W9-AZO-071

DRAFTING

technical communication

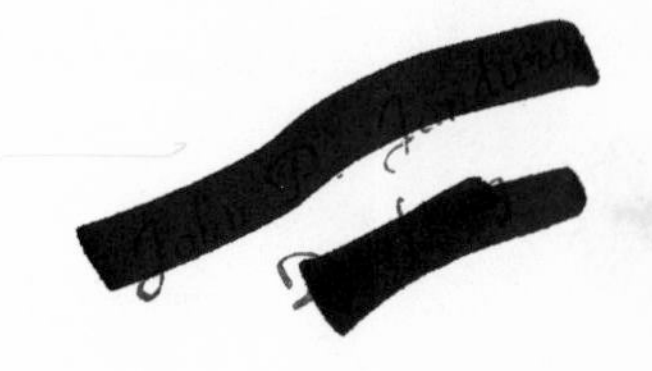

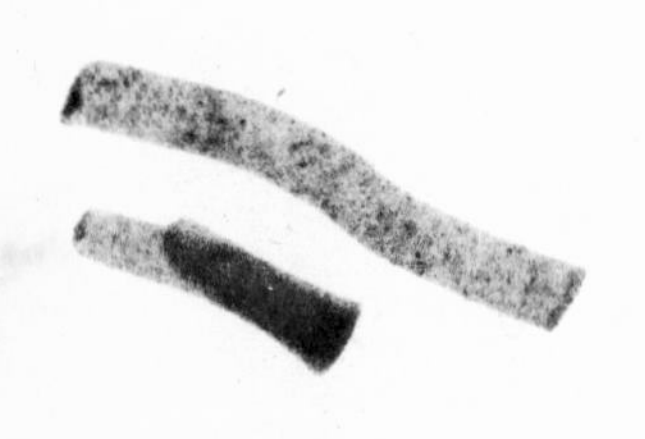

McKNIGHT & McKNIGHT PUBLISHING COMPANY • BLOOMINGTON, ILLINOIS

DRAFTING

technical communication

Lawrence S. Wright, Ed.D.
Stout State University
Menomonie, Wisconsin

First Edition

Lithographed in U.S.A.

Library of Congress Catalog Card Number: 68-18244

preface

Drafting — Technical Communication is designed as a first book for students of drafting. It is written for high school, trade school, technical institute, or college and university students who desire an authoritative and careful examination of drafting as a tool of technical communication and as a tool for solving typical problems.

Besides serving those who need to study the fundamentals of drafting, this book can be a resource for those who work with drafting daily. It can serve as an excellent review for those who have had one or two courses in junior or senior high school drafting. It should be especially helpful to students and craftsmen who need to plan and prepare the working drawings for products that they will make.

This book is designed as a helpful, well-organized tool for the teacher. Its organization is "first-things-first" — presenting information and techniques as the draftsman actually needs them in solving typical problems. The subjects covered may be studied in any order, but the arrangement of the content is entirely suitable to follow as it is presented.

The key words appearing at the top of each page are designed to give the student, the draftsman, and the teacher a clear indication of what is to be found on that page. They also will help the student review the chapter, as well as aiding the teacher in checking significant instructional content.

The problems and projects presented at the close of each chapter are designed to give the student controlled experiences in drafting practice and theory. Some of the problems are taken directly from industry; some are "tried-and-true" problems from the author's own teaching files; others are new problems designed especially for this book.

The *Technical Data Section* at the end of the book will be useful to support the planning of products. Its pages are designed primarily as resources when one desires to review such materials as: common geometrical constructions; characteristics of various woods, metal, etc.; formation of typical letters and numerals used on drawings; information on decimal and metric conversions; tolerances; or the specifications for a standard weld, bolt, screw or nail.

Suggestions for revision will be welcomed.

Lawrence S. Wright

acknowledgments

A book of this sort cannot be written without a great deal of help from many sources. The practices outlined in it are in keeping with published national standards and industrial standards and practices.

The published drafting standards of the following groups have been extremely useful, are gratefully acknowledged, and are referenced in the text where quotations have been made:

United States of America Standards Institute (USAS): a number of illustrations and quotations referenced in this book have been extracted from the *American Standard Drafting* manual, with the permission of the publisher, The American Society of Mechanical Engineers, E. 9 West 39th Street, New York, N.Y. 10016.

American Welding Society, Inc. (AWS), United Engineering Center, 345 East 47th St., New York, N.Y. 10017

International Organization for Standardization (ISO), United States of America Standards Institute, 10 East 40th Street, New York, N.Y. 10016

Military Standards (MIL-STD), Engineering Drawing Practices, Department of Defense, Washington, D.C.

Society of Automotive Engineers (SAE), 485 Lexington Avenue, New York, N.Y. 10017

Grateful appreciation is expressed to my wife, Jeanette, whose patience, encouragement, and typing and retyping of the manuscript contributed to the completion of this book in greater measure than most can imagine.

The author is indebted to Marshal Duke, a student at the University of Northern Iowa, who assisted in the preparation of the drawings for illustrations. Without his help this book would have required at least another year in preparation.

A number of teachers and prospective teachers have contributed drawings as illustrations and as problems. Each of these is identified in the text and their names follow:

Gary Anderson
Jim Arnold
Jack Becker
Regan Bell
Leonard Bengtson
Ward Bickford
Roger Ceilley
Tom Clark
Mike Cotton
William Ditch
Forrest Frownfelter
Edwin Geers
Bob Guetzlaff
Lester Hambly
Tim Harper
A. J. Hoiland
Milton Kreb
Jerald Mertens
G. I. Nowack
James Paglia
Richard Partridge
V. P. Patrilla
Albert Sherick
T. Sherwood
Larry Simmons
Lester Slater
Everett Traylor
Jack Ulveling
Bill Wagner
Richard Winey
Bill Ziesche

Examples of industrial practice help to relate the information given in this textbook to industry. The following companies kindly submitted materials, photographs, industrial drafting room standards manuals, examples of drawings, and the like. These are gratefully acknowledged and are referenced where quoted in the text.

Alvin & Co., Inc., 611 Palisado Ave., Windsor, Connecticut
American Builder, 30 Church St., New York, New York
American Screw Co., Textron Division, Wytheville, Virginia
American Steel and Wire Co., 4170 Rockefeller Bldg., Cleveland, Ohio
Atlas Tack Corp., Fairhaven, Massachusetts 02719
Barkley and Dexter, Inc., 50 Frankfort St., Fitchburg, Massachusetts
Battelle Memorial Institute, Frankfort am Main, Germany
Charles Bruning Co., Division of Addressograph-Multigraph Corp., 1800 West Central Road, Mount Prospect, Illinois 60058
California Computer Products, Inc. 305 Muller Ave., Anaheim, California
Caterpillar Tractor Co., Peoria, Illinois 61611
Cherry-Burrell Corp., 2400 Sixth St., S.W., Cedar Rapids, Iowa
Chicago Rivet and Machine Co., Bellwood, Illinois
Chrysler Corp., Detroit, Michigan 48231
City Engineers Office, Cedar Falls, Iowa 50613
College Relations Office, University of Northern Iowa, Cedar Falls, Iowa 50613
Deere & Co., Moline, Illinois 61265
Des Moines Register, The Register and Tribune Syndicate, Des Moines, Iowa
Design News, Cahners Bldg., Englewood, Colorado 80110
Eugene Dietzgen Co., 2425 N. Sheffield Avenue, Chicago, Illinois 60614
The Joseph Dixon Crucible Co., Jersey City, New Jersey
Doerfer Engineering & Design, Inc., 314½ Main St., Cedar Falls, Iowa 50613
Eastman Kodak Co., Rochester, New York 14650
Eberhard Faber Pen & Pencil Co., Inc., Wilkes-Barre, Pennsylvania
Fisher Governor Co., Marshalltown, Iowa
Ford Motor Co., 20000 Rotunda Drive, Dearborn, Michigan
The Franklin Glue Co., Columbus, Ohio 43207
Gisholt Machine Co., Madison, Wisconsin
Gramercy Co., 846 Elati St., Denver, Colorado 80204
General Motors Corp., General Motors Technical Center, Warren, Michigan 48090
Graphic Science, Kinelow Publishing Co., 9 Maiden Lane, New York, New York 10038
Greenlee Tool Co., Rockford, Illinois 61101
H. M. Harper Co., 8200 Lehigh Ave., Morton Grove, Illinois
Harvey Hubbell, Inc., Bridgeport, Connecticut 06602
John Hassall, Inc., Westbury, Long Island, New York 11591
Holo-Krome Co., West Hartford, Connecticut 06110
Hyatt Bearings Div., General Motors Corp., Harrison, New Jersey
The Independent Nail Corp., Bridgewater, Massachusetts
Industrial Arts and Vocational Education, 400 N. Broadway, Milwaukee, Wisconsin 53201
International Business Machines Corp., Princeton, New Jersey 08540
Iowa State Highway Commission, Ames, Iowa 50011
Welton V. Johnson Engineering Co., Inc., 95 Summit Avenue, Summit, New Jersey
Jones & Lamson, Springfield, Vermont 05156
Keuffel & Esser Co., Adams and 3rd Sts., Hoboken, New Jersey
Koh-I-Nor, Inc., Bloomsbury, New Jersey
Martin Co., Baltimore, Maryland 21203
Materials in Design Engineering, 430 Park Avenue, New York, New York 10022
Mayline Co., Inc., Sheboygan, Wisconsin

Minnesota Mining and Manufacturing (3-M) Co., 2501 Hudson Road, St. Paul Minnesota 55119

National Lock Co., Rockford, Illinois 61101

New Home Sewing Machine Co., P.O. Box 25901, Los Angeles, California

Ohaus Scale Corp., 1050 Commerce Avenue, Union, New Jersey 07083

Olson Manufacturing Co., P.O. Box 109, Ames, Iowa 50011

Product Engineering, 330 West 42nd St., New York, New York 10036

Ray-O-Vac Co., Division of Electrical Storage Battery Co., 212 East Washington Ave., Madison, Wisconsin

Recordak Corp., 770 Broadway, New York, New York 10003

Republic Steel Corp., Cleveland, Ohio 44101

R-Way Furniture Co., Sheboygan, Wisconsin

Schield Bantam Division, Koehring Co., Waverly, Iowa 50677

W. A. Sheaffer Pen. Co., Fort Madison, Iowa

South Chester Corp., Lester, Pennsylania

J. S. Staedtler, Inc., Montville, New Jersey

Titus Manufacturing Corp., Waterloo, Iowa

United States Plywood Corp., Protection Products Div., 2305 Superior Ave., Kalamazoo, Michigan 49003

United States Steel Corp., 5 Gateway Center, Pittsburgh, Pennsylvania 15230

V. & E. Manufacturing Co., 758 S. Fair Oaks Ave., Pasadena, California

Viking Pump Co., Cedar Falls, Iowa 50613

Wallace & Holland, Consulting Engineers, Mason City, Iowa

Wood-Reagan Instrument Co., Nutley, New Jersey

Xerox Corp., Rochester, New York

contents

Technical Data Section

Appendices

tables and technical data

TEXTBOOK SECTION

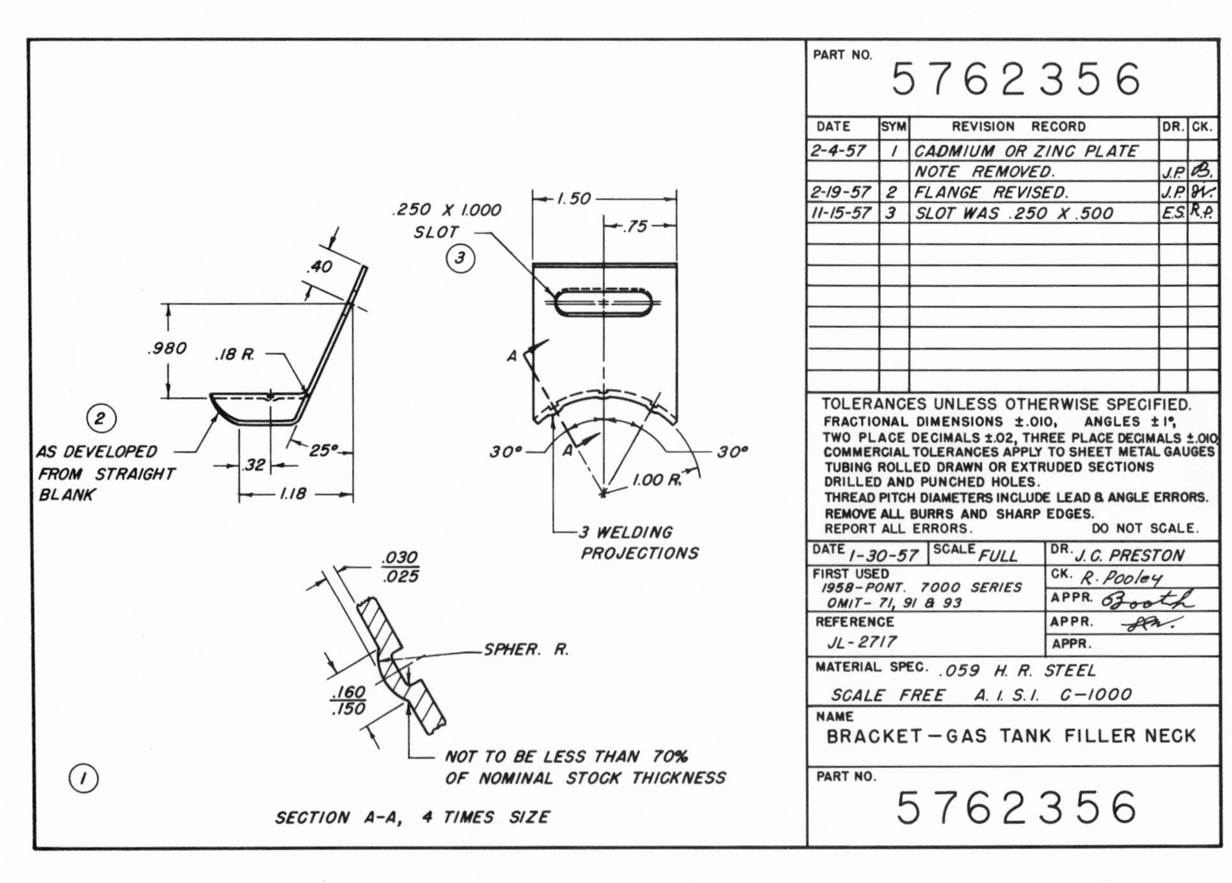

FIG. 1-1. Drawing of Bracket
(General Motors of Canada)

Technical drafting is characterized by standard practices and precision. Note standard line conventions, projection, sectioning practice, and revision block. Use of decimal dimensioning throughout is standard practice and implies precision.

CHAPTER ONE

introduction to technical drafting

The Language of Technical Drafting

Man's understanding of the principles of science and mathematics is increasing continuously. With this understanding, he has further applied these principles to the physical objects that surround him. Rapid expansion of industrial research and development and the continuous search for production efficiency result in *technological advance.* The language of this advance must meet technical demands; there is no room for sloppiness. *Technical drafting,* one means of communication in industry, is characterized by precision and standardization, Fig. 1-1. Through your study you will learn how uniform practice ensures correct interpretation, thereby conserving time and reducing cost, error, and waste, Fig. 1-2.

what is drafting?

Drafting is an Occupation

An estimated 260,000 draftsmen were employed in 1962 throughout the United States in all types of productive enterprises.[1] *The Dictionary of Occupational Titles* describes 57 drafting occupations ranging from "Detailer" to "Chief Design Draftsman." As new industry evolves, new drafting specialities are created. Practically all draftsmen specialize in a particular field, the largest of which include: mechanical, electrical, electronics, aeronautical, structural, architectural, naval architectural, and topographical drafting. Ability to read drawings is a success factor in many fields, Fig. 1-3.

[1] *Occupational Outlook Handbook,* 1963-64 edition; U. S. Department of Labor, Bureau of Labor Statistics.

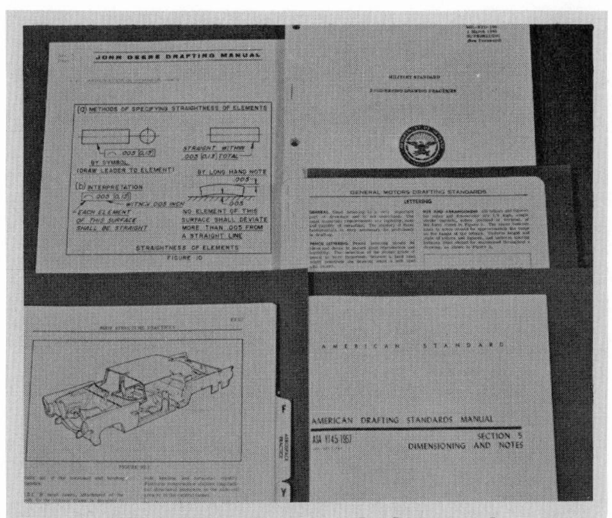

Fig. 1-2. Drafting Standards Manuals
Such manuals suggest standard procedures for the development of drawings.

INTRODUCTION

Although some of the newer techniques (such as photo-drafting and use of electronic equipment) may eliminate some routine jobs, expansion in employment for well-qualified draftsmen is anticipated in the years ahead. Further information about drafting occupations appears in Chapter 14.

Drafting is Useful to a Variety of People

Drafting skills are used by the printer in planning layouts, Fig. 1-4; by the geographer and civil engineer in map making, Fig. 1-5; by writers in expressing ideas through graphs, Fig. 1-6; by the mathematician to show relationships, Fig 1-7; and by the teacher as he helps the student learn to read drawings, Fig. 1-8. Drawings are read by the housewife in following instructions for home appliances, Fig. 1-9; by the business man and banker in reading trends of business and finance, Fig. 1-10; by the family in planning for a new house, Fig. 1-11; and many others.

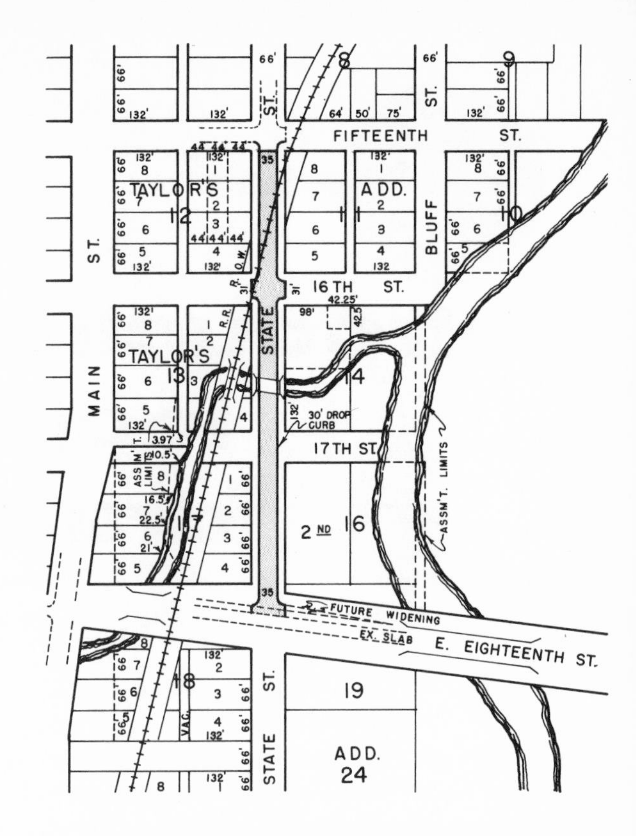

FIG. 1-5. Preliminary Plat of Paving Project (City Engineer's Office, Cedar Falls, Iowa)

FIG. 1-3. Draftsmen at Work (Chrysler Corp.) The design department is located at their Central Engineering Division in Highland Park, Michigan.

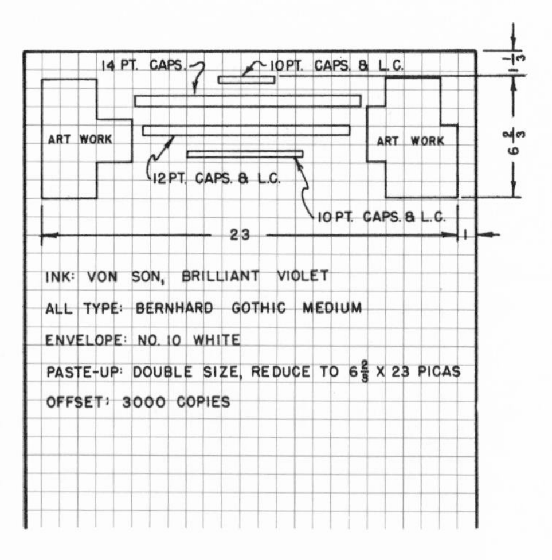

Third Annual
IOWA INDUSTRIAL ARTS FAIR
State College of Iowa, Cedar Falls, Iowa
Saturday, April 25th, 1964

(B) ART WORK COPY

FIG. 1-4. Layout and Copy for Envelope Return Address
Dimensions shown are in picas, the unit of measurement used in printing.

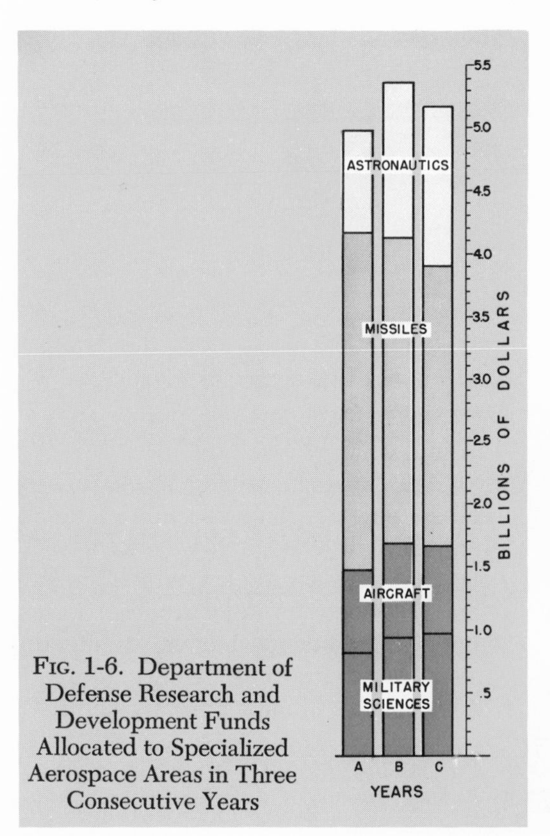

FIG. 1-6. Department of Defense Research and Development Funds Allocated to Specialized Aerospace Areas in Three Consecutive Years

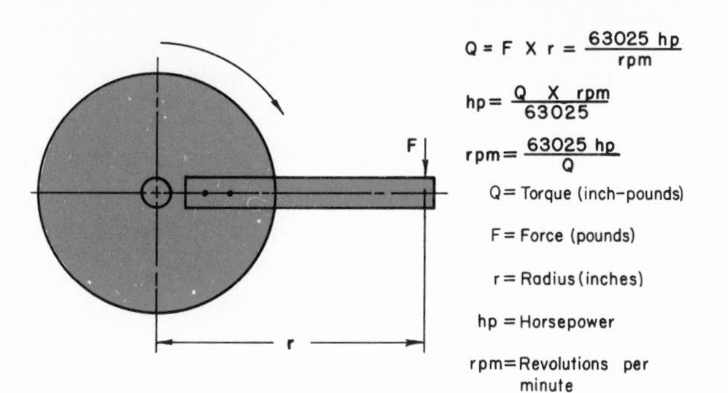

FIG. 1-7. Mathematics of Torque and Horsepower Shown Graphically (Hyatt Bearing Division, General Motors Corporation)

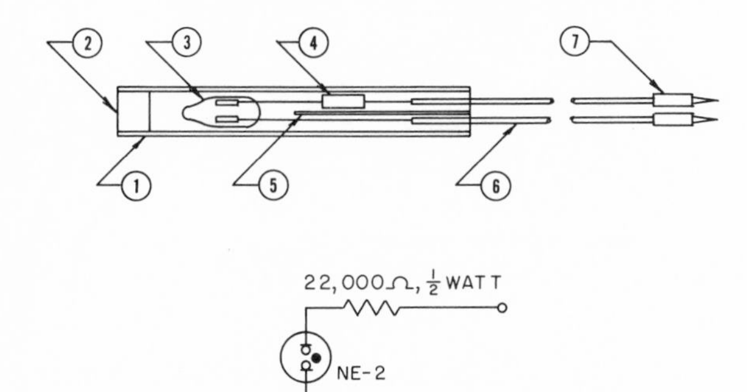

FIG. 1-8. Schematic and Assembly Drawings of Neon Test Lamp (Professor Albert M. Sherick, Iowa State University)

BILL OF MATERIAL

Part No.	Quan.	Description
1	1	Plastic tube, OD, ⅜″ – ID ⁵⁄₁₆″ x 3″
2	1	Plug, plastic, ⁵⁄₁₆″ D x ¼″
3	1	Neon bulb, NE – 2, 105-600 watts
4	1	Resistor, carbon, 22,000 ohm, ½ watt
5	1	Fish paper insulation, ⁷⁄₁₆″ x 1½″
6	2	Lead wires, #16 AWG Standard, 1000 volt insulation, 6″
7	2	Phone tips

Procedure:

1. Solder components.
2. Place plug in end of tube.
3. Insert soldered components into plastic tube, and separate them with fish paper.
4. Optional: Make a plug for the bottom end.

TO SEW BLIND STITCH HEM

Use cam No. 12.

Move the zigzag width lever to "3" and set it with the left zigzag limiter.

Set the needle position selector at "M".

Set the stitch length dial at about "1".

With the fabric inside out, fold it to the desired size of hem. (No. 1)

Fold it again leaving a margin of 1/16 inch on the bottom fold. (No. 2)

Sew on the fold as shown in the figure.

Then unfold the sewn fabric (No. 3) and you will have a blind stitch hem (No. 4).

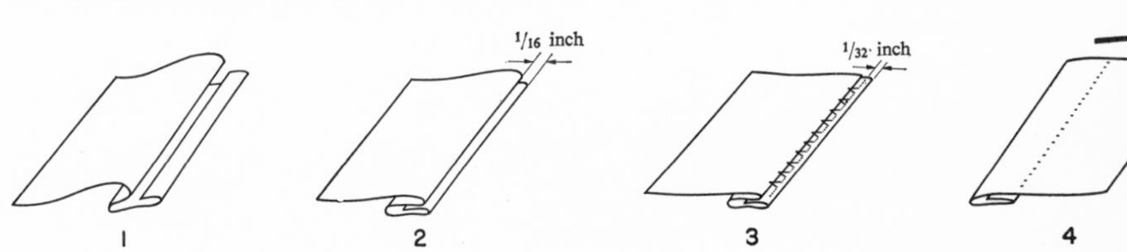

FIG. 1-9. Instructions for the Housewife on How to Sew a Blind Stitch Hem (New Home Sewing Machine Co.)

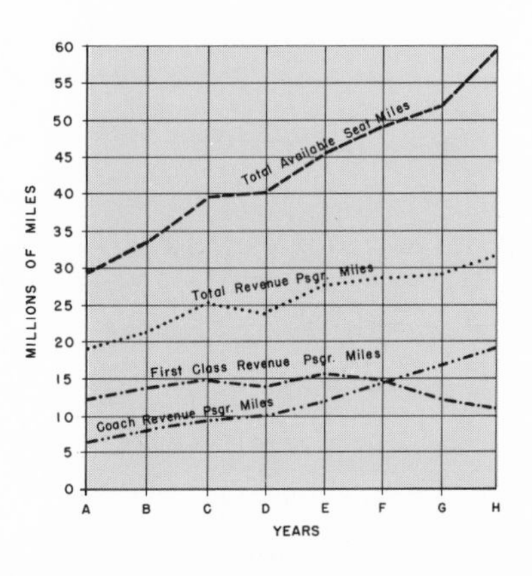

FIG. 1-10. Trends in Commercial Airline Passenger Service Shown Graphically

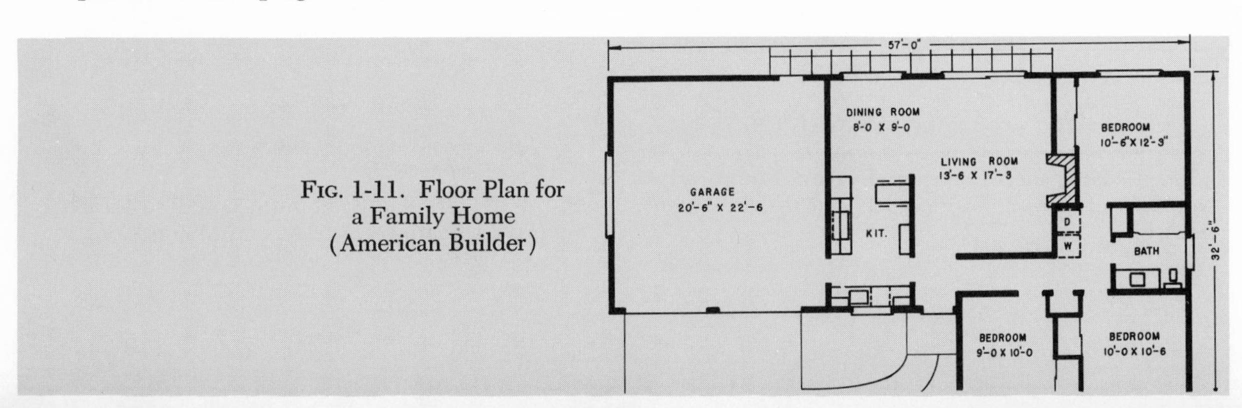

FIG. 1-11. Floor Plan for a Family Home (American Builder)

Drafting is a Universal Language Important to World Trade

Trade between countries is facilitated by efficient communication and transportation. As common markets develop and products are imported and exported, drawings are needed to explain the installation, use, and maintenance of these products. Drawings representing objects and ideas about objects are a universal language, Fig. 1-12. If you understand the theory behind drawings and are able to visualize, you have some foundation for communicating in any language.

Drafting is Analysis

Drafting is the study and recording of mathematical relationships. One variable is plotted against another to give a *visible* and precise form to ideas. Many problems in mathematics may be solved graphically. The advantage of a graphical solution is that errors often are more readily visible. Systematic recording of data in tables is part of graphic analysis. When you then record this data in a graph, you are using a direct form of data analysis, Fig. 1-13.

Drafting is Solving Space Problems

Space problems may be simply the representation of three-dimensional drawings in orthographic projection, or they may center around the concept of movement through space, Fig. 1-14. A line may be described as *the motion of a point through space*. The path of a line describes a plane, while the path of a plane describes space itself. Man has become more interested in moving through space and has become more aware of the relationships of space problems. These are recorded, studied, and solved graphically. It is becoming increasingly important to study drafting as a means of solving problems in space, Fig. 1-15.

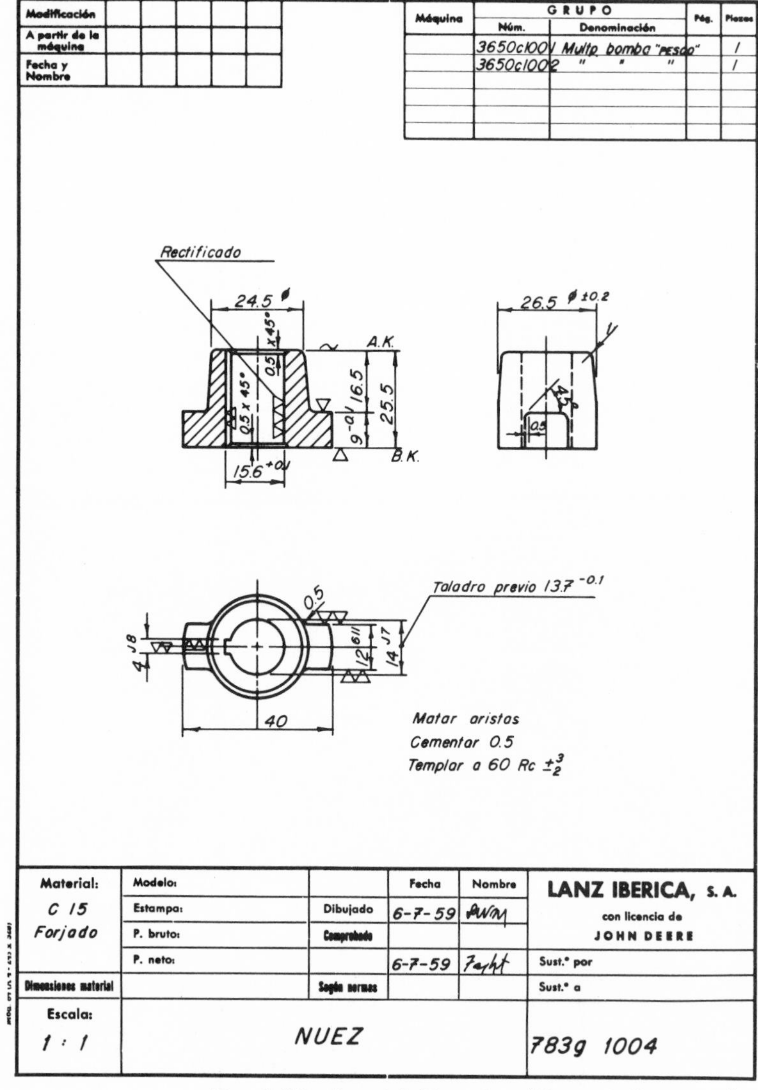

Fig. 1-12. Spanish Drawing (Deere & Company) Note use of first-angle projection and metric dimensions.

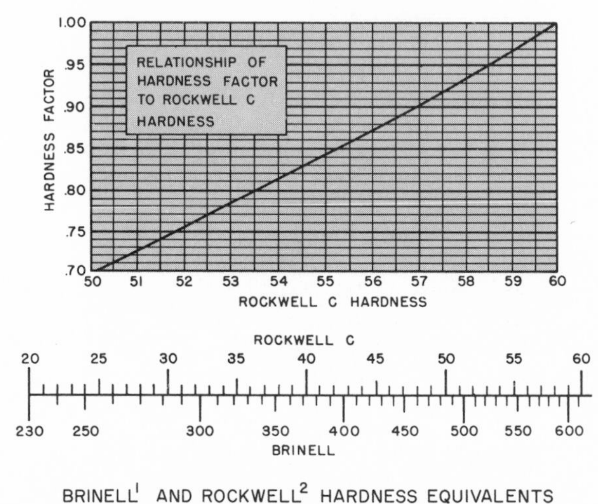

Fig. 1-13. Graphic Relationships of Two Variables (Hyatt Bearing Div., General Motors Corp.)

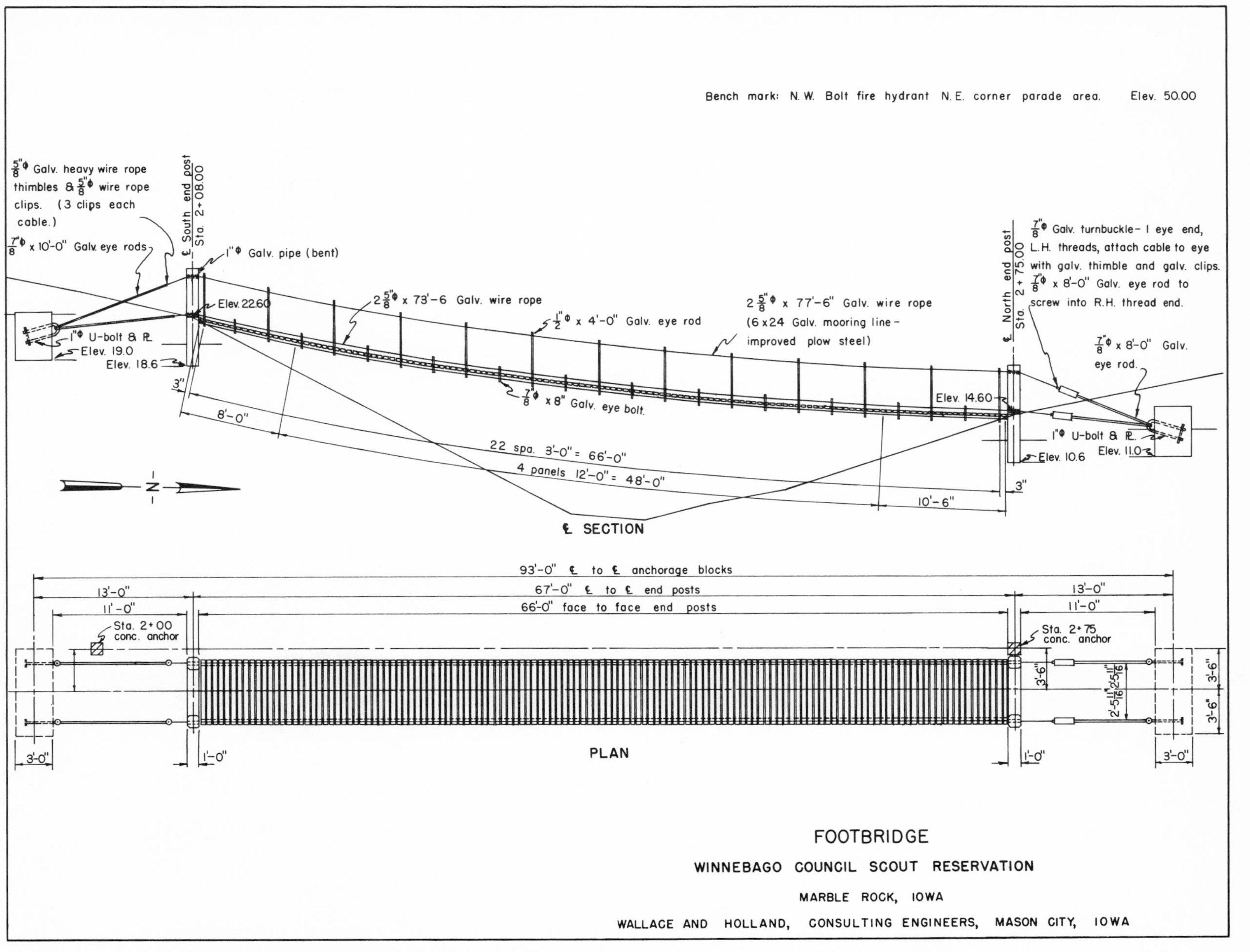

Fig. 1-14. Solution to a Space Problem Confronting the Civil Engineer (Wallace and Holland)

Drafting is Thinking and Planning

The engineer works on the solution to a product design problem. He must consider several alternative ideas and make a series of sketches to show variations, so that he can determine how each will function.

The problem may be to design the taillight for an automobile so that it fits in with the overall appearance of the car. In addition, the de-

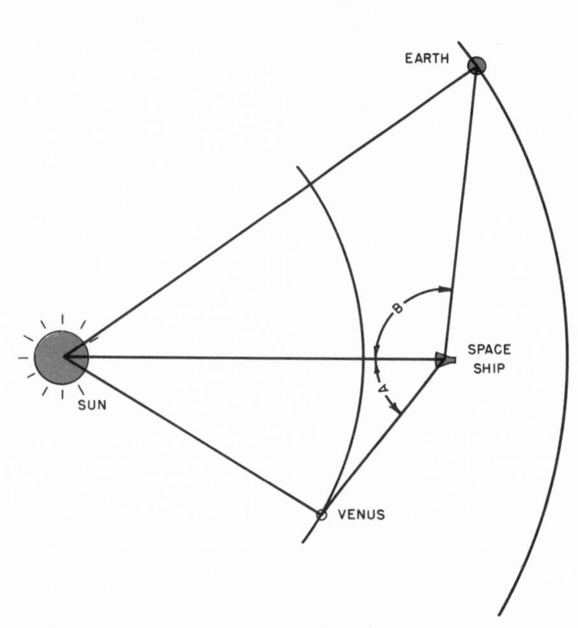

Fig. 1-15. Space Ship Navigates by Reference to the Known Positions of Other Bodies

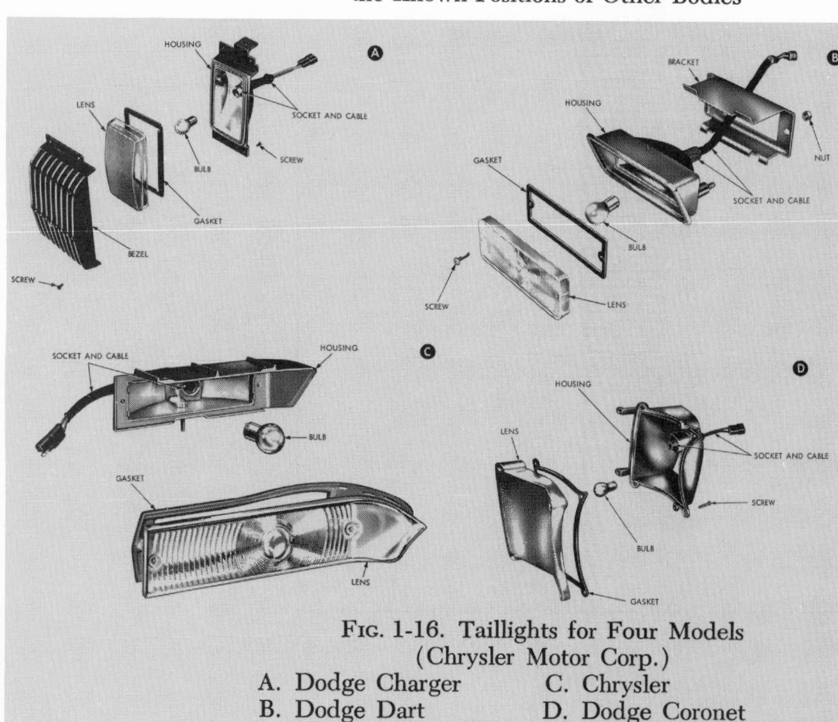

Fig. 1-16. Taillights for Four Models (Chrysler Motor Corp.)

A. Dodge Charger C. Chrysler
B. Dodge Dart D. Dodge Coronet

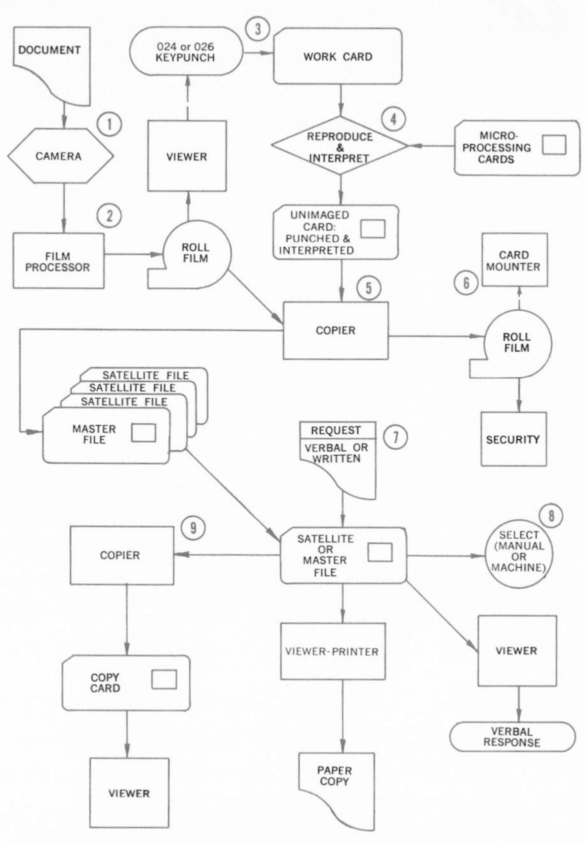

Fig. 1-17. Work Flow for Complex, Information-Handling System (International Business Machines Corp.)

Record

1. The documents are microfilmed.
2. The film is processed.
3. The information necessary to identify the microfilmed document is keypunched into a work deck. The keypunch operator works directly from the roll film, screened in enlarged form on a viewer.
4. Unimaged cards are produced and interpreted from the work desk.
5. Imaged copy cards, produced in a copier, establish the master file and initial satellite files. The roll film is placed in a security vault for permanent records protection.
6. Each frame in the original roll of film can be mounted in an aperture card to create a machine-processable security file.

Retrieve

7. Inquiries directed to the master file or a satellite file may be made by telephone . . . in writing . . . or in person.
8. Cards may be selected manually or by machine depending upon the number of cards required to answer the request.

Refer

9. Requests for information are filled by the production of (a) copy cards to be used for visual reference on a viewer, or (b) paper copies where documentation or revision is necessary. (This procedure prevents the unnecessary production of paper copies.)

sign must be *functional;* that is, it must be visible at a standard distance and must show the corners of the car. A number of different design ideas are developed and evaluated, Fig. 1-16. These are submitted to management.

As planning, drafting has many forms. The student who determines the relationship of parts for a project he will build is certain to use drafting. He makes tentative decisions about a set of working drawings and refines these. The construction procedure must be developed, requiring careful planning of what must be done and the order in which it may best be accomplished.

The industrial process engineer (the efficiency expert, studies the flow of materials in an industrial plant, the arrangement of machines, and all things related to efficient production. *Flow charts* are plans for efficient production, Fig. 1-17. This planning may be shown better through written and graphic representation than by written description alone.

standardization of drafting practices

Origin of Standard Practices

Development of standard practices in the drafting room usually begins within companies and corporations. A company, realizing the commercial advantages of such practices, develops its own "Drafting Standards Manual." These manuals grow out of practices within the company as harmonized with recommended practices of organizations who have long seen the need for standardization at the national level.

United States of America Standards Institute

In 1918 five American engineering societies formed an organization to coordinate the development of national standards. Growing out of this was the American Standards Association (ASA). In 1966 the ASA was reconstituted as United States of America Standards Institute. Standards approved as American Standards are now designated USAS. Today it is a federation of national trade associations, technical and professional societies, and consumer organizations with companies affiliated as members. Its purpose is to develop, promote, approve, and coordinate standards practices among industries.

The *USAS Drafting Manual* consists of 17 separately published sections, each developed by a subcommittee. Those sections marked with an asterisk were in preparation when this book was written:

USAS No. Y14. 1-1957	Size and Format
USAS No. Y14. 2-1957	Line Conventions, Sectioning and Lettering
USAS No. Y14. 3-1957	Projections
USAS No. Y14. 4-1957	Pictorial Drawing
USAS No. Y14. 5-1966	Dimensioning and Tolerancing for Engineering Drawings
USAS No. Y14. 6-1967	Screw Threads
USAS No. Y14. 7-1958	Gears, Splines, and Serrations
USAS No. Y14. 8	Castings*
USAS No. Y14. 9-1958	Forging
USAS No. Y14.10-1959	Metal Stamping
USAS No. Y14.11-1958	Plastics
USAS No. Y14.12	Die Castings*
USAS No. Y14.13	Springs, Helical and Flat*
USAS No. Y14.14-1961	Mechanical Assemblies
USAS No. Y14.15-1966	Electrical and Electronics Diagrams
USAS No. Y14.16	Tools, Dies and Gages*
USAS No. Y14.17-1966	Fluid Power Diagrams

Note: When using these data, keep in mind that the manuals produced by the Association will refer to the numbers with a prefix "ASA." The new manuals from the Institute will refer to the same numbers with a prefix of "USAS."

Society of Automotive Engineers

Various subcommittees of the Society of Automotive Engineers (SAE) met the need for national standardization of drafting practices in the aeronautical and ground vehicle industries by publishing drafting manuals. An outstanding comprehensive volume, *Aerospace-Automotive Drawing Standards,* was released in late 1963. It is in harmony with the USAS *Drafting Manual* and includes information on drafting room procedures, components and features, materials and processes, ground vehicle practice, aerospace practice and tables and charts.

It must be understood that both of these standards are approved as *advisory* only.

International Organization for Standardization

Because industries are decentralized both in this country and abroad, international standardization has become an important and desirable goal. Drawings of products and their components go from one country to another. The responsibility for engineering and manufacture may shift within a decentralized company, resulting in the transfer of personnel.

The International Organization for Standardization (ISO) is composed of the national standardization bodies of some 44 countries including the United States. Presently there is no international drafting standards manual, although *agreements* reached by the ISO are reflected in the current USAS and SAE manuals.

Standards Used in This Text

This text closely follows the drafting practices approved standards by the USAS and SAE. Company standards occasionally are used to supplement these.

solving drafting problems

Technical Sketching — A Basis

Ideas stem from needs. Management, the engineer, the draftsman, a customer, or you — anyone may have an idea. From needs and ideas about them, you can identify problems, examine trial solutions, and then synthesize the best of these to form specifications. The draftsman deals with problems requiring a graphic solution. He works with sketches which come to him from several sources — the engineer, the architect, the designer — or he may create them himself. These sketches may take the form of freehand work or rough mechanical work, but they must communicate ideas. *Specifications* which accompany them may be written in longhand, lettered, typewritten, or presented orally. More often, preliminary planning is done at a conference between the draftsman and one or more individuals. Sketches, verbal comments, and notes are used to make certain that all parties understand precisely what the problem is and the best method to solve it.

Technical sketching is a basic drafting skill. The draftsman must be able to sketch, both as a means of expression and as a means of visual communication. Sketching is an essential skill for the competent engineer, architect, and designer, as well as being important to teachers and students.

For example, consider just this one design problem: a new library building is scheduled for construction on a college campus and money has been allocated for 200 carrels (individual student study desks). A major furniture company has been asked to submit tentative designs for these carrels. Fig. 1-18 shows the sketches prepared for each of three carrel types, the designs of which are very similar. Type *A* has a low back; Type *B*, a high back with a book shelf; Type *C*, a high back without a book shelf. Generalized specifications and the cost of production for each of these carrels are furnished to the college authorities. They select the one they believe best fits their needs and budget, and they order 200 of this type. Now the designer confers with the draftsman who must prepare *working drawings* so that the selected design can be produced. The designer and the draftsman must understand and agree

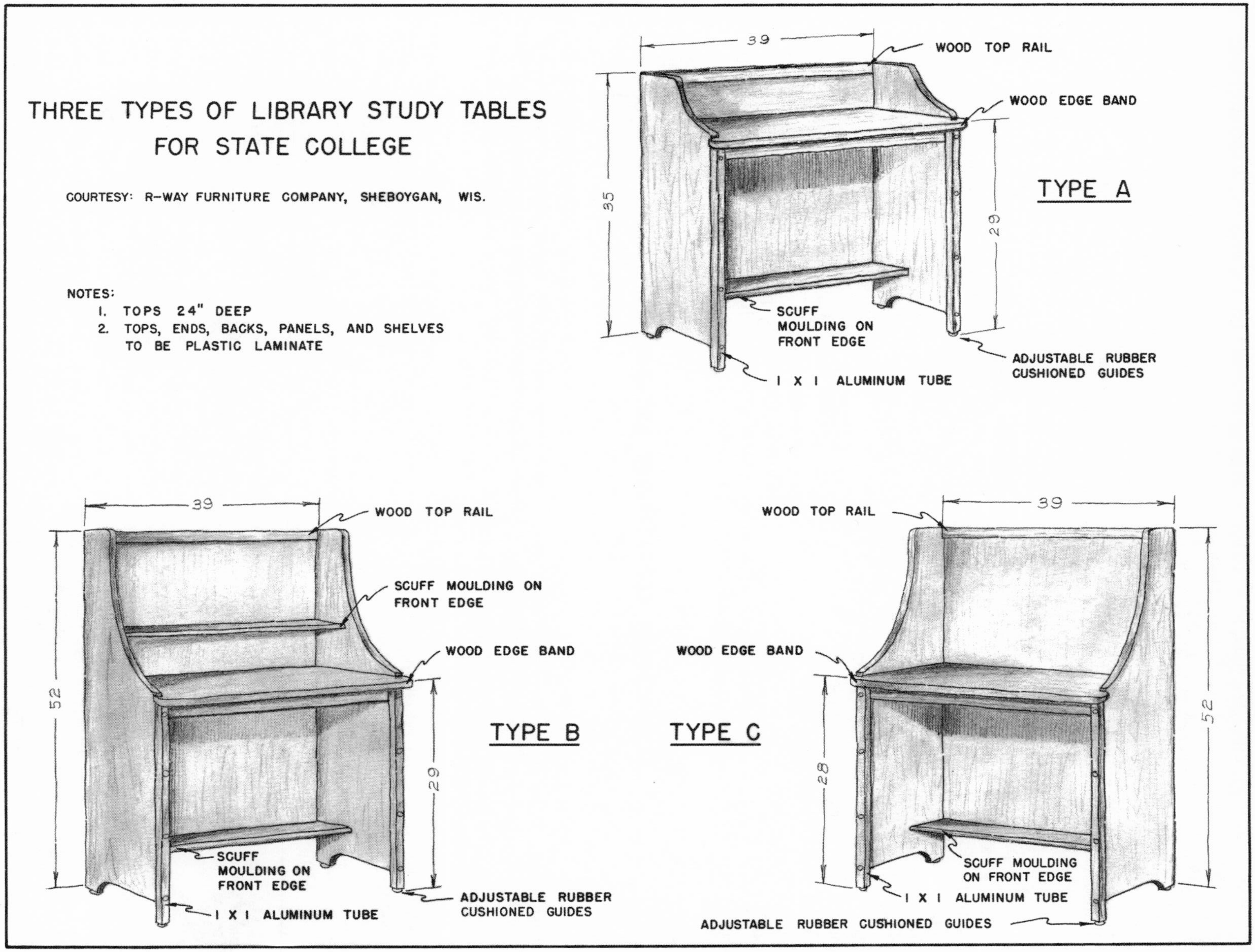

Fig. 1-18. Proposed Library Study Tables (R-Way Furniture Co.)

on the specifications. The experienced draftsman proceeds on the basis of these agreements. He has sufficient knowledge and experience to lay out the details common to this piece of furniture as normally constructed by this company. Any changes are sketched and discussed with the designer. When the drawings have been completed, they are approved by the designer, re-evaluated by the college authorities, and contracts for production are executed.

A second example involves the construction of a spindle for a drop bow pen used by the draftsman to ink small circles and circle arcs. An engineer has prepared a sketch of the part, together with specifications, Fig. 1-19. After conferring with this engineer, the draftsman develops the working drawing as shown in Fig. 1-20. This is reproduced and sent to the shops where the part is made according to the specifications.

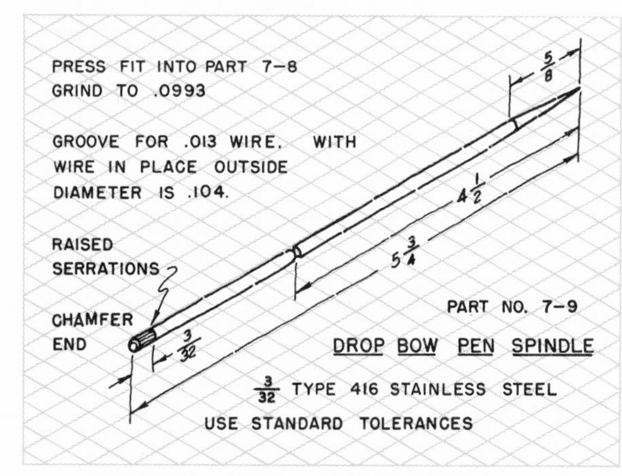

FIG. 1-19. Sketch and Specifications for Drop Bow Pen Spindle (Vemco Co.)

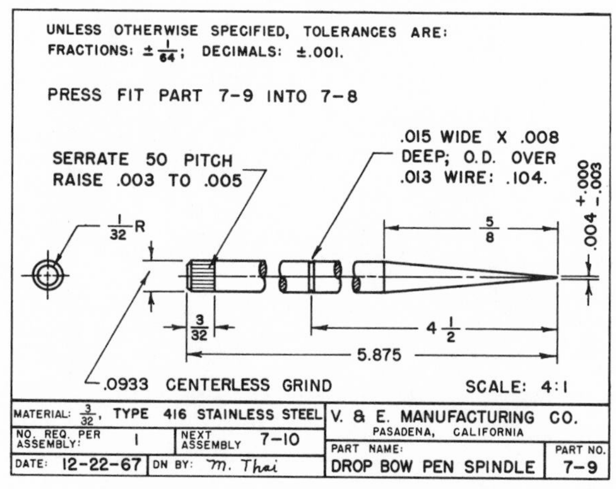

FIG. 1-20. Working Drawing for Drop Bow Pen Spindle (Vemco Co.)

As a final example, a student may be given this problem: develop a planter which can hold approximately 2 quarts of dirt spread 2″ deep.

The student must do some trial calculating and sketching, a portion of which is shown in Fig. 1-21. After discussing this preliminary work with his instructor, he selects the most desirable design for further development and final preparation of working drawings.

The furniture designer, the engineer, the draftsman, the student, the teacher – all need sketching as a basic tool of efficient communication. Similar illustrations could be given for the architect, the contractor, business executive, scientist, mathematician, and others from many walks of life. Communication through sketching involves not only the *technique* of sketching various lines but also the *ability to visualize* in pictorial form. The illustrations in Figs. 1-18 and 1-19 are *pictorial drawings* showing each of the three dimensions. The draftsman may use any of the forms of pictorial shown in Chapter 2 to communicate his ideas. When you study the techniques of line sketching and acquire the ability to make pictorial representations, you will have established the groundwork for visual communication.

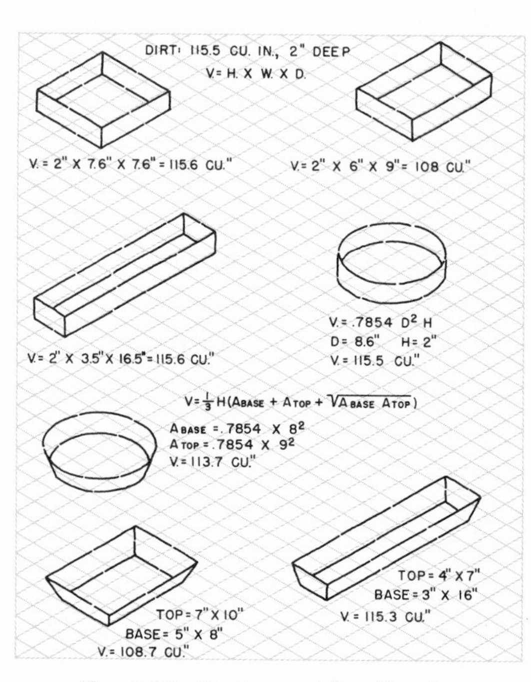

FIG. 1-21. Design or Idea Sketches

Orthographic Projection and Visualization

The pictorial sketch in Fig. 1-18 shows, in a general way, the object's shape and form. However, a piece cannot be mass-produced from a pictorial sketch since the description is not precise and the construction details are not shown. The pictorial view in Fig. 1-22 does not describe *exactly* how this part is to be made. You might assume that the drilled holes go through the mounting plate. Screw threads are not shown, although a note tells about them. The wise draftsman does not leave important details to be assumed by the workman. With one wrong assumption, innumerable unusable parts may be produced.

To describe precisely and accurately, the draftsman must draw one or more surfaces of each object in *true representation.* Position yourself at right angles to the surface of an object and look directly at it, Fig. 1-23. You can see only two of its three dimensions. To coordinate the projection of these surfaces, *multi-view projection* is required. This is done by the system of *orthographic projection* discussed in another chapter. Sketching techniques also can be used advantageously with this system.

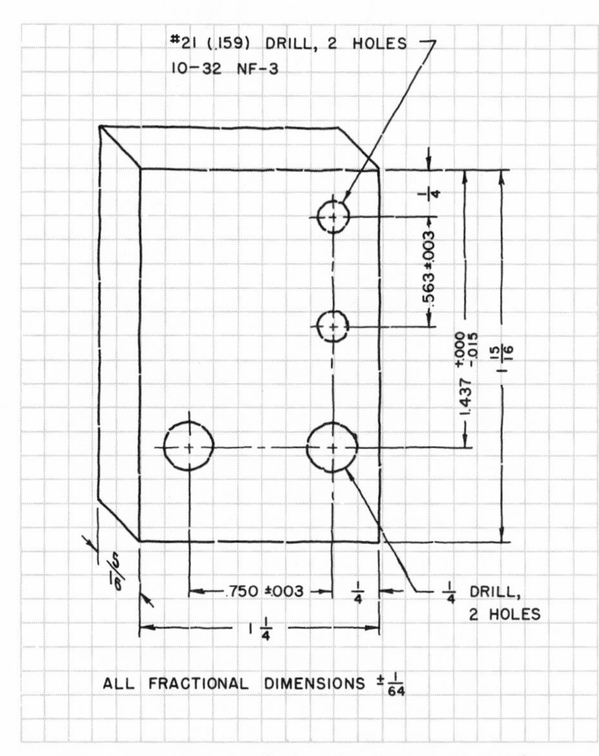

Fig. 1-22. Pictorial Sketch of Mounting Plate

Instruments and Constructions

Mechanical devices will help the draftsman accurately construct the required views. In general, the more complex the object, the more necessary is the *mechanical drawing* of that object. The drafting instruments and tools enable

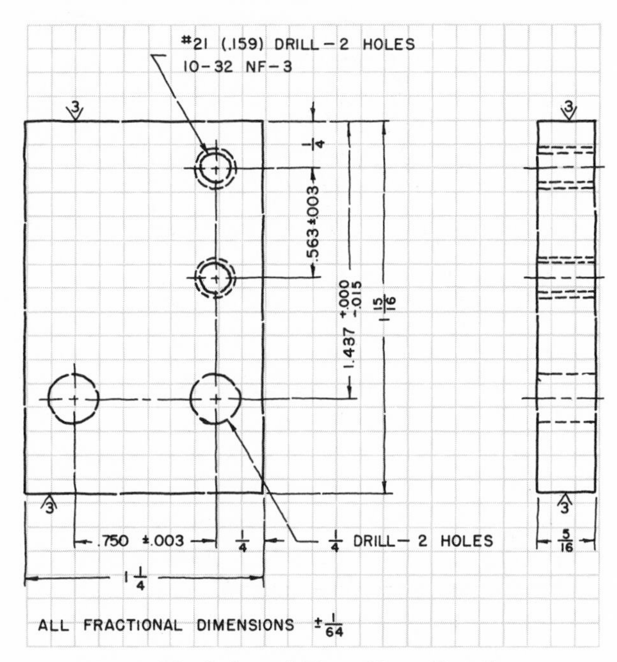

Fig. 1-23. Side and Front View Sketches of Mounting Plate

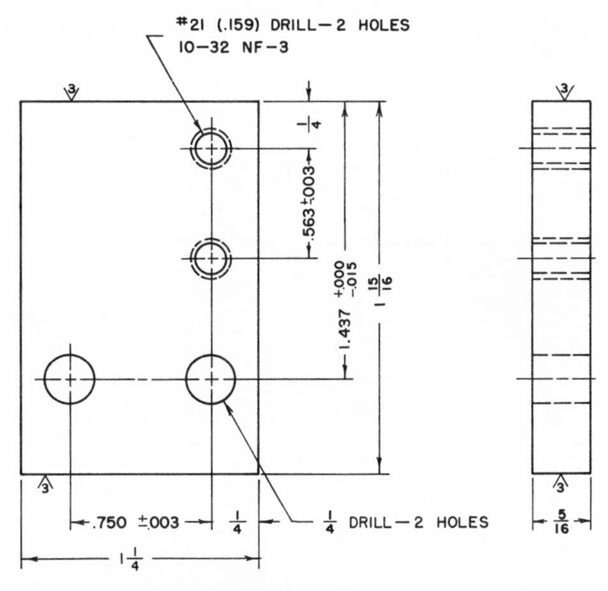

Fig. 1-24. Orthographic Projection of Mounting Plate (Gisholt Machine Co.)

the draftsman to make accurate and precise instrumental drawings. Compare the drawings of the mounting plate, Fig. 1-24 and Fig. 1-22. Both are legible, but the orthographic representation is more precise. You can see from the hidden lines in the profile view that the holes (and the threads on the upper two holes) go through the plate.

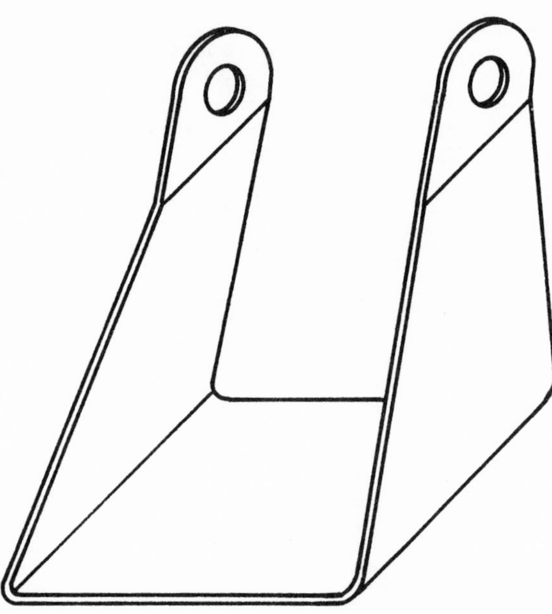

FIG. 1-25. Sheet Steel Bracket

Standard geometrical construction techniques must be used in mechanical drawing. To construct the layout for the bracket in Fig. 1-25, the draftsman must construct a line tangent to an arc of a circle. He proceeds as shown in Fig. 1-26. In this particular case, he is given specifications which originate from point *P*. He must draw a tangent to a circle of a given radius whose center is located at *O*. The line tangent to the circle *O* must pass through point *P*.

1. Locate given point *P* and arc originating at *O*.
2. Draw *PAB* through point *P* and intersecting the arc at any two points *A* and *B* in the straight line *PAB*.

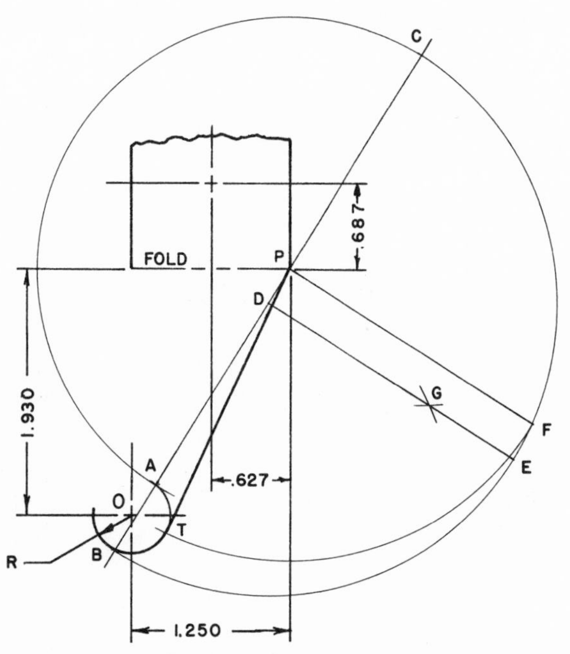

FIG. 1-26. Constructing a Tangent from a Given Point to a Given Circle Arc

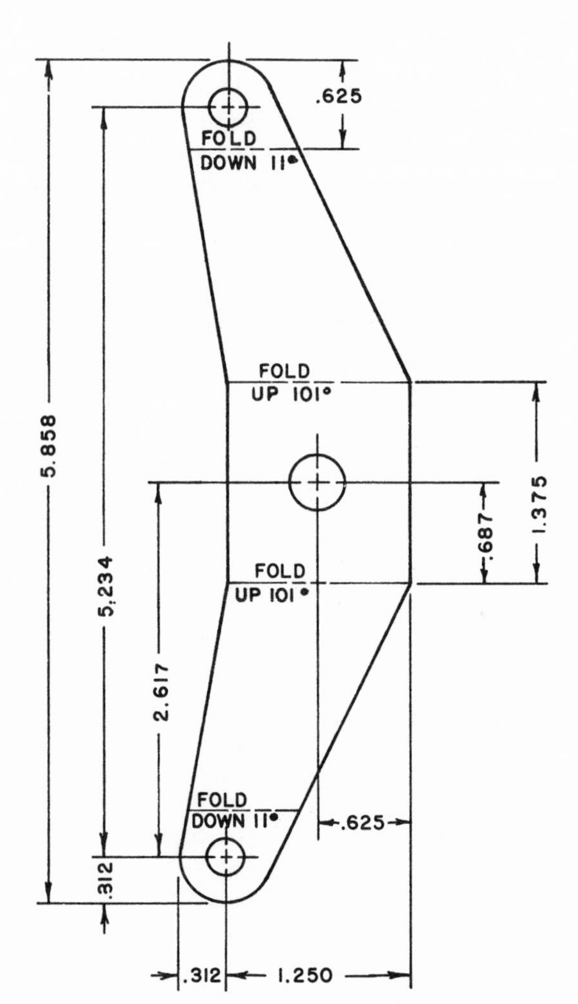

FIG. 1-27. Dimensioned Layout for Sheet Steel Bracket

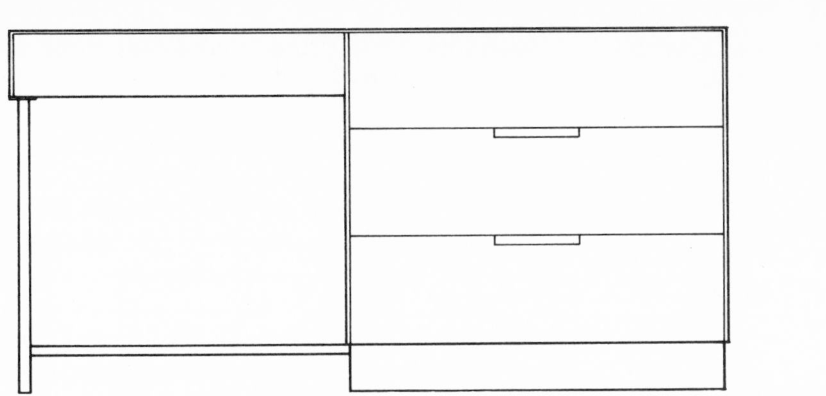

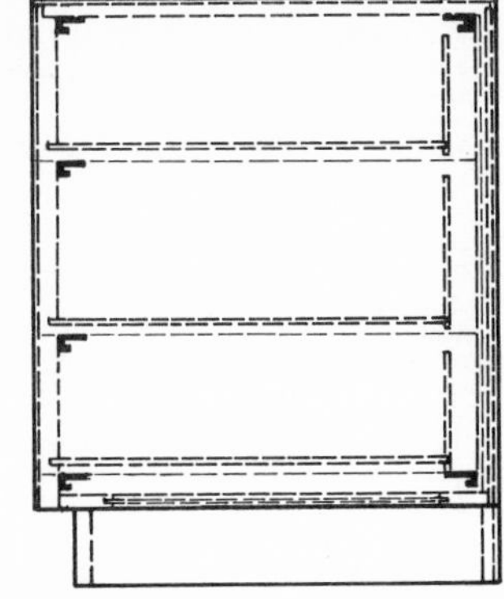

FIG. 1-28. Front and Profile Views of Desk (R-Way Furniture Co.)

3. Extend PAB to C such that $PA = PC$.
4. Erect a perpendicular bisector of line CB at DE.
5. Draw the mean proportional of PA and PB by erecting a perpendicular from P to intersect arc CEB at F.
6. With P as the center and PF as the radius, draw an arc intersecting the given arc at point T.
7. Draw line PT which is the required line tangent to the arc at point T.

This procedure will locate accurately the required points of tangency for the blank in Fig. 1-27. You can find some of the elementary geometrical constructions in the Technical Data Section at the end of this book. Other more advanced constructions are presented in Chapter 4.

Interior Detail

Many times the draftsman cannot show construction details with only the surfaces of an object. In Fig. 1-28, there are so many hidden lines that it is not clear just what each one means. To delineate this interior detail, the draftsman makes an enlarged section view with symbols showing wood edge grain (Fig. 1-29). Note also the use of break lines which permits a certain telescoping of the profile into a smaller space, yet reveals enlarged details. The handwheel in Fig. 1-30 also requires a section view in order to indicate clearly the true form of the rib and the specific features of the casting. The illustration used shows true projection; for typical practice, see Fig. 5-15.

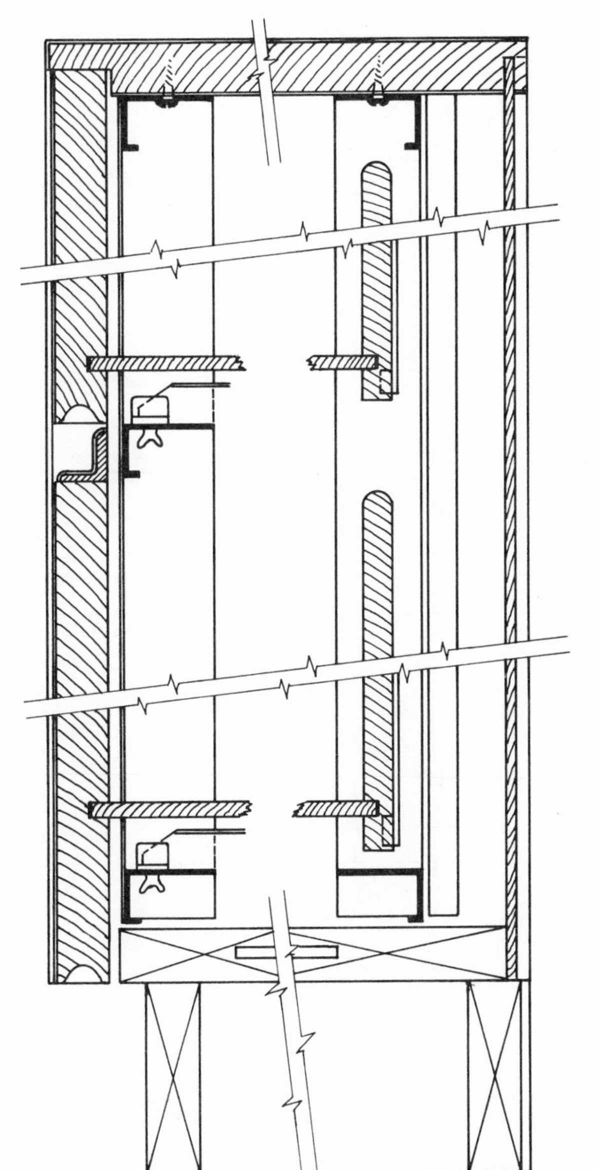

FIG. 1-29. Enlarged Section View of Desk Profile (R-Way Furniture Co.)

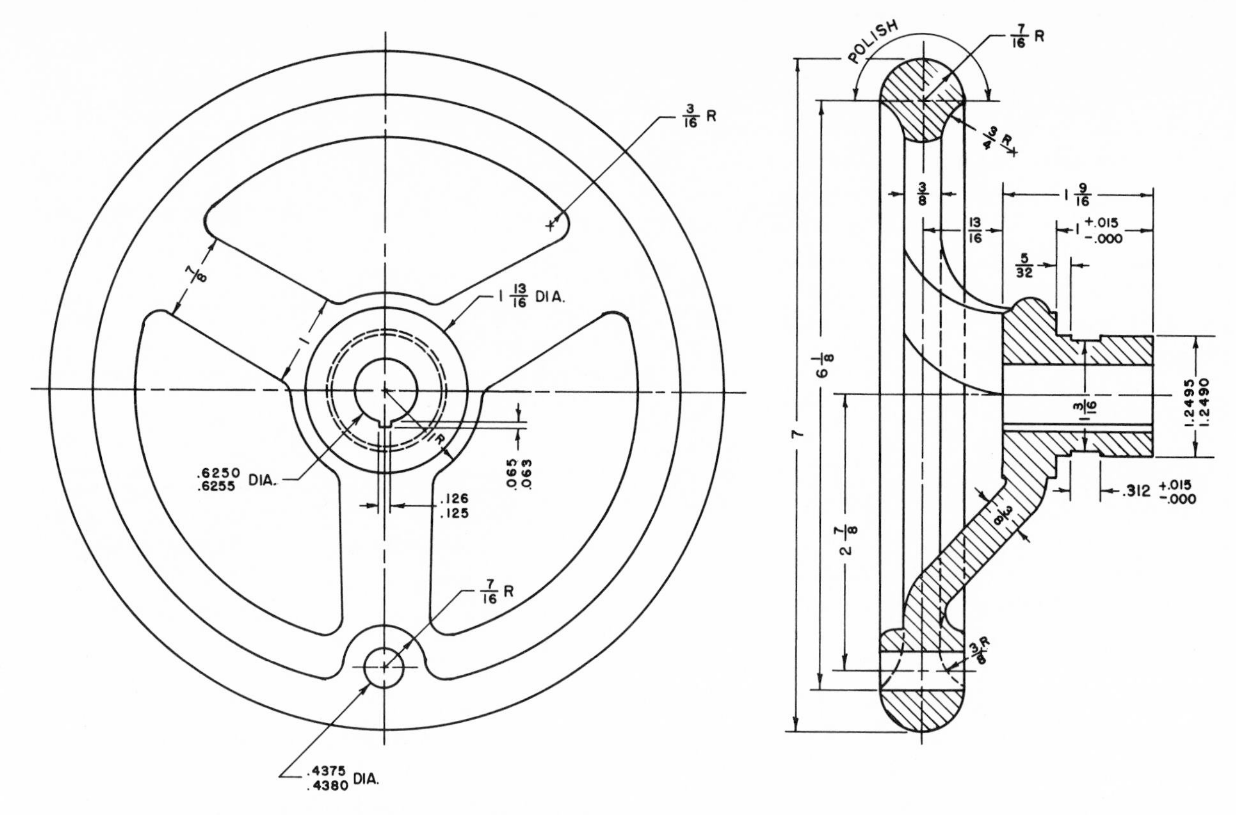

Fig. 1-30. Section View of Handwheel (Gisholt Machine Co.)

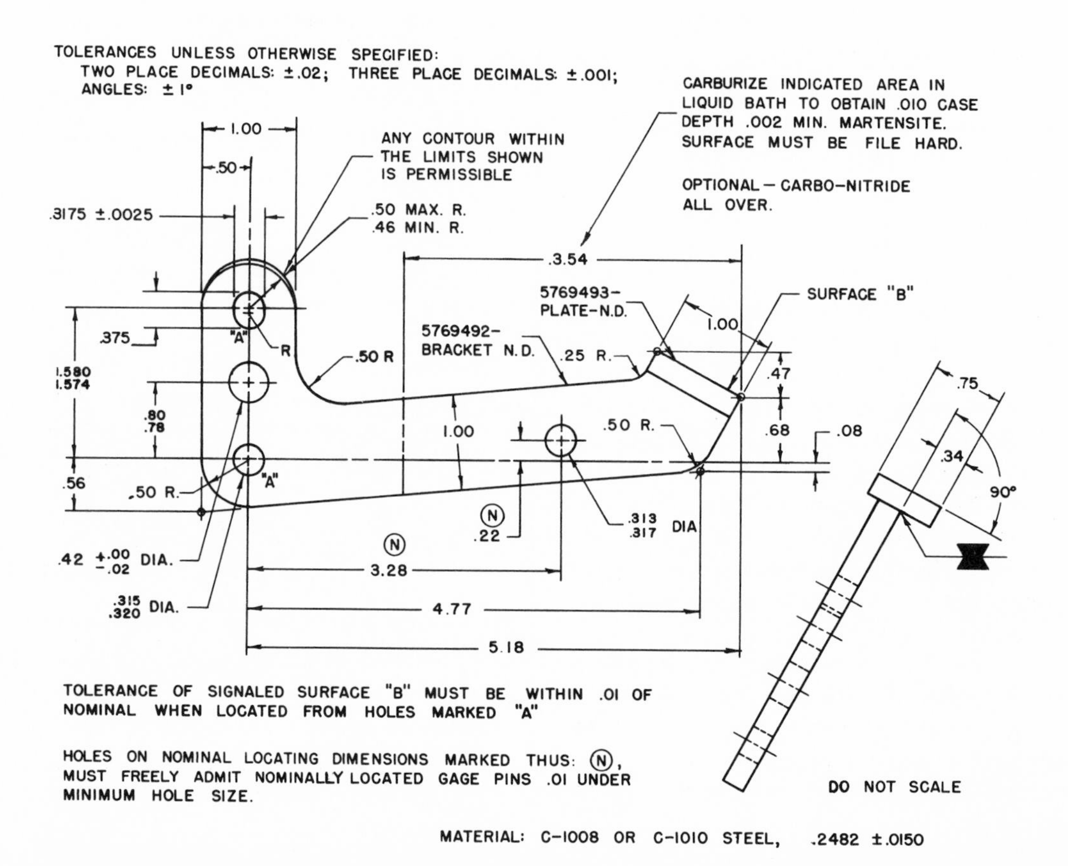

Fig. 1-31. Dimensioned Drawing of Clutch Pedal Push Rod (General Motors of Canada)

Dimensioning

Once the idea has been transformed into a multi-view projection with any necessary sectional views, the drawing must be *dimensioned* – *i.e.*, sizes of each part must be indicated. As the draftsman develops the drawing, he must leave ample space between the views for the dimensions. His objective is to convey to others the exact appearance of the object – its *true size* and *true shape*. Nothing should be left to chance or assumption.

Shop Processes

To dimension, the draftsman must understand the industrial process used to cut, shape, form, and assemble the object. To dimension the drawing in Fig. 1-20, he needs to know what serrations are and how to indicate them; also, he needs to know what a chamfer is, how it is produced on round stock, and how to specify this on the drawing. Fig. 1-24 requires knowledge of methods for drilling holes and of types of surface finishes. In Fig. 1-31 an understanding of welding is needed for fastening the plate to the bracket in dimensioning the clutch pedal push rod.

Lettering

Notes and dimension figures on a drawing must be written so that they cannot be misinterpreted. Any draftsman will emphasize the importance of lettering neatly, legibly, and with reasonable speed.

Dimensioning the Drawing

Most of the figures shown thus far have used the *aligned system* of dimensioning – *i.e.*, the dimensions are aligned in their relationship to the dimension and extension lines. Fig. 1-31 illustrates the *unidirectional system* frequently used in both the ground and space vehicle industries. With either system, dimensions are placed according to standard practices. It should be remembered that there is more chance for error in lettering and dimensioning than in any other aspect of drawing preparation.

Reproducing the Drawing

The objective of industrial drawing is to transmit graphic ideas to someone else. Once the idea has been conceived, refined, recorded, and dimensioned, it is reproduced and put into the hands of those for whom it was intended. Copies of house plans are submitted by the architect to the client for approval, and then to several contractors for bids and later to those selected for building. Copies of plans for industrial products go to the shops where the product is to be built. Formerly these copies often were blueprints; however, newer types of reproduction prints (including microfilming) are being used today. More information on finishing and reproducing drawings can be found in Chapter 9.

Summary

As a summary of the steps in preparing a set of drawings, the procedure in the development of one simple product is outlined. The Engineering Department has suggested a design for towel holders. It makes use of a marble, an inclined plane, and a finger which holds the marble. Gravity pulls the marble down. The towel is inserted under the finger. The weight of the towel pulls the marble down, and this keeps the towel hanging. To release the towel, one simply pulls the towel up and out.

The results of the first six steps in the solution of this drafting problem are shown in Fig. 1-32. The seventh step which results in the mechanical drawing is shown in Fig. 1-33. The final step (reproducing the drawing) is not illustrated. In actual practice, one or more pilot models would be made to check appearance and also the operation of parts. Any modifications would be entered on the original drawings, and then final prints for production would be released.

In the outline which follows, note the skills needed for each step. Note also how these accumulate so that the seventh step requires several abilities.

Outline — Solving a Drafting Problem

The Towel Holder

1. Idea occurs.
2. Blocked out idea in pictorial form for purposes of visualization, study and communication.

   Ability to:
   a. Sketch lines.
   b. Sketch using pictorial representation.

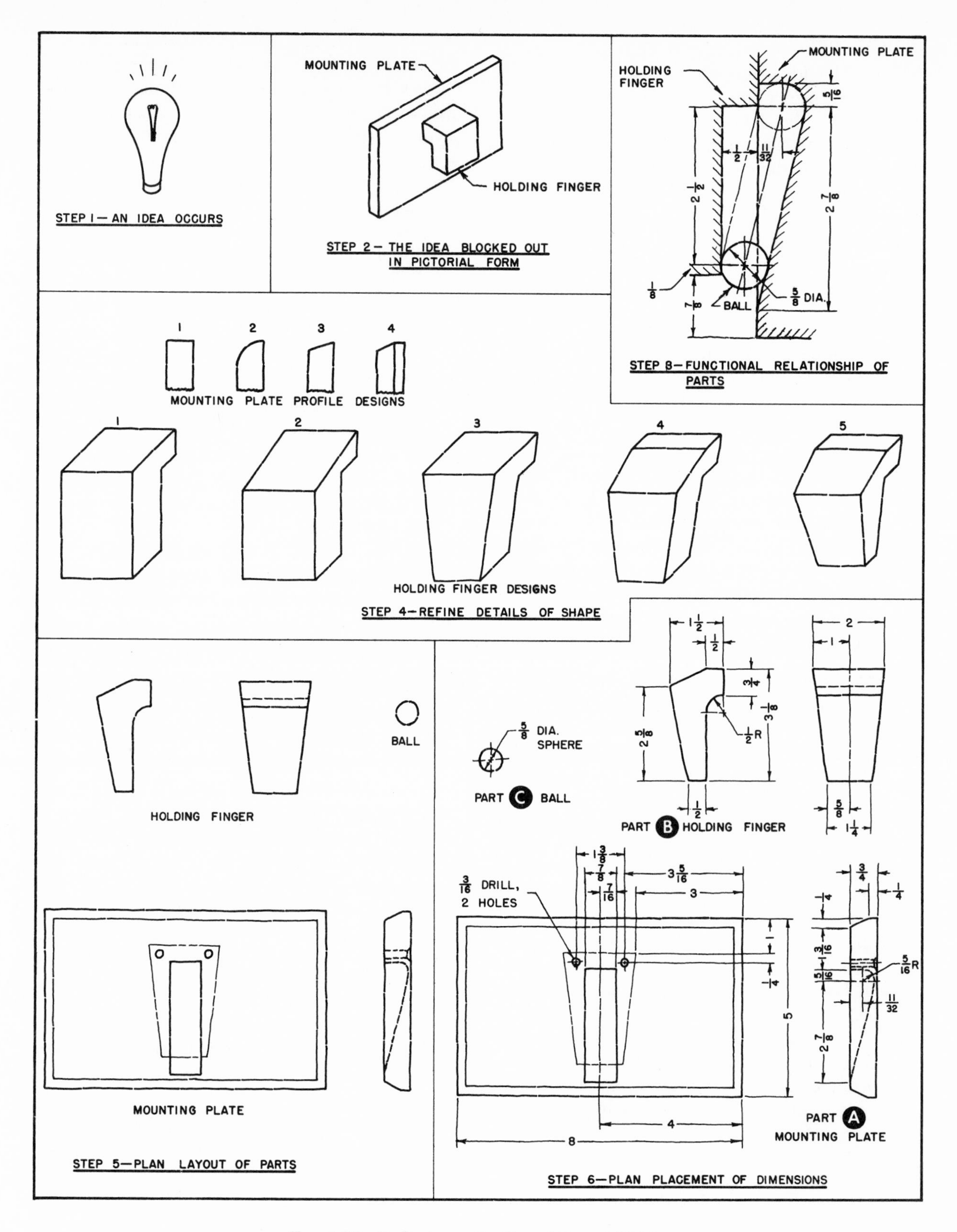

Fig. 1-32. Preliminary Studies of Towel Holder

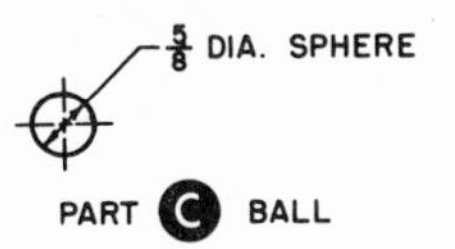

SOFTEN ALL ARRISES

PARTS LIST

NO.	NAME	REQD.	MATL.
A	MOUNTING PLATE	1	BIRCH
B	HOLDING FINGER	1	BIRCH
C	BALL	1	MARBLE
	1 3/4 — NO. 9, F.H. WOOD SCREW	2	STEEL
	FLAT LACQUER FINISH		

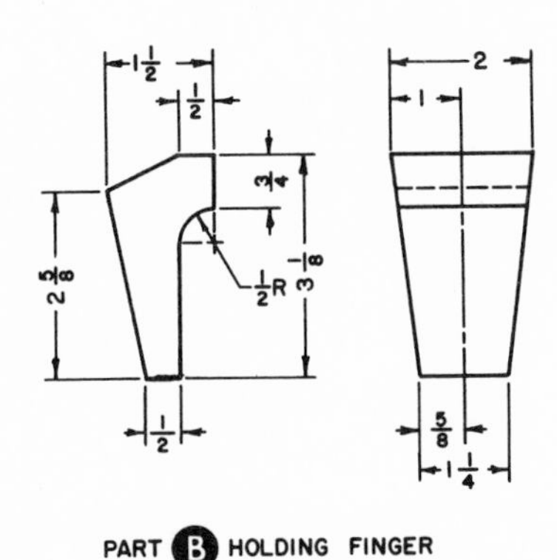

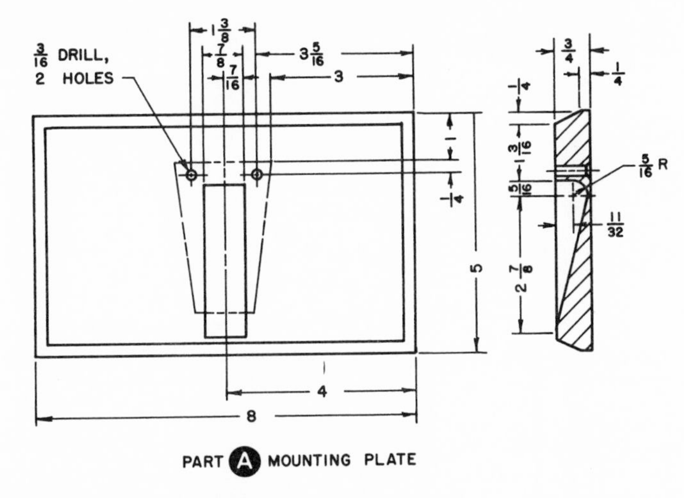

STEP 7—PREPARE WORKING DRAWINGS

Fig. 1-33. Towel Holder

3. Develop functional relationship of parts.
   Ability to:
   a. Sketch lines.
   b. Make a one-view sketch.
4. Refine details of shape for parts.
   Ability to:
   a. Sketch lines.
   b. Make pictorial sketches.
   c. Visualize.
5. Plan for layout of parts.
   Ability to:
   a. Sketch lines.
   b. Make multi-view sketches.
   c. Visualize.
6. Plan for placement of dimensions of parts.
   Ability to:
   a. Apply an understanding of shop processes to selection of dimensions.
   b. Letter notes and figures.
   c. Dimension of multi-view drawing.
7. Prepare working drawing of Parts *A*, *B*, and *C*.
   Ability to:
   a. Layout multi-view drawings.
   b. Visualize.
   c. Use basic mechanical drafting equipment.
   d. Make geometrical constructions.
   e. Show interior detail.
   f. Dimension a drawing, including understanding of shop processes and lettering.
   g. Make parts lists.
8. Make any needed changes; reproduce and distribute copies.

This exact order of steps may not always be followed by draftsmen. An experienced draftsman, especially for such a simple product, might omit the sketching in steps 5 and 6 and go directly to the mechanical drawing in step 7. He might even begin with step 7. From a practical standpoint, the draftsman uses all of his knowledge at almost the same time. However, for instructional purposes, an analysis of the draftsman's work procedure is helpful. These steps form the outline for this book which follows this pattern of development.

Chapter 1 — Problems and Projects

1. What local sources can you use to learn more about drafting?

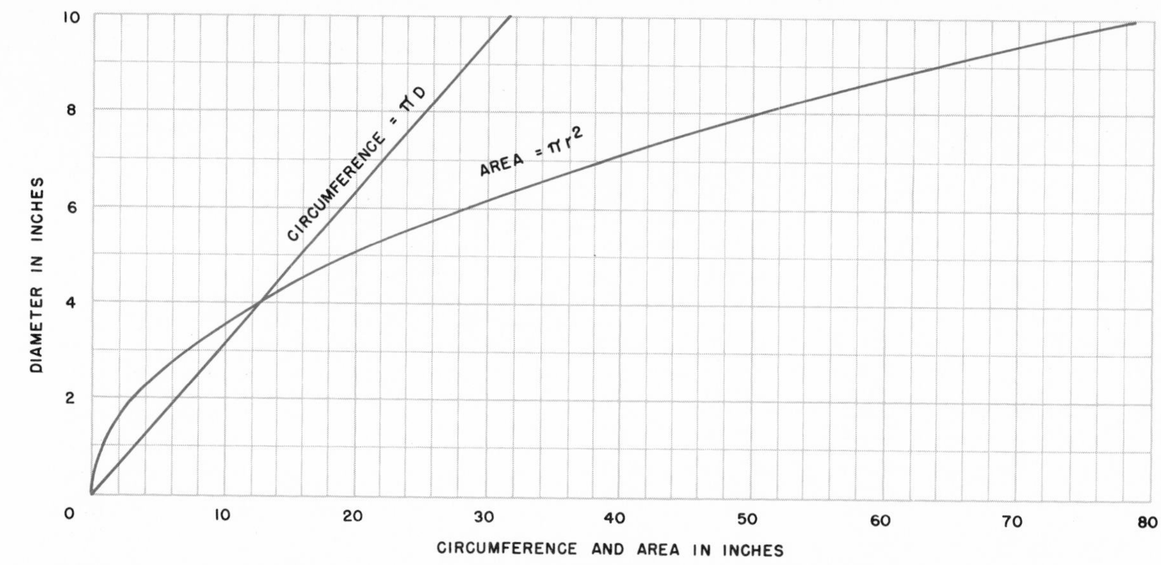

FIG. 1-34. Comparison of Circumference with Area of Circles for Diameter Ranging from 0 to 10 Inches

2. Select some specialized field of drafting that interests you. What are the advantages and disadvantages of this occupation? What are the wages a beginner can expect? What are the normal paths of advancement? What education is needed?
3. Visit your nearest State Employment Security office. What is the employment outlook for draftsmen? What kinds of drafting jobs exist in the community? Approximately how many draftsmen are employed in your city?
4. Visit a draftsman on the job. What does he like about his work? What does he dislike? What professional organizations has he joined? Find out what he feels are the basic skills required in drafting. Ask him about the procedure he follows in using these skills to solve a typical drafting problem. Do you think you would get the same answers from a draftsman who works primarily with sheet metal? machine drawings? structural drawings? Explain.
5. What are the requirements for becoming a drafting teacher?
6. Keep a record of the drafting jobs listed in the Want-Ad section of your daily paper over a period of time.
7. What is the nearest industry that markets some of its products in foreign countries? Does the company furnish drawings in the language and style of that country?
8. Make a list of the adults you know who do not make or read any form of drafting.
9. Name one industrial product that does not require drawings somewhere in the process of its manufacture.
10. What is the purpose of published drafting room standards? Are standards unchangeable? Explain.
11. Make any one of the following:
    a. A list of products that you would like to make.
    b. A list of products that should be invented.
    c. A list of products that should be redesigned.
12. Solve one of the following problems. (Show your arithmetic and sketch for each design.)
    a. Design two differently shaped containers, each of which will hold 1½ gallons of water. (There are 231 cubic inches in one standard gallon liquid.)
    b. Design two different devices, each of which will accommodate twelve 20-exposure rolls of 35mm film as they come in their cardboard container from the store. (Cardboard container size for each roll is 1⁹⁄₁₆″ x 1⁹⁄₁₆″ x 2⅜″.)
    c. Design a device for the coin collector to sort the following United States coins — maximum of fifty 10¢ pieces, forty 1¢ pieces, and thirty 5¢ pieces.

13. Read the graph in Fig. 1-34 to answer these questions:
    a. A circle has a 3″ diameter, what is its circumference? What is its area?
    b. What diameter must a circle have if its circumference is equal to its area?
    c. Read from the graph the area of a circle 60″ in diameter. Check your result by substituting in the appropriate formula and solving.
    d. Read from the graph the circumference of a circle 0.7″ in diameter. Check by substituting in the formula and solving.
    e. Read directly from the graph both the circumference and the area for a circle 2.5″ in diameter.
    f. What is the effect on the area of a circle when the diameter is doubled? What is the effect on the circumference?
14. Read the drawings of the magazine rack shown in Fig. 1-35 to answer the following questions:
    a. How many different pieces are required to make the magazine rack? What is the total number of parts required?
    b. What width magazine will this rack accommodate?
    c. How is the sheet metal shelf to be fastened to the shelf supports?
    d. How are the cross braces to be fastened to the two circles?
    e. With reference to the perforated metal shelf, Part 5, why is one end folded twice?
    f. Explain how you think the circle (Part 4) will be formed so that each is the same size and shape.
    g. Using the formula for circumference of a circle (πD), calculate the length of the piece needed for one of the circles. Check your arithmetic against the graphic solution you obtain by using the graph in Fig. 1-34.
    h. Is this the same as the given blank length in Fig. 1-35? Explain any difference that you may find.
15. Read the Italian drawing of Fig. 1-36 to answer the following questions:
    a. What units of measurement are used on this drawing?
    b. At what scale was this drawing made? (See title block.)
    c. What is the Italian title of this drawing? (This means "bracket" in English.)
    d. What is the overall size in mm of this subassembly? (There are 25.4mm per inch. Convert the overall size to inches).
    e. How are the parts of this subassembly fastened together?
    f. How many different parts are there in this subassembly? How many total parts?
    g. There are two ways to find the overall size of Part 4. What are these? Does the overall size for Part 4 come out to be the same using each of the two methods?
    h. How many holes are there in Part 1? What is their diameter?
16. Read the drawings of the industrial clamp shown in Fig. 1-37 to answer the following questions:
    a. How many parts are required to make one clamp?
    b. With reference to the base (Part 1), how many holes are drilled all the way through this part?
    c. To what depth are these holes in the base drilled?
    d. What drill is used for the two threaded holes?
    e. What are the overall dimensions of the base?
    f. With reference to the top clamp plate, are the two holes threaded? Do they go all the way through the part? What drill is to be used?
    g. What is the distance between centers of the two holes in the top clamp plate?
    h. What is the largest diameter for which this clamp is designed to be used?
17. Read the drawings of the bookcase shown in Fig. 1-38 to answer the following questions:
    a. How many parts are required to make the bookcase?
    b. What is the overall finished size of the bookcase?
    c. What parts fit into detail A?

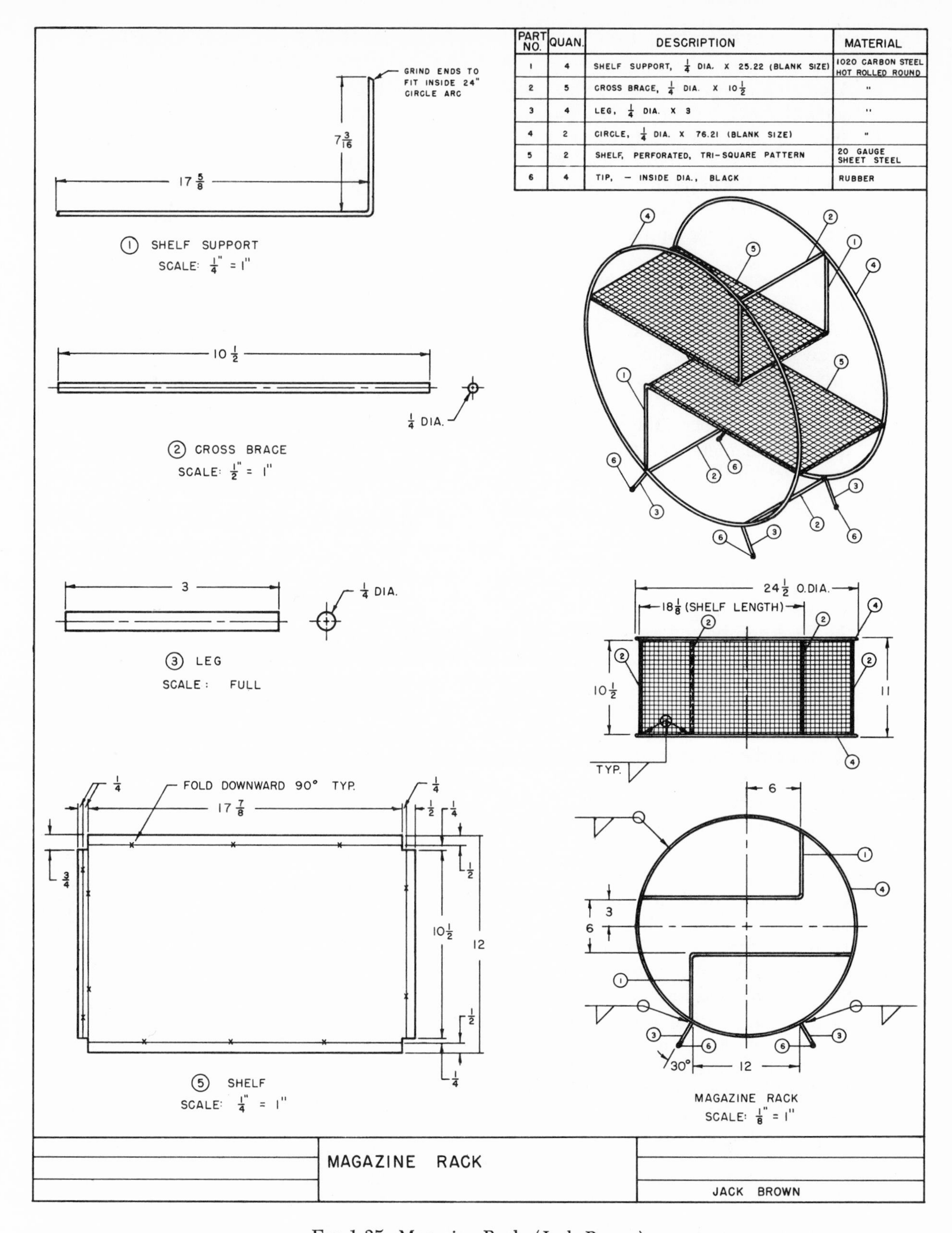

PART NO.	QUAN.	DESCRIPTION	MATERIAL
1	4	SHELF SUPPORT, $\frac{1}{4}$ DIA. X 25.22 (BLANK SIZE)	1020 CARBON STEEL HOT ROLLED ROUND
2	5	CROSS BRACE, $\frac{1}{4}$ DIA. X $10\frac{1}{2}$	"
3	4	LEG, $\frac{1}{4}$ DIA. X 3	"
4	2	CIRCLE, $\frac{1}{4}$ DIA. X 76.21 (BLANK SIZE)	"
5	2	SHELF, PERFORATED, TRI-SQUARE PATTERN	20 GAUGE SHEET STEEL
6	4	TIP, — INSIDE DIA., BLACK	RUBBER

FIG. 1-35. Magazine Rack (Jack Brown)

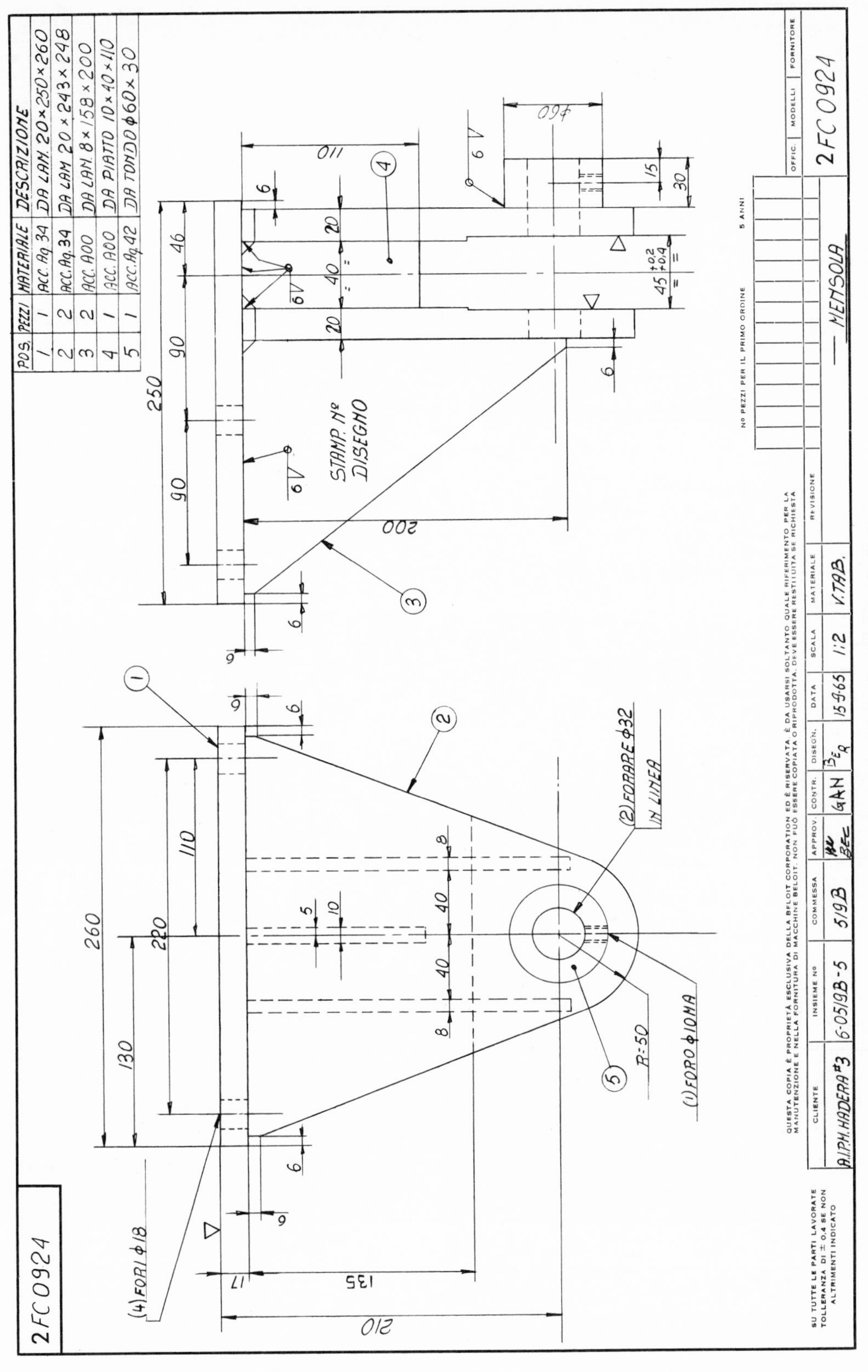

FIG. 1-36. Mensola (Beloit Italia)

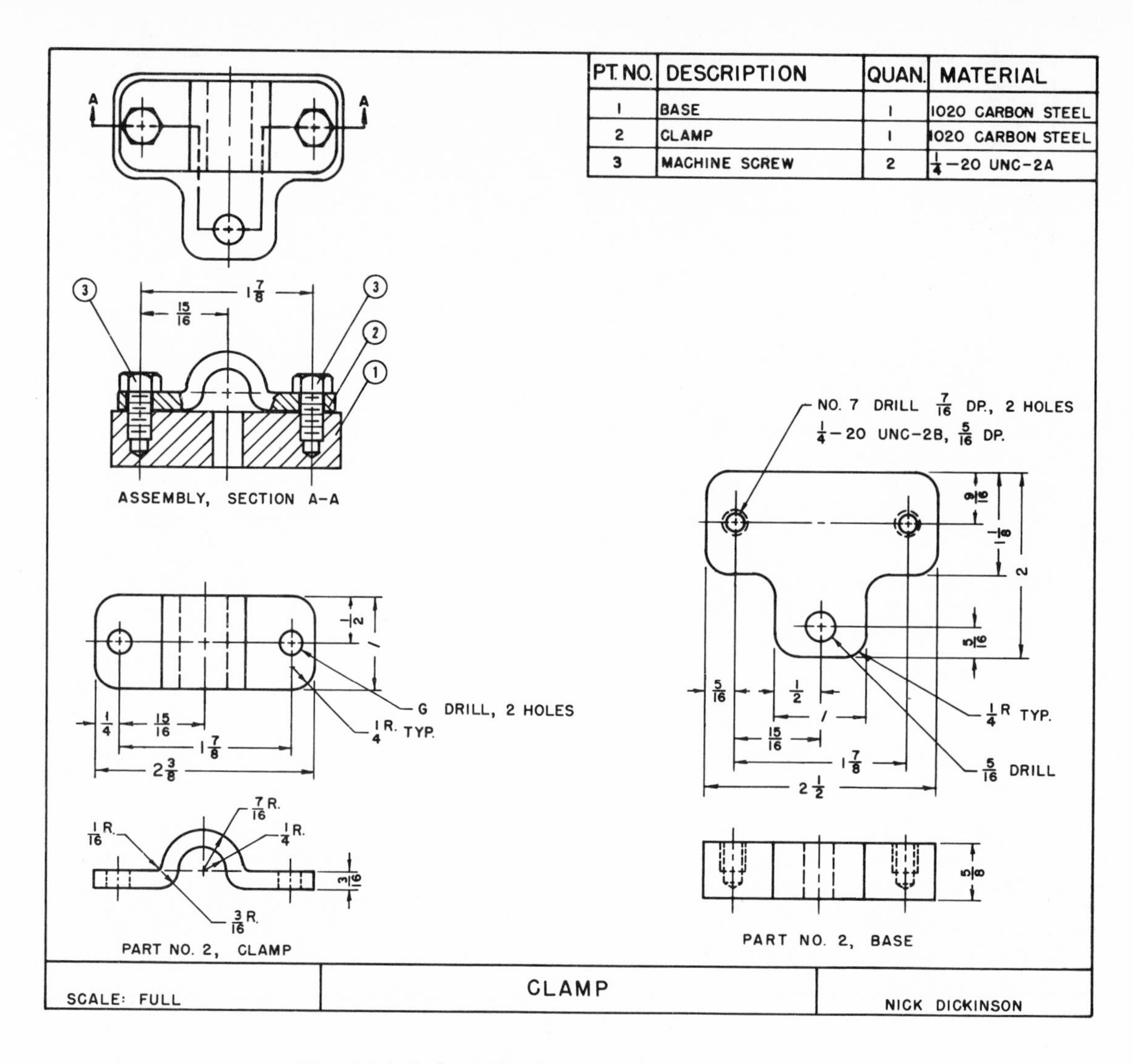

Fig. 1-37. Industrial Clamp (Nick Dickenson)

d. If the glass doors (Parts 8 and 9) are exactly ¼″ thick and the grooves shown in sections *A-A* and *B-B* were exactly ¼″ wide, what would happen when the doors were fitted into these grooves?

e. After the bookcase has been completed and books are placed in it, one of the glass doors is broken. Can a new one be put in without disassembling the bookcase? Explain your answer.

f. Why is detail *B* enlarged? Why is it shown in section view?

g. Are the two sides (Parts 3 and 4) identical? Explain.

h. What details, if any, were drawn larger than full size? Why?

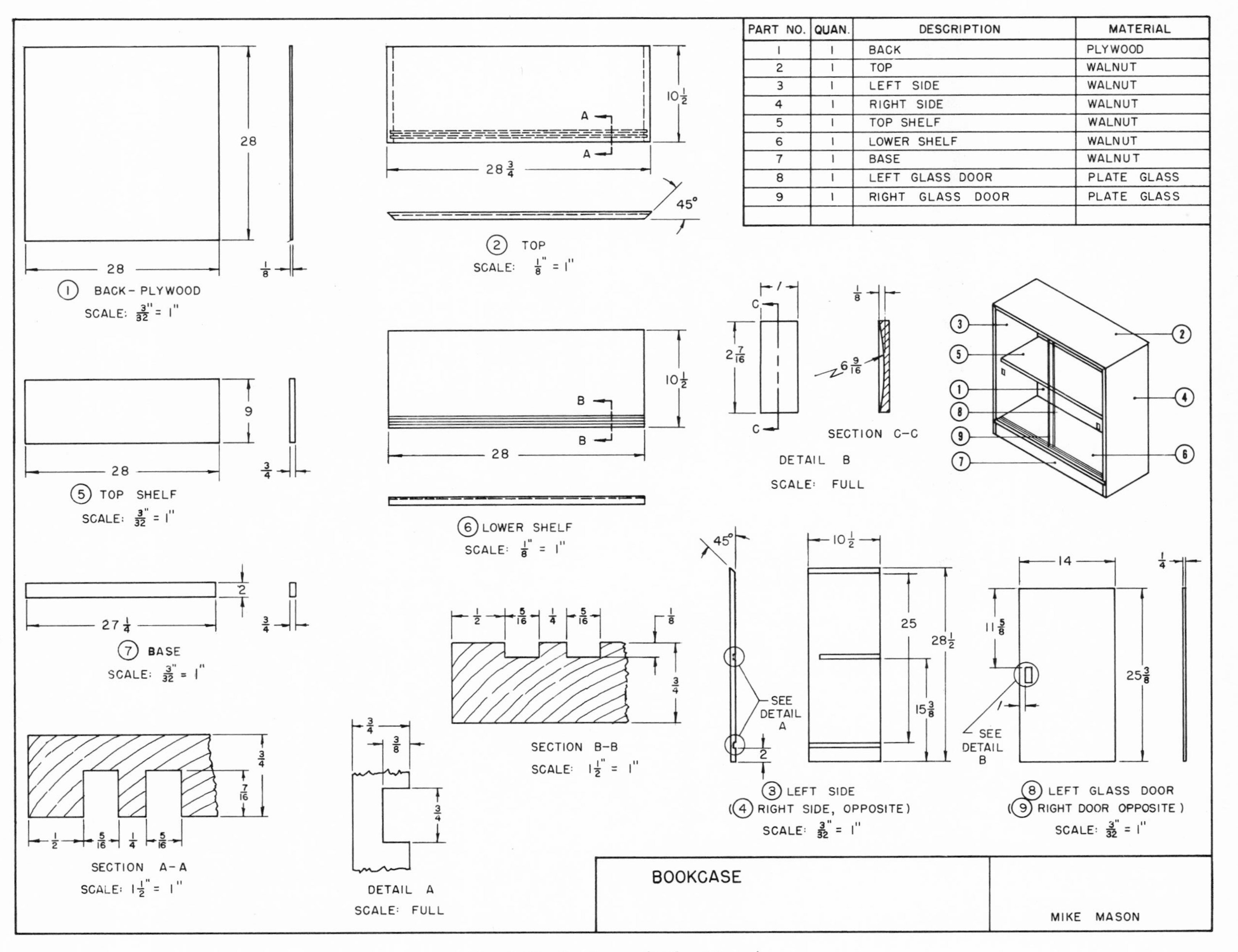

PART NO.	QUAN.	DESCRIPTION	MATERIAL
1	1	BACK	PLYWOOD
2	1	TOP	WALNUT
3	1	LEFT SIDE	WALNUT
4	1	RIGHT SIDE	WALNUT
5	1	TOP SHELF	WALNUT
6	1	LOWER SHELF	WALNUT
7	1	BASE	WALNUT
8	1	LEFT GLASS DOOR	PLATE GLASS
9	1	RIGHT GLASS DOOR	PLATE GLASS

FIG. 1-38. Bookcase (Mike Mason)

CHAPTER TWO

TECHNICAL SKETCHING

technical sketching

Preliminary studies are necessary in solving drafting problems. Because sketching can be done with pencil, paper, and eraser, it is an efficient aid in the planning that precedes mechanical drafting. For the draftsman, sketching is a means of communication which must be used every day. This chapter will help you review technical sketching and will also extend your knowledge of three-dimensional sketching.

tools and techniques

Papers

Sketches can be made on opaque or translucent papers with or without grid lines. Grid lines are helpful in sketching straight lines, in measuring, and in estimating proportion.

Pencils

A medium-soft pencil (such as *H*, *HB*, *F*, and *B*) will produce dense, black lines that are easy to see. A harder pencil (such as *3H* or *4H*) may be used for layout or constructions to be darkened later. Classification and grades of pencils are discussed in Chapter 4. See Fig. 4-19.

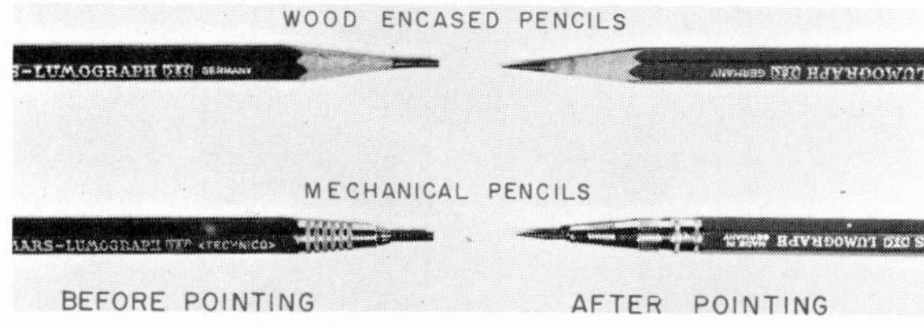

Fig. 2-1. Pencils Sharpened in Draftsman's Pencil Sharpener

Erasers

A soft eraser that effectively cleans graphite from the paper should be chosen. Some of the plastic erasers recently developed for use with plastic pencils and film tracing media are especially good.

Preparing the Sketch Pencil

Sharpening

When sharpening pencils use either a knife or a draftsman's pencil sharpener. Be sure to sharpen the *unlettered* end so the pencil can always be identified. Remove only the wood. The draftsman's pencil sharpener automatically will remove the wood about 1½″ back and leave ⅜″ of the lead exposed, Fig. 2-1.

Pointing

Point the lead to a uniform cone shape, Fig. 2-2. Use a pencil pointer, a sandpaper pad, a small mill file, or any other mechanical pencil pointer, Fig. 2-3.

1. Hold the tang end of the pointer in your hand; rest the other end on a solid surface such as the edge of the drafting table.
2. Move the pencil point over the pointer towards your body, and, at the same time, rotate the pencil in a clockwise manner, Fig. 2-4.
3. After each stroke, reposition your fingers so the next stroke begins where the preceding one ended. In this way, you can make a full cone shape along the entire 3/8″ length of exposed lead.

Before using the point, burnish it slightly on a piece of scratch paper to make it less likely to snap during use. However, do not dull the point too much, since a dull pencil point makes fuzzy, wide lines.

You will need to repoint your pencil after every few lines. Wipe the pencil point on a cleansing tissue after each repointing. Tap the pointer gently on the edge of the desk to dislodge the graphite so that it falls in a waste basket or on scrap paper. Separate your pointer from other tools by keeping it in an envelope.

Point and repoint the lead in a mechanical lead holder by this method also. The cone length should be 3/8″ after pointing.

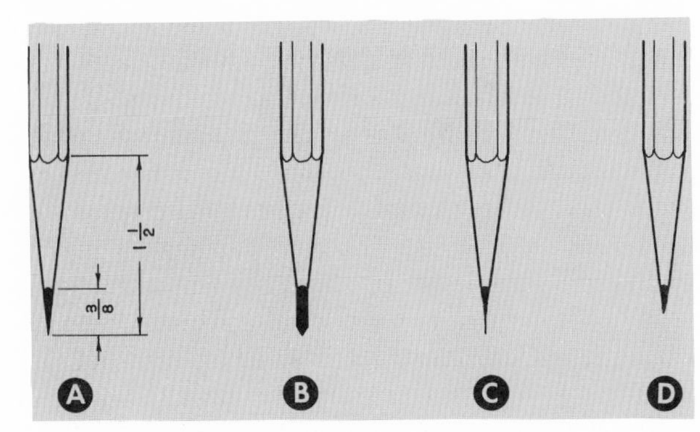

Fig. 2-2.
A. Properly sharpened and pointed for technical sketching
B. Too blunt from pointing
C. Too fine from pointing
D. Too dull from use

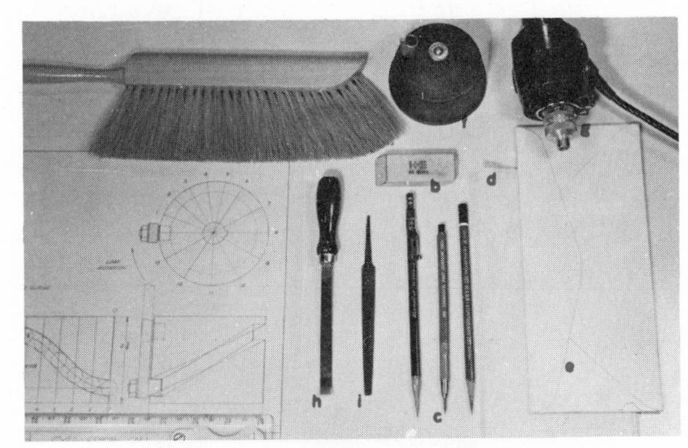

Fig. 2-3. Pencil Pointing Equipment
A. Dusting brush
B. Eraser
C. Pencils
D. Cleansing tissue
E. Envelope for pencils and pointers
F. Mechanical pencil pointer
G. Attachment for electric eraser for pointing pencil leads
H. Draftsman's pencil pointer
I. Small file used for pointing pencils

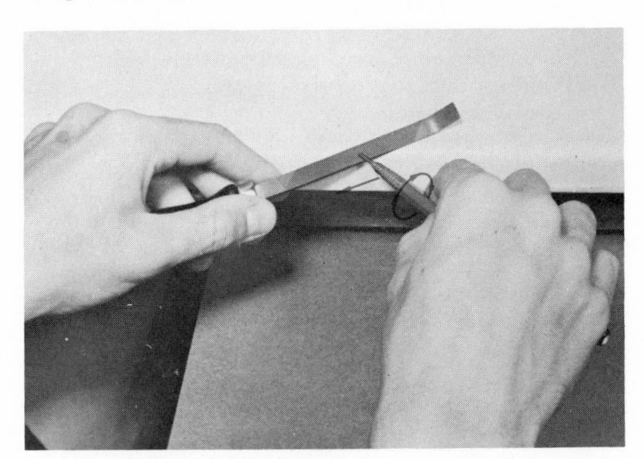

Fig. 2-4. Note Direction of Movement and Rotation

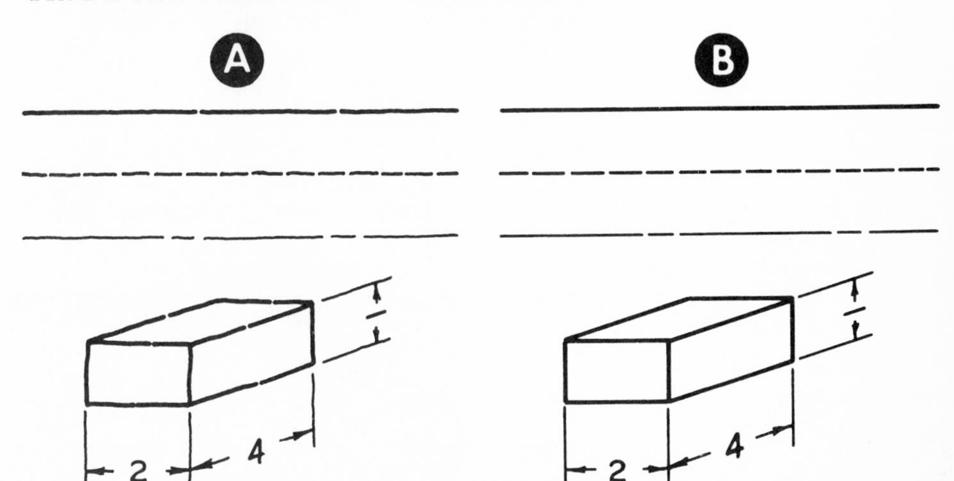

Fig. 2-5. Compare (A) Sketched Lines with (B) Mechanically Drawn Lines

Sketching Lines

In drafting, the most basic element is the straight line. You can combine horizontal, vertical, and inclined lines with curved lines to describe any object graphically.

Lines of technical sketches have a fundamental uniformity with freedom and flexibility in their execution. Mechanically drawn lines are rigid, Fig. 2-5.

Contrast the lines used by the draftsman in sketching technical objects with that used by the artist. The artist's strokes have varying width and weight. The draftsman's single strokes are sharp and clear, Fig. 2-6. In your home workshop, you may not be very fussy about the quality of your sketch. Industrial sketches prepared to show ideas to others are carefully done.

Fig. 2-6. Types of Lines
A. Make sharp clear, single-stroke sketch lines.
B. Avoid art-type feather sketch lines.
C. Avoid lines that are too light.
D. Avoid lines that are too wide.

Straight Lines

If you are right-handed, sketch *horizontal lines* from left to right. The arm and wrist should combine to make this movement, Fig. 2-7. Holding the pencil in the usual manner, sketch a series of straight lines from ¾″ to 1½″ long, end to end, to make the desired line. After sketching each line, rotate the pencil slightly. Frequent rotation keeps the point uniformly cone-shaped so that the lines are a consistent width. Also, the pencil will not require pointing as often.

Sketching a series of short lines (rather than one continuous line) will enable you to draw a straighter line. Your wrists and arms act as natural pivots. If you move your wrist and not your arm, a curved line will result, Fig. 2-8. Similarly, if you move your forearm but hold your elbow, a curve of larger radius will be drawn. Shorter strokes, up to 1½″ in length, actually may be slight curves, but, being short, they appear to be straight lines.

Sketch *vertical lines* in either of two ways — (1) by turning the paper so that the line becomes a horizontal line or (2) by holding the pencil so that you can use a finger and wrist movement to make the vertical line, Fig. 2-9. Again, use a series of strokes with a maximum length of 1½″.

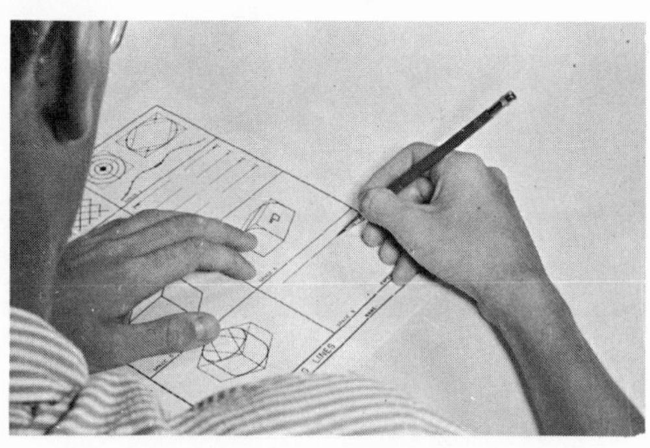

Fig. 2-7. Position of Hands and Pencil for Sketching Horizontal Lines

Fig. 2-8. The Wrist Acts as a Natural Pivot

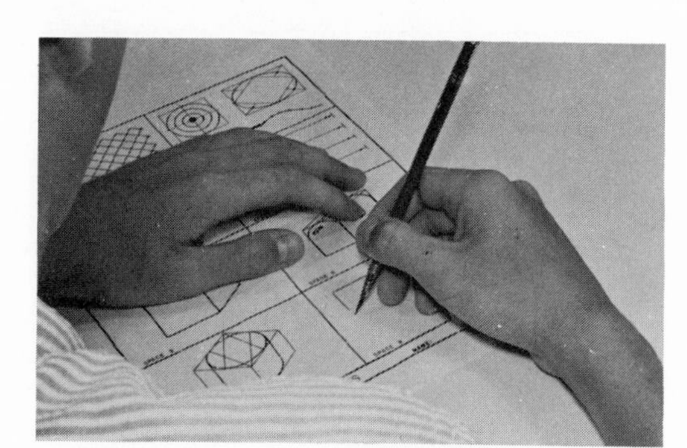

Fig. 2-9. Position of Hands and Pencil for Sketching Inclined Lines

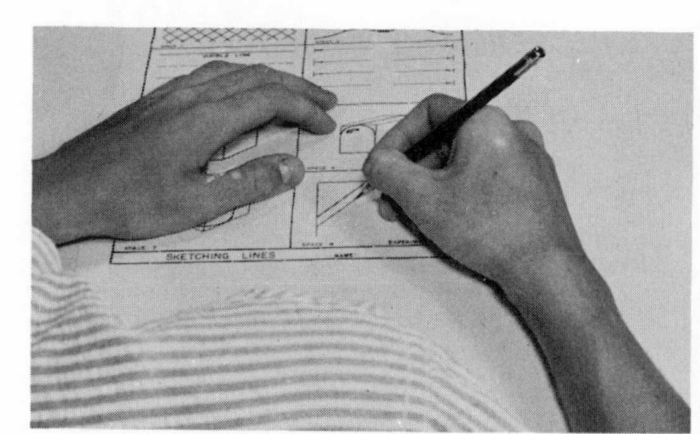

Fig. 2-10. Change the Position of the Paper to Sketch Inclined Lines

To sketch *inclined lines,* move yourself or the paper so that you use either horizontal strokes or vertical strokes, Fig. 2-10.

Regular Curves

CIRCLES AND CIRCLE ARCS. If you have not done technical sketching before, you will need an aid for sketching circles and arcs. Sketch a square with the length of any side equal to twice the radius of the desired circle. Then sketch the circle inside it, Fig. 2-11.

Another method is to construct the circle as shown in Fig. 2-12.

Always position the center lines for the circle or arc first to determine its location. Use either method of construction to make a neat sketch.

ELLIPSES. Construct an ellipse much like a circle by sketching a rectangle and inscribing the ellipse. See Fig. 2-13.

Use the method shown in Fig. 2-14 to construct an ellipse as a representation of a circle in a pictorial view. This method should be used when sketching circles in an isometric representation.

Irregular Curves

Many curved forms are neither circular nor elliptical. Fig. 2-15 shows how to sketch these irregular curves. Generally, if points are placed closer together, less approximating is needed to obtain a smooth curved form.

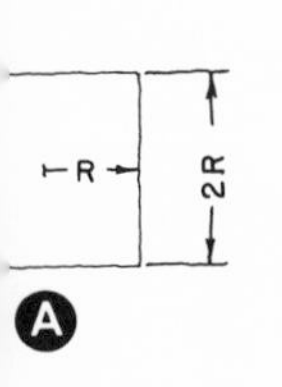

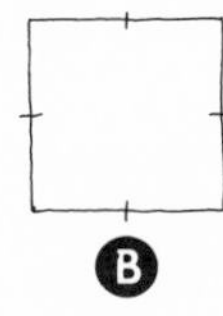

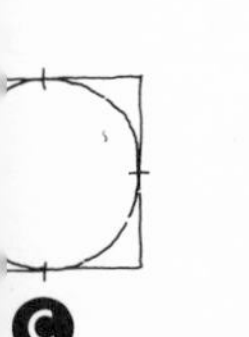

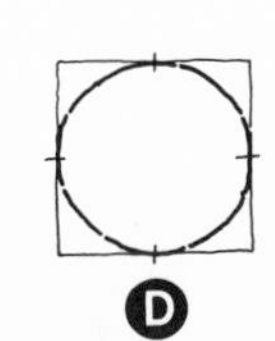

FIG. 2-11. Sketch a Circle by Inscribing it in a Square
Sketch a square in light, construction-weight lines. The length of the sides should be twice the radius of the desired circle.
Mark the mid-points of each side of the square.
Make trial arcs for the circle.
Complete the circle, and darken the object lines.

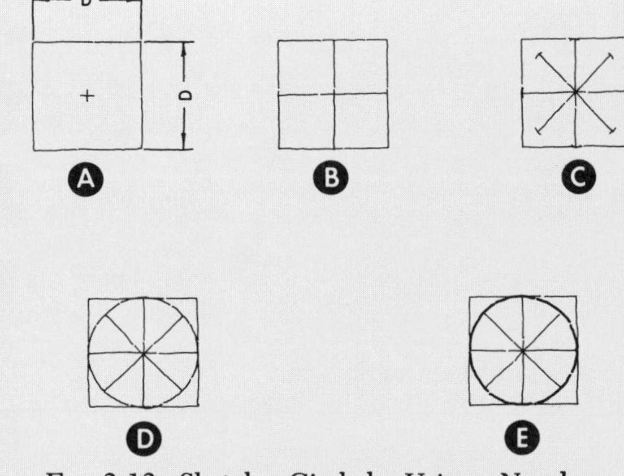

FIG. 2-12. Sketch a Circle by Using a Number of Diameters as Guides

A. Sketch a square in light, construction-weight lines. The length of the sides should be the same as the diameter of the desired circle. Locate the center of the square.
B. Through this point, construct two lines the same length as the diameter of the desired circle, perpendicular to each other and intersecting at their mid-points.
C. Add two more diameters, placing them halfway between those already constructed. Mark the end-points with circle arcs.
D. Connect the end-points with circle arcs.
E. Darken the object lines.

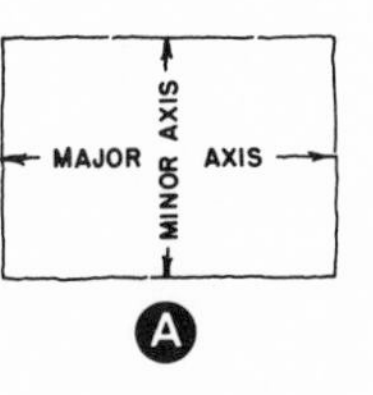

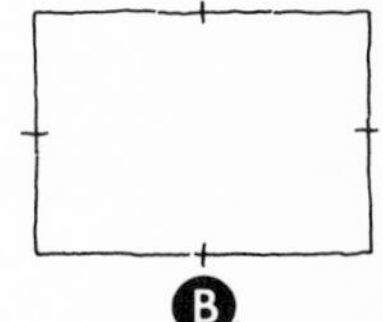

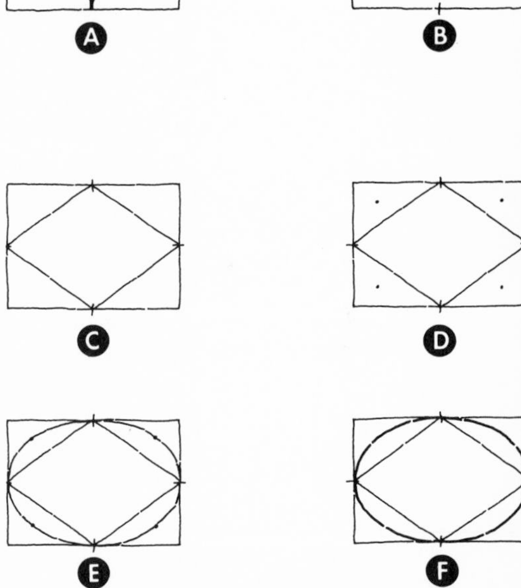

FIG. 2-13. Sketch an Ellipse by Inscribing in a Rectangle

A. Construct a rectangle of the desired size. The length should be the same as the major axis of the ellipse; the height should be the same as the minor axis of the ellipse.
B. Locate the mid-points with straight lines.
C. Connect successive mid-points with straight lines.
D. Place a dot in the approximate center of each triangle thus formed.
E. Sketch a smooth curve, passing alternately through the mid-points of the rectangle and the mid-points of the triangles.
F. Darken the ellipse.

TECHNICAL SKETCHING

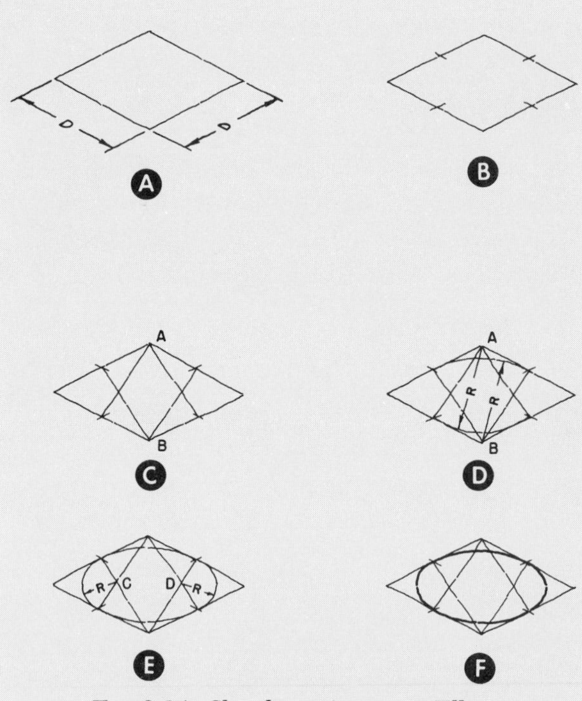

FIG. 2-14. Sketch an Apparent Ellipse Using the Four-Center Method

A. Sketch a rhombus. (A rhombus is a parallelogram with equal sides). Use light, construction-weight lines. This type of construction usually is used when viewing a circle in such a way that it appears as an ellipse. Therefore, the length of each side of the rhombus should be equal to the diameter of the circle which is to be placed as an ellipse.
B. Locate the mid-point for each side of the rhombus.
C. Using the vertices (*A* and *B*) of the obtuse angles, sketch lines to the two mid-points opposite.
D. Using the length of the constructed lines from *A* and *B* as radii, sketch circle arcs.
E. Using the intersections of the two sets of lines as at points *C* and *D*, sketch circle arcs to complete the outline.
F. Darken the ellipse.

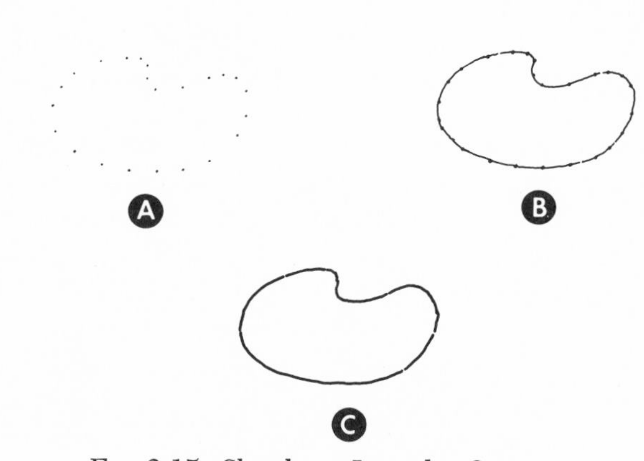

FIG. 2-15. Sketch an Irregular Curve

A. Locate several points through which the curve must pass.
B. Smoothly sketch the curve through these points.
C. Darken the curve.

Conventional Lines

In technical sketching as in mechanical drafting, each line element conveys a specific meaning. These have become standardized through use over a period of years. Fig. 2-16 identifies these lines as they are sketched, drawn in pencil, and drawn in ink. Study these conventions. Note that there is variation among the lines based on line width: some lines are thick, some medium, and some thin. This variation, coupled with the use of different grades of pencil lead, gives all necessary flexibility. Because there are no ink grades the variation in width of the ink lines is more pronounced that that for the pencil lines.

Note carefully the suggested sizes for line segments. Draftsmen do not measure each segment to get its precise length; but, they do develop an "eye" for estimating this length.

These are not "hard-and-fast" measurements. Drawing to a small scale or in a confined space may require that conventional lines be shorter than these recommendations. For example, a sketch is being made in which a hidden line must be placed in a space ⅛″ long. Hidden lines require at least two, and preferably three, short dashes. The minimum length of each dash is ⅛″; consequently, dashes shorter than the recommended length will have to be used.

For sketching thick lines, use pencils in the medium-soft range such as *H*, *F*, *HB* and sometimes *B*. Use a well-pointed *2H* or *H* pencil for thin lines. Keep in mind that all pencil lines (with the single exception of construction lines) must be sufficiently black and dense to reproduce well. Even though you may not reproduce your sketches, it is a good habit to develop this awareness of whether pencil lines will reproduce. Construction lines should be just barely visible.

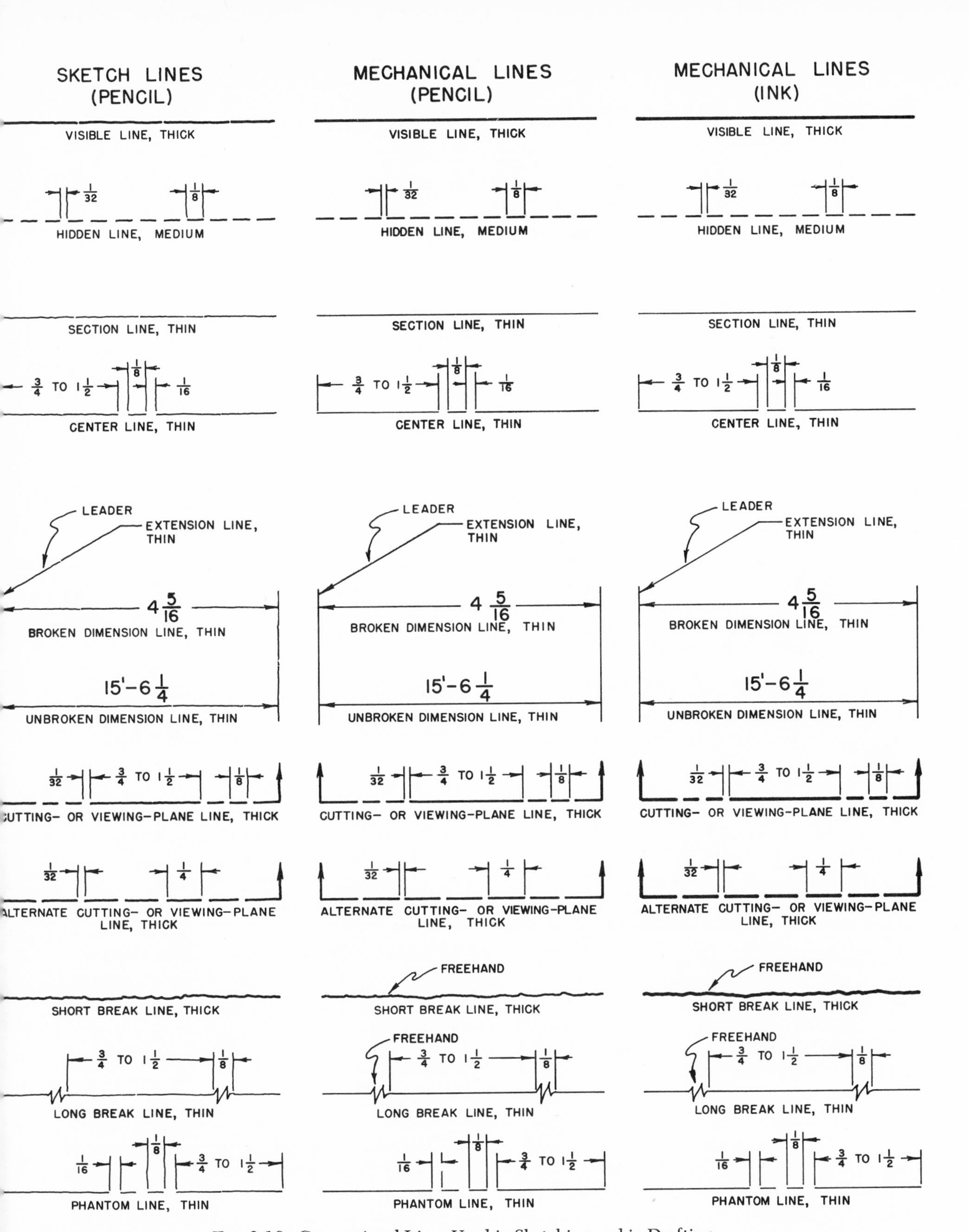

FIG. 2-16. Conventional Lines Used in Sketching and in Drafting

TECHNICAL SKETCHING

sketching in three dimensions

Basic Terms

The word *pictorial* originates from picture, which means image or likeness. You see things as they are in three dimensions: height, width, and depth. When you take a picture with a camera, or sketch a likeness on a piece of paper, you are making a representation of a three-dimensional object on a two-dimensional surface. This causes certain problems. To be sure you understand them, see whether you can define these key words: "true shape," "true size," and "representations" of shape and size.

True shape means that the sketched shape is, in fact, true. If a face of an object is physically square, and if your sketch of this face is physically square, then the sketch is in true shape. However, if a face of an object is physically square and if the sketch of it is not square, then this sketch is only a *representation* of a true face, *not* a true face. In Fig. 2-18 A(1) on page 31, the front face shows in true shape. The top and right-side faces both represent a true shape but are foreshortened.

All sketches are representations of an object, but only some faces show true shape. All sketches *represent* true shape.

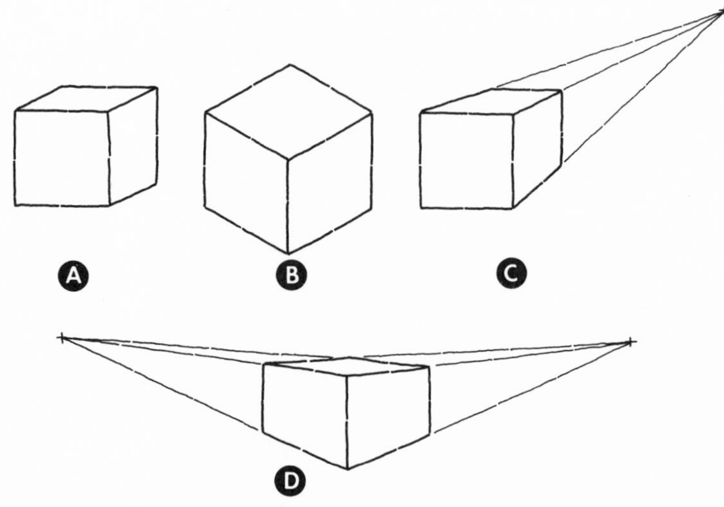

Fig. 2-17. Basic Forms of Pictorial Representation
A. Oblique
B. Isometric
C. Parallel perspective
D. Angular perspective

A line may be *true length* or a *representation* of true length. Any given object is physically a certain size. When an object is sketched, its size is represented. Objects larger than the paper upon which they are sketched are made *proportionately* smaller. Conversely, extremely small objects may require that the sketch be enlarged. In either case, this is *scaling* the object.

The height of a box will be the same regardless of the point along the bottom from which it is measured. Both the width and depth are also constant. Yet, in a pictorial representation of the object this may not be so.

When height is shown between two lines which recede to a common vanishing point, the height lines cannot be physically the same length. Refer to Fig. 2-17, *C* and *D* on page 30. The lines can, however, being different physical lengths, both represent the same true length.

The size of an object can be represented by lines which are true length or scaled length; or by lines which only represent the length but are neither true nor scaled length. The discussions which follow should clarify these concepts.

Classification of Three-D Sketches

Three-dimensional representations are classified as: *oblique, axonometric* and *perspective*. This classification is based upon the relative position of (1) the object, (2) the observer, and (3) a plane upon which the image of the object is imagined to be projected.

Four basic forms of pictorial representation, their characteristics, uses, and procedure for sketching are presented on the following pages. See Fig. 2-17. Think of the illustrations as a 2″ plastic cube used as a paperweight.

Oblique

Characteristics

See Fig. 2-18 and note that:

1. The front face appears in true shape.
2. Faces other than the front appear distorted.
3. Height lines are both vertical and parallel to each other.
4. Width lines are both horizontal and parallel to each other.

5. Depth lines recede at any convenient angle and are parallel to each other.
6. All lines show in their true length (or scaled length).

Uses

Oblique 3-D representation is used when quick work is desired with a minimum of construction. Features of an object which are circular, or irregular, if placed in the front view will retain their true shape. This is a useful form for students and teachers who may be solving problems of visualization. Different faces may be shown or two faces may be emphasized at the expense of the third merely by changing the angle of the receding lines. See Fig. 2-19.

A disadvantage of this type of pictorial is that long objects not properly positioned may be very distorted, Fig. 2-20.

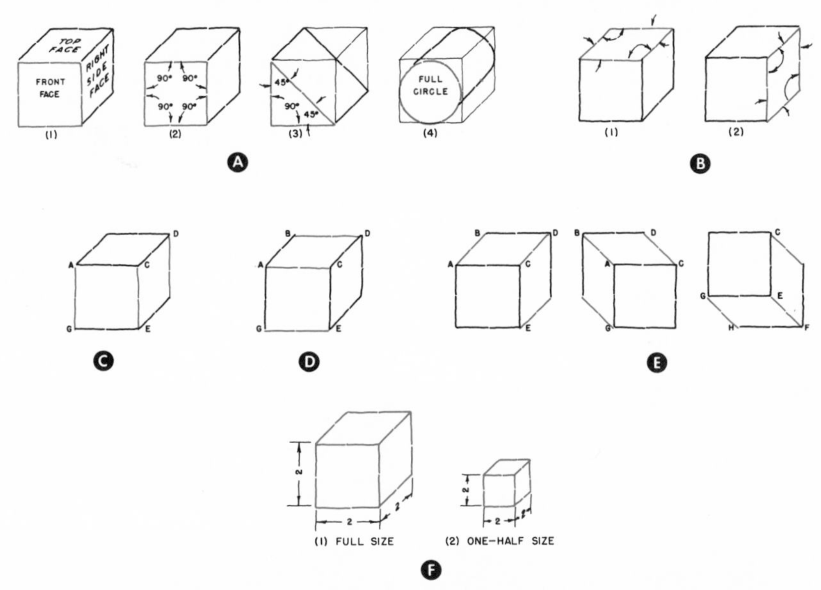

FIG. 2-18. Characteristics of Oblique Pictorial Representation

A. (1) The front face shows in true shape.
   (2) If lines make 90° angles with each other on the object, then these lines are 90° in the front face of the oblique.
   (3) If lines are at an angle on the front of the object, they are at the same angle on the oblique front face.
   (4) If the front face has a circular feature in it, this will show on the front face of the oblique as a circle.
B. Faces other than the front face and the rear face (the rear face usually is hidden from view) do not show true shape.
C. Height lines are vertical and parallel to each other.
D. Width lines are horizontal and parallel to each other. Note lines *GE*, *AC*, and *BD*.
E. Depth lines may recede at any convenient angle from the front view. For a given sketch, all depth lines are parallel to each other. Note lines *AB*, *CD*, *EF*, and *HG*.
F. All lines show in their full length or in their scaled value from full length.

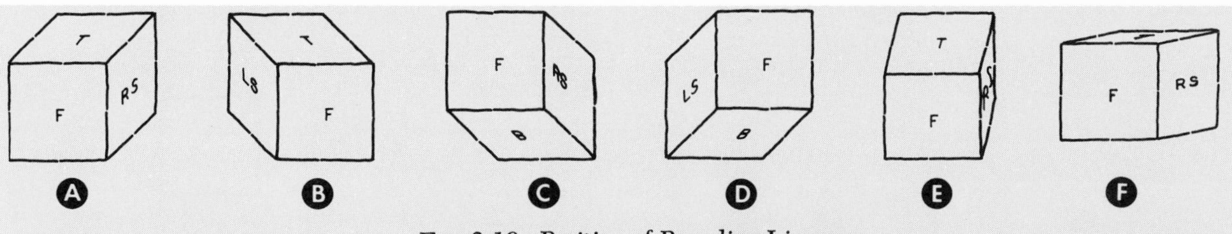

FIG. 2-19. Position of Receding Lines

A. Front, top and right side
B. Front, top and left side
C. Front, bottom and right side
D. Front, bottom and left side
E. Emphasis of top and front at the expense of the side face
F. Emphasis of front and side at the expense of the top face

Sketching Procedure

1. Select the face to be used as the front face. If the object is quite long, select this length as the front view to obtain the minimum distortion. See Fig. 2-20A. If the object has a circular feature or an irregular shape, select this for the front face to show its true shape. Refer to Fig. 2-18 A(4).
2. Determine which other faces will show, e.g., the left side and top; right side and bottom; top and right side. Review Fig. 2-19.
3. Sketch the front face of the oblique pictorial. (For the remaining steps, see Fig. 2-21.)
4. Sketch the receding lines.
5. Complete the construction of the sketch.
6. Darken all object lines.

One-Point or Parallel Perspective

Characteristics

See Fig. 2-22 and note that:

1. The front face appears in true shape.
2. Faces other than the front appear somewhat distorted.
3. Depth lines recede to a common vanishing point.
4. Height lines are both vertical and parallel to each other.
5. Width lines are both horizontal and parallel to each other.
6. Of the height and width lines, only those in the front face are true length.
7. Only one depth line can be true length.

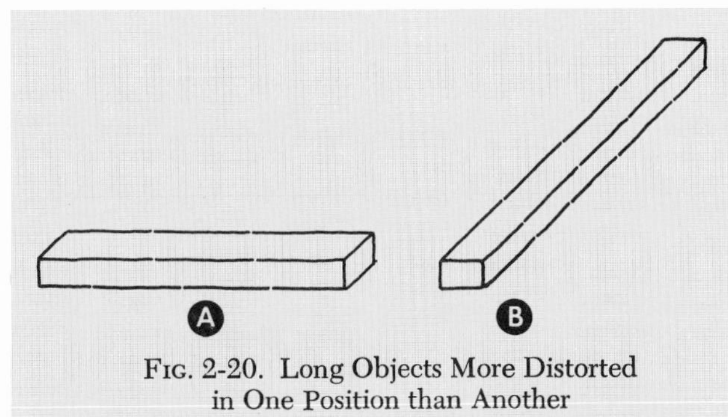

Fig. 2-20. Long Objects More Distorted in One Position than Another
A. Properly positioned
B. Improperly positioned

Uses

One-point, or parallel, perspective is used chiefly for interior views of rooms by interior decorators and architects, Fig. 2-23. It also is used by students and engineers to obtain a pictorial somewhat more like the original object than can be done with oblique. It has the advantage of showing one true face in the front view, thus enabling quick transposition from the object to the sketch. Different faces of the object can be shown by changing the position of the vanishing point. See Fig. 2-24. This also can be done to vary the amount of distortion to emphasize two faces at the expense of the third, Fig. 2-25. For example, the front and side faces may be emphasized at the expense of the top face.

The chief disadvantage of the one-point perspective is that long objects, if placed with their length as the depth dimension, will be quite distorted just as in oblique representation, Fig. 2-26.

Sketching Procedure

1. Select the faces which are to be shown. Choose which of these is to be the front view. In the case of a long object, this length should be chosen as the front view to minimize distortion.

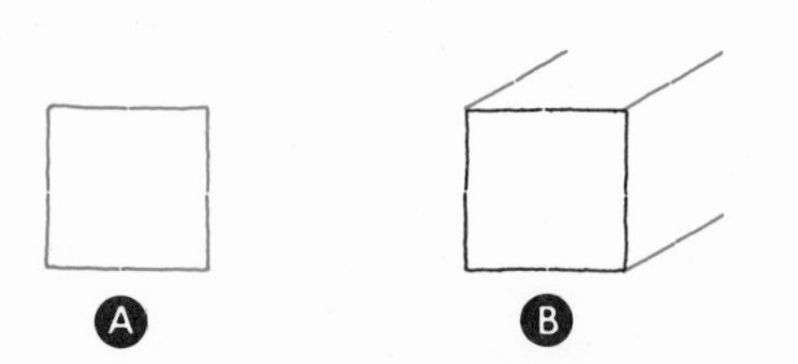

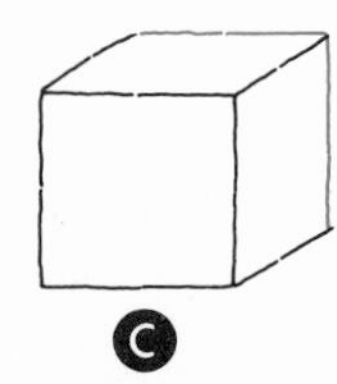

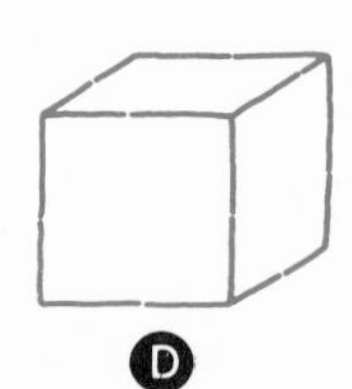

Fig. 2-21. Steps for Sketching Oblique Pictorials
A. Sketch the front face full size or to whatever scale seems reasonable. Use light construction lines.
B. Sketch the receding lines with the appropriate angle. Use construction lines. The angle of inclination for the receding lines will be determined by the detail in the surface other than the front view which you want to display most prominently.
C. Sketch the remaining horizontal and vertical lines to complete the outline.
D. Darken all object lines. Note: *Hidden lines usually are not shown in pictorial representation.*

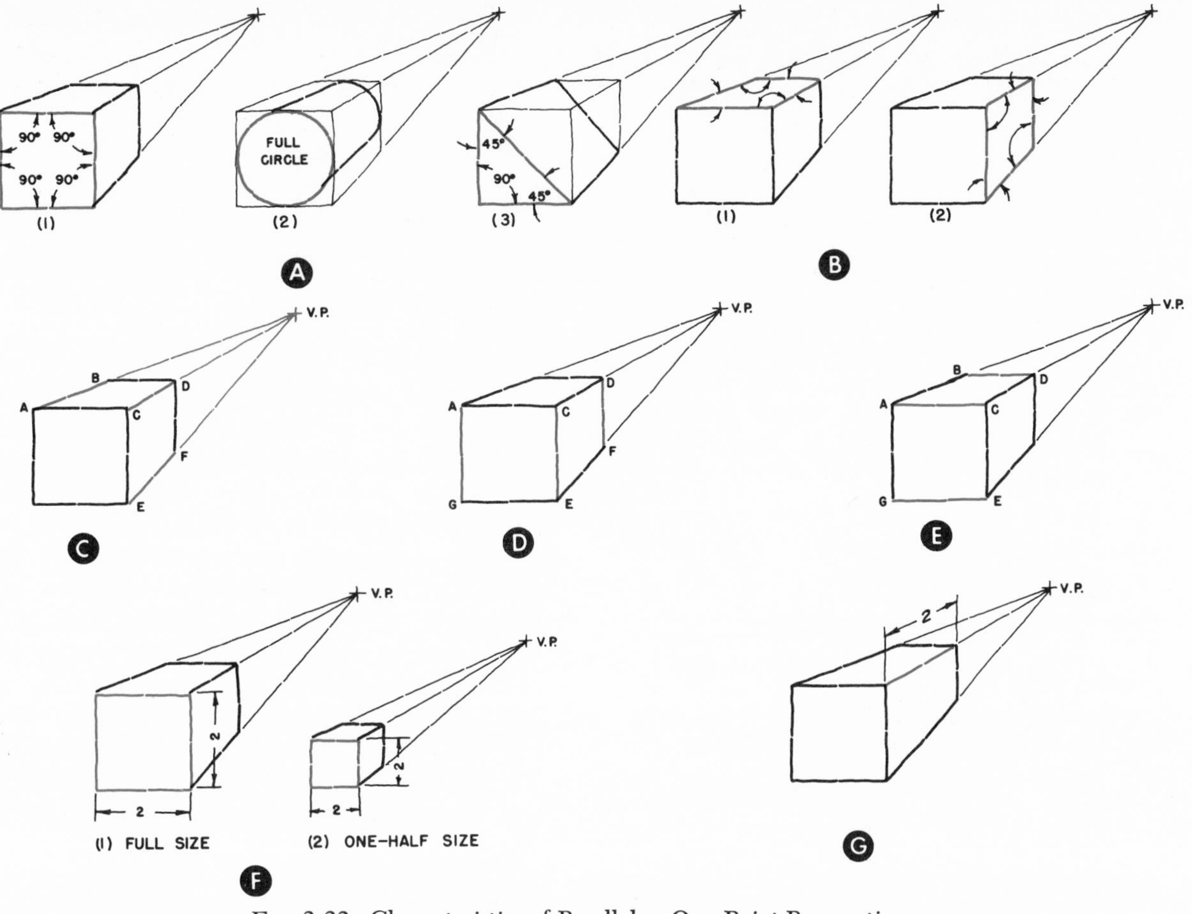

FIG. 2-22. Characteristics of Parallel or One-Point Perspective

A. (1) The front face will appear in true shape just as in oblique.
   (2) If a circular feature appears in the front face of the object, it will appear in its true shape in the front view.
   (3) An angular feature in the front face will appear as a true shape in the front view.

B. Faces other than the front face and rear face (the rear face is usually hidden) do not show true shape.

C. Extensions of the depth lines recede to a common vanishing point. This means that these lines cannot be parallel. Note lines *AB, CD,* and *EF*.

D. Height lines are vertical and parallel to each other. Note lines *AG, CE,* and *DF*.

E. Width lines are horizontal and parallel to each other. Note lines *GE, AC,* and *BD*.

F. Of the height and width lines, only those in the front face are full or scaled size. Because the height and width lines limit the rear of the object, and yet are terminated by a pair of lines which recede to a common vanishing point, they cannot be physically the same length even though they represent the same distance.

G. Since the depth lines originate at different points but recede to a common point, only one can be true length. The center one of the three receding lines usually is selected as the one upon which to layout the depth dimension.

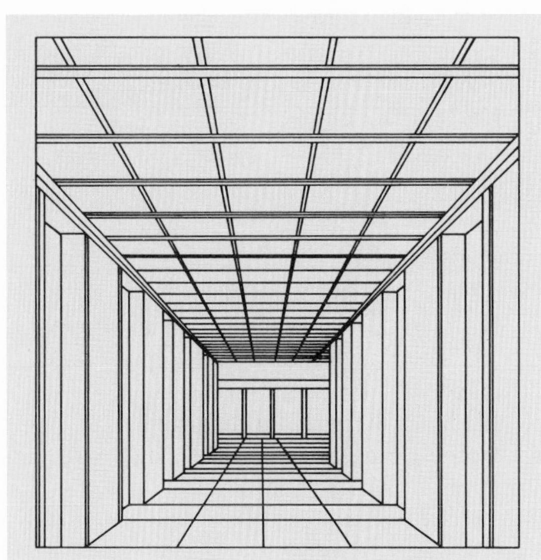

FIG. 2-23. Designers Use One-Point Perspective Representation for Interiors of Rooms

TECHNICAL SKETCHING

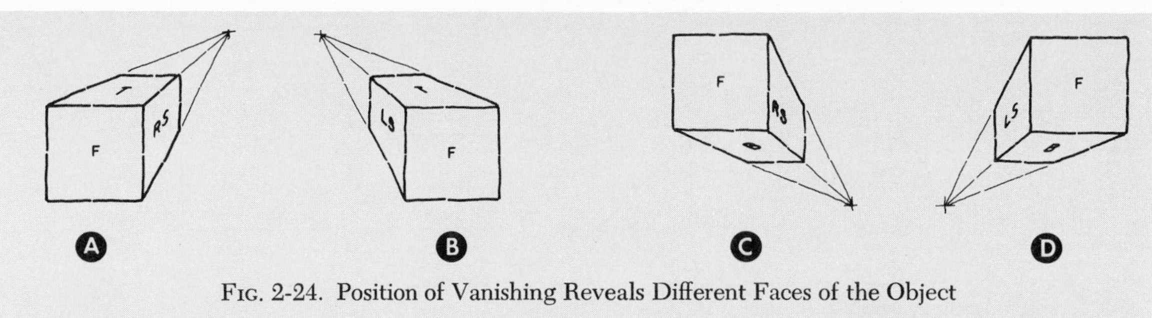

Fig. 2-24. Position of Vanishing Reveals Different Faces of the Object

A. Front, top, and right side
B. Front, top, and left side
C. Front, bottom, and right side
D. Front, bottom, and left side

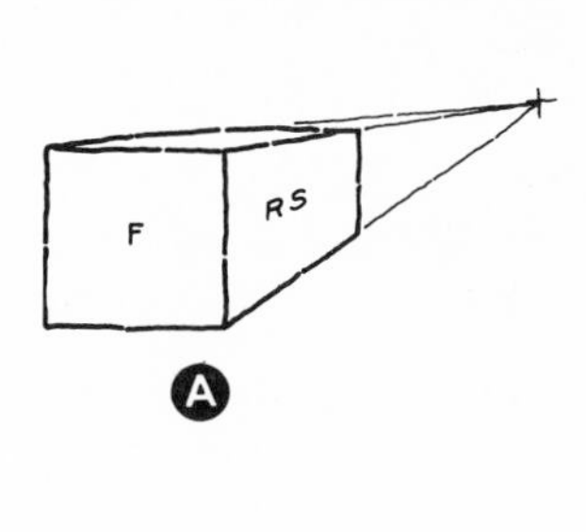

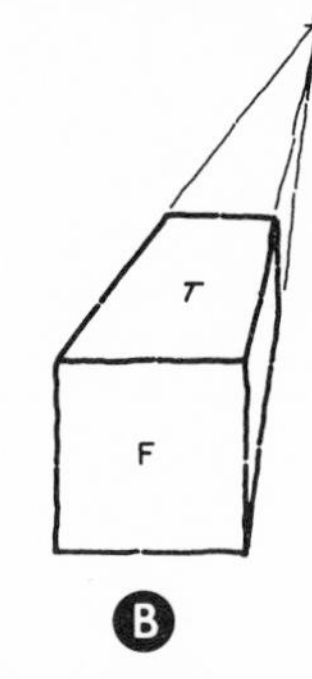

Fig. 2-25. Position of Vanishing Point May Emphasize Two Faces of the Object at the Expense of the Third

A. The front and side faces may be emphasized at the expense of the top face.
B. The front and top faces may be emphasized at the expense of the side face.

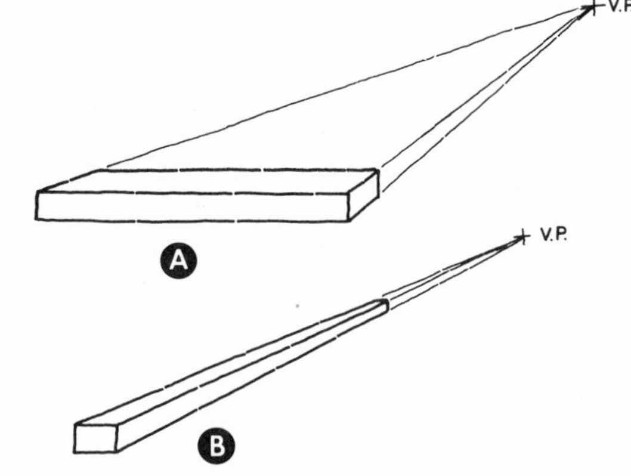

Fig. 2-26. Long Objects in One-Point Perspective May Appear Distorted in One Position

A. Properly positioned
B. Improperly positioned

2. Sketch the front face. (For the remaining steps see Fig. 2-27.)
3. Position the vanishing point.
4. Connect the vanishing point and front view with construction lines.
5. Establish the length of the depth lines.
6. Sketch the remaining lines.
7. Darken the object lines.

Isometric

Characteristics

See Fig. 2-28 and note that:

1. No face of an isometric is true shape.
2. All circular features are represented by ellipses.
3. All faces are *equally* distorted.
4. Isometric axes are at 120° angles to each other.
5. Height, width and depth lines are true length.
6. Height lines are vertical and parallel.
7. Width and depth lines recede at 30° to the horizontal. (There are exceptions, but this is the common position.)
8. Width lines are parallel to each other.
9. Depth lines are parallel to each other.

Uses

Isometric pictorial presentation most often is used in engineering when drawing ease is required. Sketches can be prepared easily because everything is equally distorted. Line length is uniform to the same scale, and the three surfaces are clearly and equally shown. When the faces are changed, different faces are displayed, Fig. 2-29. If the receding lines come downward 30° from the horizontal, the bottom face will be shown.

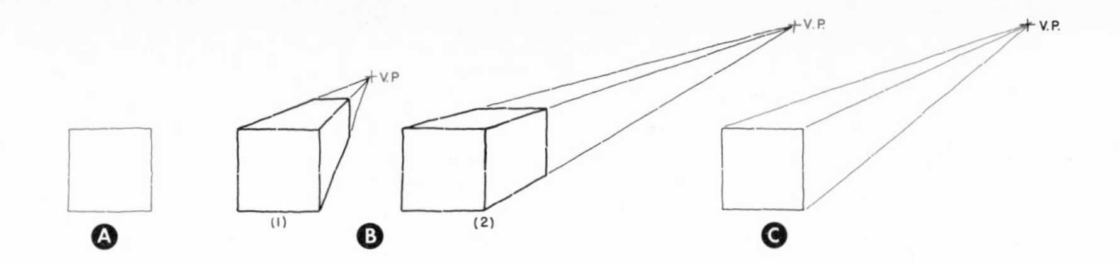

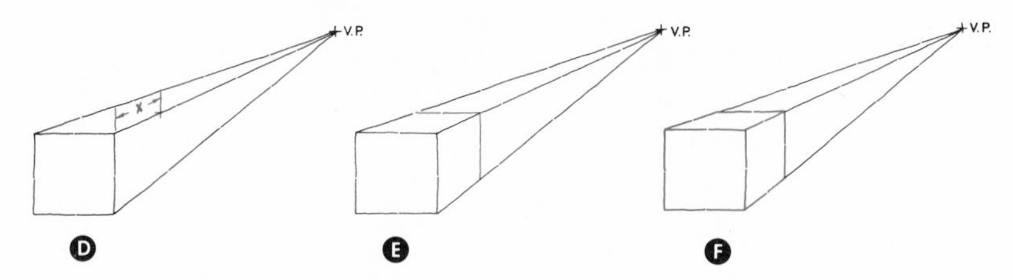

FIG. 2-27. Steps for Sketching One-Point Perspective Pictorials

A. Using construction-weight lines, sketch the front face full size or to a reasonable scale.
B. Select a vanishing-point position sufficiently far away from the object to provide the least amount of distortion.
C. From the nearest three corners of the front view, sketch construction lines which meet at the vanishing point. These lines should be very light.
D. Using the full or scaled length on one of these lines (generally the center one), establish the depth of the object.
E. From this end of the depth lines, sketch the remaining width line; then, the height line. The outlines of the object should now be complete in construction weight.
F. Darken the object lines.

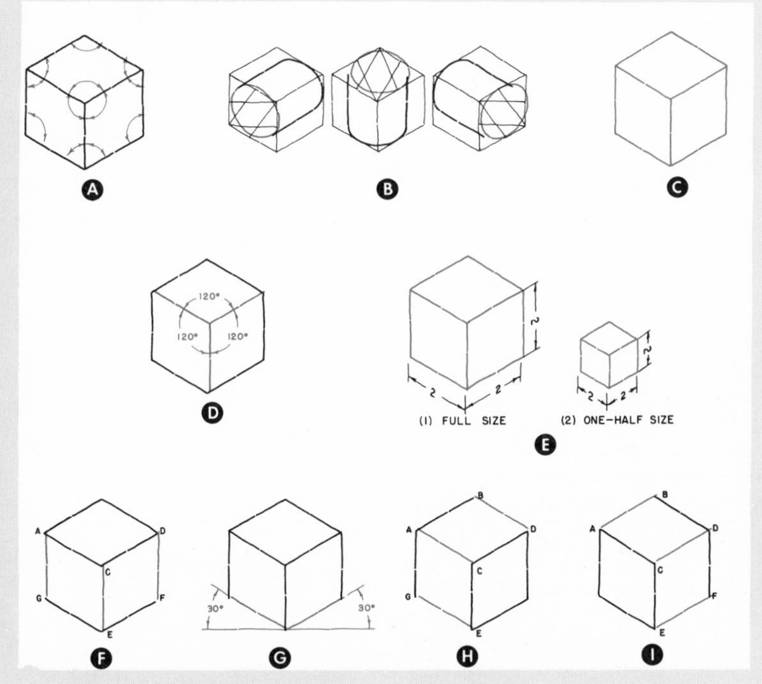

FIG. 2-28. Characteristics of Isometric Pictorial Representation

A. No face will show in its true shape. Angles of 90° on the object will not be 90° on the isometric but will be represented by either 60°- or 120°-angles depending upon location.
B. Circular features are always represented by ellipses.
C. All faces are equally distorted.
D. Because of its position, the object appears tipped with respect to the observer. The isometric axes are always at 120° angles to each other.
E. Height, width, and depth lines are
 (1) full length,
 (2) proportionately scaled.
F. The height lines are vertical and parallel.
G. The width and depth lines generally recede at 30° to the horizontal. (For variations, see Fig. 2-29.)
H. Width lines are parallel to each other.
I. Depth lines are parallel to each other.

However, true shape never can be shown, and no one view can be emphasized because the angle between the isometric axes is inflexible.

Sketching Procedure

1. Refer to Fig. 2-30 for the sketching procedure described below.
2. Select the three faces which are to show. Choose which of these will be the front face. It makes little difference whether one face is long, since the distortion will be equal in any view.

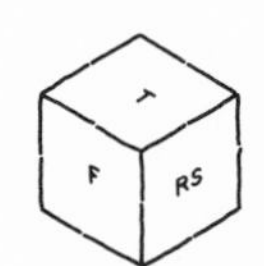

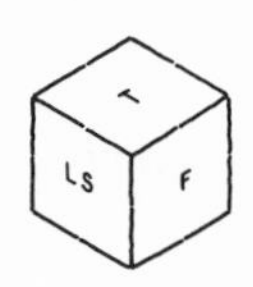

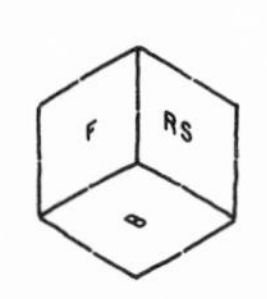

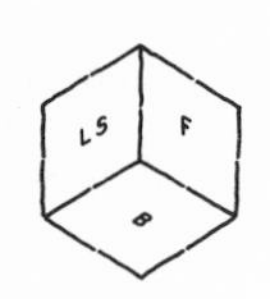

FIG. 2-29. Show Different Faces of Object in Isometric by Changing Position

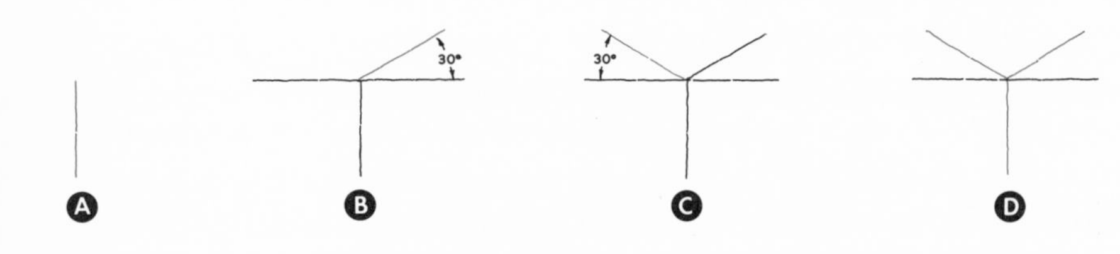

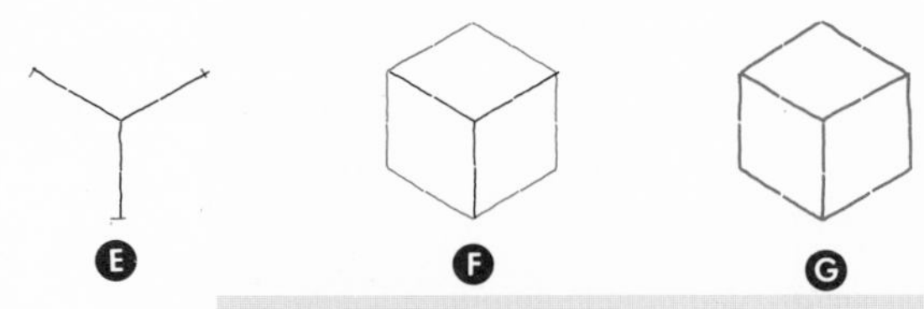

FIG. 2-30. Steps for Sketching Isometric Pictorials

A. Construct a vertical height line. Use construction-weight lines.
B. Starting at the top of this line, construct a line upward and to the right 30° from an imagined horizontal base line passing through this point.
C. Again starting at the top of the height line, construct a line upward and to the left 30° from an imagined horizontal base line passing through this point.
D. These three lines become the isometric axes upon which all measurements may be based. These axes will be called the vertical isometric axis, the right isometric axis, and the left isometric axis.
E. Layout on the appropriate axes, the overall height, width and depth measurements.
F. Complete the construction of the sketch by adding height lines parallel to the vertical height line, depth lines parallel to the right isometric axis, and width lines parallel to the left isometric axis.
G. Darken the object lines.

3. Construct the isometric axes.
4. Lay out the height, width, and depth dimensions.
5. Complete the construction.
6. Darken the object lines.

Two-Point or Angular Perspective

Characteristics

See Fig. 2-31 and note that:

1. No face will show in true shape.
2. Objects are viewed by the observer as though he were looking at a corner.
3. Height lines are vertical and parallel but are not usually the same length.
4. Width lines recede to a common vanishing point at the left.
5. Depth lines recede to a common vanishing point at the right.
6. Only one height line, one width line, and one depth line can be true length.
7. Changing the location of the vanishing points will display different faces. See Fig. 2-32.

Uses

Angular or two-point perspectives are used primarily by architects to show exterior features of houses and buildings. See Fig. 2-33. The civil engineer uses this method for large structures such as dams. In contrast to the others, this type pictorial most nearly approximates an object as it appears to the eye. (Of course, the positions of the vanishing points must be chosen carefully.)

On the other hand, no views have true features, thus making this type the most difficult to sketch.

Sketching Procedure

1. Refer to Fig. 2-34 for the sketching procedure described below.
2. Select the three views to be shown.
3. Construct a height line of random length.
4. Establish the position of the right and left vanishing points.
5. Layout the length of the height line.
6. Sketch lines from the extremes of the height line to each vanishing point.
7. Establish the length of the width and depth lines.
8. Complete the construction of the other width and depth lines.

TECHNICAL SKETCHING

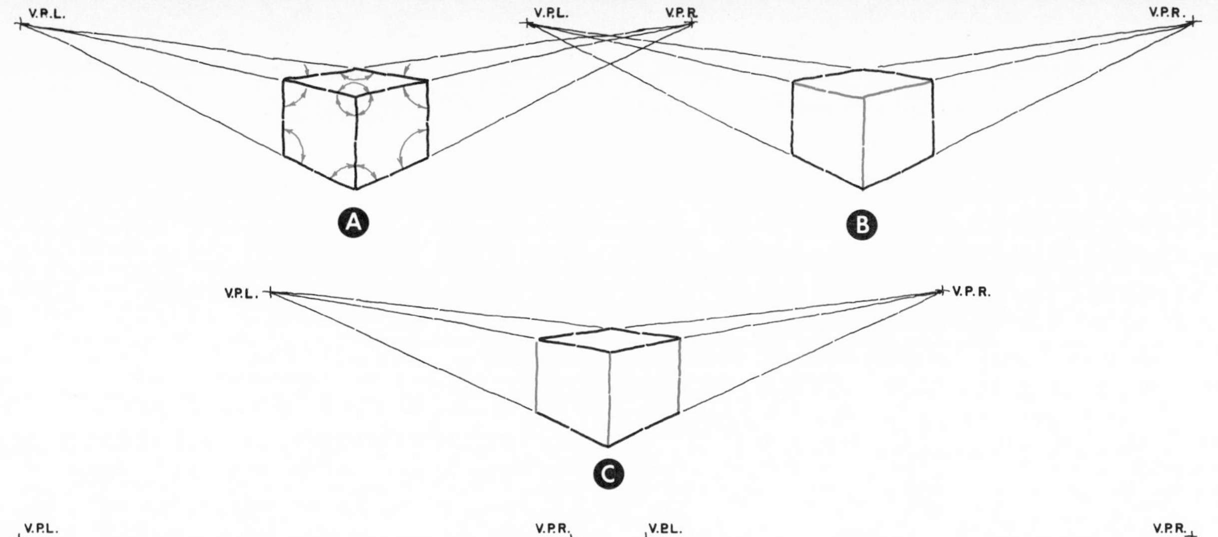

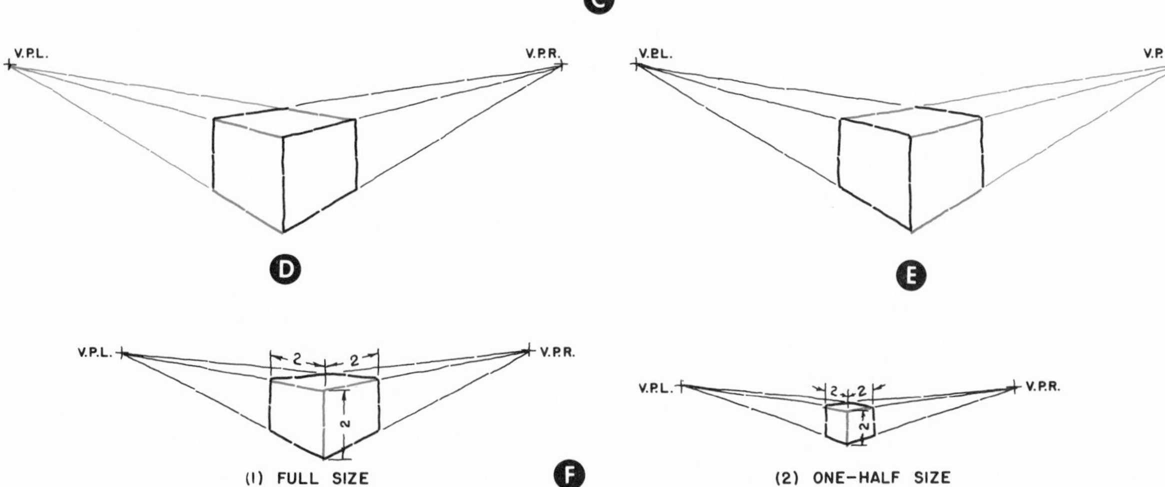

FIG. 2-31. Characteristics of Angular or Two-Point Pictorial Representation

A. No face will show true shape. The distortion of the faces may not necessarily be the same in each face for a given object.

B. Objects are shown as from a corner view.

C. Height lines are vertical and parallel but are not all the same length.

D. Width lines recede to a common vanishing point at the left.

E. Depth lines recede to a common vanishing point at the right.

F. Only one height line, one width line, and one depth line can be true length. All measurements are made on the selected lines.

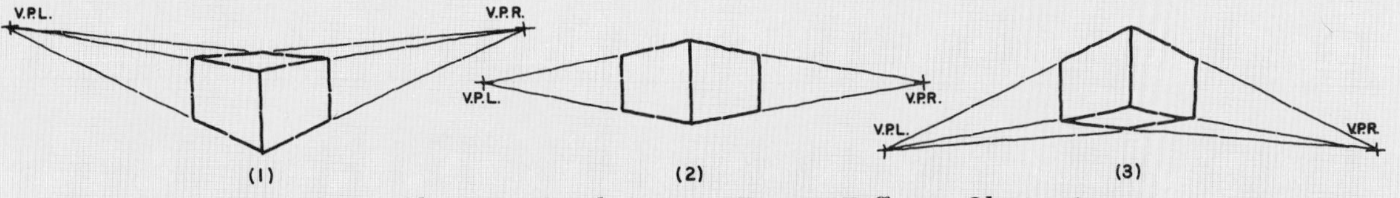

FIG. 2-32. Changing Vanishing Point Permits Different Observations

1. From above
2. From the middle, thus seeing only two faces
3. From below

FIG. 2-33. Two-Point Perspective Used in Architectural Rendering of Building Exteriors (University of Northern Iowa)

Place a sheet of tracing paper over the high rise dormitory in the foreground and locate the two vanishing points.

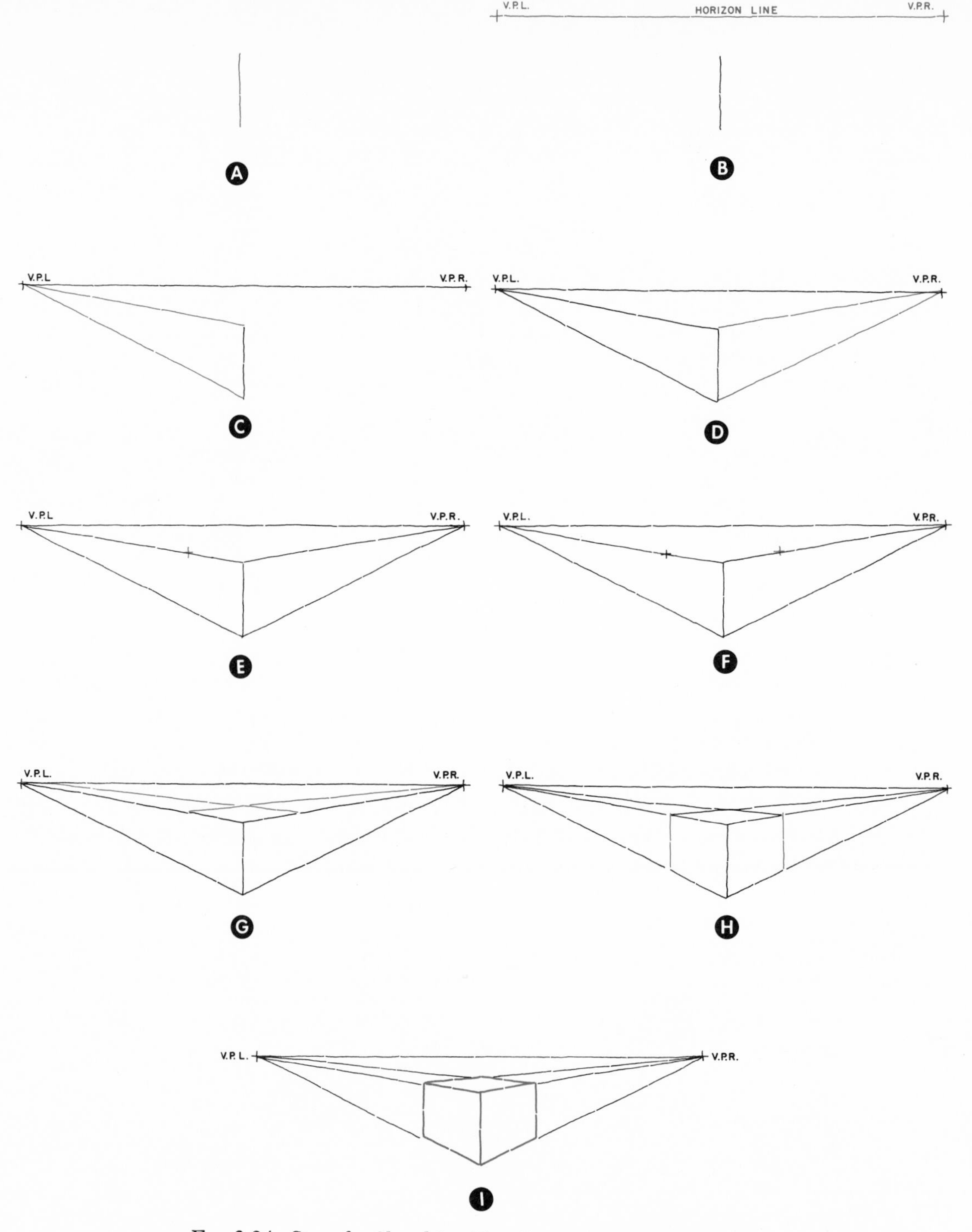

FIG. 2-34. Steps for Sketching Two-Point Perspective Pictorials

A. Construct a vertical height line. This will position the front corner of the object.
B. Establish left and right vanishing points so as to provide the least amount of distortion. This selection may be such as to show the bottom, only two sides, or the top (Fig. 2-32). Vanishing points most frequently are placed on a horizontal line representing the horizon and usually are spaced an equal distance from the vertical height line.
C. From the height line, measured in its true length, sketch two lines to the left vanishing point.
D. Then sketch two lines to the right vanishing point.
E. On the upper line receding to the left, establish the width.
F. On the upper line receding to the right, establish the depth dimension.
G. From the two points just established, sketch a line to the farthest vanishing points.
H. Drop height lines parallel to the first and originating from the two points just established.
I. Darken the object lines.

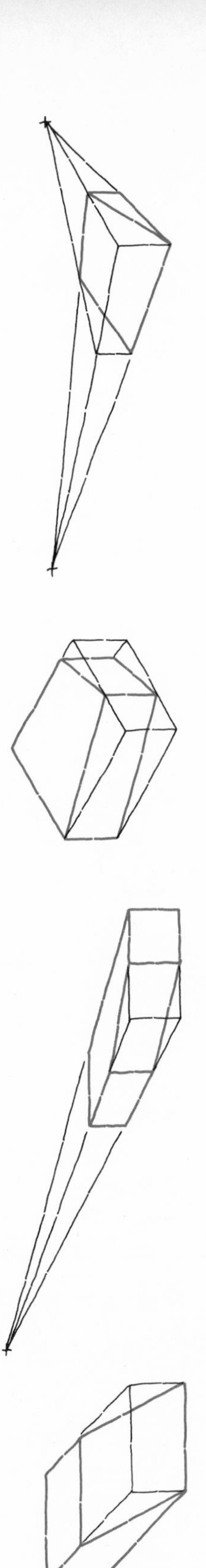

FIG. 2-35. Steps for Sketching Inclined Faces in Pictorial

A. Construct a basic box. The size should be that of the overall dimensions of the object.
B. Mark the location of the inclined lines on the faces of the basic box.
C. Sketch the required inclined surfaces.
D. Darken the object lines.

9. Add the height lines.
10. Darken the object lines.

Effect of Changing the Depth Dimension

Now that you are familiar with the four basic kinds of pictorial and the procedure for sketching each, try an experiment. Use a familiar object such as a sugar cube (½″ cube) or a one-pound box of butter (2½″x2½″x4½″). Make a full-size oblique sketch. Next make a second sketch similar to the first except use one-half the depth dimension. Which sketch looks more like the object?

Repeat this experiment with one-point perspective. Which of these two sketches is more realistic?

Try the experiment again using isometric and then two-point perspective.

Which of the four kinds of sketches is improved by reducing the depth dimension? Which, if any, appears more realistic without reducing the depth dimension?

You may not always want to reduce the depth dimension by a full one-half. The amount of reduction which makes the object look best is the amount which should be used. When an object is sketched to scale, the depth dimension is scaled and then, beyond this, is reduced the desired amount. As your experiment showed, do *not* reduce the depth dimension for isometric sketches.

Geometrical Breakdown and the Basic Box

Objects may be classified by their basic geometrical forms. The objects presented thus far have been simple, rectangular prisms. Other forms can be constructed easily by inscribing them in rectangular prisms, because all physical objects have the three dimensions: height, width, and depth. This method of construction is called *basic box* construction.

Methods for inscribing the more complex forms in a basic box for the four types of pictorial representation are alike. The illustrations show the procedure step by step. You may choose any pictorial, or you may wish to compare the steps for each kind.

Inclined Features

1. Sketch a basic box. (See Fig. 2-35.) Use the overall dimensions of the object and the appropriate form of pictorial representation.
2. Locate the position of the inclined face on the basic box by placing plus (+) marks representing the origin and termination points of the inclined lines.
3. Sketch the required inclined surfaces.
4. Darken the object lines.

The procedure is the same for oblique surfaces, as shown in Fig. 2-36.

Regular Curves

1. Construct a basic box. For example, the basic rectangular shape will be shown in Fig. 2-37*A*, if the object is a food can, three units in diameter and six units in length. The desired position of the object will determine the position in which to sketch the basic shape. If the object is upright, then the basic shape must be in that position. If the can is on its side, the basic shape must appear in the position shown in Fig. 2-37.
2. Sketch the circular feature. Assuming the can to be on its side, in *oblique* and *one-point perspective,* the circular view of the end should be sketched as a circle, Fig. 2-37*B*(1). Refer to Figs. 2-12 and 2-13, page 27, to review how to sketch circles.

In the *isometric pictorial,* the circular view should be sketched as an ellipse, Fig. 2-37*B*(2). Use the construction method shown in Fig. 2-15, page 28.

In a like manner, the circular view of the can will appear somewhat distorted in the *two-point perspective.* Refer to Fig. 2-37*B*(3). Use a method of approximation for construction. (See Fig. 2-14, page 28.) Even though the figure will not be a true ellipse, it will be quite satisfactory.

3. Use the same technique to sketch the circular feature in the rear face. Note Fig. 2-37*C*.
4. Complete the sketch by constructing the receding lines, Fig. 2-37*D*. Check that they are all tangent to the circular feature and recede according to the rules for the type of pictorial used.
5. Darken the object lines, Fig. 2-37*E*. Note: If the object is in an upright position, use the same procedure. For circular features appearing in the top or side view of either

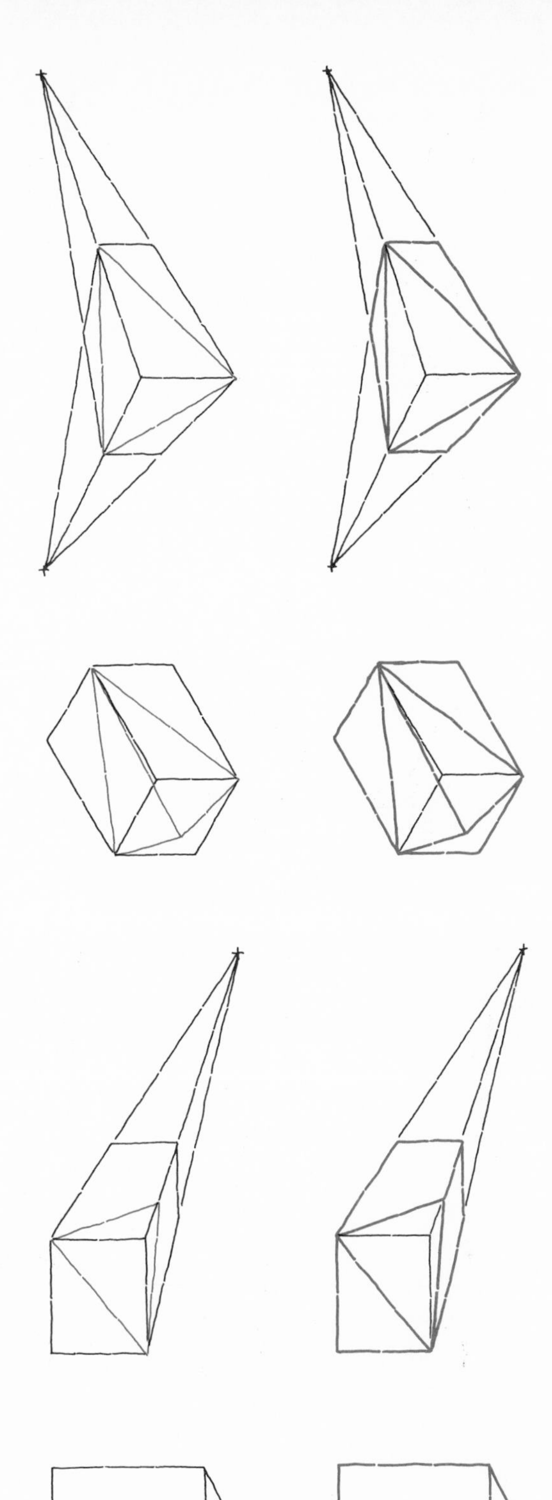

Fig. 2-36. Steps for Sketching Oblique Faces in Pictorial

A. Construct a basic box. The size should be that of the overall dimensions of the object.
B. Mark the location of the inclined lines on the faces of the basic box.
C. Sketch the required inclined surfaces.
D. Darken the object lines.

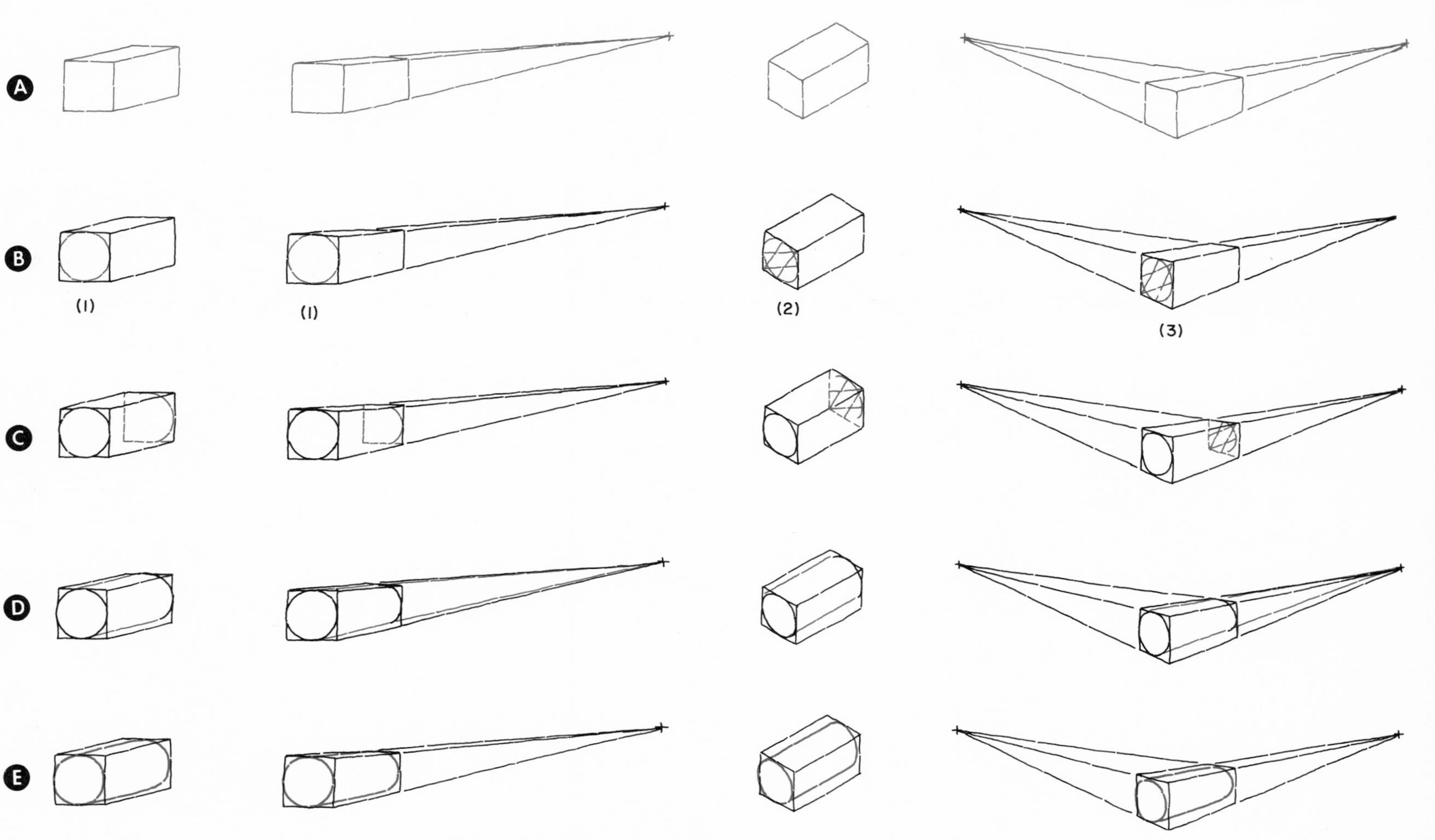

Fig. 2-37. Steps for Sketching Regular Curves in Pictorial

A. Construct a rectangular prism of the overall dimensions of the object. The prism must be constructed on its side if this is the circular feature in the front face.

B. Sketch the circular feature in the front face.

(1) The circle view in both oblique and one-point perspective will be a circle if placed in the front view.

(2) The circular face will be an ellipse in isometric.

(3) The circular face will be a distorted ellipse in two-point perspective.

C. Sketch as much of the circular feature in the rear face as is visible.

D. Complete the sketch by constructing receding lines.

E. Darken the object lines.

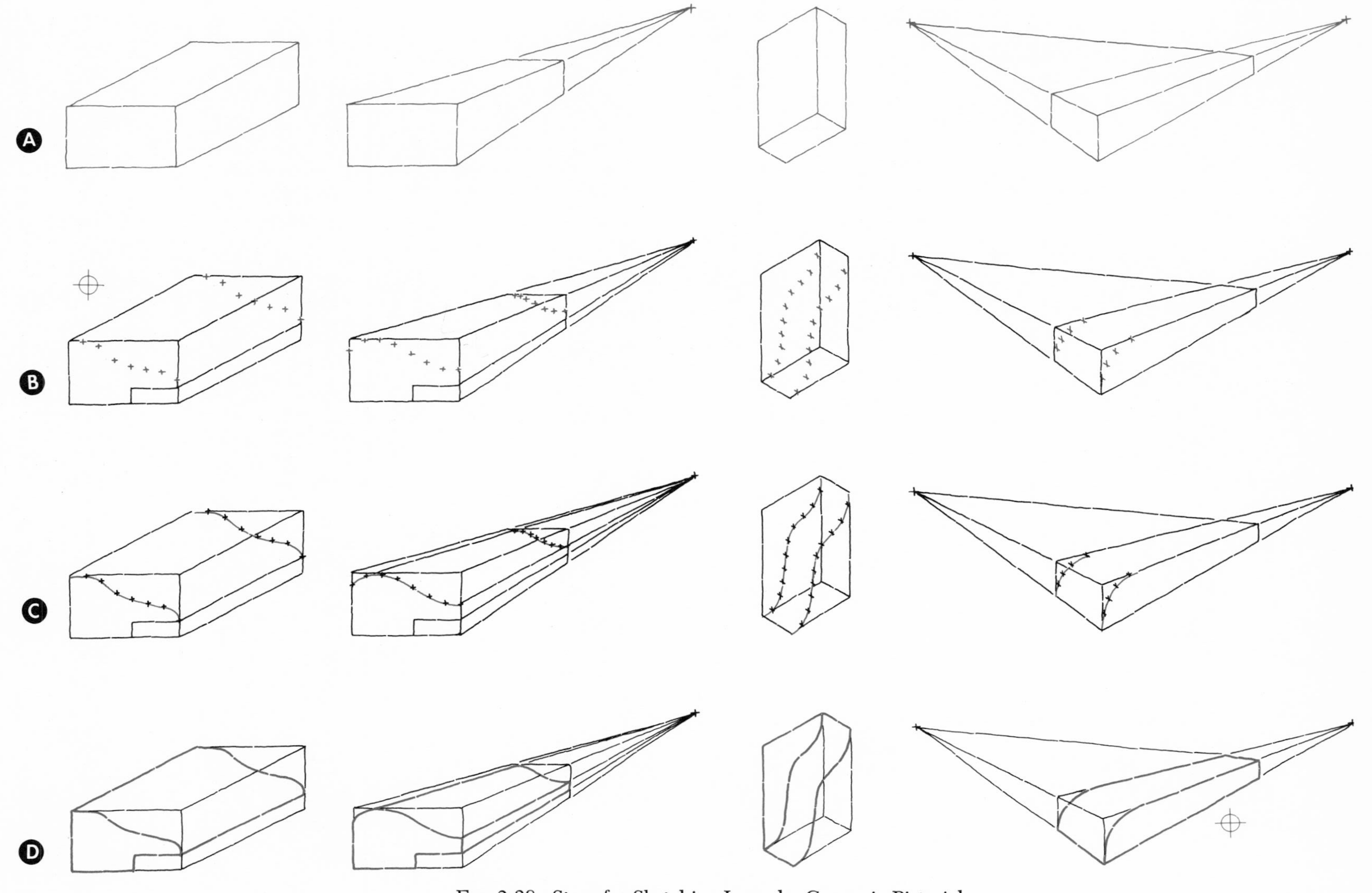

Fig. 2-38. Steps for Sketching Irregular Curves in Pictorial

A. Sketch a basic box.
B. Locate several of the points of the curve on the appropriate face.
C. Sketch a smooth curve through these points.
D. Darken the object lines.

oblique or one-point perspective, one of the methods suggested in Figs. 2-14 or 2-15 for construction of ellipses should be used.

The same procedure also applies to portions of a circle (such as circle arcs) with the final darkening done only for that portion of the circle needed. Notice that the shape at the rear of the object is a partial circle in both oblique and one-point perspective. See Figs. 2-37 *C, D,* and *E.*

Irregular Curves

1. Sketch a proportioned basic box, as shown in Fig. 2-38.
2. Locate several points of the curve on the face of the basic box where the curve is to appear.
3. Draw a smooth curve through these points.
4. Darken the object lines.

Combining Geometrical Forms

You have seen how rectangular prisms, regular curves, inclined features, and irregular curves may be sketched in 3-D representation. Any object may be divided into these basic geometrical forms. By breaking more complex objects into a number of these basic forms and by sketching them in the appropriate place, the object can be drawn with little difficulty.

1. Determine and sketch the controlling geometrical form. See Fig. 2-39. This is generally the largest or most important one, although occasionally the whole object can be inscribed. Each geometrical subdivision is then placed on the controlling form. At this stage you are concerned with separate basic boxes to locate the separate features of the object.
2. Construct the several geometrical subdivisions of the object using the methods you have already learned.
3. Darken in the object lines.

Student-Made Sketches

Fig. 2-40 shows sketches made by students to solve the design problems indicated.

Chapter 2 — Problems and Projects

For most of these problems, you should use grid paper ruled with either 4 or 8 squares to the inch.

1. Sharpen and point each of your drafting pencils following the instructions given earlier. Check their shape against that shown in Fig. 2-2.
2. Sketch some straight lines, concentrating on straightness and stroke. Use Fig. 2-6A as your guide. Be sure the lines are dense, black, and sharp, and that the strokes are between ¾″ and 1½″ in length. Any gap between strokes should be very small.
3. Carefully sketch the conventional lines shown in the first column of Fig. 2-16. Choose the appropriate pencil, and make your lines the same width as those in the figure.
4. Sketch a series of horizontal lines, vertical lines, and inclined lines.
5. Sketch a design for a 10-foot section of picket fence with pickets 1′ and 2′ in height, arranged pleasingly.
6. Sketch a series of circles of different diameters.
7. Sketch five concentric circles. Make the diameter of the inner circle 1″ and increase the diameter of each succeeding circle ½″.
8. Sketch several ellipses of different sizes.
9. Sketch four concentric ellipses. Decide upon the size of the first. Uniformly increase the size of each succeeding one.
10. Plot several points at random. Sketch a smooth curve through them. Make several different irregular curves by this process.
11. Sketch as many of the plane geometrical figures as you can, *e.g.*, square, triangle, trapezoid, circle, star, octagon, *etc.*
12. Make design sketches of several rose-trellis patterns.
13. Sketch a design for a new perforated sheet-metal pattern.
14. Design a textile pattern for a speaker cover of a stereo or television set.
15. Design the grille for a new-model car.
16. Sketch the layout for a school athletic field.

For the following problems use 8½″ x 11″ cross-sectioned paper with 8 squares to the inch. Divide the paper into four equal parts by sketching lines. Make four sketches of each object assigned — oblique pictorial in the first section of the paper; one-point perspective in the second; isometric representation in the third; and two-point perspective in the last.

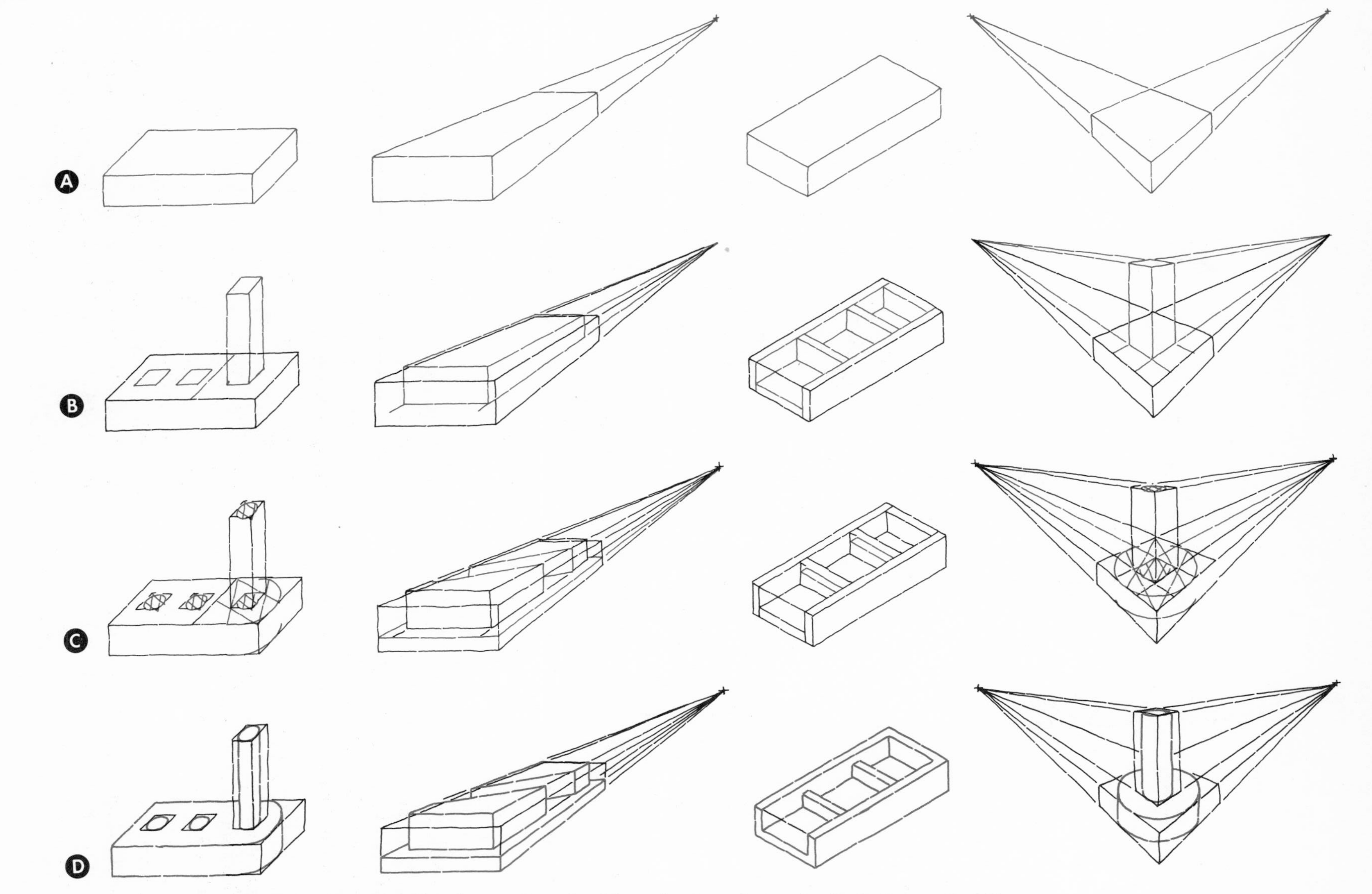

FIG. 2-39. Steps for Sketching a Complex Object by Considering the Basic Geometrical Forms.

A. Layout the controlling basic shape.
B. Position basic shapes of each geometrical subdivision of the object.
C. Sketch the geometrical subdivisions in the basic box constructed for each.
D. Darken the lines.

TECHNICAL SKETCHING

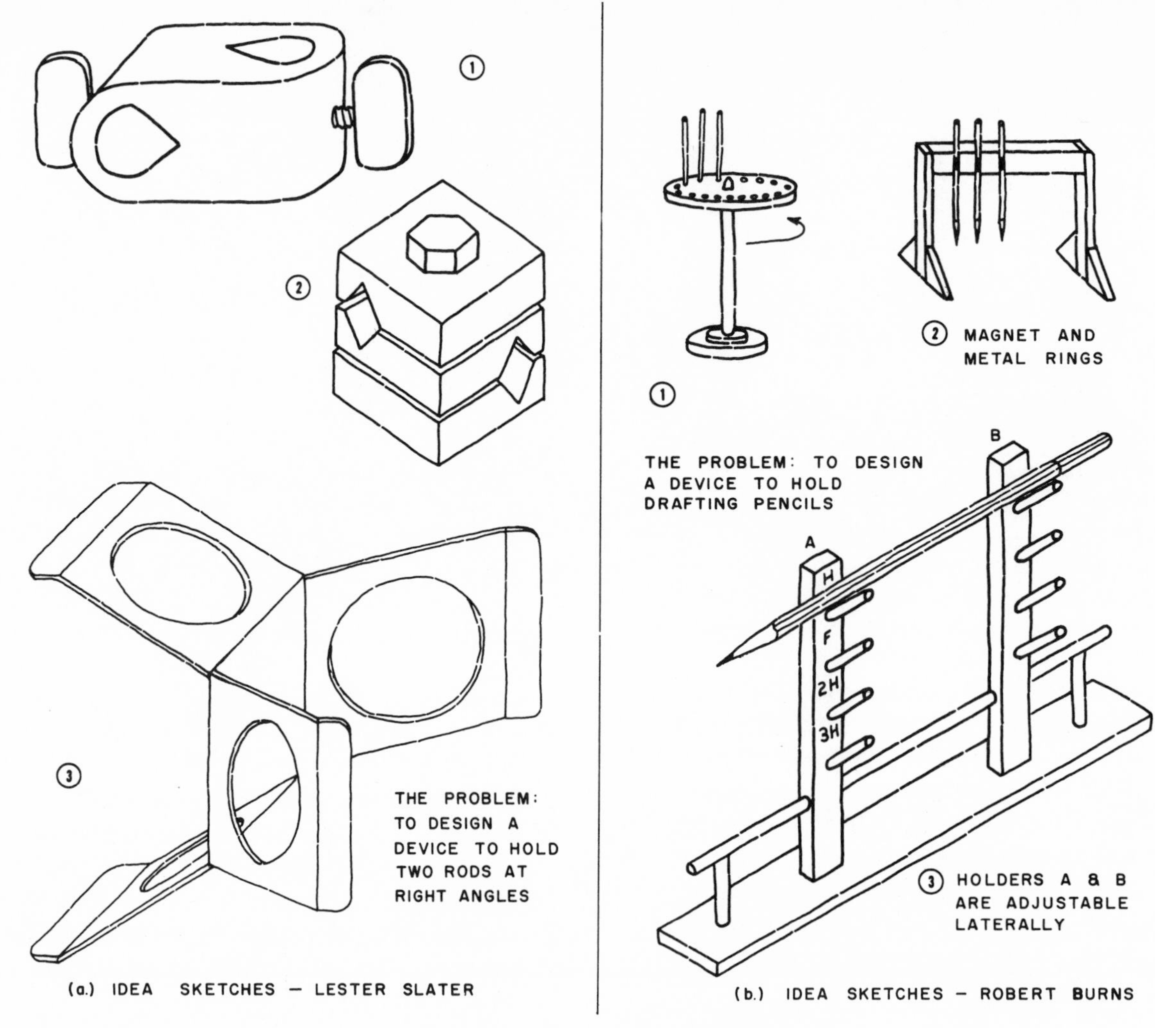

FIG. 2-40. Student-Made Sketches

Rectangular Solids:

17. Cube of sugar, ½″ x ½″ x ½″.
18. Child's block, 2½″ x 2½″ x 2½″.
19. Cake of ice, 18″ x 18″ x 18″.
20. One-fourth pound of butter, 1¼″ x 1¼″ x 4½″.
21. Eraser, ¾″ x 1″ x 1⅞″.
22. Art gum eraser, ⅞″ x ⅞″ x 1¾″.
23. Artificial sponge, 1½″ x 3″ x 6″.
24. Gold brick, 3″ x 4″ x 6″.

Cylindrical Solids:

25. Croquet mallet head, 2″ diam. x 7″.
26. Rolling pin blank, 2½″ diam. x 10″.
27. Dowel rod, 1″ diam. x 3″.
28. Plastic paperweight, 2½″ diam. x 1½″.
29. Unground magnifying glass prism, 4″ diam. x ½″.
30. A ten-dollar roll of 50 cent pieces, 1³⁄₁₆″ diam. x 1⁷⁄₁₆″.

Triangular Solids:

31. Sketch your 30° to 60° triangle.
32. Sketch your 45° triangle.
33. Sketch your triangular scale rule.

For the following problems, choose the pictorial form you wish to use, the scale or proportion in which it is to be done, and the most desirable combination of faces to show. Make the pictorial as realistic as possible. Use basic box construction and think of the parts of the object in their simplest geometrical form. Sketch any of the following as assigned:

34. Drafting table.
35. Chair.
36. Stool.
37. Wastebasket.
38. Roll of drafting tape.
39. Each of the parts of a pair of shears.
40. An opened textbook.
41. Slide rule components.
42. T-square head and blade.
43. Each of the parts of a mechanical pencil.
44. The component parts of a mechanical pencil pointer.
45. Any one of the instruments in your drafting instrument list.

Many times the draftsman does not have objects from which to make his sketches. He sketches from ideas that he creates. Select from among the problems that follow those ideas that appeal to you. Choose the pictorial form you wish to use. Make four proposed solutions for each idea. Each idea sketch should suggest a different treatment of the problem.

46. Design a device upon which a telephone can be placed. The base of the telephone is 5″ x 9″. The telephone weighs 4 lbs.
47. The draftsman needs to keep his pencils and erasers handy, yet organized, on his desk. Sketch four design ideas for accommodating an HB, 2H, and 4H pencil together with a pencil eraser measuring ½″ x 1″ x 2″. Remember that the pencil is sharp when pointed and that the points should not be broken unnecessarily.
48. Obtain the specifications for a soldering iron (Measure your own, get one from the school shop, or look in a hardware catalog.) Sketch design ideas for holding the soldering iron when it is hot.
49. Most families eat at a "drive-in" on occasion. When the tray of food is brought to the car, there often is a need for more places to put sandwiches, drinks, and the like. Sketch four solutions to the problem of providing extra space in a car for these items. The objects may be optional equipment or be built into the car at the factory.
50. Sketch four desk lamp shades that will permit light to fall where it is needed without a glare. Any type lamps may be assumed, *e.g.*, wall lamp, table lamp, fluorescent lamp or others.
51. A source of power delivers a uniform rotary motion of 1750 revolutions per minute (rpm) to a ¾″ shaft. Suggest through sketches at least two methods to convert this motion to another shaft which is rotating in the opposite direction at 2800 rpm. Suggest through two more sketches how to produce from this original power source (1750 rpm) a uniform, rotating motion of 100 rpm.
52. Sketch four ideas for a hub cap design for a new-model car. (You may substitute some other piece from a car such as a door handle, bumper guard, or arm rest.)
53. Sketch design ideas for the front of a sporting goods store. Use your name as the firm name.
54. Sketch appropriate designs for a sign to be hung over the front of the sporting goods store developed for problem 53.
55. Near your house is a ditch three feet wide. Plan a foot bridge wide enough to accommodate two persons walking side by side. Although a professional designer would be concerned with live load weights, dead weight, etc., your problem is simply to suggest four design ideas as to how the bridge might look.

CHAPTER THREE

orthographic projection

theory of orthographic projection

Need for Precise Representation

Pictures as well as pictorial sketches and drawings provide a visual impression of an object. A camera records the three-dimensional image on the surface of photographic paper; a pictorial sketch or drawing records it on drawing paper, Fig. 3-1. In each case, a three-dimensional object is represented on a two-dimensional surface — such a representation, obviously, cannot be precise.

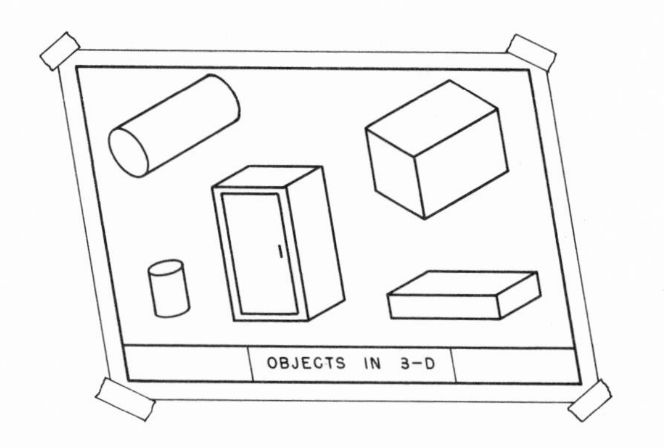

Fig. 3-1. Three-Dimensional Objects Represented by Pictorial Drawings on Drawing Paper

For many purposes, pictorials do not provide sufficient detail. To make a product exactly as the designer intends requires a *precise* description of the shape, the size of each part, and the way these parts fit together.

One surface of an object has only two dimensions; these can be represented easily on drawing paper. By relating and coordinating representations of several faces, a systematic and precise description can be made which will permit construction exactly as intended. This type of coordinated representation is *orthographic projection.*

Orthographic Projection Defined

The term *orthographic* is a combination of the word *orthogonal,* meaning "at right angles," and *graphic,* meaning "to draw." The word *projection* has several meanings, but when used with orthographic, its meaning is geometrical. The following geometrical definition of *projection* dates back more than 300 years:

> The drawing of straight lines or "rays" through every point of a given figure, usually so as to fall upon a surface and produce upon it a new figure each point of which corresponds to a point of the original figure. Hence, each of such rays, or of such points of the resulting figure, is

said to be the projection of a point of the original one; or the whole resulting figure is said to be a projection of the original one.

This definition suggests that a projection of an object can be made by drawing straight lines through every point of the original figure to produce a new figure on some surface, Fig. 3-2. This surface is called a *plane of projection.* Each point formed by the intersection of the projection line on the plane represents a corresponding point on the original object. However, this yields a "pictorial projection" when the lines converge to a vanishing point and are not at right angles to the object nor to its projected image. Therefore, this projected image often is not accurate enough.

Orthographic means "to draw at right angles." When projection lines are at right angles both to the object from which they originate and to the plane upon which they are projected, the projected image is called an *orthographic projection.* This does describe the shape and size of one surface accurately.

Since the projected lines are at right angles both to the surface of the object and to that of the plane of projection, they are parallel to each other. For the same reason, the surface of the object is parallel to that of the plane of projection.

To summarize:

1. Projection lines or rays are at right angles to both the surface of the object and to that of the plane of projection.
2. Projection lines are parallel to each other.
3. The surface of the object and the projection plane are parallel to each other.

For orthographic projection, each of the above statements must be true. Study Fig. 3-3 so that you become very familiar with these conditions.

Use of More Than One Plane of Projection

To describe more than one surface of an object, more than one plane of projection is needed. A different plane is needed for each different surface. If a separate plane of projection is placed parallel to each surface of the object, each may be described, Fig. 3-4. Observe that the six surfaces of the object are at right angles to one another, and, therefore, the six projection planes are at right angles to each other. Thus, the projection planes are *mutually perpendicular* or *orthogonal.*

The Three Basic Dimensions

All objects have three dimensions: height, width, and depth. See Fig. 3-5. Height is measured from bottom to top; width from side to side; depth from front to back. The measurement is taken from a point on one face of the object to a corresponding point on the opposite face. These same dimensions are projected from the object to the corresponding planes of projection.

Fig. 3-2. Rays to Plane of Projection Form New Image of Original Figure

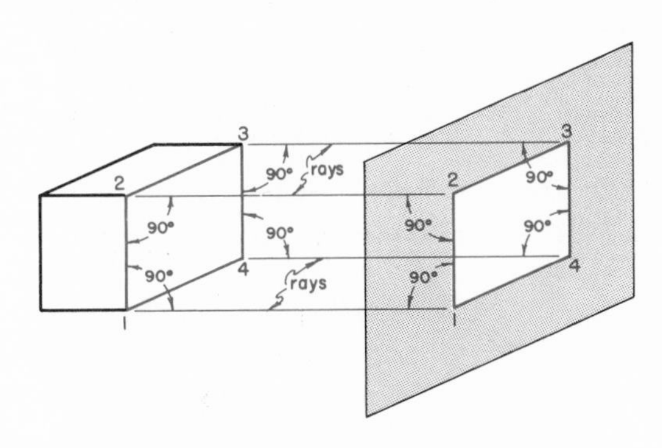

Fig. 3-3. Conditions Necessary to Have an Orthographic Projection

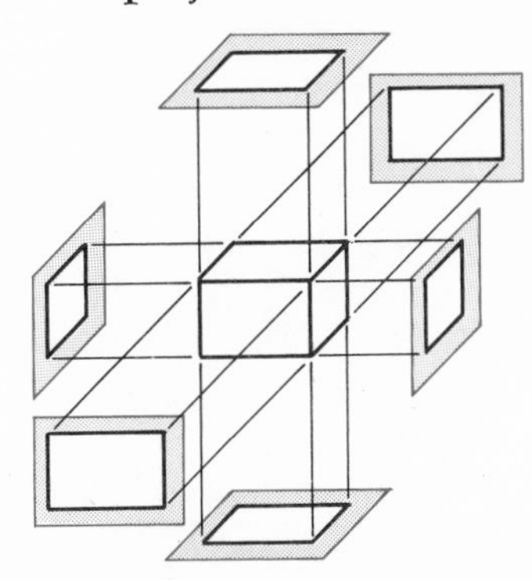

Fig. 3-4. A Separate Plane of Projection for Each Surface View in Orthographic Projection

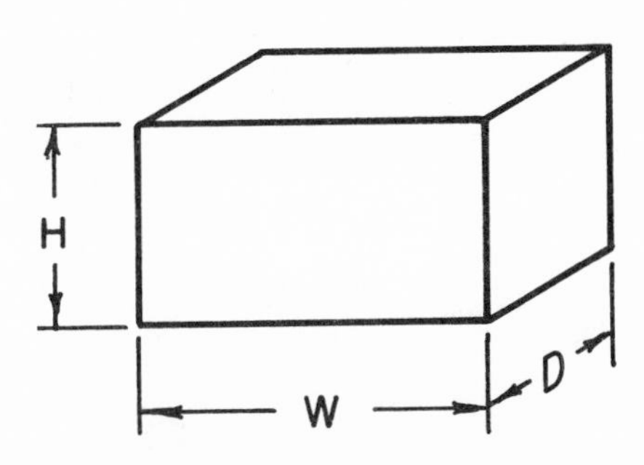

Fig. 3-5. Three Basic Dimensions – Height, Width, and Depth

ORTHOGRAPHIC PROJECTION

Notice in Fig. 3-6 that of the three basic dimensions (height, width, and depth) only two may be seen on any given surface and, therefore, only two may be seen on any given plane of projection. Notice further in Fig. 3-7 that height as a dimension shows in each projection of the front, right side, left side, and rear views; width shows in each projection of the front, top, rear, and bottom views; depth, in each projection of the right side, top, left side and bottom views.

The front and rear views show the same two dimensions; the right and left side views show the same two dimensions; also the top and bottom views, the same two dimensions. Thus, all six principal views are not needed to describe an object completely. The three views usually chosen are the front, right side, and top views.

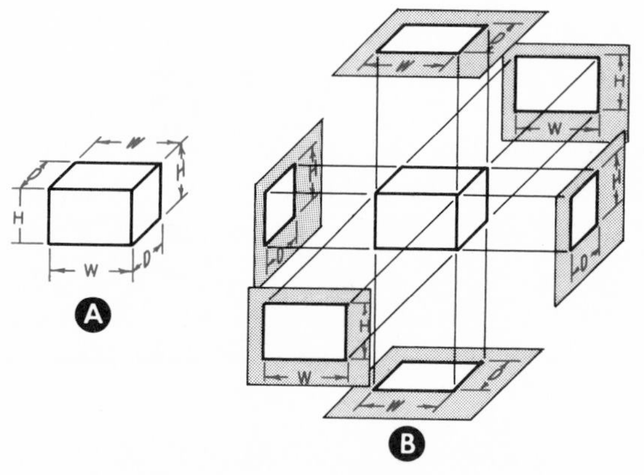

Fig. 3-6. Two Basic Dimensions Seen
A. On any given surface
B. On any given projection of a surface

For each set of two principal views (such as the front view and right side view, Fig. 3-8), there is one dimension common to each, with the other two dimensions independent. This suggests two things. First, when any two views are given, they are coordinated because one of the dimensions is common to each view. Secondly, when any two views are given, all three basic dimensions are given. Thus, the projection of the front and right side views is coordinated by the height dimension; that of the front and top views is coordinated by the width dimension; and that of the top and right side views, by the depth dimension.

Correlating the Views in Orthographic Projection

A three-dimensional object can be represented clearly by orthographic projection if the views are drawn in a certain relationship to each other. For convenience, the common or principal views (front, top, and right side) should be used.

Consider the object as having been placed inside a transparent projection box, Fig. 3-9. The use of the projection box will enable you to visualize the coordination of the views.

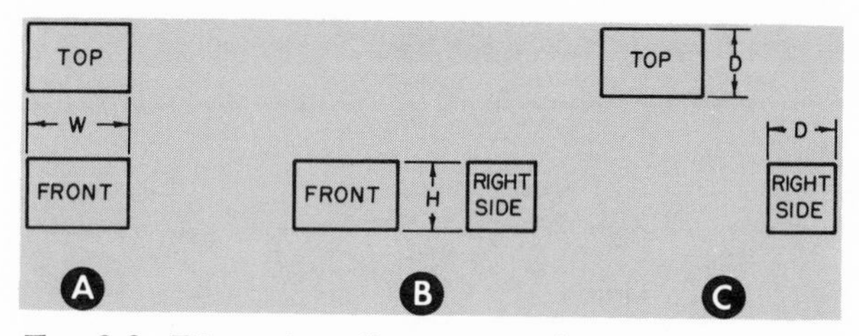

Fig. 3-8. Dimensions Common to the Principal Views

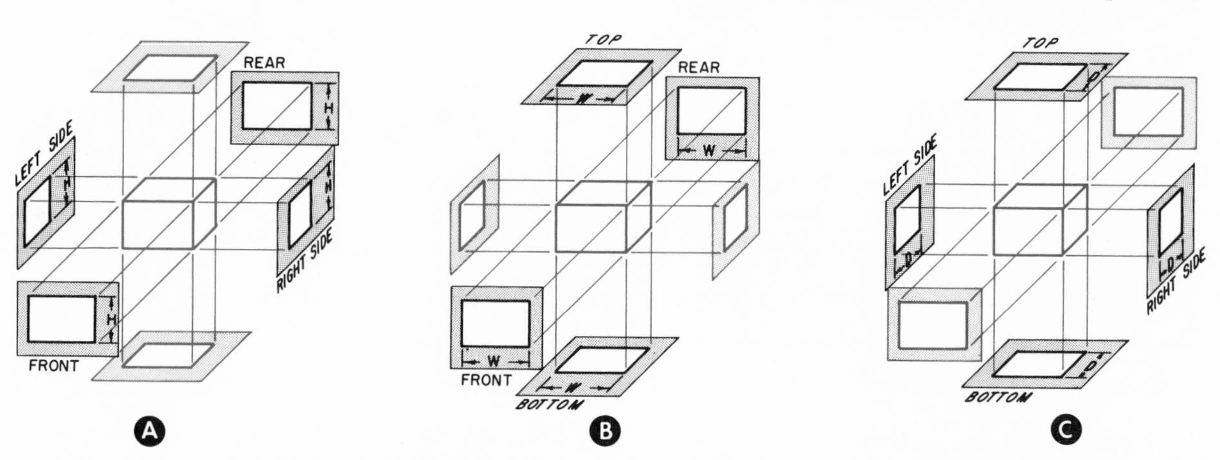

Fig. 3-7. Projections Showing (A) Height, (B) Width, and (C) Depth Dimensions

By imagining the projection planes to fold, you have placed them in a certain relationship, and they may be considered to have been folded into the flat surface of a piece of paper.

Observe the relationships of this arrangement:

1. The top view is aligned vertically with the front view.
2. The right side view is aligned horizontally with the front view.
3. Both the front and top views show the width dimension in common.
4. Both the front and the right side views show the height dimension in common.
5. The front view coordinates the top and right side views.
6. Both the top and right side views show the depth dimension in common.
7. The top view is in a natural position: above the front view.
8. The right side view is in a natural position: at the right of the front view.

If you need to show more than the three principal views, they can be envisioned as projections of the several surfaces of the object, each of which is folded into the plane of the piece of paper, Fig. 3-10. Thus you may have all six views of the object, if they are needed. In actual practice, you seldom will need all six views. Information shown in the front, top, and right side views merely duplicates the other three views. However, when one of these other surfaces is needed to clarify detail, the relationship of the chosen views is that shown in Fig. 3-10.

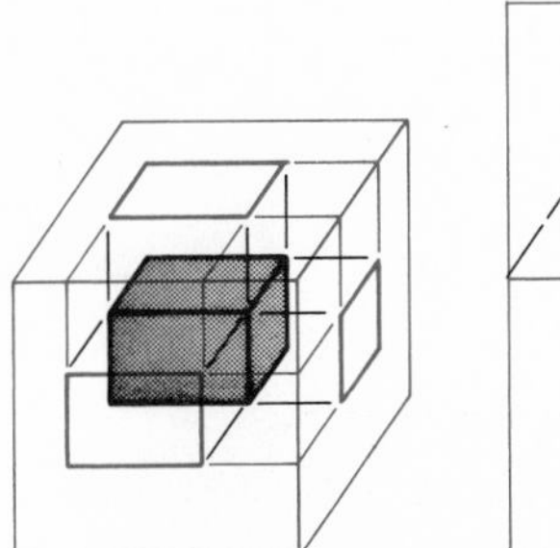

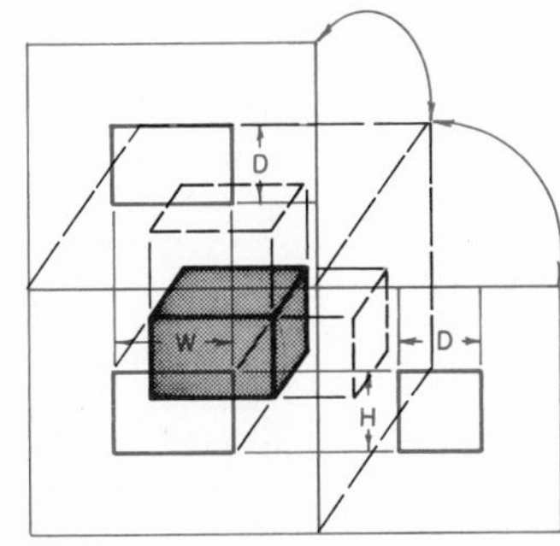

Fig. 3-9. A Projection Box Coordinates the Three Principal Views of an Object

Alternate Views

Although views generally are arranged as shown in Fig. 3-10, alternate positions may be used to give a more satisfactory spacing arrangement. When one of the alternate positions is used, it should be identified clearly so that the projections will not be misread. See Figs. 3-11 and 3-12.

Third-Angle Projection

The natural positions of the views as they have been developed here are said to be in *third-angle projection*. This refers to the position of four quadrants commonly used in mathematics to identify positions in space. See Fig. 3-13.

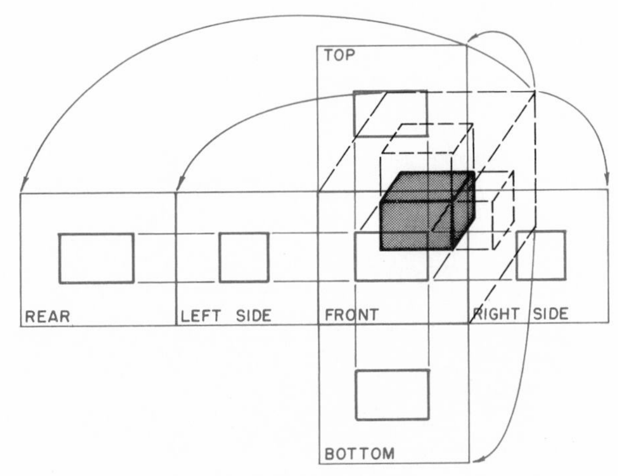

Fig. 3-10. All Six Projections of an Object Opened into Plane of a Piece of Paper

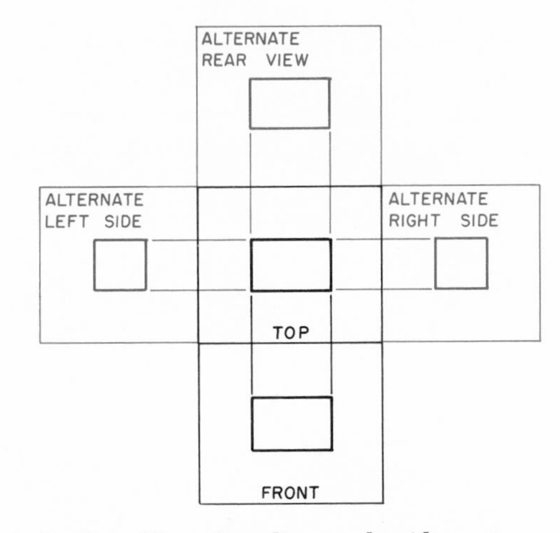

Fig. 3-11. Top View Coordinates the Alternate Position of Right Side, Left Side and Rear Views

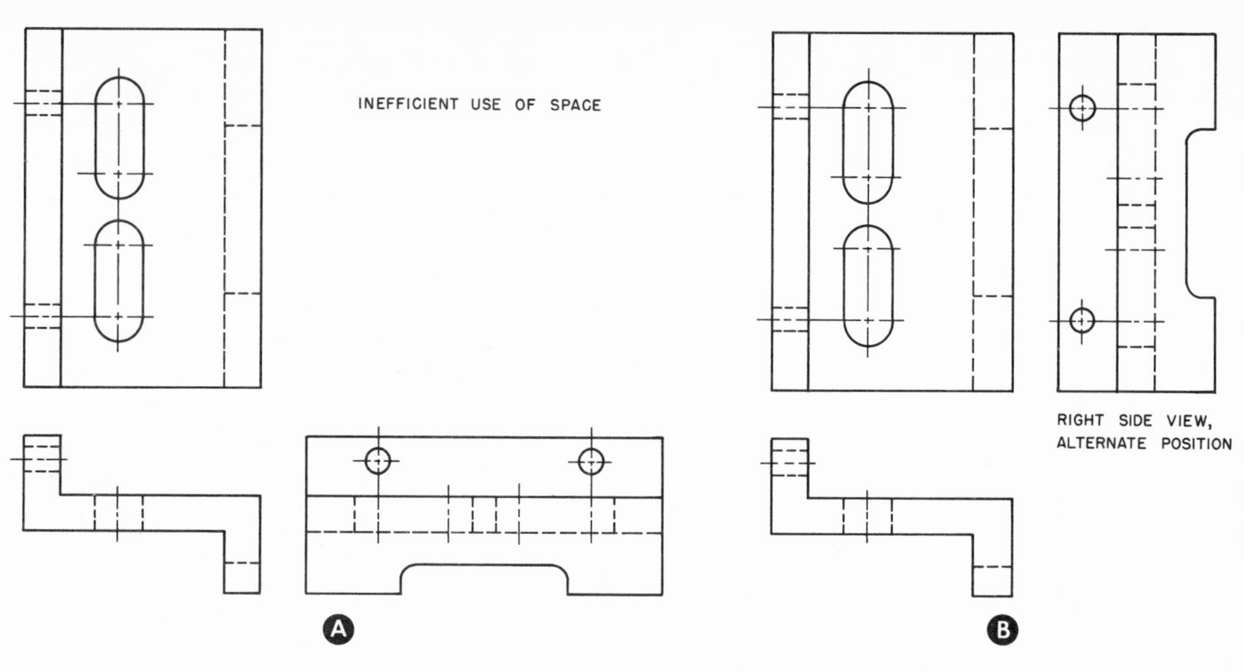

FIG. 3-12. Best Spacing Arrangement of Alternate View

A. Normal arrangement

B. Alternate arrangement

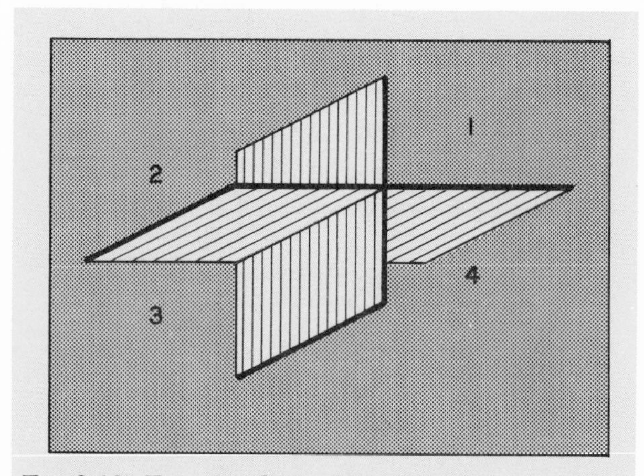

FIG. 3-13. Four Quadrants Identify Position in Space

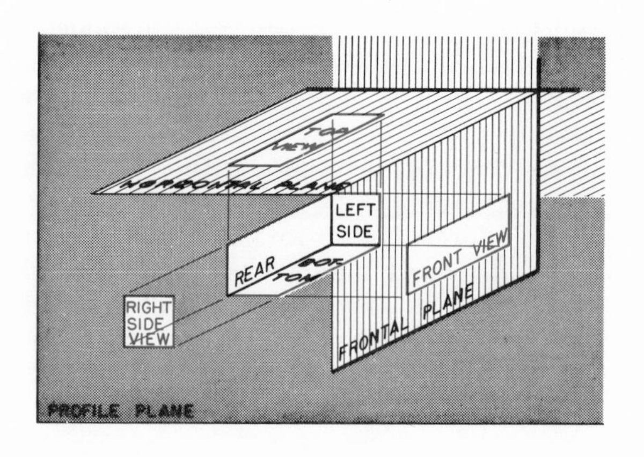

Projections in the third angle of these quadrants are standard for the United States and Canada, Fig 3-14. Since the views of the object occupy their natural positions, this method of projection is easier to use. The top view is above the front view, and the right and left side views are, respectively, at the right and left of the front view. Thus, each view is placed so that it represents the near side of the actual object.

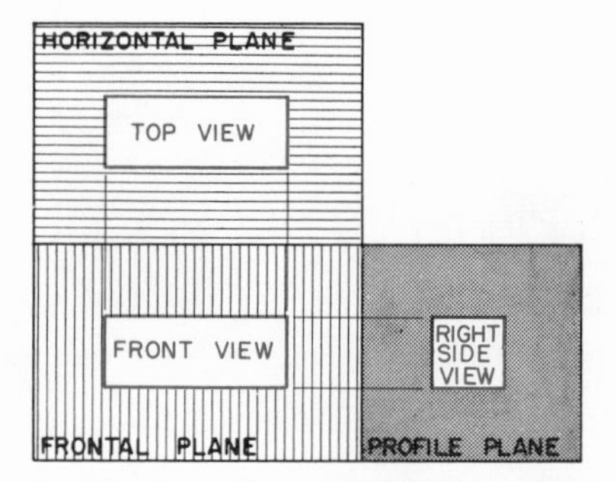

FIG. 3-14. Third-Angle Projection — Used in the United States

First-Angle Projection

Although projections from any one of the four quadrants could be used, only the first- and third-quadrant projections are practical. Third-angle projection, of course, is used in the United States; however, first-angle projection should be understood because it is used in western Europe and many other countries. Our industries are seeking foreign markets. As these markets develop, there is a greater demand for draftsmen who can read drawings that use first-angle projection. On the other hand, the trend in industries coming into North America (as a foreign market) is to use the third-angle projection of the United States.

First-angle projection results in a front view with the top view below it; the right side view appears to the left of the object, and the left side view appears at the right of the object. See Fig. 3-15. Each of the views is projected through the object from a surface of the object to the corresponding projection plane. One advantage of first-angle projection is that drafting sheets can be used more economically with the title block in the lower right corner, Fig. 3-16.

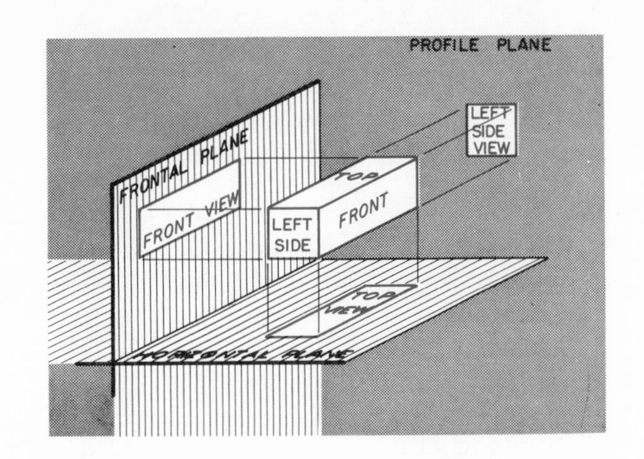

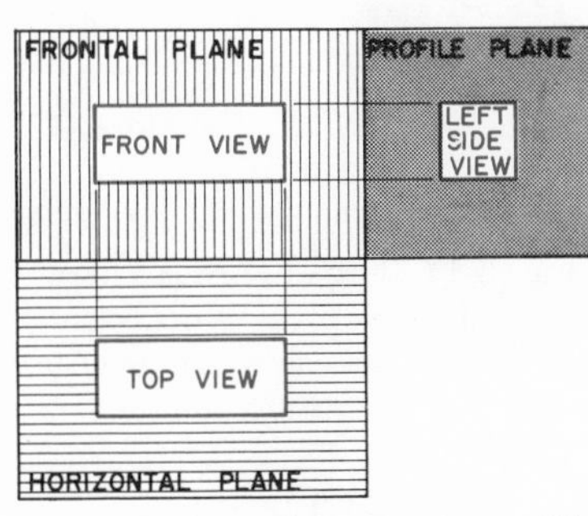

FIG. 3-15. First-Angle Projection — Used in Some Countries

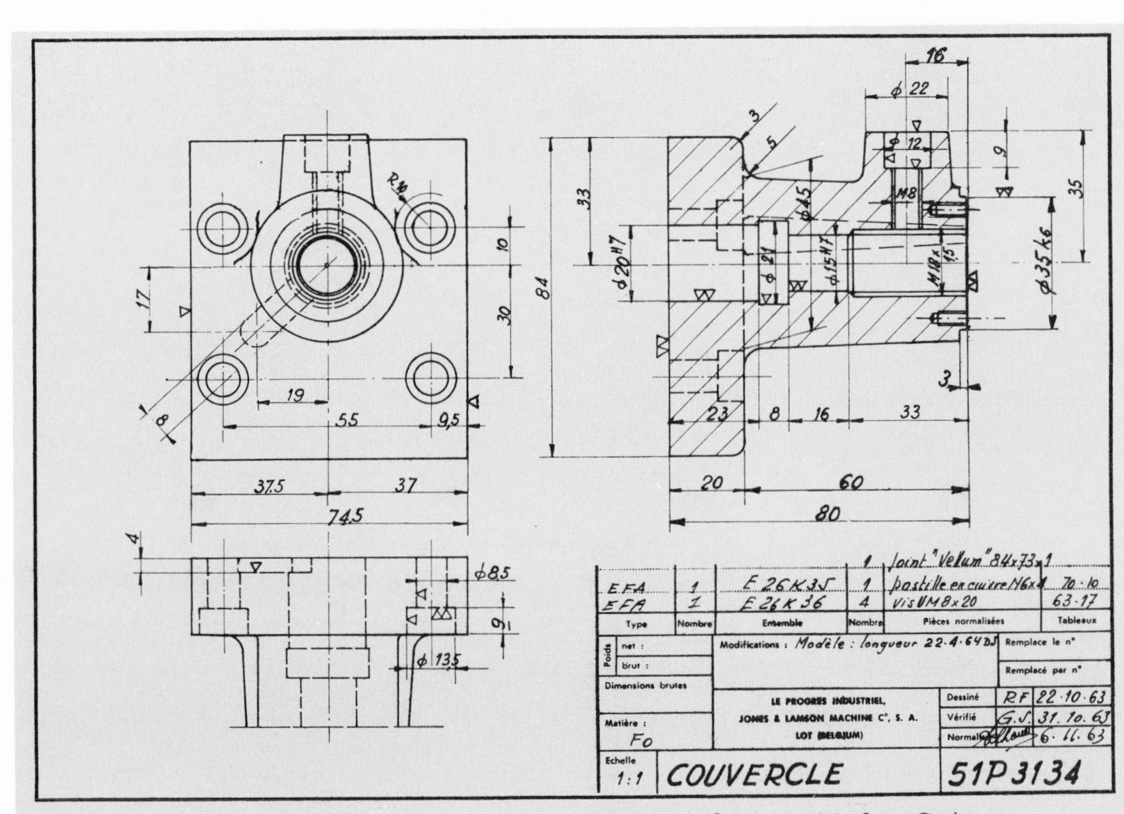

FIG. 3-16. Belgian Drawing of a Cover (Jones and Lamson Machine Co.)

Some countries using first-angle projection also use third-angle projection. In this case, it is most important to identify the type of projection being used on each drawing.

Partial Views

Partial views save space and time. They are used to represent symmetrical objects by half views, Fig. 3-17. When the adjacent view is an exterior view, the near half of the symmetrical view is shown. When the adjacent view is a full or half-section, the far half is shown. Partial views always are placed on the drawing sheet in direct projection from the adjacent views.

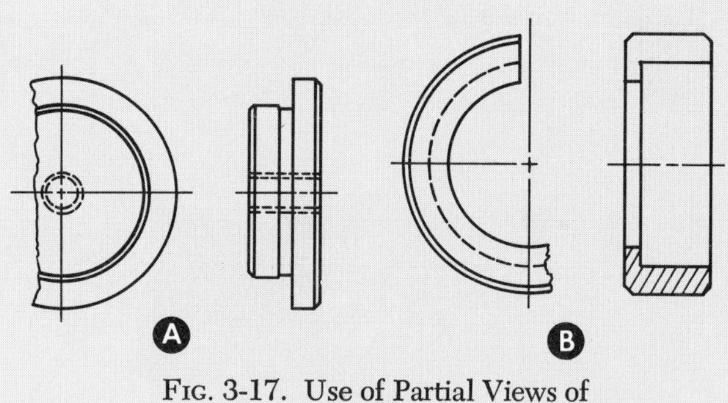

FIG. 3-17. Use of Partial Views of Symmetrical Objects
A. External partial views show the near portion.
B. Internal partial views show the far portion.

Removed Views

A removed view may show detail most clearly. (Refer to Fig. 3-25 on page 57.) In such cases, the view should be identified clearly, and the position from which the view is taken should be easy to see. A cutting plane line with arrows showing the viewing direction and identified by letters is common practice. This is an exception to the somewhat ironclad rule of orthographic projection and the relationship of views to each other. The removed view may be placed at any convenient place on the drawing.

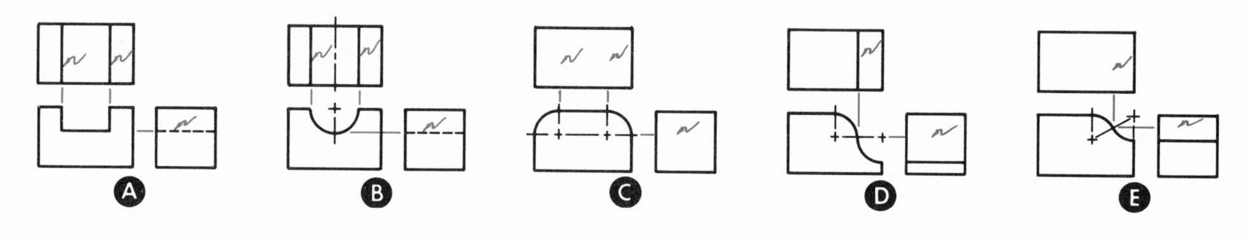

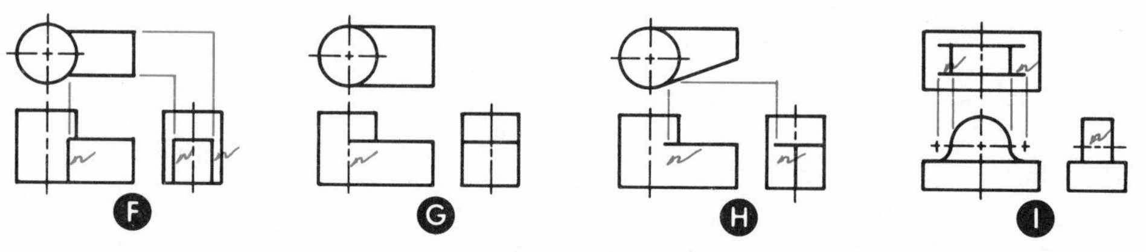

FIG. 3-18. Conventional Representation of Line Intersection

A. The edge views of the walls of the groove are projected to the adjacent view.
B. Intersections of curved and plane surfaces are projected to the adjacent view when the change of direction at this intersection is definite.
C. Curved surfaces tangent to plane surfaces are not projected.
D. Tangent points of curved surfaces with direction changes of 90° are projected to the one adjacent view but not to the other.
E. Tangent points of curved surfaces with less definite changes of direction are not projected.
F. Definite change in direction is projected.
G. Plane surface tangent to a curved surface of a cylinder is not projected.
H. Inclined plane surface tangent to a curved surface of a cylinder is not projected.
I. Note projection of full edge view to top view. Note also, no projection of two tangent curved surfaces in the profile view.

Conventional Representation of Projection

When you have a projection of a figure whose surface has a rectangular groove cut in it, there is no question as to whether you can see the lines representing the walls of the groove. On the other hand, with curved surfaces, there are numerous special cases that can be identified. Fig. 3-18 illustrates some of these.

Projection of Intersections with Cylinders

Fig. 3-19 shows several applications of conventional practice relating to forms intersecting with cylinders. Study each carefully.

Fillets and Rounds

External corners are sharp when they have been formed by machining. This is especially true for metal but is also true of other materials. A sharp corner in wood may splinter in addition to cutting. For these reasons, external corners often are rounded and then are called *rounds,* Fig. 3-20.

Internal corners may be rounded to add strength to the corner and (especially in the metal industries) to make the production of the castings somewhat easier. Rounded internal corners are called *fillets.*

Fillets and rounds are shown only where their curved shape shows. On working drawings, they never are shaded. They should be drawn with a template or compass, although in some cases, they may be drawn very carefully freehand.

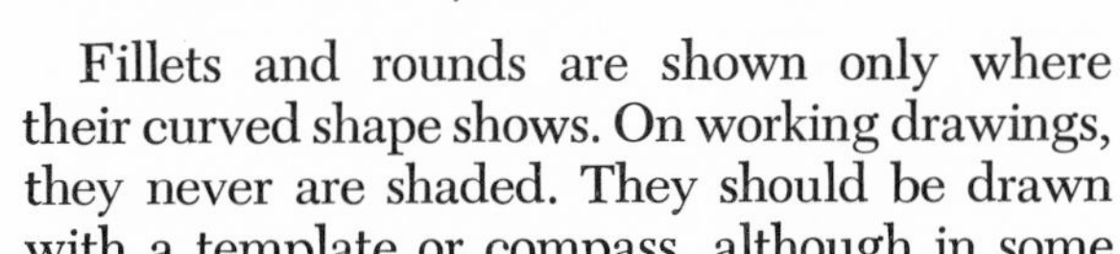

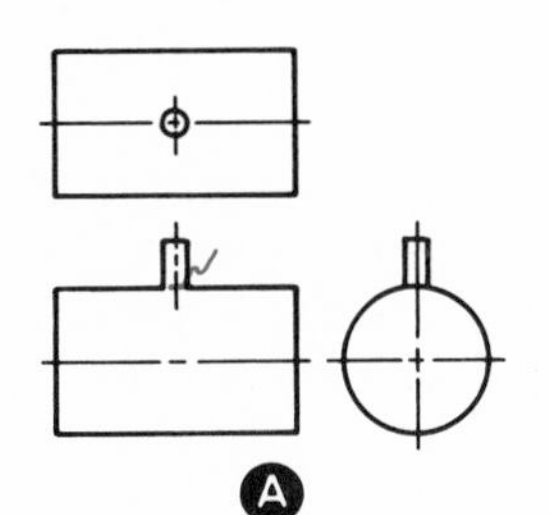

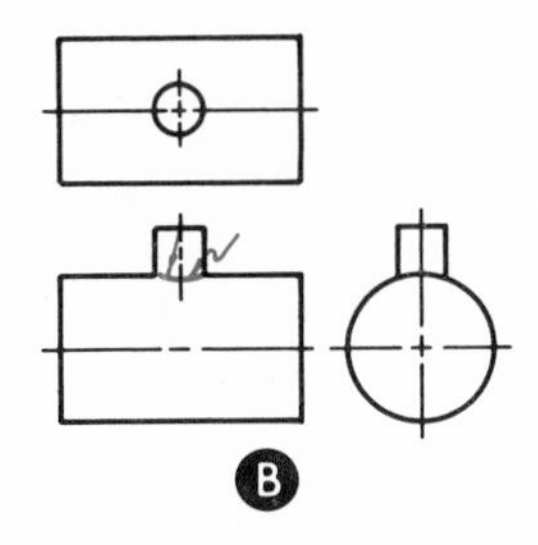

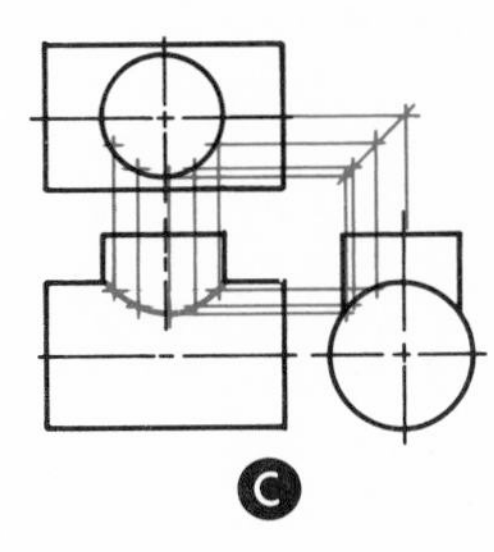

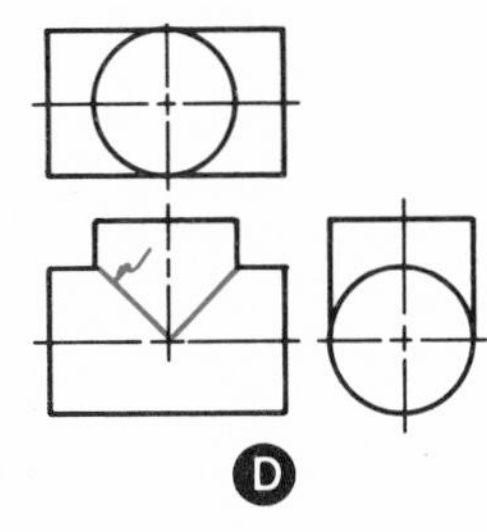

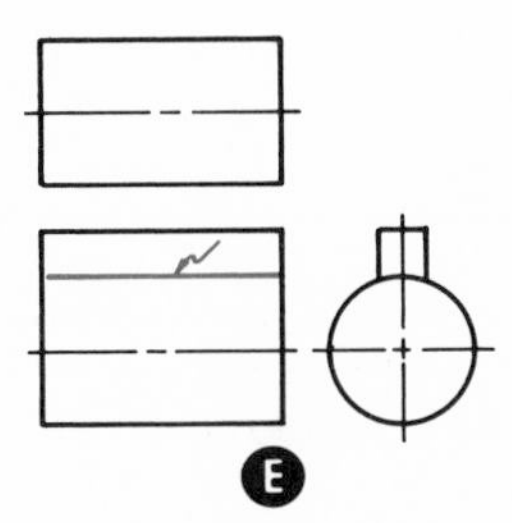

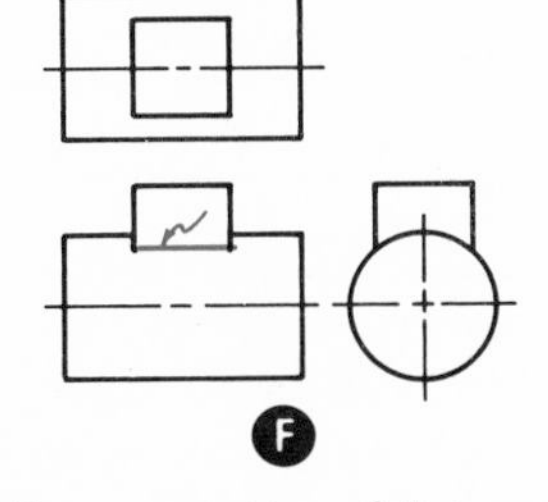

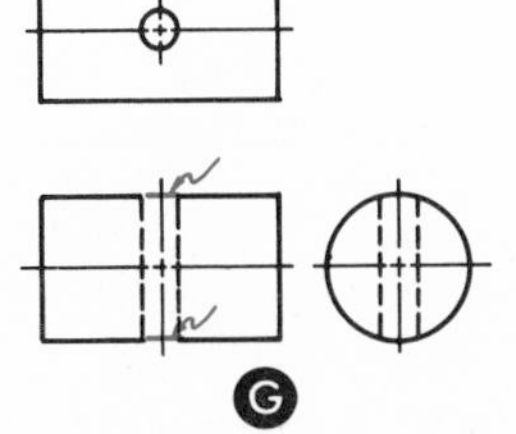

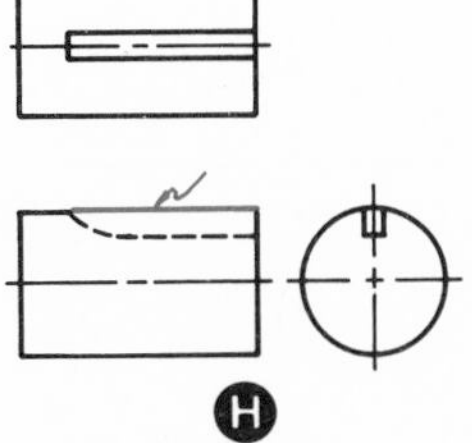

FIG. 3-19. Conventional Representation of Intersections of Cylinders and Prisms with Cylindrical Surfaces

A. A small cylinder intersecting a large cylinder results in an insignificant curve which is projected simply as a straight line.
B. An approximation for true projection, representing the intersection of a small with a large cylinder.
C. Intersection of large cylinders may be shown by plotting points of intersection and joining these through the use of the irregular curve.
D. Intersection of two cylinders of the same size.
E. Intersection of small prism with a large cylinder does not require special construction.
F. Projection of the intersection of a cylinder with a prism.
G. True projection of a small hole drilled in a large cylindrical surface is not important enough to construct.
H. True projection of a keyway in a large cylindrical surface is not important enough to construct.

Runouts

Runouts are the projections of fillets and their intersection with plane and cylindrical surfaces. Runouts have a radius equal to that of the fillet. About one-eighth of a circle arc is drawn to represent them. Runout treatment varies with the shape of different intersecting members. The examples in Fig. 3-21 show typical runouts.

Conventional Edges

Fillets and rounds often eliminate lines which, if the corners were sharp, would help in reading a drawing. See Fig. 3-22. In such cases, you may violate the rules so that a more readable drawing results. In Fig. 3-23, lines are drawn to show the change of direction and to make the reading as clear as possible.

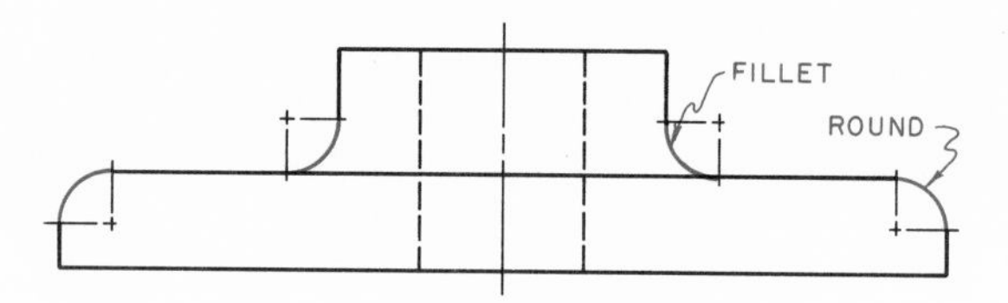

Fig. 3-20. Fillets and Rounds

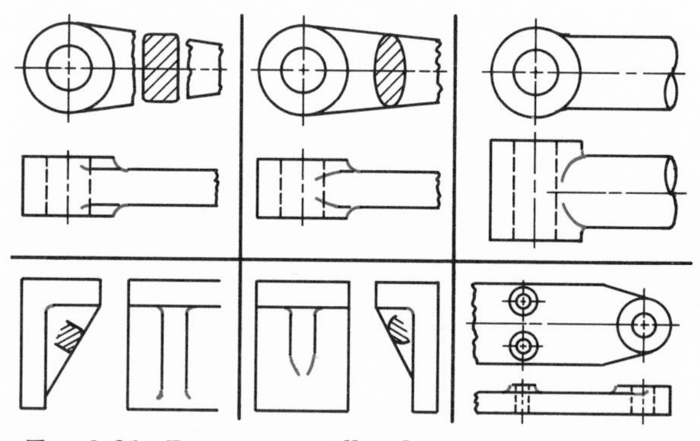

Fig. 3-21. Runouts on Filleted Intersections (USAS)

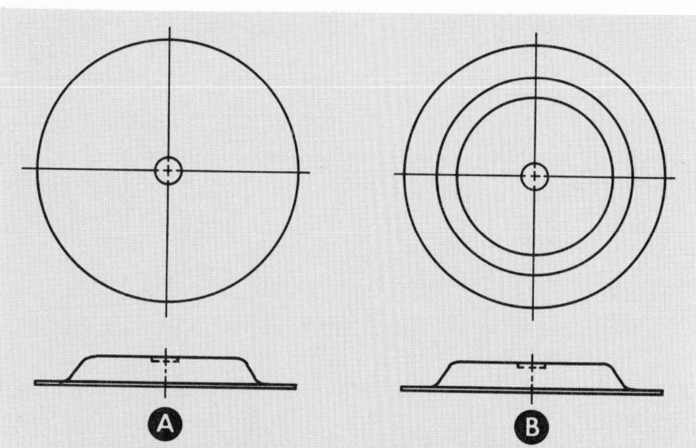

Fig. 3-22. Drawings of Filleted and Rounded Corners
A. In some cases, the practice suggested in Fig. 3-18 E results in a misleading projection.
B. This conventional practice improves readability.

Right-Hand and Left-Hand Parts

Right- and left-hand parts may be identical; that is, by turning the right-hand part around, it may become a left-hand part. This is desirable for manufacturing articles, but it cannot always be achieved. The right-hand glove, for example, does not properly fit the left hand. The abbreviations LH and RH are used to distinguish which view is which. In most cases, it is necessary to draw only one of the two parts, together with a note saying: RH PART SHOWN; LH PART OPPOSITE. See Fig. 3-24. In cases where more detail than this is needed, separate parts must be drawn and identified.

Conventional Lines

Study Fig. 3-25 to review the meanings of conventional lines used in orthographic projection. Reexamine Fig. 2-16 in the previous chapter to review the technique for sketching these lines.

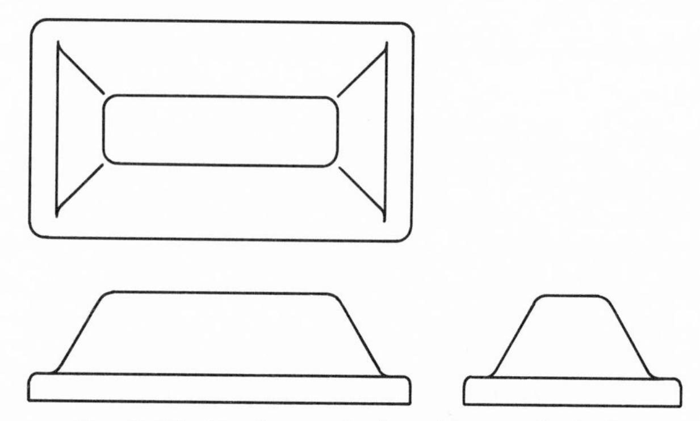

Fig. 3-23. Draftsman Judges Lines to Include

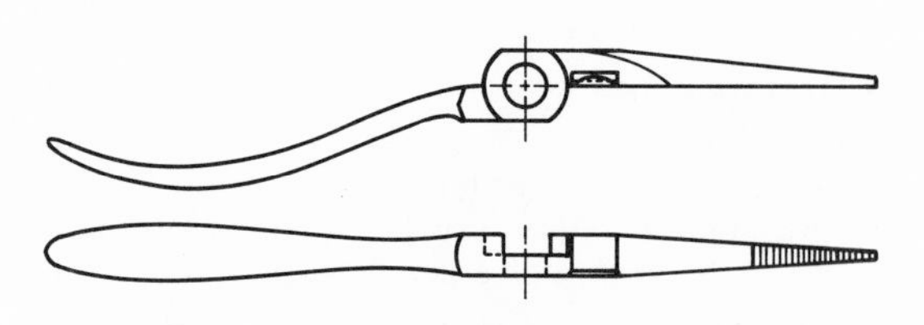

Fig. 3-24. Treatment of Right-Hand and Left-Hand Parts

Fig. 3-26 shows techniques used to show hidden features under several special conditions:

1. Dashes of hidden lines that run up to a visible outline should touch the visible outline (a).
2. Dashes representing hidden lines do not intersect other hidden lines nor object lines not in the same plane as the hidden line (b).
3. Dashes of hidden lines representing a hidden feature lying in the same plane such as "L" and "T" corners should intersect (c) and (d).
4. When two or more hidden lines meet on a plane, the dashes should intersect (e).
5. When the dash line gives the appearance of extending the length of a visible outline, a gap should appear (f).
6. When drawing hidden features such as arcs of a circle, the dashes of the arc come up to and touch the center line. Then a gap appears on the straight line side of the center line (g).
7. The dashes of parallel hidden lines fairly close together should be staggered rather than aligned. Notice those for the drilled hole at (a).

To add snap to the drawing of hidden lines, press down on the pencil at the beginning and end of each dash line.

It has been pointed out earlier that views of an object should be chosen so as to have the least number of hidden lines (consistent with other requirements). As you become proficient as a draftsman and begin to make more complex drawings, hidden lines may be omitted wherever they are not needed for clarity, Fig. 3-27.

Fig. 3-25. Use of Conventional Lines (USAS)

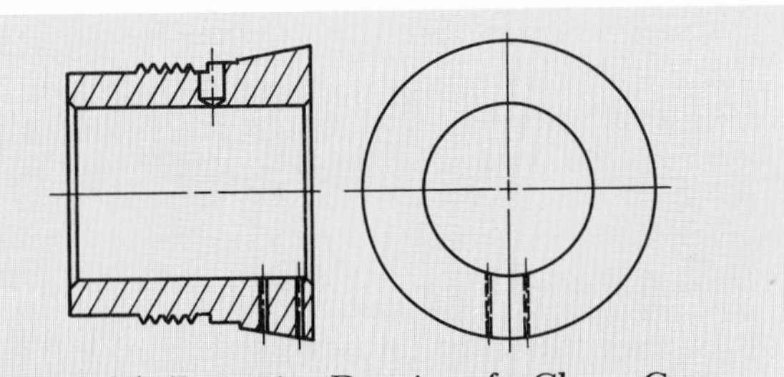

Fig. 3-27. Projection Drawing of a Clamp Cone (Gisholt Machine Co.)
Note that several hidden lines are intentionally omitted for clarity.

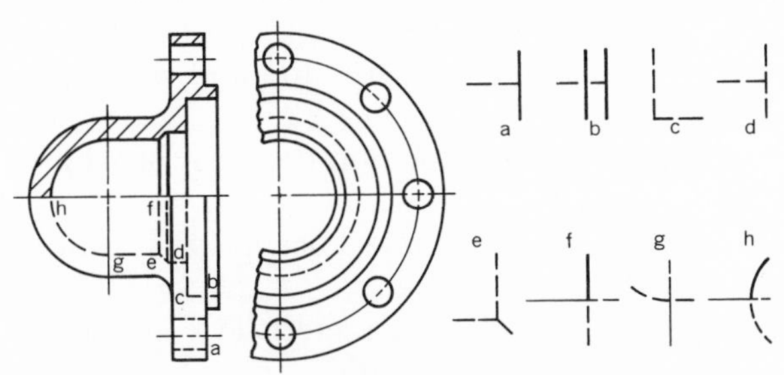

Fig. 3-26. Conventional Hidden Line Technique (SAE)

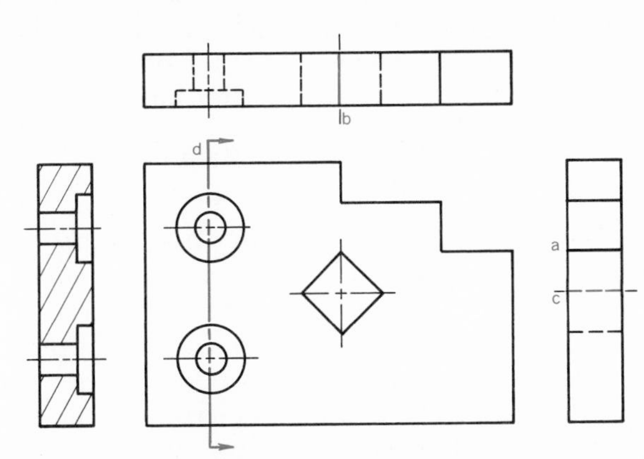

Fig. 3-28. Lines Taking Precedence over Other Coinciding Lines

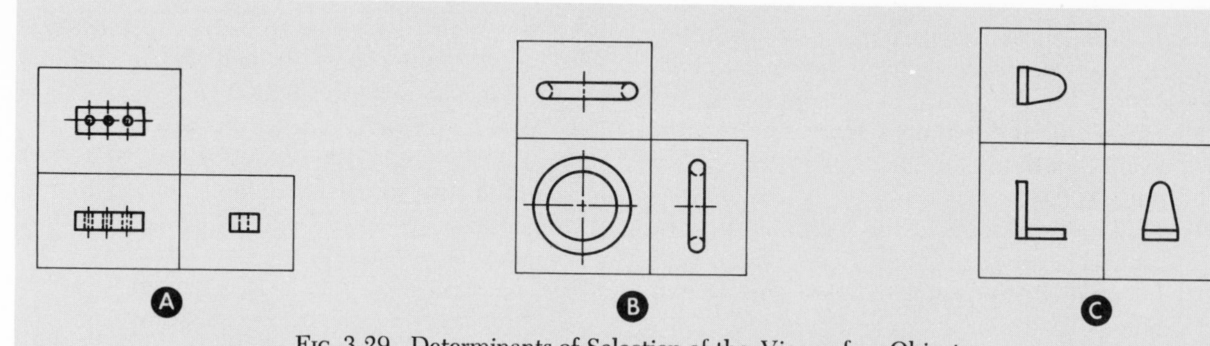

FIG. 3-29. Determinants of Selection of the Views of an Object
A. Natural position of the object
B. Characteristic contour of the object
C. Least hidden lines in the several views

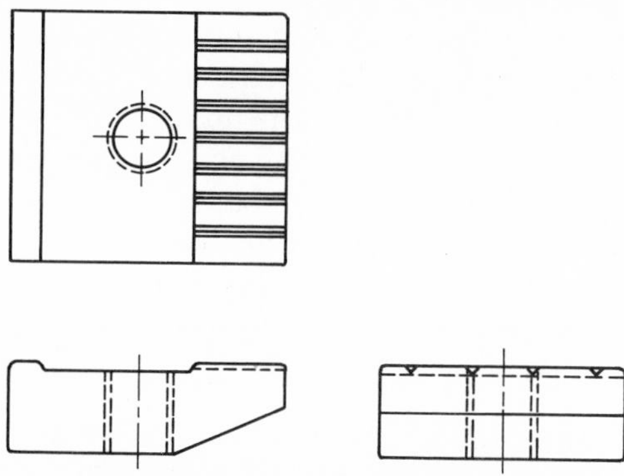

FIG. 3-30. Carriage Clamp (Gisholt Machine Co.) Front view is upside down from natural position but has the advantage of making all grooves in the top view visible.

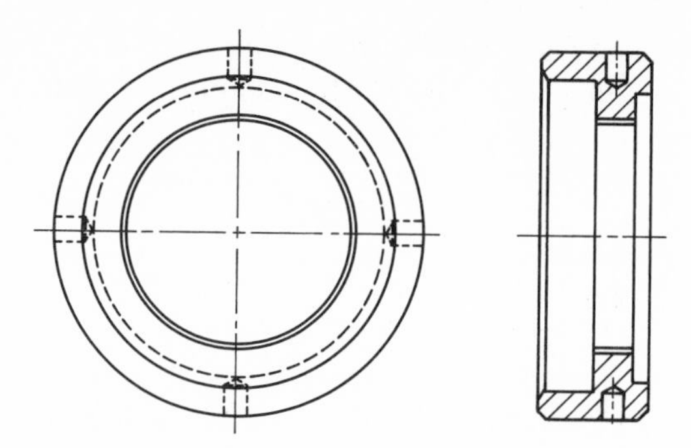

FIG. 3-31. Clamp Nut (Gisholt Machine Co.) Hidden lines show in front view but has advantage of a clear section as right side view.

Precedence of Lines

In the projection of a surface, several lines often come in the same place. In general, the more important lines take precedence over the lines of lesser importance, Fig. 3-28. Visible lines take precedence over both hidden lines (a) and center lines (b). Hidden lines take precedence over center lines (c). Cutting-plane lines take precedence over center lines (d).

Preliminary Decisions to the Layout of Orthographic Views

Intelligent work at the drafting board is based upon making wise decisions *before* mechanical drawing is done. The first objective of the draftsman should be to make correct preliminary decisions. Then when actual layout of the drawing is done, attention can be given to important matters such as correct visual representation, legible lettering, and clear dimensioning technique.

Choose the Best Views

Decide which are the best views for clear and accurate presentation of the object to be drawn. The experienced draftsman may make this decision mentally. However, the beginning draftsman should sketch the proposed views, as this step can save considerable time. If you start a mechanical drawing without first selecting the best views, you may find later that you must start over with your drawing. Since the front view coordinates the top and right side views, you must decide which view of the object should be the front view. Selection depends in part upon the other surfaces to be shown, which then will become the top and right side views.

A front view is chosen on the basis of which view:

1. Is seen when the object occupies its natural position, Fig. 3-29A.
2. Best shows the characteristic contour of the object, Fig. 3-29*B*.
3. Produces the fewest hidden lines in all three views, Fig. 3-29 *C*.

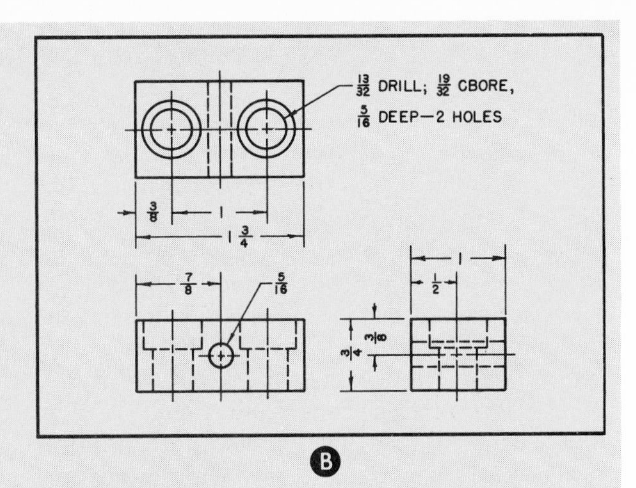

FIG. 3-32. Stop Block (Gisholt Machine Co.)

A. Crowded, poor arrangement, and undesirable dimensioning practice

B. Good spacing, good arrangement, and good dimensioning practice

Whenever possible, all three of these considerations should be used to select the best front view. However, one of these factors may be more important than either of the other two. In such cases, make your decision on the basis of the most important factor. The object always must be shown so that it conveys meaning clearly to the reader. This is the most important single rule in selecting which views to use, Figs. 3-30 and 3-31.

Select the Paper

Decide on the size and quality of paper. Draftsmen use a tracing medium and select a standard size upon which the sketch or drawing will not appear cluttered.

Choose the Appropriate Scale

Decide on the scale to use, keeping in mind the size of the drawing paper you have chosen and the relative size of the object you are describing. Select the largest possible scale, but leave an adequate amount of room for dimensioning and notes without making the drawings appear crowded. More on scaling a drawing appears in Chapter 4.

Decide on the Spacing Between Views

Spacing of a drawing is good when the drawing does not appear crowded. It will seem crowded if either the object, its extension or

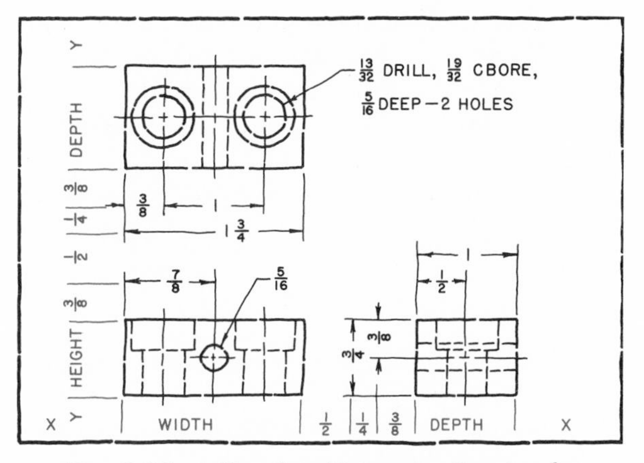

FIG. 3-33. A Sketch to Determine Spacing for the Views of a Drawing

dimension lines, or its notes are too close to the border lines or too close to each other, Fig. 3-32. Dimensioning is discussed later in Chapter 8. The arithmetic for spacing is important but simple, Fig. 3-33. Subtract the total amount of horizontal distance required by the views of the object from the total horizontal distance available within the border lines. Divide this figure by the number of spaces required. For vertical placement on the page, use the total vertical distance required by the object. Subtract this from the space available. Divide the result by the spaces needed. When dimensions are to be used, allow space for their placement.

Visualizing Points

Objects are composed of points, lines, and planes organized into three-dimensional solids. Consider first the point. The geometrical definition of a *point* is: "that which has neither height, width, nor depth." Practically, a point is the intersection of two lines, or it may be the end view of a single, straight line. By imagining an object to have planes of projection around it, with projection lines from points on the object to corresponding points on the appropriate projection planes, you can completely describe the object on these projection planes, Fig. 3-34.

Notice in Fig. 3-35 how a single point in space, *A*, is located on a projection box and how this looks when it is folded into a single plane. Now refer again to Fig. 3-34, and consider point *A*. In the frontal plane, is it the end view of a line? Is it the intersection of two lines? Ask yourself these questions about point *A* in the profile and horizontal planes.

Studying the position of points, lines, and planes in space requires careful specification. We already have used the terms *frontal plane, frontal view, horizontal plane, horizontal view, profile plane* and *profile view*. Be sure you understand these terms.

The distance of a point from known surfaces (such as projection planes) establishes its position in space, Fig. 3-36. The lines from which distances are measured in this figure are of special importance because they are imaginary edge views of projection planes. See Fig. 3-36*D*.

In Fig. 3-36*E*, they become hinge lines or folding lines for the projection planes. These lines are *reference lines* used as a guide from which to measure distance and locate points. They are identified by a letter or numeral representing the projection planes which lie on either side of them. The reference line *HF* separates the horizontal plane (H) from the frontal plane (F). Note also in Fig. 3-36 how the projection lines are related. In which view(s) is one of the projection lines represented as a point? At what angle to the planes of projection are the projection lines? In which planes of projection do projection lines appear as images of a projection line?

Visualizing Lines

Because you now can locate points in space by measuring their distance from the planes of projection, you can also locate *straight lines* because they are merely the shortest distance between two points. They may represent an edge view of a plane. Theoretically, a line has length but neither width nor depth.

In (A) of Fig. 3-37, the location of line *AB* is fixed by the distances which points *A* and *B*

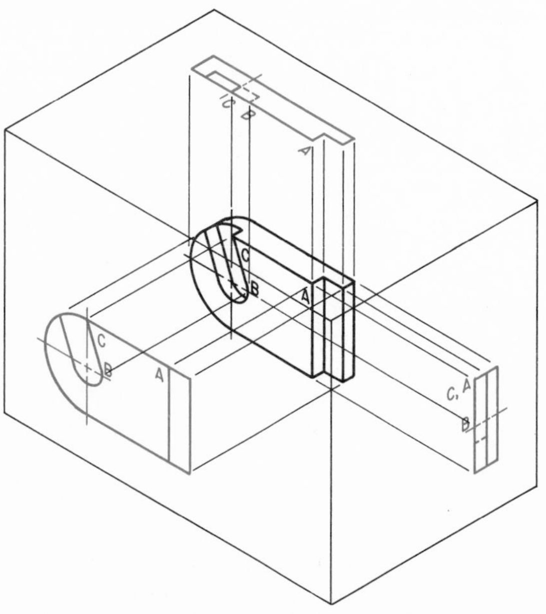

Fig. 3-34. Complete Description of the Object by Projection to the Appropriate Projection Planes (Jerald Mertens)

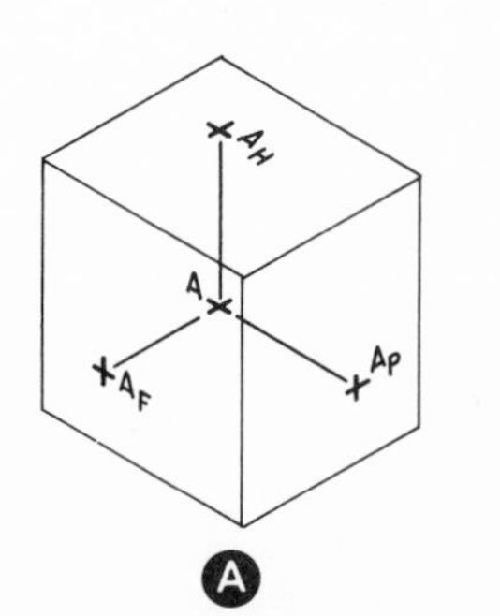

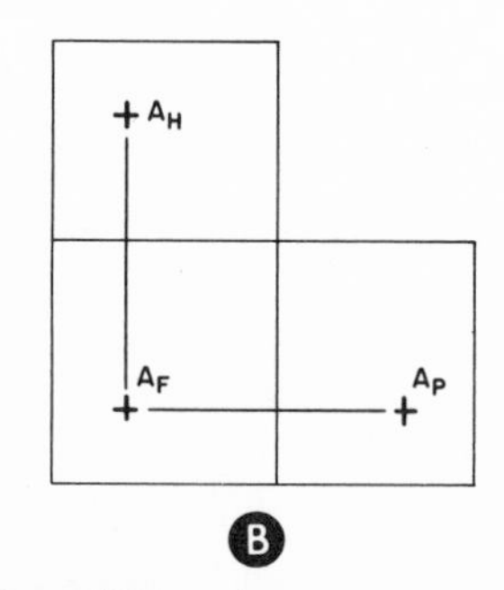

Fig. 3-35. Projection of Point *A*
A. On the projection box
B. When the projection box is folded flat like the surface of drafting paper

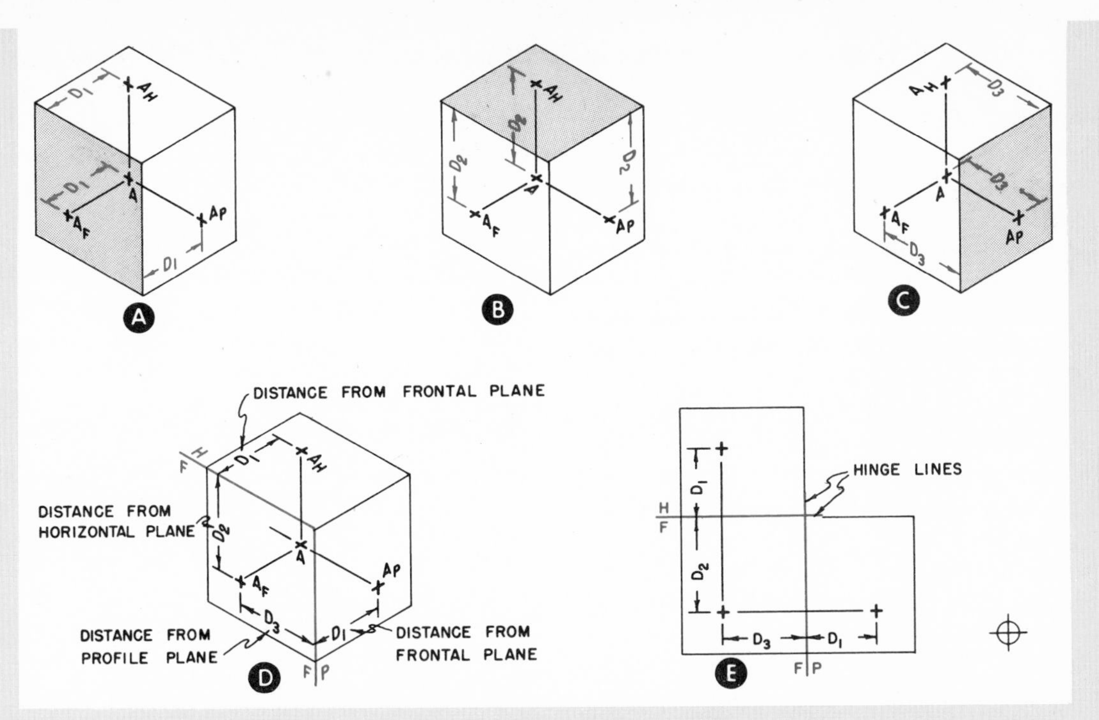

FIG. 3-36. Distance of Point from Known Surfaces Establishes Position in Space

A. Projections of point *A* are located the same distance (D_1) from the frontal plane.
B. Projections of point *A* are located the same distance (D_2) from the horizontal plane.
C. Projections of point *A* are located the same distance (D_3) from the profile plane.
D. Note intersection of planes at *H* and *F* and how distances locate the point.
E. Note how line *HF* becomes a reference line from which distances are measured.

are from the three projection planes. It is easy to make a three-view drawing of line *AB* as it appears in space by using projection lines from points *A* and *B* to the projection planes and then by connecting these points with a straight line. To make such a drawing, you would imagine the projection planes folded into the plane of your drafting paper as at (*B*). Explain how to locate line *AB* on each of the three principal planes of projection.

A given line appears as its true length when it is parallel to a projection plane and when the projection lines from it are parallel to each other and at right angles to both the given line and the plane upon which it is projected. See Fig. 3-37*B* (horizontal view and frontal view). When the plane upon which a line is projected is at right angles to the line, the projection will appear as a point, as in the profile view in Fig. 3-37*B*. When a line is neither at right angles nor parallel to a projection plane, it appears foreshortened. Note the frontal and profile views of Fig. 3-38. This simply means that it looks shorter than it really is. There is no way to project a line longer than its true length.

To review, refer again to Fig. 3-34 and answer these questions.

1. Is line *CB* as it appears in the horizontal view true length? Explain.

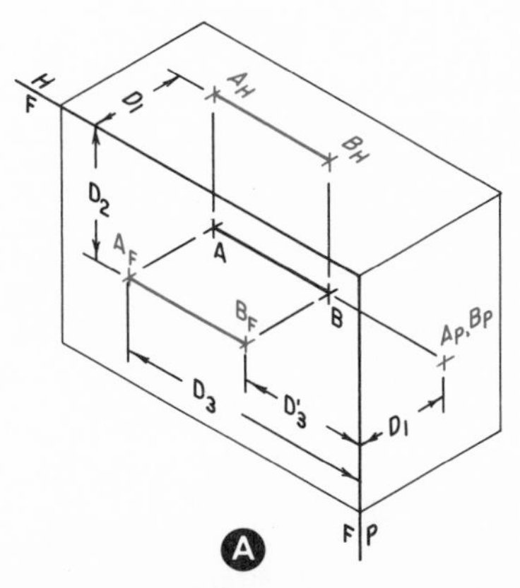

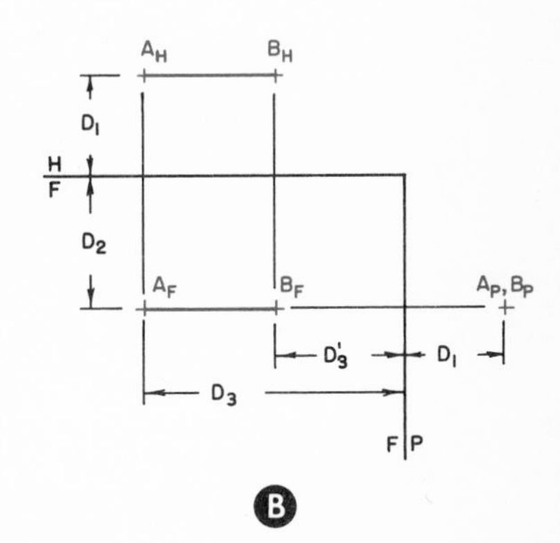

FIG. 3-37. Projections of Line *AB*
A. Pictorial B. Orthographic

2. Which point (C or B) on the angle bracket is farther from the profile plane?
3. How does line CB appear in the profile view?
4. Does line CB appear in its true length in the front view?
5. Does line CB appear in any of these three views as a point? Why?
6. Which point (C or B) on the object is farther from the frontal plane of projection? the horizontal plane of projection?
7. In which planes of projection does the projection of line CB represent an edge view of a plane surface?

Refer to Fig. 3-39 (line CD), and answer the first six of these same questions. Make a flat 3-view sketch of Fig. 3-39. Fig. 3-40 shows only the curved-end element of the bracket of Fig. 3-34. Curved line DEF is represented as a true-length curve in the front view because the curve is parallel to the frontal plane of projection. This same curve is represented by a straight line in the horizontal and profile planes. Why? Is curve DEF true length in either of these two planes?

Visualizing Planes

Lines representing boundaries of planes can be located in space by laying out their distances from the planes of projection. Fig. 3-41 shows a plane surface located on the three principal planes of projection. Because the plane figure $ABCD$ is parallel to the frontal plane, its image on this plane is true. However, the plane figure

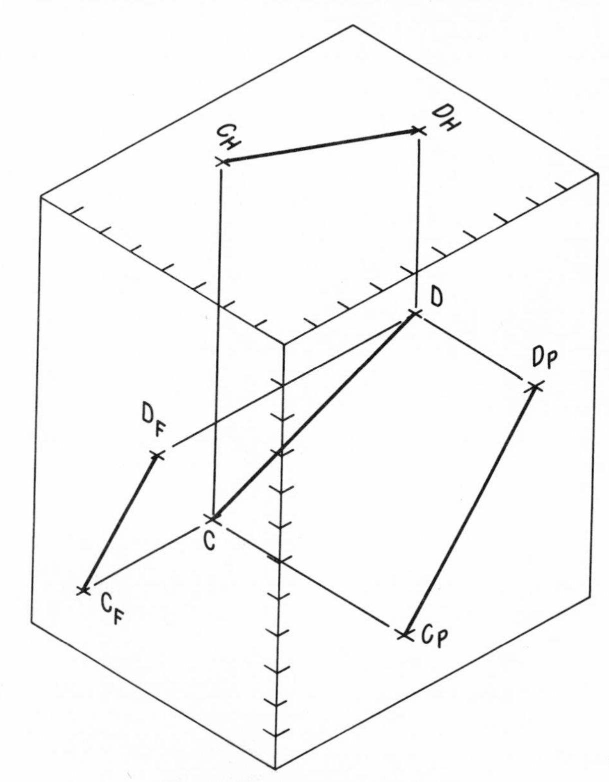

FIG. 3-39. Projections of CD

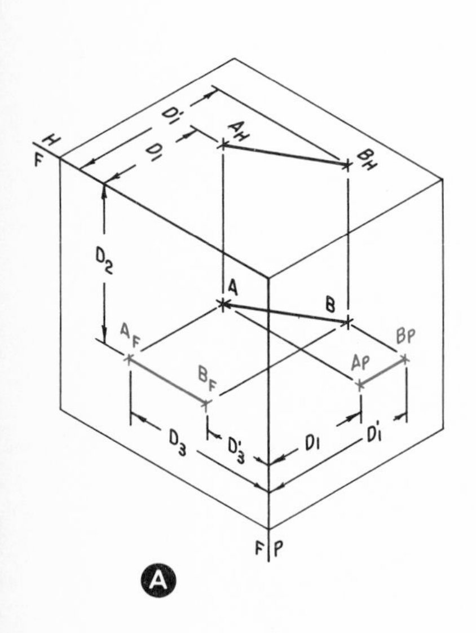

A

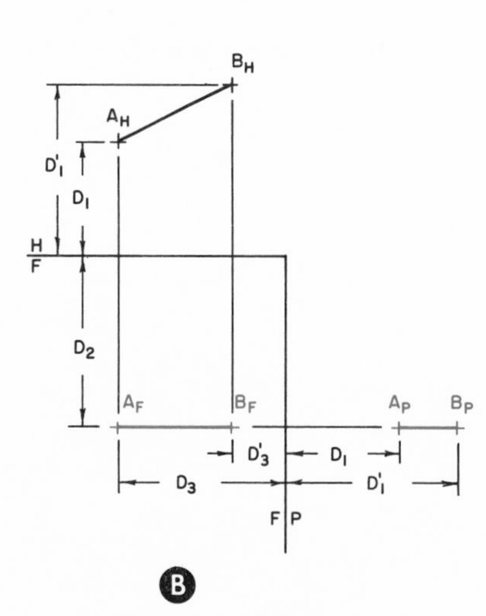

B

FIG. 3-38. Foreshortened Frontal and Profile Views of AB
A. Pictorial
B. Orthographic

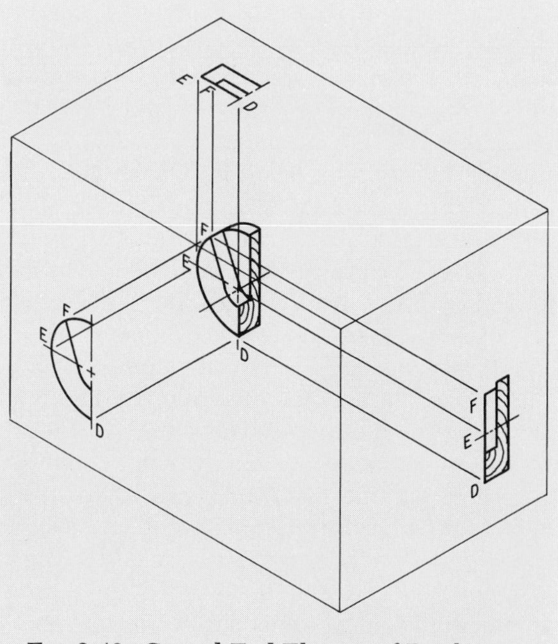

FIG. 3-40. Curved-End Element of Bracket

is at right angles to the profile and horizontal planes so that its image on these planes is an edge view. Fig. 3-42 shows a plane figure *ABCD* which is inclined to two of the principal planes of projection and at right angles to the third. In this case, the plane figure is foreshortened on the planes to which it is inclined and appears as an edge view on the third plane.

A plane figure may be inclined to all three of the principal planes of projection, Fig. 3-43. In this case, all three views are foreshortened. None of the principal views is a true view.

Plane figures which have curved forms may be described in the same manner. Select points on the object, and project these to the principal planes of projection. See Figs. 3-44 and 3-45.

Refer to the end bracket in Fig. 3-46 to review and answer the following questions:

1. Is the top view a true view?
2. Is any surface in the top view foreshortened?

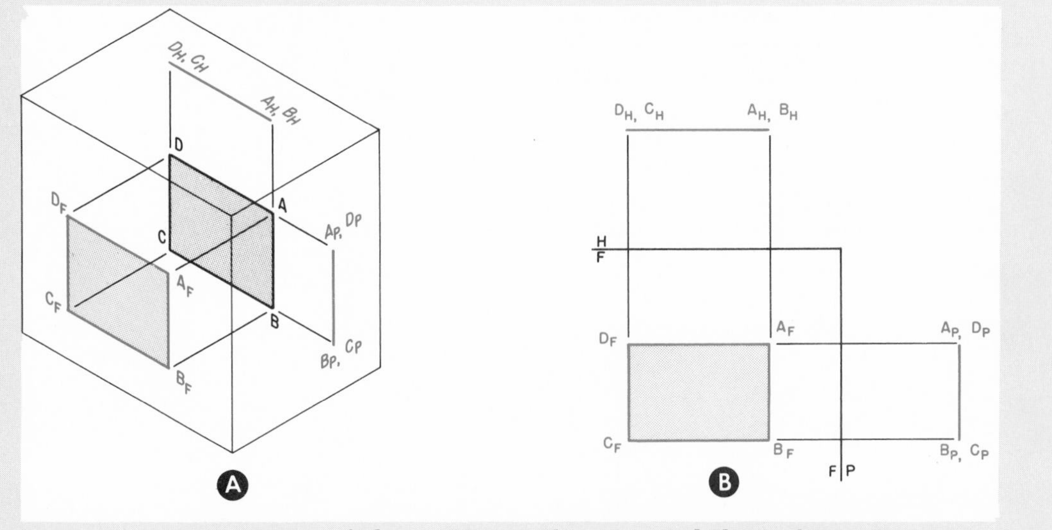

Fig. 3-41. Location of Plane *ABCD* on Three Principal Planes of Projection

A. Pictorial B. Orthographic

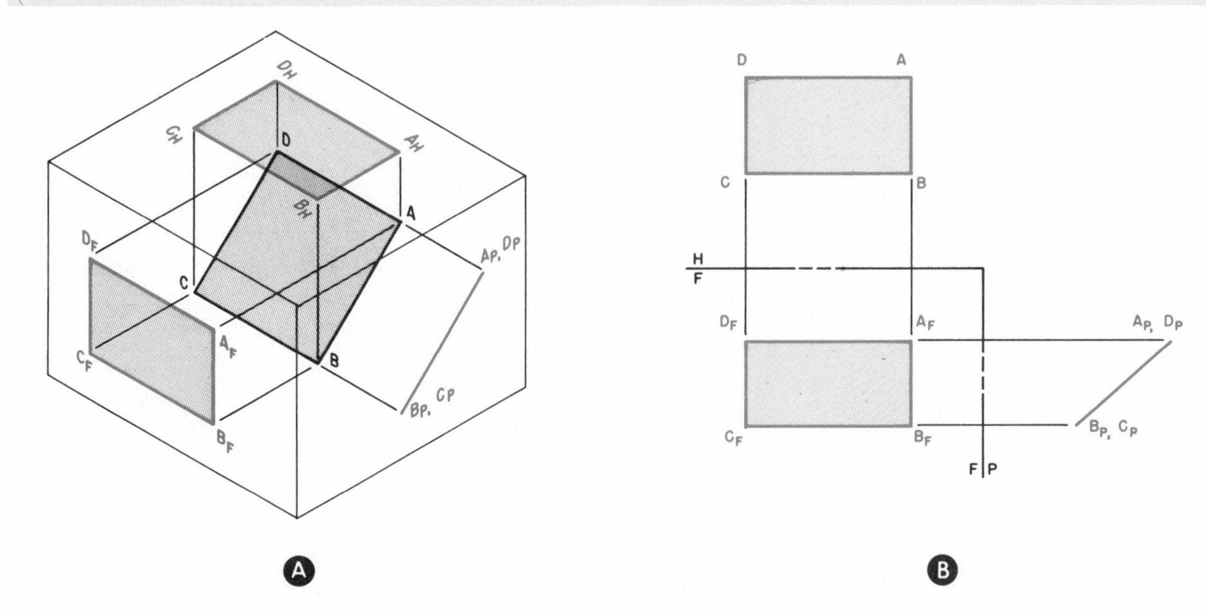

Fig. 3-42. Plane *ABCD* Inclined to Two Principal Planes of Projection is Foreshortened

A. Pictorial B. Orthographic

ORTHOGRAPHIC PROJECTION

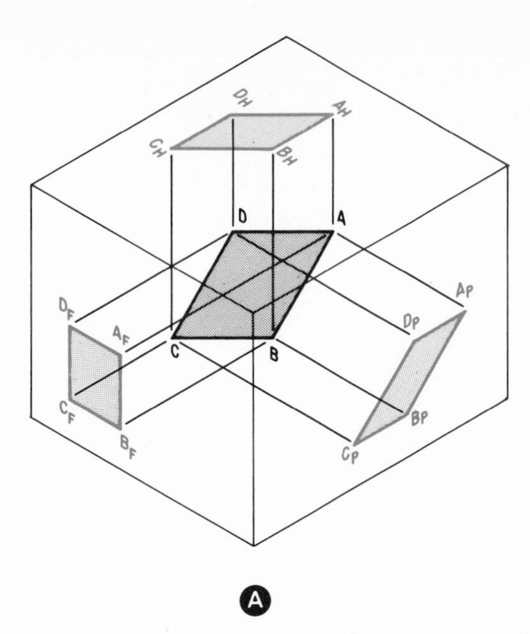

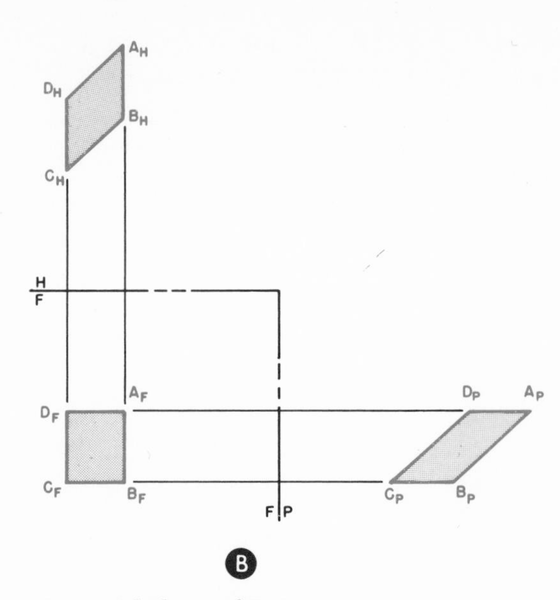

FIG. 3-43. Plane *ABCD* Inclined to All Three Principal Planes of Projection
A. Pictorial
B. Orthographic

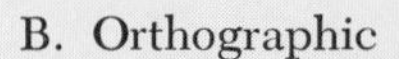

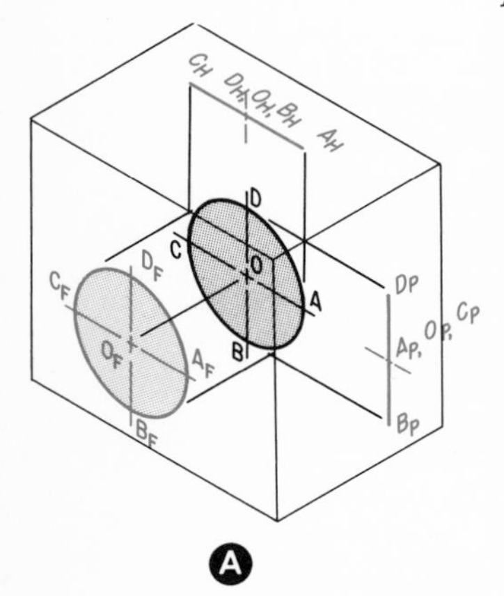

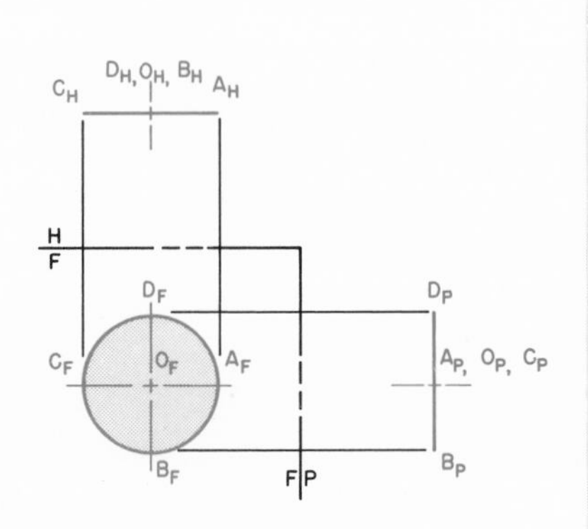

FIG. 3-44. Projection of Curve, Circle *O-ABCD*, Parallel to the Frontal Plane
A. Pictorial
B. Orthographic

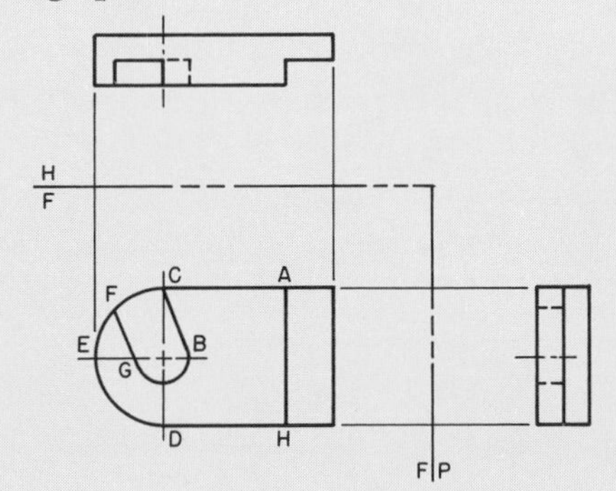

FIG. 3-46. Orthographic Projection of Bracket

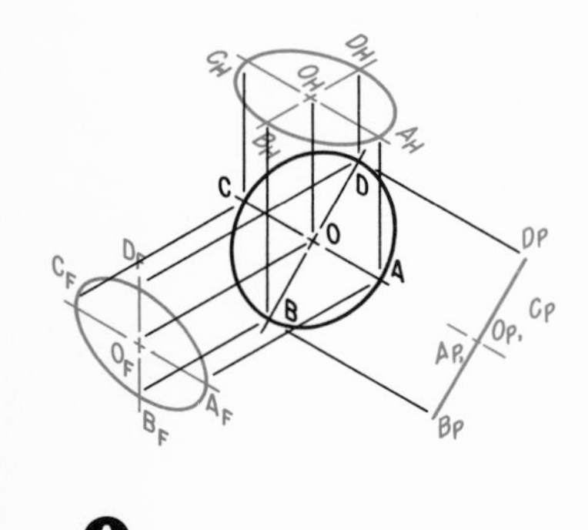

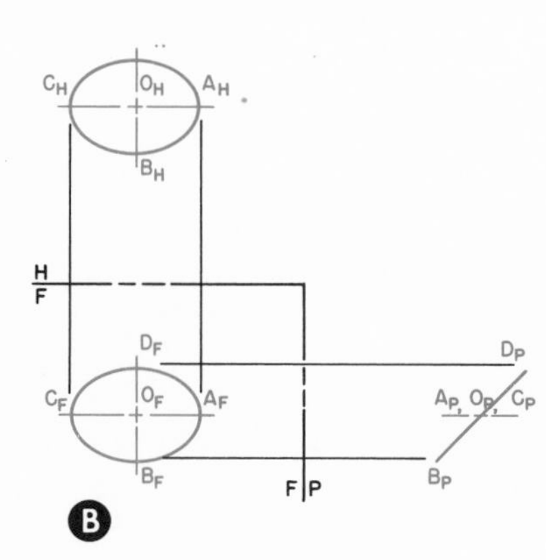

FIG. 3-45. Projection of a Curve Inclined to Two of the Principal Planes of Projection
A. Pictorial
B. Orthographic

3. To which of the planes of projection was the top surface of the end bracket parallel?
4. What surfaces of the object are edge views in the top view?
5. Do the circular features appear in their true projected shapes in the front view? How do you know?
6. In which views does the base of the slot *CBGF* appear in the edge view?
7. In which views does line *CB* appear as a true-length line? as a foreshortened line?

It is a short step from describing a single plane surface in space to describing more than one. In so doing, you can describe solids. By analyzing the point, line, and surface elements of an object, you will be able to locate these elements in pictorial. *Or*, from a pictorial, you

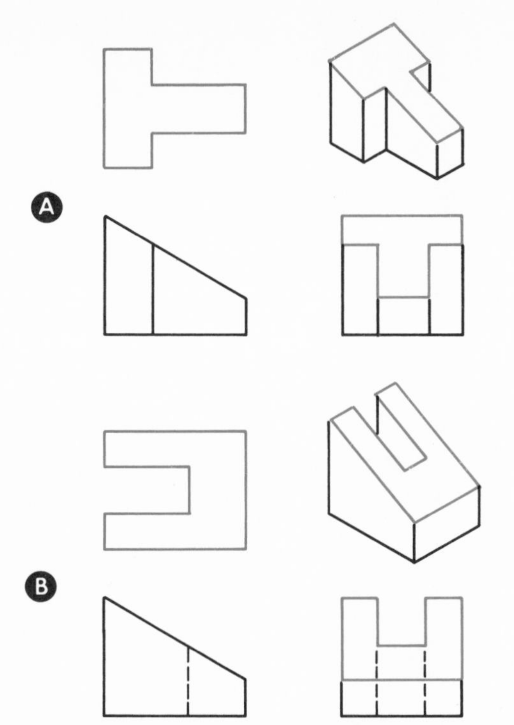

FIG. 3-47. Characteristic Shapes of Inclined Surfaces
A. Inclined "T"
B. Inclined "U"

can relocate the elements in an orthographic projection. Note again the importance and function of the reference lines to this type of study.

Characteristic Shapes of Inclined Surfaces

Surfaces will have the same general shape in every view in which the surface is not shown as a line. If a T-shaped surface appears in the top view, the same shape also will appear in an adjacent view, Fig. 3-47.

Terminology

You have examined the practical relationship of points, lines, and surfaces in space. The following terms are needed to help you understand these relationships in a more formal way. Study them carefully. For each definition, think of an object that will illustrate it.

NORMAL LINE. A line parallel to two of the three principal planes of projection and perpendicular to the other. Such a line will show its true length in the planes to which it is parallel. It will appear as a point in the plane to which it is perpendicular, Fig. 3-48. Make a three-view, orthographic sketch of line *AB*.

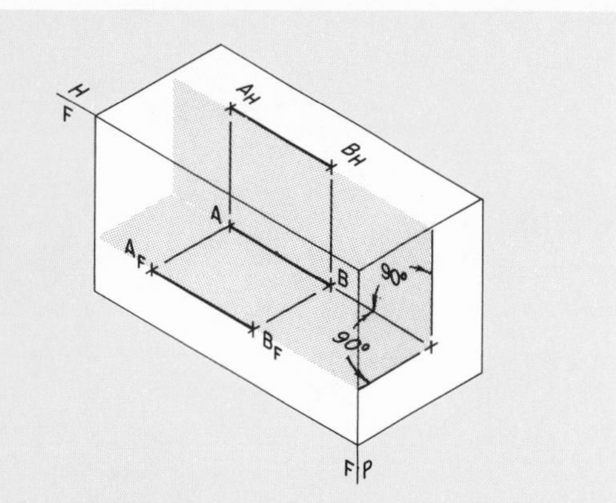

FIG. 3-48. Normal Line
It is parallel to two of the principal planes of projection.

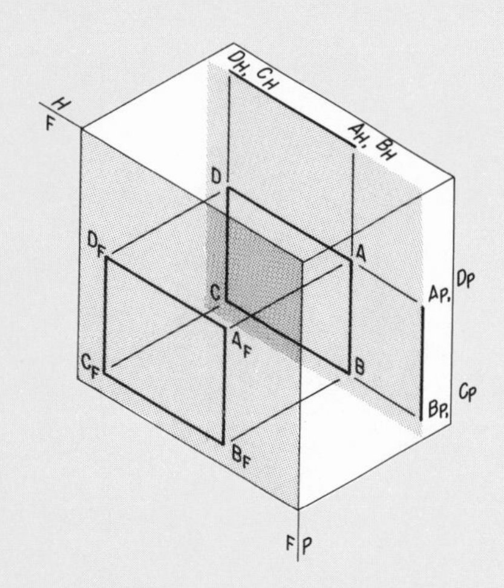

FIG. 3-49. Normal Plane
It is parallel to one of the principal planes of projection.

NORMAL SURFACE. A surface parallel to one of the principal planes of projection. It will produce a true view on that plane. If such a surface is at right angles to one of the other principal planes of projection, it will show as an edge view in that plane, Fig. 3-49. Make a three-view, orthographic sketch of plane *ABCD*.

INCLINED LINE. A line parallel to one plane of projection but inclined to the other two. Thus, it will appear in its true length in the plane to which it is parallel, Fig. 3-50. Make a three-view sketch of line *AB*. It will appear foreshortened in each of the other planes of projection. In general, the closer the line is to becoming perpendicular to a plane of projection, the more distortion or foreshortening

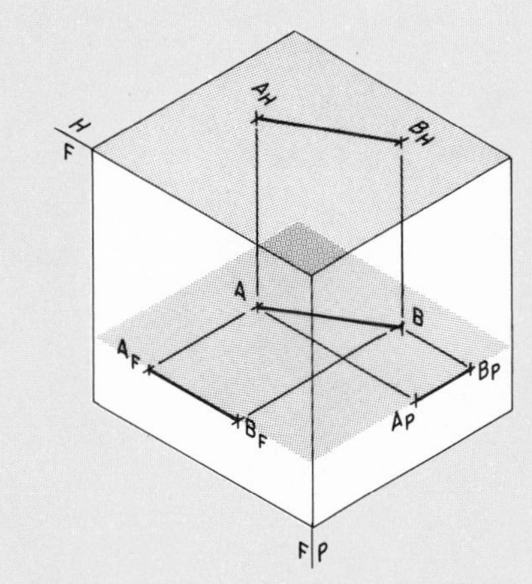

FIG. 3-50. Inclined Line
It is inclined to two of the principal planes of projection and parallel to one.

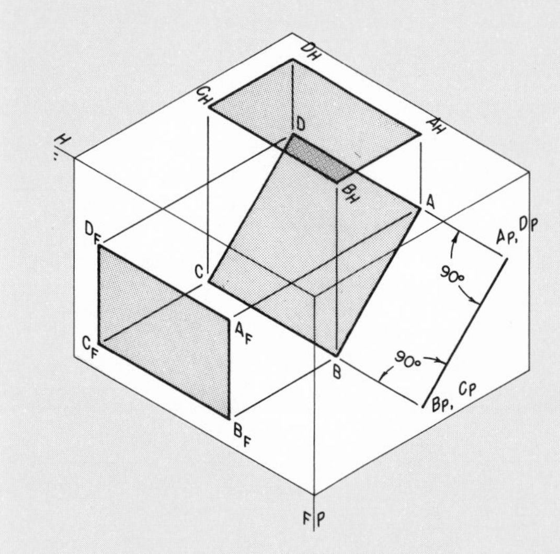

FIG. 3-51. Inclined Surface
It is inclined to two principal planes of projection and perpendicular to one.

of its projection. Conversely, the closer the line is to being parallel to a plane of projection, the more nearly its projection approaches its true length.

INCLINED SURFACES. A surface inclined to two planes of projection and perpendicular to one. In the plane to which it is perpendicular, the surface will appear as a line or edge view. In the planes to which it is inclined, it will appear as a foreshortened plane (one which does *not* show true size nor shape). See Fig. 3-51. Make a three-view sketch of plane *ABCD*.

In general, the closer an inclined surface is to being perpendicular to a plane of projec-

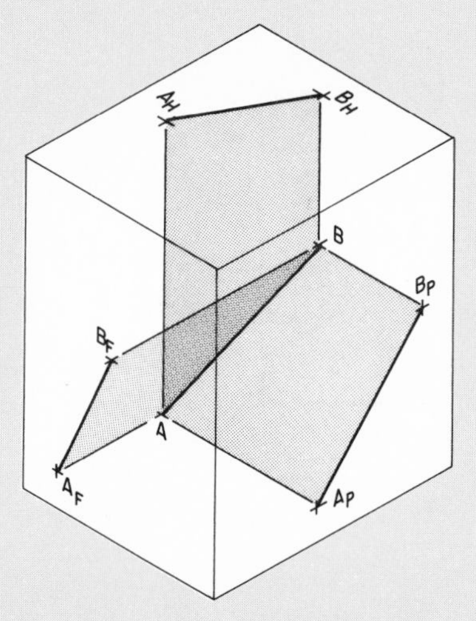

FIG. 3-52. Oblique Line
It is inclined to all three of the principal planes of projection.

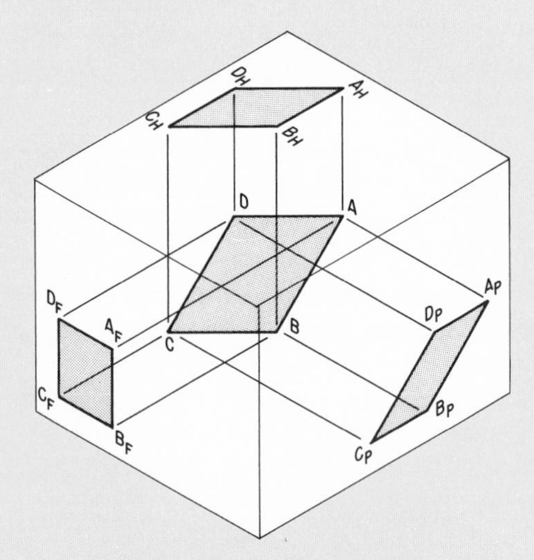

FIG. 3-53. Oblique Surface
It is inclined to each of the three principal planes of projection.

tion, the more foreshortened its projection on that plane will be. The closer an inclined surface is to being parallel to a plane of projection, the more nearly its projection on that plane will be like its true size and shape.

OBLIQUE LINE. A line neither parallel nor perpendicular to any of the normal planes of projection. Thus its projection on any of the planes always is foreshortened, Fig. 3-52. Make a three-view sketch of line *AB*. Its projection is somewhat more foreshortened as it approaches being perpendicular to a projection plane and somewhat less foreshortened as it approaches

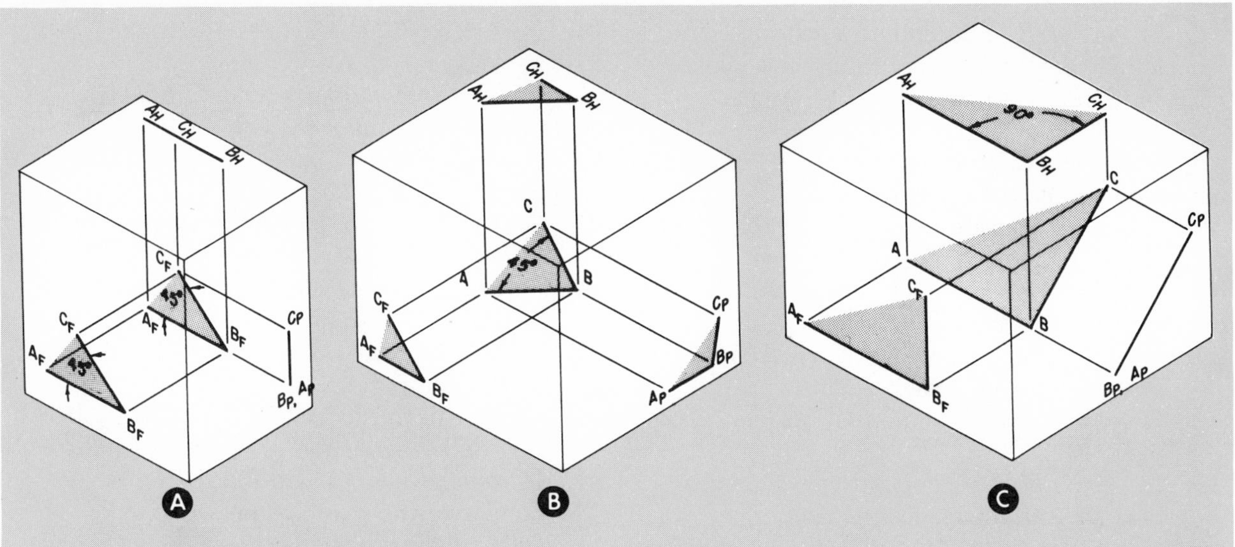

FIG. 3-54. Projection of Angles
A. A 45° angle parallel to a principal plane of projection. Note how an edge view is related to the projection in which the true angle shows.
B. A 45° angle inclined to each of the three principal planes of projection.
C. A right angle with only one leg inclined to a plane of projection.

being parallel to a projection plane. Its projection is never in true length and neither does it ever appear as a point view on any one of the normal projection planes.

OBLIQUE SURFACE. A surface neither perpendicular nor parallel to any of the normal planes of projection. Thus, its projection on the normal planes always is foreshortened. Its projection becomes more foreshortened as it approaches perpendicularity to a plane of projection and less foreshortened as it approaches being parallel to a plane of projection. It does not show in any of the normal views as a true surface nor as an edge view, Fig. 3-53. Make a three-view sketch of plane *ABCD*.

ANGLES. Angles parallel to a plane of projection show in their true size, Fig. 3-54A. The image of an angle *inclined* to a plane of projection may be projected as either larger or smaller than the true angle depending on its position. In the case of a 90° angle, when only one leg of the angle is inclined to a plane of projection and the other leg is parallel to a plane of projection, the image of the angle still will be 90°. Make three-view, orthographic sketches of the angles shown in Fig. 3-54.

Sketch a pictorial for an angle other than one that is 45°, 90°, or 180°. The legs of the angle chosen should be inclined to each of the principal planes of projection. Then make a three-view, orthographic sketch of this angle.

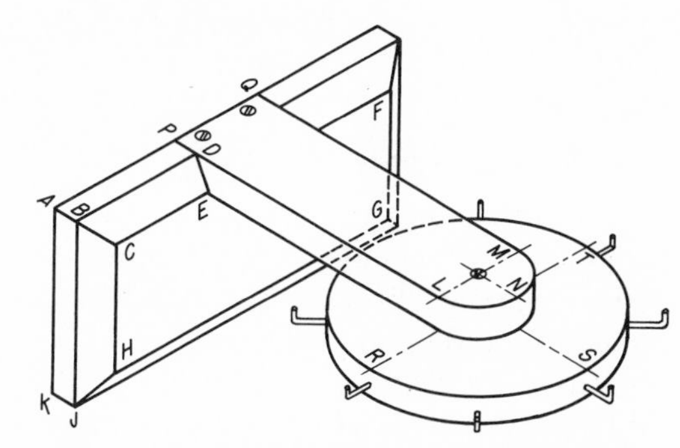

FIG. 3-55. Wall-Mounted Kitchen Utensil Holder (James Paglia)

Summary

Answer the following questions about the kitchen utensil holder in Fig. 3-55. (All questions assume you are making a three-view, orthographic projection of the holder.)

1. In what view does line *AB* appear as a point?
2. Will line *AB* appear in any of the principal views in its true length? If so, which?
3. Is line *AB* considered a normal line? Explain.
4. In what view (if any) does line *DE* appear as a point?
5. Will line *DE* appear in any of the principal views in its true length? If so, in which?

6. Is line *DE* considered a normal line? Why? By what name is this line known?
7. In what view does line *BC* appear as a point?
8. Will line *BC* appear in any of the principal views in its true length?
9. Is line *BC* considered a normal line? Why? By what name is this line known?
10. In what view(s) will surface *ABJK* appear in true shape?
11. In what view(s) will surface *ABJK* appear as an edge view?
12. Is surface *ABJK* a normal surface? Explain.
13. In which of the principal views does surface *BCED* appear in true shape?
14. Is surface *BCED* a normal surface? Is it an oblique surface?
15. In what view does surface *PLNMQ* appear in true shape?
16. In what view(s) does surface *PLNMQ* appear as an edge view?
17. Will the circular end *LNM* appear in its true shape in the top view?
18. In what view(s) will the thickness of the holder wheel show in true size?
19. To which plane of projection will surface *CHGF* be parallel?
20. What will the surface of the holder wheel *RST* look like in the profile view?
21. In which view(s) will line *BJ* be perpendicular to the plane of projection?

methods of visualization

Analysis of Elements

In the preceding paragraphs you have seen how objects are made up of various combinations of geometrical elements and forms. By visualizing these in combination, you can visualize the object, Fig. 3-56.

When you are reading an orthographic drawing, use this technique to help visualize the pictorial of the object.

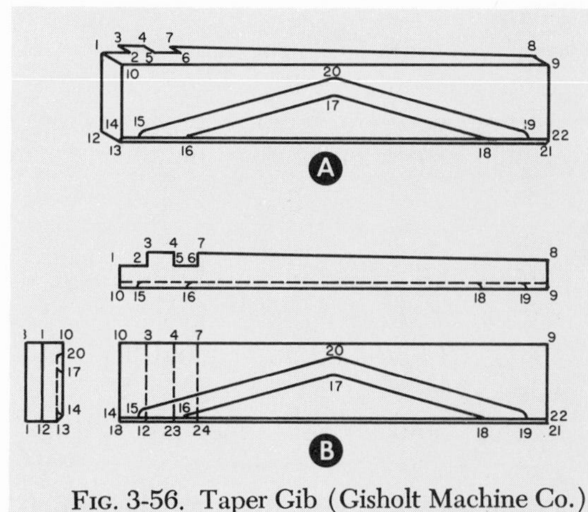

FIG. 3-56. Taper Gib (Gisholt Machine Co.)
A. Pictorial
B. Orthographic

1. Number the various points of intersection on the main view of the drawing.
2. Number all known points on the other views of the drawing.
3. Sketch a pictorial of an imaginary box using the overall dimensions of the object.
4. Place all known positions of numbers on this box.
5. Darken all known lines.
6. Study the object to complete its visualization.

When making the transformation from a pictorial to the orthographic projection, number the intersections on the pictorial. Make the basic two- or three-view layout by sketching the outline of each view. Then study the pictorial, and add the elements to the orthographic projections.

Adjacent Views

Still another way to study visualization is first to identify each surface of an object with a letter and then to examine carefully the orthographic views to see where these surfaces are located. Sometimes the surfaces will be true shape, sometimes foreshortened, and sometimes in edge view, Fig. 3-57. Objects can be

	Horizontal View	Frontal View	Profile View
A			
B			
C			
D			
E			
F			
G			
H			
I			
J			
K			
L			
M			

studied either from pictorial to orthographic or from orthographic to pictorial. No two adjacent surfaces can be in the same plane.

Modeling

Industrial designers use modeling as a means of visualizing what an object really looks like. However, before a model can be made, design sketches and sufficiently detailed preliminary drawings must be produced. Models are made from clay, plastic, wood, and other materials, Fig. 3-58. Based on what the proposed product looks like in model form, decisions are made with respect to its design; then, final drawings are prepared.

Student draftsmen also find modeling useful in studying projection. Modeling clay is easily formed and may be cut with a knife and re-

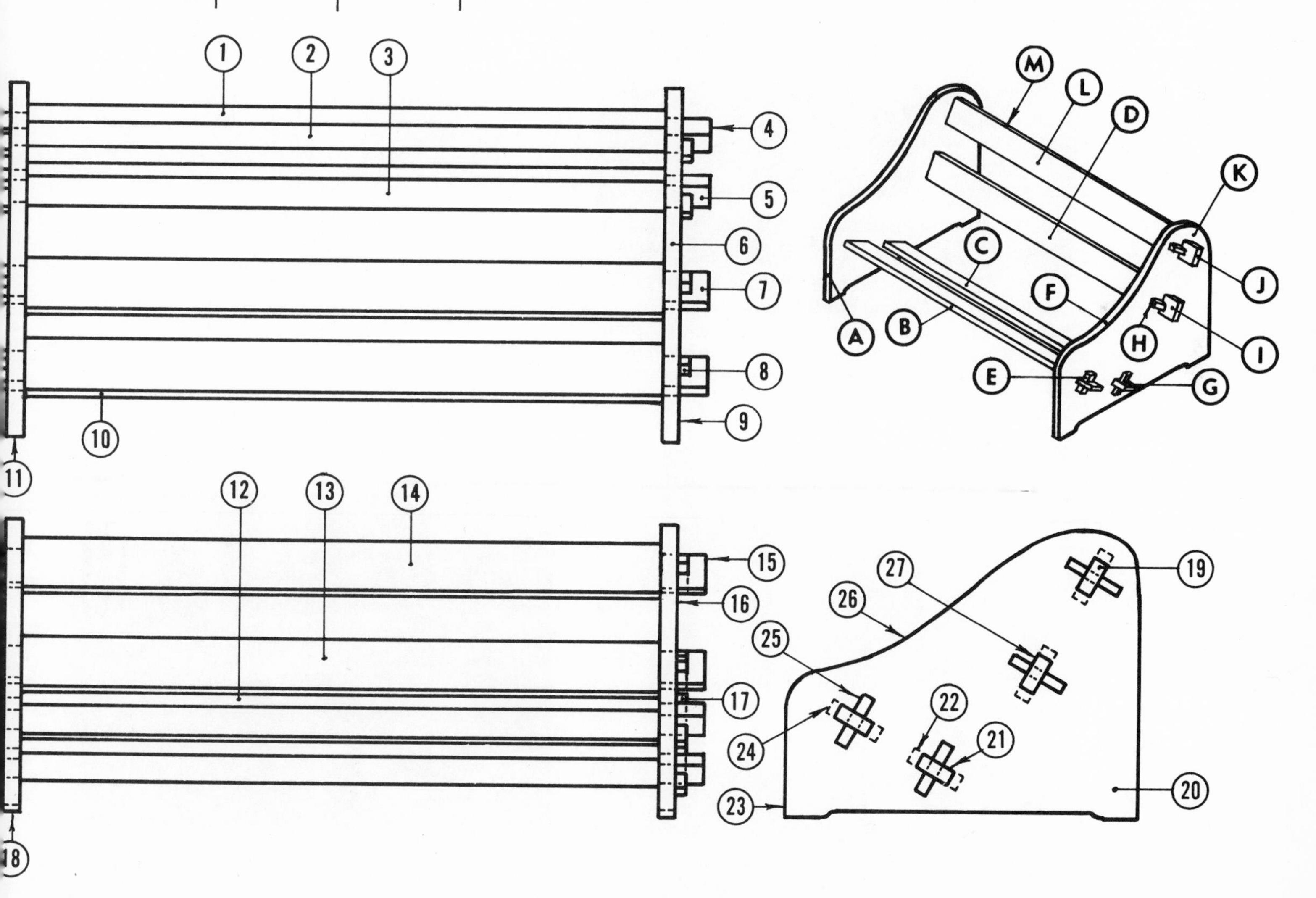

Fig. 3-57. Visualizing Adjacent Views (Richard Winey)

Place tracing paper over the table in this illustration. Then place numerals from the three orthographic views opposite the lettered surfaces which they represent on the pictorial.

used. Frequently models are used to visualize an object from its orthographic projection. Typically the three orthographic views of a figure are given. These then are carved into clay, soap, wood, or any solid easily cut. For working with missing-line problems or missing-view problems, the technique shown in Fig. 3-59 is very helpful. The process is simple and direct:

1. Examine the given orthographic views.
2. Transfer the given lines to the basic block from which the model is to be cut.
3. Cut as necessary to satisfy the conditions of the several given views.
4. If lines or views are missing, add them to the sketch or drawing as needed.

Making a Fold on the Reference Line

When a set of orthographic views is given, you may sketch them on a sheet of scratch paper and fold the paper on the reference plane lines. This often is helpful in visualizing an object, since it provides the three principal surfaces of a basic box, Fig. 3-60.

Fig. 3-58. Work on Clay Models (General Motors Corp.)
These are prepared to give the designers and management an accurate, three-dimensional impression of the finished car. Car at far right is a fiber-glass prototype.

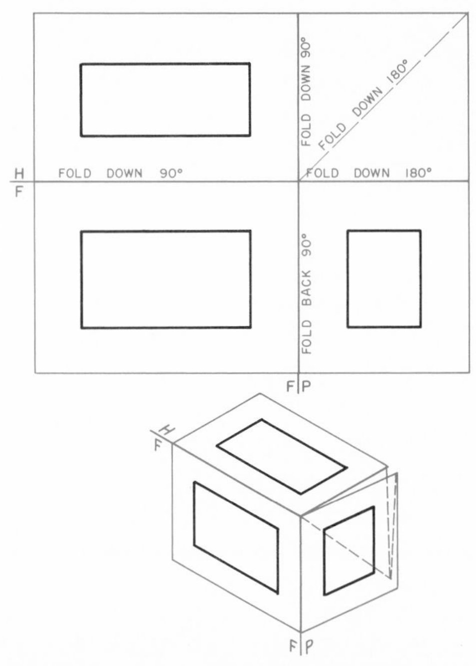

Fig. 3-60. Study Objects by Folding Paper on its Reference Hinge Lines

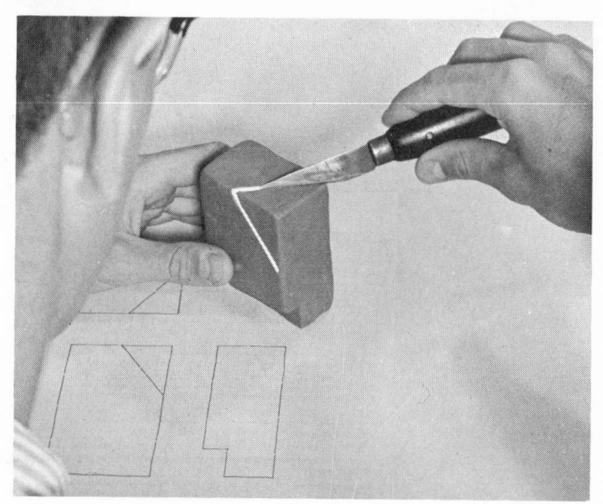

Fig. 3-59. Student Studying Missing-Line Problem by Modeling in Clay

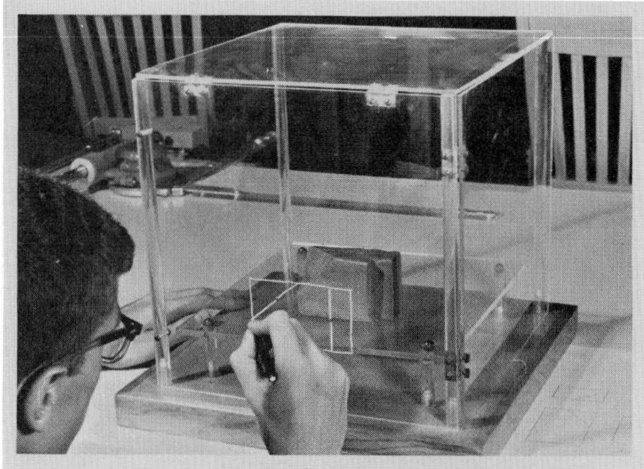

Fig. 3-61. Student Working with a Projection Box to Visualize Object

Use of a Projection Box

If you have a projection box available for your studies, you are indeed fortunate. See Fig. 3-61. Use a grease pencil on each surface of the box to draw the edges of the objects which are seen. Then open the box into its flat plane to observe the three views in their correct relationship. Several illustrations of this have been used in this chapter.

Many drafting supply houses provide a small, inexpensive kit which has three pieces of plastic hinged with tape. This may be most helpful to students in visualizing and studying objects.

Missing-Line Problems

Missing-line problems take the form of three orthographic views with one or more lines deliberately omitted. The problem is to discover which lines are missing and to sketch or draw them in. The procedure recommended for solving these problems is shown in Fig. 3-62.

Some problems have more than one solution, as does Fig. 3-62. Can you find a second solution? It is not considered "sporting" to add lines outside the contours given. If the ground rules say that only one line is missing from a given set of three views, a solution which adds more than one line is considered wrong. Generally, when there is more than one solution, the simpler solution is preferred.

Missing-View Problems

As the name implies, in a missing-view problem, an entire view is missing. Almost always in these cases there are several possible solutions. The procedure is essentially the same as for missing-line problems. See Fig. 3-63.

1. Sketch a basic box in pictorial.
2. Add the views which are given.
3. Complete sketching the object.
4. Sketch or draw the missing view as required.

Sketch the missing view suggested by solutions *B* through *E* in Fig. 3-63. Also sketch at least one more possible solution.

Problems in Reading a Drawing

One of the best ways to learn to read drawings is to make drawings. However, not all people who need to read drawings have the time to learn to make them. By answering questions and solving problems about particular

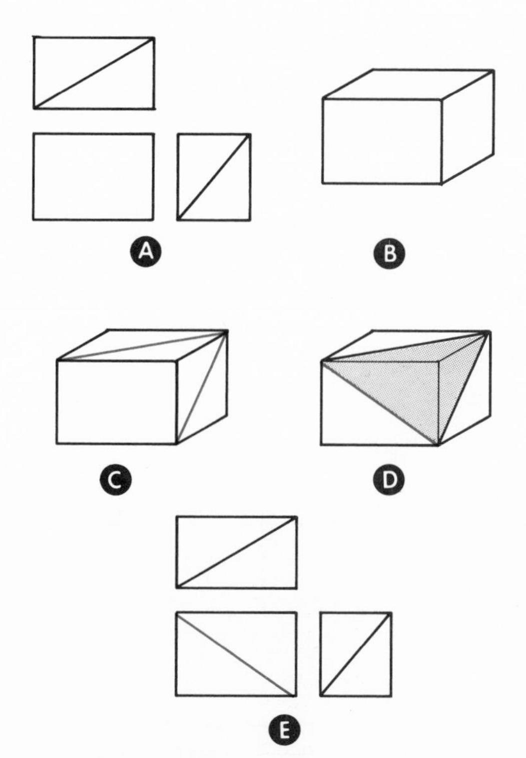

FIG. 3-62. Solving Missing-Line Problems
A. Missing-line problem.
B. Sketch a basic box in pictorial (a box having the overall height, width, and depth).
C. Add the lines to the surfaces, as they are given.
D. Complete sketching of the pictorial.
E. Add the discovered missing lines to the orthographic projections.

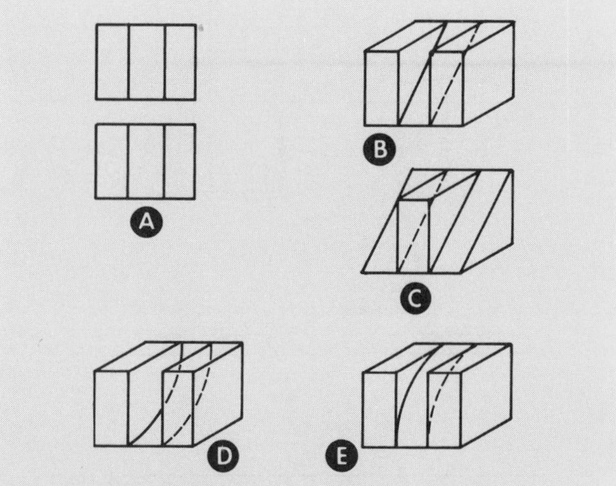

FIG. 3-63. Missing-View Problems
A. Given front and top views
B. Various solutions

ORTHOGRAPHIC PROJECTION

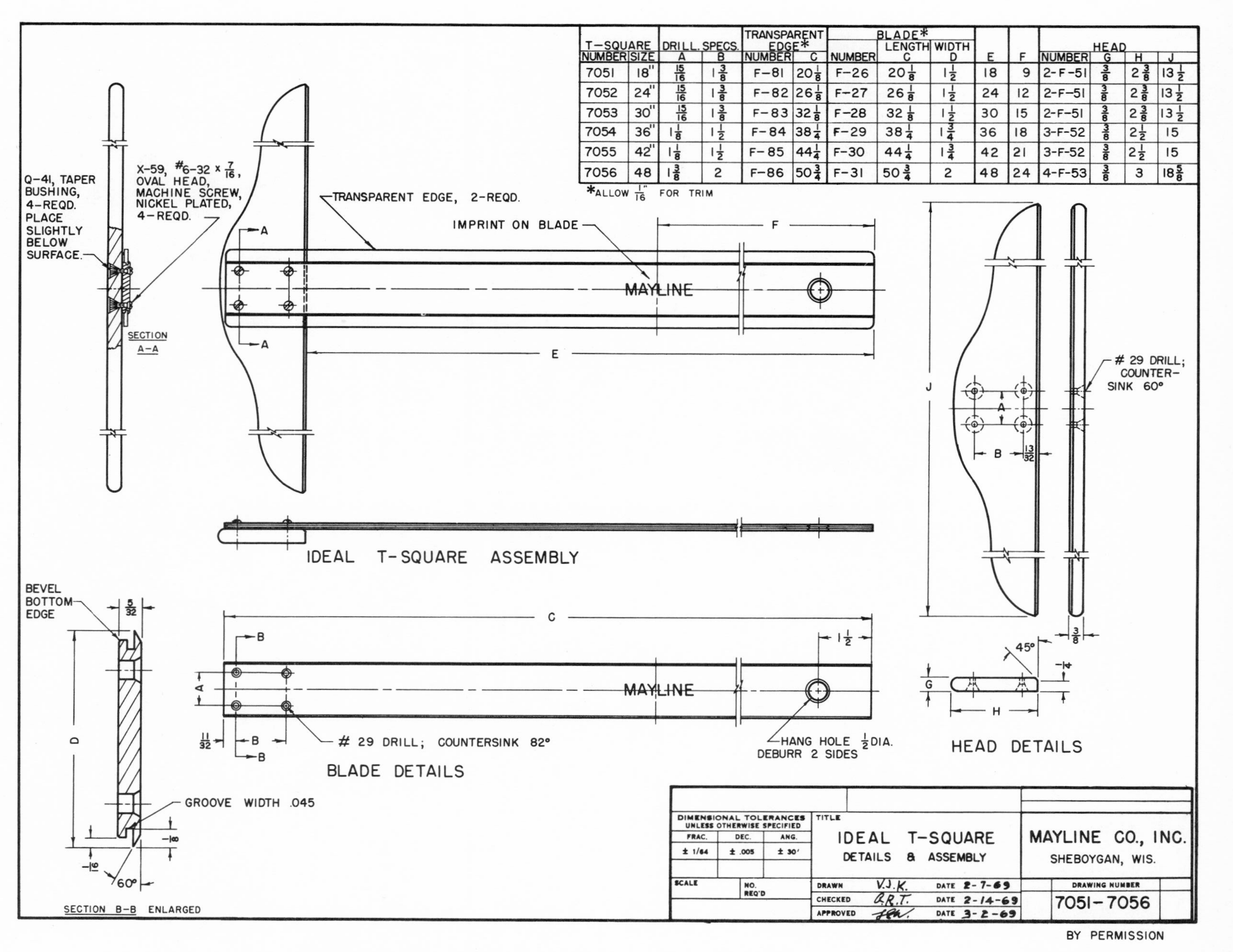

T-SQUARE NUMBER	T-SQUARE SIZE	DRILL. SPECS. A	DRILL. SPECS. B	TRANSPARENT EDGE* NUMBER	TRANSPARENT EDGE* C	BLADE* NUMBER	BLADE* LENGTH C	BLADE* WIDTH D	E	F	HEAD NUMBER	HEAD G	HEAD H	HEAD J
7051	18"	15/16	1 3/8	F-81	20 1/8	F-26	20 1/8	1 1/2	18	9	2-F-51	3/8	2 3/8	13 1/2
7052	24"	15/16	1 3/8	F-82	26 1/8	F-27	26 1/8	1 1/2	24	12	2-F-51	3/8	2 3/8	13 1/2
7053	30"	15/16	1 3/8	F-83	32 1/8	F-28	32 1/8	1 1/2	30	15	2-F-51	3/8	2 3/8	13 1/2
7054	36"	1 1/8	1 1/2	F-84	38 1/4	F-29	38 1/4	1 3/4	36	18	3-F-52	3/8	2 1/2	15
7055	42"	1 1/8	1 1/2	F-85	44 1/4	F-30	44 1/4	1 3/4	42	21	3-F-52	3/8	2 1/2	15
7056	48	1 3/8	2	F-86	50 3/4	F-31	50 3/4	2	48	24	4-F-53	3/8	3	18 5/8

*ALLOW 1/16" FOR TRIM

Fig. 3-64. Ideal T-square Details and Assembly

drawings, one may learn how to read drawings and improve his ability to visualize. Answer the following questions related to Fig. 3-64.

1. How many separate pieces are required for a completed 18″ Mayline T-square?
2. What is the shape of the bottom edge of the T-square blade?
3. Is the allowance for trimming the transparent edge of the T-square allowed on its width, thickness, or length?
4. Why are the taper bushings which help to hold the blade and the head together set "slightly below" the head surface?
5. One edge of the T-square head is beveled at 45°. Is this bevel on the same side or the opposite side from the side in which the taper bushings are placed?
6. What drill and what countersink are used to make the holes in the head for the taper bushings?
7. What drill and what countersink are used to make the holes for the machine screws?
8. What is the thickness of the blade for the 48″ – #7056 Ideal T-square? for the 18″ – #7051?
9. What is the width of the groove which receives the transparent edge?
10. How long is the transparent edge for a 36″ – #7054 T-square?
11. What are the thickness, width, and length dimensions for the blade of the 24″ – #7052 T-square?
12. What is the diameter of the hang hole? Why is it deburred on two sides?
13. How far from the blade end is the center line of the "MAYLINE" imprint located for the 48″ – #7056 T-square?
14. What length of the blade extends beyond the head of a 24″ – #7052 T-square?
15. What is the length of the blade of a 24″ – #7052 T-square?
16. What generalization can you make with respect to the size specification of T-squares, such as a 30″ or 48″ T-square?
17. What are the specifications for the machine screws which fit into the taper bushings?
18. To make the six different sizes of T-squares, how many different sizes of T-square heads are needed?
19. The thickness of the T-square heads is shown to be 3/8″. What is the thickness of the thickest and the thinnest T-square heads which would be acceptable? (Answer must be in 64ths.)
20. In the assembly drawing, left end view, the hidden line which would have shown the beveled edge of the T-square head was omitted. Why do you think this was done?

Chapter 3 — Problems and Projects

1. In each of the problems in Fig. 3-65 certain lines have been omitted from one or more views. First, make a pictorial sketch of the problem. Then sketch the three views of the missing-line problem on cross-sectioned paper (4 x 4 ruling recommended). Add the missing lines. Add center lines where needed. Consider the "precedence of lines" where appropriate.

2. Make an orthographic sketch of each object in Fig. 3-66. First choose the best front view. Then decide upon how many orthographic views to use. (Remember, too many views is just as inaccurate as too few views.) Use cross-sectioned paper as an aid for sketching.

3. Make two different orthographic sketches of Problem 6, milling jack base, from Fig. 3-66. For the first sketch, make a three-view sketch using third-angle projection. For the second sketch, make a three-view sketch using first-angle projection. Write a paragraph suggesting the advantages and disadvantages of each of these two methods of representation.

4. Make a three-view sketch of Problem 12, Fig. 3-66. Use the surface with the holes in it as the top view. Instead of the usual right side view, make an alternate view at the right of the top view. Why is this appropriate for this object?

5. Answer the following questions with respect to Fig. 3-67:

1. Of what material is the input pump cover to be made?
2. How many section views are shown on this drawing?
3. What is the maximum draft angle?
4. For cast fillets not otherwise specified, what is the radius? cast corners?
5. Where on the input cover pump may the part number be cast?

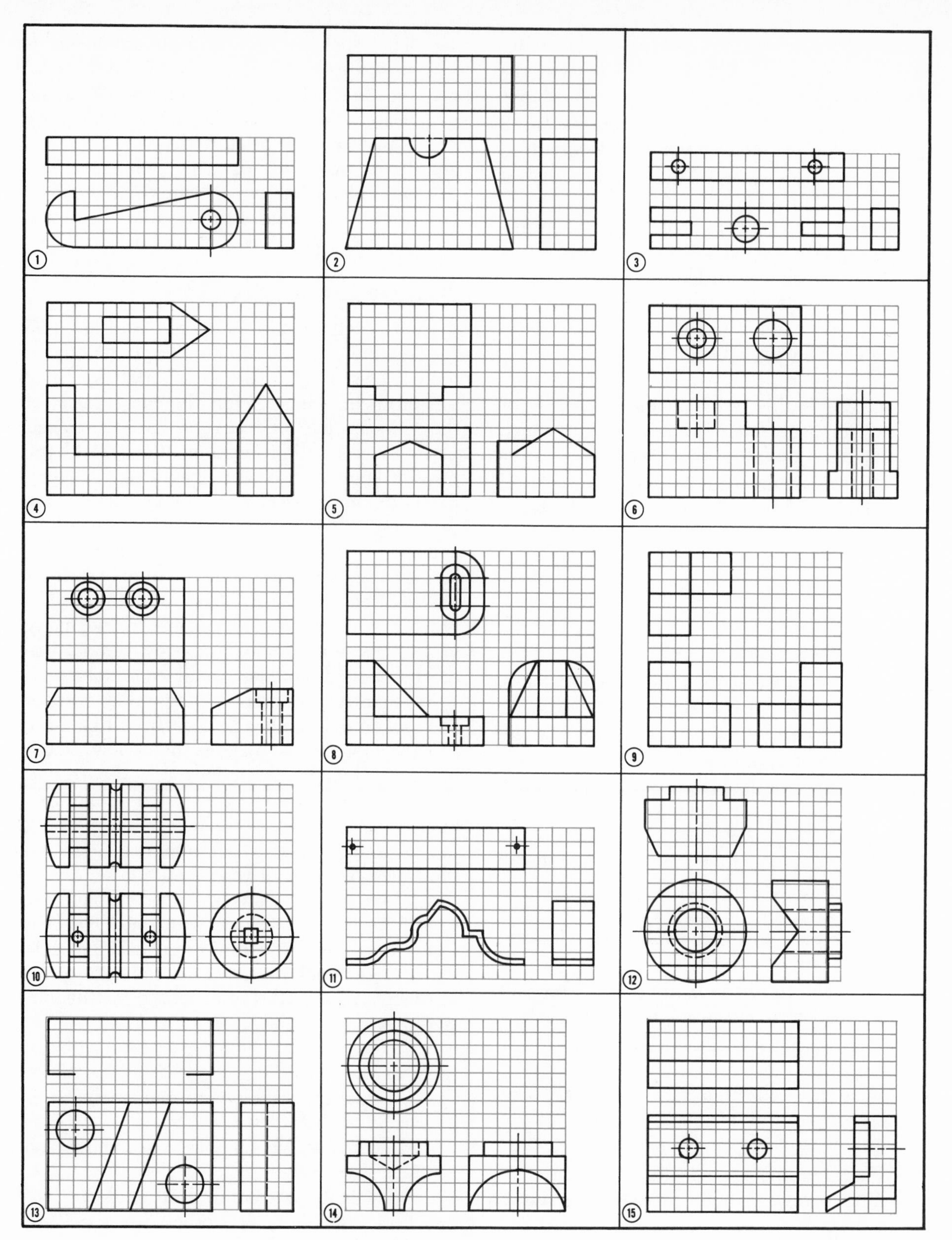

Fig. 3-65. Missing-Line Problems

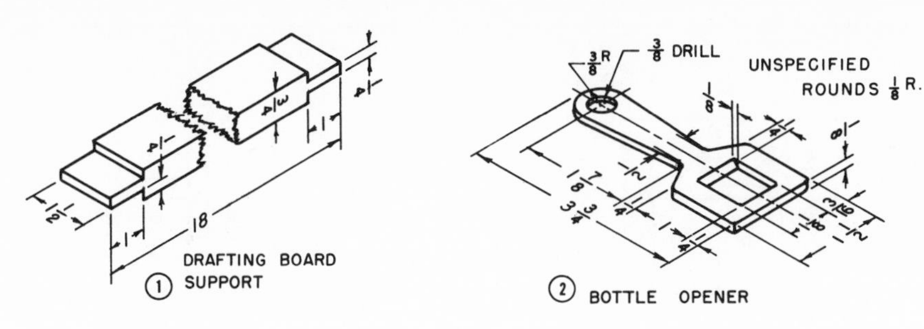

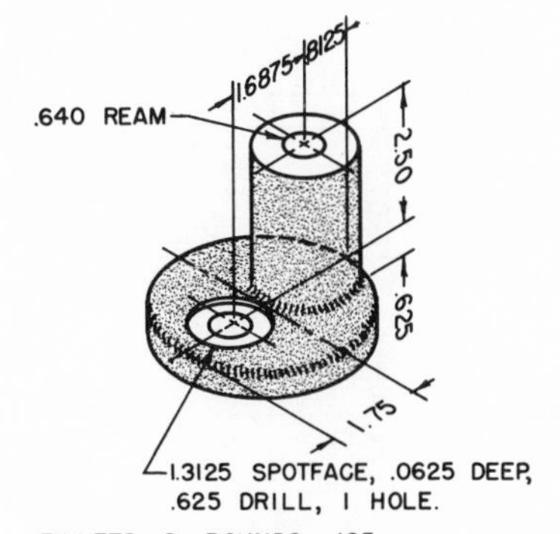

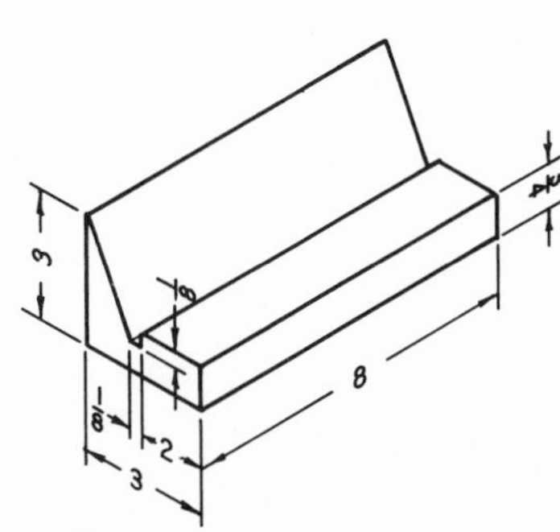

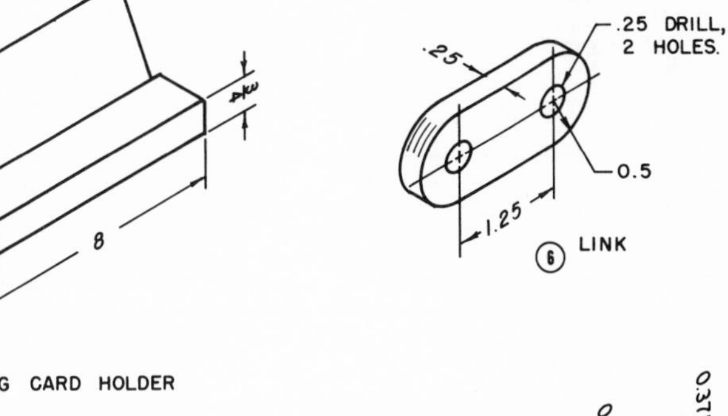

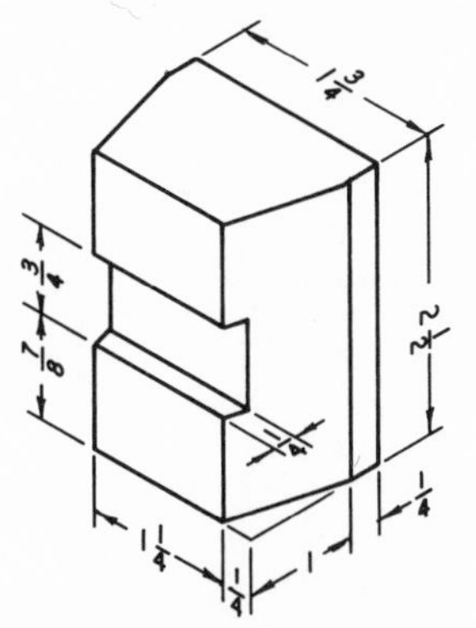

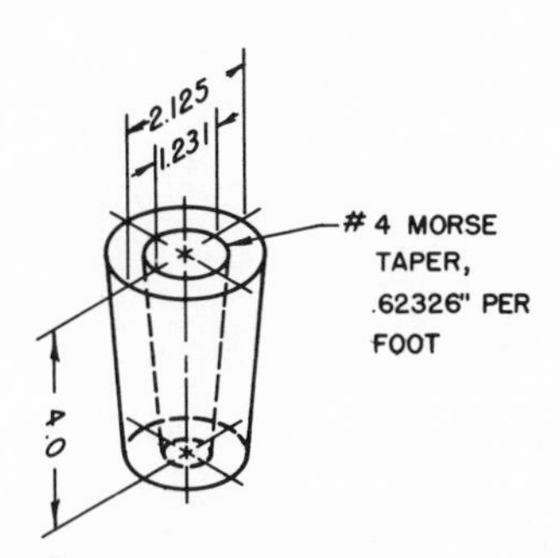

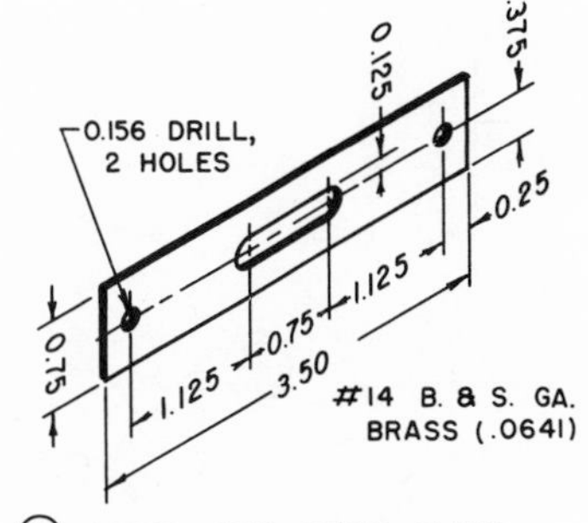

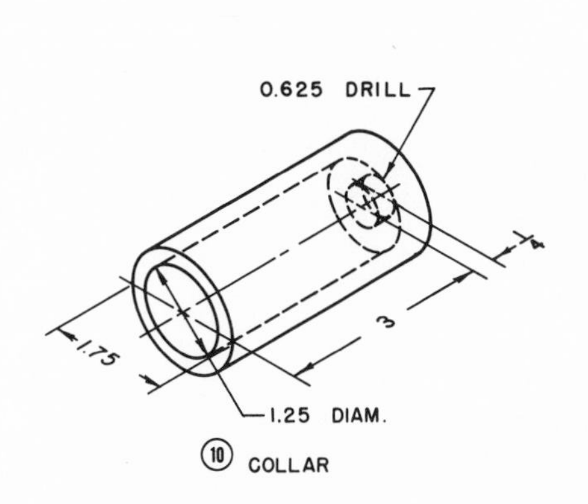

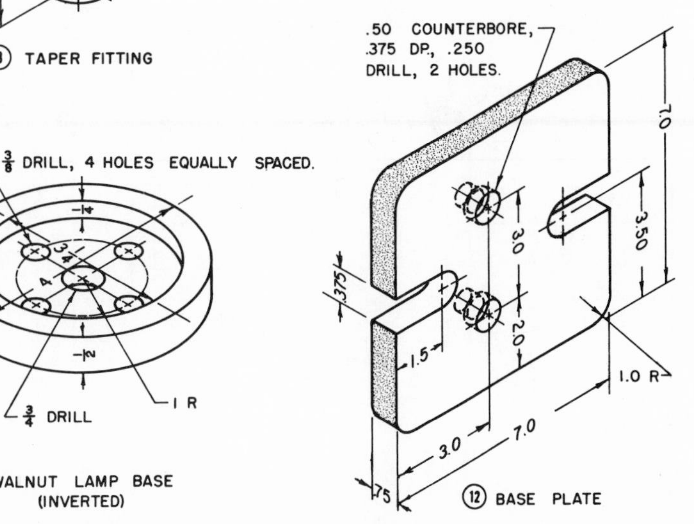

Fig. 3-66. Problems

ORTHOGRAPHIC PROJECTION

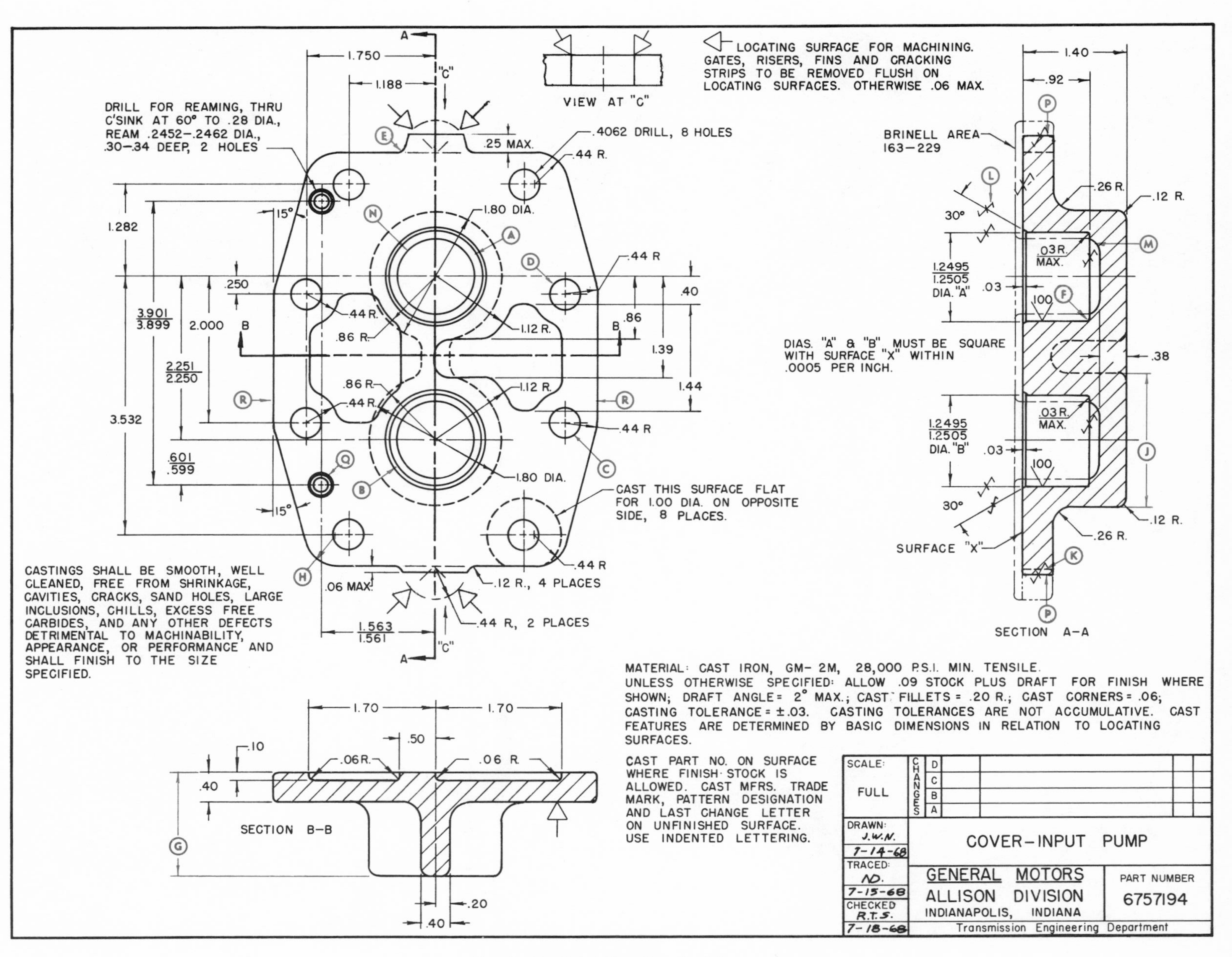

FIG. 3-67. Print-Reading Problem

6. What does the following symbol mean: —▷?
7. What is the relationship of hole *A* to surface *X*?
8. What is the distance between holes *C* and *D*?
9. What is the value of radius *E*?
10. What is the value of radius *F*?
11. What is the value of distance *G*?
12. What is the value of radius *H*?
13. What three machining operations are performed on hole *Q*?
14. What is distance *J*?
15. What feature does hidden line *K* represent?
16. What does the symbol at *L* represent?
17. How many surfaces of the inlet pump cover are finished surfaces?
18. What is the range of Brinell hardness required?
19. What is the purpose of the locating surface shown in view C-C? Why is this called *view* C-C rather than *section* C-C?
20. At what scale was this drawn?
21. What is the value of radius *M*?
22. Does circle *N* represent a hole which goes clear through the cover?
23. What is the overall width of the cover between the arrows lettered *R-R*?
24. What is the overall distance between the arrows lettered *P-P*?
25. What is the maximum diameter permitted for hole *B*?

CHAPTER FOUR

ORTHOGRAPHIC PROJECTION

tools, materials and constructions

After you have developed an understanding of orthographic and pictorial representations, the methods and skills of using mechanical drawing instruments are utilized to express your ideas. The primary function of tools, materials, and construction techniques is to help you communicate ideas accurately.

Observe the minimum set of tools and materials in Fig. 4-1. General tools used by the professional and in many up-to-date school drafting rooms are shown in Figs. 4-2 and 4-3. Additional tools are shown in Fig. 4-4.

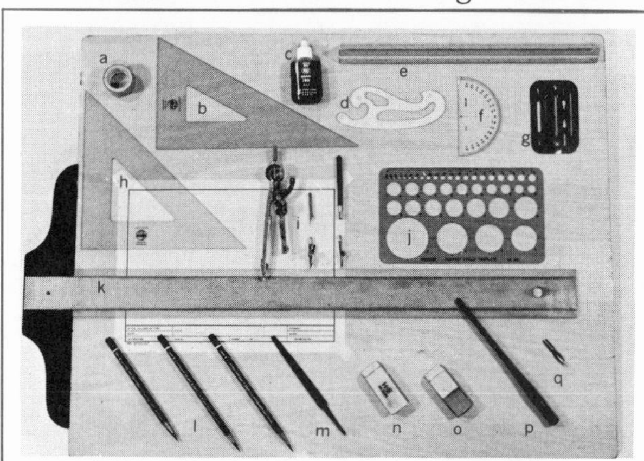

FIG. 4-1. Minimum Tools for Drafting

A. Drafting tape
B. 30-60° triangle
C. Ink
D. Irregular curve
E. Triangular scale rule
F. Protractor
G. Erasing shield
H. 45° triangle
I. Combination compasses, dividers and ruling pen
J. Circle template
K. T-square
L. F, H, and 2H pencils
M. Pencil pointer
N. Vinyl eraser
O. Combination eraser
P. Pen holder
Q. Medium pen point
R. Drafting board

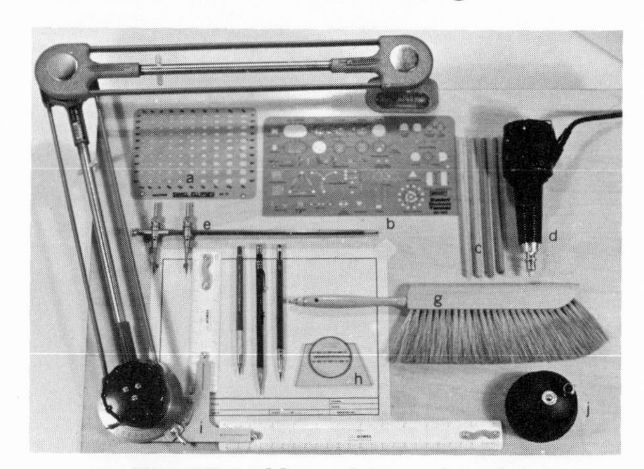

FIG. 4-2. Additional General Tools

A. Small ellipse template
B. Electrical symbol template
C. Erasers for electric eraser
D. Electric eraser
E. Beam compasses
F. Mechanical pencils
G. Dusting brush
H. Ames lettering guide
I. Arm-type drafting machine
J. Mechanical pencil pointer

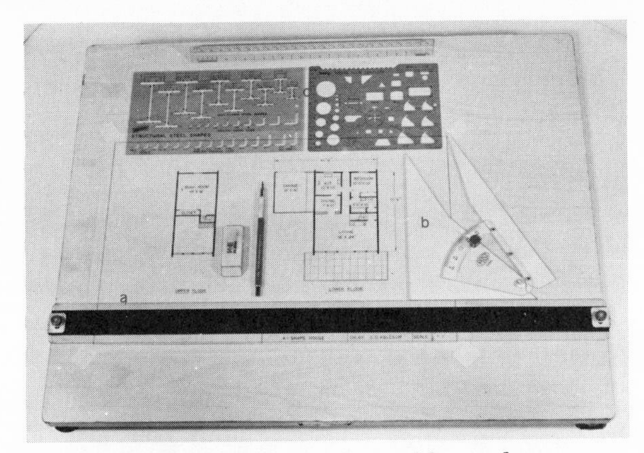

FIG. 4-3. Drafting Tools Used by Architect
A. Parallel bar
B. Combination triangle and protractor
C. Structural steel and house plan templates

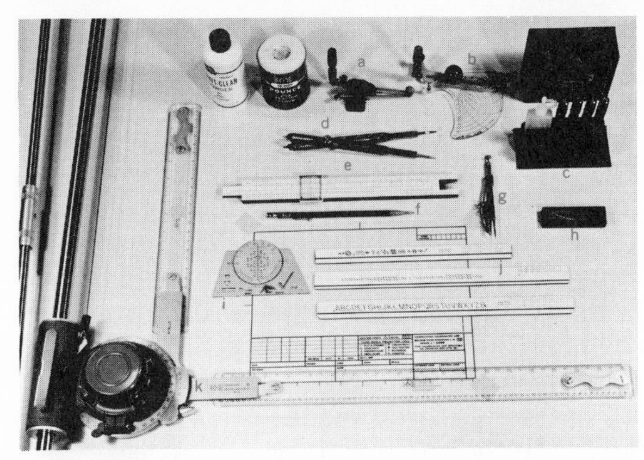

FIG. 4-4. Professional Tools for Special Purposes
A. Scriber for LeRoy lettering
B. Letter guide
C. Technical fountain pens
D. Proportional dividers
E. Slide rule
F. Mechanical pencil
G. Drop bow compasses
H. Sharpening stone
I. Lineograph
J. Templates for LeRoy lettering
K. Track type drafting machine

Trends in Drafting Room Furniture

To many people, the word *draftsman* brings a vision of a man perched on a fairly high stool and bent over a drafting board that is nearly horizontal. Studies made by industry have shown that desk-height tables with an accompanying chair are better for the draftsman's health, comfort, prestige, and efficiency. In equipping new drafting rooms, the trend is toward this newer type of drafting work station, Fig. 4-5. In schools, these work stations have the advantages of permitting dual use of rooms, providing for student comfort, and (to the extent to which they are more efficient) permitting more instructional material to be covered in a given amount of time.

FIG. 4-5. Drafting Room with Professional-Height Tables (University of Northern Iowa)

tools and materials

T-Square

The T-square, triangles, and the protractor have been the prime instruments of graphic communication for many years, and it is a reasonable assumption that they will be of value for many years to come.

There are several types of T-squares available to the draftsman, but the most popular and functional has been the clear plastic blade edge and the clear plastic blade.

The draftsman must always be concerned with the quality and condition of his tools. Form the habit of checking the tools at the beginning of a work period. The following inspections should be performed on the T-square:

TOOLS, MAT'LS
CONSTRUCTIONS

1. Check the working edge straightness of the blade, Fig. 4-6. Examples *A* and *B* show the error that is prevalent when the blade is placed on a sheet of paper and a line is scribed from the working edge; then the blade is revolved 180° and the working edge is aligned to the scribed line. Blades that have a positive or negative curvature must not be used. However, example *C* illustrates a true working edge, and the T-square is in condition to do accurate work.

2. Check the head and the blade for a secure, tight fit at the assembly joint. If the blade cannot be securely fastened in a 90° angle to the head, the blade must not be used.

In example *A*, Fig. 4-7, a reference point (A) is placed on the working edge of the T-square. After placing the paper, move the T-square to the top of the paper and accurately scribe point (B) on the paper from the alignment of reference point (A). Then move the square to the lower edge of the paper and place a triangle so that the edge will align with point (A) on the T-square. If the T-square is out of adjustment, point (B) will not align with the triangle edge as shown in example *A* or *B*. Example *C* illustrates a true workedge that is properly aligned with the blade in a 90° angle to the head.

Parallel Bar

When long lines must be drawn, such as those on floor plans and elevations of buildings, the parallel bar may be preferred. Triangles and protractors are used with the parallel bar to layout angular features. Refer again to Fig. 4-3. Since the parallel bar is somewhat more efficient to use than the T-square, many architects, structural draftsmen, and some draftsmen in the civil and mechanical fields prefer to use this instrument.

Drafting Machines

There is one chief reason why many industries and some schools use drafting machines — *increased output*. They have been shown to

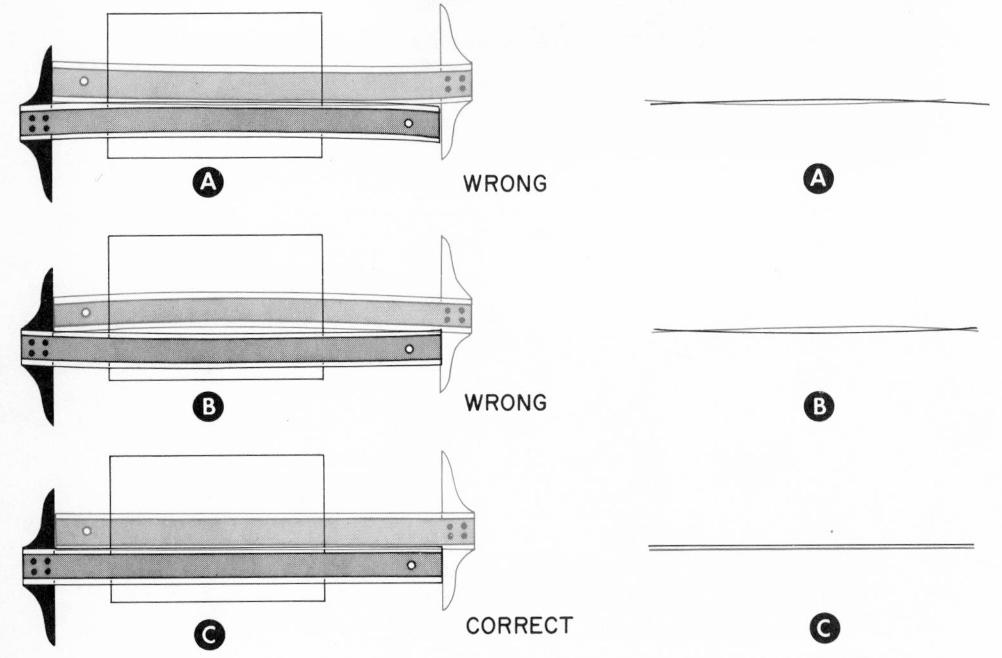

Fig. 4-6. Check the T-square Work Edge for Straightness

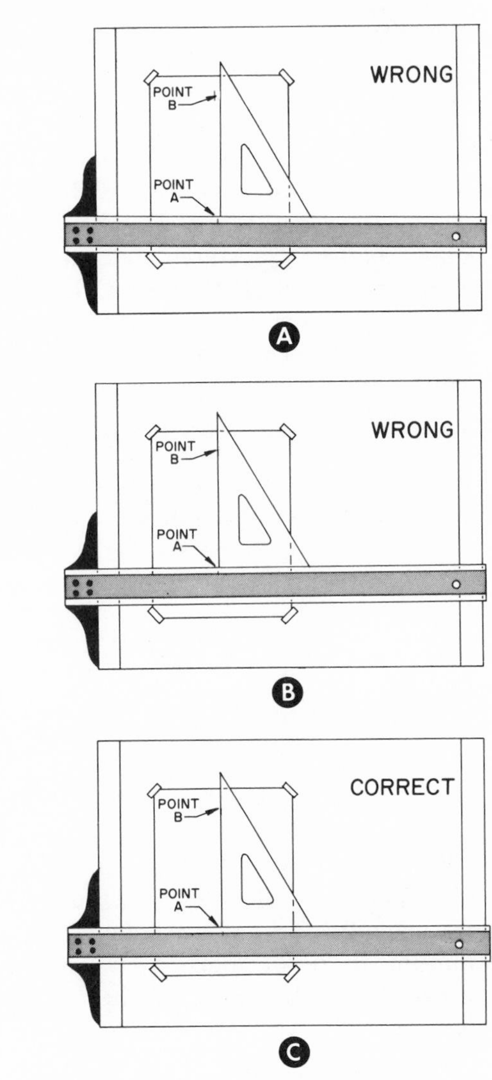

Fig. 4-7. Check the 90° Angle of a T-square

increase drafting efficiency by up to 30%. They replace the T-square or parallel bar, the 30° - 60° triangle, the 45° triangle, the protractor, and the scale rules, Figs. 4-8 and 4-9.

There are two types of drafting machines: (1) the arm-type machine, Fig. 4-10 (which was the first type produced), and (2) the X-Y, track-type machine, Fig. 4-11. Although the arm type is less expensive, the track type is more efficient and versatile. The operational techniques for both are essentially the same. Read the instructional manual accompanying the machine as the first step to effective use. It describes how the machine is mounted, what the controls are, and how these are used. Features of the drafting machine which should be thoroughly understood include base-line adjustment, index control, vernier scale, and verification for accuracy.

Base-line adjustment permits the machine to be aligned to any base line rather than constantly working from the horizontal, as is the case with the T-square or the parallel bar.

1. Set the protractor head so that the zero and the vernier zero are opposite each other, Fig. 4-12.

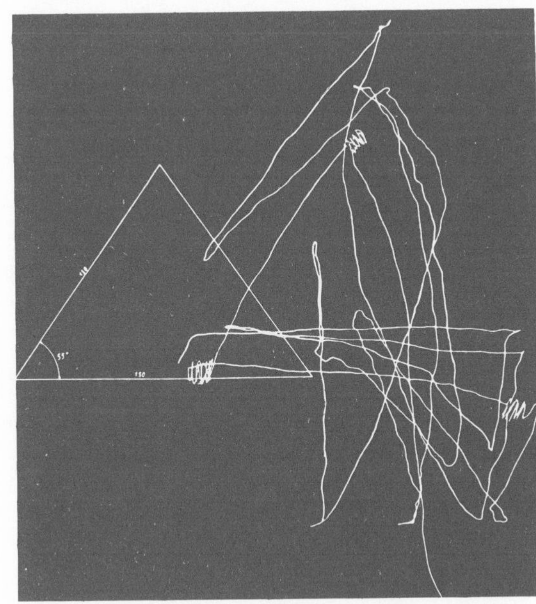

FIG. 4-8. Motions of Right Hand Required to Construct Equilateral Triangle with Conventional T-square and Triangle (Battelle Memorial Institute)

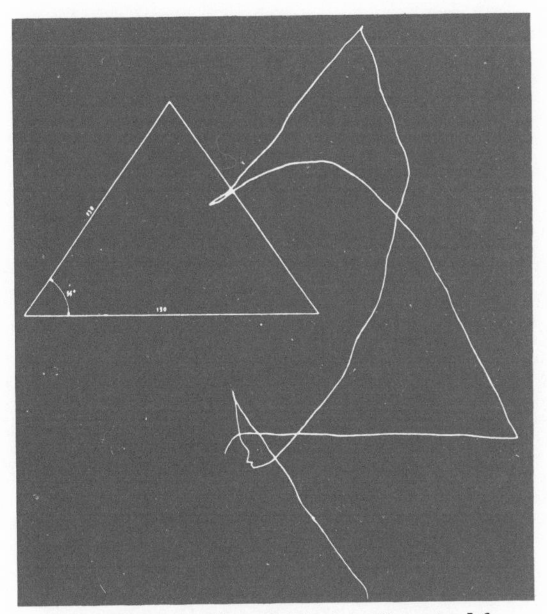

FIG. 4-9. Triangle and Motions Required for Construction with a Drafting Machine (Battelle Memorial Institute)

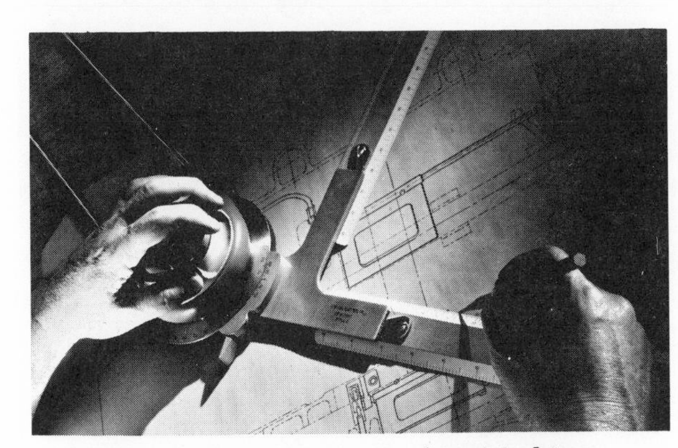

FIG. 4-10. Arm-Type Drafting Machine (Keuffel & Esser Co.)

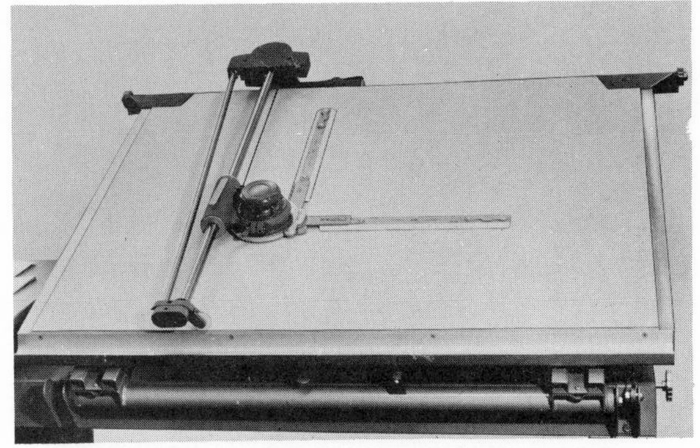

FIG. 4-11. Track-Type Drafting Machine (Keuffel & Esser Co.)

2. Loosen the base-line wing nut, Fig. 4-13.
3. Set the horizontal scale on any reference line, Fig. 4-14.
4. Finger-tighten the base-line wing nut.

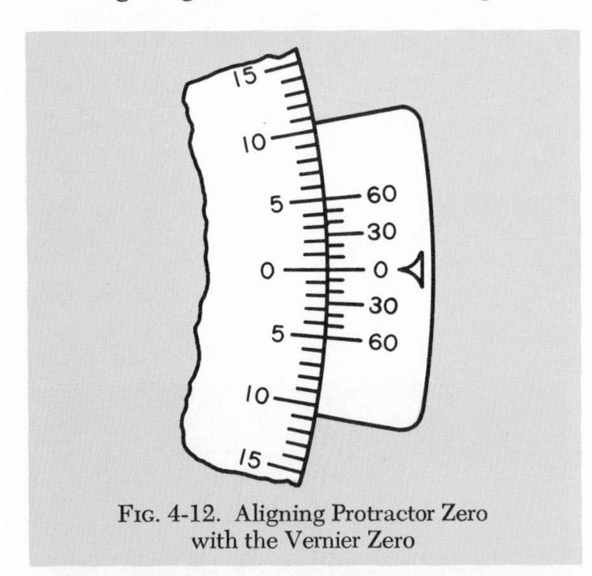

FIG. 4-12. Aligning Protractor Zero with the Vernier Zero

FIG. 4-13. Loosening the Base-line Wing Nut (V. & E. Mfg. Co.)

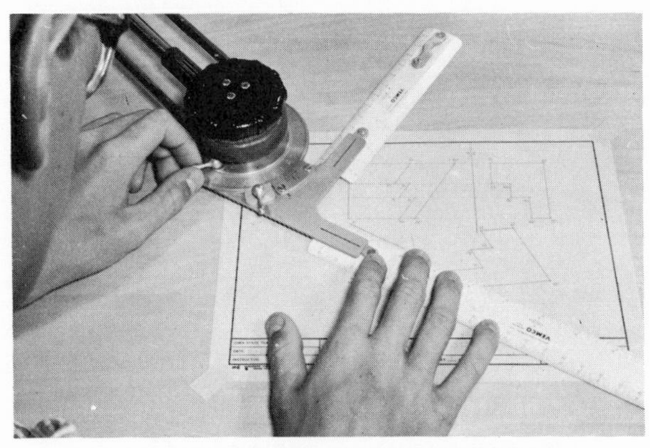

FIG. 4-14. Aligning the Horizontal Scale at the Desired Position

The 90-degree relationship of the two scales is now oriented to the new base line. Machines with full 360° base-line adjustment are the more versatile and will be found especially useful when working with auxiliary projection.

Occasionally the 90° relationship between the two blades becomes out of adjustment. This angle must be inspected frequently to insure accuracy in graphic communication. Use the procedure outlined in Fig. 4-15 to check the blade. Adjust the blade to the 90° angle when an error occurs such as in example *A* or *B*.

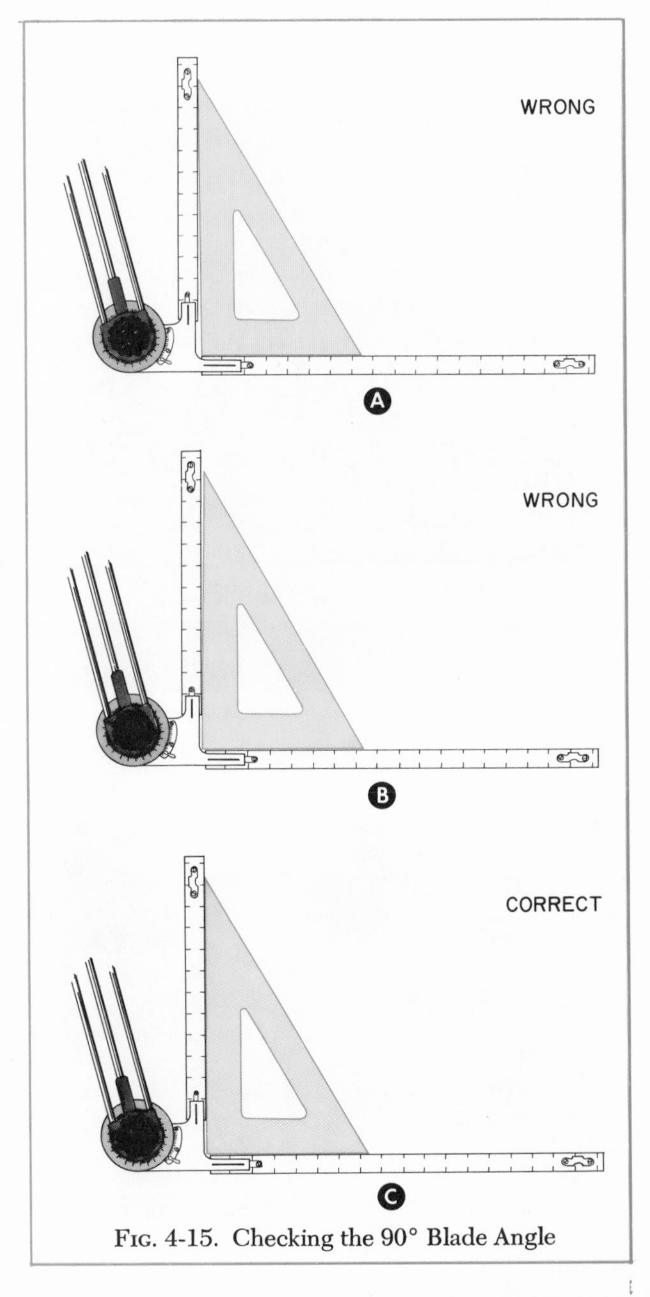

FIG. 4-15. Checking the 90° Blade Angle

The *index control* permits automatic stops every 15°. These standard angles can be measured or drawn easily. A large hand control usually facilitates easy adjustment, Fig. 4-16. To set the machine for angle layouts other than every 15 degrees, an indexing clamp tightened by finger pressure can be used.

The *vernier scale* permits readings of parts of one degree, thus allowing more accuracy than a protractor whose readings generally are accurate only to ± ½ degree. To read a vernier scale, you first must know the number of full degrees needed, together with the number of minutes (one degree = 60 minutes). The vernier zero line shows the degrees. The vernier line exactly in line with the protractor reading shows the minutes. For example, in Fig. 4-17, the zero line of the vernier is upward past 10° but not quite 11°. Therefore, the angle is 10° plus part of the next one. The 20-minute line of the vernier (up from the zero line) exactly aligns with a protractor line. Adding this to the number of degrees gives 10 degrees 20 minutes (10° 20′) as the value of the measured angle. See also Fig. 4-18.

Verification for accuracy is as important with machines as it is with triangles and T-squares. Instructions for checking individual machines are easy to follow and are a part of the manual. You should make periodic checks against horizontal and vertical reference lines to give assurance that all is in alignment. When a paper is removed from the board and replaced, checking reference lines is most important.

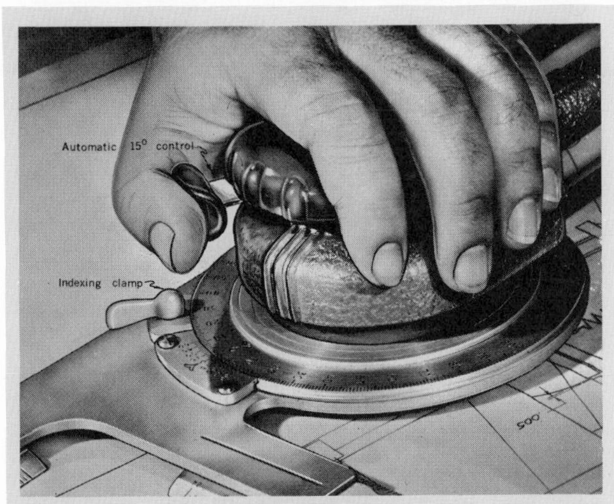

Fig. 4-16. Indexing Clamp and Automatic 15° Control (V. & E. Mfg. Co.)

When a machine is out of adjustment, check these items:

1. Loose board mounting.
2. Loose scale mounting.
3. Loose clamps.
4. Loose bands (when using the arm-type machine).

If these are not the fault, your instructor will help you with the machine.

To use the drafting machine follow these steps:

1. Check the machine for correct scale alignment daily before starting to draw.
2. Draw horizontal lines from left to right (reverse for left-handers).
3. Draw horizontal lines by placing the pencil above the scale.

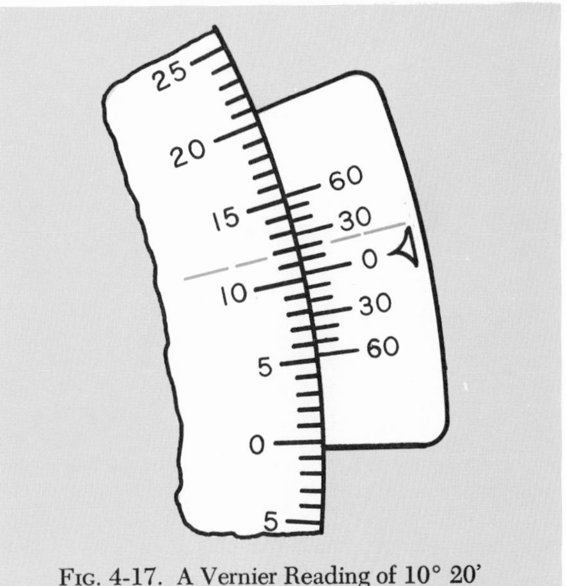

Fig. 4-17. A Vernier Reading of 10° 20′

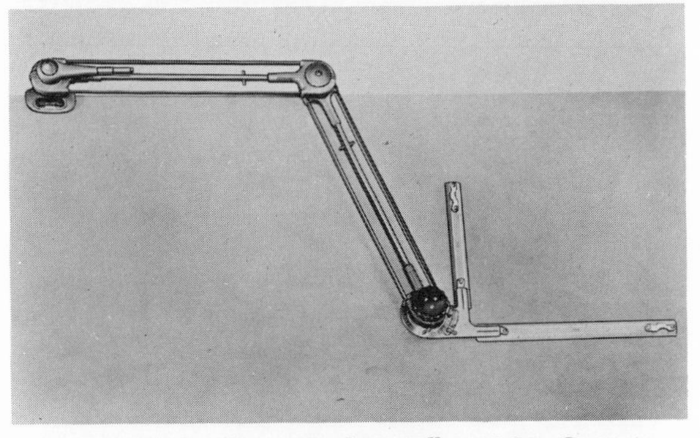
Fig. 4-18. Drafting Machine Elbow May Occupy Either of Two Positions (V. & E. Mfg. Co.)
If one position partially covers the vernier scale, shifting to the other will avoid the difficulty.

TOOLS, MAT'LS CONSTRUCTIONS

4. Draw vertical lines from the lower end upward.
5. Draw vertical lines from the left-hand side of the vertical scale (reverse for left-handers).
6. Hold the scale of the machine down firmly with one hand when drawing a line along its edge.
7. Use light pencil pressure along the scale to avoid deflecting it through increased leverage at the far end of the line.
8. Whenever possible, draw lines in their final form the first time.
9. The beginner should draw all long lines lightly until some experience has been gained.
10. Do not subject the drafting machine to sudden shocks or bumps.

Drafting Boards and Surfaces

Drafting boards range in size from 12″ x 18″ to 43½″ x 84″ (or larger if made to order). A common student size is 18″ x 24″. This permits work on drawing papers in standard sizes up to 18″ x 24″.

Surface quality desired is a strong, fine-grained material such as basswood, a special permanent board covering made of multi-layer laminates, or a cover material for boards made of flexible, cellulose-acetate film which is laminated to a tough paper base. Unusually hard surfaces such as those made from glass or plastic laminate should be avoided, as they have very little resilience. When circles are drawn on these tops, the pricker leg of the compasses almost always enlarges the hole in the center of the circle.

TABLE 4-1

Comparison of Common Drafting Media*

	Strength	Reproducibility	Flexibility	Stability	Erasibility	Aging	Approx. Cost $/yd.	Comments
Vellum (solid transparentizer)	Fair	Good	Excellent	Poor	Fair	Good	0.40	Most popular general-purpose material
Vellum (mobile transparentizer)	Fair	Fair	Excellent	Poor	Fair	Good	0.35	Popular general-purpose
Polyester film	Excellent	Excellent	Excellent	Excellent	Excellent	Excellent	2.00	Best all-around drafting material
Tracing Cloth (pencil)	Good	Good	Excellent	Poor	Good	Excellent	2.00	Moisture resistant, accepts ink poorly
Tracing Cloth (ink)	Good	Good	Excellent	Poor	Good	Excellent	1.60	For permanent drawings
Paper (all rag)	Fair	Fair	Excellent	Poor	Fair	Good	0.20	For drawings requiring few copies
Paper (part rag)	Poor	Fair	Excellent	Poor	Poor	Fair	0.12	Chiefly for sketches and preliminary drawings
Paper (all sulfite)	Poor	Good	Excellent	Poor	Poor	Poor	0.07	Chiefly for sketches and preliminary drawings
Glass cloth	Excellent	Excellent	Excellent	Excellent	Excellent	Excellent	9.00	Little used, replaced by stable base polyester film
Vinyl film	Good	Excellent	Fair	Excellent	Excellent	Excellent	1.50	Little used, except for scribe-coated stock
Acetate film	Fair	Excellent	Excellent	Good	Excellent	Excellent	1.00	Little used, except for overlays

*Reprinted from *Product Engineering*, August 28, 1961. Copyright 1961 by McGraw-Hill, Inc.

The sides of drafting board surfaces must be straight and true to provide a guide for the T-square used from the left- or right-hand edge. Tongue-and-groove joints are used along the edge, or a steel cleat is fastened to the edge to prevent warping.

Drafting Papers and Mediums

To cover the wide range of materials available, you should study the catalogs of manufacturers and suppliers. Tracing papers are available in a range of rag contents, thicknesses, colors, and degrees of transparency. *Drafting vellums* have the strength and drafting qualities of the fine papers along with the transparency of the thinnest tracing paper. *Drafting cloths* are available in a variety of surfaces, some designed to take pencil and others to take ink. Various types of *drafting films* are available. They are receptive to inks or pencil, erasable, exceptionally stable (fluctuations in humidity and temperature do not affect them), permanent, and waterproof. See Table 4-1 for a comparison of common drafting media. Papers, vellums, cloths, and films come in assorted sizes of rolls, cut sheets, and pads. They may be pre-printed with grids which are reproducible or nonreproducible and/or title strips and borders. They may be sensitized or plain.

Size and Format

The USA Standards Institute recommends five standard flat-sheet sizes for both trimmed and untrimmed papers as shown in Table 4-2.

TABLE 4-2

Trimmed and Untrimmed Sizes of Flat Sheets*

Letter Designation	Trimmed Size (Inches)		Untrimmed Size (Inches)	
	Width	Length	Width	Length
A	8½	11	9	12
B	11	17	12	18
C	17	22	18	24
D	22	34	24	36
E	34	44	36	48

*USAS

Formats for title strips, revision strips, and borders are shown in Figs. 4-19 through 4-23. Note in Fig. 4-21 that size "C" and larger use zoning for reference purposes.

Placement of Paper

When drawing with the T-square and triangles, place the drawing paper downward and to the left side of the drafting board (for right-handlers); for left-handers, downward and to the right, Fig. 4-25. Check that the drawing paper is placed (1) to produce the least error caused by the leverage between T-square head and blade, (2) to give plenty of room for the blade to be fully on the table, and (3) to insure that the entire length of the head of the T-square is in contact with the edge of the drafting board. Use relatively small pieces of tape over the four corners of the paper.

When using a drafting machine, place your paper so that it is in the most comfortable and convenient position, since the entire board surface should be available to this machine.

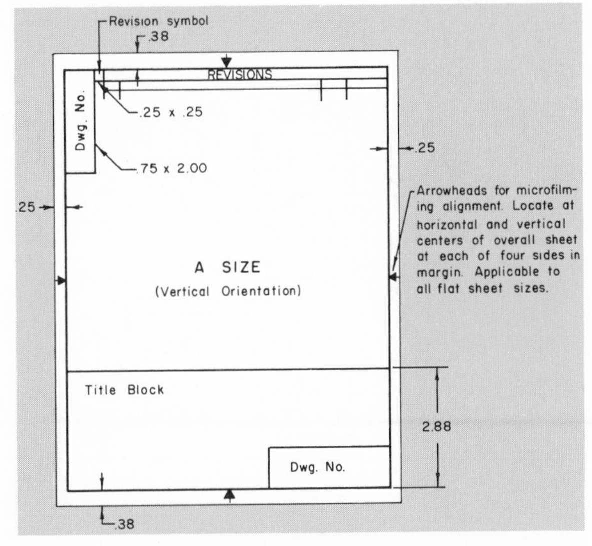

FIG. 4-19. Alternative Format for Vertical "A" Size (SAE)

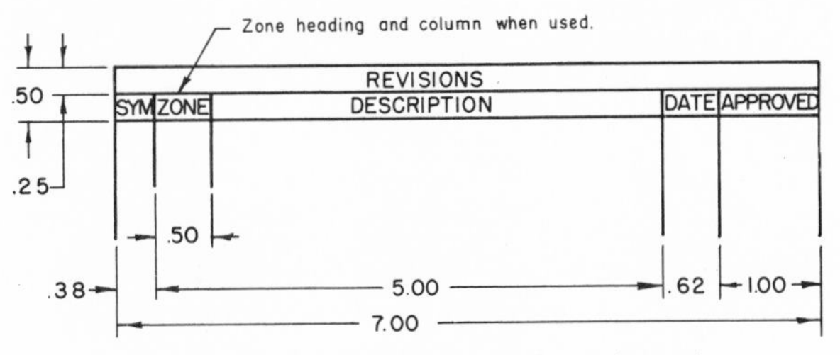

FIG. 4-20. Basic Revision Block (SAE)

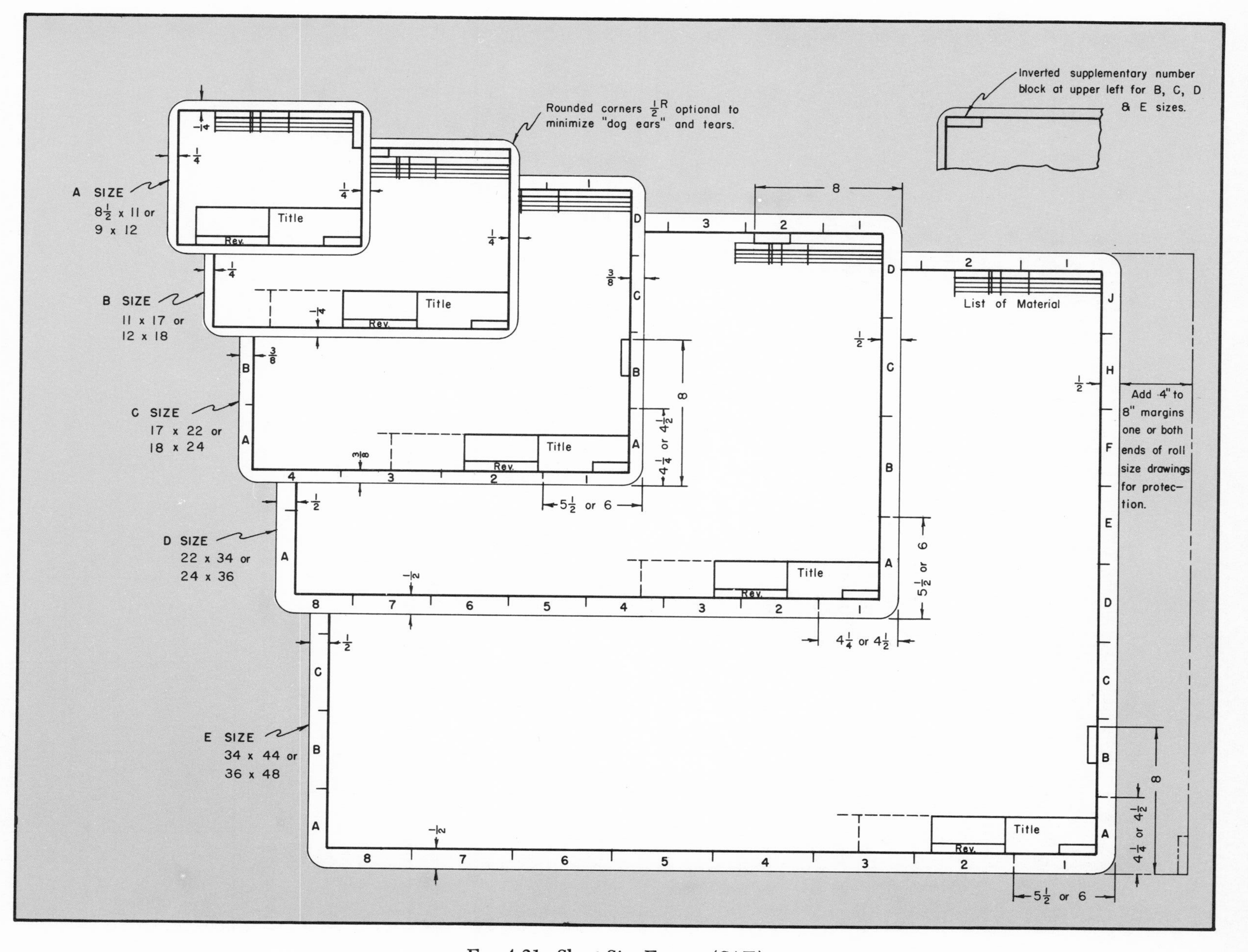

FIG. 4-21. Sheet Size Format (SAE)

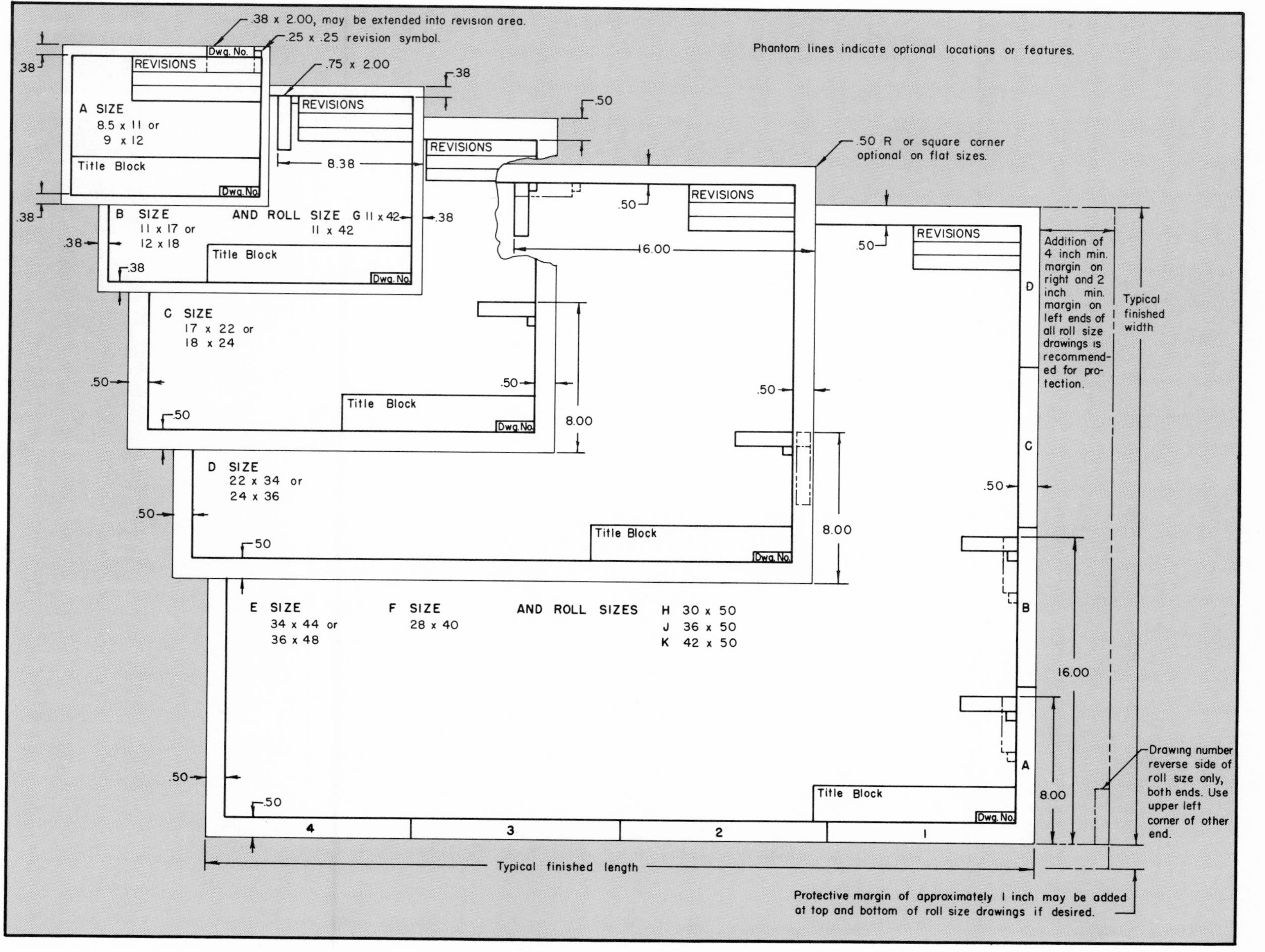

FIG. 4-22. Sheet Size Format (USAS)

Pencils

The pencil is such a common tool that its importance to drafting might be overlooked. Forerunners of modern pencils in the form of colored ore and flint instruments were used 20,000 years ago. The words *lead pencil* suggest that the composition is of lead. This was true in the times of the ancient Egyptians and Romans, but it is not the case today. The pencil of today is composed of a mixture of graphite and pipe clay. The graphite for drafting pencils is ground, separated into varying degrees of fineness, powdered, and mixed with pipe clay. In general, the more clay, the harder the pencil lead and vice versa. A pictorial story of the manufacture of lead pencils is shown in Fig. 4-27.

Pencils come in nineteen degrees of hardness ranging from ExExB to 9*H*, Fig. 4-26. Those

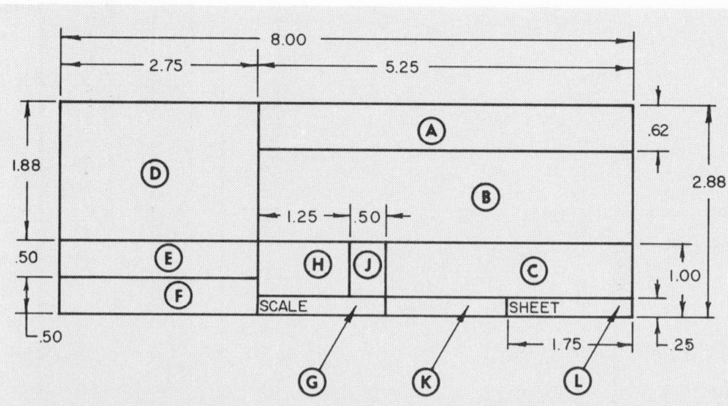

Fig. 4-23. Basic Title Block (SAE)

Labeled spaces are for the following:

A. Company name and address
B. Drawing title
C. Drawing number(s)
D. Data for recording the preparation, checking, approval, and date of drawing (Information may vary to suit the company's internal administrative practices.)
E. Approval by the design activity
F. Approval by activity other than the design activity
G. Scale of drawing
H. Code identification number assigned by Military for identification of company when such number exists
J. Drawing letter size identification
K. Actual or estimated weight of the item, reference to a specification, report, etc.
L. Recording the first sheet and the total number of sheets of a multisheet drawing

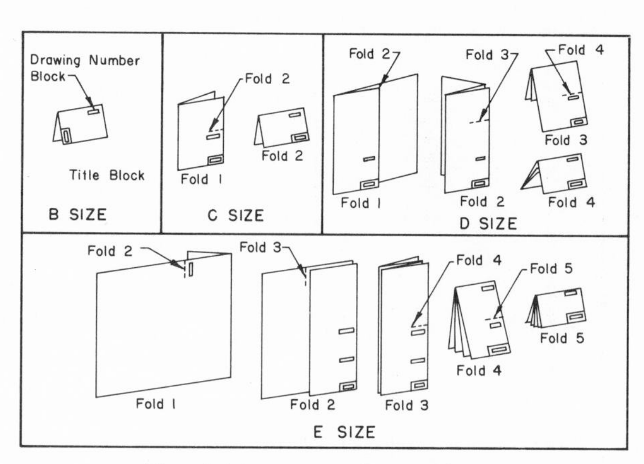

Fig. 4-24. Print Folds (SAE)

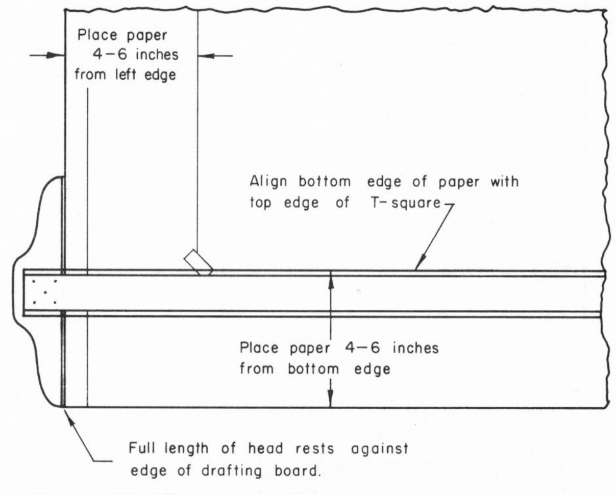

Fig. 4-25. Placement of Paper on Drafting Board for Use with T-square

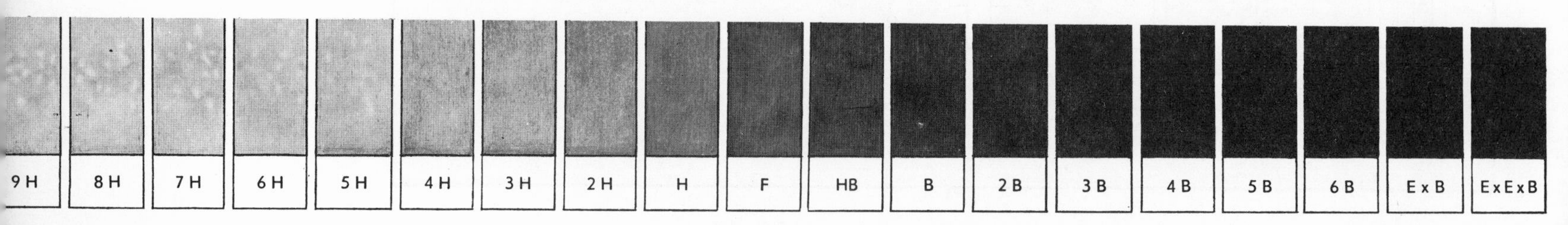

Fig. 4-26. Nineteen Degrees of Lead Pencils (J. S. Staedtler)

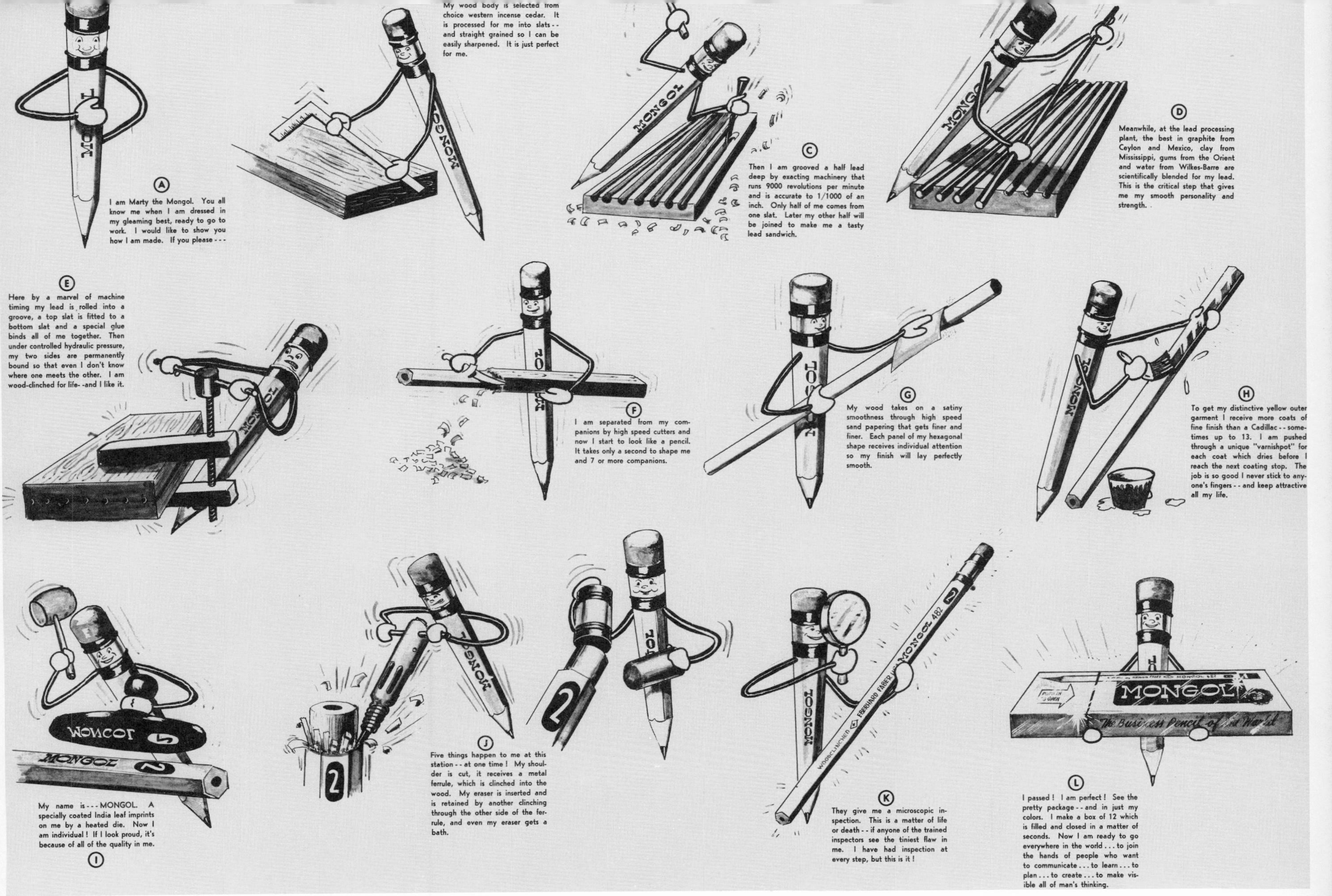

Fig. 4-27. Pictorial Story of Pencil Manufacture (Eberhard Faber Pencil Co.)

TABLE 4-3

Standard Procedure for Rating Drafting Pencils*

Quality Being Tested	Method of Testing	Determinant
1. Rate of Wear	With comparable degrees and equal points and pressure, draw one 18″ line with each pencil.	Note which pencil wore more quickly, and which line broadened more.
2. Point Strength	Re-point pencils equally. Hold each in turn in normal working position, and gradually bear down until the point snaps off.	Note which pencil withstood greater pressures.
3. Opacity of Line	Re-point pencils equally. Draw four 4″ intersecting lines with equal pressure with each pencil.	Make 3 prints at very slow, medium and very fast speeds and note which lines "come up stronger".
4. Erasibility	Re-point pencils equally. Draw four 4″ lines alternately with each pencil, beneath one another. Make single pass down through all lines with eraser.	Note which lines removed more easily, with less matte damage. Erase one line of each completely, and re-draft in same spot. Note which line re-drew more easily.
5. Uniformity of Line	Re-point pencils equally. Draw four 4″ intersecting lines with each pencil.	Hold up to light source such as lamp or window, and note which line blocks more light, has less graying or feathering at edges.
6. Smearing	Re-point pencils equally. Draw 2 medium-light lines and 2 medium-dark lines with each pencil.	Lay straightedge atop lines, and move back and forth across lines with slight pressure. Note which lines smear, and if smear "ghosts" on print.
7. Contrast	Re-point pencils equally. Draw 4″ cross-hatched lines with each pencil, 1/8″ spacing.	Microfilm, reduce and blow back. Note clarity and "cobwebbing" of intersections.
8. Versatility	Overlap and tape 3 pieces of film, cloth and vellum. Draw single line across each medium with various degrees of each pencil.	Note which lines "take" and erase best. Run prints; note clarity.

*The Joseph Dixon Crucible Company, Jersey City, New Jersey.

usually used for general drafting are *HB* to *3H*, with *4H* through *9H* used for layouts, graphical computations, and the like. The more common drafting pencils are *HB*, *F*, *H*, and *2H*. These are used for the heavy and medium lines such as object lines, hidden lines, lettering, and borders. The *3H* pencil is used for thin lines such as section, center, extension, and dimension lines. Harder pencils are used primarily for layout work. Test drafting pencils as shown in Table 4-3.

The use of mylar films requires specially-made pencils. The lead of these pencils has a plastic base, rather than graphite, and it is smear proof, yet erases easily. Drawings made on tracing film with these pencils may be washed with soap and water to remove dirt and grime. These pencils come in five grades as shown in Fig. 4-28.

Pointing the Drafting Pencil

The same techniques are used to sharpen and point a pencil for mechanical drafting as are used for technical sketching, Chapter 2, page 25. Frequent pointing is required for best line work results. Be sure to keep your pointing equipment in an envelope or box so that graphite particles will not get on your drawings nor on your instruments. A wiping cloth or pad of cleansing tissue is needed to remove excess graphite from the pencil point after each pointing.

Mechanical and electrical pencil pointers are more expensive than ordinary pointers but are a real convenience for those who do much drafting, Fig. 2-3.

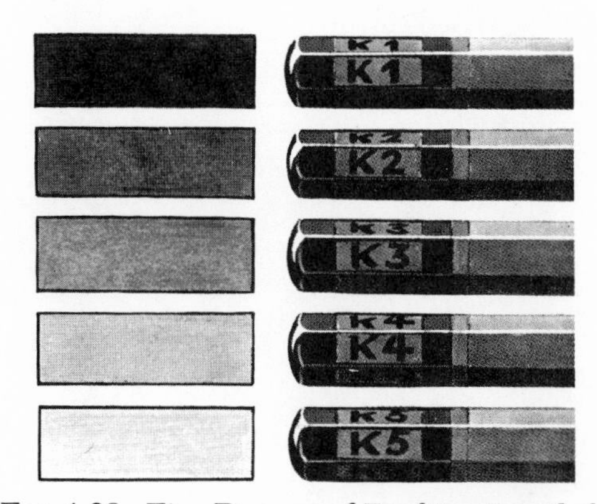

Fig. 4-28. Five Degrees of Drafting Pencils for Use on Drafting Films (J. S. Staedtler)

Line Technique

Horizontal lines are drawn by the right-handed draftsman from left to right; left-handers, from right to left. The pencil is rotated slightly as the line is drawn to maintain a uniform cone-shaped point on the pencil and thus to obtain a uniform line width. Note in Fig. 4-29 that the pencil is in a plane 90° to the paper and that it leans at an angle of 60° to the paper in the direction in which the line is drawn.

Vertical and inclined lines are drawn using the same technique and are drawn in the directions shown in Fig. 4-30.

See Fig. 4-31 for drafting techniques for film. Except for point *4* in the figure, these techniques generally are desirable for good drafting of pencil lines on any drafting media.

Triangles

Triangles are of the 45°, 30° - 60°, or adjustable type. They should be of professional-grade, optically-clear plastic to enable you to see the work underneath. They may have finger lifts or bevels on the inside of the triangle. Triangles are used in combination with each other or with the T-square or parallel bar. In the latter cases, lines in any multiple of 15° can be constructed.

Triangles also are used to draw parallel lines and lines at right angles to given lines, Figs. 4-32 and 4-33. For best control and best line weight, lines should be drawn in the directions shown in these illustrations.

Erasers

You will hope to make as few mistakes as possible. When you do make one, you should know how to erase it. Your supplies and equipment should include a pencil eraser, an eraser for ink, and a cleaner type eraser. Of these, the ink eraser is the most abrasive and the cleaner type the least. Erasers made from vinyl for use on drafting films do not contain abrasives and are especially good for use with both graphite and plastic pencil lines.

Eraser Techniques

1. Select an eraser that removes the lead deposit thoroughly without damaging the surface of the drafting medium.
2. Avoid the use of coarse erasers, knives, razor blades, and the like.
3. Use an erasing shield to protect the lines not being erased and to avoid wrinkling the paper.
4. Use a hard surface such as an extra erasing shield or plastic triangle to back up the area during erasure. If the hard surface used is metal, it will tend to carry away some of the heat generated while erasing.

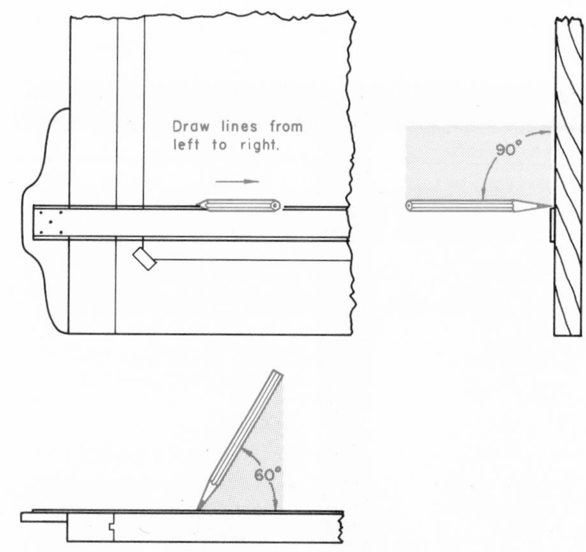

Fig. 4-29. Position of Drafting Pencil for Drawing Lines

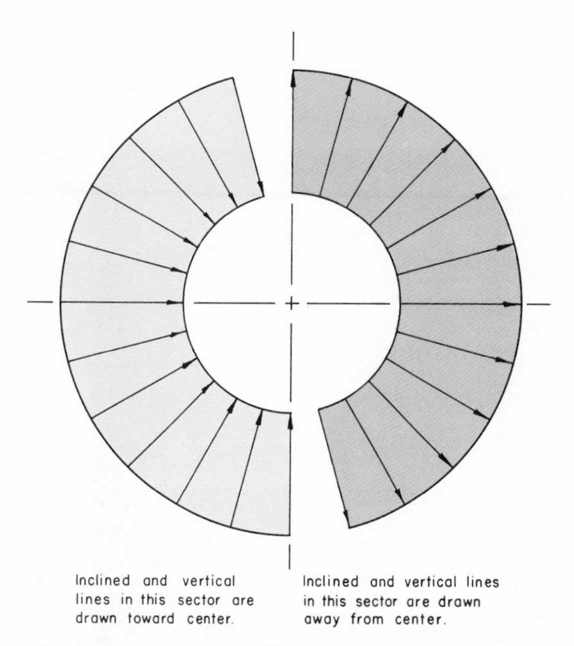

Fig. 4-30. Directions for Drawing Various Lines

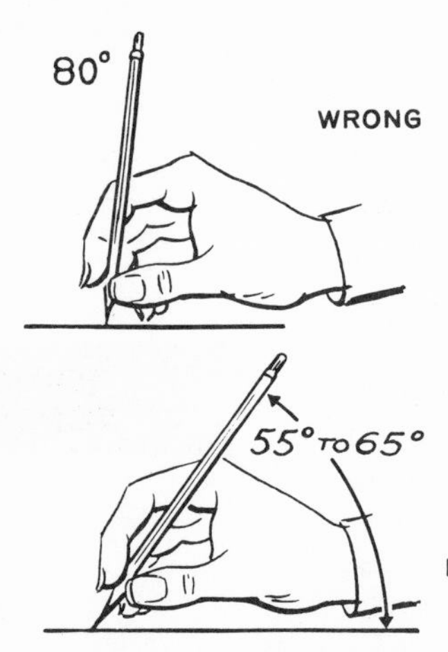

NO. 1

Reduce the angle of pencil to film to 55° to 65°. Sharper angles may penetrate the matte.

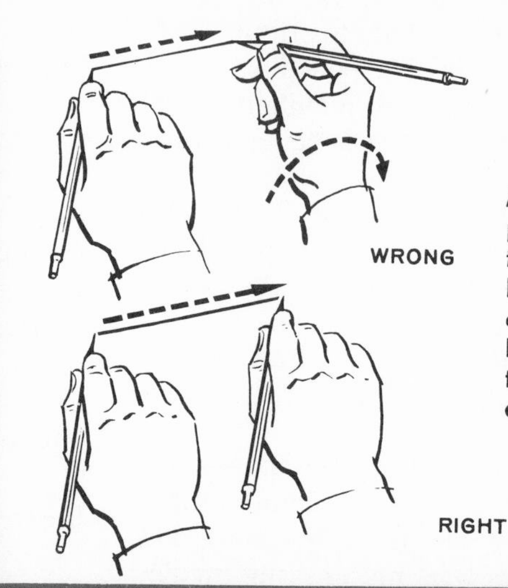

NO. 2

Maintain this constant pencil and wrist angle throughout an entire line. The tendency to increase the perpendicularity toward the end of the line is a chief cause of film "gouging".

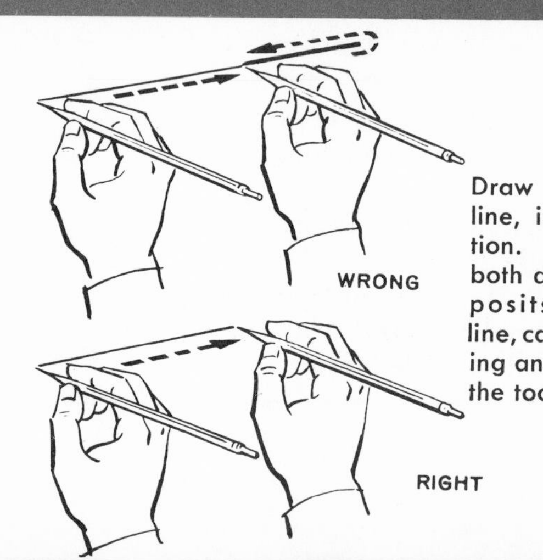

NO. 3

Draw with a single line, in one direction. Retracing in both directions deposits a double line, causing smearing and damage to the tooth.

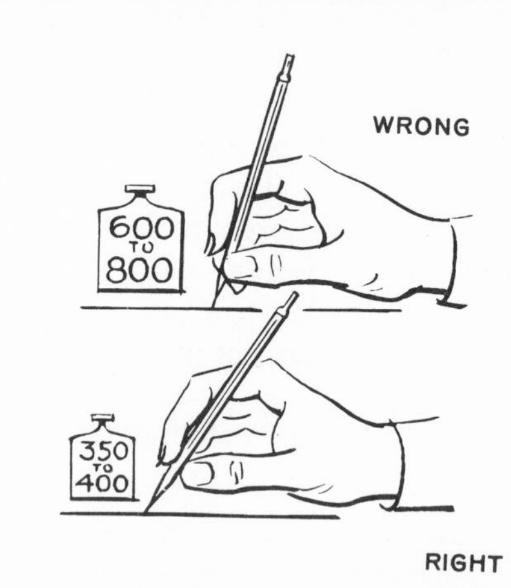

NO. 4

Draft with a light touch. Drafting films require up to 40% less pressure than other media. Smearing and embossing can be checked by reduction of pressure from about 600 grams to 350 grams.

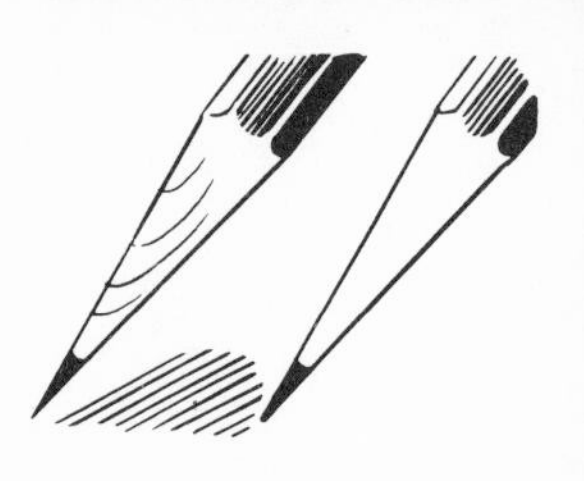

NO. 5

Draw with a slightly blunted point. Needle points or burrs left in pointing may gouge the film and should be removed by stroking the point on a scrap of paper.

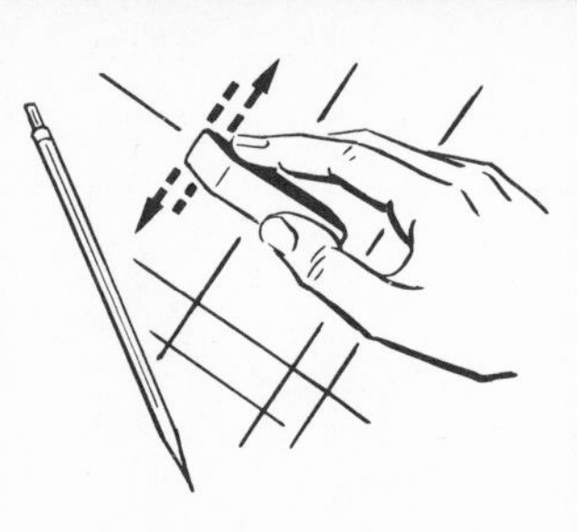

NO. 6

Erase at right angles to the direction of the work with a non-abrasive manual eraser. This minimizes tooth damage, eases re-draws.

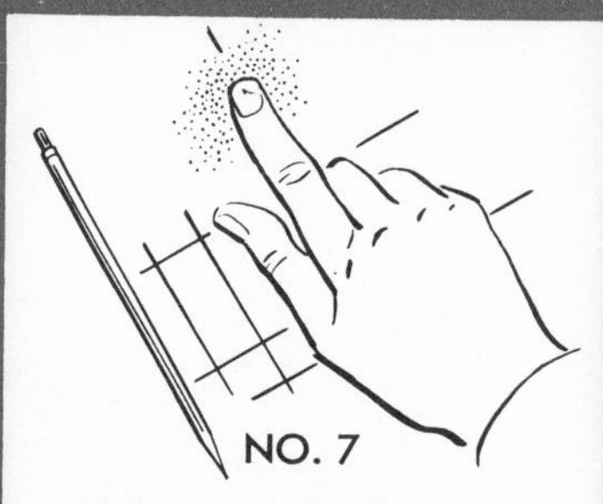

NO. 7

If the tooth is burnished and the line will not "take", restore the tooth by roughening the surface with an abrasive (typewriter) eraser or by rubbing in a slight amount of "pounce" with the finger.

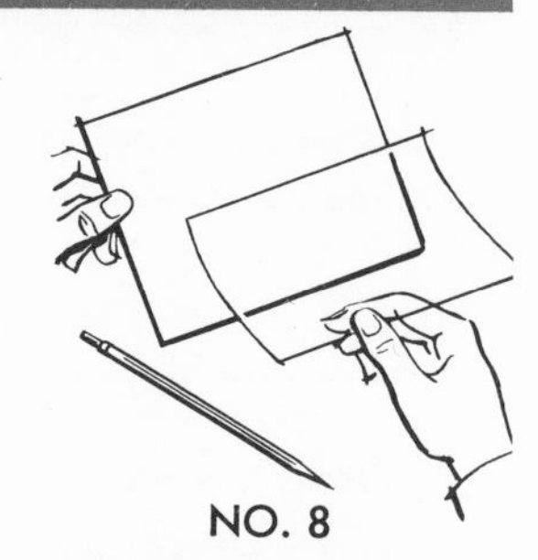

NO. 8

Use a non-pliable backing (glass, metal, fibreboard, etc.) under the drawing to reduce embossing (impressions) on the reverse side, and lessen the possibility of these ghosting.

FIG. 4-31. Drafting Techniques for Use on Film (The Joseph Dixon Crucible Co.)

5. Erase the back side of the paper where the erasing was done to remove any dirt and to offset discoloration that the erasing might have caused.
6. Lines that may have been made too heavily and thus actually embossed the paper may be taken out in part by burnishing the back to help restore the damaged fibers of the drafting medium.
7. Make a series of slits, about ⅛″ deep and ⅛″ apart, in the eraser. This promotes cleaning and helps prevent burn-through.
8. Vary the direction of the eraser strokes to prevent burn-through and surface damage.
9. Erase thoroughly but over a longer period of time and a somewhat larger area than that actually required.
10. Keep the drafting surface free from eraser crumbs by brushing with a good dusting brush.
11. When the tooth of the paper has been damaged by erasing, use *pounce* to improve the area for pencil work and a *soapstone stick* for ink work.
12. Avoid the use of chemical eradicators.

Professional draftsmen may prefer an electric erasing machine, Fig. 4-34. The techniques of erasing are the same, but the beginner should be very careful not to use too much pressure. Move the machine around. Place a piece of copper, brass, or aluminum sheet metal under the area to be erased to help dissipate the heat. Several grades of erasers are available, and it is easy to change from one to another.

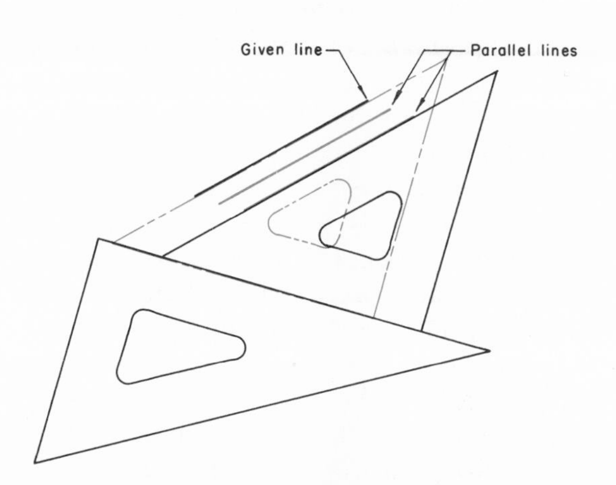

Fig. 4-32. Triangles Used in Combination to Draw Lines Parallel to a Given Line

Layout of the Border and Title Strip

Draftsmen usually use preprinted paper with the border and the company title strip on it. However, the student draftsman sometimes must layout the border and title sheet, Fig. 4-35. To do this, proceed methodically:

1. Select a standard border and title block layout from standards on pages 86-87.
2. Draw a horizontal trim line near the lower edge of the paper. Use a lightweight construction line. (If you are using precut, trimmed paper, omit steps 2 and 3.)
3. Draw a vertical trim line of construction weight near the left edge of the paper. (Left-handers will find it more convenient to draw the vertical line at the right-hand side of the paper.)

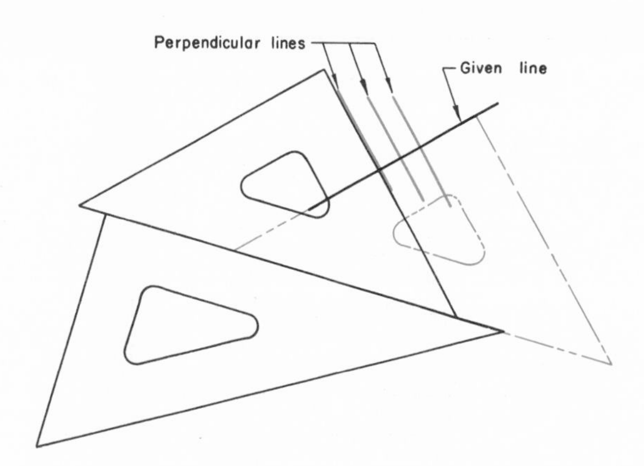

Fig. 4-33. Triangles Used in Combination to Draw Lines at Right Angles to a Given Line

Fig. 4-34. Electric Eraser (Charles Bruning Co.)

4. Place the full-size scale face up along the horizontal trim line or along the edge of the paper if it is precut. Layout at the required distances along the scale by marking lightweight, short, horizontal dash lines at each of the required distances. Do not use dots; they are not as accurate as carefully made dashes.

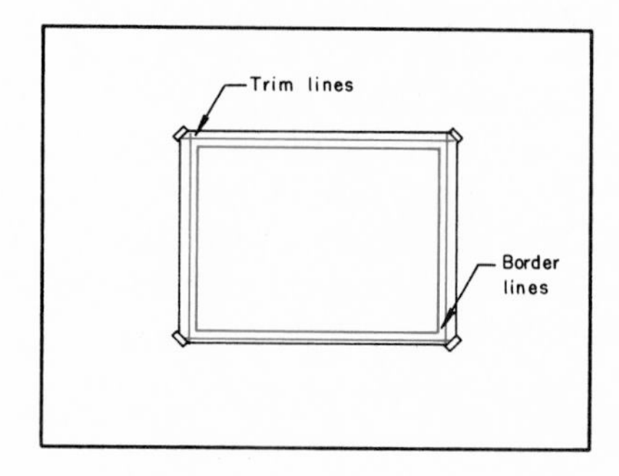

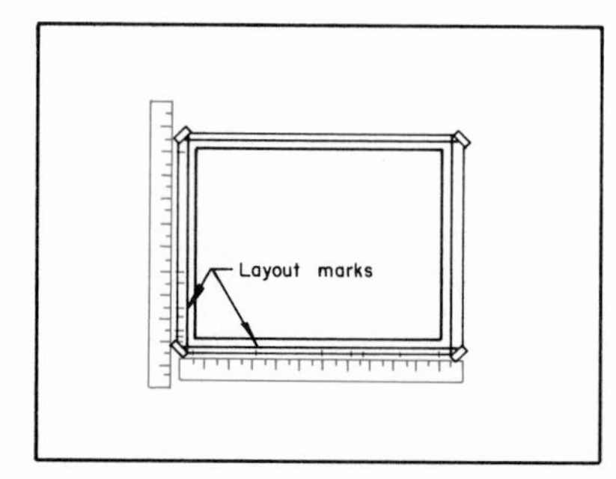

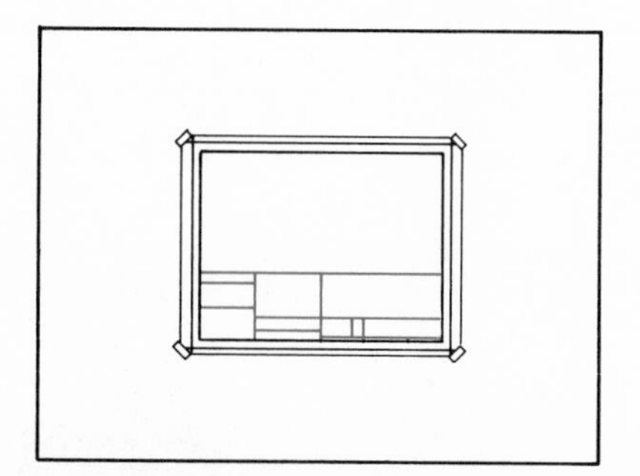

FIG. 4-35. Layout Procedure for Border and Title Strip

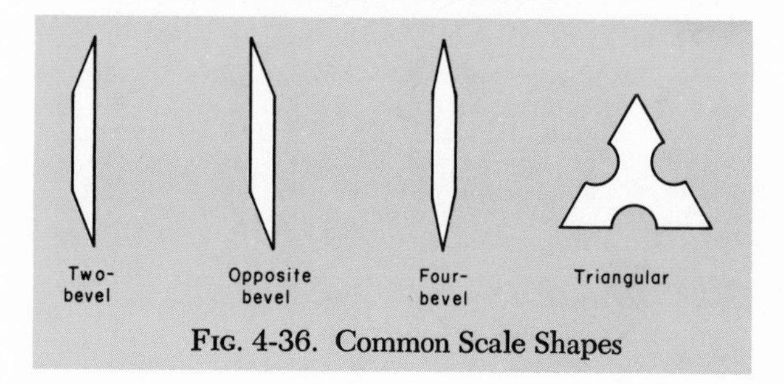

FIG. 4-36. Common Scale Shapes

5. Place the scale along the vertical trim line or the vertical edge if paper is precut, and layout the distances with short dashes at the required places.
6. With the help of the T-square, draw horizontal construction lines through the marks along the vertical trim lines or edges.
7. Draw vertical construction lines through the dashes laid out on the horizontal trim lines or edges. Darken in the border lines with an *H* or an *F* pencil. Border lines usually are the darkest lines on a drawing.

Scale Types

Drawings may be made full size, less than full size, or greater than full size. The relationship of the representation of the object to its actual size is its *scale*. Large objects (such as a house, an office building, a bridge, a rocket, a car, or a table) require a scale to reduce the size so that it will fit on one of the standard-size sheets of drawing paper. Very small objects and objects with minute detail (such as precision instrument pivots for electrical devices) will need to be enlarged so that the detail may plainly be seen and dimensioned. The scale chosen should give the largest size possible on the drawing paper being used, while leaving adequate room for dimensions.

Scales are made of boxwood, wood with plastic faces, all plastic, or all metal. They are available in four basic shapes, each having a particular advantage, Fig. 4-36.

The *two-bevel* scale has a wide base and both faces are completely visible.

The *opposite-bevel* scale has two faces, one of which is visible on each side of the scale and is easy to lift by tilting the scale.

The *four-bevel* scale has four faces, thus increasing the number of scales on one instrument. It is also easy to lift by tilting.

The *regular triangular* scale has six faces and permits full-face contact with the drawing. This is the scale most commonly used in schools.

A variation of the triangular scale is the *concave triangular* scale, which has only the edges of the bottom scales in contact with the drawing. It is usually plastic and is somewhat lighter in weight than a comparable regular triangular scale.

There are three methods of placing scale graduations on the scale. The engine-divided scale is the most common and generally preferred. Each graduation is cut into the scale face by machine-controlled knives, then filled with a permanent black pigment.

Die-engraved graduations are carefully die-cut in black on the faces of the scale.

Molded graduations are a part of the mold from which the scale itself is made. The graduations are filled with permanent black pigment.

The divisions of a scale are either *fully divided* or *open divided*. On the full-divided scale, each unit is fully subdivided along the entire face of the scale, Fig. 4-37. The open-divided scale has only the main unit divisions along the scale with one fully subdivided extra unit at one end, Fig. 4-38.

The mechanical engineer's scales and the civil engineer's scales usually are fully divided. The architect's scales usually are open divided.

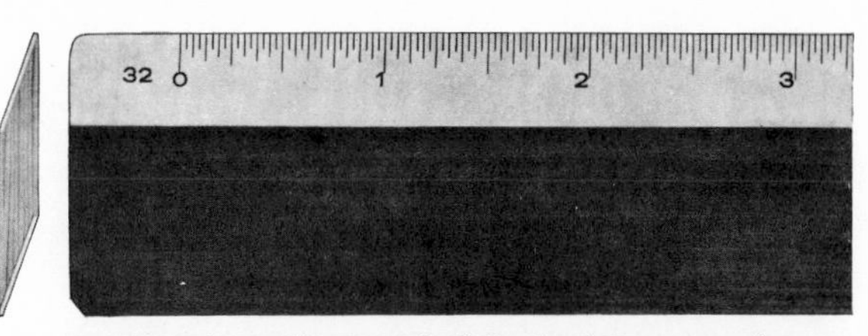

FIG. 4-37. Fully-Divided Scale (Gramercy)

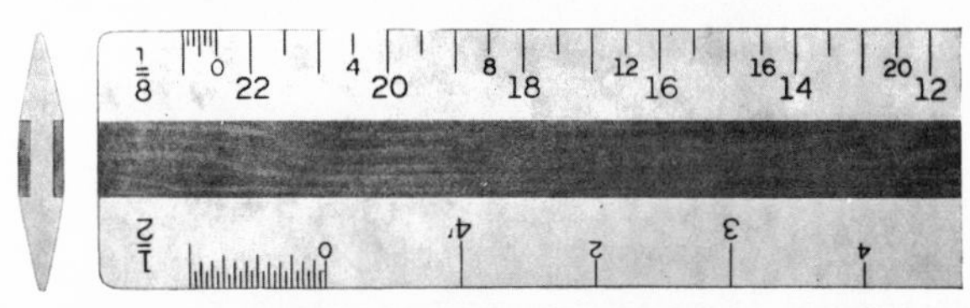
FIG. 4-38. Open-Divided Scale (Gramercy)

Mechanical Engineer's Scales

The mechanical engineer works with objects for which drawings may be full size, half size, one-quarter size or one-eighth size. The scales he uses are made so that he can use these sizes directly to lay off distances and to measure them. The full-size scale is subdivided into fractional parts of an inch. On the other scales, a unit which *represents* an inch is subdivided into parts representing fractional parts of an inch in the English system, Fig. 4-39. Just as the divisions on a full-size scale determine the fractional parts of an inch, the subdivisions of an inch on the mechanical engineer's scales determine the fractional part of an inch that is represented. A special mechanical engineer's scale with half-size graduations is shown in Fig. 4-40. Full-size graduations are on the reverse side of this scale.

In recent years there has been a movement in the drafting rooms of automotive industries,

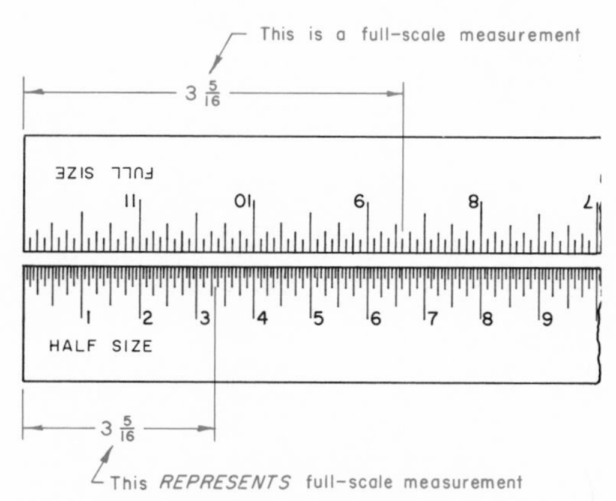

FIG. 4-39. Half-Scale Measurement Represents Full-Scale Size

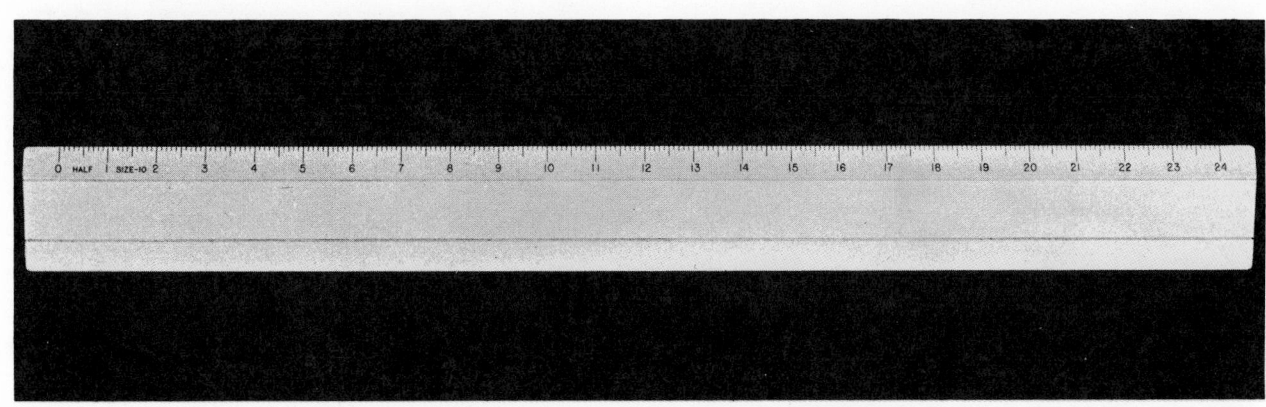
FIG. 4-40. Mechanical Engineer's Scale Uses Decimal Inch

aircraft and related industries, and other generally large industries to use the decimal inch as the basic unit of measurement. This trend is likely to spread in these and other industries in the years ahead.

Fig. 4-41 is a metric scale.

Architect's Scales

The architect develops plans for buildings, and the scales he uses range from 1″ = 1′ (1/12 size) to 3/32″ = 1′ (1/128 size). The units of division on the architect's scale *represent feet*. These are further divided into inches and, in some of the larger scales, fractional parts of an inch, Fig. 4-42. Common architect's scales are shown in Fig. 4-43.

Civil Engineer's Scales

Civil engineers may work with even larger distances than architects. They may be concerned with the layout of a highway, an airport, or the pipes in a city water system. The units of division are in multiples of ten parts of an inch, ranging from ten to sixty or seventy, Fig. 4-44. These may represent single units or any multiple of ten such as 100, 1000, or 10,000, Fig. 4-45.

Student Scales

Students must learn how to use each of these three kinds of scales. A special student-model, triangular-scale rule is available with the following scales on it:

1. Full scale subdivided into 16ths of an inch.
2. Mechanical engineer's scales: ¾ size, ½ size, ⅜ size, ¼ size.
3. Architect's scales: 1″, ½″, ¼″, and ⅛″ to the foot.
4. Civil engineer's scale: 50 parts to the inch.

How to Use the Scales

Review full-size dimensions and measurement:

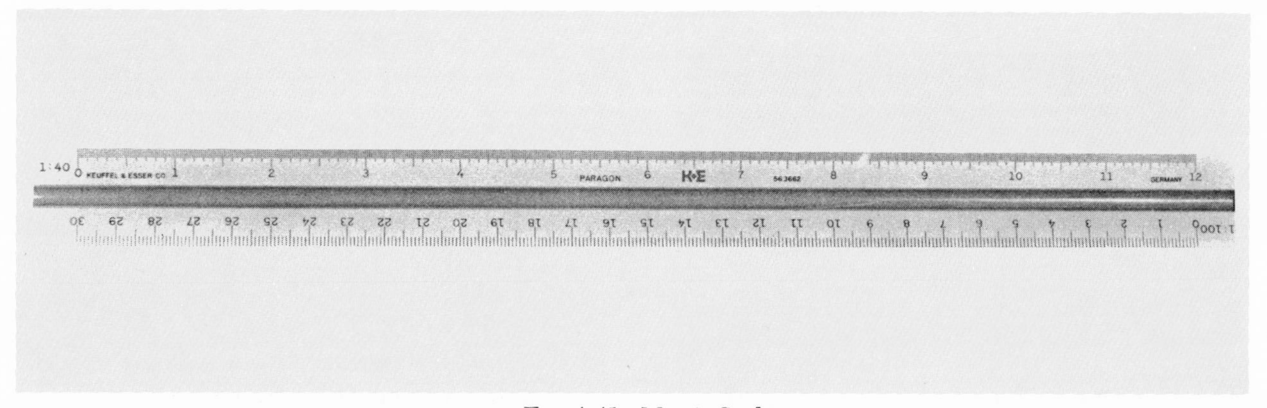

FIG. 4-41. Metric Scale

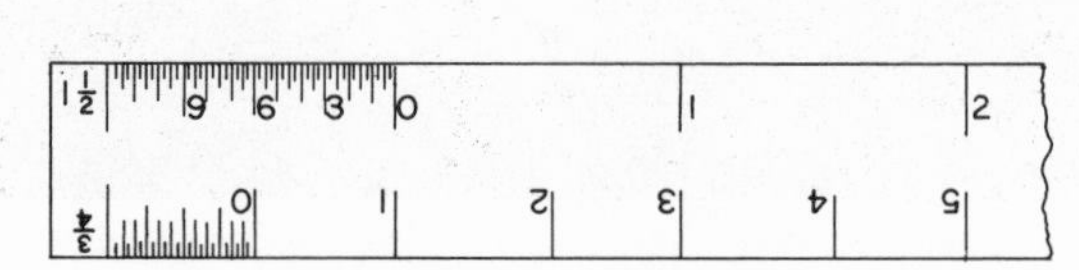

FIG. 4-42. Feet and Inches Represented on the Architect's Scale

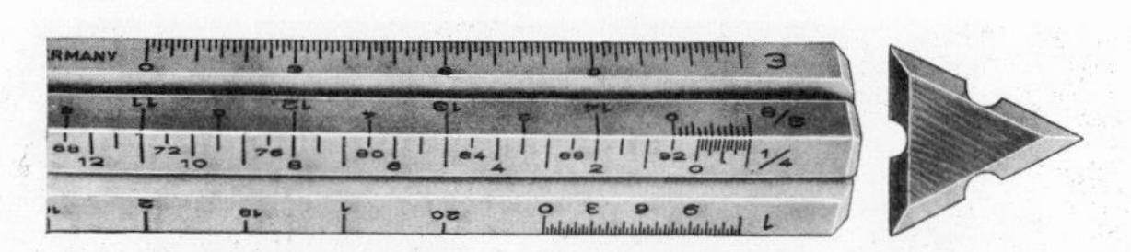

FIG. 4-43. Common Architect's Scale (Gramercy)

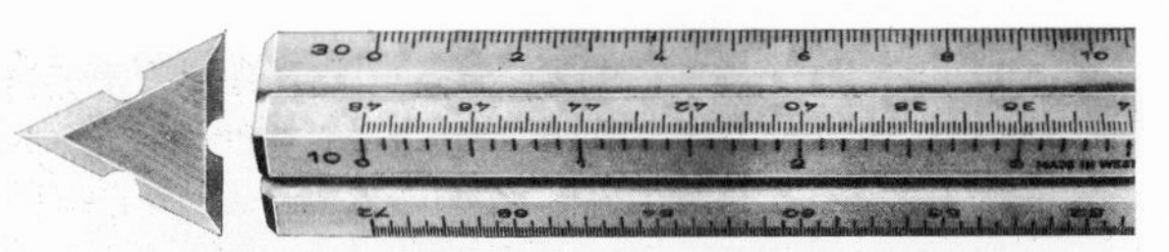

FIG. 4-44. Civil Engineer's Scale (Gramercy)

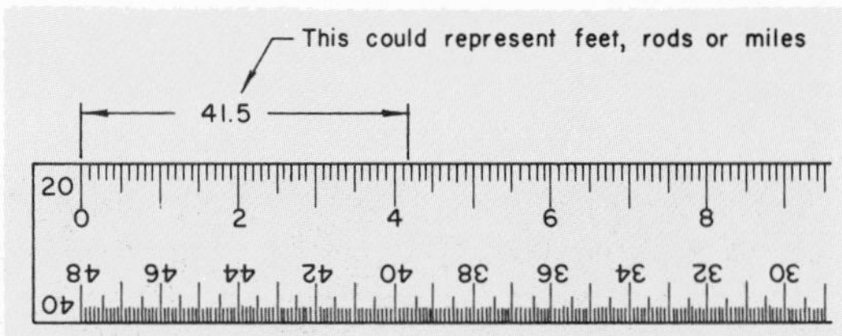

FIG. 4-45. Civil Engineer's Scale Units Representing Different Units

1. The common one-foot rule is divided into 12″.
2. Each inch is divided into a number of divisions, the more common of these being 16.
3. The name of these divisions or fractional parts of an inch is derived by placing a one over the number of divisions in an inch such as 1/16. Then say "each of these subdivisions of an inch is 1/16 of an inch" and "the inch is divided into sixteenths."
4. When you measure several sixteenths of an inch, the result always is expressed in the form of the least common denominator. *Example:* two-sixteenths is one-eighth of an inch; four-sixteenths is one-fourth of an inch; twelve-sixteenths is three-fourths of an inch.
5. Odd numbers cannot be reduced, such as three-sixteenths, seven-sixteenths, and thirteen-sixteenths.
6. For easier reading, the scale divisions which can be reduced to a least common denominator are made longer. These scale markings are read directly in terms of the least common denominator, Fig. 4-46.
7. In the English system, full-scale rules may be subdivided into 64ths, 32nds, 16ths, 8ths, 4ths, and halves. Common rules are divided into 16ths.

Drawings are made full size whenever possible.

To measure a full-scale line, place the zero of the full-size scale at one end of the line. Line up the scale with the line. Read the result on the scale to the fraction of the least common denominator.

To layout a line using the full scale, place the zero mark of the full scale at the place where the line begins; mark a short dash opposite the zero. If the line is to be 1¾″ in length, place another dash opposite the 1¾″ marking. Then connect these dashes using a straightedge.

Caution: Do not use dots nor punch holes in your paper. Dash lines are more accurate.

When the mechanical engineer's, architect's or civil engineer's scales are used, the layout procedure of marking dash lines is the same. The chief difference is in reading the divisions on the scales.

For example, assume you are to use the mechanical engineer's scale to lay off the distance of 8⅝ inches at the scale of one-quarter size.

1. Locate the one-quarter size scale on the scale rule.
2. Locate the full unit divisions on the scale, and observe the position of the one marked 8.
3. Place the 8 on the point of origin of the 8⅝″ line.
4. Direct your attention to the zero mark from which the 8 full-divisions were counted off.
5. Using the full-divided unit next to this zero mark, observe the position of the 5/8ths distance.
6. Mark this end of the line representing 8⅝″.

Each of the mechanical engineer's scales other than full scale is used in this same manner. Locate the scale, find the full units in one direction from the zero point, and then find the fractional parts in the opposite direction from the zero point.

The architect's scale is used in much the same way. For example, assume you are to layout a line representing 12′ - 4″, at a scale of ¼″ = 1′ - 0″.

1. Locate the scale ¼″ = 1′ - 0″ on the scale rule.
2. From the zero mark on this scale, read the full units, namely 12′.
3. Place this 12′ division mark on the point of origin for the line you are to draw.
4. Locate the zero mark from which the 12 full divisions were counted.
5. Using the full-divided unit next to this zero mark, find the distance which represents 4″.
6. Mark this end of the line representing 12′-4″.

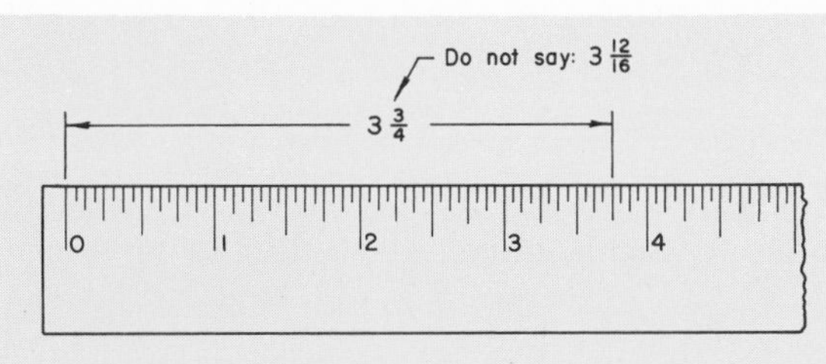

FIG. 4-46. Use Least Common Denominator to Read Scale

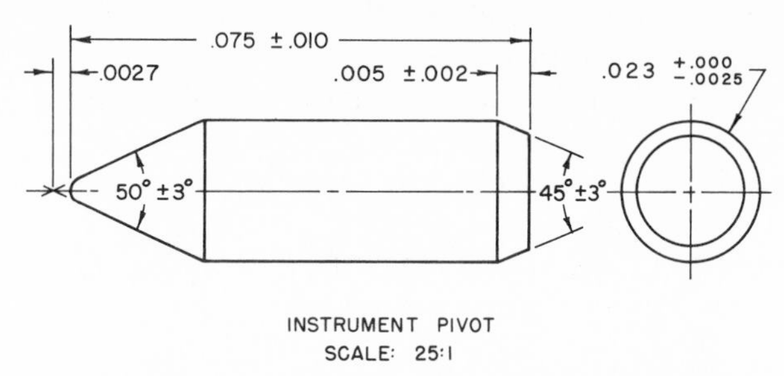

FIG. 4-47. Enlargement Scale of 25 to 1 (Welton V. Johnson Co.)

Other of the architect's scales are used in the same way. Some have enough divisions that the fractional parts of an inch may be laid out directly, Fig. 4-42.

The civil engineer's scale usually is full-divided, Fig. 4-44. Therefore, once the scale has been chosen, the layout of distances is somewhat similar to the layout of full-scale distances. For example, assume you are to lay-out a line representing 148′, using the scale 1″ = 50′ - 0″.

1. Locate the scale in which the inch is divided into 50 parts.
2. Place the zero mark of this scale at the point of origin for the line you are to draw.
3. Read the full divisions as equal to ten units until you come to 14 on the scale. This represents 140′.
4. Read the subdivisions between 14 and 15 to locate 8′ more.
5. Make the layout for this end of the line which represents 148′.

Other scales used by the civil engineer are read in the same way. Had you been using 148 miles instead of 148 feet, you might have used the same scale. Similarly, had you been using 14,800 feet, you also might have used the same scale, but each marked full division on the scale would have equaled 1000 feet instead of 10 feet. In each of the three cases just cited, the physical distance of the line is the same, even though it *represents different actual lengths.*

Enlarging

Sometimes rather than making a drawing smaller than the object is (reducing its size), it must be enlarged or made larger than the object. This may be done to show detail which is not otherwise clear, Fig. 4-47. The full scale for enlargement is used, but each dimension

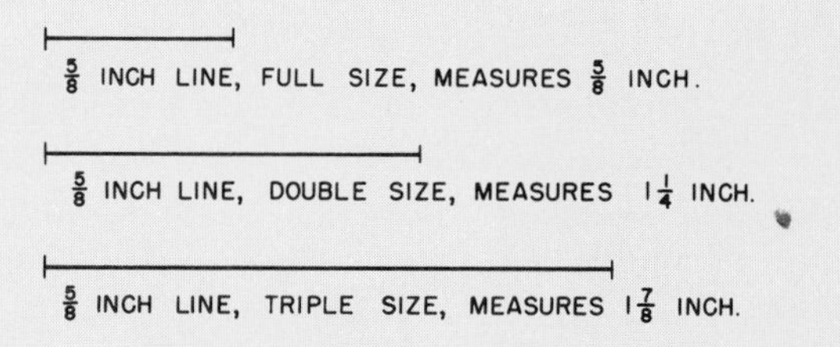

FIG. 4-48. Enlargements are Multiplications of the Full-Scale Measurements

must be multiplied by the enlargement ratio. For example, to draw a line representing 5/8″ double size, multiply 5/8 x 2. Layout this new length (1¼″) directly on the page, Fig. 4-48. If it were triple size, you would multiply by three, and so on.

Another technique, which uses squares, is especially helpful with irregular patterns. One may use each square as a pair of coordinates. He may either enlarge or reduce by using a pattern of squares which is larger or smaller than that of the original, Fig. 4-49.

Drawing to Scale

Since all drawings are not made to scale, drawings must be identified clearly as to the scale used. This information frequently appears in the title strip, but it also may appear with subtitles when more than one scale is used on one sheet of paper. See Figs. 3-64 and 3-67.

No matter where this information appears on the drawing, the format is the same. The word *scale* is lettered and is followed immediately by a colon. Then the scale used is carefully lettered.

Mechanical engineer's scales will read *full size, ½ size, ¼ size* or *double size.* They may be abbreviated such as *full, half, quarter, eighth,* or *double.* The scales also may be converted into inch equivalents such as 1″ = 1″, ½″ = 1″, ¼″ = 1″, ⅛″ = 1″, or 2″ = 1″ (which is double size).

Architect's scales will read 1″ = 1′ - 0″. Notice that this is a precise way of saying one inch equals one foot and no inches. Both the hyphen and the "no inches" are important in assuring us, for example, that the architect meant exactly what the scale says to the nearest inch. Other architect's scales read the same way: 3″ = 1′ - 0″, 1½″ = 1′ - 0″, ¾″ = 1′ - 0″, ½″ = 1′ - 0″, ¼″ = 1′ - 0″, 3/16″ = 1′ - 0″, ⅛″ = 1′ - 0″, 3/32″ = 1′ - 0″.

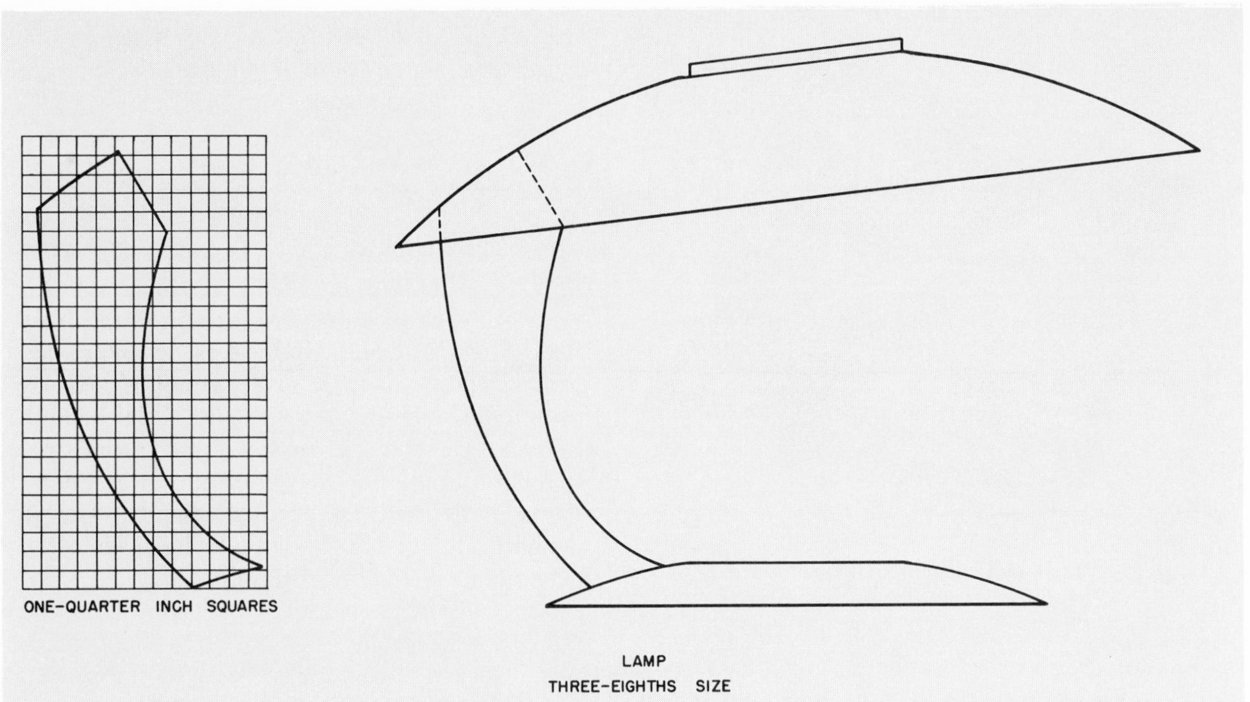

FIG. 4-49. Squares Used for Enlargement or Reduction of Irregular Curve Parts (Richard Partridge)

Civil engineer's scales may read: 1″ = 1000 feet, 1″ = 50′ - 0″, or 1″ = 100 miles. On map drawings, a graphic scale may be used, Fig. 4-50. Sometimes a fraction is used, such as 1/6250, meaning 1″ = 6250″.

Accuracy in Layout

Use of a scale requires accuracy. When you are making a drawing at one hundred twenty-eighth size, an inaccuracy may be magnified 128 times when the object is constructed. This means that it is important to use a sharp and well-pointed pencil for layout work, that layout lines be carefully drawn, and that consistency in layout practices be followed. Cumulative errors can be avoided by setting the scale in position for layout and making as many layout marks as possible without moving the scale, Fig. 4-51. Consistency can be practiced by selecting and then using only one method of layout. The preferred method for reading a scale and laying out a line is to measure from the center of the graduations on the scale and from the centers of the layout lines drawn on the page. Follow this method consistently – in other words, do not measure to the outside of one line and the inside of another. Error will be reduced substantially and good work will result.

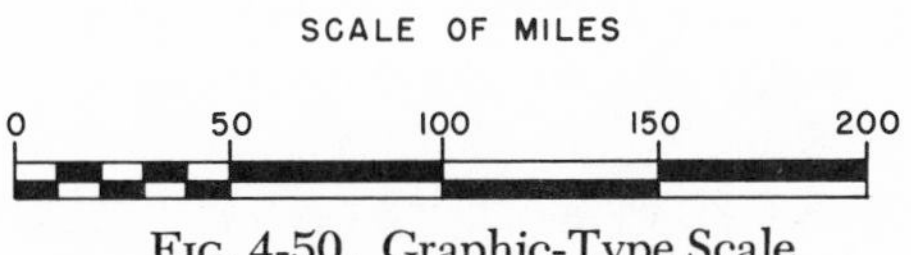

FIG. 4-50. Graphic-Type Scale Commonly Used on Maps

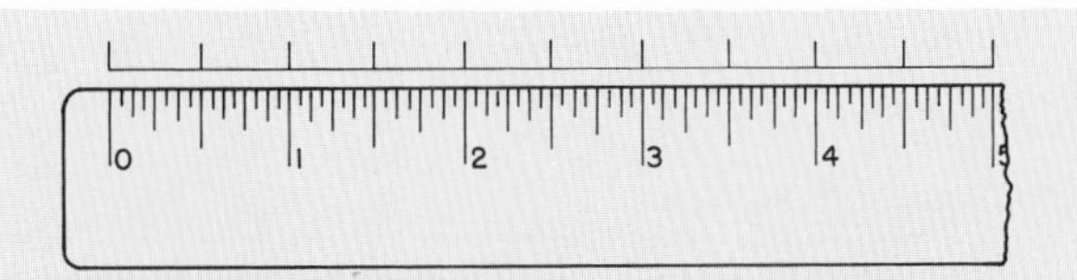

FIG. 4-51. Make as Many Layout Marks as Possible before Resetting the Scale

Drafting Instrument Set

A minimum set of drawing instruments for general use should include: 1 ruling pen, 1 combination pen and pencil compasses and dividers, 1 beam compasses, 1 dividers, Fig. 4-1. Purchase of fewer instruments with better quality will result in better fitting of mating parts, longer wear, easier operation, and less maintenance, Fig. 4-52. Almost any combination of instruments can be obtained in sets by consulting suppliers' catalogs or by arrangement for special needs with the company.

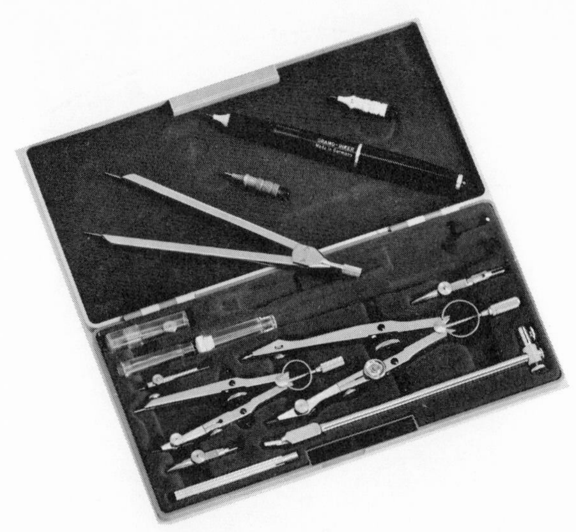

FIG. 4-52. A Set of Instruments with India Ink Fountain Pen and Interchangeable Pen Point Sections (Gramercy)

FIG. 4-53. Centering Tacks for Compasses (Keuffel & Esser Co.)

A *centering tack* is included in some instrument sets. Its purpose is to provide a pivot point for the compasses, especially when describing concentric circles. It prevents the compasses point from enlarging a hole in the paper, Fig. 4-53.

Care of Instruments

Drafting instruments are precision made for accurate work. Do not permit them to fall from the drafting surface. If dividers or compasses points become dull, carefully repoint them on a small carborundum stone. Figs. 4-54 through 4-60 show special instruments used in drafting.

Perspiration and oils from the draftsman's hands may stain some instruments. Use a cleaning and polishing cloth to help keep the instruments in good condition.

Use caution in working with the threaded parts of instruments. Do not strip the threads by forcing or handling carelessly. Instruments are made to give a lifetime of satisfactory service with normal care in use.

Sharpening the Ruling Pen

Sharpening the pen consists of two major steps – *first* shape the nibs; *then* sharpen them.

TO SHAPE THE NIBS:

1. Tighten the thumbscrew so the nibs just barely touch.

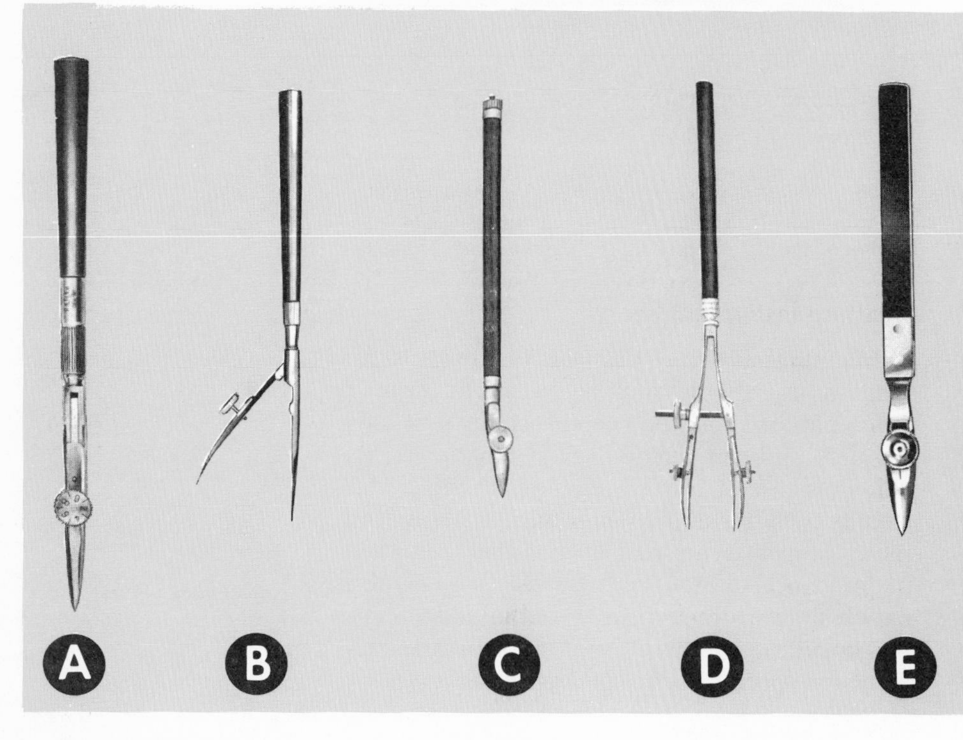

FIG. 4-54. Special Pens (Gramercy)

A. Calibrated thumbscrew for accuracy in setting and re-setting the line widths
B. Jacknife pen with hinged blade to facilitate cleaning
C. Offset pen for drawing irregular curves
D. Railroad pen for drawing double curves
E. Wide pen for drawing long lines

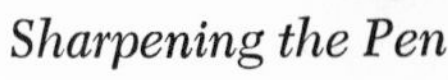

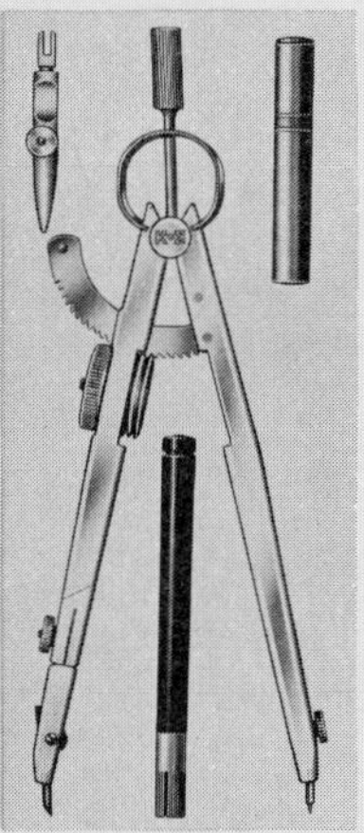

FIG. 4-55. Quick-Set Bow Compasses (Keuffel & Esser Co.)

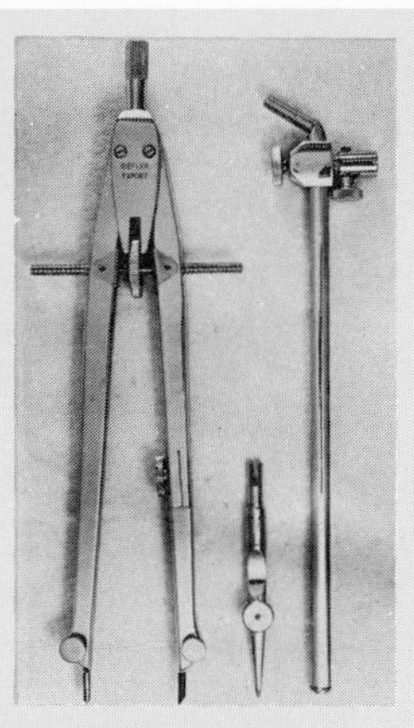

FIG. 4-56. Rapid-Action Riefler Compasses (Gramercy)

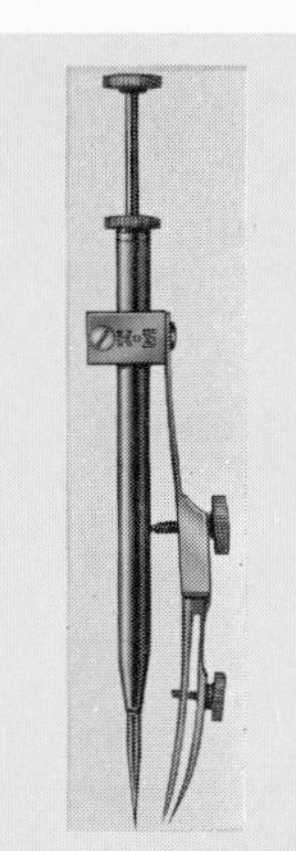

FIG. 4-57. Drop Bow Pen for Precise Control of Small Diameter Circles (Keuffel & Esser Co.)

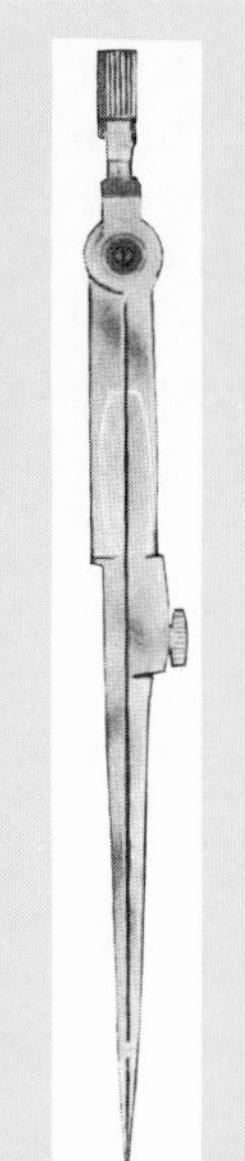

FIG. 4-58. Hairspring Dividers for Accurate Work (Gramercy)

FIG. 4-59. Proportional Dividers for Obtaining Proportional Parts of Lines, Planes, and Solids in Ratios from 1:2 to 1:10 (Gramercy)

2. Hold the pen in a vertical plane over the sharpening stone.
3. Move the pen in the vertical plane from side to side in contact with the stone, until the desired shape is obtained, Fig. 4-61.

TO SHARPEN THE NIBS:

1. Loosen the thumbscrew so that the nibs are about ¼″ apart.
2. Hold the pen in a nearly horizontal position over the sharpening stone.
3. Use a half-moon stroke to sharpen the outside of the nib only.
4. Sharpen the other nib on the outside. Both nibs should be equally sharp — just short of razor-sharp.

The nibs *never* should be sharpened on the inside, since to do so will destroy the capacity of the pen to hold ink. The nibs should make slight indentations, but not cuts, in the drafting paper, in order to hold the ink.

To help determine when a pen needs to be sharpened, close the nibs until they barely

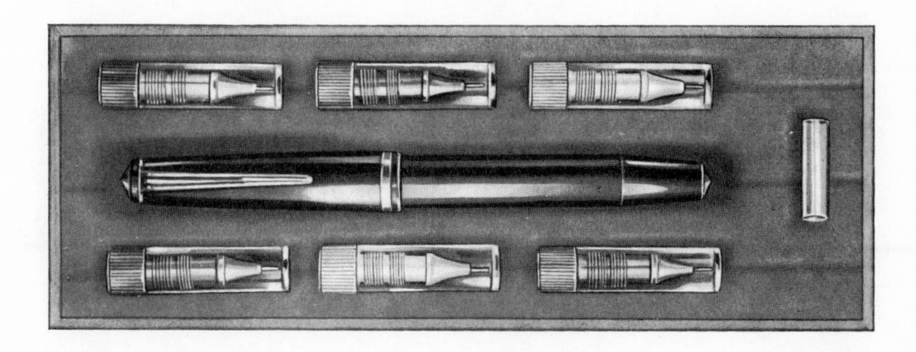

No. 1	White	Very Fine	.006″	0.15 mm	
No. 2	Grey	Fine	.008″	0.25 mm	
No. 3	Yellow	Medium	.012″	0.40 mm	
No. 4	Green	Medium Broad	.018″	0.60 mm	
No. 5	Blue	Broad	.032″	0.80 mm	
No. 6	Red	Very Broad	.040″	1.00 mm	

FIG. 4-60. Fountain Pen Set Rules Lines of Uniform Width (Gramercy)

touch. Then hold the pen so you are looking directly at the end of the nibs. If there is a bright spot, the nibs may need sharpening. If there is practically no reflection of light on the nibs, then they are properly sharpened. A well-sharpened pen should *not* need resharpening often.

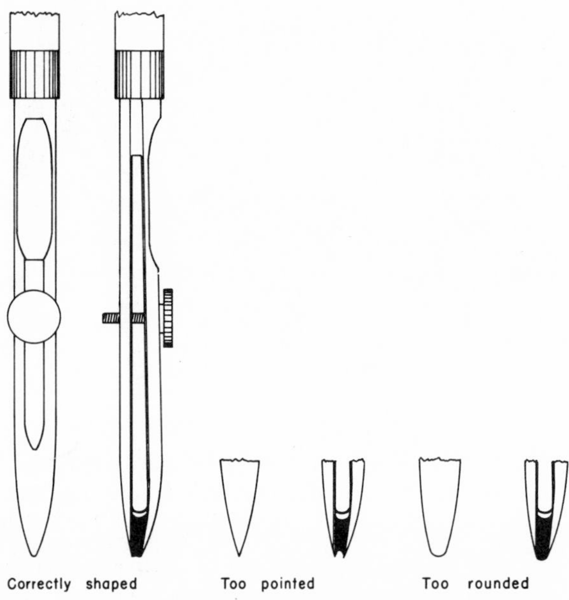

Fig. 4-61. Ruling Pen Nibs

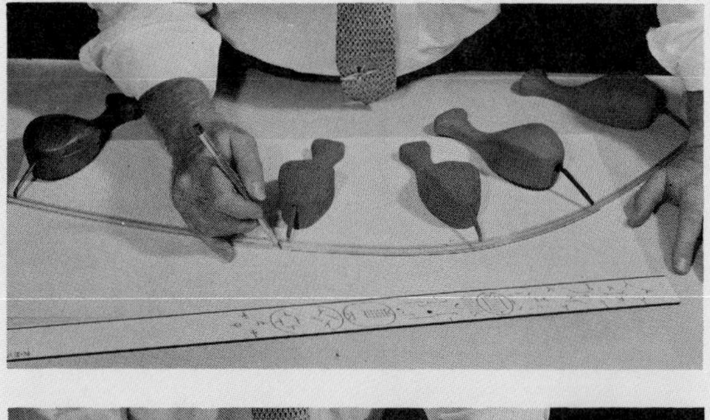

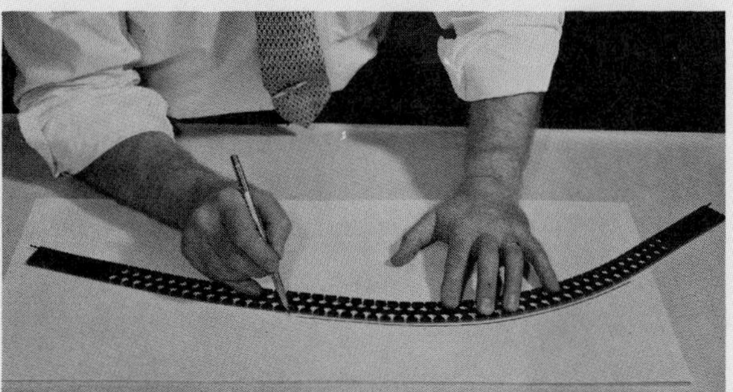

Fig. 4-62. Adjustable Curves Formed to Contour (Keuffel & Esser Co.)

Use this same procedure to sharpen the pen inserts for the compasses.

Technical Fountain Pens

Information on the use and care of technical fountain pens may be found in Chapter 9, page xxx. See Fig. 7-4.

Irregular Curves

Irregular curves are used to draw curves that are neither circles nor circle arcs. They are made of transparent plastic about .060″ thick.

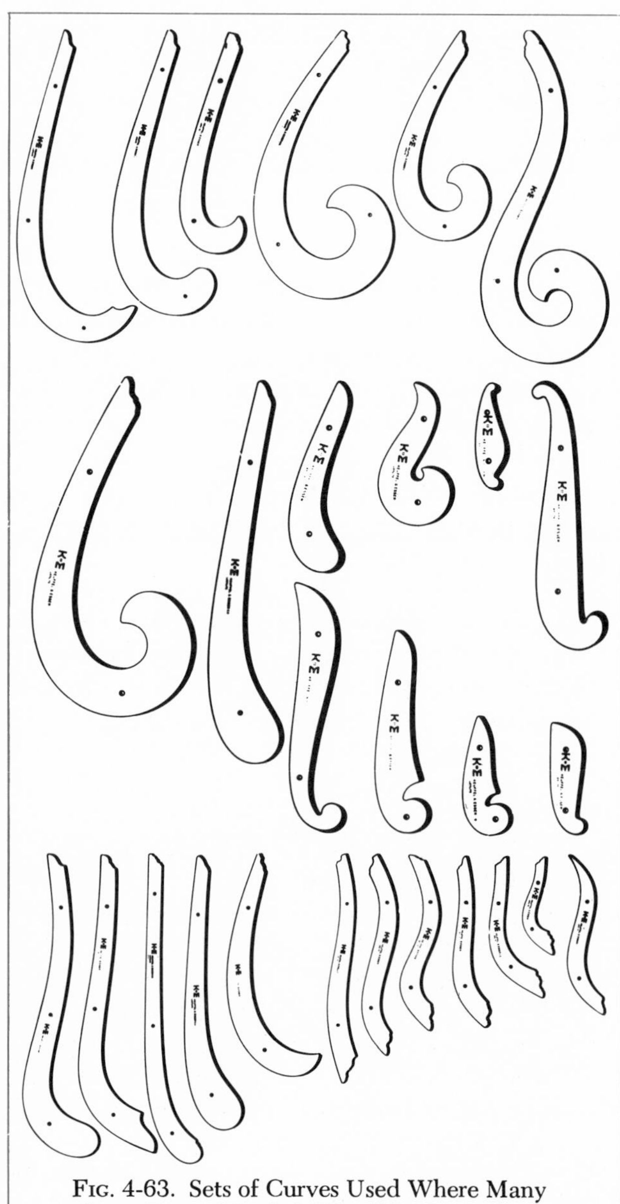

Fig. 4-63. Sets of Curves Used Where Many Curve Forms Needed (Keuffel & Esser Co.)

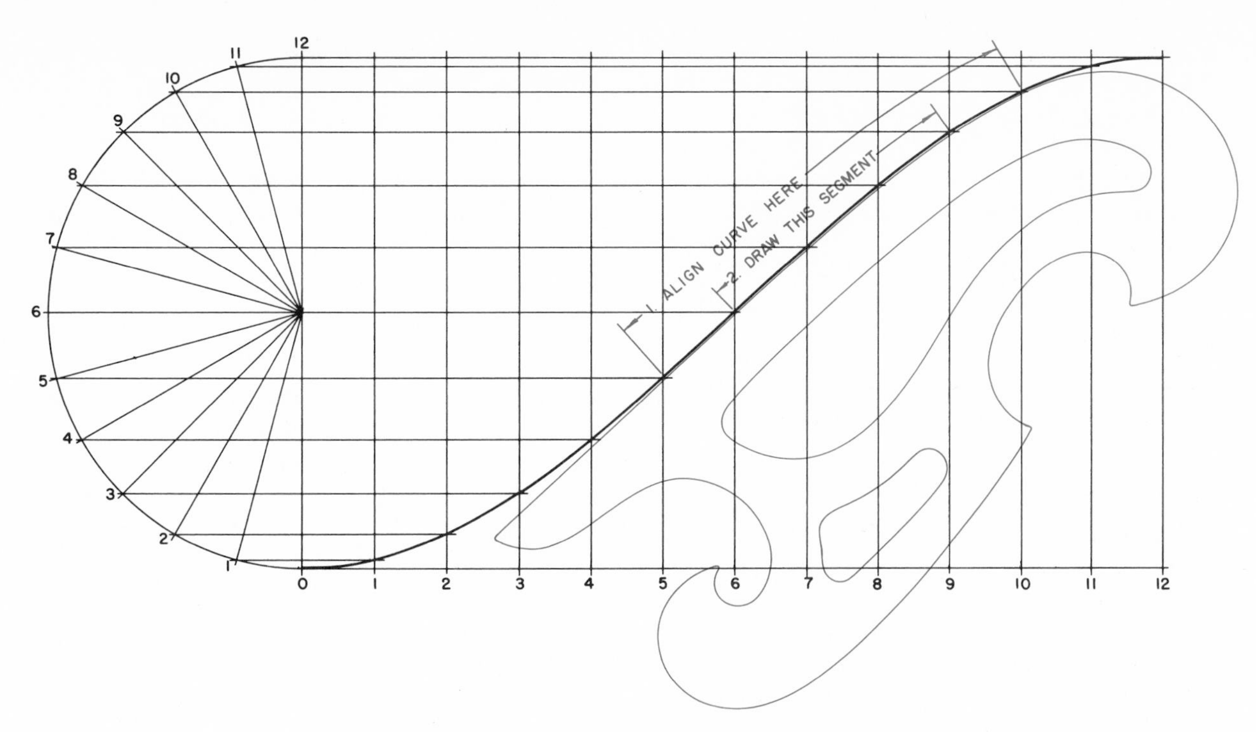

FIG. 4-64. Align Curve Through a Minimum of Five Points

One or two curve forms should meet the requirements of most student draftsmen. See Figs. 4-62 and 4-63.

To use the irregular curve to produce a smooth curve between several points, you must select a segment of the curve that fits the points. For accuracy, align the curve with one more point on each end of the curve than you plan to draw through, Fig. 4-64. Then reset the curve for another segment, using the same procedure. Repeat this until the desired curve is completed.

Templates

As a time-saver for the draftsman, many special templates are available. Templates of circles, squares, hexagons, ellipses, mathematical symbols, chemistry symbols, architectural symbols, electrical and electronic symbols, welding symbols, nut and bolt templates, pipe fitting, and others may be seen in suppliers' catalogs, Fig. 4-65.

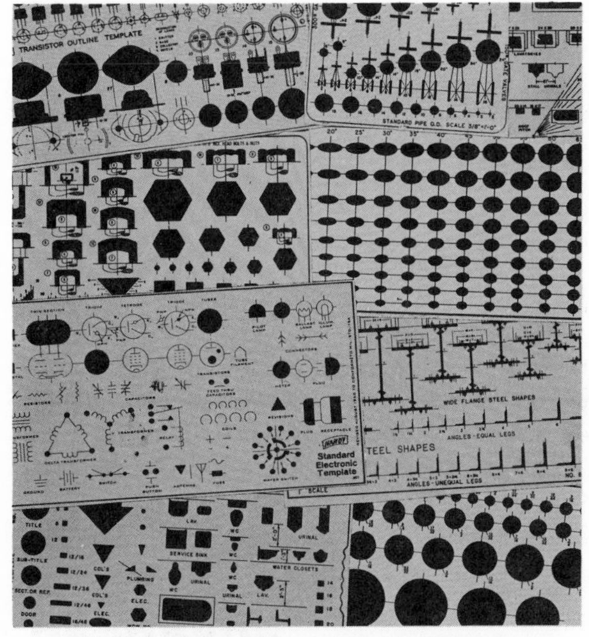

FIG. 4-65. Selected Common Templates (Alvin Co.)

In using templates, be sure you have accurately aligned the symbol with the position it is to occupy on a drawing. In inking, check that the template is off the drawing far enough that ink will not run under it. This can be accomplished by putting tape under the template or by using the template over a triangle or another template.

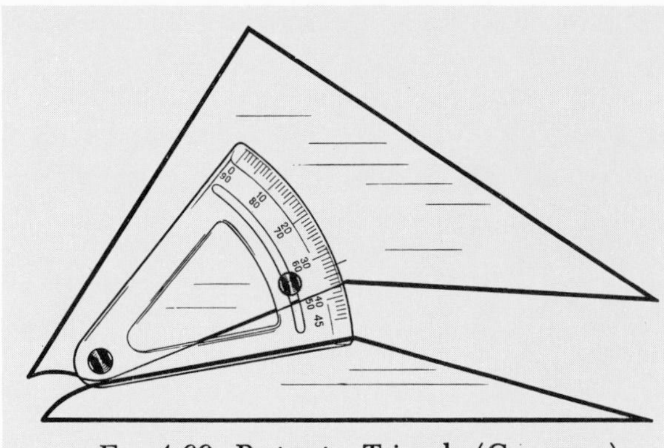

FIG. 4-66. Protractor Triangle (Gramercy)

Circle Templates

The traditional set of drafting instruments can be used to draw circles of any diameter falling within the range of the instrument. Instruments must be set carefully to the size circle or circle arc needed, and (with compasses) the lead must be the same weight as that in your pencils.

The circle template was developed to save time in drawing certain standard-size circles. In addition, uniform line weight is insured because the same pencil or pen can be used as those used for drawing the straight lines. The standard template has circles of various diameters ranging from 1/16" to 1⅜". Special templates have even larger circles. Templates with decimal circle diameters and those with metric circle diameters are available.

Drawing circles with a template is easy, but a few pointers should be observed.

Templates usually have a note printed on them if an allowance for width of pencil leads has been made. To make certain, choose one of the circles and measure its diameter. If a pencil allowance exists, the measured diameter will be very nearly 1/16" over the size of the printed diameter.

1. Locate the center lines of the circle or arc to be drawn.
2. Align the center lines of the circle from the template with those on the drawing. (This step must be done *very* carefully every time but especially where concentric circles or arcs are to be drawn.)
3. Right-handed draftsmen draw the circle clockwise with the pencil or pen held at right angles to the paper.

When concentric circles or arcs are made, the smaller ones should be drawn first.

Fillets and rounds are one-quarter of a circle arc. In drawing these arcs, you can draw a construction-weight, right-angle corner intersection to help properly align the template.

Runouts are one-eighth of a circle arc. Their location is not quite so critical, since they are more symbolic than precise.

Protractors

Angles are measured in degrees (°), minutes (′), and seconds (″). Most protractors can be used to measure fairly accurately to the nearest degree. Some protractors have a sufficiently large radius to be subdivided into half or quarter degrees. The protractor of the drafting machine can be read to the nearest 1, 5, or 10 minutes, depending on the divisions of its vernier scale.

To use a protractor, you need a base line and a point or origin. To layout an angle of given size, place the center mark of the protractor at the point of origin, align the *0* mark with the base line, and make a short dash mark opposite the desired number of degrees. Connect this mark and point *0* to finish the layout of the angle. Fig. 4-66 is a triangle with a protractor adjustment.

advanced geometrical constructions

This section contains selected geometrical constructions of the conic sections (except the circle), spirals, and cycloids. For those who may want to review basic geometrical constructions, refer to the Technical Data section, TD 4-1 through TD 4-23, at the end of this book. Some reference is made to the equations for these geometrical forms. Although the derivation of these equations is left to books on analytical geometry, students who read through the material, study illustrations, and work intelligently on the problems should gain an understanding of these curve forms and their construction.

Ellipse

An ellipse is formed by a point moving in a plane so that the sum of its distances from two fixed points is a constant.

Set your compasses on the *focal radius,* F_1P_1 in Fig. 4-67. Lay out this distance along a straight line on a scrap of paper. Then adjacent to and extending beyond it, add the focal radius P_1F_2. Starting from the same origin on your scrap paper, lay out focal radius F_1P_2. Adjacent to it and extending beyond it, layout P_2F_2. These total distances will be equal, as should any like distances from the foci to a given point on the ellipse.

A standard form of the equation for the ellipse is $\frac{x^2}{a^2} + \frac{y^2}{b^2} = 1$. Figure 4-68 shows the basic terminology of the ellipse where A_1 and A_2 are the vertices of the ellipse and the distance between them, A_1A_2, is the major axis; B_1B_2 is the minor axis; a is one-half the major axis and also equals one-half the sum of the focal radii; b is one-half the minor axis. The line through either focus, perpendicular to the x axis and terminating at opposite points on the perimeter of an ellipse is the *latus rectum.* Its length is $\frac{2b^2}{a}$.

Ellipses may be quite round or very flat and narrow. *Eccentricity* (e) is the measure of this characteristic and is always less than 1. Eccentricity is a ratio of the distance between the foci to the length of the major axis: $e = c/a$ where c is the distance from a focus to the intersection of the major and minor axes of the ellipse. Substitute some numbers in the above equation to determine whether a value for eccentricity which approaches 1 is a very round ellipse or a very flat ellipse. As an ellipse approaches roundness, do the foci approach the vertices of the ellipse or the intersection of the major and minor axes of the ellipse?

Applications

Applications of the ellipse occur in many places. The earth's orbit around the sun is approximately elliptical with the sun at one focus. Orbits of all the planets likewise are elliptical with the sun at one focus.

Orbits of our man-made satellites about the earth are elliptical. With known eccentricity of these orbits and a specified path angle, burnout conditions can be specified.

The ellipse has both optical and acoustical properties. The "Whispering Gallery" in the Capitol in Washington, D. C. is base on an

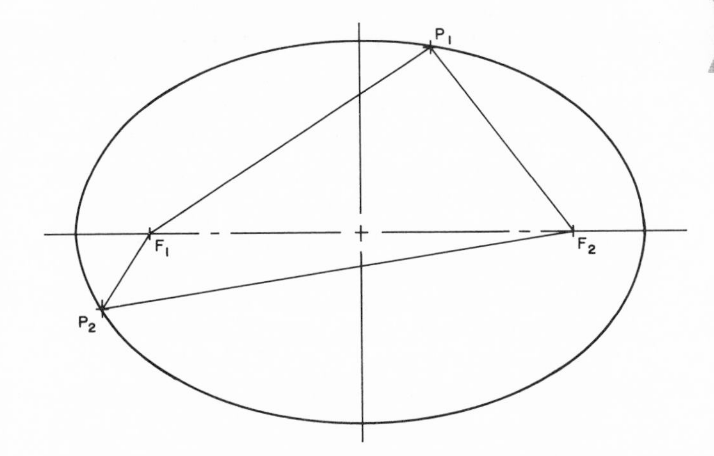

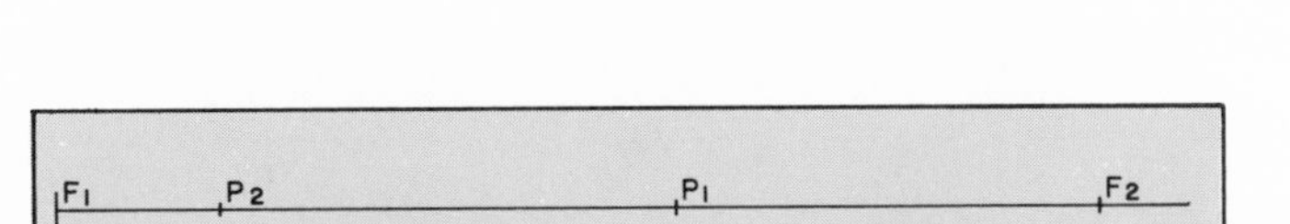

FIG. 4-67. The Sum of the Two Focal Radii from a Point on the Ellipse Equals the Major Diameter of the Ellipse

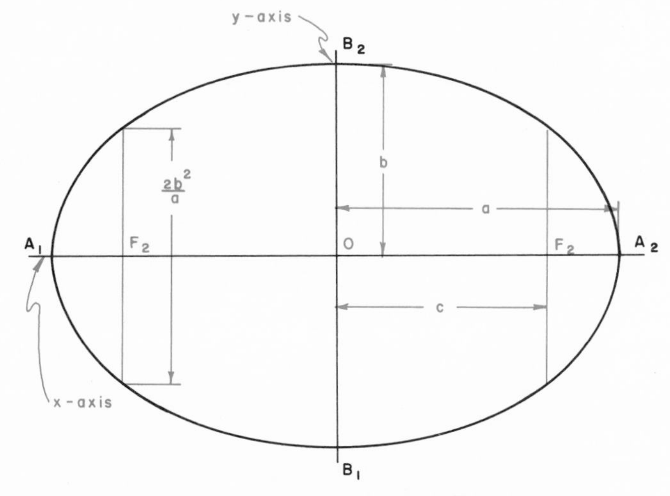

FIG. 4-68. Terminology of the Ellipse

ellipsoidal ceiling structure and the use of the two focal points as the sending and receiving points for those who whisper, Fig. 4-69.

The ellipse is used in the construction of arches, and although it is not the strongest type of arch, it is pleasing to the eye.

The cross section of spokes on hand wheels may be elliptical, with the length of the major and minor axes given. See Fig. 4-70.

An ellipse is formed by the orthographic projection of a circle inclined to the plane of projection, as has been seen in Chapter 3, Fig. 2-45.

An ellipse is formed by the intersection of a plane and a cone when the plane is oblique to the axis of the cone and its angle is greater than those of the elements.

This is one of the examples of a *conic section.* Conic sections are produced by planes intersecting a right circular cone, Figs. 4-71 through 4-74.

The ellipse is used for both gears and cams where slow, powerful motion is to be transmitted.

Constructions

The easiest way to draw an ellipse is to use an ellipse template. These are available in a wide range of sizes through most of the drafting supply firms.

TRAMMEL METHOD. Draw an ellipse using the trammel method, Fig. 4-75.

1. Layout the given major and minor axes A_1 A_2 *and* B_1 B_2 bisecting each other at O.
2. On a scrap piece of paper (preferably tracing paper, in order to see the image from either side), construct a trammel by laying out from an end point P distance a equal to one-half the major axis. From this same end point, layout distance b equal to one-half the minor axis.
3. Place the trammel so that the end points P_1 and P_2 lie on the respective axes; P will then be a point on the ellipse. Mark this position.
4. Find a sufficient number of random points to draw a smooth curve and to complete the ellipse.

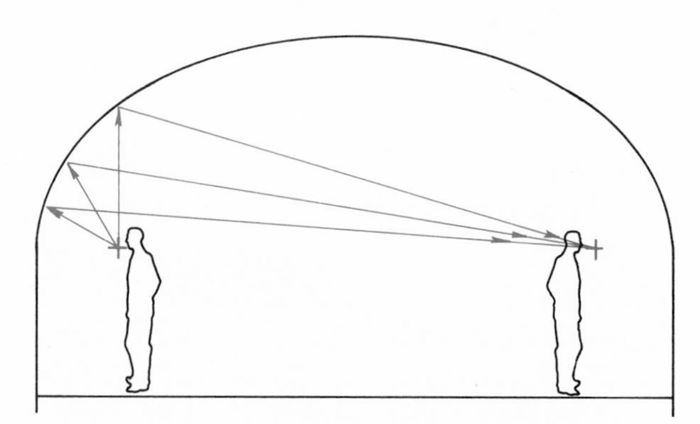

Fig. 4-69. Reflective Property of the Ellipse Illustrated through "Whispering Galleries"

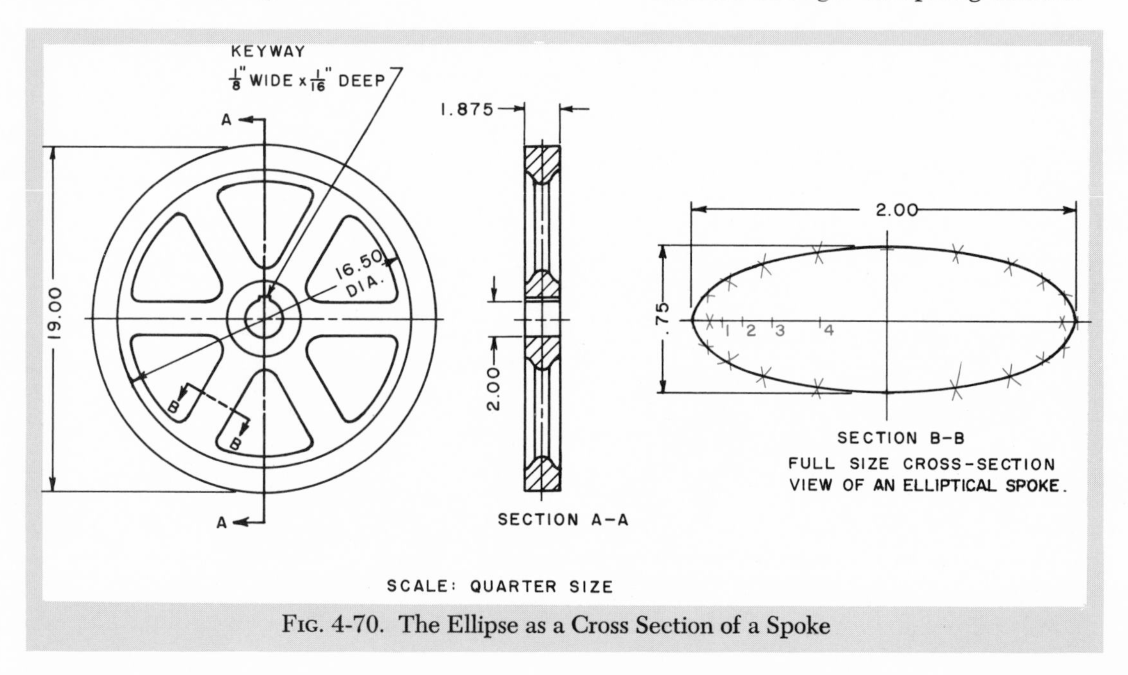

Fig. 4-70. The Ellipse as a Cross Section of a Spoke

APPROXIMATE FOUR-CENTER METHOD. Draw an ellipse using the approximate, four-center method, Fig. 4-76. This construction is used for ellipses which are representations of circles in isometric planes.

1. Layout the given major and minor axes A_1A_2 and B_1B_2 so that they bisect each other at O.
2. Draw lines connecting A_1B_1, B_1A_2, A_2B_2, and B_2A_1. These lines represent the diameter of the circle.
3. Find the mid-points of these lines by measurement or construction.
4. Connect these mid-points to the opposite vertices at B_1 and B_2.

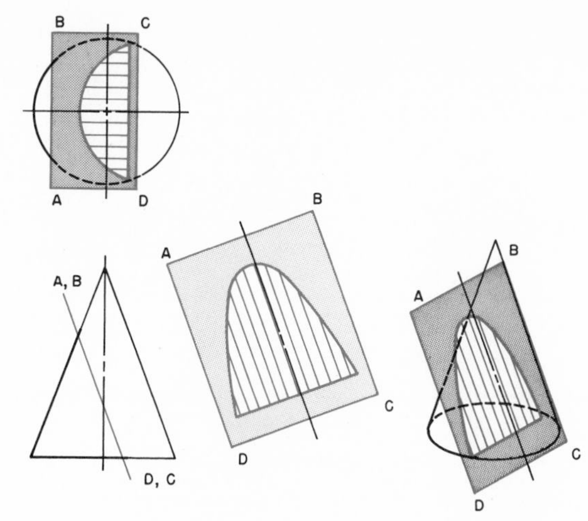

FIG. 4-73. The Parabola as a Conic Section

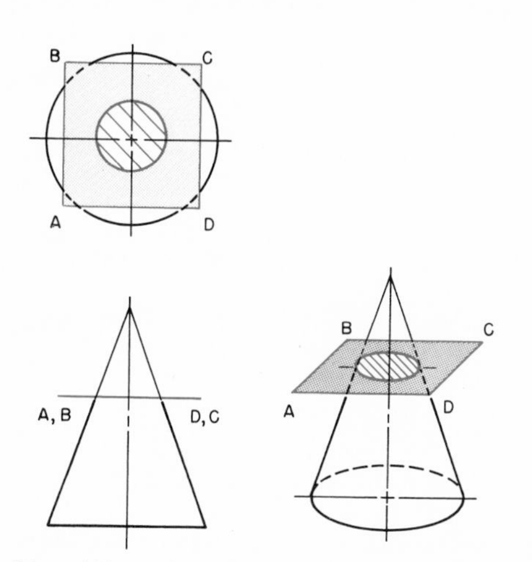

FIG. 4-71. The Circle as a Conic Section

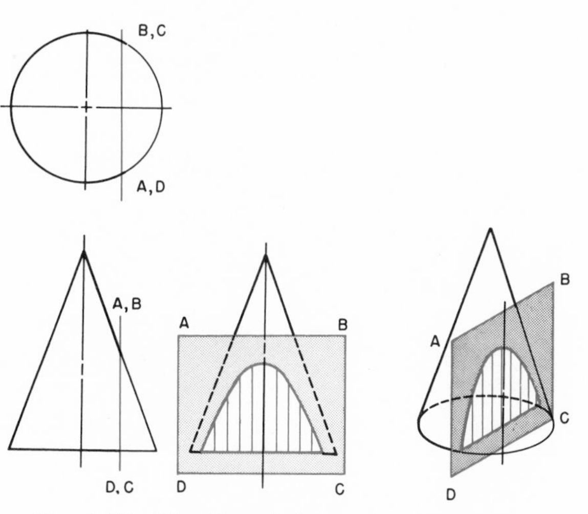

FIG. 4-74. The Hyperbola as a Conic Section

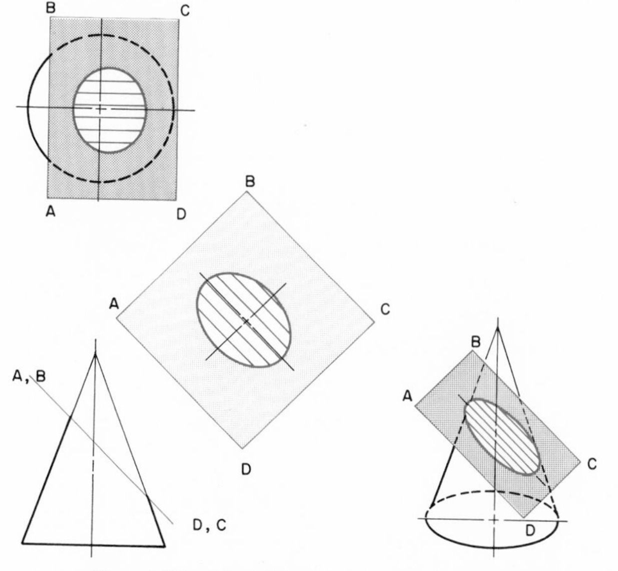

FIG. 4-72. The Ellipse as a Conic Section

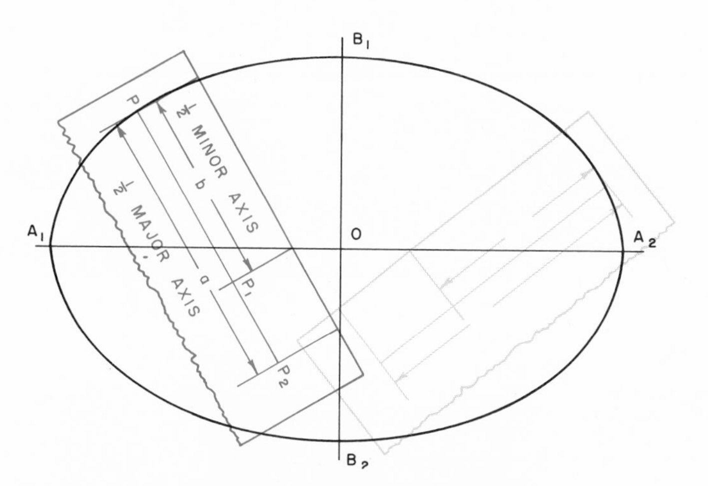

FIG. 4-75. Trammel Method of Constructing Ellipse

5. With B_1 as the center, draw an arc from point *4* to *3*. With B_2 as the center, draw an arc from point *1* to *2*.
6. With point P_1 as the center, draw an arc from *4* to *1*. With P_2 as the center, draw an arc from *2* to *3* to complete the ellipse.

FOCI METHOD. Draw an ellipse using the foci method, Fig. 4-77.

1. The major and minor axes are given so that A_1A_2 is a perpendicular bisector of B_1B_2 and conversely.
2. With OA_1 as the radius and B_1 as the origin, strike arcs on opposite ends of A_1A_2.
3. Repeat with B_2 as the origin. This locates the foci F_1 and F_2.
4. Space points along the major axis at random from F_1 to O. Points at the left of the line should be closer together than those at the right. The larger the ellipse, the more points you should use.
5. Select any one of the points just spaced, such as *1*. With F_1 as the origin and radius *A-1*, draw a circle arc at *1′*. (Note that this is in 4 places.)
6. Use F_2 as the origin and *A-1* as the radius. Draw four circle arcs intersecting at the four positions of *1′*.
7. Repeat for each of the spaced points along A_1A_2.
8. Connect each of the prime points (such as *1′*, *2′*, *3′* and the like) with an irregular curve to complete the ellipse.

CONCENTRIC CIRCLE METHOD. Draw an ellipse using the concentric circle method, Fig. 4-78.

1. Lay out the given major and minor axes A_1A_2 and B_1B_2.
2. With O as the center, draw two concentric circles — one with radius equal to one-half the major axis; the other with radius equal to one-half the minor axis.
3. In any two opposite quadrants, draw any number of diagonals through O with each diagonal intersecting both circles in two places such as at points *1*, *2*, *3*, and *4*. The

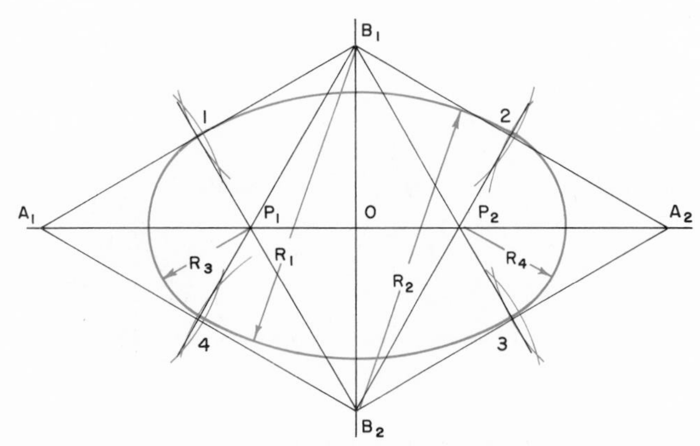

FIG. 4-76. Approximate Four-Center Method of Constructing Ellipse

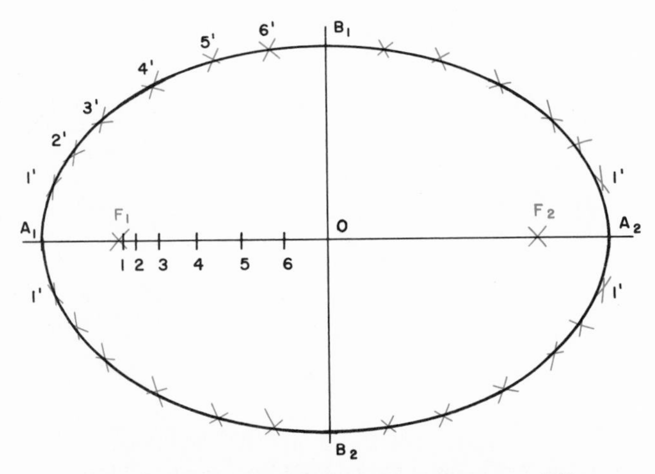

FIG. 4-77. Foci Method of Constructing an Ellipse

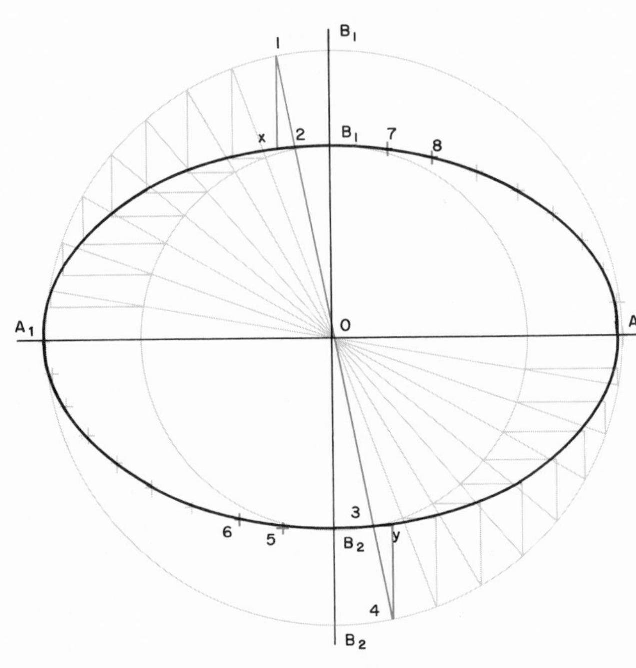

FIG. 4-78. Concentric-Circle Method of Constructing Ellipse

larger the number of diagonals, the more accurate will be the ellipse.

4. From the intersection of each diagonal with the outer circle (such as at points *1* and *4*) draw a line perpendicular toward the major axis, such as lines *1-x* and *4-y*.
5. From the intersection of each diagonal with the inner circle such as at points 2 and 3, draw a line perpendicular to the minor axis and intersecting the lines drawn in the previous step as at *x* and *y*.
6. By projection from lines already drawn, establish points in the other two quadrants such as points *5, 6, 7, 8* and other points not numbered in the illustration.
7. Draw a smooth curve through the points to complete the ellipse.

Parabola

A curve form with each point of the curve equidistant from a fixed point (focus) and a fixed line (directrix) is a parabola, Fig. 4-79. This definition is restated in terms of the path of motion of a point: A parabola is a curve form generated by a point moving in a plane so that everywhere on its path of motion it is at the same time equidistant from the focus and the directrix.

The standard form of the equation of the parabola is $y^2 = 2\ kx$ where y is the distance along the y-axis, x is the distance along the x-axis, and $2k$ is a constant modifier. Accordingly, by selecting an arbitrary value for k and choosing several convenient values for x, y can be calculated and the parabola fitting this equation can be plotted by sketch or mechanical drawing, Fig. 4-80. To complete both halves of the parabola, one set of values for y must be assigned negative numbers. Notice that the equation for the directrix is the line $x = \frac{-k}{2}$ and that the location of the focus is conveniently $(\frac{k}{2}, O)$.

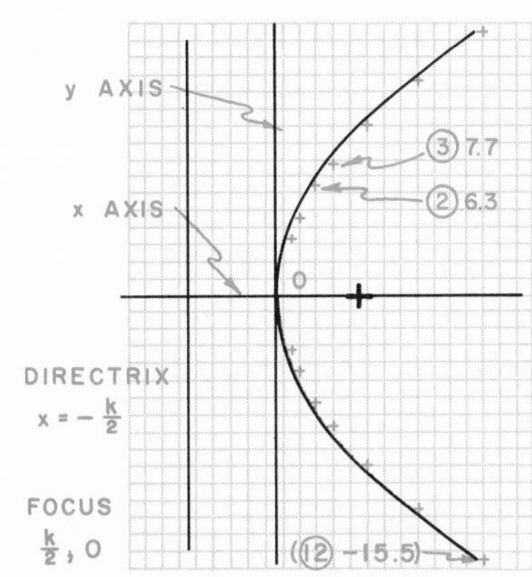

Fig. 4-80. Parabola Plotted from an Equation

Standard Form of Equation
for Parabolas: $y^2 = 2\ kx$
Equation for this Curve: $y^2 = 20\ x$

Table of Values

x	$\sqrt{y}$	y	*Neg. y*
.5	$\sqrt{10}$	3.2	− 3.2
1	$\sqrt{20}$	4.5	− 4.5
2	$\sqrt{40}$	6.3	− 6.3
3	$\sqrt{60}$	7.7	− 7.7
5	$\sqrt{100}$	10.0	−10.0
8	$\sqrt{160}$	12.6	−12.6
12	$\sqrt{240}$	15.5	−15.5

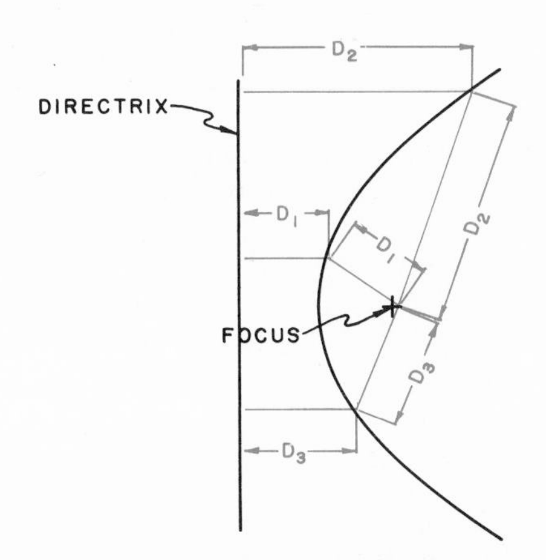

Fig. 4-79. Equal Distances from Fixed Point on a Parabola to the Directrix and to the Focal Point

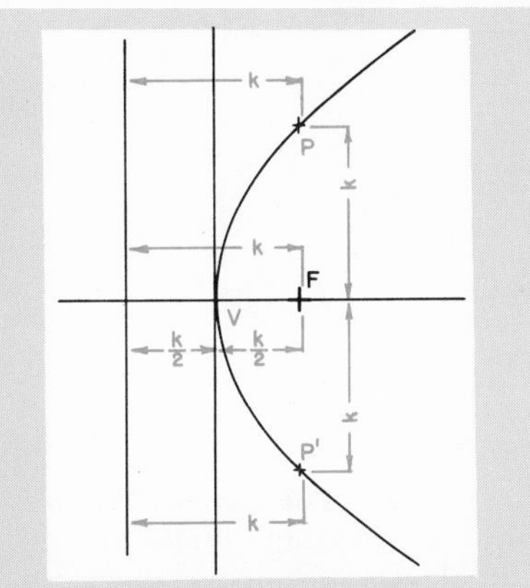

Fig. 4-81. Relationships of the Constant k for a Parabola

In Fig. 4-81, notice that k is the perpendicular distance from the directrix to the focus. The vertex V of the parabola is a point half way from F, the focus along the line k such that $FV = \frac{k}{2}$ and the distance from V to the directrix equals $\frac{k}{2}$. This, of course, is in harmony with our definition that each point on a parabola, in this case V, is equidistant from the focus and the directrix.

Also notice that the two points P and P' are located a distance k directly above and below F, and that both P and P' are also k distance from the directrix. Armed with this information, it is easy to sketch approximate parabolas knowing the location of the directrix, the focus, and the value of the constant k.

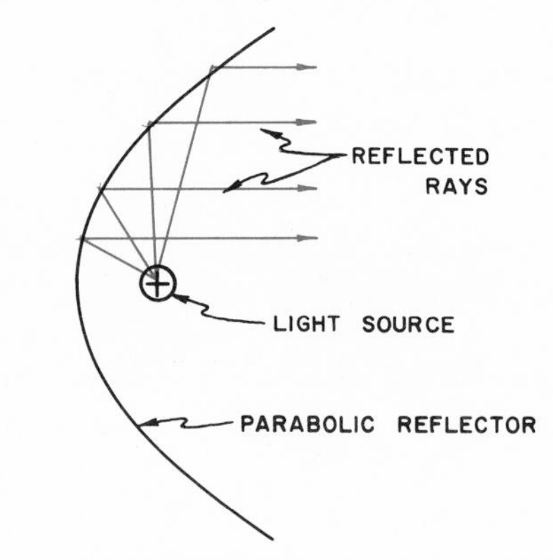

FIG. 4-82. Reflective Property of the Parabola

Applications

The parabola has many practical applications; one most often mentioned is its use in reflectors, Fig. 4-82. Rays of light or sound coming in parallel to its axis of symmetry will be reflected in such a way that they will pass through the focal point. Conversely, if a light bulb or sound mechanism is located at the focus point in a parabolic reflector, the light rays or sound waves will be reflected out parallel to this same axis of symmetry, Fig. 4-83.

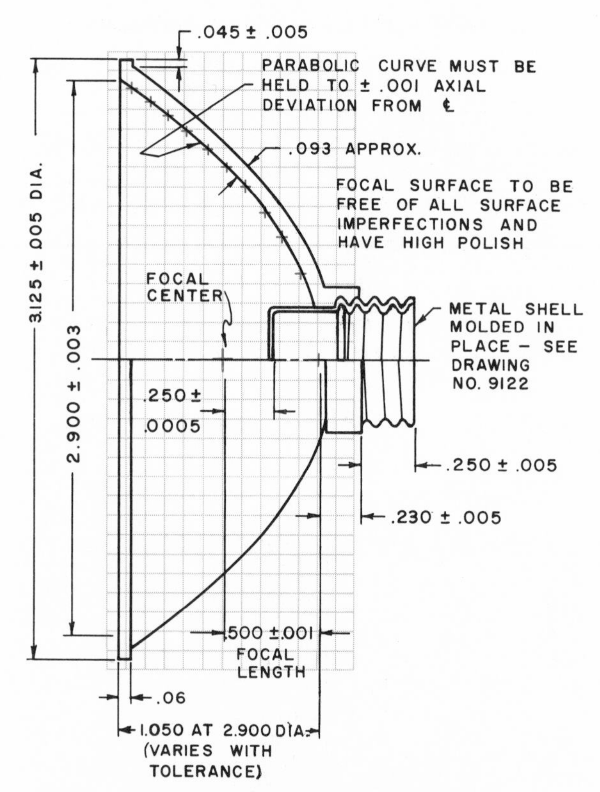

FIG. 4-83. Polystyrene, Prefocused Flashlight Reflector
Color shows layout information and does not show on original industrial drawing. Can you determine the equation for the parabola from the information given?

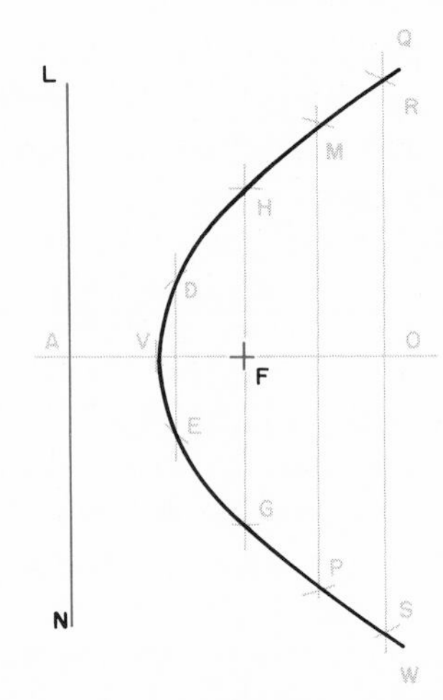

FIG. 4-84. Constructing Parabola with Focus and Directrix Given

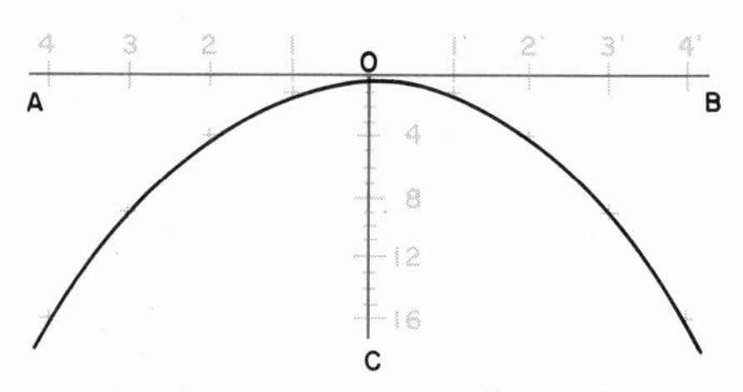

FIG. 4-85. Constructing Parabola with Rise and Span Given

Other applications include parabolic reflecting mirrors used in telescopes and parabolic curves or envelopes used in highways and railroads. To provide for smooth transition between various elevations in the vertical plane, parabolic support arches are used for bridges and other structures. Calculations in ballistics make use of parabolic curves, *e.g.*, a bomb dropped from an airplane falls in an approximate parabolic path. Students of mathematics study the parabolic curve in analytic geometry. In physics, if one body is attracted to another by an inverse square force, one of the possible paths of motion is parabolic with the second body at the focus. Some cam profiles in machine design use parabolic curves.

Constructions

The constructions shown in Figs. 4-84, 85, and 86 are typical drafting problem solutions.

FOCUS AND DIRECTRIX GIVEN, Fig. 4-84.

1. Layout the focus *F* and directrix *LN*.
2. Through *F*, draw a line perpendicular to *LN* and intersecting it at *A*.
3. At a convenient point *O*, on *AF* extended, draw a line *QW* to *AF* and parallel to *LN*.
4. Use *AO* as a radius and *F* as the origin to draw arcs intersecting *QW* at *R* and *S*.
5. Draw any convenient number of equally spaced lines on *AO* parallel to *QW*.
6. On each of these, locate points as you did *R* and *S* using a radius equal to the distance from the line to *A*.
7. Draw the parabolic curve through the points located with an irregular curve. (Note that the vertex is located half way between *F* and *A*.)

RISE AND SPAN GIVEN, Fig. 4-85.

1. Layout the rise and span at right angles to each other.
2. Divide one-half of the span *AO* into any convenient number of equal spaces.
3. Square the number of spaces used in the previous step, and divide the rise into that many equal spaces.
4. Plot the points of intersection of the numbers along the *half* span and their squares along the rise.
5. Construct similar points using the other half span.
6. Draw the parabola through these points.

THROUGH ANY TWO GIVEN POINTS, Fig. 4-86.

1. Layout the two given points *U* and *V*.
2. Locate any point *Z* and draw *UZ* and *ZV*.
3. Divide *UZ* and *ZV* into any number of equal parts, and number these divisions as shown.
4. Draw lines connecting like-numbered divisions.
5. Draw the parabolic curve tangent to these intersecting lines.

Hyperbola

A hyperbola is a curve form with its points so located that the difference between the distance of a given point to each of two fixed points called *foci* is constant, Fig. 4-87. Stated in terms of a path of motion of a point: A hyperbola is a curve form generated by a point moving in a plane so that the difference of its distance from each of two fixed points (*foci*) is constant.

The standard form of the equation for an hyperbola is $\frac{x^2}{a^2} - \frac{y^2}{b^2} = 1$ when the foci are placed on one of the coordinate axes and the center is at the origin. In the equation,

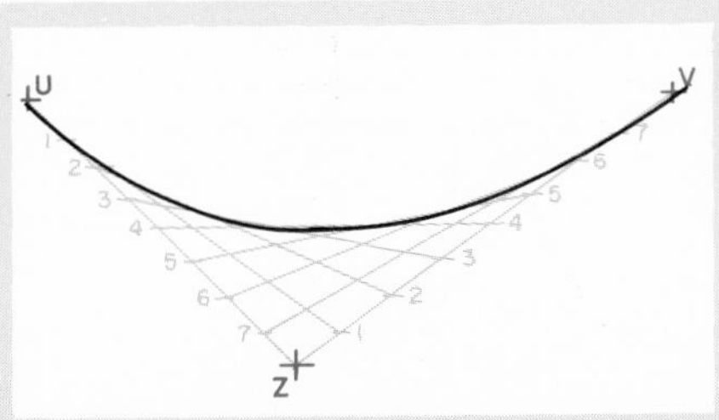

FIG. 4-86. Constructing Parabola Through any Two Points

Standard Form of Equation for Hyperbola:

$$\frac{x^2}{a^2} - \frac{y^2}{b^2} = 1$$

Given: $a = 2 \quad b = 3$

$$y = \sqrt{2.25\,x^2 - 9}$$

$$\text{Foci} = c = \sqrt{a^2 + b^2}$$

x	y
2	0
3	3.4
4	5.2
5	6.9

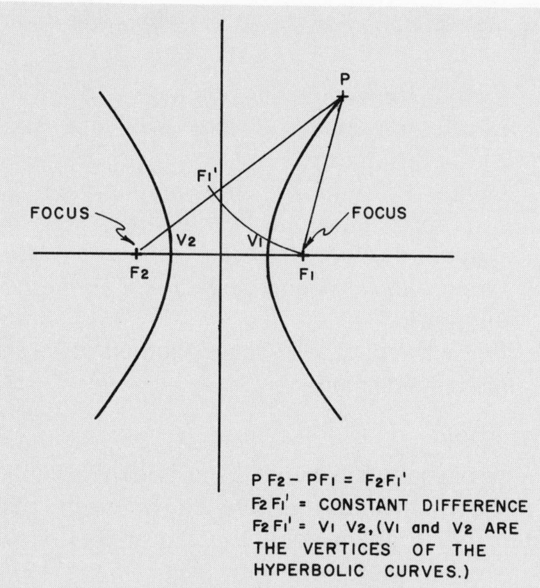

FIG. 4-87. Constant Difference Exists from All Points *P* on Hyperbola to Foci
Choose any second point *P* on the hyperbola, and use your dividers to check this statement.

a represents one-half of the transverse axis (semi-transverse axis); b represents the semi-conjugate axis; x and y are the values along the coordinate axes. Figs. 4-88 and 4-89 show the terminology and basic relationships for hyperbolic curves. The use of plus and minus values for both x and y will complete the halves of the hyperbola.

Notice the relationship between c and the distance of each focus from the center.

Notice also that b, the semi-conjugate axis, is not necessarily the same length as the perpendicular distance from the focal points to the hyperbolic curve directly above or below them. This distance directly above and below a focal point extending to the curve is calculated from the formula $\frac{2b^2}{a}$.

Asymptotes are the straight lines which a given hyperbolic curve approaches as the curve recedes from the center. Note that the asymptotes are straight lines originating at the center of a rectangle whose sides are $2a$ and $2b$ and a segment of which is $2c$ in the key triangle.

Applications

Hyperbolic curves find wide use in the graphical representation of equations. A frequently used type is the equilateral hyperbola with its asymptotes as axes. For all equilateral hyperbolas, $a = b$ and the equation $\frac{x^2}{a^2} - \frac{y^2}{b^2}$

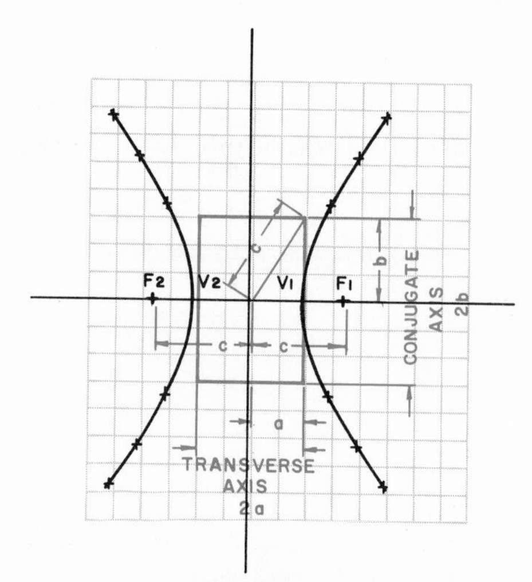

FIG. 4-88. Hyperbolic Curve Terminology

x	y	k
1	5	5
2	2.5	5
3	1.66	5
4	1.25	5
5	1	5

x	y	k
1	1	1
2	.5	1
3	.33	1
4	.25	1
5	.20	1

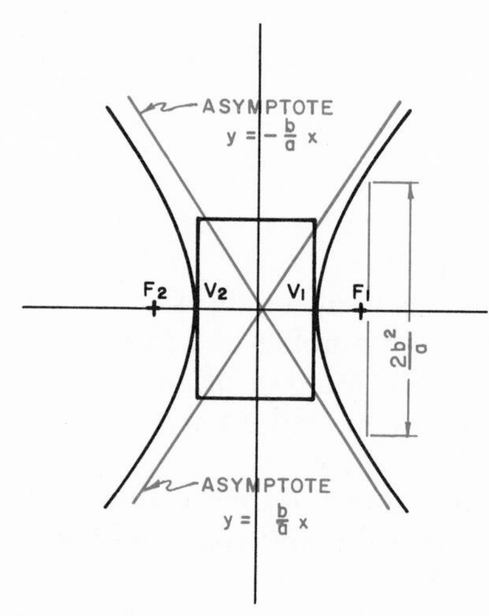

FIG. 4-89. Asymptotes — Straight Lines which the Curves Approach
The equation of these lines is their slope.

= 1 can be re-written $xy = k$ where the product of two variables, x and y, equals a constant k. When k is positive, the branches of the hyperbola will be located in the first or third quadrants. When both x and y are positive, and this is a usual practical condition, the useful branch is in the first quadrant. Note in Fig. 4-90 that the asymptotes are the axes an that $a = b$. Boyles law illustrates an application of the equilateral hyperbola. It states that if the temperature and mass of a gas remain unchanged, the product of pressure and volume is constant, $PV = K$. A pressure-volume graph is shown in Fig. 4-91.

Applications of the hyperbola may be found in sound ranging and radar navigation. Assume that you are the navigator of an aircraft and are attempting to discover your location. Radio signals tell you that you are 200 miles closer to station *A* than to station *B*, and that you are 100 miles closer to station *C* than *B*. The location of stations *A*, *B* and *C* are fixed and known. From *A* to *B* is 400 miles and from *B* to *C* is 500 miles, Fig. 4-92. Establish first that you are on hyperbolic curve line *RS*. Then establish that you are also on hyperbolic curve line *MN*. The only place where you could be on both curves at once is at point *O*, their intersection. This locates your position.

No doubt you observe that stations *A* and *B* are foci for the hyperbolic curve *RS*, as are stations *B* and *C* for hyperbolic curve *MN*. This is a typical problem of hyperbolic navigation as used, for example, in the Loran (*LOng RAnge Navigation*), Decca, and Gee systems of navigation.

Hyperbolas have application to space travel. A relatively fast-moving body, such as a comet, coming under the influence of gravitational pull of the earth, will travel in a hyperbolic path. The launch path of satellites and space vehicles may be either a parabolic or a hyperbolic path in order to escape the pull of the earth's gravitational field.

Constructions

MECHANICAL.

Given: the location of the foci F_1 and F_2 and the length of the transverse axis, Fig. 4-93.

1. Layout the given data, and extend the transverse axis through F_1 any convenient distance to *T*.

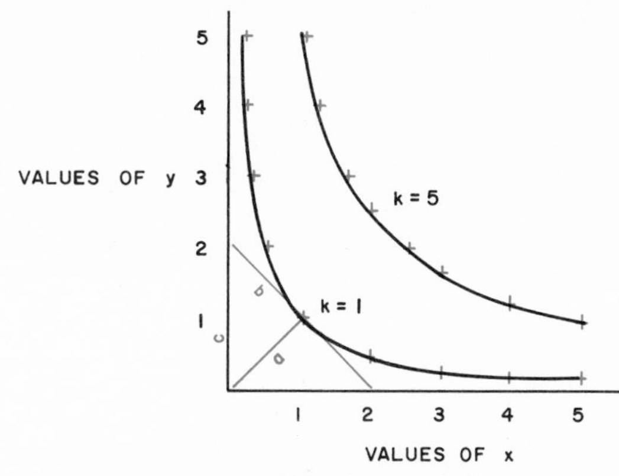

Fig. 4-90. Equilateral Hyperbolic Curves of Form $xy = k$
Curves were derived by plotting products of numbers from 1 to 5 where $k = 1$ and plotting again for $k = 5$.

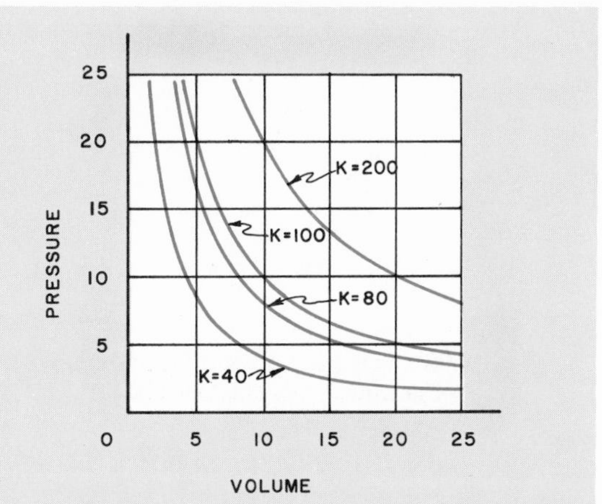

Fig. 4-91. Pressure-Volume Graph – Based on Boyles Law and Using Various Constants

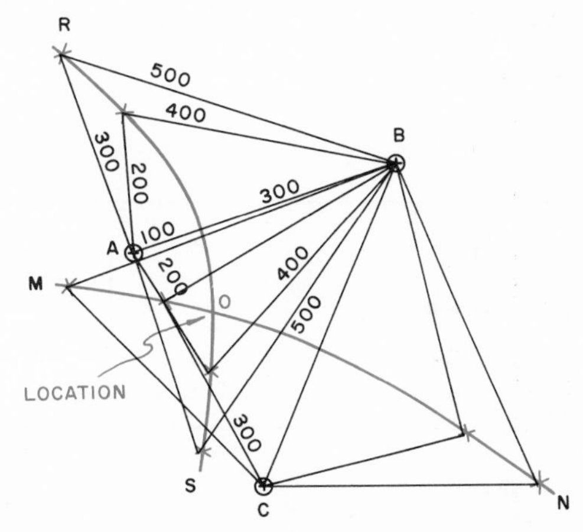

Fig. 4-92. Hyperbolic Navigation to Determine Position from Known Stations

2. With F_1 as a center and V_1T as the radius, layout arcs R and S.
3. With F_2 as a center and V_2T as the radius, layout intersecting arcs at R and S.
4. Layout a convenient number of additional points such as T_1, T_2, and T_3 and locate points R_1, R_2, R_3, S_1, S_2, and S_3.
5. Draw the two branches of the hyperbola through these points. The other two branches may be constructed in a like manner.

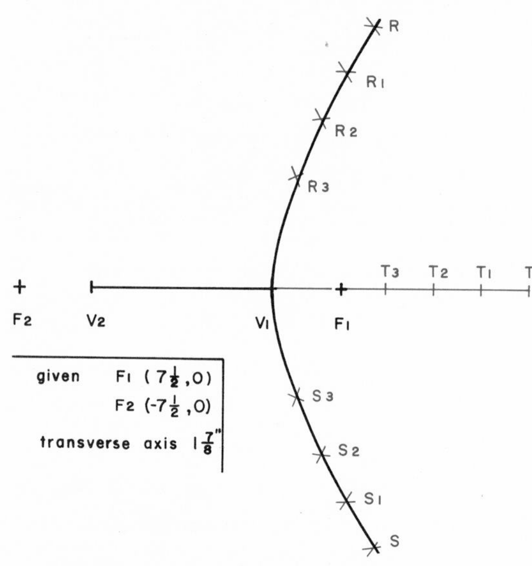

FIG. 4-93. Construction of a Hyperbola with Foci and Traverse Axis Given

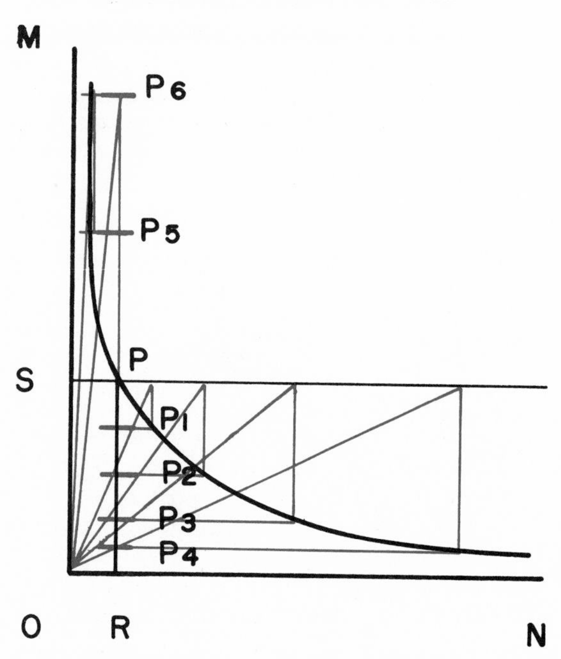

FIG. 4-94. Construction of Equilateral Hyperbola with Asymptotes and a Point on the Hyperbola Given

EQUILATERAL.

Given: the asymptotes OM and ON and point P, (2, 8) of an equilateral hyperbola, Fig. 4-94.

1. Layout asymptotes OM an ON and point P. Draw PR parallel to OM, intersecting ON and extending as far as M. Draw PS parallel to ON, intersecting OM and extending as far as N.
2. Through each of these points, draw a line parallel to SP extended.
3. Draw lines originating at O and extending to SP.
4. From the intersections of these lines on SP, draw perpendiculars to the lines drawn parallel to SP.
5. Draw the equilateral hyperbola through the points of intersection found.

Spirals

Applications

Spirals have practical application to the design of springs such as watch springs and some springs in upholstered furniture. Spiral bevel gears have teeth that approximate a spiral and which are designed to give a continuous contact to secure a steady and quiet drive. Spirals may be used in cam design. For example, a

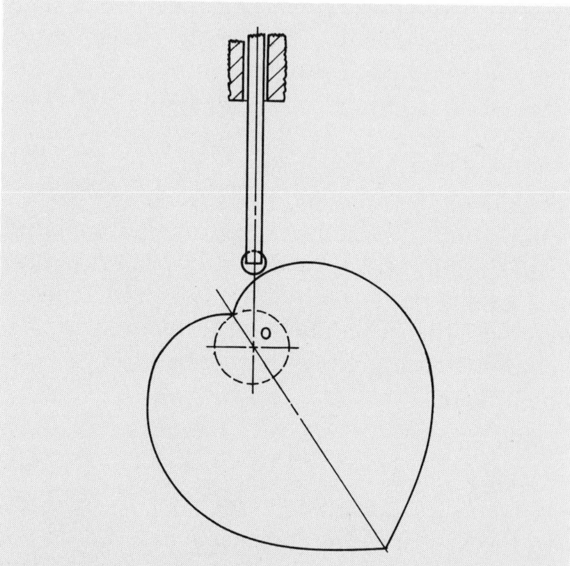

FIG. 4-95. Follower (based on spiral) Moving with Reciprocating Motion at Uniform Velocity as the Cam Rotates through 360°

cam designed on the basis of the spiral of Archimedes may convert uniform angular motion into uniform linear motion, Fig. 4-95.

Constructions

A spiral is a curve form traced by a point moving around a fixed point and continually receding from that point. The *spiral of Archimedes* is one such spiral. It may be defined as the path of a point moving uniformly along a straight line as the line revolves with uniform angular motion about a fixed point. Such a spiral is easily constructed. Fig. 4-96.

1. Layout the fixed point *O* as an origin. Through this point, draw a series of lines at equal angles, such as 15°.
2. Beginning on any one of these lines, lay off a distance such as ⅛″. On each succeeding line proceeding in either a clockwise or counter clockwise direction, lay off successive distances such as two times ⅛″ on line two, three times ⅛″ on line three, etc.
3. Use an irregular curve to draw the spiral beginning at the origin, and passing through each succeeding point.

An *equiangular spiral* may be drawn by starting with the basic layout as for the spiral of Archimedes. From any point on one of these lines, construct a perpendicular to the next. From the intersection of the perpendicular with the succeeding radial line, construct another perpendicular, continuing about the basic layout. Construct a smooth curve through the foot of each perpendicular, so located to draw the equiangular spiral. Try the construction of this spiral by sketching.

Involutes and Evolutes

Involutes and evolutes are related to the root words *involve* and *evolve,* respectively. To involve means to envelop within the folds of some condition or to wind in a spiral form. To evolve means to unfold, to open out, or to expand.

Involutes and evolutes are interrelated in such a way that every example of one includes an example of the other. For instance, the evolute for an involute of a given circle arc is the given circle arc, Fig. 4-97. An involute is described by the path of a point on a string as the string remains tight, but is unwound from any plane figure. Note in Fig. 4-97 how each of the points *C, D, E, F, G, H, I,* and *J* represents positions which the point on a string wrapped along the circle arc *OAB* would occupy as it is being unwound from this evolute.

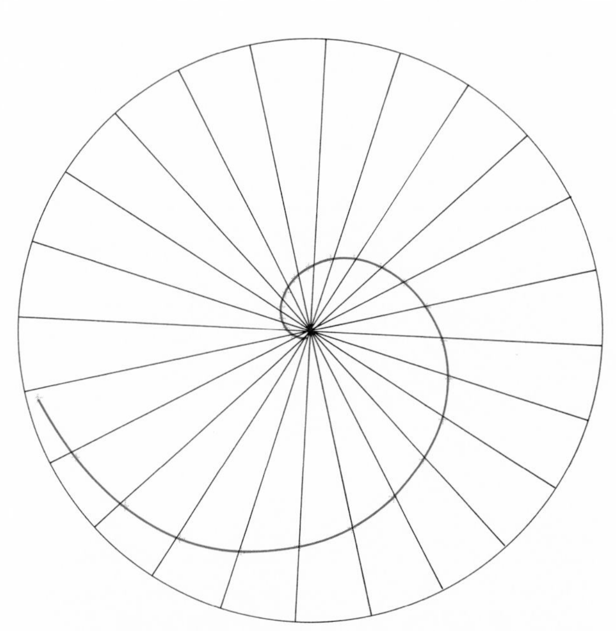

FIG. 4-96. Construction of the Spiral of Archimedes

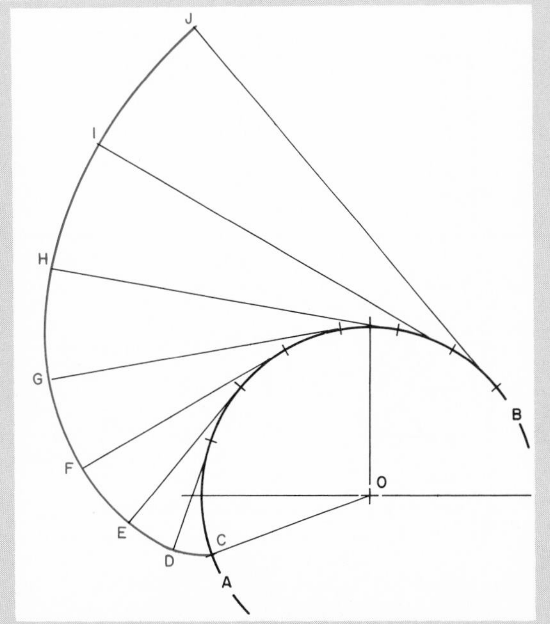

FIG. 4-97. Circle Arc *OAB* is Evolute of Curve *CJ* — Curve *CJ* is Involute of Circle Arc *OAB*

Applications

The involute is the basic curve form used on gear teeth. Involute gear teeth permit gears to mesh without breakage or interference as they turn. Note in Fig. 4-98 that the involutes of the profiles on adjacent gear teeth make use of the principle of *parallel* curve construction described in the succeeding paragraphs. See also Fig. 4-99.

Another industrial application of the involute is found in centrifugal pumps. In Fig. 4-100, the evolute is a square whose diagonals are ⅝″ and which is constructed in the center of the section view. The lightweight colored lines in the figure represent the construction used to obtain the involute and was not a part of the drawing as it was released for production. The heavy colored line is that part of the involute used in the construction of the pattern for the production of the water pump housing.

Constructions

INVOLUTE OF A CIRCLE. Construct the involute of a circle or a circle arc, as shown in Fig. 4-101.

1. Draw a number of tangents, such as *2-A*, to points which have been spaced uniformly about the given curve.
2. With the center of the compasses at the intersection (such as *J*) of two adjacent tangents, draw a circle arc from one of the tangent points (1) on the curve to the adjacent tangent (*A*).
3. Using the intersection of the second and third adjacent tangents (*K*) as the center, draw the second segment (*AB*) of the involute. Continue in this manner to complete the involute.

Observe in Fig. 4-101 that the tangents of the evolute, such as *D5*, are also normals to the involute. (A *normal* to a curve at any given point is a line drawn at right angles to the tangent to the curve at that point.) The length of these tangents is the radius of curvature of the involute when an infinite number of these is used to construct the involute. In actual practice, as in Fig. 4-101, when a finite number of tangents is drawn, the centers of curvature for the involute are not coincident with the evolute. For example, the tangent length of *D5* is *D5*, but the center of curvature of the normal to the larger involute is *DM*. The larger the number of tangents to an evolute, the more accurate will be the construction of its involute.

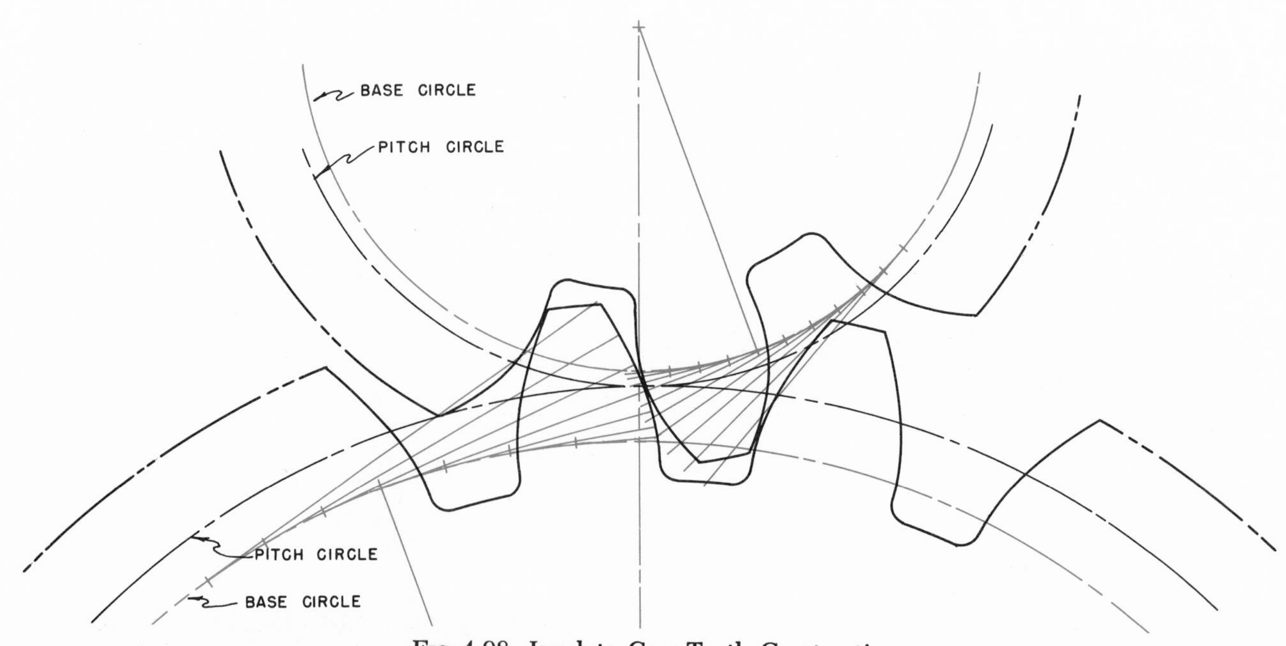

FIG. 4-98. Involute Gear-Tooth Construction

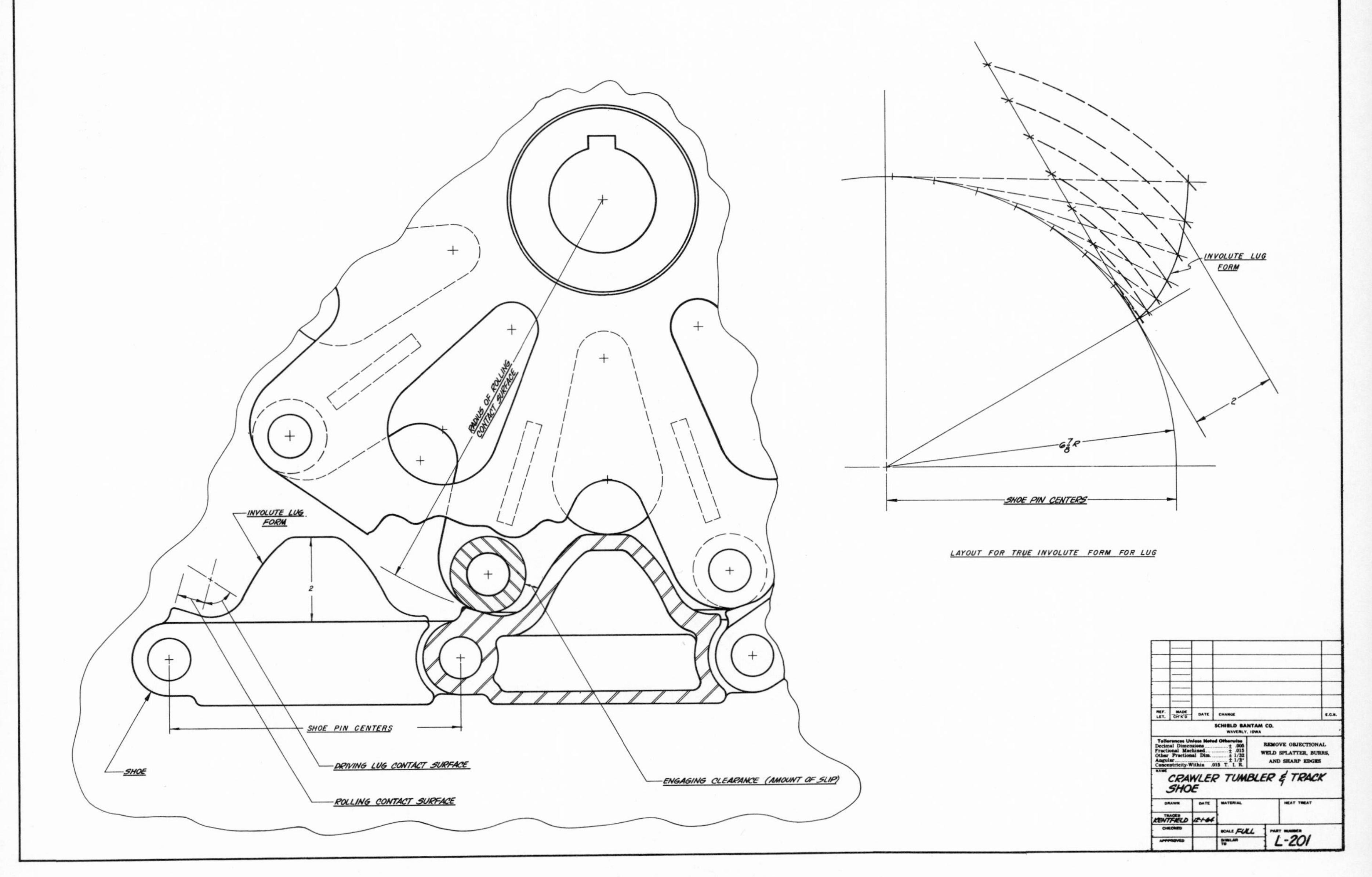

Fig. 4-99. Industrial Application of Involute of a Circle Arc (Schield Bantam Co.)
Note layout in upper right-hand part of illustration for the development of the required involute form for the track shoe lug.

TOOLS, MAT'LS CONSTRUCTIONS

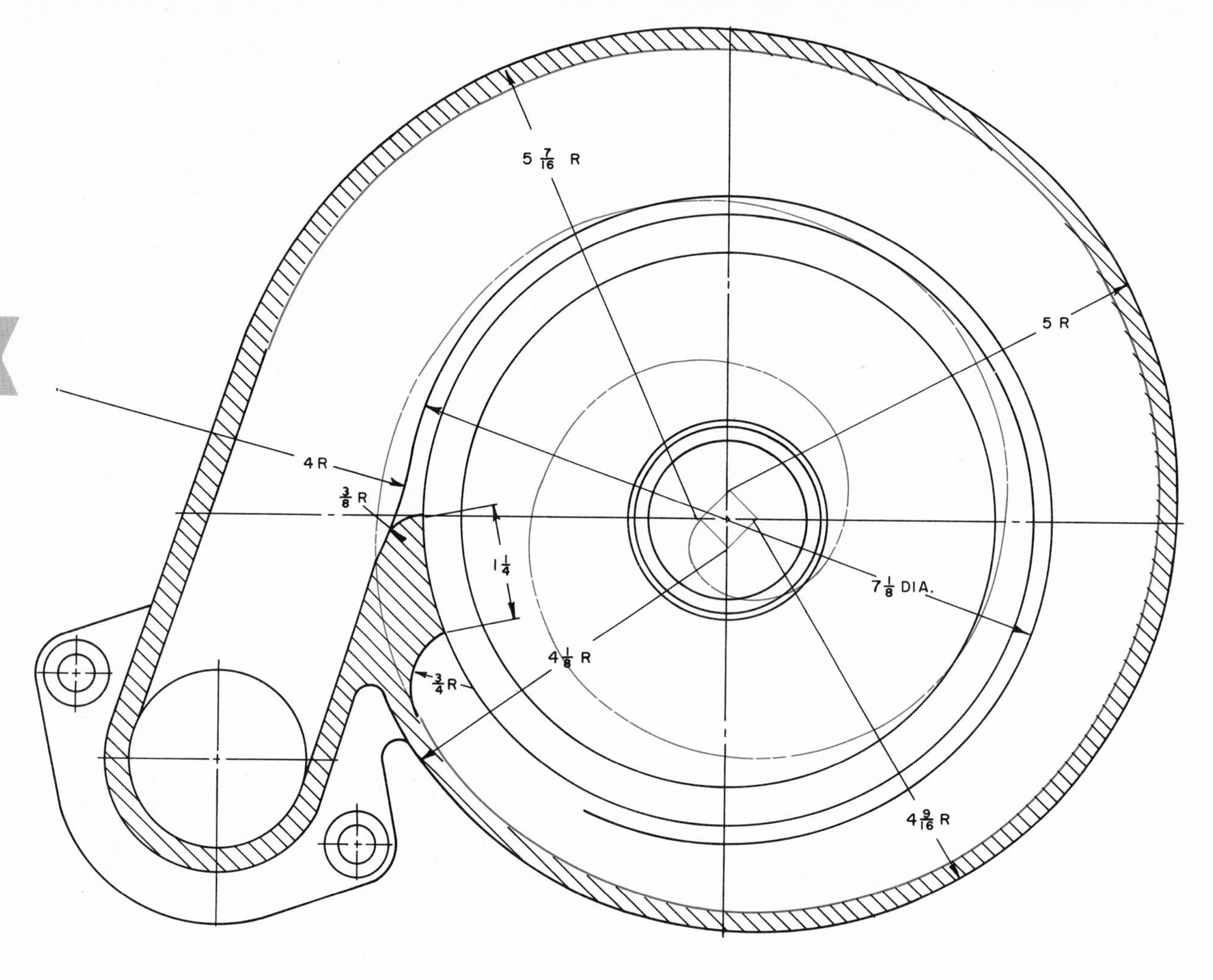

FIG. 4-100. Water Pump Housing Showing Application of an Involute of a Regular Polygon In this case, the polygon is a square whose diagonals are ⅝″.

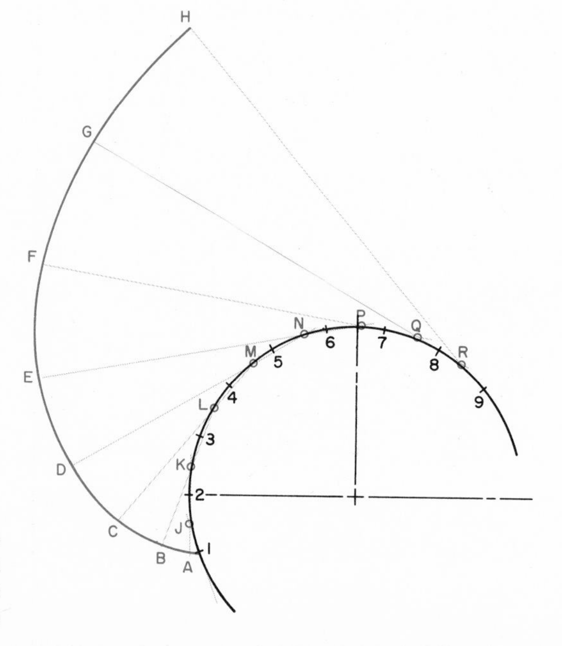

FIG. 4-101. Construction of an Involute of a Circle Arc

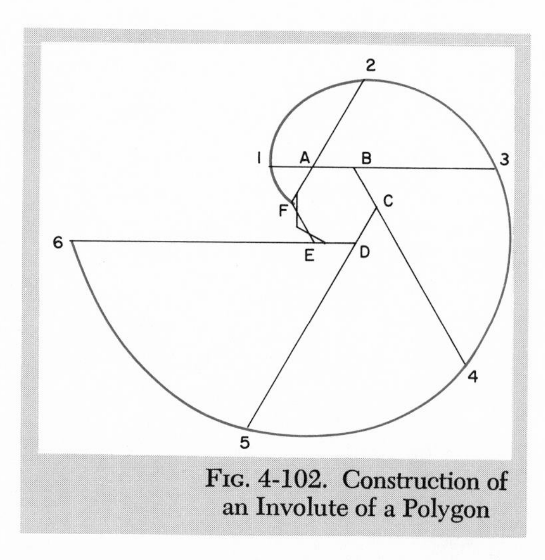

FIG. 4-102. Construction of an Involute of a Polygon

INVOLUTE OF A POLYGON. To construct an involute of a polygon, Fig. 4-102:

1. With hexagon *ABCDEF* as the given polygon and *A* as the center and *AF* as the radius, strike arc F_1.
2. With *B* as the center and radius B_1, strike arc 1-2. Repeat in a like manner until the desired involute is constructed.

Summary

At this point, you should sketch or draw the involute of a circle 1-inch in diameter and the involute of a square, pentagon, or triangle with 1-inch sides, to see whether you understand this type of construction.

A given involute has only one evolute. A given evolute has many involutes because the initial point may be chosen arbitrarily. You may test this statement by working with a given involute such as that in Fig. 4-101 or 4-102. In each case, only one evolute exists. However, place a piece of tracing paper over one of these figures, and choose an origin to construct an involute other than that used to construct the one in the illustration. Notice that the two involutes derived from the same evolute produce parallel curves. Any two such involutes are a constant distance apart.

Involutes of a given circle and involutes of various given regular polygons are identical. In some other cases, varying shapes are produced.

Cycloids

A cycloid is generated by a fixed point on the circumference of a circle as the circle rolls in a plane along a straight line in that plane. For example, if you drive your car in a straight line on a level stretch of road and have a thumb tack in the tread of one of the tires, any point on the head of the tack will travel in a cycloidal path as the car moves over the road.

If the circle with a fixed point on its circumference rolls along the outside of the circumference of another circle, the path generated by the fixed point is an *epicycloid.*

If the circle rolls along the inside of the circumference of another circle, the path of the fixed point traces a *hypocycloid.*

Applications

The cycloid curves are used in machine design for the construction of certain gear-tooth profiles, blower impellers and the like. The cycloidal arch sometimes is used in bridge and building construction.

Constructions

A cycloidal arch may be constructed as shown in Fig. 4-103. The span is $2\pi r$ which will be recognized as the formula for the circumference of the circle, which will roll along the straight line (a distance equal to the span). The angle θ is any arbitrary number of degrees which comes out in an even number when divided into 360°; in this case, it was 24°. The constant k, which is set off along the center line of the given circle, is:

$$k = 2\pi r \div \frac{360°}{\theta}$$

In the example problem, $r = 1.5$ and $\theta = 24°$, so the calculated value of k is 0.628. To

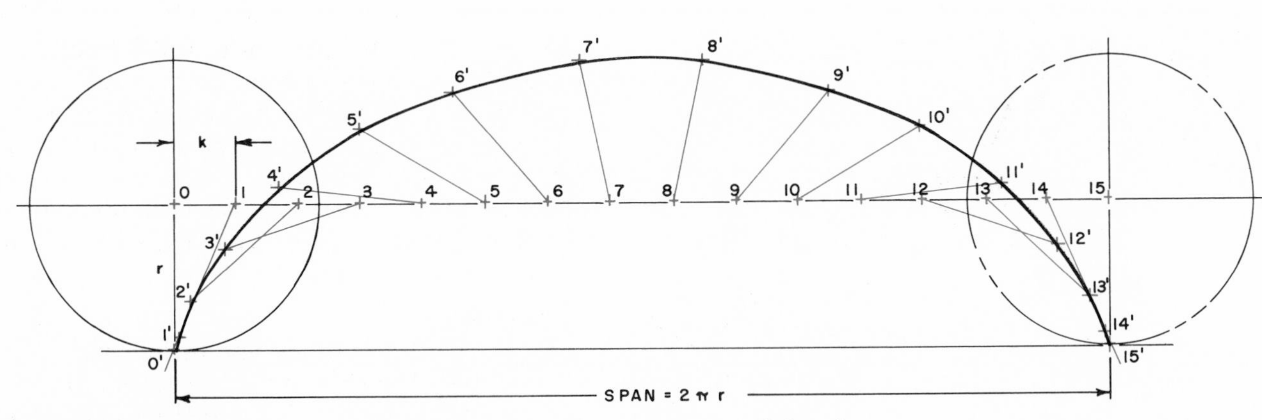

FIG. 4-103. Construction of a Cycloidal Arch

find the number of units of k needed, use the quotient found in the above formula when you calculated $\frac{360°}{\theta}$.

Note in the example problem that *0-0′* equals r, as does *1-1′*, *2-2′*, and so on. Layout from the successive positions of 0, 1, 2, 3 and so on, a distance equal to r. Using 0-0′ as the base line, draw each succeeding radius at θ degree increments in a clockwise direction until all of the "prime" positions have been located. These positions represent the fixed point on a circle as the circle rotates along a straight line, thus describing a cycloid which is drawn in with the irregular curve.

The above construction is presented to show basic geometrical relationships. In practice, the following method is quicker, Fig. 4-104.

1. Divide the circle into an equal number of parts, such as 12.
2. Layout distances along the center line from 0 to 12 equal to the length of the arcs of the circle.
3. Through the intersections of the lines dividing the circle into equal parts and the circle arcs, layout horizontal lines *A* through *G*.
4. Using the radius *0-0′* and successive positions such as 0, 1, 2, and the like, plot the positions on successive horizontal lines *A*, *B*, *C*, etc.
5. Use the irregular curve to draw the cycloid.

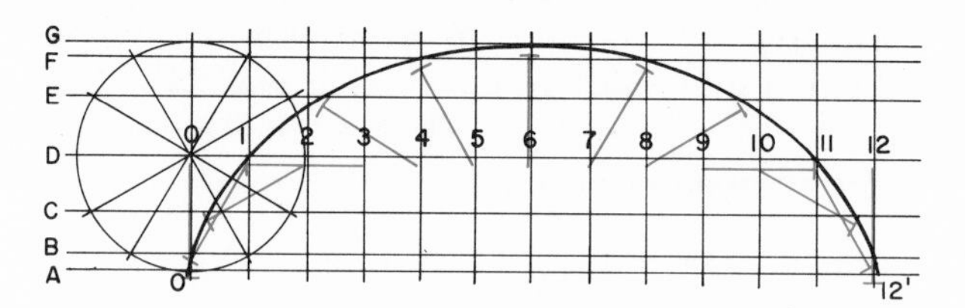

FIG. 4-104. Shorter Method for Cycloid Construction

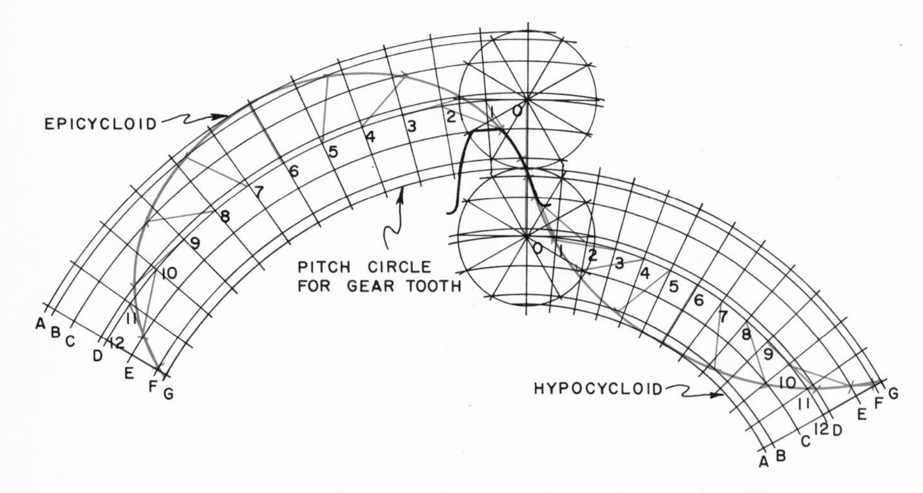

FIG. 4-105. Epicycloid and Hypocycloid Construction

Epicycloids and hypocycloids are constructed essentially the same way as a cycloid, Fig. 4-105. Note the cycloidal gear tooth superimposed on this figure. The addendum is an epicycloidal profile, and the dedendum profile is hypocycloidal.

Helix

A helix is generated by a point moving uniformly both around and up or down the surface of a cylinder or a cone. A helix is understood to be derived from a cylindrical surface unless it is designated as a *conical* helix. The perpendicular distance along the axis from the beginning of one revolution about the surface to the beginning of a second revolution is the *lead* of the helix.

A stretch-out development of the surface about which the helix moves will show the helix as a straight line. The angle between a base line and the development of the helix is the helix angle.

The helix may be (1) right-hand, in which case if it were a thread on a bolt it would advance into a nut when turned in a clockwise direction; or (2) left-hand, in which case the bolt would advance into its nut when turned in a counterclockwise direction.

Applications

There are many practical applications of the helix such as: the flutes of a drill bit and the auger bit, post hole augers, feed auger elevators, screw and bolt threads, helical gears, spiral stairs, coil springs, cork screws, and barber pole stripes. Even a point on a propeller driving a boat through the water moves in the path of a helix. Fig. 4-106 is an example of the helix from an industrial drawing.

Constructions

1. Layout the cylinder upon which the helix is to be formed using a front and top view with the base circle divided into an equal number of parts, as shown in Fig. 4-107.

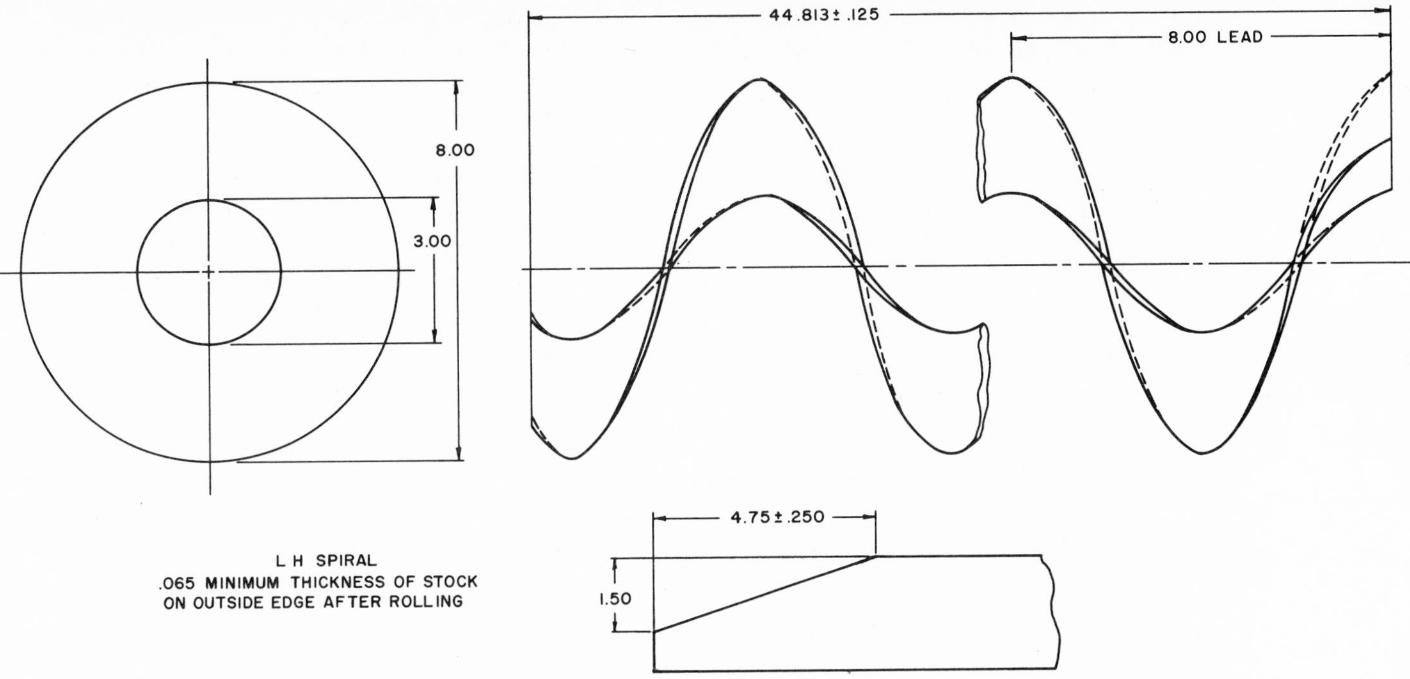

FIG. 4-106. Helical Auger Flighting

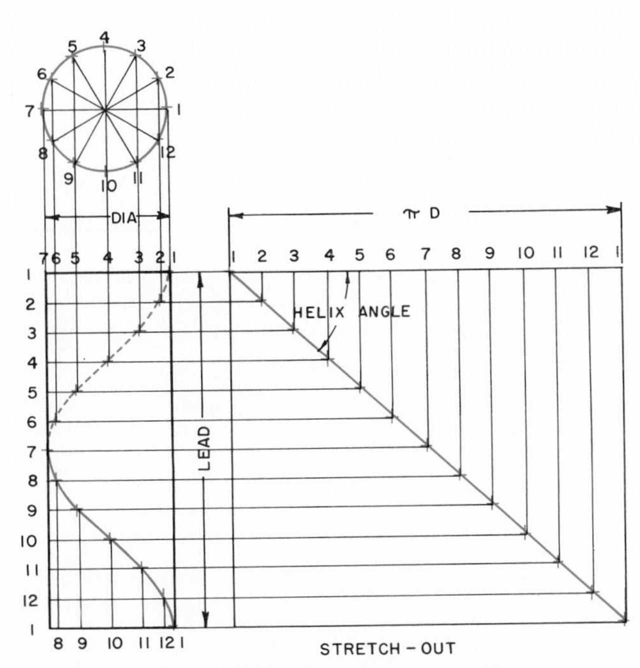

FIG. 4-107. Construction of a Helix

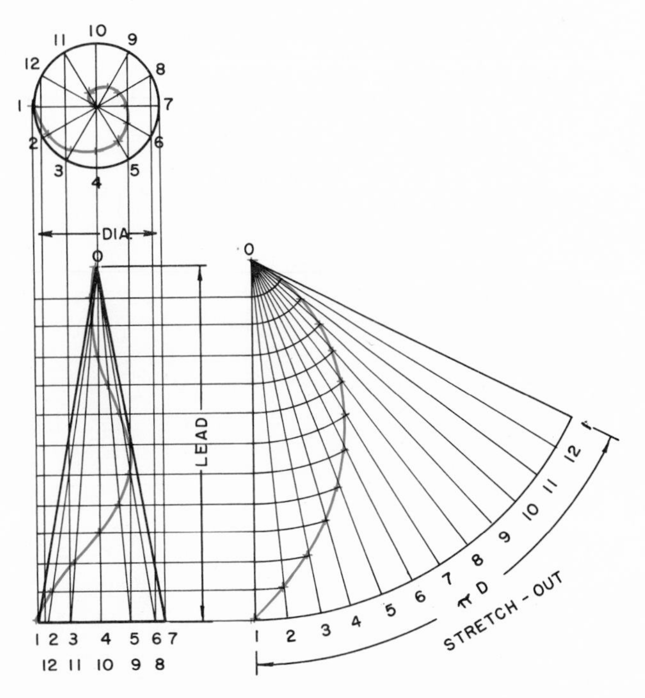

FIG. 4-108. Construction of a Conical Helix

2. Layout the lead on the rectangular view, and divide the lead into the same number of equal parts as was used to divide the base circle.
3. Project upward from point 1 on the base circle to point 1 in the cylindrical view. This will locate a point of the helix.
4. Proceed in a like manner to locate other points.
5. Draw the helix through these points with the irregular curve.

A conical helix is constructed in a like manner as shown in Fig. 4-108. Note that the projection of the conical helix in the circle view is a spiral of Archimedes. The development of the helix on the stretch-out is an equiangular spiral.

Chapter 4 — Problems and Projects

1. Assume you are a draftsman for a company which is changing to pre-printed title blocks. It is your job to prepare these for "A," "B," and "C" size cut sheets. Make rough sketches first. Then make a mechanical layout for each of these title blocks.
2. Figure 4-109 shows several lines. Measure each line and record your answer on a sheet of paper using the following scales:
   a. full size
   b. mechanical engineer's: one-half size
   c. mechanical engineer's: one-eighth size
   d. 4:1
   e. architect's: ½″ = 1′ - 0″
   f. architect's: ¼″ = 1′ - 0″
   g. civil engineer's: 1″ = 50′
   h. civil engineer's: 1″ = 10 miles
   i. mechanical engineer's — decimalized inch: quarter size
   j. metric scale: full-size
   k. metric scale: half-size
3. On a separate sheet of paper draw twelve lines ½″ apart. Make them all exactly 10″ long, and label them *a*, *b*, *c*, etc. Make the following layouts on the appropriate lines:
   a. full scale: 5⁹⁄₁₆″
   b. mechanical engineer's scale, half size: 14⅞″
   c. mechanical engineer's scale, quarter size: 27.82″
   d. mechanical engineer's scale, quarter size: .08″
   e. architect's scale, 1″ = 1′ - 0″: 8′ - 3¼″
   f. architect's scale, ¼″ = 1′ - 0″: 33′ - 9″
   g. civil engineer's scale, 1″ = 100′: 288.5′

FIG. 4-109. Problem 2

h. civil engineer's scale, 1″ = 500 miles: 4,200 miles
i. 10:1 enlargement: ⅝″
j. double size: 3.09″
k. full size: 2.48″
l. mechanical engineer's scale, decimal inch, double size: $^{31}/_{64}$″

4. (a) Make a 4-times-size inch; show the common *fractional* divisions of a full-size inch.
   (b) Make a 4-times-size inch; show the common *decimal* divisions of a full-size inch.
   (c) Make a 4-times-size inch; show the common divisions for its metric equivalent of a full-size inch.
5. Explain the difference between the scale called "quarter size" and the one called ¼″ = 1′ - 0″.
6. Using the four-center method, make an isometric pictorial drawing of a tin can measuring 3.5″ in diameter at its base and 5″ in height.
7. A hand wheel is to have five spokes whose cross section is elliptical at the point of a section view of the spokes. The major axis is 1.25″, and the minor axis is .875″. Using the concentric-circle method and making the elliptical section four-times full size, construct the layout for this section.
8. An elliptical arch is to be constructed over a span of 18 feet. If the foci are located 2½′ from the respective vertices, what is the eccentricity of the ellipse? What is the height of the highest point of the arch as measured from the major axis? (Hint: a equals one-half the sum of any pair of focal radii.) Construct this elliptical arch using the foci method.
9. A right circular cone has a 5″ diameter at its base with an altitude of 8″. At a height of 4½″ from the base, a plane is passed through the cone, making an angle of 40° with the base. Make a drawing showing the true view of the conic section.
10. Construct an ellipse whose major axis is 6″ and whose minor axis is 4″. Use the foci method. Make a second ellipse to these specifications using the trammel method. Then compare their shapes. Are they the same shape? Should they be the same shape?
11. Imagine you threw a baseball straight upward into the air at a velocity of 64′ per second. Using the formula, $d = vt - 16t^2$, make a table of values for each half-second that the ball is in the air, showing the distance the ball traveled during that time period. (d represents the distance above the point from which the ball was thrown, v represents the velocity at which it was thrown, and t represents the time in seconds that the ball has been in the air.) Plot this information on a graph, placing the values of d along the y axis and the values of t in half-seconds along the x axis. What kind of a curve form results? Based on this graph, what path do you think the booster for a satellite follows from blast off until it is jettisoned?
12. Referencing the standard form of the equation for a parabola, $y^2 = 2\,kx$, what is the effect of writing the equation $y^2 = -2\,kx$? $x^2 = 2\,ky$? $x^2 = -2\,ky$? Make a sketch of each of these parabolas when $k = 20$.
13. Draw four parabolas with the same vertex and axis, but vary the position of the focus. What generalization can you make about these four parabolic curves?
14. The cross section of a parabolic reflector is described by the equation $y^2 = 60x$. Make a drawing of the cross section of this reflector. The focus on this reflector is 15″ from the vertex.
15. Explain how a shop might build a wooden form into which this reflector could be shaped into its form of a parabaloid.
16. A cable hanging in a parabolic shape is 100′ apart at its end points, which are in the same horizontal plane. The lowest point of the cable is 62.5′ below the points of suspension, and the focus is 10′ from this lowest point. Draw the parabolic curve. Find the height of the cable above the lowest point, 10′ from a point of suspension, measured horizontally. At this point, a guy wire is to be attached. Write the equation for the parabolic curve form of the cable.
17. The elevation of a highway at the top of hill A is 240′ above sea level. The top of the next rise, hill B, is 200′ and is located horizontally 500′ from hill A. Assume a

point *O* located 250′ horizontally from hill *A* at an elevation of 160′. Make a parabolic envelope showing the smooth curve form which the highway should take. Find the elevation of the highway at each 100′ interval along the 500′ distance separating hill *A* from hill *B*.

18. *Given:* asymptotes *OA* and *OB* and point *P*. (8, 16). Construct the equilateral hyperbola.
19. *Given:* foci located at (10,0) and (−10,0) and a transverse axis of 1″. Construct the branches of this hyperbola lying in the first and second quadrants.
20. With the same foci as in problem 19 and a transverse axis of 4″, construct the first and second quadrant branches of the hyperbola.
21. A steel oxygen tank is known to contain 2 cubic feet of oxygen at a pressure of 200 lbs./sq. inch. Make a hyperbolic graph from which you can read the various volumes of gas as the pressure decreases from 200 to 10 lbs./sq. inch. What is the effect of choosing different units of measure for graphing the pressure as compared to those used for graphing the volume?
22. The pressure capacity of a steam boiler is 100 lbs./sq. inch. The volume of steam at 10 lbs./sq. inch is 1000 cubic feet. How many cubic feet of steam at full pressure is this boiler designed to hold? Make a hyperbolic graph showing the volume for various pressures in increments of 10 lbs./sq. inch.
23. The navigator of an aircraft is flying over a large storm system and cannot see the ground. His navigational aids tell him that station *A* is located 450 miles due north of station *B* and that station *C* is located 250 miles due east of *B*. Radio signals show him to be 150 miles closer to *A* than to *B* and 200 miles closer to *B* than to *C*. Find his location at the time of observing the radio signals.
24. Assume you are commanding a field piece on a battlefield. The locations of three of your listening stations are known. S_1 is 2500 yards due east of you; S_2, 2000 yards due north; and S_3, 1500 yards northeast. Station S_2 heard the sound of enemy fire 3 seconds later than S_3. Station S_1 heard the same sound 4 seconds later than S_3. S_3 reported the sound generally northeast. Assume there is no wind and that your position, all three stations, and the enemy emplacement are at the same elevation. Knowing that sound travels at 1100 feet per second, what is the bearing (measured in degrees from north) and for what range should you set your field piece in order to return the fire?
25. The equation of a hyperbola is given as $\frac{x^2}{25} - \frac{y^2}{100} = 1$. Construct the four branches of this hyperbola using a grid sheet and solving for several values of x.

    Hint: $x = \sqrt{\frac{a^2 y^2}{b^2} + a^2}$

    $y = \sqrt{\frac{b^2 x^2}{a^2} - b^2}$
26. Construct a spiral of Archimedes through a series of lines at 30°, from a center *O*, by layout of successive distances of ¼″ from the origin. Superimpose on this layout an equiangular spiral starting at the first point beyond the origin plotted for the spiral of Archimedes.
27. Construct the involute of an evolute whose diameter is 1½″. Construct a parallel curve ½″ from the involute.
28. Construct an involute of an octagon whose sides are ¾″ long.
29. Construct an involute of an isosceles triangle whose base is 1″ and whose altitude is 1½″. Construct two parallel curves to the first involute.
30. Draw an involute of the parabola described by the equation in problem 14: $y^2 = 60x$.
31. Draw the involute of one branch of the hyperbola in problem 20.
32. Construct a cycloidal arch which has a span of 30′. In the center of the arch will be a supporting column. This column is directly under the vertex of the evolute of the cycloid. Construct the evolute of the given cycloid, and determine the minimum distance from the base of the cycloid to the top of the supporting column upon which its evolute rests.

33. Using a circle of 2″ in diameter, construct an epicycloid directly above a hypocycloid. The radius of the circle upon which both curve forms are derived is 6″.
34. Layout a right-hand helix generated on the surface of a cylinder which is 2″ in diameter and whose altitude is 4″. The lead is 2″.
35. Layout a conical helix for a cone whose base is 2″ in diameter and whose altitude is 4″. The lead is 1″.
36. Two imaginary concentric cylinders have as their diameters .5′ and 4.5′. The smallest is a center post for a spiral stairway. The largest is the outline of the helical path of the outside of the spiral stairs. This stairwell rises 12′ from the first to the second floor, with a lead of 6′. Each step rises 7.2″. How many steps are required to reach the second floor from the first floor? How many revolutions around the center post does one make in ascending the stairs? What is the widest tread measurement for each step? (*Hint:* measure the chord of the largest circle arc for one step.) What problem, if any, do you foresee for a man 6′ tall as he climbs this spiral staircase?

CHAPTER FIVE

describing interior detail

Interior detail may be shown by hidden lines. When these, alone, do not show the internal construction clearly enough or too many lines result in confusion, a section may be drawn, Fig. 5-1. A *section* shows how an object would look if an imaginary cutting plane were passed through the object, perpendicular to the direction of sight. To the observer, a portion is then

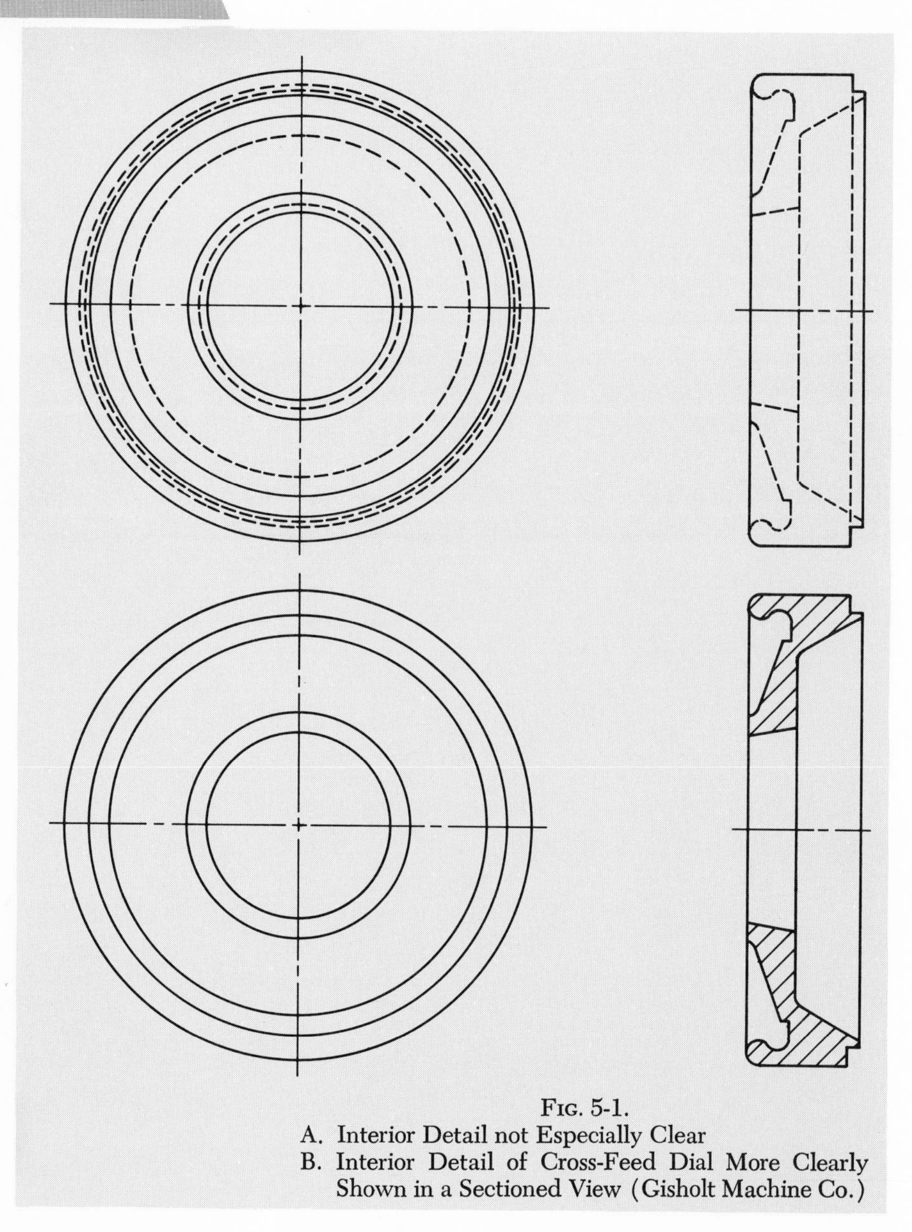

FIG. 5-1.
A. Interior Detail not Especially Clear
B. Interior Detail of Cross-Feed Dial More Clearly Shown in a Sectioned View (Gisholt Machine Co.)

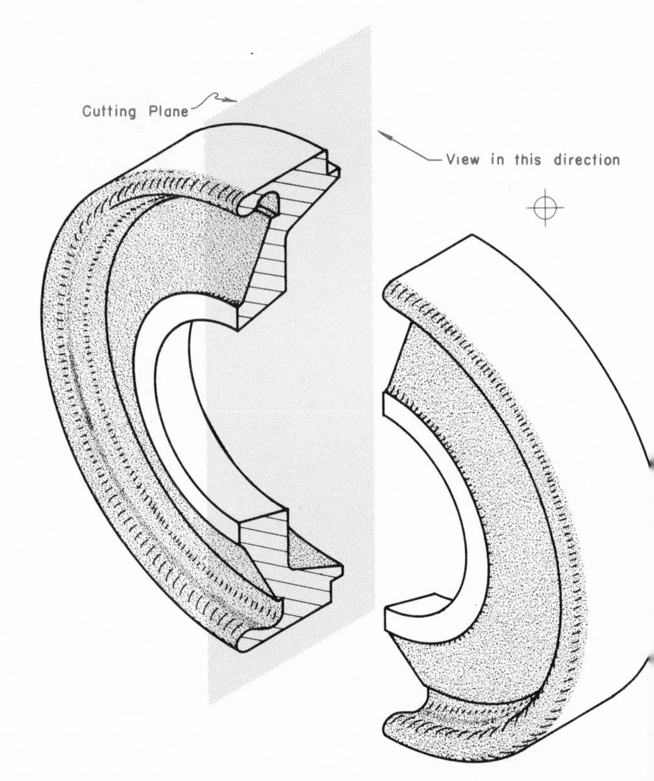

FIG. 5-2. Section Lining Used to Distinguish Surfaces an Imaginary Cutting Plane Passes Through

imagined to be removed or broken away, Fig. 5-2. The cut surface exposed by an imaginary cutting plane is shown by section lining. Portions which are not cut are shown in visible outline form as usual.

Symbols Used

Fig. 5-3 shows common symbols used for different materials. Note that the symbol for cast iron is a general-purpose symbol as well. This generalized symbol may be used to represent any material. Then, when a material is changed, it takes less time to draw and makes redrawing unnecessary. The use of generalized symbols is confined primarily to drawings of individual parts. When sectioned views of assembled objects are shown, the various symbols are generally used for clarification, Fig. 5-4.

When these general-purpose symbols are used, exact specifications should be given in a note on the drawing.

Section Lines

Whenever possible, section lines are spaced ⅛″ or slightly farther apart. The tendency of beginners is to crowd the section lines together. This not only spoils the appearance of the drawing, it also wastes time drawing more lines than are needed.

Section lines are relatively lightweight lines much like extension and dimension lines. They should be drawn firmly enough to insure good reproduction. These lines are as follows:

a. On a single piece, section lines are at 45° angles to the outlines of the view, Fig. 5-1 (b).

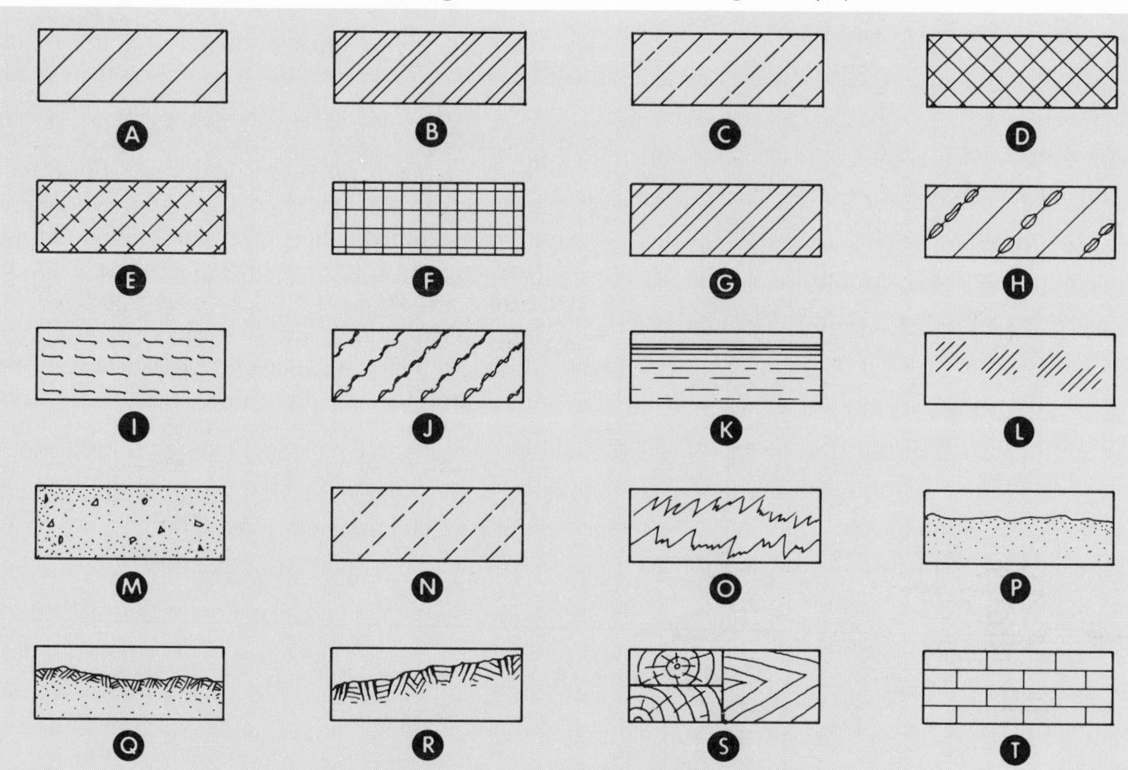

FIG. 5-3. Symbols for Section Lining (USAS)

A. Cast iron and general purpose symbol
B. Steel
C. Brass, bronze, copper and copper and compositions
D. White metal, zinc, lead, babbitt and alloys
E. Magnesium, aluminum, and aluminum alloys
F. Electric windings, electromagnets, resistance, *etc.*
G. Rubber, plastic, electrical insulation
H. Sound insulation
I. Cork, felt, fabric, leather, fiber
J. Thermal insulation
K. Water and other liquids
L. Transparent materials, glass, *etc.*
M. Concrete
N. Marble, slate, glass, porcelain, *etc.*
O. Exterior marble
P. Sand
Q. Earth
R. Rock
S. Wood
T. Exterior brick

b. On a second part adjacent to the first, section lines are drawn at 45° angles opposite the first, Fig. 5-4.

FIG. 5-4. Relief Valve (Fisher Governor Co.) How many different materials does the section lining represent? How many parts are there in the relief valve?

c. For additional parts, section lines are drawn at any convenient angle using first, common angles such as 30° and 60°, to clearly distinguish between the various parts, Fig. 5-4.

In assembly sections where detailed parts are put together in their correct working order, do not draw section lines that purposely meet at the boundary lines. Special angles may be chosen when section lines otherwise would be nearly parallel or perpendicular to the visible lines. See Fig. 5-5 and the auxiliary section, B-B, Fig. 5-9.

Section lines are parallel and equidistant throughout a given part.

Outline sectioning may be used to section relatively large areas, Fig. 5-6.

The Cutting Plane

Cutting plane lines were identified in Fig. 2-16, page 29. This line represents the edge view of the imaginary cutting plane. Observe the cutting plane lines used in Figs. 5-8 and 5-9. Arrowheads on these lines show the direction in which the observer is looking. Bold capital letters identify the particular section. These letters are reprinted on the sectional view to identify it when the section is removed or whenever identification is needed.

It is preferred practice to show the cutting plane through exterior views and not through sectional views.

The cutting plane line may be omitted when it is perfectly clear where the section is cut along a center line, Fig. 5-1 (b).

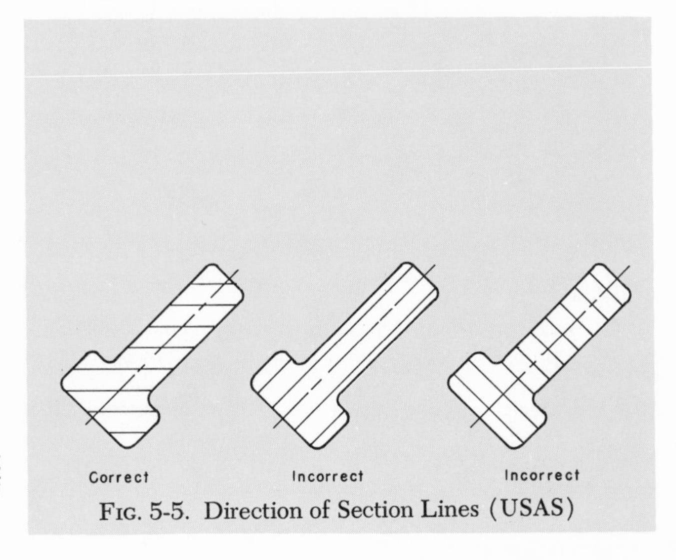

FIG. 5-5. Direction of Section Lines (USAS)

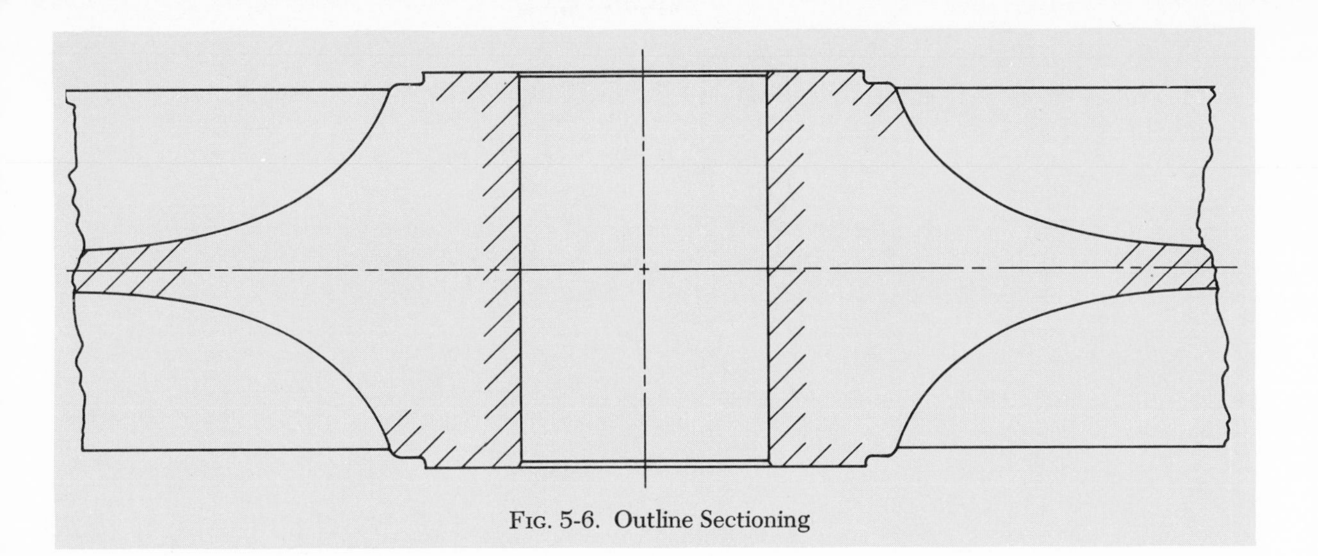

Fig. 5-6. Outline Sectioning

types of sectional views

Full Sections

A full section is obtained by passing a cutting plane entirely through the object as in Fig. 5-2. One-half of the object is removed. The remaining half shows the interior detail.

Half Sections

A half section is obtained by passing two cutting planes, at right angles to each other, through a symmetrical object, thus removing one-quarter of the object, Fig. 5-7. The advantage of this type of section is that both external and internal detail may be shown. The cutting plane line, arrows, and letters may be omitted on symmetrical objects if the cutting plane lines are coincident with the center lines.

Either a center line, as shown in Fig. 5-6, or a visible line may be used to divide the sectioned from the unsectioned portion.

Offset Section

Offset sections show features which are not located in the usual line of the cutting plane. The cutting plane line may be offset to pass through the desired features, Fig. 5-8. The offset is not shown in the section view since the cutting plane line is an imaginary division.

Broken-Out Section

Broken-out sectional views are shown when a small portion of the object is all that is needed to show the required detail, Fig. 5-9. The area sectioned is limited by a break line.

Revolved Section

Revolved sectional views are taken by passing a cutting plane perpendicular to elongated or like features and then imagining this plane to be revolved in position at a 90° angle, Fig. 5-8.

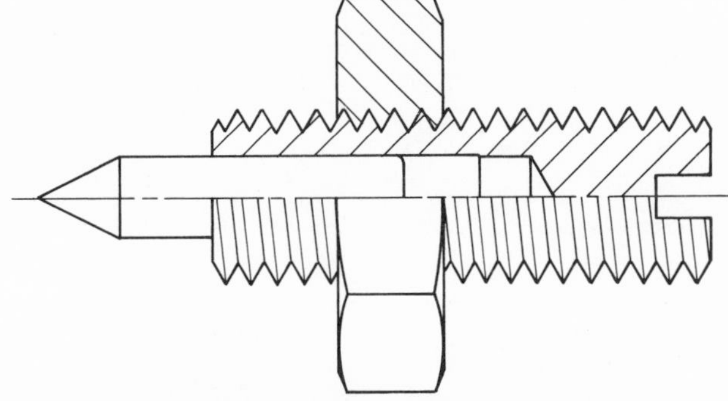

Fig. 5-7. Half-Section View of Instrument-Type Pivot-Bearing Assembly (Welton V. Johnson, Engineering Co., Inc.)

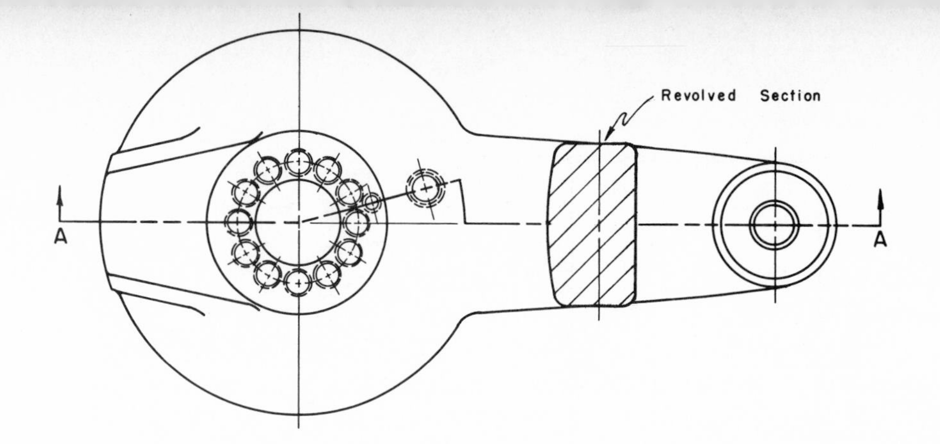

INTERIOR DETAIL

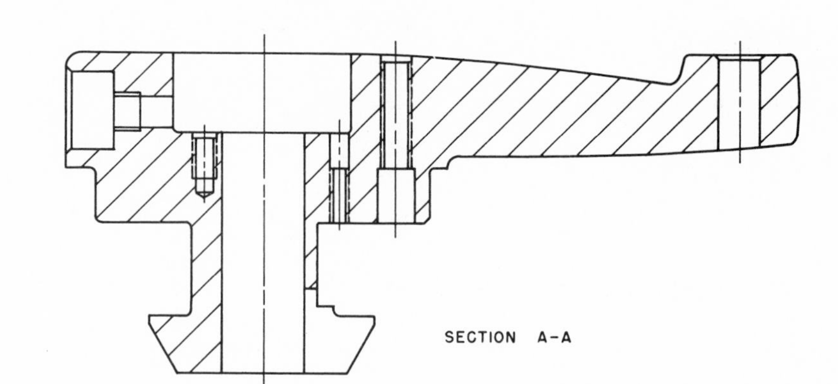

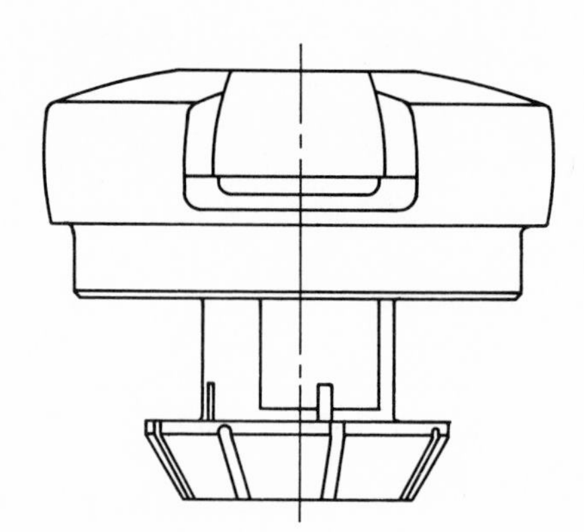

Fig. 5-8. Tool Post Lever (Gisholt Machine Co.)

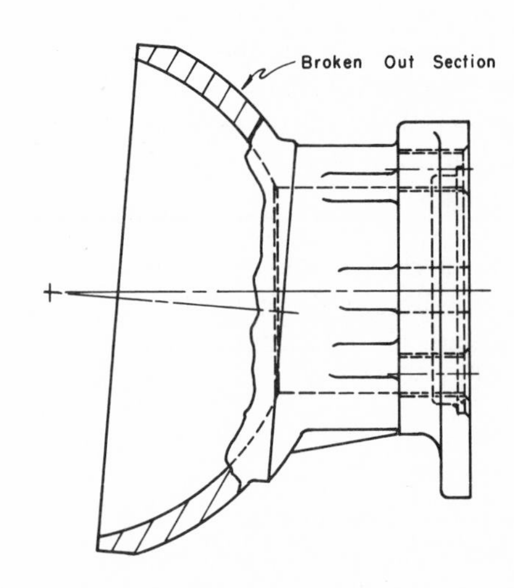

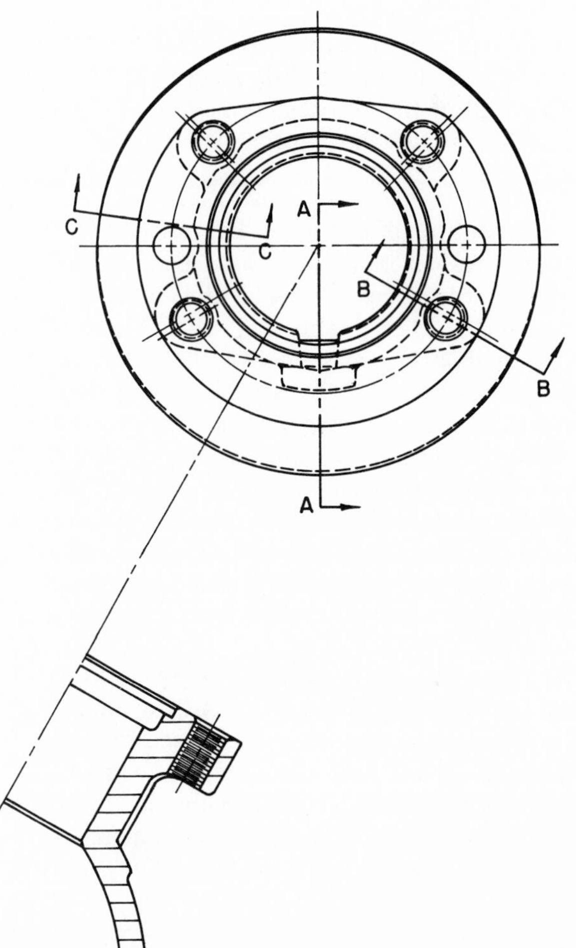

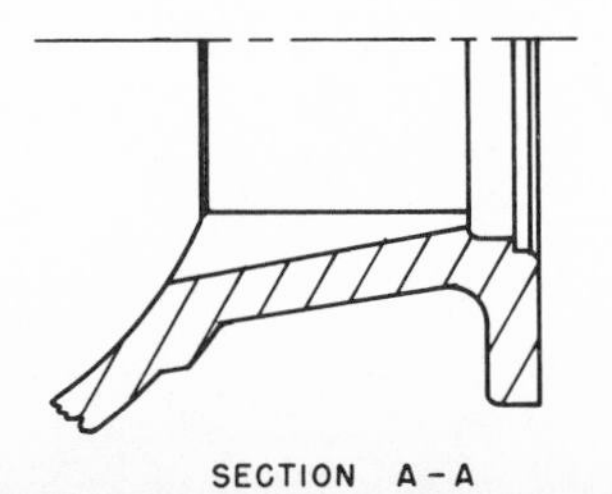

Fig. 5-9. Ball Joint (Buick Motors Div., General Motors Corp.)

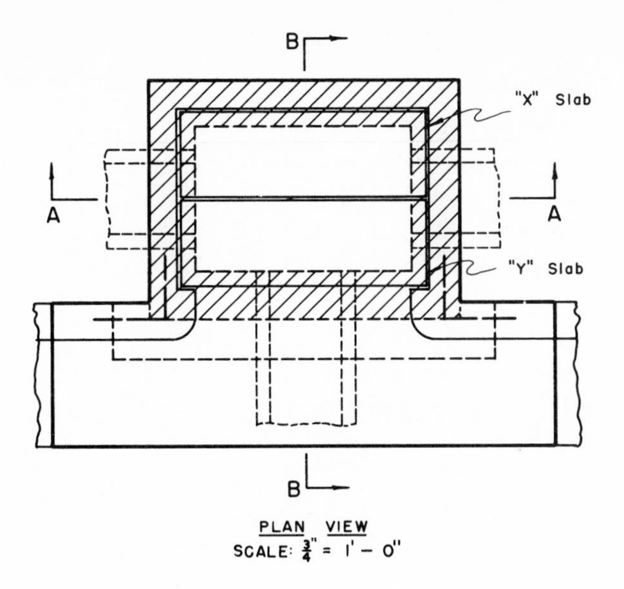

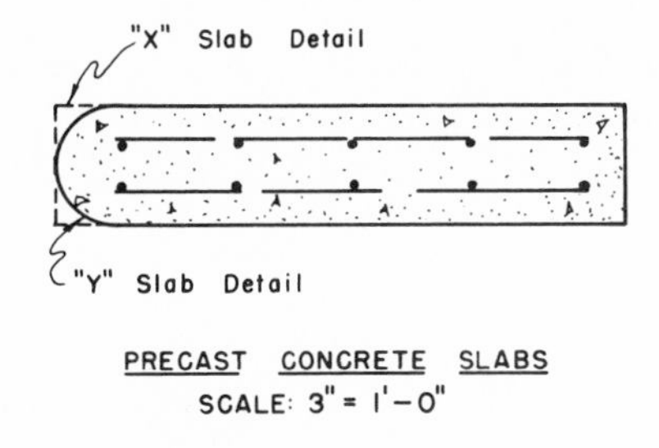

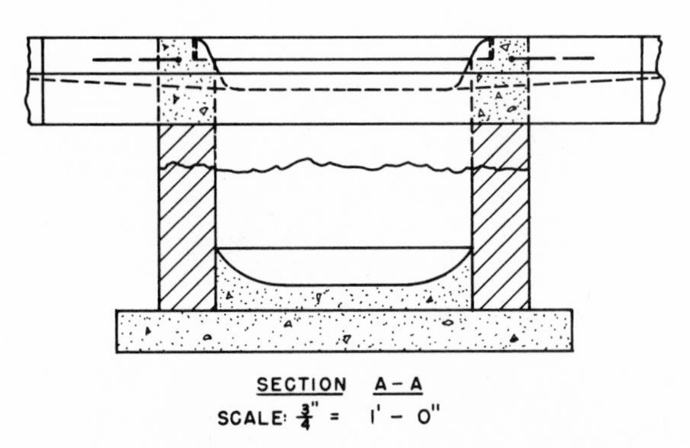

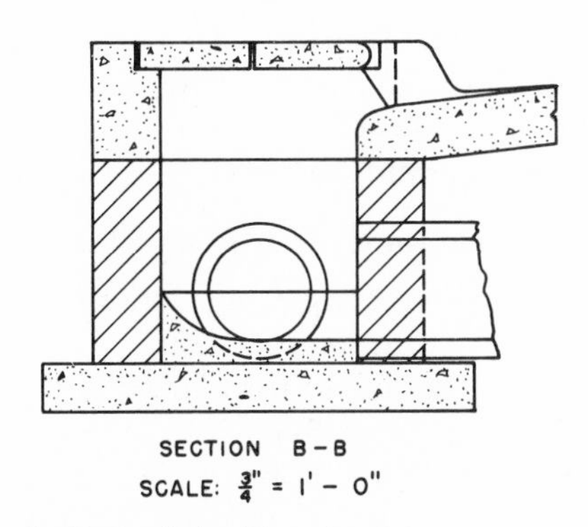

FIG. 5-10. Clearly Marked Sections at a Different Scale than the Rest of the Drawing (City Engineer's Office, Cedar Falls, Iowa)
Note practice shown in the plan view and section A-A of placing section lines behind visible features. Note also the use of cutting plane lines in civil engineering drawings.

Removed Section

Sectional views usually appear on the same sheet and in the normal projected arrangements shown for orthographic projection. However, instances may arise in which a section view should be placed in a location other than those in standard view arrangements. These section views are *removed* sections and should be clearly labeled to identify the view such as sections *AA* and *CC*, Fig. 5-9.

Whenever possible, removed views should be placed on the same sheet with the regular views. There may be occasions on multiple-sheet drawings where a sectional view must be placed on a different sheet from the one showing the cutting plane line. In such cases, a note should be placed both below the section title and on the drawing where the cutting plane is found. A note might read: *Section AA on sheet 5, zone B-2.*

When two or more sections appear on the same sheet, they should be placed in alphabetical order from left to right. Identifying letters should be used in alphabetical order except for the letters I, O, and Q which might be confused with numerals 1 and 0. When more than 23 sections are used, additional sections are designated by double letters such as *AA-AA*, or *BB-BB*.

Removed sectional views may be drawn at a different scale than that of the original drawing. In these cases, the scale used for the removed sectional view should be clearly shown with identification of the view, Fig. 5-10.

Removed sections should not be changed in position from the normal attitude. They may be placed on center lines extended from section cuts as shown in Fig. 5-9 section *B-B*.

Auxiliary Section

An auxiliary sectional view is one taken from any direction other than that of the principal view as shown in Fig. 5-9 section *B-B* and *C-C*

Thin or Narrow Sections

Sections through materials such as sheet metal, packing, gaskets, and the like may be shown solid, Fig. 5-4. Such materials are generally too thin to show section lining effectively.

INTERIOR DETAIL

conventional practices

A number of sectioning practices are used which do not meet all of the rules of technique and projection. These practices are quite standard. They are sometimes for the benefit of the draftsman because the practice makes it easier to draw, and sometimes for the benefit of the reader because some practices make it easier to read the drawing.

Lines Behind the Cutting Plane

Lines representing hidden features behind the cutting plane should be omitted except where required for clarity of presentation and reading, Fig. 5-1 (b). Hidden lines on half-section views appear only on the unsectioned half if needed for clarity or dimensioning, Fig. 5-11.

Sections Through Webs and Ribs

In order to avoid a false impression when a cutting plane passes through a web, rib, or similar element, the SAE recommends that the element should be section lined with double spacing as shown in Fig. 5-12 (a). In this case, hidden lines may be used to show the inter-

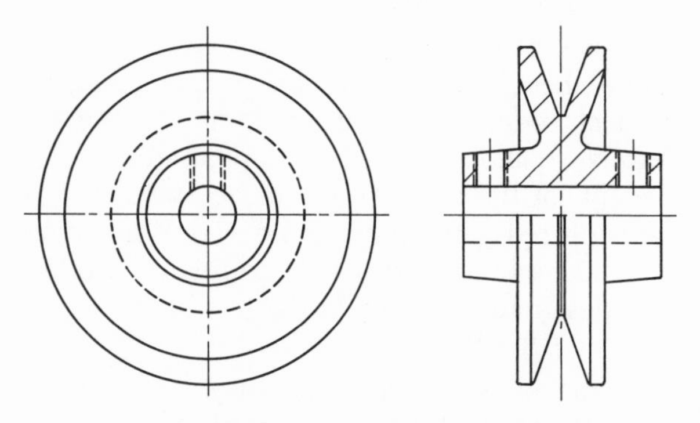

Fig. 5-11. Hidden Line in Unsectioned Half of Pulley Aids in Reading and Clarity
Note that not all possible hidden lines are included in the lower or in the upper half.

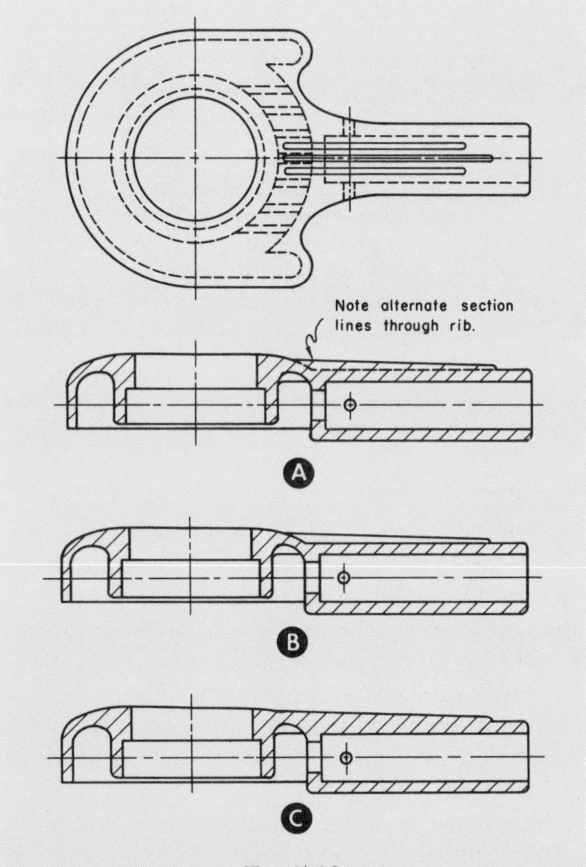

Fig. 5-12.
A. Vemco Drafting Machine Elbow (V. & E. Manufacturing Co.)
B. Alternate practice for treatment of ribs.
C. Do not use this technique for sectioning a rib. Either *A* or *B* should be used.

section between the solid body and the rib or similar element.

When the cutting plane cuts across ribs, they should be section lined as in Fig. 5-13.

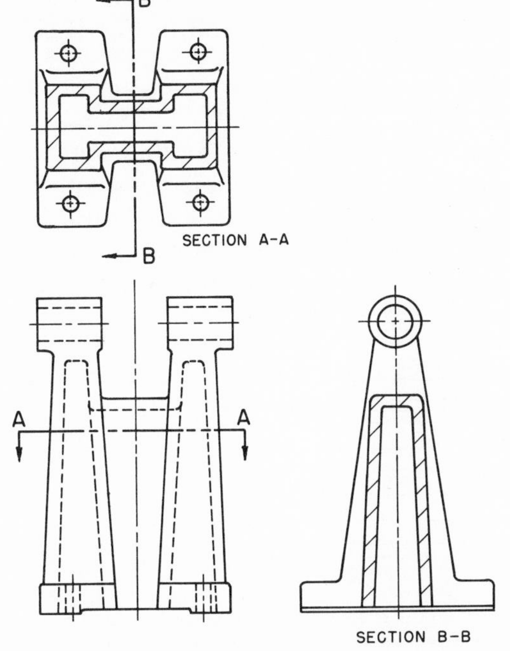

FIG. 5-13. Treatment of Ribs in Section

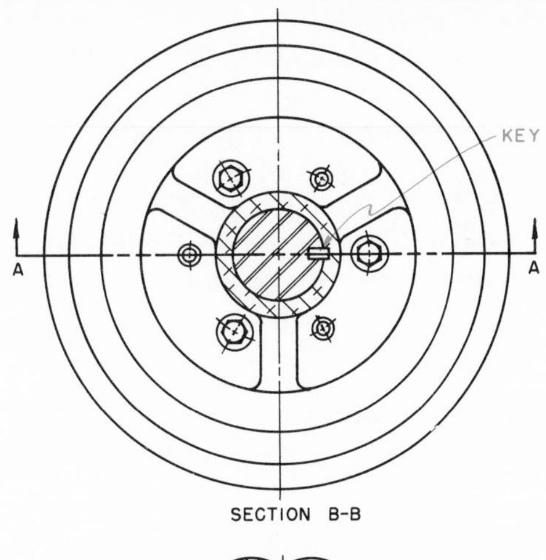

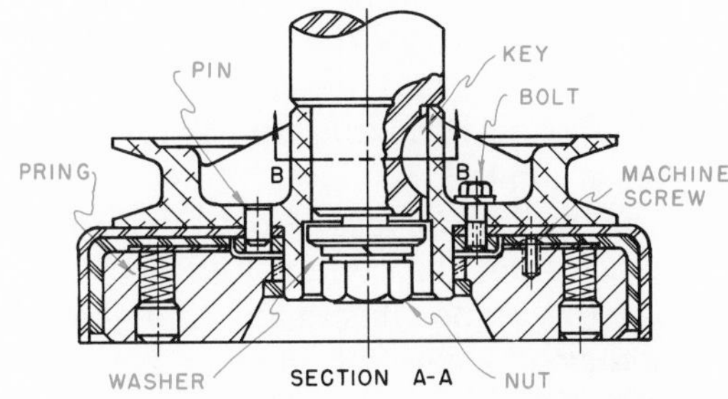

FIG. 5-14. Elements not Revealing Interior Detail are not Sectioned (Deere & Co.)

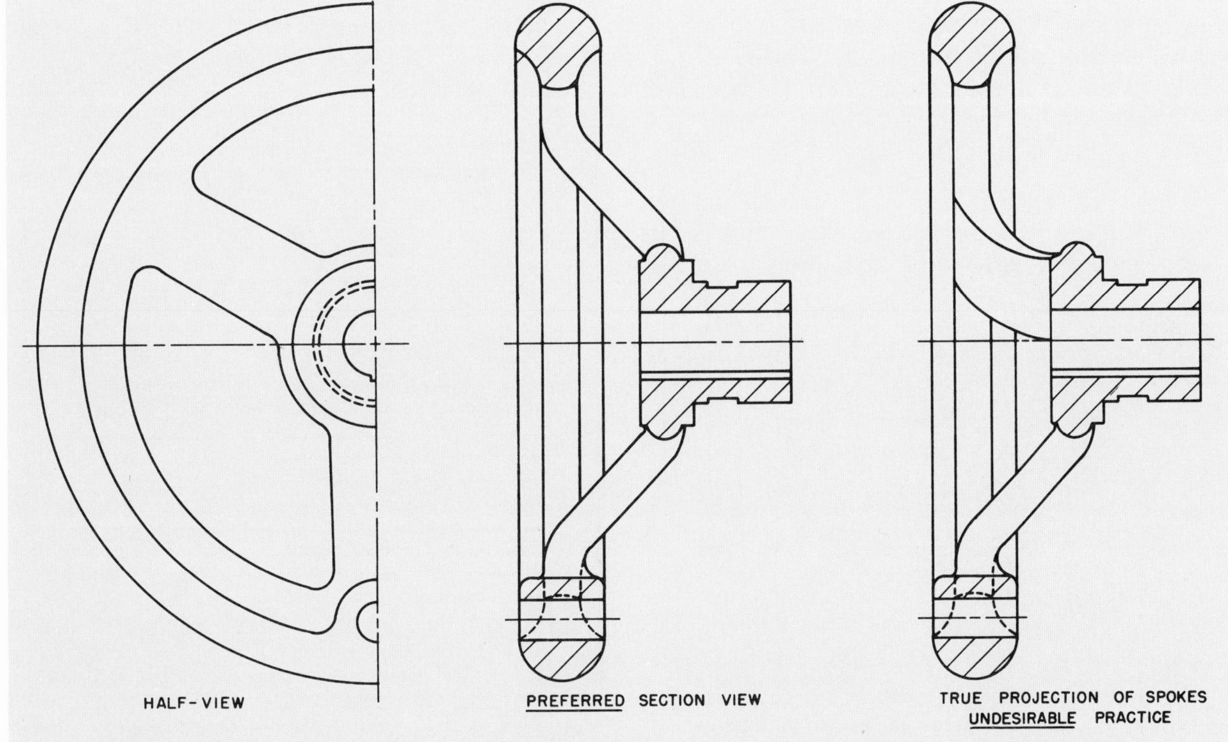

FIG. 5-15. Hand Wheel (Gisholt Machine Co.) Note preferred practice for treatment of spokes.

Non-Sectioned Parts

Sectioning is not required in areas that can already be seen or imagined from an exterior view. Thus when the cutting plane passes through the center lines of these features, they should not be sectioned, Fig. 5-14. Elements usually falling into this classification include shafts, bolts, nails, rivets, rods, keys, pins, spokes, screws, both ball and roller bearings, nuts and the like.

Alignment of Features

INTERIOR DETAIL

Many times, especially in showing the interior detail for castings, true projection of a feature is both time consuming and not especially revealing. In such cases the draftsman should rotate these features into the plane of the paper, Fig. 5-15. Spokes, ribs, arms and like elements should be so rotated.

Holes in drilled flanges should be rotated true distance from the center, Fig. 5-16.

Note in this same illustration that features not located along a straight line may be rotated into the plane of the paper so that interior detail may be included. The cutting plane may be bent to facilitate the drawing of such features.

Intersections in Section

Curves of little or no consequence caused by intersections may be simplified as shown in Fig. 5-17, *A* and *B*. Larger curves may be projected or approximated by circle arcs.

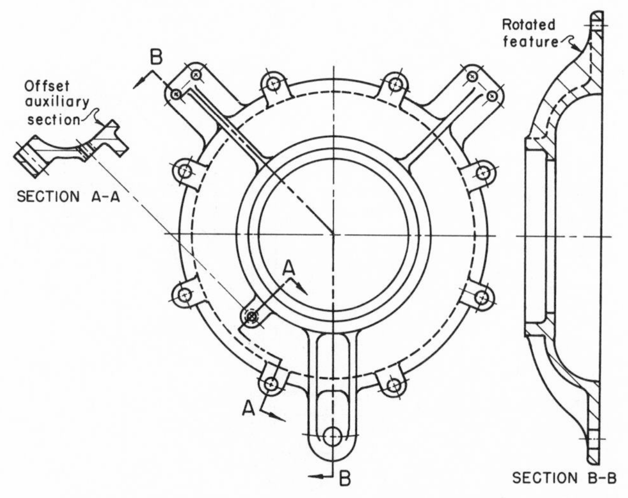

Fig. 5-16. Conventional Treatment of Drilled Holes and Features Not Located for Advantageous True Projection (USAS and SAE)

Conventional Breaks

Elongated objects may be shortened with conventional break representation as shown in Fig. 5-18.

Review also the conventional long break treatment shown for wood in Fig. 2-12, page 27.

Chapter 5 — Problems and Projects

I. Can you read a foreign drawing? Answer each of the following 20 questions with respect to Fig. 5-19. Answer the questions in English as far as possible. Use Arabic numerals when called for. Answer each question fully including the limits where appropriate.

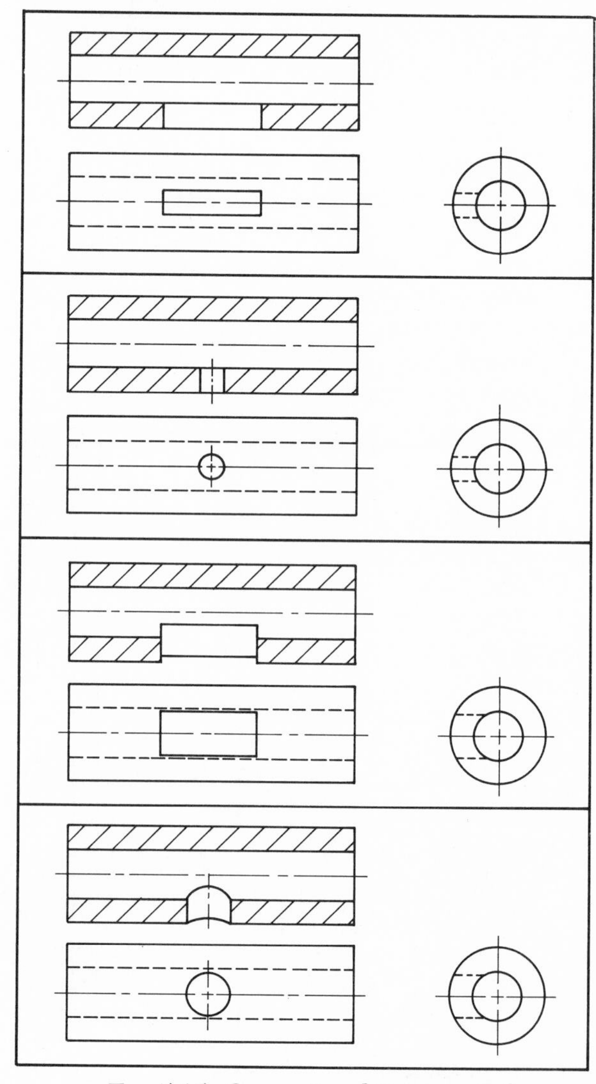

Fig. 5-17. Conventional Treatment of Intersections in Section (USAS)

1. What is the name of the part?
2. What is the drawing number?
3. What is the number of the Assembly of which this is a part?
4. At what scale are the basic views drawn?
5. What system of measurement is used?
6. From what country is this drawing?
7. What system of projection is used on this drawing?
8. The view with cutting plane *a-a* in it is taken from which end of the view that has cutting plane *b-b* in it?
9. The view with cutting plane *a-a* in it matches which end of *coupe a-a*?
10. What type of section view is *coupe a-a*? *Coupe b-b*? *Coupe c-c*?
11. What is the meaning of the view marked *Echelle 1/1*?
12. Is there a difference between any of the French numerals as compared with standard numerals on drawings made in this country?
13. What is the overall length of the object? What is the diameter?
14. What is the radius of the fillets shown at *A*?
15. In what view is the diameter of hole *B* found? What is the diameter of hole *B*? Does this hole go through the object?
16. Where are the cross-sectional dimensions for slot *C* found? How deep is slot *C*? How wide? What is the radius of the fillets at the bottom of the slot?
17. In what view is distance *D* found? What is its value?
18. What is the diameter of circles *E* and *F*? Does hole *F* go all the way through the object?
19. What are the dimensions of the chamfer shown at *G*? *H*?
20. In what view is the feature at *J* shown in profile?

II. Answer these questions with respect to the Exhaust Manifold in Fig. 5-20.

1. How many section views appear on the drawing of the Exhaust Manifold?
2. How many different types of sectional views appear on the drawing?
3. Which views are removed, partial-sectioned views?
4. What is the scale of this drawing?
5. Are all parts of the drawing at the same scale? If not, what scales are used?
6. What is the allowance on all decimal figures with 2-places? 3-places? Angular dimensions?
7. What is the wall thickness of the manifold?
8. What is the diameter of the exhaust opening shown in section *R-R*?
9. How many holes will be drilled identical to that in section *S-S*?
10. How many holes will be drilled identical to that shown in section *D-D*? What is the diameter of the hole shown?
11. What is the chief difference between the hole shown in section *W-W* as compared

INTERIOR DETAIL

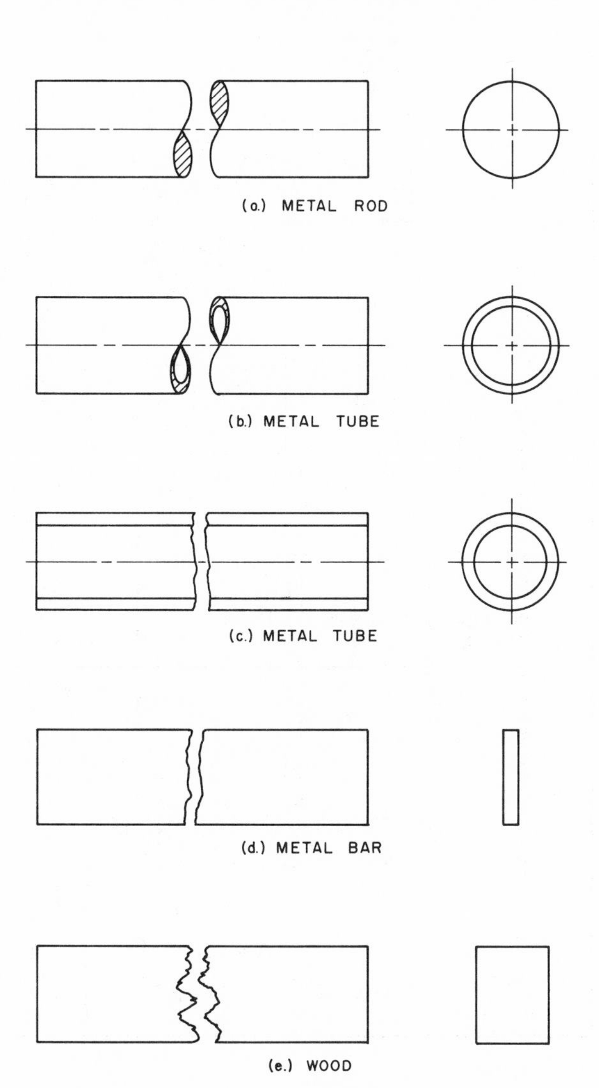

FIG. 5-18. Conventional Breaks (SAE)

INTERIOR DETAIL

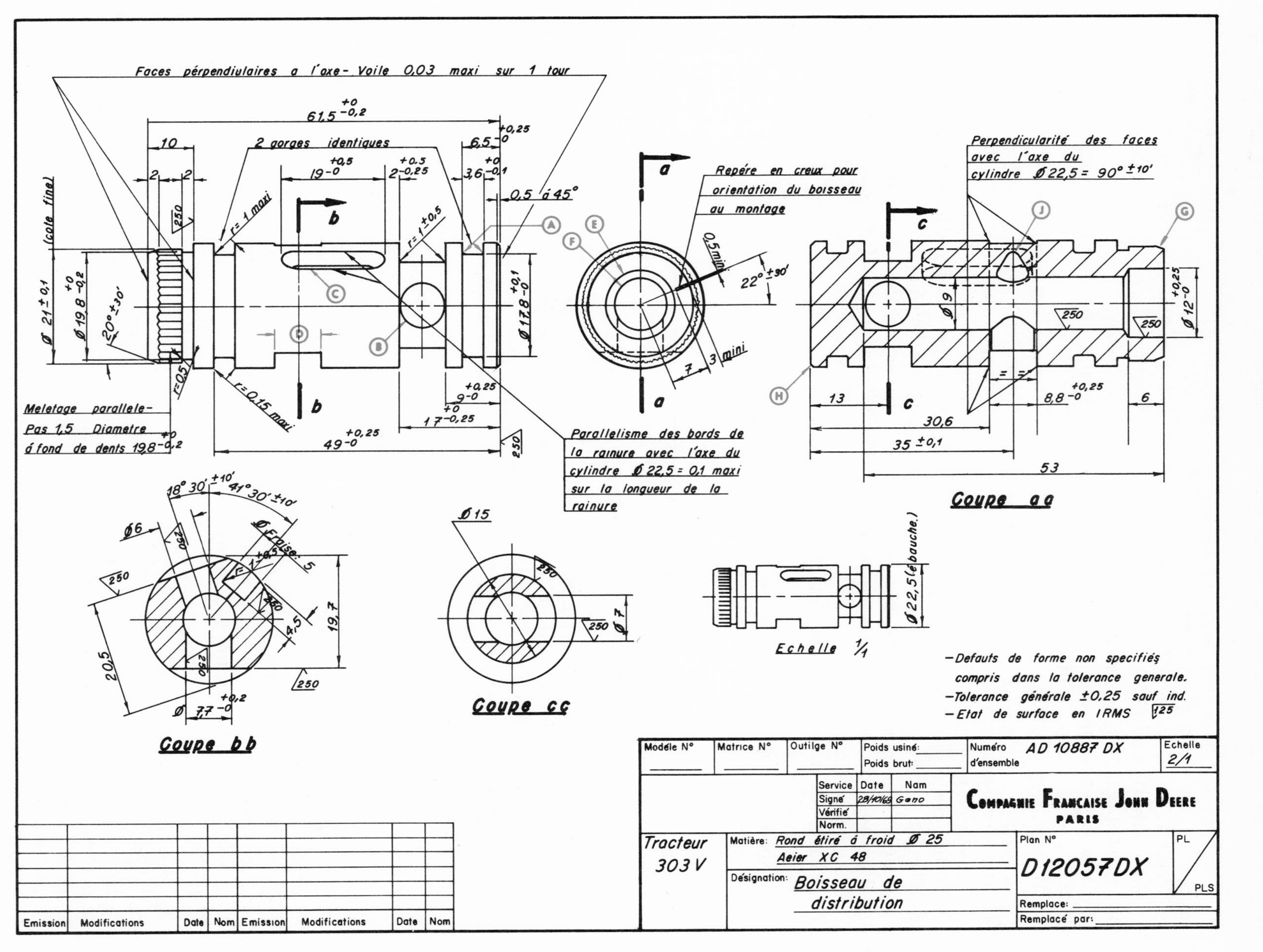

FIG. 5-19. French Print-Reading Problem (Deere & Company)

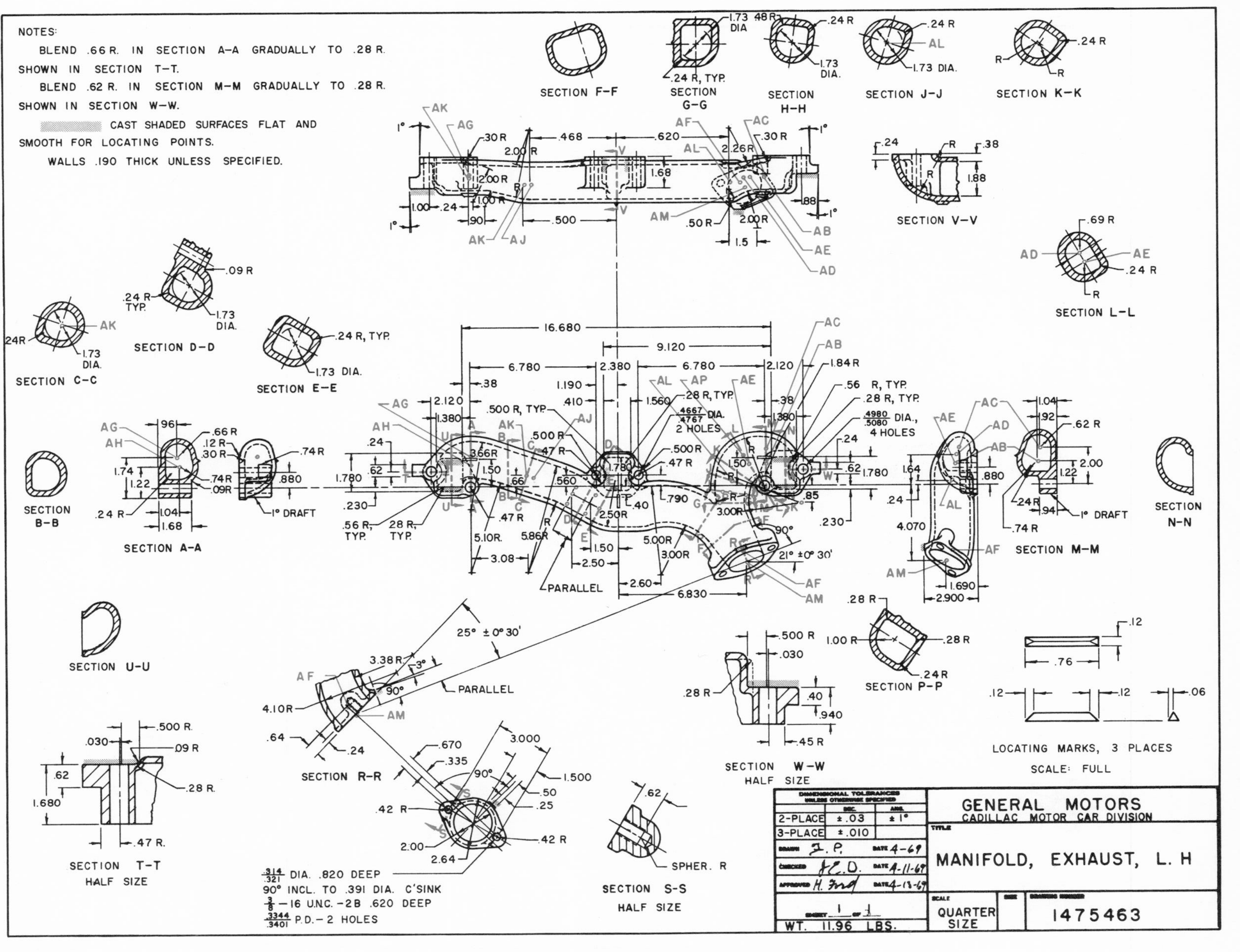

Fig. 5-20. Exhaust Manifold (General Motors)

INTERIOR DETAIL

INTERIOR DETAIL

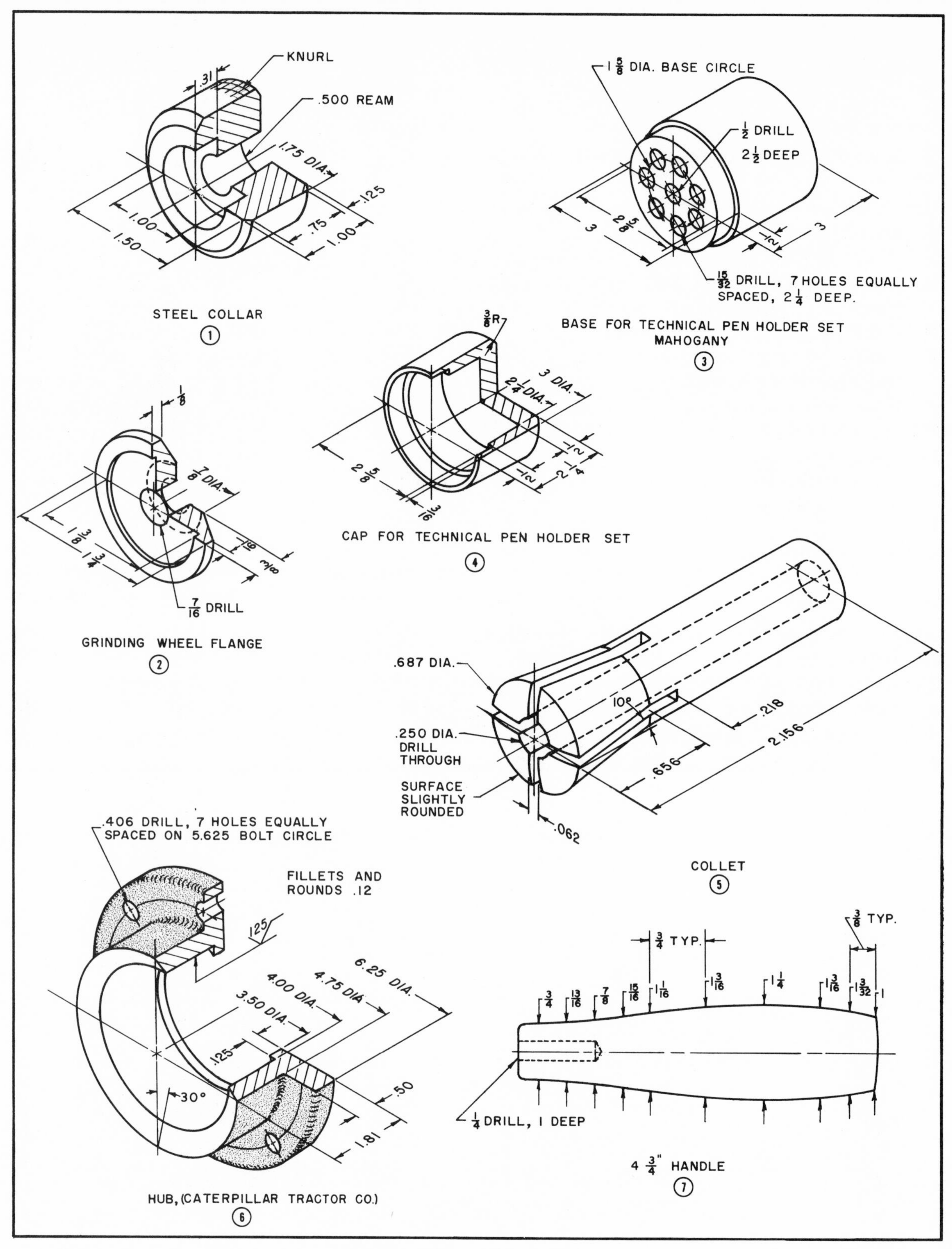

FIG. 5-21. Problems 1-7

with that in section *T-T*? What is the relationship of the diameter of the holes in these two sections?

12. What is the overall length of the exhaust manifold? What is its weight?
13. How many principal views of the manifold are shown?
14. Where do the locating marks shown just above the title block go?
15. What does the abbreviation *TYP* mean?
16. Generally, what is the pattern for placing the several section views in the position that they occupy on the drawing?
17. Make a full-size sketch of one of the three intake openings.
18. How far from the basic longitudinal center line are the bolt holes for the center intake opening located?
19. What is the distance between centers of these two holes?
20. There are four arcs in the interior of section *E-E*. What is the radius of each of these arcs?

III. Make sketches and/or drawings of the problems as assigned from Figs. 5-21, 5-22, and 5-23.

Problems, Fig. 5-21:

1. Make a two-view drawing of the steel collar including a half-section view.
2. Make a two-view drawing of the grinding wheel flange including a full-section view.
3. Make an appropriate mechanical drawing of the base for the technical penholder set including a full-section view.
4. Make a drawing of the cap for the technical penholder set. One view should be a half-section view.
5. Make a drawing of the collet including a partial-section view showing the construction of the collet end.
6. Make a mechanical drawing of the hub. Choose an appropriate section view.
7. Make a mechanical drawing of the handle and show removed section views from these dimension points: $^{13}\!/_{16}$, $^{15}\!/_{16}$, and $1\,^{3}\!/_{16}$.
8. Make an appropriate sectional view drawing of problems as assigned from 8 through 13, Fig. 5-22.
14. Make an appropriate drawing including sectional view of the bearing cap, Fig. 5-23.
15. Make a sectional drawing of the sheave at section *A-A*.
16. Make an offset section drawing of the brake ratchet at section *A-A*.

INTERIOR DETAIL

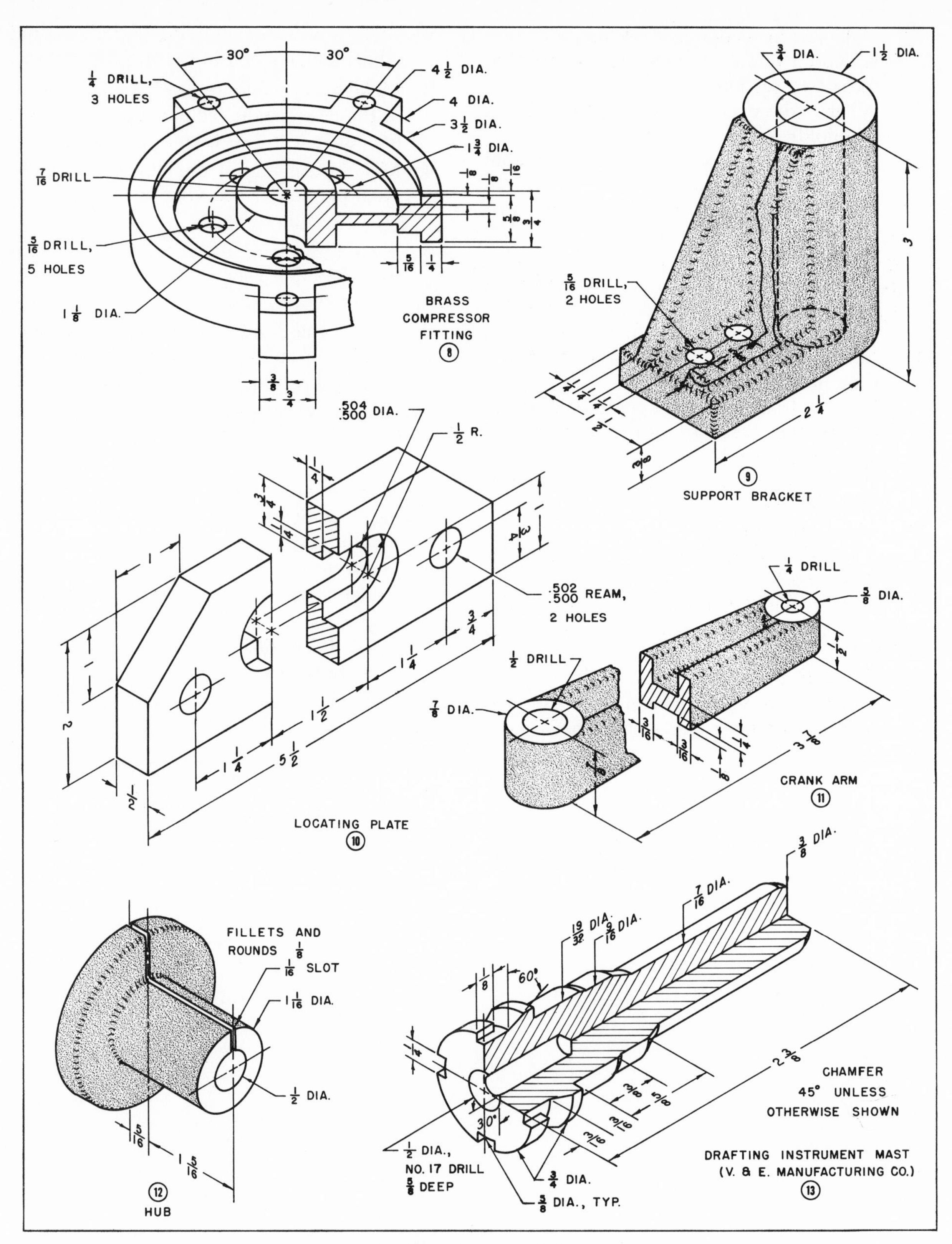

Fig. 5-22. Problems 8-13

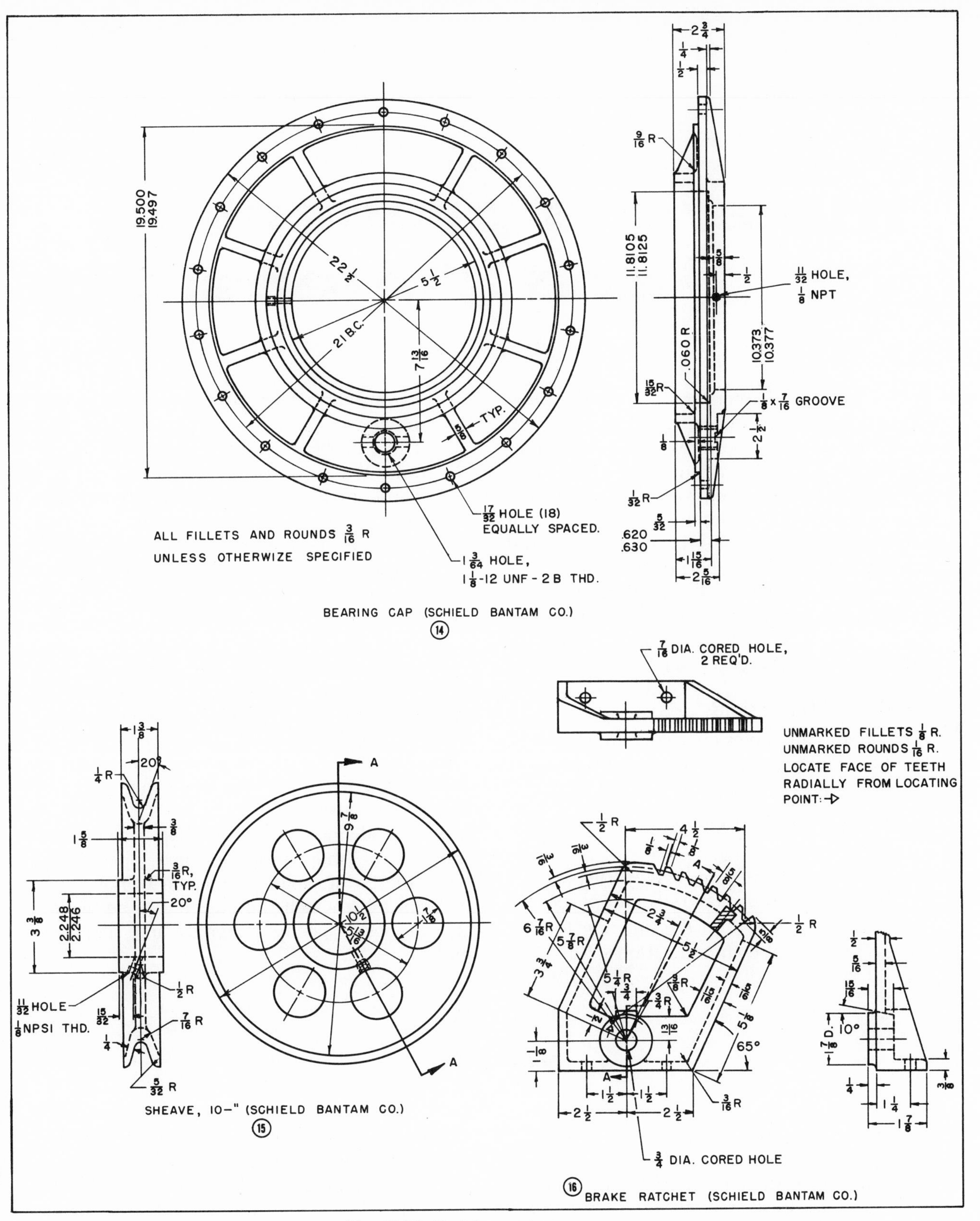

FIG. 5-23. Problems 14-16

CHAPTER SIX

materials processes and dimensions

The first five chapters bring us to the point where dimensions, notes, and specifications must be added to the drawings. Dimensions are required by whoever processes the materials and fabricates the product. For this reason, you need a general understanding of common materials used in production and common processes applied to those materials in the shop. Such an understanding will provide a base for making intelligent decisions with respect to choosing dimensions to use on a drawing and where to place them.

Functions of Dimensions

Dimensions and notes on a drawing show:

1. Size and location of parts and their geometrical subdivisions.
2. Permissible variations of size and location dimensions.
3. Special operations to be performed.
4. Specifications of materials and parts.

All of this is placed on the drawing for the express purpose of communication with:

1. Those who design, draw, and check the drawings.
2. Those in the purchasing department who order the materials and supplies.
3. Those in the methods department who plan the production procedures.
4. Those in the shop who make the product.
5. Those who inspect, check, and test the product.
6. Those who use the product.

The goal of private industrial enterprise is to produce something which will sell at a profit. If the draftsman should specify an impossible process, a process for which the company does not have the physical facilities or a process which is not the most economical, he will be endangering his job as well as endangering the life of the company.

The draftsman must develop an understanding of shop processes and operations, know the terminology peculiar to working the material from which the object is to be made, and properly specify materials and standard parts.

woods

Specifying Wood

Wood is a common material and easy to work. The dimensioning of a drawing from which a wood product is to be made requires an understanding of how wood is specified and processed. Lumber is sold by the board foot. A board foot is 1″ thick by 12″ wide by 1′ long.

Nominal and Actual Sizes

Lumber is specified by its nominal size. This is the actual size of a rough board as it is cut from the log. A common specification such as 2″ x 4″ x 8′ gives nominal thickness and width in inches by length in feet. Such a piece may be rough, S2S (surfaced two sides), or S4S. Table 6-1 shows rough sizes and corresponding actual sizes of hardwoods S2S, and softwoods S4S.

Grading and Classification

Hardwood and softwood lumber is classified by grade as shown in Table 6-2. Lumber is either kiln dried (KD) or air dried (AD). It also can be either plain sawed or quarter sawed, Fig. 6-1.

A wide variety of plywoods is available. They are of interior, exterior, or special types and are graded by appearance and quality of veneers

PLAIN-SAWED
WOOD TENDS TO WARP

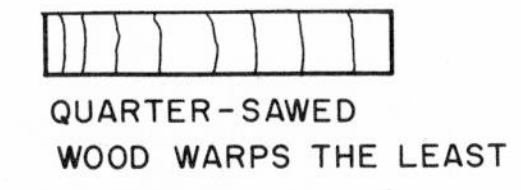

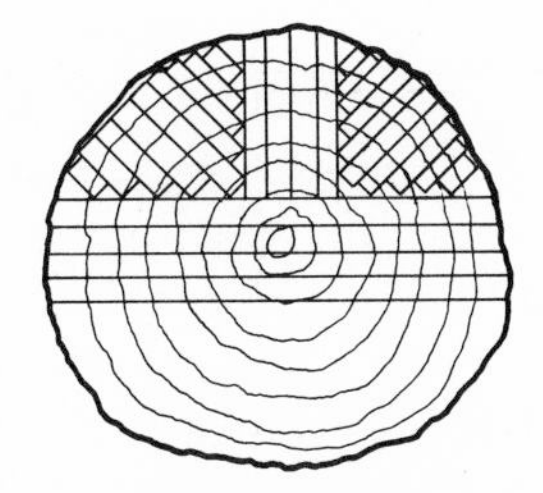

FIG. 6-1. Plain-Sawed and Quarter-Sawed Lumber Cuts

TABLE 6-1

Nominal Sizes and Actual Sizes of Common Lumber

Nominal Size	Surface Two Sides Hardwoods (S2S)	Surface Four Sides Softwoods (S4S)
½	5/16	
5/8	7/16	
¾	9/16	
1	13/16	
1½	1 5/16	
2	1¾	
1 x 2		¾ x 1 5/8
1 x 4		¾ x 3 5/8
1 x 6		¾ x 5 5/8
2 x 4		1 5/8 x 3 5/8
2 x 6		1 5/8 x 5 5/8
2 x 8		1 5/8 x 7 5/8

TABLE 6-2

Grades of Lumber

Softwood	Hardwood
Yard Lumber — less than 5″ thick, intended for general building purposes. Select — Good appearance and finishing quality. Grade A — practically clear, suitable for natural finishes. Grade B — generally clear, suitable for natural finishes. Grade C — for high quality paint finishes. Grade D — can be painted. Common — general utility grade not of finishing quality. #1 Common — sound and tight knotted, suitable for use without waste. #2 Common — larger and more pronounced defects but sound — suitable for use without waste. #3 Common — coarser features than #2 — some waste expected. #4 Common — low quality — waste expected. #5 Common — lowest quality; waste expected but, must be usable. Factory and Shop Lumber — for manufacturing purposes, equal to Grade B select or better. #1 Average 8″ wide. #2 Average 7″ wide. Structural Lumber — lumber 5″ thick or more; grade is based on the strength of the piece.	First and Seconds, FAS — a combination of first grade which is at least 91.66% clear and second grade which is at least 83.33% clear. Selects — face side must be as good as seconds, reverse side as good as #1 common. #1 Common — some defects #2 Common — with defects but suitable for small cuttings.

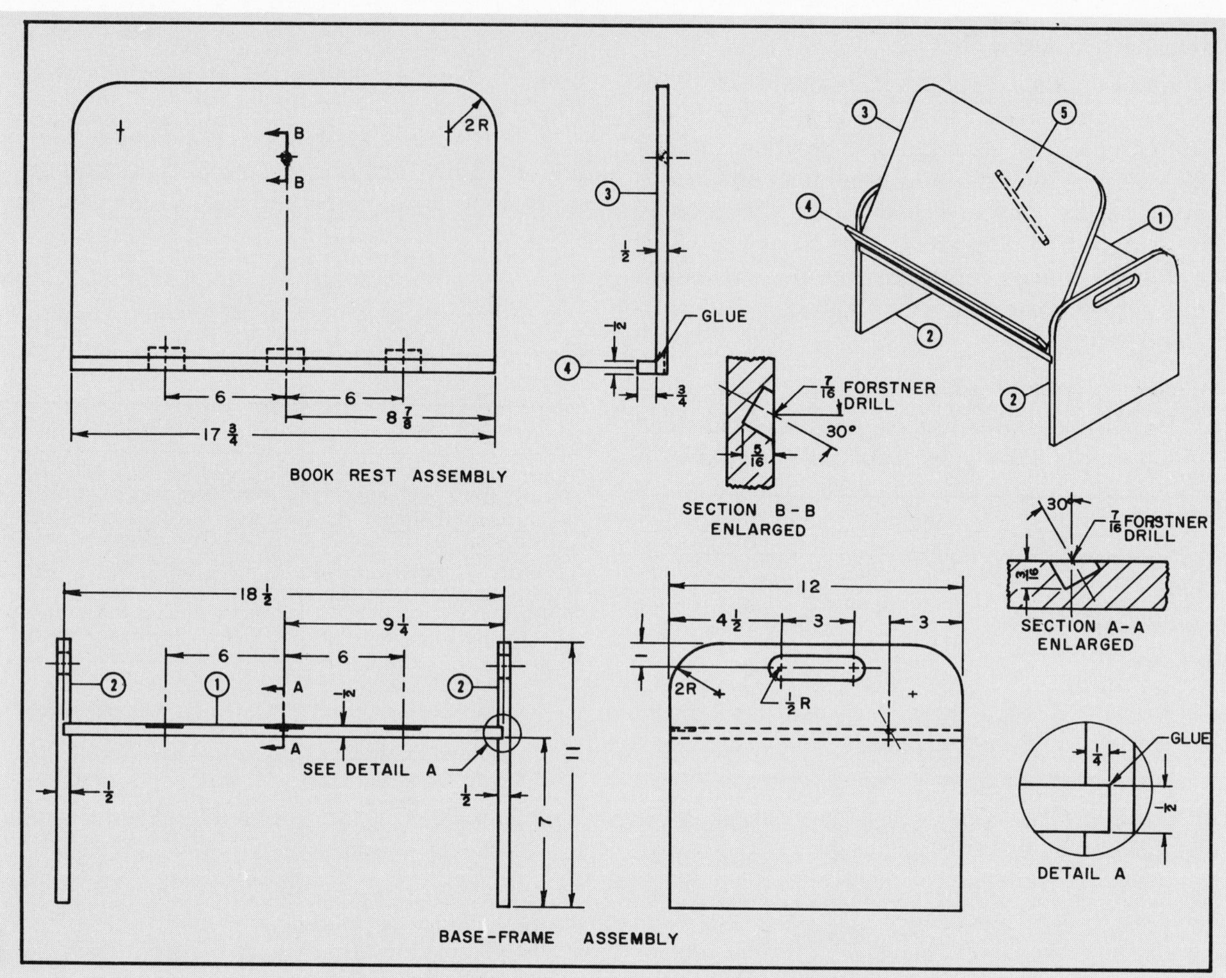

FIG. 6-2. Portable Book Rest (Gary Anderson)

used. Plywood is sold by the square foot and should be specified by the standard thicknesses of less than ¼″ to more than 1″. The number of plys in the plywood will be in odd numbers such as 3-ply and upwards. The most common plywood panel size is 4′ x 8′.

Wood substitutes such as masonite, particleboard and many others are now on the market.

For further information on woods and/or wood substitutes, consult the various manufacturers' catalogs, or phone or visit your nearest wood products dealer.

Dimensions for Overall Size

Finished Bill of Materials

As an illustrative example, consider the requirements for the portable book rest in Fig. 6-2. The material must be of mahogany and specified in the proper quantities[1]. To obtain the required dimensions for the finished bill of materials, you need the overall dimensions for Parts 1, 2, 3, and 4, Fig. 6-3. In addition to these, you need the specifications for the standard parts such as the hardware items: screws, hinges, and the prop rod. Appropriate finishing materials and supplies such as glue will also need to be identified for the bill of materials as shown in Table 6-3.

Stock List

From the bill of materials and with an understanding of the grading and specifying of lumber, a stock cutting list can be made which will show the nominal sizes of pieces of lumber to be ordered or taken from the stock room. Allowances will have to be made for building up

[1] See TD-6-1 for characteristics and uses of various woods.

TABLE 6-3

Bill of Materials for Book Rest

Part No.	Name	Material	Quantity	Size
1	Base	Mahogany	1	½ x 12 x 18½
2	Side	Mahogany	2	½ x 11 x 12
3	Book rest	Mahogany	1	½ x 12 x 17⅞
4	Stop	Mahogany	1	½ x ¾ x 17¾
5	Prop rod	Birch dowel	1	⅜ x 9
6	Hinges, butt	Wrought brass (narrow)	3	1½ x ⅞
7	Screws	F. H. brass	6	½″ x No. 2
	Glue			
	Wood filler			
	Stain			
	Sanding sealer			
	Lacquer			

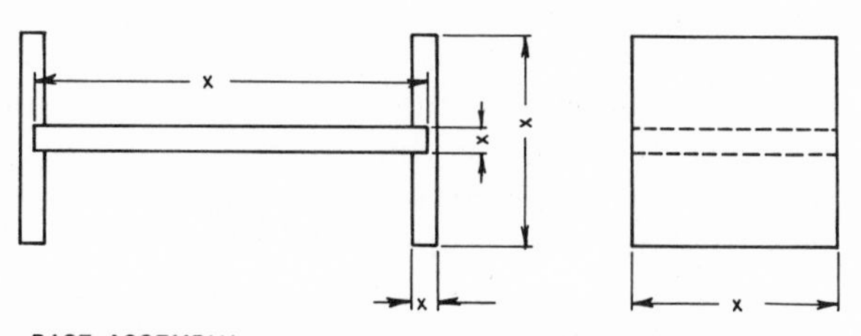

BASE ASSEMBLY
DIMENSIONS REQUIRED FOR BILL OF MATERIALS

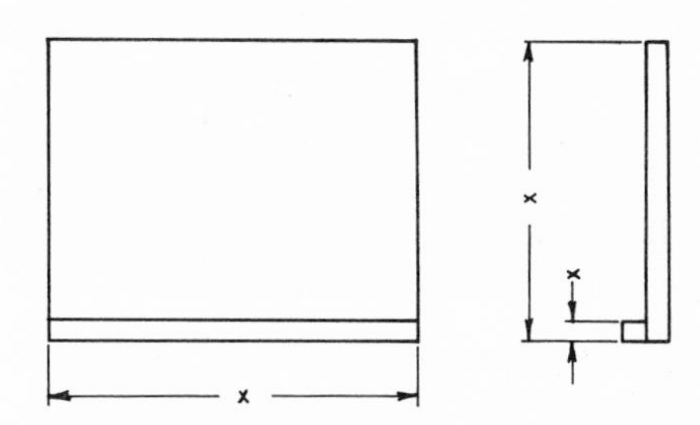

BOOK REST ASSEMBLY
DIMENSIONS REQUIRED FOR BILL OF MATERIALS

Fig. 6-3. Dimensions Required for the Bill of Materials

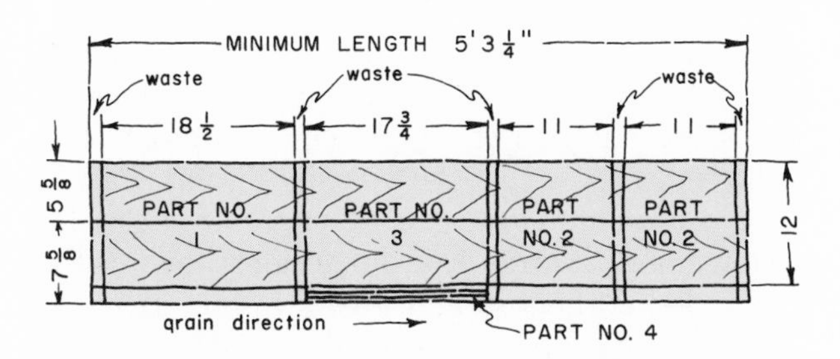

A NOMINAL 1 x 6 IS ACTUALLY ¾ x 5⅝.
A NOMINAL 1 x 8 IS ACTUALLY ¾ x 7⅝.

STOCK LIST

NO. PCS.	SIZE	KIND OF WOOD	QUAN.
1	1x6x6	FAS MAHOGANY S2S	3 BD. FT.
1	1x8x6	FAS MAHOGANY S2S	4 BD. FT.

Fig. 6-4. Planning the Stock List

stock to the required width, for the width of saw cuts for trimming, as well as for the amount to be taken off by planing, Fig. 6-4.

Plan the Layout for Cuttings

When the stock has been gathered together and you have looked over the pieces that are to be used, make a rough layout of the pieces to be cut. These dimensions can be taken from the drawing or from the finished bill of materials. The layout is made with white chalk and a framing square. Allowances of $\frac{1}{16}$″ for planing, ¼″ for each saw cut, and ½ to 1″ for the length of each piece are made.

Surface to Thickness

When the boards have been built up to rough width by gluing, the piece is surfaced. This operation is performed by planing and may be done on a machine surfacer or by hand with a plane. In either case, the dimension required is the final thickness of the boards to be cut from this stock.

Cut to Size

The various pieces are now carefully cut to length (cross-cut sawing) and width (rip sawing). These dimensions should be taken directly from the drawings although they appear in the bill of materials. An allowance of about $\frac{1}{16}$″ is left for jointing or planing to the final width. Cutting to length should be done as accurately as possible so that planing end grain need not be done. Cut the prop rod to length as shown in the bill of materials.

Permissible Variation

Dimensions are not absolute. If a wood piece is specified in the drawing as 11″ in length, it would not be reasonable to require it to be exactly 11″. If it seems important to do so, a note may appear on a drawing indicating the level of precision required for the dimensions. In rough carpentry one might be off on some dimensions by a half inch without making much difference. In some furniture and cabinet work you might want to hold a close tolerance such as "hold all dimensions to ± 1/64″.

Dimensions for Details of Shape

The main pieces have been surfaced, cut to length and cut to width. So far, the dimensions used have left all of the pieces rectangular. The drawings show that the two side pieces, Part 2, have rounded corners at the top and a slot for convenient lifting. The dimension showing the rounded corners should give a radius. Because both corners are obviously alike, only one need be dimensioned. The center of the radius can be located by measuring in 2″ from each side, and the location for the rounded corner can be scribed or marked with dividers set at a radius of 2″. The rounds can be made by band sawing, paring with a chisel, or jig sawing — all followed by sanding. The same reasoning follows for dimensioning the rounded ends of Part 3, the book rest.

The overall size of the hand-hole slot is 1″ x 4″ with the ends rounded. The important dimensions for this slot, however, are the locations of the centers for the rounded ends because the slot will probably be laid out with dividers and straightedge. Cutting of the slot may be done by using a brace and an expansion bit with a diameter of 1″, and then keyhole sawing to the straight lines with final finishing of the exterior surfaces by filing and sanding. Another method is to drill a suitable hole through which a jig saw or coping saw blade is placed. Just enough wood for filing and sanding is left inside the layout lines. In either case, the important dimensions, in both layout and construction, are the location from two working edges of each center line and the radius of the two rounded ends. Because the slot is obviously symmetrical about the center lines, it is *not* necessary to show the radius at both ends, the width of the slot, the length of the slot, nor the distance of either edge of the slot from a working edge. If the edges of all pieces are to be slightly rounded so that they are not dangerously sharp, a note should appear to "soften all arrises". This is usually done by sanding and should be done before assembly.

By way of summary you should remember that details of shape require dimensions of size as well as dimensions of location.

Dimensions for Subassembly

To assemble the sides to the base frame, a *dado joint* is called for in the side pieces. Again you will need both a location from a working edge and the size of the dado cut. Because of the lack of space for dimensioning a dado of this size on a drawing at this scale, it is necessary to show a separate detail properly keyed and labeled. Assembly is to be made with glue. The location dimension is shown on the main drawing. In a simple drawing such as this one, it is understood that the same dado is cut on the opposite side in the same relative place. In more complicated drawings, both dadoes could be encircled and referred to as detail *A*.

It is clear that the stop, Part 4, comes at the base of the book rest so the only needed instruction is to use glue for assembly.

Dimensions for Assembly

The assembly hardware has been specified in the bill of materials. The gain for the hinges must be located and cut. The steady holes for the prop rod must be located and cut.

Hinges are generally located by center lines. The hinge is then placed over the center line, outlined with a very sharp pencil, and cut to depth. Depth of the gain cut is determined by the thickness of the hinge and need not be shown on the drawing. Notice that the centers for the gain cuts in the base are located from a working edge which is not common to that used for the same purpose for the book rest. Therefore, it is particularly important to locate these gain cuts by appropriate center line dimensions for both pieces. Because these two subassemblies must fit together to function properly, the middle center line is located first and the two outside gain-cut center lines are dimensioned from this. If a large number of these units were to be made, it would be worthwhile to carefully detail and dimension the gain cuts since one would obviously not fit each hinge, if producing a large number of these units.

The center of the steady holes for the prop are located by center lines. Then an angle for drilling the hole is shown. A forstner bit (which does not have a lead screw making a small extra hole) is specified to get a flat bearing surface for the prop in the steady holes. The depth of the hole is specified. Enlarged sectional views are shown for added clarity.

To dimension drawings using wood as the chief material involves the understanding of many operations and processes not shown in this illustrative example. You can learn more about these from actual experience in a wood shop and from consulting a standard textbook on woodworking.

metals

Much of today's manufacturing is based on the processing and fabricating of metals. To dimension products having metal parts, the draftsman must understand how metals are processed and fabricated in the shop.

Specifying Metal

Metal is sold by the pound and comes in a wide variety of plates, sheets, bars, rods and shapes. Consult suppliers' catalogs for specific needs.

Metals are generally classified as ferrous or non-ferrous. TD-6-2 summarizes some characteristics and uses of metals. Further information about these materials and others will be found in various engineering handbooks.

Metals are manufactured to actual sizes usually holding a relatively small tolerance range.

Parts lists on drawings identify each part whether manufactured or purchased.

Parts lists or bills of materials show the assigned part number, name, number of parts required for it and the material from which it is to be made, Fig. 6-4.

Dimensioning Metal Parts

Examine the working drawings for the parts of a can holder, called the "Food Warmer," to observe how the dimensions are placed on these drawings, Fig. 6-5.

TABLE 6-4

Parts List for Food Warmer

Part No.	Name	Quantity	Material/Size
1	Base	1	Cast aluminum
2	Lower bracket	1	1⁄16 x 1 1⁄8 steel
3	Lower bracket	1	1⁄16 x 1 1⁄8 steel
4	Lower bracket	1	1⁄16 x 1 1⁄8 steel
5	Upper bracket	1	1⁄16 x 1 1⁄8 steel
6	Clamp bar	1	1⁄16 x 1 1⁄8 steel
7	Regular square nut	1	1⁄4 x 20-NC
8	Thumb screw	1	1⁄4 x 20-NC 2″ Long
9	Handle shaft	1	3⁄8 diam. x 5 17⁄64 blank length steel
10	Handle	1	Wood
11	Ferrule	1	1⁄32 x 2″ diam. blank size steel
12	Round head bolt	1	5⁄16 x 18-NC 7⁄8″ long
13	Plain heavy washer	1	I. D. 3⁄8, O.D. 7⁄8, 14 Ga.
14	Wing nut	1	5⁄16 18-NC
15	Knock-out core	1	#14, .083 x 1.50 for use in casting only

MAT'LS, PROCESSES
DIMENSIONS

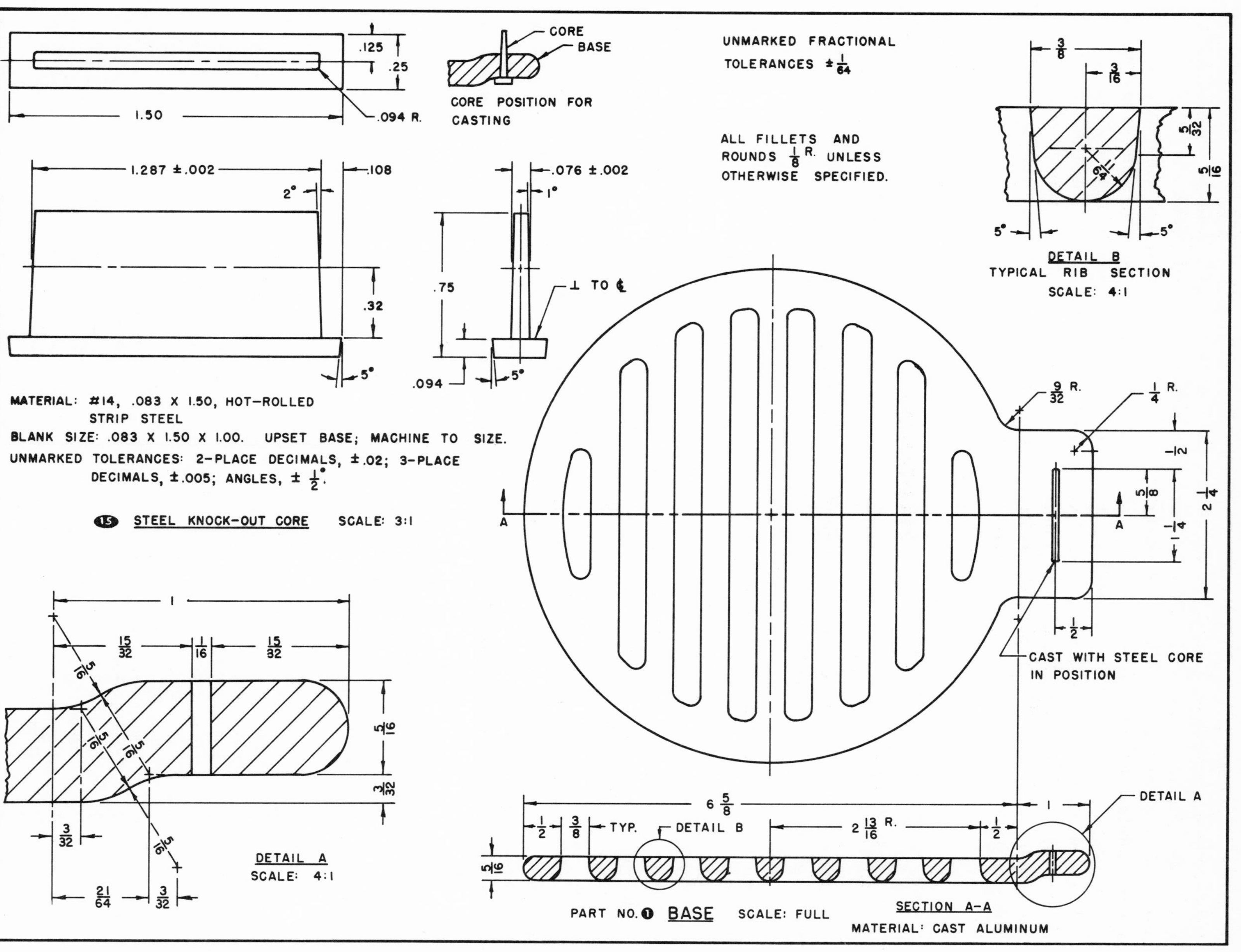

Fig. 6-5A. Drawings for Food Warmer

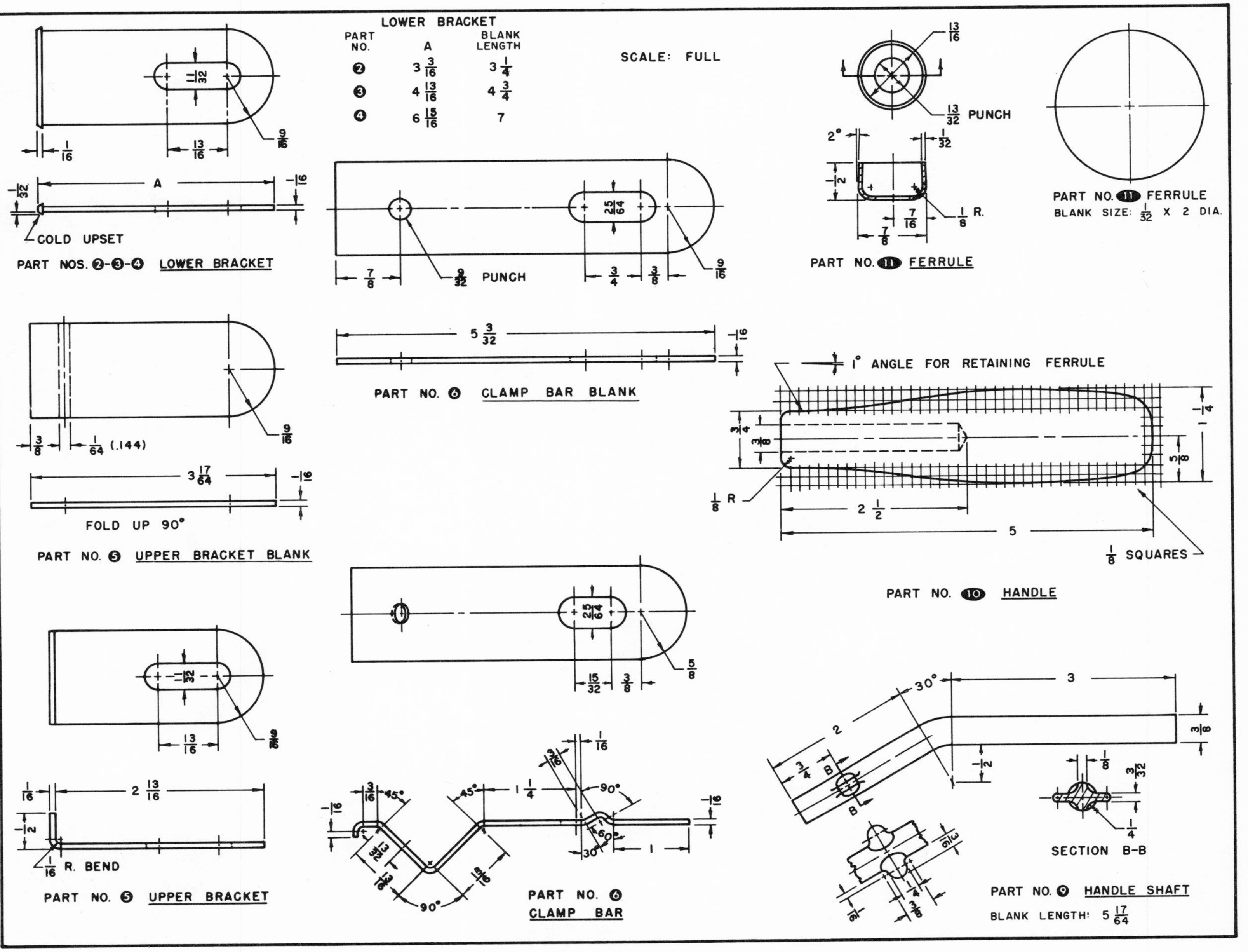

FIG. 6-5B. Drawings for Food Warmer

MAT'LS, PROCESSES DIMENSIONS

Blank Lengths

First look at Part 5, the upper bracket. This part will be produced from carbon steel which comes in strips 1/16″ x 1⅛″. The first step will be one in which the parts are blanked, *i.e.*, sheared on a large press to the blank size shown. To produce this cut, a cutting die will have to be made which will cut the contour form shown at the semi-circular end of the strip and cut the piece to length at the opposite end at the same time. The radius of the semi-circular end and the overall blank length are given so that the piece can be blanked.

Punching

The second step will probably be to punch the slot in the bracket. Here you need to know the width of the slot, the length of the slot between centers, the radius of the semi-circular ends, and the location of the slot with respect to both the end and the sides of the bracket. Notice in the drawing the importance of the 9/16″ radius dimension at the end, giving the location both from the end and from the side, as well as defining the shape of the end.

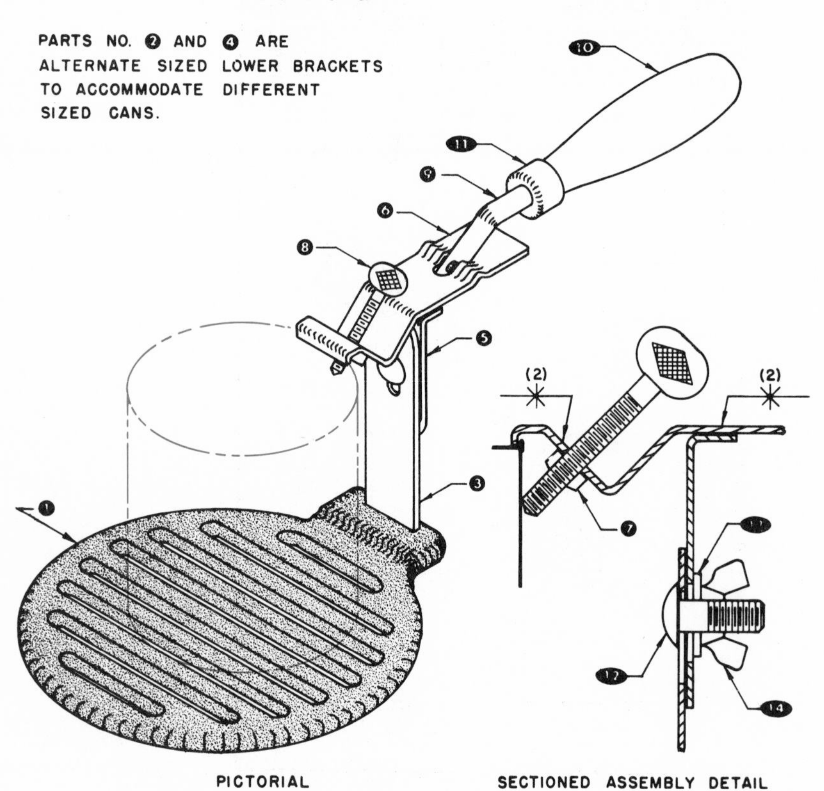

FIG. 6-5C. Pictorial for Food Warmer

Bending

The third step will be to make the right angle bend. The blank drawing shows the position at which the bend is to be made, the bend allowance, and the direction and number of degrees in the bend.

Checking and Inspection

The finished drawing shows sizes and locations of geometrical features of the finished bracket for checking and inspection.

Study the drawings of Parts 2, 3, and 5 to observe the requirements of the shop with respect to placement of dimensions.

Note on Parts 2 and 3 that a forging process called *upsetting* is required. What dimensions are given to tell the location and size of the upset? What is the effect of upsetting on blank length?

Drawing and Trimming

To make the ferrule, Part 11, requires a *drawing* operation. The piece is blanked and drawn into shape, the hole is punched, and the piece is trimmed. Which dimensions are required for blanking? drawing? punching? turning?

Forging

Part 9 requires forging and bending. Part 10, the handle, is turned from wood. Note that the handle contour is defined by a grid pattern as well as overall dimensions. From this a template can be made which will permit the handles to be turned to the desired shape.

Casting

Part 1, the base, is a casting. Note the draft angle which permits the pattern to be withdrawn from the foundry sand without breaking the cavity.

A pattern of the base must be made. Generally it is made of wood in the pattern shop. Allowances must be made by the patternmaker both for the shrinkage of the metal from which it is to be cast and for machining to finished size. Study the drawing of Part 1.

Dimensions for Assembly

The ferrule, Part 10, fits over the end of the handle, Part 9. Note that the ferrule is of slightly smaller diameter at the open end so that it won't slip off the handle after assembly.

The slot in the clamp bar, Part 5, must be long enough after bending so that the lugs can be slipped through to seat the handle, and so the handle can be unseated and removed after the holder is placed over the fire for cooking.

When the ferrule is in place on the wood handle, the handle shaft is driven as a *force fit* into the handle.

Slots in the upper and lower brackets are placed so that the device is adjustable for cans of different heights. The round head bolt with a square neck must fit the slot. A washer and wing nut for tightening must also fit this.

The thumb screw must be positioned so that it can be turned toward the can, thus gripping the top of the can securely so it won't slip off the holder.

How would the slot in Part 1, which receives the lower bracket, be processed if only one unit were to be produced? How would this slot be produced if the production run was for 1000 units? *Hint*—if the slot is too costly to produce, the functional relationship may have to be re-designed to reduce the cost. This is a typical engineering problem. As this is designed, a steel knockout core is cast into the base. When the part is cooled, the core is knocked out. The lower brackets should then fit the slot.

Dimensions for Standard Parts

Standard parts (purchased parts) are not drawn in detail and dimensioned. They are carefully specified on the parts list and are shown in the assembly drawing together with appropriate part numbers.

It is not the purpose of this chapter to present all of the metals processes. Additional information may be found by reading standard references on this subject and by doing some of the problems at the end of this chapter. Whenever possible, men at work and the operations and jobs they perform can be studied.

TD-6-3 shows some characteristics and uses of materials other than woods and metals.

Chapter 6 — Problems and Projects

1. Assume that 200 units of the portable book rests are to be produced by a manufacturer of furniture. Make out the order for the lumber needed. Allow 10% waste. Make out the order for the necessary hardware including screws. Estimate the amount of glue, wood filler, sanding sealer, and lacquer for this production run. Using prices found in catalogs, estimate the total cost of materials for 200 units.
2. Make a layout for the lumber cuttings of one portable book rest to be made from plywood.
3. List the operations required to produce the wall-mounted corner study unit, Fig. 6-6. Show the layout for cutting the lumber from plywood sheets. Make a bill of materials. Plan to assemble it with glue and screws. What dimensions are required to produce the study unit?
4. List the operations required to make the vise, Fig. 6-7. Make a bill of materials for the vise. Through a sketch show what dimensions are required to make a vise.
5. Consult one or more references on woodworking to answer these questions with a dimensioned sketch.

MAT'LS, PROCESSES
DIMENSIONS

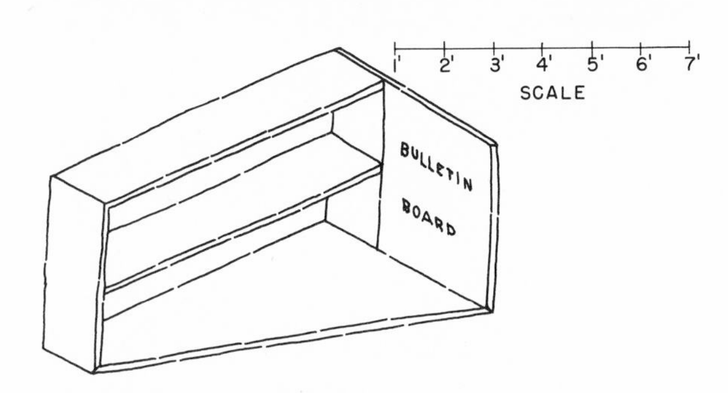

Fig. 6-6. Wall Mounted Corner Study Unit (Lester Slater)

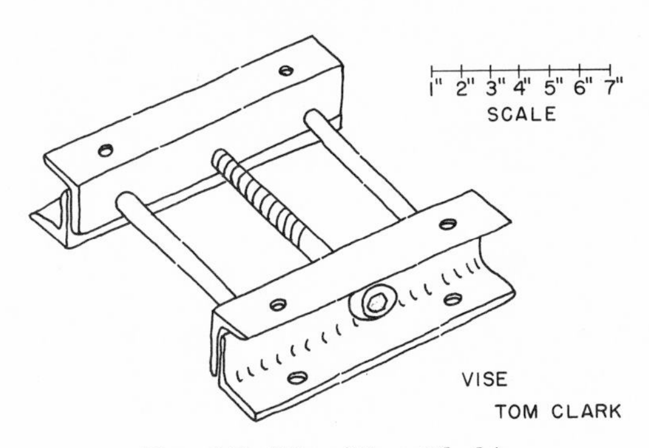

Fig. 6-7. Vise (Tom Clark)

a. What dimensions are required to construct a dado joint? Mortise and tenon joint? Miter joint? Half lap joint?
b. What dimensions are required to drill the pilot and shank holes for wood screws?
c. What is the difference between a chamfer and a bevel? Show how each is dimensioned.
d. What dimensions are required to produce an irregular curve form such as a free-form coffee table top?

6. Consult an engineering handbook or other standard references on metalworking to answer these questions.
   a. What is a metal extrusion?
   b. What is the difference between drilling and reaming?
   c. What is the difference between counterboring and countersinking? Show with a sketch how each is dimensioned.
   d. What are SAE steels?
7. What differences are there, if any, between the dimensions for a product when only one item is produced by a student in a shop class as compared with those industry would use to make a production run of 500 units?

CHAPTER SEVEN

lettering the drawing

Is Lettering Ability Really Important?

Lettering on a drawing has the simple function of communication. This is so evident that its significance is often overlooked. Unless the intended meaning is given the reader, the effort to communicate has failed. Engineers, draftsmen, and those who read their drawings know the importance of lettering.

The formation of a single number on a drawing may make a great deal of difference in the mass production of a product. For example, one chief draftsman reports that a poorly made *3* was misread as a *5* in the shop. Before the error was recognized, $10,000 worth of parts — all the wrong size — had been processed. The parts had to be scrapped, the correction made, and new parts run.

An architect reported an illegible lettering error that cost him $76,000. During the excavation layout on a home for the elderly, a numeral *3* was misread as an *8*. This error was discovered after the excavation had been completed and the foundation had been poured. The error resulted in the foundation being 5 feet lower in the ground than was required. To correct this error, special concrete columns were designed, fill dirt was purchased and trucked into the cavity, and the concrete was poured to raise the building to the required foundation height. The owners demanded that the architect pay the cost for the original foundation because of the error. When all associated expenses were tallied, the communication error cost the architect $76,000.

Proper Position for Lettering

If you are a golfer, you probably know that the "pros" take a certain "stance" or position when "addressing" the ball. Many books have been written on this important subject. In most sports there are certain body positions that are vital to playing the game well. It is the same with lettering a drawing.

As you address (sit facing) the drafting table, you should be sitting squarely in your chair or on your stool. Your weight should be evenly distributed over the chair seat. Your feet should be on the floor or foot rest like the profile view in Fig. 7-1.

Do not slump over the table. Slumping results in a cramped position that will not contribute to effective letter formation.

For effective lettering, the paper must be free to be moved so that the draftsman can maintain the best sitting position for lettering. On large drawings, where it is not possible to move the drawing conveniently, the draftsman must move about the board in various stances and positions to do the lettering.

Fig. 7-1. Suggested Position for Lettering

LETTERING

Place both elbows on the drafting table surface while maintaining the position in the profile view of Fig. 7-1. Right-hander's should place their left hand at the top of the paper and bring their right hand so that a comfortable triangle is formed between the two elbows and the left hand. Left-hander's should place their right hand so that the triangle is formed between the two elbows and the left hand. The result will be a natural position both for writing and for lettering.

The pencil should be held firmly but not tightly, for lettering should be done in an attitude of relaxation rather than one of tenseness. If you become tense when lettering, you should stop and go on with some other activity or move your hands about to increase the circulation of blood in the hand. When you go back to lettering, it will be done more easily.

Use Standard Lettering

The USAS states that "the most important requirement for lettering on drawings is legibility." *Single-stroke Gothic* is the style of lettering recommended for general use. It has the advantages of simplicity and legibility, and the lettering may be done quickly and easily. Both vertical and inclined styles of this lettering are approved by the USAS. See TD-7-1 and 2. *Inclined* lettering is easier for some draftsmen, while *vertical* is easier for others. An important consideration is that all lettering on a given drawing should be of one style. Study these two tables in the TD section carefully. As you practice lettering, keep your text open to the style of lettering you choose to use.

The USAS recommends that for "mechanical or equipment industries, capitals be used for all lettering on working drawings." Types 1, 2, 3, 4, and 5 as shown in TD-7-3 are all capital letters. Type 6 is an optional group used for lower case letters. USAS standards are used for fractional and decimal dimensioning. Notice in TD-7-3 that SAE does not use lower case letters.

Lettering on drawings is the same size whether the draftsman is working on a small sheet of paper or a large one. When you are going to reduce the size of a drawing, the letters should be larger. Standardization of lettering is desirable, and the student draftsman should carefully follow the standards.

Lettering Must Reproduce Well

Pencil Lettering

The choice of pencil for lettering depends on the draftsman. The *HB, F, H,* and *2H* are among the common pencils used. The draftsman should choose one that will yield — with his lettering pressure — an intense black image for each letter or numeral made. Fig. 7-2 shows several samples of lettering made by using different pencils. Which one should this draftsman choose?

Good lettering should be of the same intensity and weight (or very nearly so) as object lines. Well-executed lines on a drawing mean very little if the lettering does not come through legibly on the reproduction. Quality reproduction of both numerals and letters is of extreme importance in industrial drawing.

Ink Lettering

Ink may be used for lettering. In a few industries a drawing made with pencil is lettered with ink. It is general practice that inked drawings are always lettered with ink.

The choice of lettering pen for ink is determined by the style and size of lettering. Regular and special pen holders are available for fine, medium, or heavy pen points, Fig. 7-3. For most freehand lettering on a drawing, a medium point such as Gillott No. 404 is appropriate. In recent years technical fountain pens that will not clog with the use of India ink have been developed. These are available with tips for making lines of different width. In addition to their use in freehand lettering, technical fountain pens may be used for inking with templates and for drawing lines mechanically. Occasional cleaning will prolong their life. The Koh-i-noor Rapidograph pen with 7 point sizes for lettering and drafting in ink is shown in Fig. 7-4.

Numerals on the Drawing

Guide Lines and Direction Lines

Lightweight *guide lines* and *direction lines* are used by the student draftsman and by many professional draftsmen. They are easy to draw and are well worth the time it takes to insure uniformity.

THIS SAMPLE IS B
THIS SAMPLE IS HB
THIS SAMPLE IS F
THIS SAMPLE IS H
THIS SAMPLE IS 2H
THIS SAMPLE IS 3H
THIS SAMPLE IS 4H
THIS SAMPLE IS 5H

FIG. 7-2. Samples of Pencil Lettering by One Draftsman

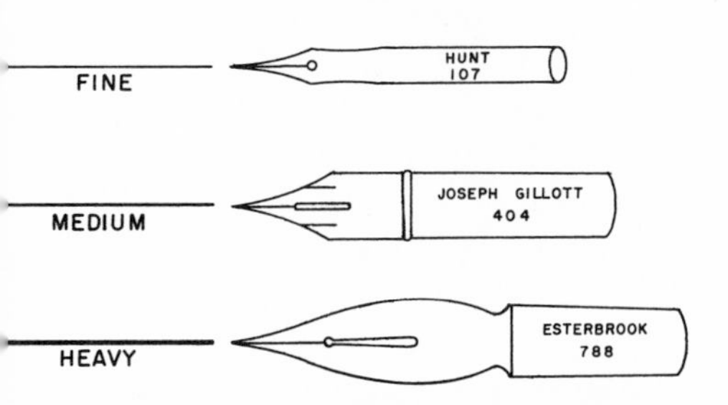

FIG. 7-3. Common Pen Points for Inking

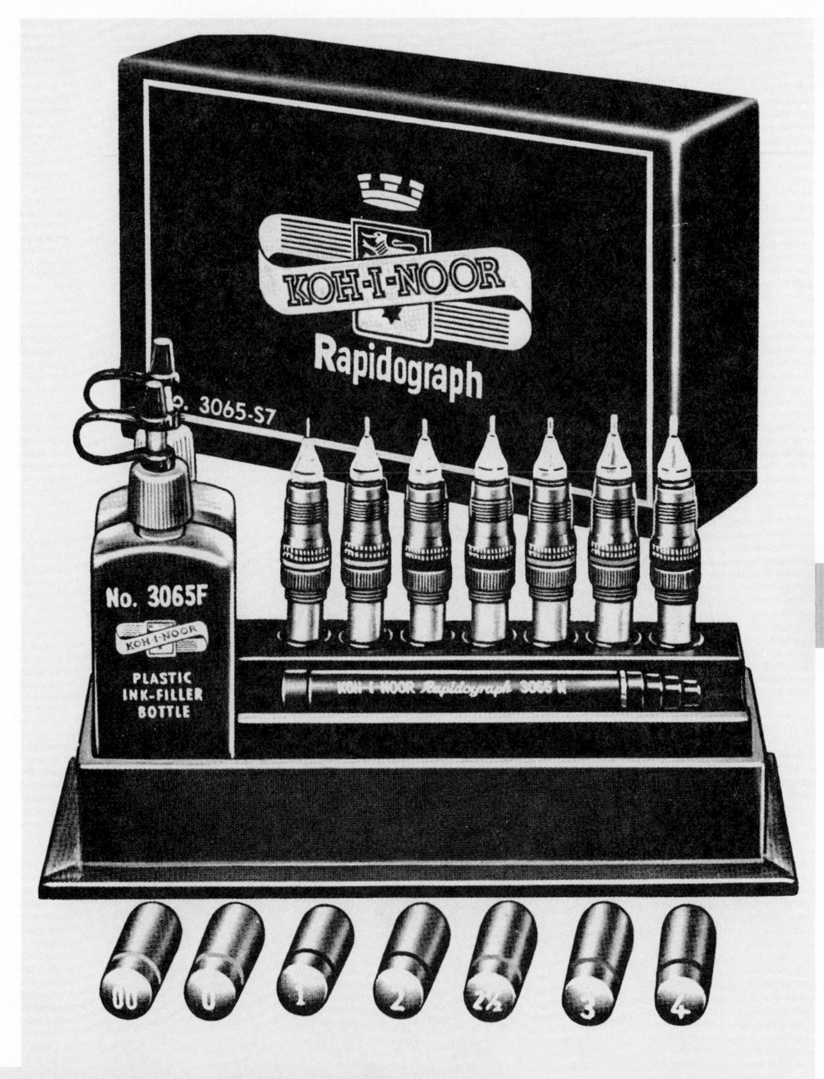

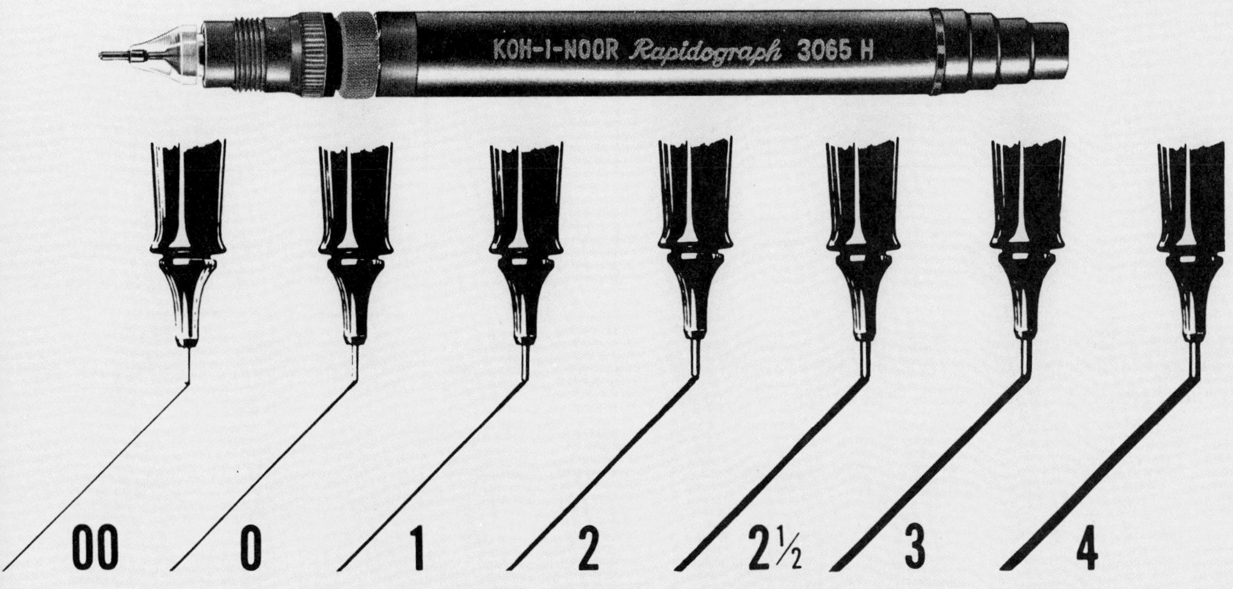

FIG. 7-4. Seven-Section Technical Fountain Pen Set (KOH-I-Noor, Inc.)

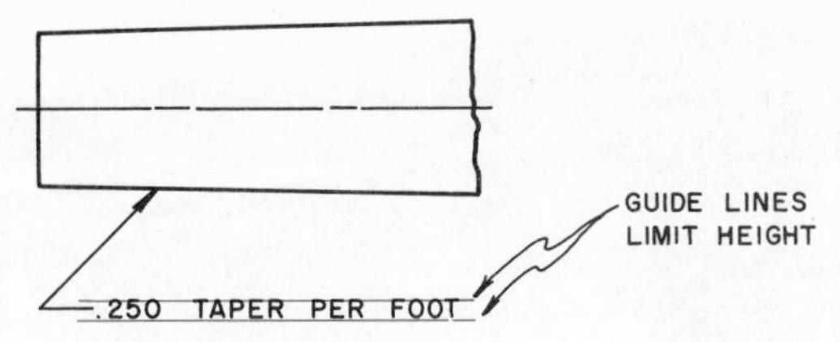

Fig. 7-5. Guide Lines Limit Height

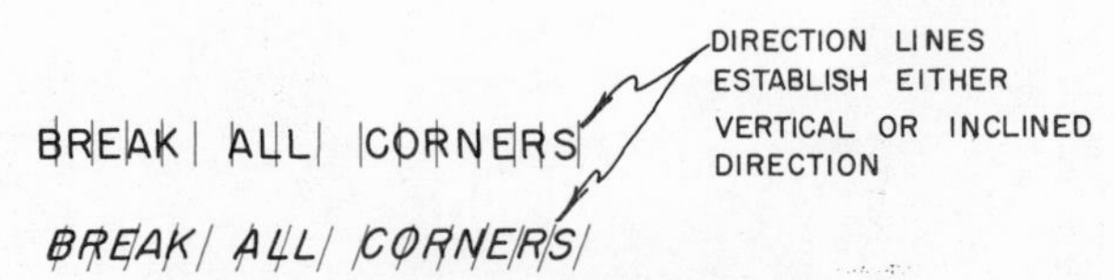

Fig. 7-6. Direction Lines Establish Vertical *or* Inclined Direction

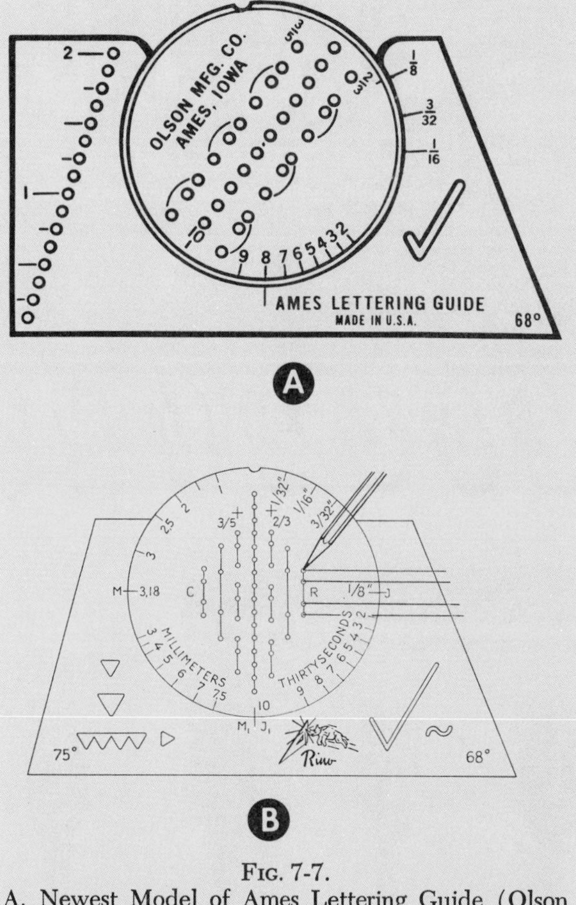

Fig. 7-7.
A. Newest Model of Ames Lettering Guide (Olson Mfg. Co.) Note: ⅛″ spaced holes along left frame.
B. Parallelograph (Gramercy) Note: Both English and metric spacing.

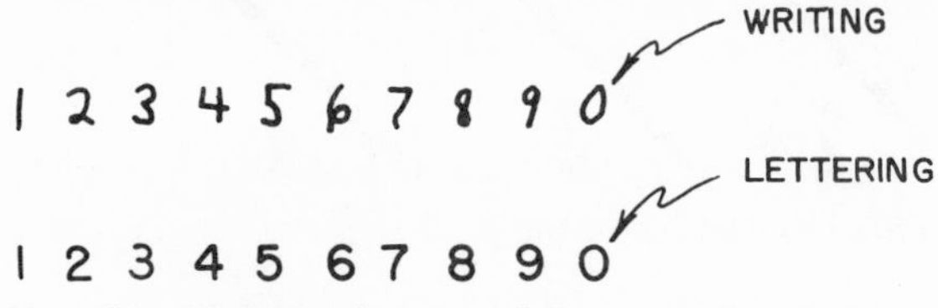

Fig. 7-8. Writing of Numerals Compared to Lettering

Guide lines are used to limit the height of both numerals and letters, Fig. 7-5. Direction lines are used to establish either vertical or inclined direction, Fig. 7-6. These may be drawn with T-square and triangles or with special instruments. The Ames guide line instrument, the Braddock Rowe Lettering Triangle, and the Parallelograph are examples, Fig. 7-7.

Numeral Formation

Use the correct form for each numeral. Compare the numerals as they are commonly written and as they should be lettered, Fig. 7-8. Numerals are carefully formed according to USAS and SAE recommendations. See TD section, 7-1 and 7-2. Numerals for dimensioning a drawing are placed between the dimension lines and should read from the bottom or from the right-hand side of the drawing. The unidirectional system of dimensioning, where all notes and dimensions read from the bottom of the drawing, is discussed in Chapter 8. Notice in Fig. 7-9 that guide lines carefully limit the height of whole numbers, and that the height is ⅛″.

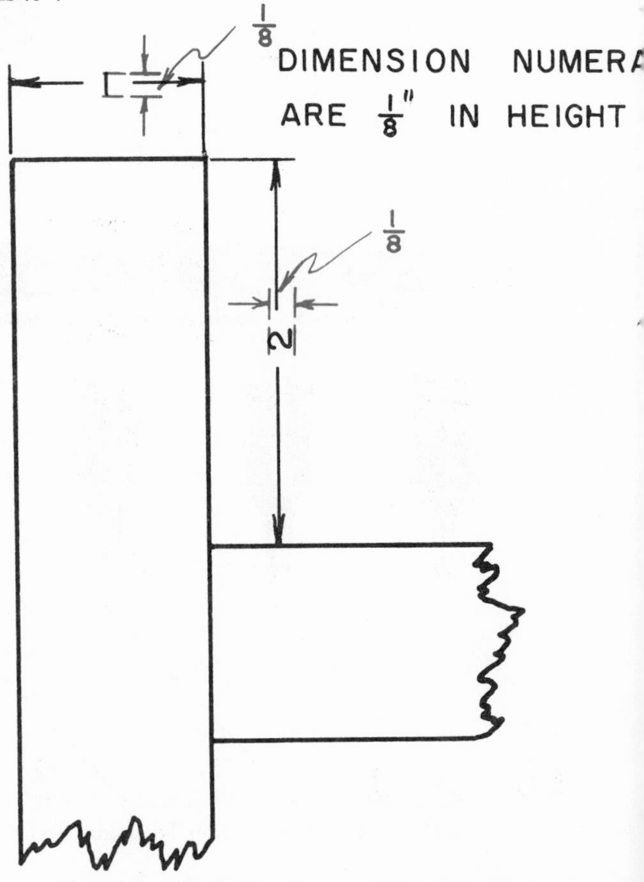

Fig. 7-9. Whole Numbers are ⅛″ in Height

Fractions

Numerals in fractions – denominators and numerators – should be smaller in size than the whole numbers. Fig. 7-10(A) shows guide lines for the whole number and the entire fraction. Notice that the numerator and denominator are three-fourths the height of the whole number in Fig. 7-10 (B).

As may be seen in Fig. 7-11, fractions read from the bottom or right-hand side of the drawing. Guide lines and direction lines are included to show how they are used in lettering. Note that the fraction bar is horizontal for fractions reading from the bottom of the page. The same relationship exists when reading from the right. The fraction bar always maintains this relationship – *even when using inclined lettering.* Note also that neither the numerator nor the denominator touches the fraction bar.

Decimals

Numerals used in decimal dimensioning are made as whole numbers, Fig. 7-12. Decimals with limits of size may appear as fractions without the bar. For example, note the distance between the centers of the holes in the shaft guide. SAE drafting standards recommend that decimal figures read from the bottom of the drawing. In the mechanical fields the trend is definitely toward SAE dimensioning.

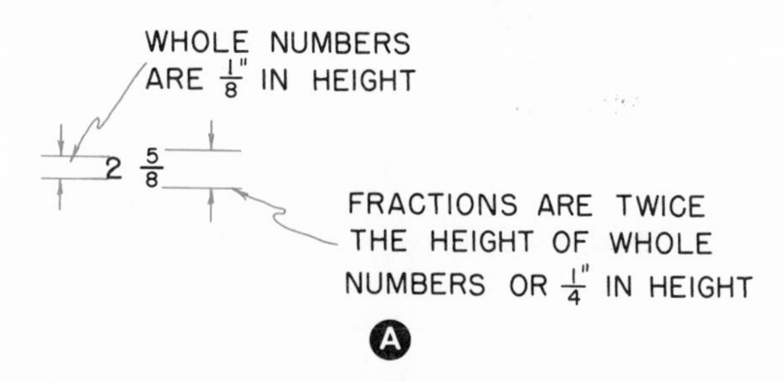

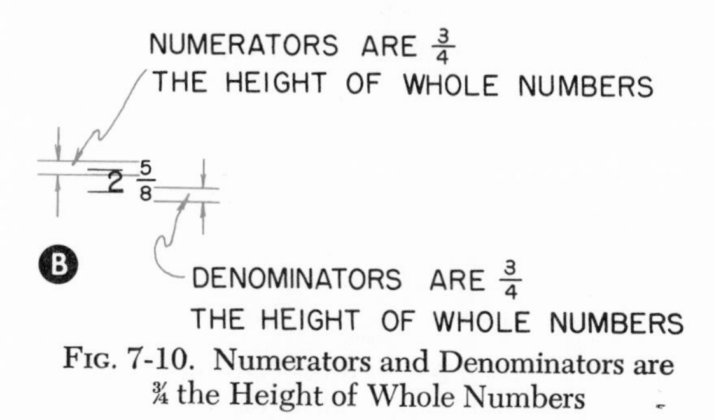

FIG. 7-10. Numerators and Denominators are ¾ the Height of Whole Numbers

Modified Numerals for Microfilming

The use of microfilm for master drawings (in which drawings are reduced to nearly one thirty-second of their original size and then enlarged or blown back to about 65% of the original size) has caused many industries to review the formation of standard numerals. One

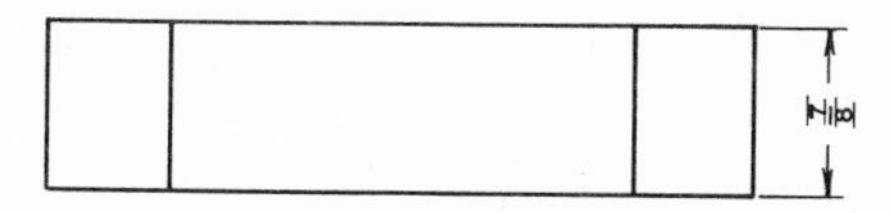

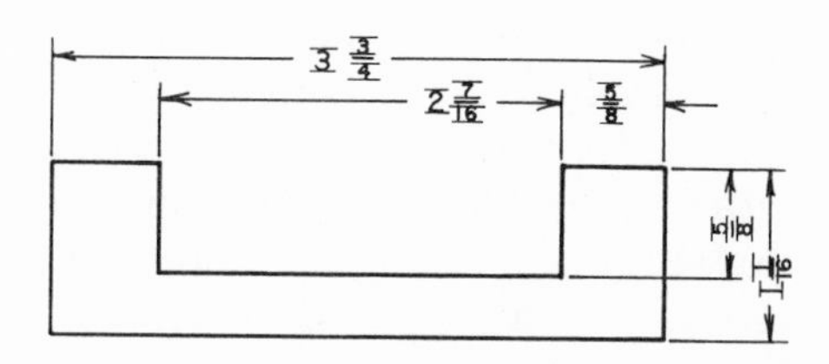

CLEAT
SCALE: FULL SIZE

FIG. 7-11. Fractions Read from the Bottom and Right Hand Side of Drawings

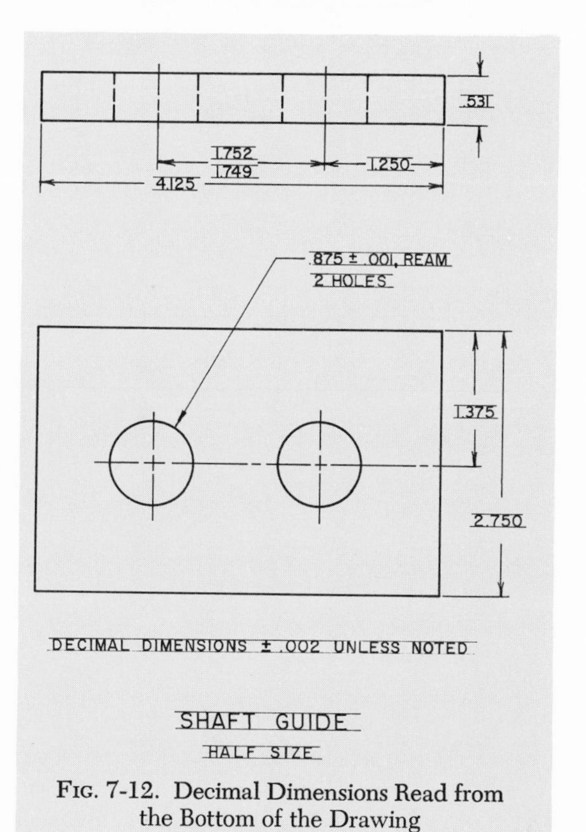

FIG. 7-12. Decimal Dimensions Read from the Bottom of the Drawing

company modified freehand lettered numerals so that misinterpretation would be less likely to occur. See Chapter 9, Fig. 9-4.

Lettering on the Drawing

Rules for Composition

Correct letter formation and uniformity are required to produce legible lettering. There are several aspects of uniformity:

1. UNIFORMITY OF STYLE. Only one style of lettering should be used on a drawing. There is a tendency for beginners to use letters which are not a part of the single-stroke Gothic style. A few of the special troublemakers are shown in Fig. 7-13. The simplicity of the single-stroke Gothic style is one reason why it is standard. Other styles may be appropriate on other drawings. For example, architectural lettering has a much different character than the lettering used in the processing industries, Fig. 7-14.
2. UNIFORMITY OF LINE WEIGHT. Lettering should be done with uniformly well-sharpened and well-pointed pencils. The weight of each letter should be dense black in order to produce a legible print from the drawing, Fig. 7-15. As a general rule, lettering should not be underlined. A few exceptions may be made by some industries where special emphasis is required.
3. UNIFORMITY OF HEIGHT. The letters of each line of lettering — and all lines of lettering on a single drawing — should be the same height. Uniformity of height is important as a matter of consistency, Fig. 7-16.
4. UNIFORMITY OF DIRECTION. Letters must carefully be made uniform in their direction. All letters on one drawing must be either vertical or inclined; never both, Fig. 7-17.
5. UNIFORMITY OF SPACING. Proper spacing of letters, words, lines, and paragraphs make for easy reading of the lettered material.
   a. SPACING OF LETTERS IN WORDS. Proper spacing of letters within a word makes the *relative space,* or area, between letters appear equal. Since the shapes of the letters are different, the space needed between adjacent parts of such letters as the capitals *H* and *I*, or *N* and *B*, is quite different from that needed between *L* and *E*, or *F* and *T*, Fig. 7-18. More space must be allowed

I J M W I AM JIM W.

a. TROUBLE MAKERS

I J M W I AM JIM W.

b. SINGLE-STROKE GOTHIC

FIG. 7-13. Troublemakers in Lettering

A B C D E F G H I J K L
M N O P Q R S T U V W X
Y Z 1 2 3 4 5 6 7 8 9 0

FIG. 7-14. Popular Style of Architectural Lettering (William P. Spence)

EACH LETTER SHOULD BE DENSE BLACK

a. TOO LIGHT

EACH LETTER SHOULD BE DENSE BLACK

b. DENSE BLACK

FIG. 7-15. Non-Uniform and Uniform Line Weights

NON-UNIFORM HEIGHT MAKES FOR POOR QUALITY!

LETTERS SHOULD BE OF UNIFORM HEIGHT.

FIG. 7-16. Uniform Letter Height Makes Reading Easier

DECIMAL DIMENSIONS ± .002

a. NON-UNIFORM INCLINATION

DECIMAL DIMENSIONS ± .002

DECIMAL DIMENSIONS ± .002

b. UNIFORM INCLINATION

FIG. 7-17. Lettering Must be of Uniform Inclination

HIM HIM LEFT L E F T

a. CROWDED b. GOOD c. GOOD d. TOO SEPARATED
ADJACENT STRAIGHT-LINE LETTERS OPEN-END LETTERS

I L L I N O I S ILLINOIS

e. POOR f. GOOD

FIG. 7-18. Spacing Between Letters Should *Appear* Equal

between adjacent *straight line letters* and less space between adjacent *open-end letters*. The result is the *appearance* that the relative spacing between letters is equal.

b. SPACING BETWEEN WORDS. Words too close together are very difficult to read. Words spaced too far apart are not easy to follow, Fig. 7-19. For most word spacing, the distance used between words is equal to the width of a capital "*O*". When the last letter of one word and the first letter of the next one are adjacent straight line letters, a little more space should be allowed between the words. When the last letter of one word and the first letter of the next one are ajacent open-end letters, a little less space should be allowed.

c. SPACING BETWEEN SENTENCE ENDINGS AND BEGINNINGS. The same principles for spacing between words are used to space between the end of a sentence and the beginning of the next sentence. The two-space rule followed in office typing is to be avoided. Good composition for lettering requires only a distance approximately equal to the width of a capital *O* after the period and before the capital letter of the next sentence.

d. SPACING BETWEEN LINES OF LETTERING. The space between lines of lettering should be equal to or slightly less than the height of the capital letters. The same amount of space is required when fractions are used and also when lower case letters are used, Fig. 7-20. Paragraphs and notes should be separated by approximately twice the height of the capital letters to keep them clearly identified, Fig. 7-21.

WORDS SHOULD BE SPACED NEITHER
TOO FAR APART NOR
TOOCLOSE TOGETHER

FIG. 7-19. Spacing Between Words

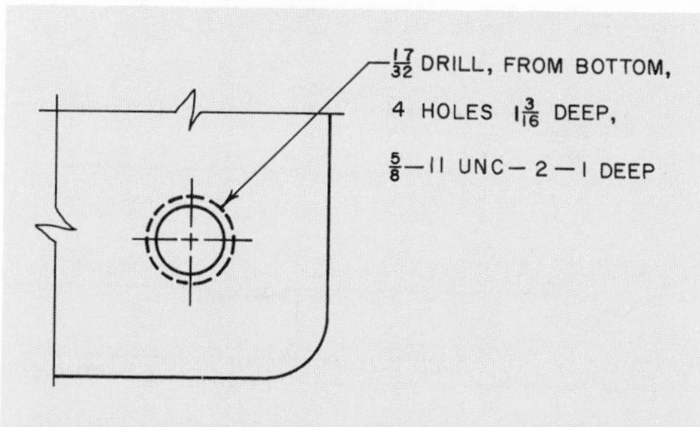

FIG. 7-20. Spacing Between Lines of Lettering

Notes

Notes are lettered on a drawing after most dimensioning has been done. Notes should always be placed to be read from the bottom of the page. The rules for good composition should be carefully observed, and guide lines should be used. The purpose of notes is to supplement direct dimensions.

General notes apply to the entire drawing. These are placed near the title strip in a central position, Fig. 7-23. *Local notes* apply to a particular location and are accompanied by a leader. Local notes should not be placed between views; they should not be crowded.

Notes are used to specify standard parts which are to be purchased. They should be brief, carefully worded, and *standard* abbreviations used. (See USAS Z32.13-1950). To draw and dimension these parts would be a waste of time.

To speed up work, notes may be typed on a drawing. Commonly used notes may be printed on a pressure sensitive material and may be transferred directly to the tracing paper.

Titles

Carefully made titles and title strip information complete a well-executed drawing. Most

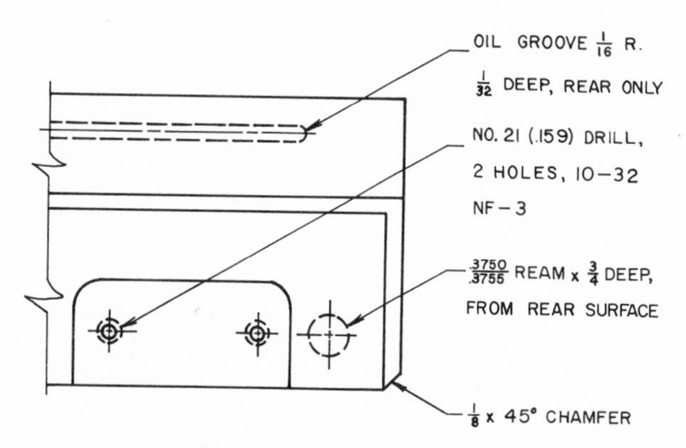

FIG. 7-21. Note Spacing

lettering on drawings is one-eighth inch in height. Titles and drawing numbers are usually the largest lettering. Titles are one-quarter inch in height and should be made with a bolder line to make them stand out clearly. See TD-7-3.

Titles may be balanced about a vertical center line, Fig. 7-22. They may be centered within the title space of a title strip, Fig. 7-23. Even experienced draftsmen have difficulty in accurately balancing lettering about a center line on the first try. Most will letter the title on a scrap piece of paper and place this under the tracing paper in the proper position. The letters are then traced. When opaque paper is used, the scrap paper is placed where it can easily be followed — above the space in which the title is lettered.

MODEL 5 LATHE
TOOL POST CROSS SLIDE
SCALE: HALF SIZE
GISHOLT MACHINE COMPANY
MADISON, WISCONSIN
2-24-65
DRAWN BY______ CHECKED BY______
DRAWING NO. 5V-9159C

FIG. 7-22. Title Centered About a Vertical Center Line

PREPRINTED TITLES. The draftsman's time, as well as that of the student draftsman, is too valuable to be making and laying out the information that should be preprinted on a title strip. Most industries and many schools use paper with *printed borders and title strips.* The draftsman fills these in with the appropriate information for each drawing, Fig. 7-23.

PRESSURE-SENSITIVE TITLES. In recent years a transfer process has been developed. Title strips are printed on translucent paper with a pressure-sensitive, adhesive backing. They have been perfected so that the heat of common reproducing machines will not adversely affect them. These transfers may be placed on tracing paper, cloth, or film. The appropriate title information may then be filled in, and the time otherwise spent in the layout of these strips is saved, Fig. 7-24.

Lettering for Microfilming

The size of the original and the reduction and blowback ratios determine the size of lettering on drawings for microfilming. Table 7-1 shows the usual microfilm reduction for USAS standard drawing sheet sizes and the recommended sizes for lettering. Letters must be carefully formed without crowding. Spacing between lines of lettering should be at least one-half of the letter height. Spacing between words should be the width of the letter *O*; spacing between sentences should be twice the width of the letter *O*; spacing between paragraphs should be at least enough to add one more line of lettering.

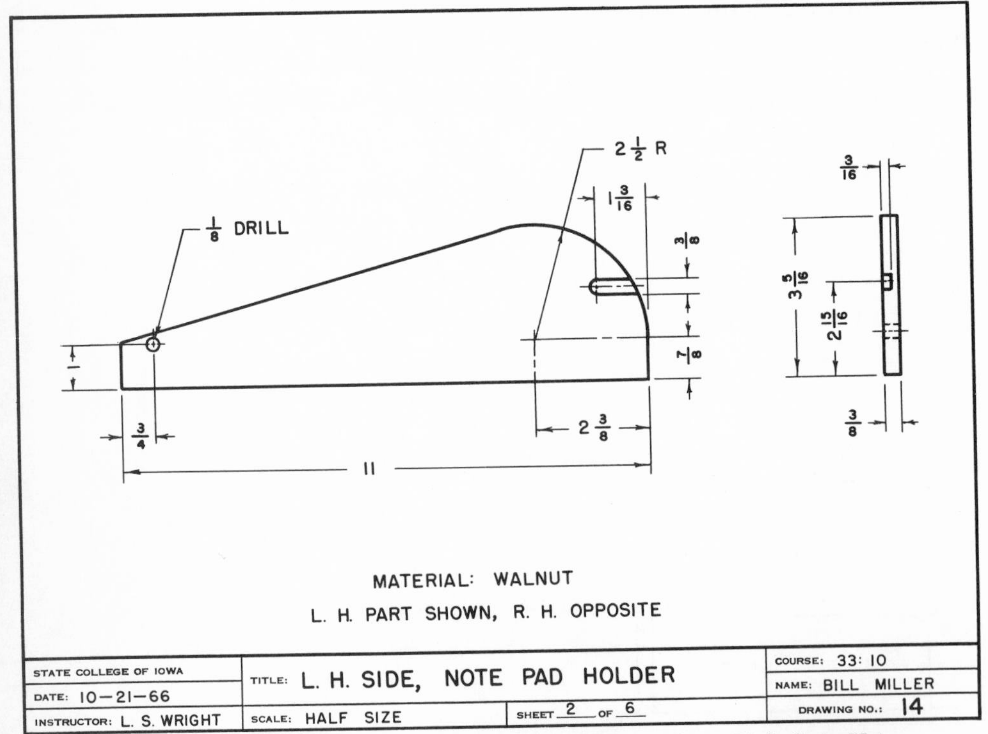

FIG. 7-23. Title within a Title Strip Using a Preprinted Title Block and Border

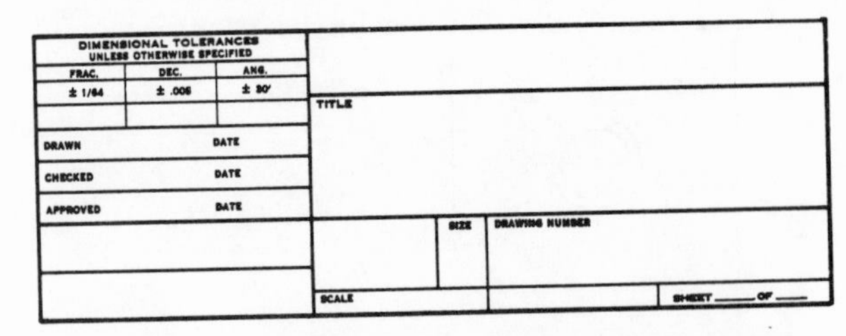

FIG. 7-24. Preprinted, Pressure-Sensitive Title Strip

Lettering on Pictorials

The same rules of composition apply to the lettering of pictorial drawings. Because the dimension figures are placed in the pictorial planes, it is most important to draw both guide lines and direction lines to aid in their correct formation. These lines should be drawn in the pictorial plane of one face of the object, Fig. 7-25. Notice that the guide lines are parallel to the object lines while the direction lines are drawn pictorially and represent right angles. Lettering on pictorial drawings is always an adaptation of vertical lettering. Inclined letter forms are never used. Notes accompanying pictorial objects are done with vertical lettering and follow the practices used for notes. All notes are lettered to be read from the bottom of the page, Fig. 7-26.

Mechanical Lettering Devices

A number of mechanical lettering devices are available today. With their aid, near perfect letters may be made in ink or with pencil. The formation of each letter is mechanical. The spacing of letters is just as important with the mechanical instruments as it is when lettering freehand. One still must understand and apply the rules of good composition.

Among the more widely used mechanical instruments is the LeRoy lettering set, Fig. 7-27. A *follower pin* moves in the groove of a carefully made letter. At the same time, the pen or pencil repeats this movement on the drawing forming the desired letter, Fig. 7-28. A wide variety of template sizes and styles of letters is available.

The Varigraph, Letterguide, Wrico and Unitech sets also use templates and a lettering pen. The cautions for these instruments are:

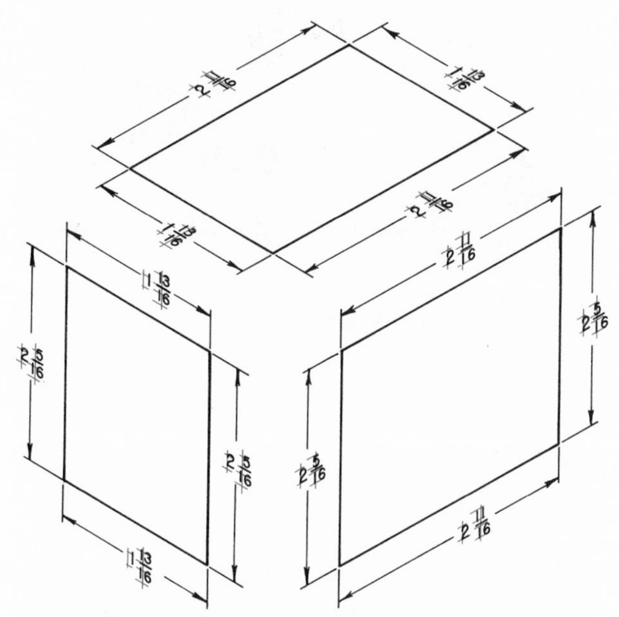

FIG. 7-25. Dimensions in Pictorial are Placed in the Pictorial Planes

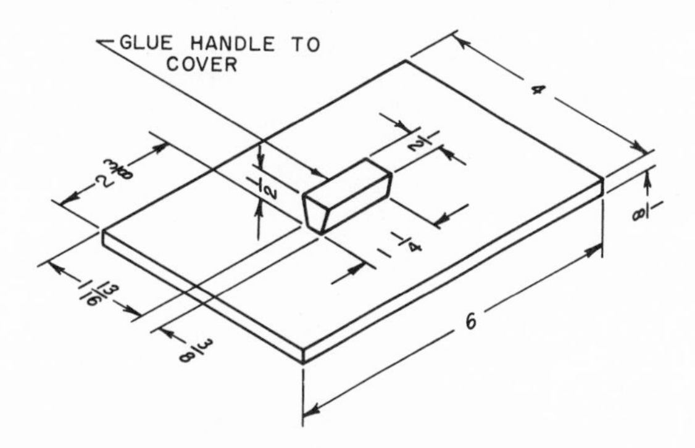

FIG. 7-26. Notes on Pictorials Read from the Bottom and Are *Not* Placed in the Pictorial Planes

TABLE 7-1

Reductions, Blowback Sizes, and USAS Standard Drafting Sizes, Microfilm Recommended Sizes for Lettering

USAS Drafting Size		35mm Film Reduction	Blowback (% of Original Size)	Recommended Lettering Height	
				Fractions	Decimals
A	8½ x 11	16	.919	1/8	.125
B	11 x 17	20	.735	1/8	.125
C	17 x 22	24	.613	5/32	.150
D	22 x 34	28	.525	3/16	.170
E	34 x 44	28 or 30	.490	3/16	.170

1. Use a guiding type pressure rather than force.
2. Be sure the pen is in the proper position for each letter before drawing it.
3. Once the letter has been started, watch the follower point in the template, since the pen will take care of itself.
4. It is highly important to clean the ink from these pens carefully in order for them to continue to function properly.

Recent developments include reservoir pens which function much like a fountain pen and do not have to be cleaned after each use.

Industrial Applications

There are many industrial uses of letter forms as three-dimensional objects. Examples come from sign services, trade marks, special patterns and castings, structural steel letters, and others, Fig. 7-29. In these instances the characters must be detailed just as any other industrial products are detailed.

Chapter 7 — Problems and Projects

1. Obtain drafting standards manuals from two local industries and compare the

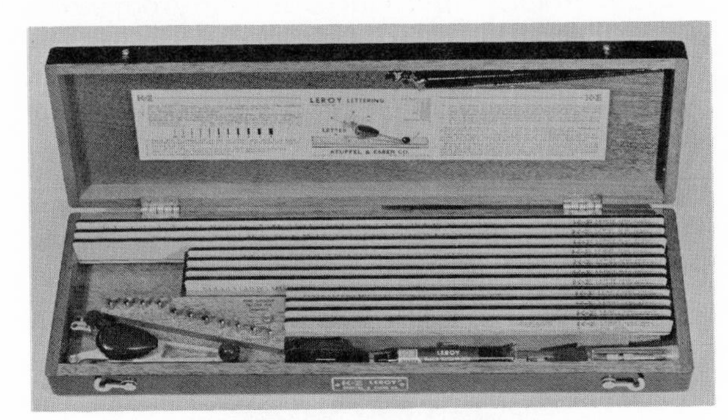

FIG. 7-27. LeRoy Lettering Set (Keuffel & Esser Co.)

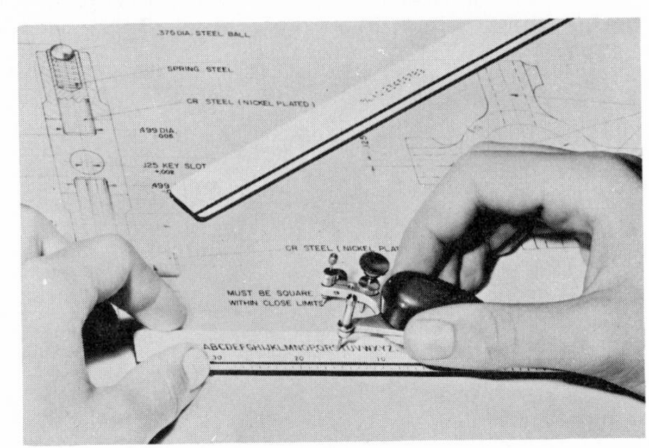

FIG. 7-28. Lettering with LeRoy Equipment

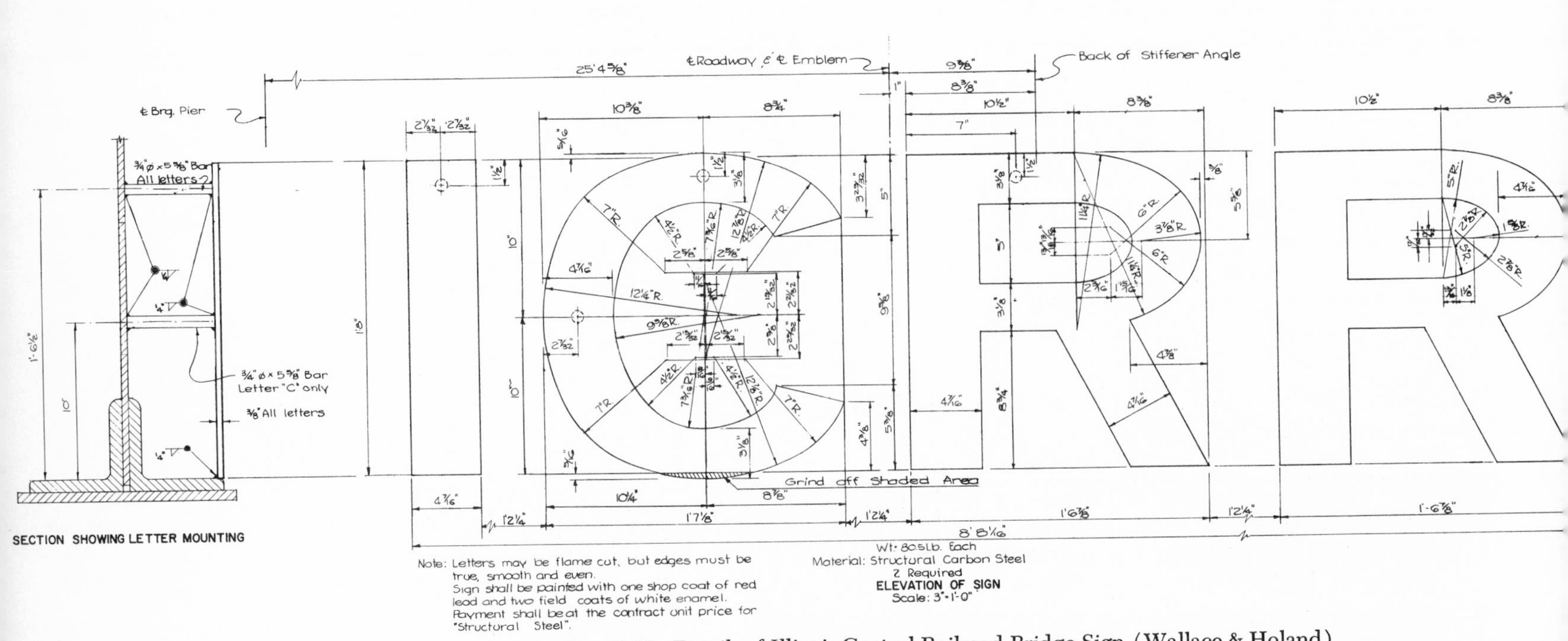

FIG. 7-29. Details of Illinois Central Railroad Bridge Sign (Wallace & Holand) Use of slanted fraction bar is not according to USAS nor SAE Standards.

alphabets with those of the USAS and SAE in TD-7-1 and 2.

2. Letter your name and school several times using a different pencil each time. Criticize your work and identify the lettering that is the most dense and which will reproduce best.
3. Obtain reproductions of drawings from local industry, and study the dimensioning and lettering on the drawings.
4. Using tracing paper over an industrial drawing, trace the lettering carefully freehand.
5. Make an illustration to show both a good and poor example of each of the following conditions:
   a. Spacing of letters in a word.
   b. Spacing between words.
   c. Uniformity of style.
   d. Uniformity of line weight.
   e. Uniformity of height.
   f. Uniformity of direction.
   g. Uniformity of inclination.
6. Make a local note showing a drilled hole $^{27}/_{64}''$ in diameter.
7. Letter a general note for a drawing indicating that "all fillets and rounds are ⅛″ unless otherwise specified."
8. Assume that you have just completed a new design for a product of your choice. Letter the title information about a vertical center line. Include at least the title, date, drawing number, scale, name of firm, and your name as the draftsman.
9. Draw or sketch a circle 6¾″ in diameter. Draw a vertical radius in the circle. Draw two more radii which divide the circle into three equal parts. Dimension the length of each line as though it were part of a pictorial drawing.
10. Even though mechanically made letters are perfectly formed, what principles of lettering must one use in placing them on a drawing?
11. Use a grid sheet, and letter the alphabet and numerals from either TD-7-1 or TD-7-2, paying particular attention to exact letter formation. Evaluate your work by using the check list, Table 7-2.
12. Letter two lines of lettering from any paragraph in this book. Select additional lines each day for two weeks. Use the check list of Table 7-2 to evaluate your work each day. Compare your work of the last day with that of the first day.

TABLE 7-2

Checklist for Improving Lettering

Performance Satisfactory	Needs Attention	Good Practice
______	______	1. Sit squarely in your chair with both elbows on the table and feet on the floor or foot rail.
______	______	2. Paper should be taped to the board.
______	______	3. Hold pencil firmly but not too tightly.
______	______	4. Use single-stroke Gothic capital letters ⅛ inch in height with all letters and numerals carefully formed.
______	______	5. Use either vertical or slanted styles.
______	______	6. Select a pencil lead of such grade that intense, black letters are made.
______	______	7. Execute all characters so that they display uniformity of style, line weight, height, direction, and apparent spacing.
______	______	8. Use typewritten or printed letters whenever possible.
______	______	9. For sharp reproduction of typewritten letters back up the work with intense black or orange carbon paper.
______	______	10. When lettering for microfilming make characters slightly larger and use a somewhat narrower, but equally intense, line so that they will not fill in on blowbacks or reductions.
______	______	11. Do not underline letters on a drawing.
______	______	12. Fraction bars are horizontal and the numerals do not touch them.
______	______	13. Practice lettering with intent to improve and practice frequently rather than less-frequent long-periods of time.
______	______	14. All notes on a drawing read from the bottom of the page.
______	______	15. Use guide lines. Use direction lines if needed.

CHAPTER EIGHT

dimensioning

Introduction

Dimensions for a drawing are like the captions which accompany some cartoons — without them the chief effect of the communication is lost. The purpose of dimensioning is to add the information not shown by the representation of the object alone. The drawing, together with the dimension figures and notes, must clearly define the parts of each object or structure in their completed condition. There should be no confusion with respect to what is intended. Enough views, sections, dimensions and notes must be displayed. Dimensions should be given only once and should not be repeated; no scaling of the drawing should be needed. The size, form and location of various features must be complete. Dimensions should be selected which show those points, lines or surfaces which are related to each other and those which control other components or mating parts.

systems of dimensioning

English and Metric Systems

Dimensions on drawings will either be in the English or the metric system. In English-speaking countries, the English system is used. In most other countries the metric system is used. It seems quite *unlikely* that those countries now using the metric system will change to the English system. Likewise, it is unlikely that in the near future the United States will change from the English to the metric system. The cost to industry for such a change in either direction would be staggering. In spite of this cost, however, there are movements underway to change from English to metric for international standardization.

With continued industrial expansion to international markets both in this country and in others, a working knowledge of both systems is important. In the product manufacturing industries of this country it is understood that all dimensions will be in the English system. In special cases where a dimension in the English or metric system must appear when the other system is in general use, this must be clearly indicated with the appropriate abbreviation, Fig. 8-1.

At least one of America's industries is presently using a system of *dual dimensioning* in its plants, both at home and overseas, Fig. 8-2.

Historically, manufacturing methods have been such in this country that fractions in multiples of 64ths of an inch have been the standard. Experiences growing out of logistics and supply relationships of countries during both world wars, technological advance in manufacturing materials and methods, together with a quest for a system of dimensioning permitting much finer divisions of the inch than those yielded by the use of fractions, have led many manufacturing industries to adopt the decimal inch as their standard. The *SAE Aerospace Automotive Drafting Manual* uses the decimal inch as its standard.

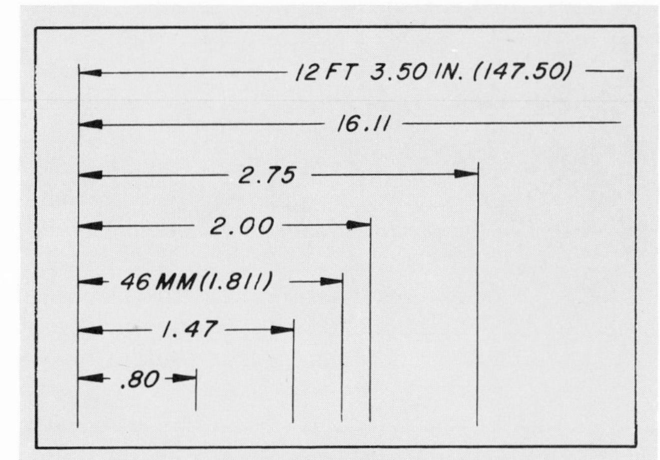

Fig. 8-1. Indicate Variations from Standard Dimensioning with Appropriate Designations such as "in" or "mm" (SAE)

Fig. 8-2. Dual Dimensioning on Drawings (John Deere Dubuque Tractor Works)
This provides for manufacture in one system of dimensions and interchangeability with parts manufactured under either system.

The elimination of fractions simplifies dimensional calculations. In the woodworking industries and in the construction and architectural fields, fractions continue to be the standard and to serve very well. A student draftsman, therefore, must gain facility with both fractions and decimals and know the appropriate use of each.

In those industries using the decimal inch, a few special cases demand the use of fractions. Many materials and processed items are customarily merchandized in fractional sizes; examples include lumber, textiles, felt, rubber, screen, mesh and threads.

Angular tolerances are generally specified in degrees, minutes or seconds; but in the fractional system, ½° may be used.

Tolerances on fractionally dimensioned parts must be expressed in fractions. When fractions are used, the fraction bar may not be omitted; the fraction bar may not be slanted; the fraction bar should be heavier than the dimension line; the numerals of the fraction should not touch the fraction bar. Usually, fractional measurements are in 64ths: 1/64, 1/32, 1/16, ⅛, ¼ and ½. Where closer accuracy than 1/64″ is required, decimal dimensioning is used.

Systems of Decimal Dimensioning

The Modular .02 System

Two basic decimal dimensioning systems are used in industry. The Modular .02 system (or two-place decimal system) is used on drawings of new products wherever practicable. It is also used when convenient in revising and redesigning products when replacement of the fractional system can be readily accomplished, Fig. 8-3.

To limit the number of arbitrarily chosen decimal values and to provide a uniformity of choice for the two-place decimal inch system of dimensioning, select values from the chart shown in TD-8-1.

Values should be chosen from the highest order of preference wherever possible. The use of the values in Column 1 should be increased. The values in Column 2 are *popular* hundredths. These correspond favorably with some commercial or industry practices and are likely to continue in use. Values in Column 3 are all even-numbered values not appearing in Column 1 or 2. These should be used only when necessary to satisfy design requirements.

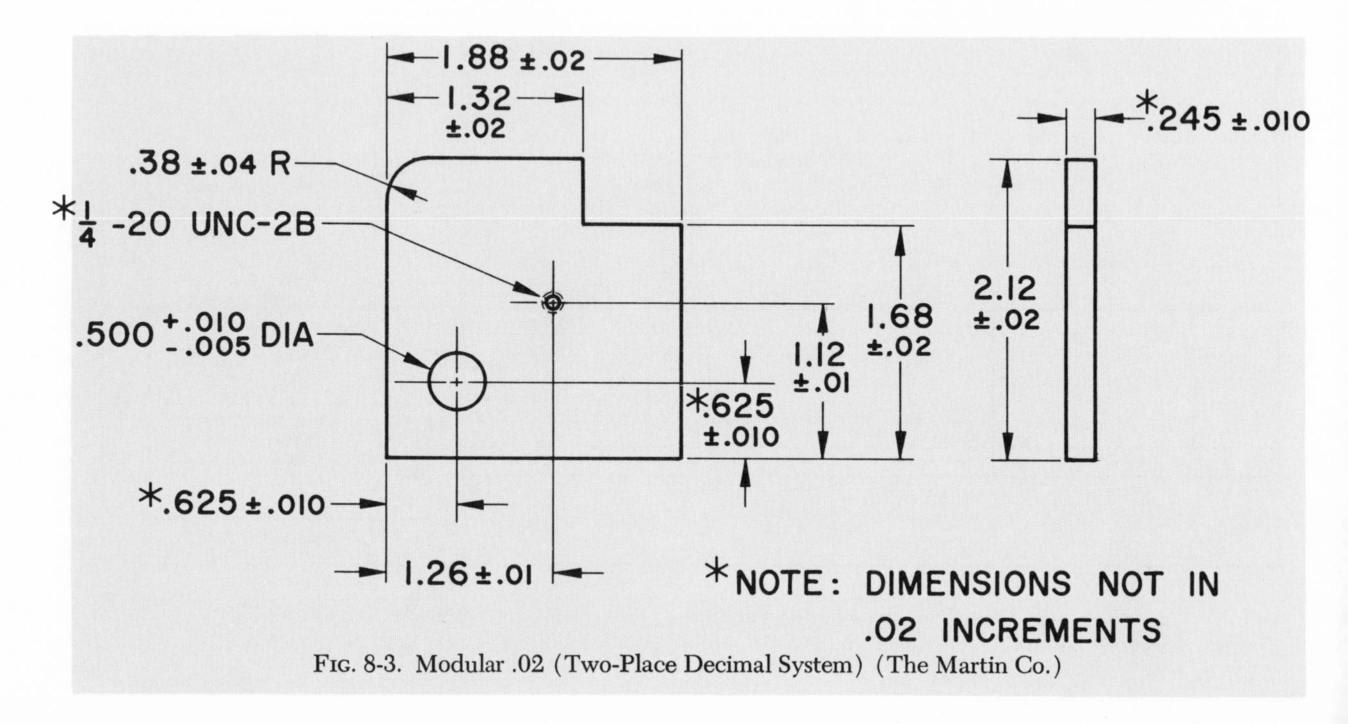

FIG. 8-3. Modular .02 (Two-Place Decimal System) (The Martin Co.)

Those remaining odd-numbered values appearing in Column 4 are used when dividing values from the first three columns and should be used only when required.

The Decimal-Equivalents-of-Fractions System

The decimal-equivalents-of-fractions system (or the three-place decimal system) is used on new drawings for only those dimensions related to mating features dimensioned in fractional or decimal equivalent systems. When revising drawings, dimensions not affected by the revision should not be altered. When redrawing completely, all fractional dimensions are converted to decimal equivalents, Fig. 8-4.

To provide for uniformity in converting from fractions to decimals, use the chart in TD-8-2. This table is especially useful in a period of transition from the fractional to the decimal system.

Standard Decimal Expressions

Whether using the two-place or three-place decimal system, all decimals should include the number of places specified. See Tables 8-1 and 8-2. The zero is omitted to the left of the decimal point in this system thus making carefully-executed decimals extremely important. The space used for the decimal point should be equal to about one-half a number space, and it should be slightly heavier than the line weight of the accompanying numerals.

Tolerances shown must be expressed in the same number of places as that of the system used.

Correct	*Incorrect*
2.80 ± .02	2.80 ± .020
3.600 ± .003	3.6 ± .003

TABLE 8-1

Correct and Incorrect Applications of the Two-Place Decimal System

Correct	Incorrect
.10	.1
1.00	1.
1.20	1.2
1.56	1.561

TABLE 8-2

Correct and Incorrect Applications of the Three-Place Decimal System

Correct	Incorrect
.200	.2
.460	.46
1.800	1.8
1.640	1.64
1.708	1.70811

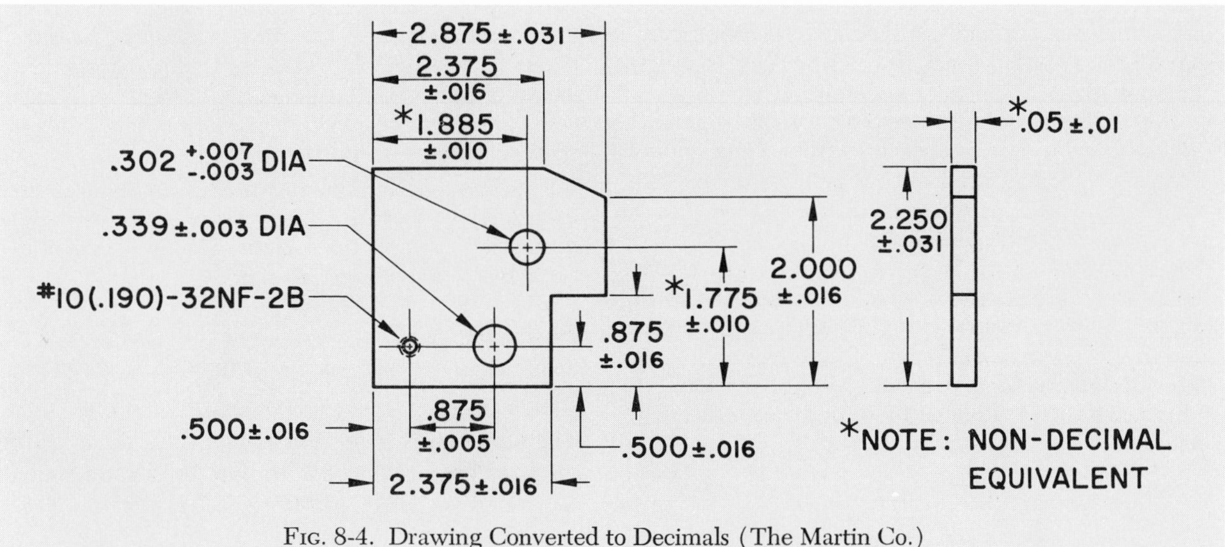

FIG. 8-4. Drawing Converted to Decimals (The Martin Co.)

No specific tolerance is to be implied in the choice of the two-place or three-place system. Tolerances should be specified when required or included as a general note in the title block when appropriate.

Rules for Rounding-off Decimals:

1. Where the figure following the last number to be retained is greater than five, the last number is increased by one. Example: 8.37662 becomes 8.377 if cut off to three places, or 8.38 if cut off to two places.
2. Where the figure following the last number to be retained is less than five, the last number remains unchanged. Example: 4.46325 becomes 4.463 if cut off to three places, or 4.46 if cut off to two places.
3. Where the figure following the last number to be retained is exactly five and the number to be retained is odd, the number is increased by one. Example: 7.6315 becomes 7.632 if cut off to three places.
4. Where the figure following the last number to be retained is exactly five and the number to be retained is even, the number remains unchanged. Example: 5.2185 becomes 5.218 if cut off to three places.[1]

General Selection of Decimal Dimensions

Two variations of decimal dimensioning are the two-place and the three-place systems. There are no tolerances implied by the number of digits in a dimension.

The fundamental basis of the two-place system is that, where practicable, dimensions shall be expressed as multiples of .02, such as .04, .10, and 1.06, rather than decimal equivalents or conversions of fractions such as .094 and 1.0625. All dimensions shall have no fewer than two decimal places.

Dimensions having more than the two decimal places may be used in the two-place system whereever required or expedient. Where necessary, dimensions may be expressed as two-place values which are not multiples of .02.

The fundamental basis of the three-place system is that, where practicable, dimensions shall be expressed as multiples of .010, such as .100 and 1.060, rather than as decimal equivalents or conversions of fractions such as .094 and 1.0625. All dimensions shall have no fewer than three decimal places.

[1]John Deere *Drafting Manual*

[2]*SAE Aerospace Automotive Drafting Standards*

Dimensions having more than three decimal places may be used in the three-place decimal system wherever required or expedient. Where necessary, dimensions may be expressed as three-place values which are not multiples of .010.

Features which are produced by commercial tools or which lend themselves to inspection by commercially available gages shall be dimensioned with limits according to the capability of the tool or the increments of the gage to be used.

a. Holes to be drilled or reamed are specified in two, three, or four decimal places, such as:
   .373-.380 DIA
   .0620-.0635 DIA
b. Counterbores and other commercial cutters are specified by decimal equivalents of fractions in two, three, or four places, such as:
   .365-.385 CBORE
c. Fillets and corner radii, up to 1.00 radius are specified in two or three decimal places, such as:
   .02-.04 R
   .484-.516 R
   High and low limits should be selected which will permit the use of commercial radius gages for the limits. These are available in fractional equivalent increments or in decimal increments.
d. Screw threads, when designated by decimals, are specified to three or four places, such as:
   .250-20 UNC-2A   .4375-14 UNC-2A
   .190-32 UNF-2A   .3125-24 UNF-2A
e. Metal tubing bends are specified to the tube axis in decimal equivalents of fractions in two or three decimal places.

Features which are produced from commercial stock sizes may be dimensioned by giving the basic stock size, in which case commercial mill tolerances will apply. If the feature is toleranced, values should be selected according to the commercial limits of the stock. (Bar stock, tubing and sheet stock frequently contribute their standard sizes to certain features of finished parts.)

Features which are functional, such as those involved in a fit or mounting distance, shall specify dimensions to the number of decimal places dictated by tolerance requirements.[2]

The Decimal Scale

In Fig. 8-5 the inch is divided into tenths with numerals every .20 part of an inch. Note that there are 50 subdivisions of .02 each. Two lines within each tenth are lengthened to facilitate reading such as .04 and .06; .14 and .16; .24 and .26.

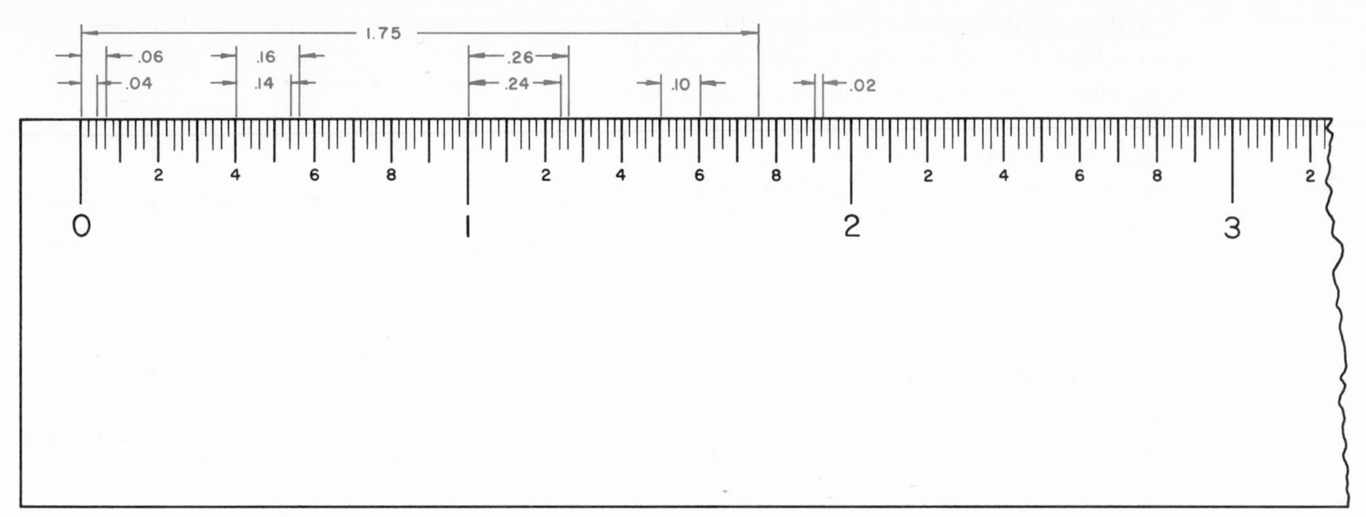

FIG. 8-5. Full-Size Scale Rule Using Decimal Inch

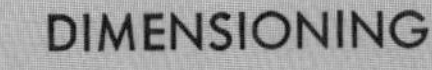

specification of lines and notes for dimensioning

Dimension Lines

Dimension lines are lightweight lines which contrast distinctly with object lines, Fig. 8-7. They are terminated with arrowheads which show the direction and extent of the dimension. They may not pass through a dimension figure.

When dimension figures are in a single line, the dimension line is usually broken, Fig. 8-6. Fractions are considered single line dimension figures. Exceptions are found in structural drawings, some architectural drawings, and in a few industrial drafting rooms.

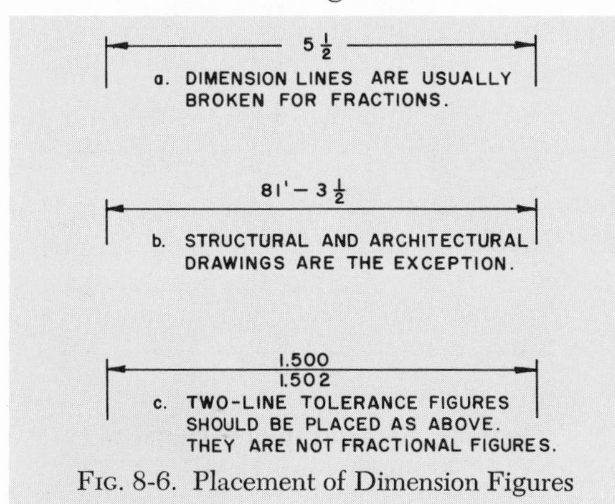

FIG. 8-6. Placement of Dimension Figures

Dimension lines should be aligned and grouped where possible, Fig. 8-7. The shorter dimensions appear close to the view, and the longest are located farthest from the view.

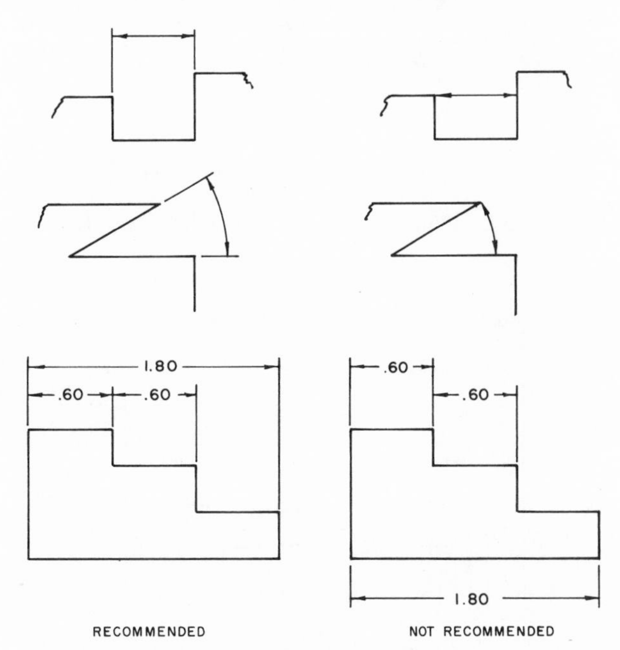

FIG. 8-7. Arranging Dimension Lines for Orderly Appearance (USAS)

Although dimension lines should not be crossed by other lines, exceptions are permissible such as *A* in Fig. 8-8 which shows acceptable methods for dimensioning in confined spaces. Where there are several parallel dimension lines, the dimensions should be staggered to make reading easier, Fig. 8-9. Neither center lines, extension lines, nor object lines should be used as dimension lines.

Dimension lines are placed ⅜″ from the object lines with successive lines ¼″ apart, Fig. 8-10. In the decimal system, SAE recommends *about* .40 space between parallel dimension lines and between dimension lines and part outlines.

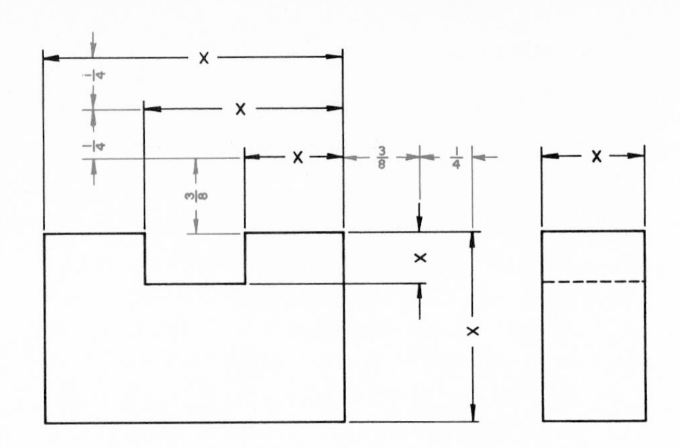

Fig. 8-10. Placement of Dimension Lines with Respect to Object Lines

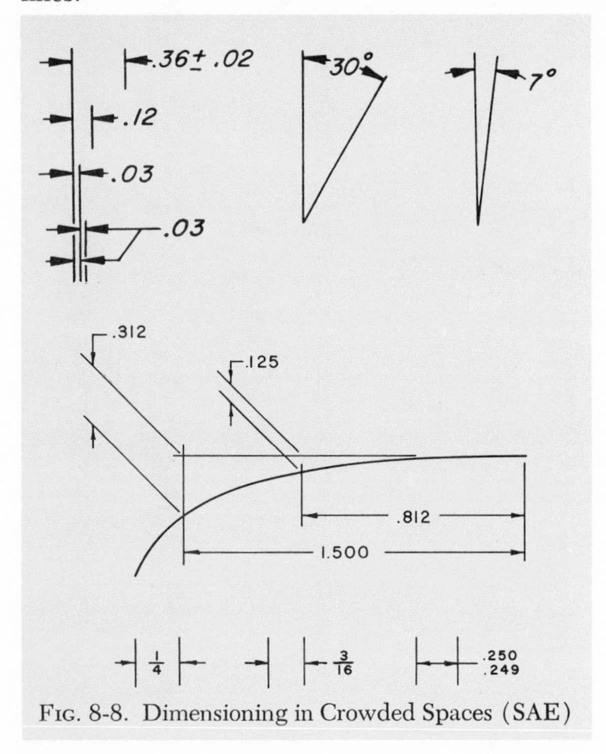

Fig. 8-8. Dimensioning in Crowded Spaces (SAE)

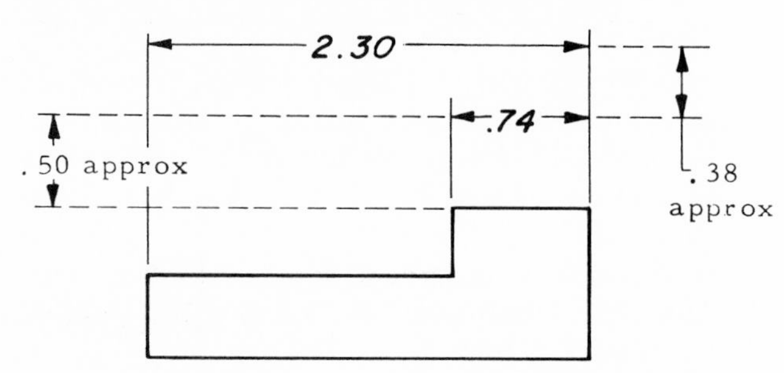

Fig. 8-11. Some Industrial Standards Recommend Dimension Lines Placed "A Reasonable Distance" from the Outline of the Part (General Motors)

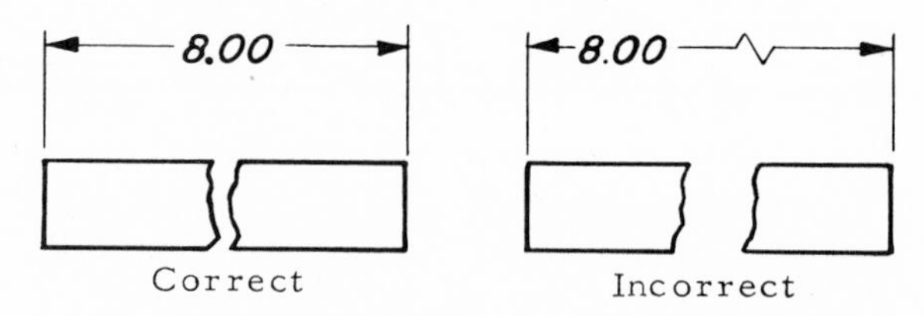

Fig. 8-12. Dimension Lines Are Not Broken when Dimensioning a Broken Part (General Motors)

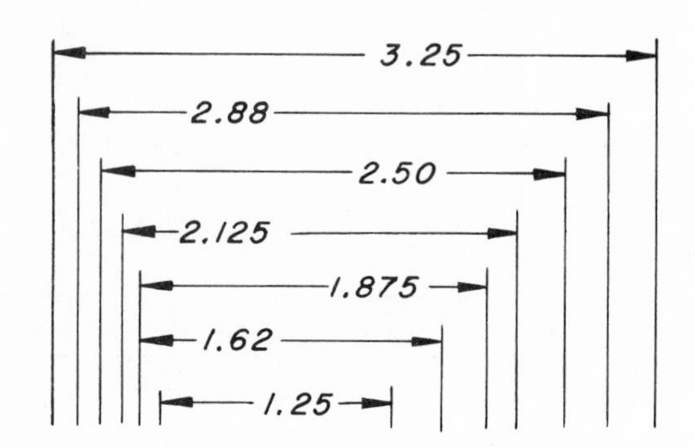

Fig. 8-9. Staggered Dimension Figures for Clarity (SAE)

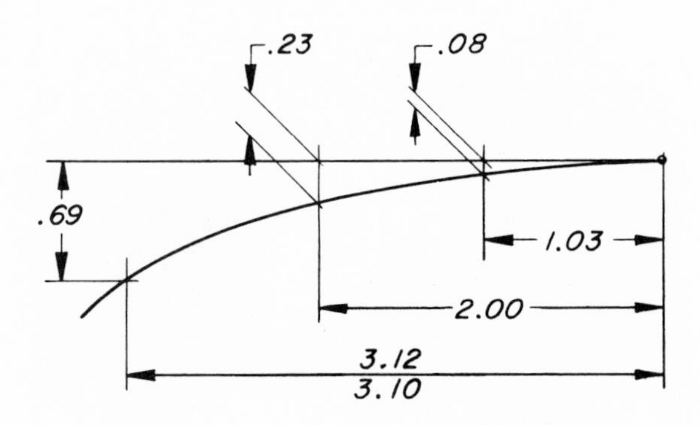

Fig. 8-13. Extension Lines Oblique to Dimension Lines (SAE)

Extension Lines

Extension lines are lightweight lines which contrast distinctly with object lines, Fig. 8-10. They are extensions of object lines which show where the dimensions actually extend. Extension lines are drawn at right angles to dimension lines. When their meaning is clear as at *a* in Fig. 8-13, other angles may be used.

Extension lines start about 1/32″ from an object line (a visible gap) and extend about ⅛″ beyond the farthest dimension line (USAS). In the decimal system it is recommended that extension lines start about .03 to .06 from the outline of the object and extend about .12 beyond the line of the referenced dimension (SAE).

Crossings of extension lines should be avoided, but where crossing is necessary the lines should not be broken at the point of intersection. However, if extension lines cross dimension lines near the arrowhead, a break in the extension line is permissible, Fig. 8-15.

A center line may be extended and used as an extension line. In such cases, the part extending beyond the body of the drawing for purposes of dimensioning is drawn as an extension line.

Leaders

Leaders are used to direct attention. They contrast distinctly with object lines. They are terminated with arrowheads except when it refers to an area within the outline of the feature, in which case a dot terminates the leader line, Fig. 8-17. Leaders are generally relatively short oblique lines drawn at 30°, 45°, or 60° to the outline of the part. Other angles may be used, but small angles (less than 30°) should be avoided. Leaders should generally be drawn parallel where possible. If not, they should be at 180° or 90° angles to each other. Leaders are generally straight lines except in the fields of architecture, and other specialized applications where curved line leaders are appropriate.

DIMENSIONING

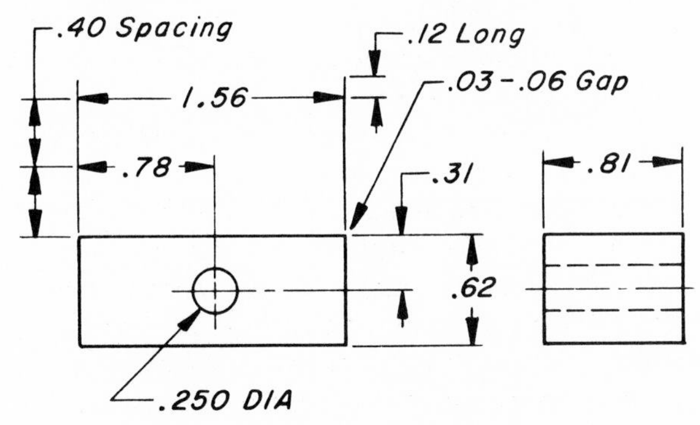

FIG. 8-14. Recommended Extension Line Placement (SAE)

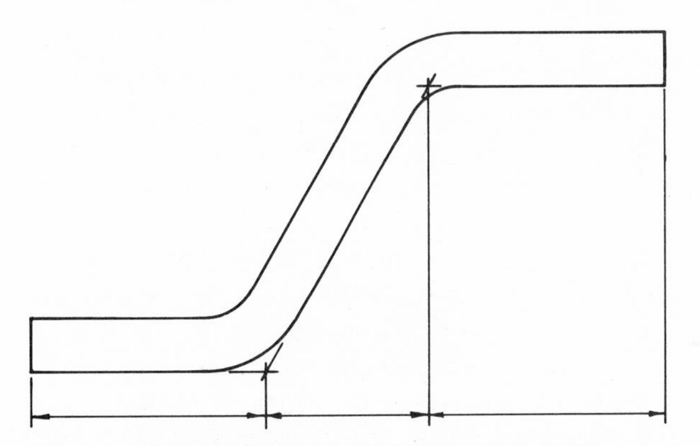

FIG. 8-16. Extension Lines Pass Through Points They Locate if Points Are Not on Outline (USAS)

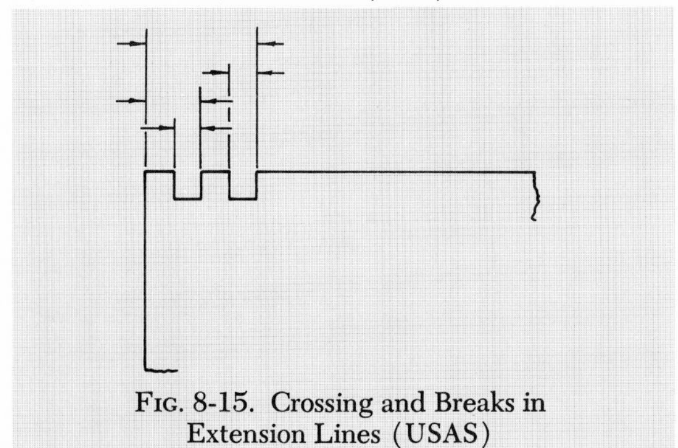

FIG. 8-15. Crossing and Breaks in Extension Lines (USAS)

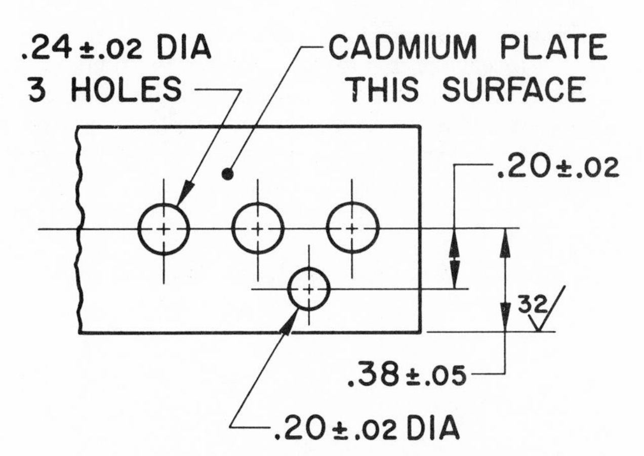

FIG. 8-17. Leaders are Terminated with Arrowheads Except when Referring to a Surface within Outlined Area (Martin Marietta)

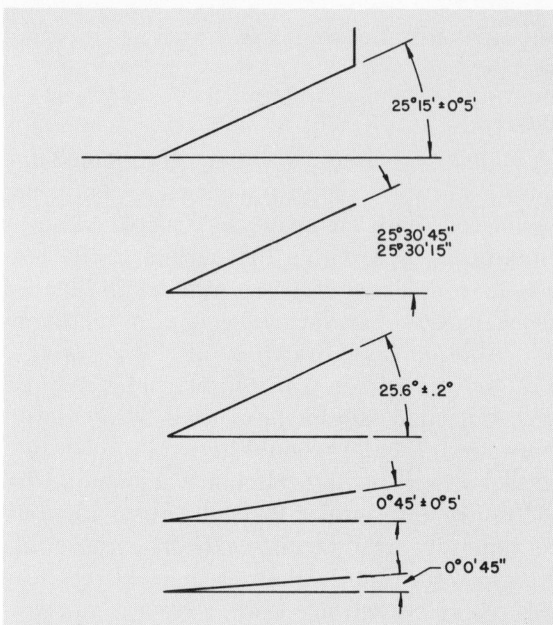

Fig. 8-18. Angular Dimensioning Practice (USAS)

The short portion of the leader is ¼″ long and should run either to the beginning or end of the note. In notes of more than one line in length, it may run to the center of the note.

Leaders directing attention to circles and circle arcs should be drawn radially. Their direction must originate at the center of the circle or arc even when they are drawn only to the outline of the circle.

Avoid crossing leaders and the use of long leaders, horizontal or vertical leaders, and leaders parallel to adjacent section, dimension or extension lines.

Notes

Note Classification:

A *local note* is one that conveys instructions or information pertinent to characteristics such as a feature, area, or dimension. It is placed adjacent to its subject and has a leader where the note applies.

A *general note* is one that conveys instruction or information pertinent to the item as a whole or to overall characteristics such as features, surfaces, dimensions, or material conditions. A general note is commonly used where it can replace a local note that would be required in more than one place on the drawing. It may refer to local characteristics by the use of symbols, letters, or numbers. General notes are grouped above, or near, the title block and may be numbered. Where required, a general note is preceded by the phrase *unless otherwise specified.* Views should be located so that a suitable area is reserved for possible expansion of general notes.[3]

Notes are lettered horizontally on the page. Guide lines should be used.

Local notes should be located with reference to the object lines in a manner comparable to the placement of dimension lines; that is, about ⅜″ unless dimension lines are in the way.

Symbols for Units of Measurement

Linear dimensions on machine drawings are understood to be in inches unless other units are specifically indicated. For this reason inch marks are not used. One exception to this is when an inch stands alone it should appear as 1″. When feet and inches are used, the form should be: 10′-0; 10′-4¾; and 10′-0¼. As a general rule, dimensions of six feet and over are in feet and inches as just expressed.

In architectural drafting rooms, both the foot and inch marks are used as indicated in the following expressions: 0′-9¾″; 28′-0½″; 32′-0″.

Note that the short dashes used above to separate feet from inches have a definite size — one letter space in length (a hyphen, not a long dash) — and are parallel to the baseline of the expression and at mid-height of the expression.

Angular expressions are in units of degrees (°) with divisions of minutes (′) and seconds (″). Parts of degrees may be expressed in decimals. When minutes are expressed alone, they should be preceded by 0° such as: 0° 15′, Fig. 8-18.

[3]*SAE Aerospace Automotive Drafting Standards*

specification and placement of dimensions

Methods of Dimensioning

Dimensions are placed on a drawing using either the *unidirectional* or the *aligned* method. The USAS recommends both methods.

Unidirectional Dimensions

Unidirectional dimensions are all read from the bottom of the page as shown in Fig. 8-19. This method was used originally in the automotive and aircraft industries where many large drawings are made which would otherwise be both awkward to draw and awkward to read. This method is becoming more widely used as attempts are made to find efficient ways of making drawings, and it is becoming standard practice to use this system with the decimal inch. In general, it takes less time to letter a drawing when the dimensions all read from the same direction.

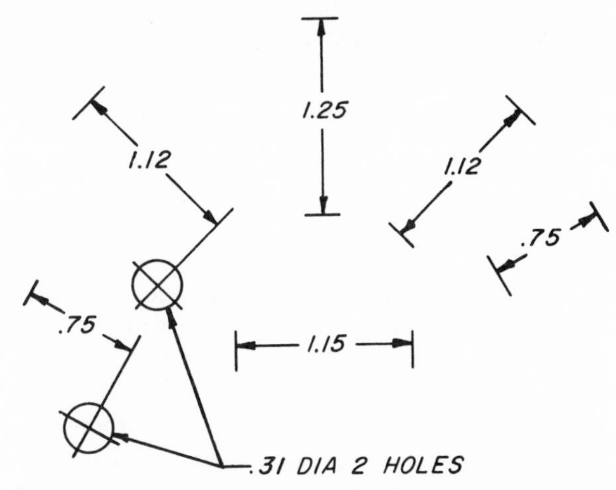

Fig. 8-19. Unidirectional Dimensions Read from the Bottom of the Page (Chrysler Corp.)

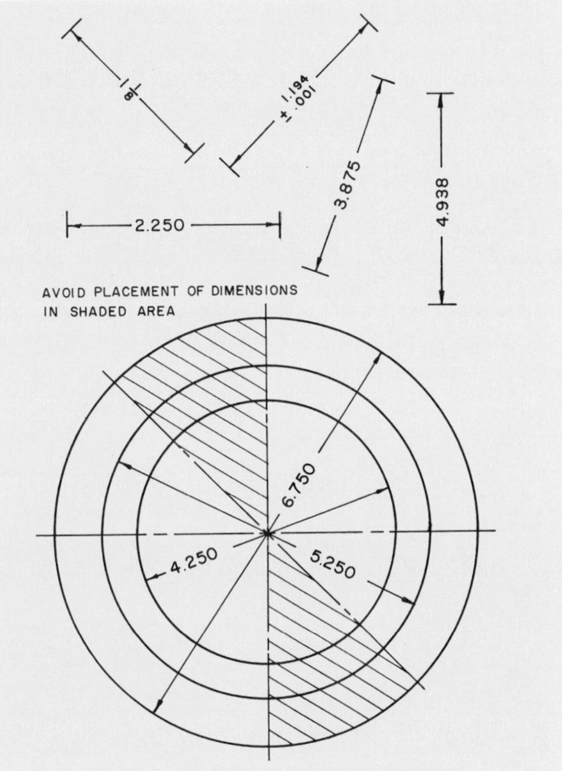

Fig. 8-20. Recommended Placement of Aligned Dimensions (USAS)

Aligned Dimensions

Aligned dimensions are placed along their dimension lines and may read from the bottom or from the right-hand side of the drawing, Fig. 8-20. Section lines are broken to permit easy reading of the dimension figures, as shown in *a* and *b* of Fig. 6-5.

Notes accompanying leaders read from the bottom of the page in both the unidirectional and the aligned methods.

General Practices

Dimensions should be taken from visible outlines whenever possible and not from hidden lines. A section view or broken-out section may be needed to avoid dimensioning hidden lines.

Dimensions should be placed between the views when the contour of the object requires. Dimensions may also be placed outside, but *never* on the view. When a dimension must be placed on a sectioned view, the section lines are broken rather than being continued through the dimension figure.

The principal view of a part should show most of the important dimensions since it is usually this view that is the characteristic contour of the part. Dimensions for surfaces in profile should be given in that view. In auxiliary views only those dimensions should be given which are not shown in their true shape in the

DIMENSIONING

principal view. Dimensions should always be placed where the features dimensioned are shown in true representation.

Those dimensions used to manufacture the product should be given rather than those used to layout the drawing, as discussed in Chapter 5.

Dimensions measured from reference lines outside the area of the drawing may be marked with a short dimension line and an appropriate note, Fig. 8-21.

Use of Finish Marks

Dimensions should be given for finished rather than rough surfaces. Although the starting dimension on a rough casting cannot come from a finished surface, once the first machining has been performed dimensions should be related to finished surfaces. Generally, therefore, location dimensions must be from finished surfaces or important center lines.

Finish marks indicate surfaces that are to be machined as contrasted to ones which are left rough on a casting or forging. The two approved styles are shown in Fig. 8-23. Parts to be machined from rolled stock do not require finish marks.

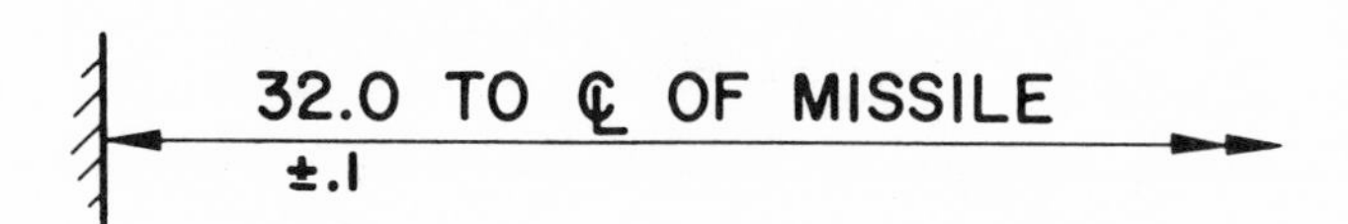

Fig. 8-21. Dimensions Extending Outside the Area of the Drawing (The Martin Co.)

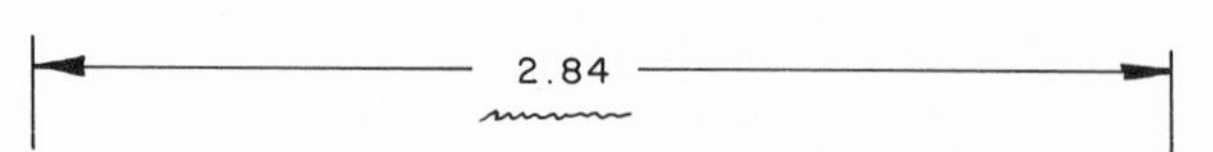

Fig. 8-22. A Wavy Line Under a Dimension Figure Indicates that this Dimension Is Not to Scale
This practice is reserved for rare use.

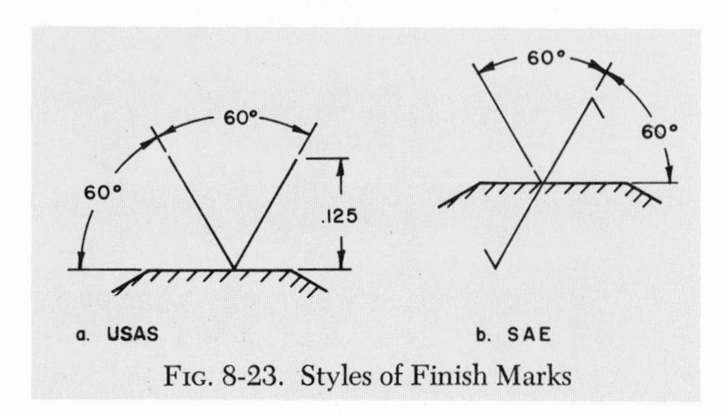

Fig. 8-23. Styles of Finish Marks

Finish marks are placed on the edge of all surfaces to be finished, including hidden lines.

Finish marks are not used when notes indicate specific machining operations. A note meaning "finish all over" should be used where this is the case.

Reference Dimensions

Reference dimensions are used for reference only as contrasted with dimensions used for sizes and locations. They are marked *REF*.

In some cases, information about the overall size is desired, but because of rounded ends this dimension is not utilized in the shop, Fig. 8-24. Fig. 8-24 is completely dimensioned without the reference dimension, but the reference dimension gives additional information.

The effect of omitting the reference mark would be to dimension the part in two different ways thus causing a repetition of dimensions. This omission would very likely lead to confusion in manufacture or inspection or both. Parts should be dimensioned without such repetition.

Dimensioning Basic Shapes

Analysis of the elements of any drawing will reveal that they are made up of basic geometrical shapes. Learn to dimension and locate these shapes with respect to each other.

The positions of rectangular shapes are located with reference to their faces. Cylindrical and symmetrical shapes are located with respect to their center lines.

Geometrical Shapes

Practices in dimensioning various geometrical shapes are shown in Figs. 8-25 through 8-40.

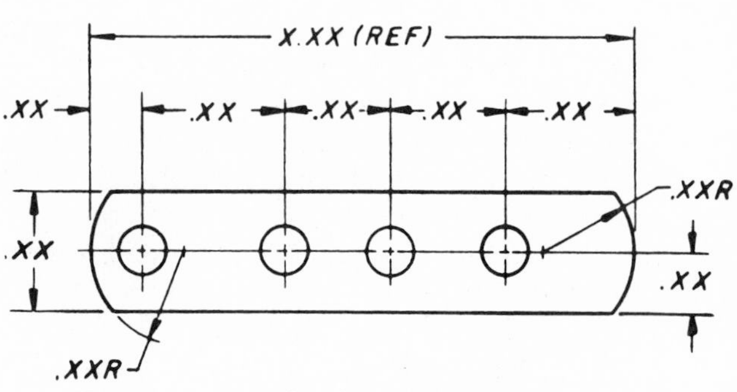

Fig. 8-24. Use of Reference Dimensions (Chrysler Corp.)

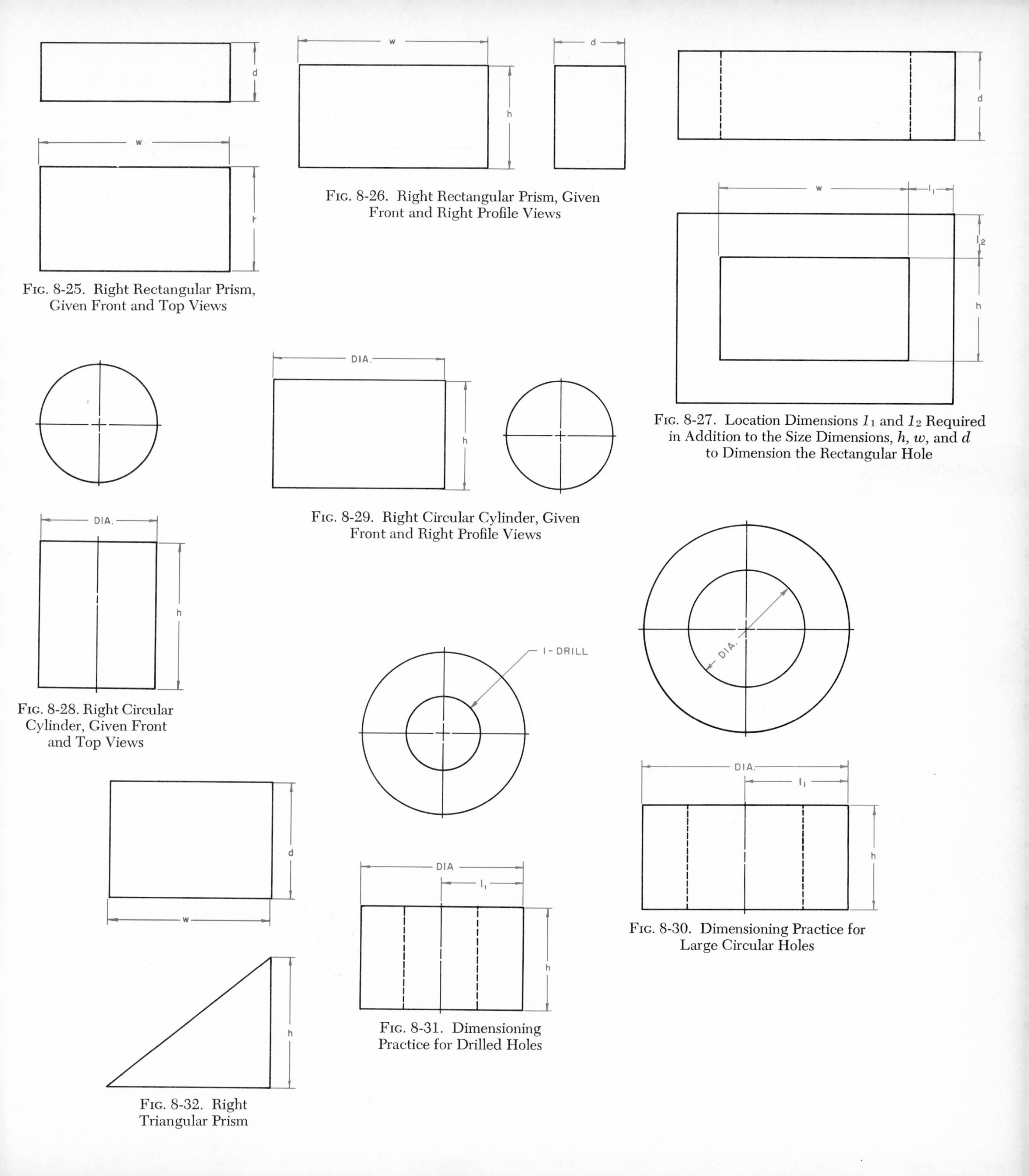

Fig. 8-25. Right Rectangular Prism, Given Front and Top Views

Fig. 8-26. Right Rectangular Prism, Given Front and Right Profile Views

Fig. 8-27. Location Dimensions l_1 and l_2 Required in Addition to the Size Dimensions, h, w, and d to Dimension the Rectangular Hole

Fig. 8-28. Right Circular Cylinder, Given Front and Top Views

Fig. 8-29. Right Circular Cylinder, Given Front and Right Profile Views

Fig. 8-30. Dimensioning Practice for Large Circular Holes

Fig. 8-31. Dimensioning Practice for Drilled Holes

Fig. 8-32. Right Triangular Prism

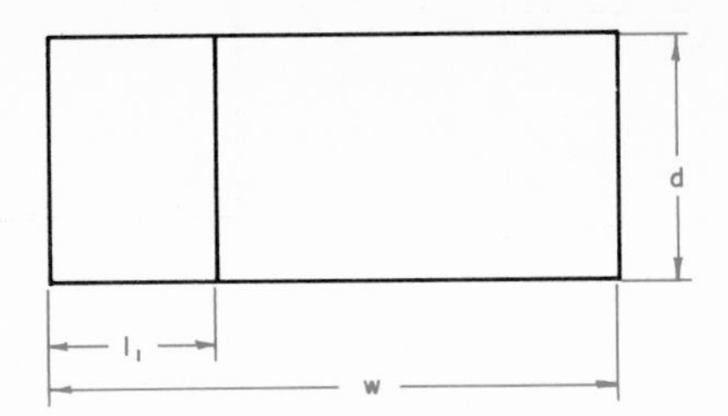

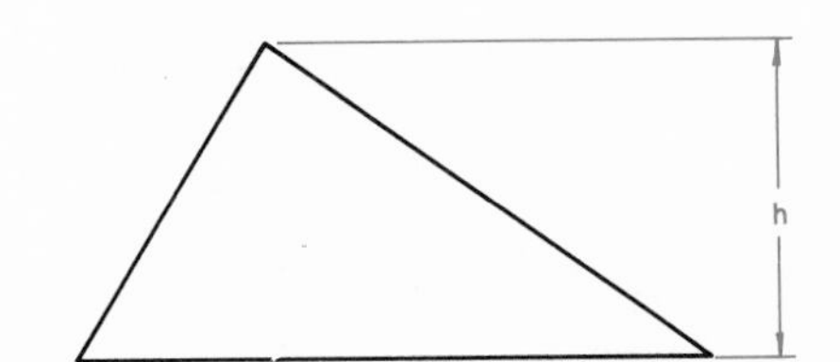

FIG. 8-33. Location Dimension Required for the Triangular Prism

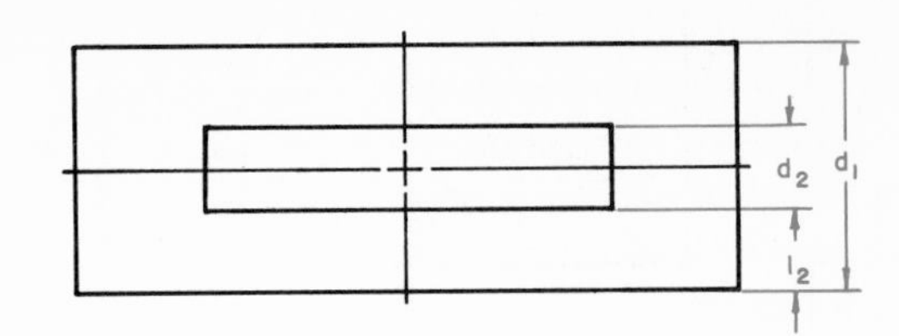

FIG. 8-34. Frustum of a Rectangular Pyramid

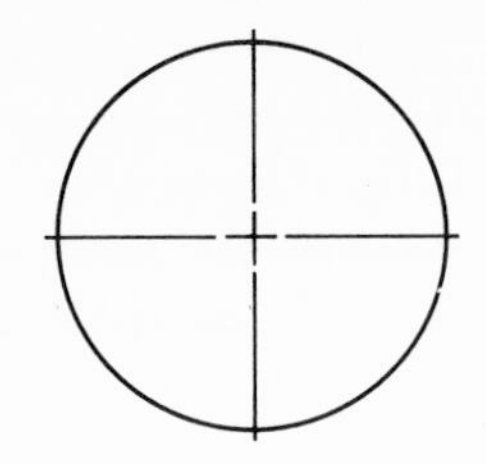

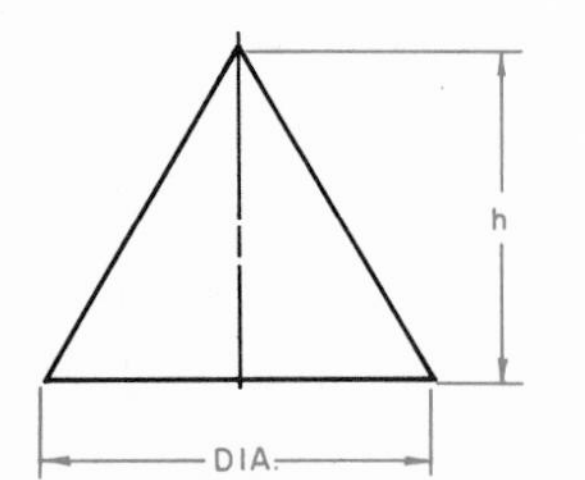

FIG. 8-35. Right Circular Cone

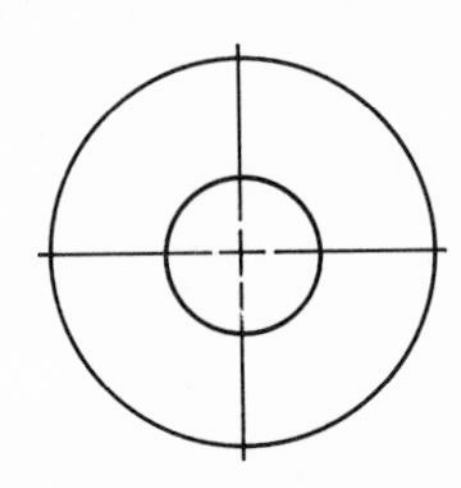

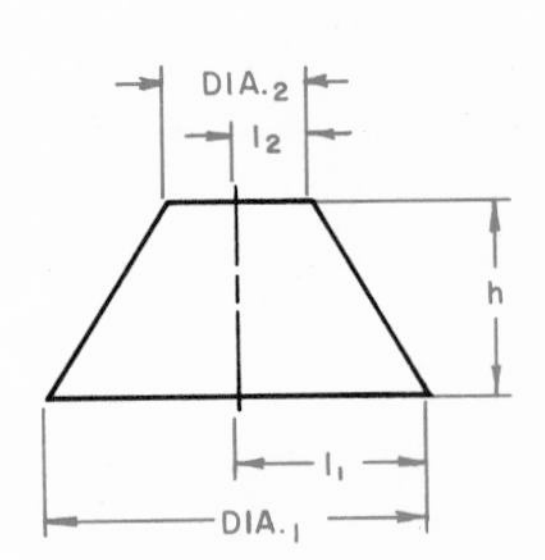

FIG. 8-36. Frustum of a Right Circular Cone

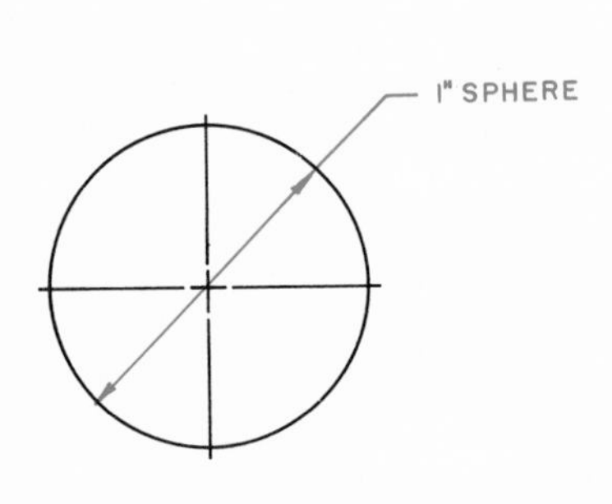

FIG. 8-37. Sphere May Require Only One Dimension Figure

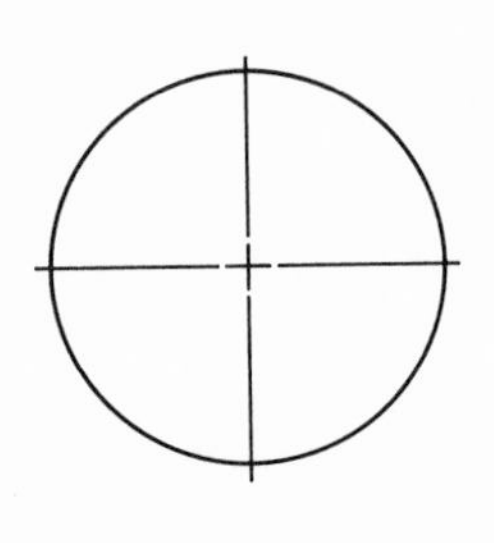

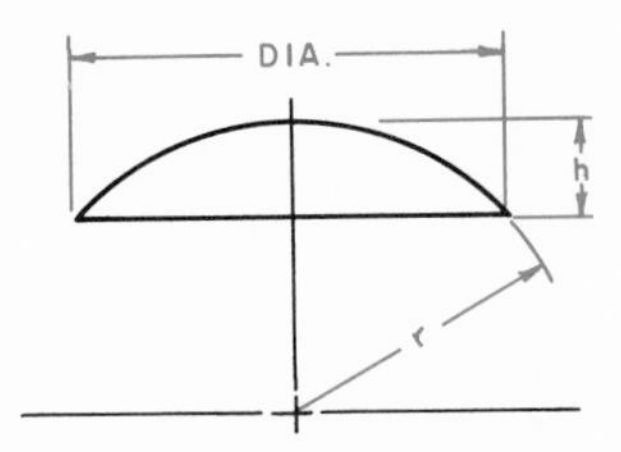

FIG. 8-38. Spherical End

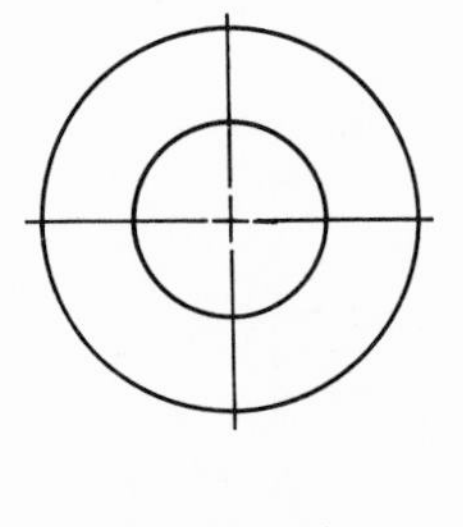

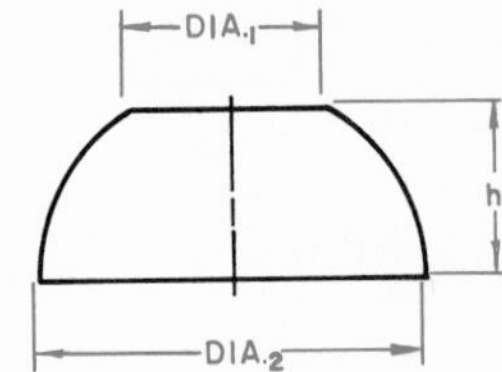

FIG. 8-39. Frustum of a Sphere

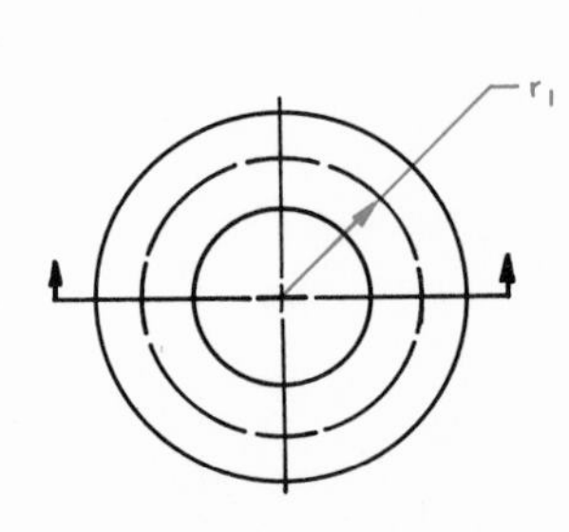

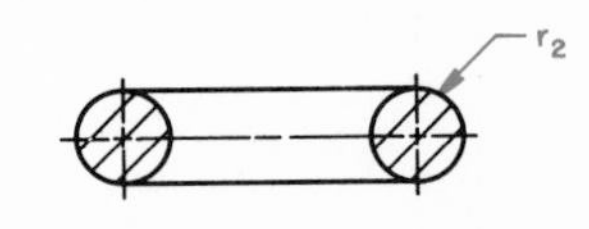

FIG. 8-40. Torus

Round Holes

Round holes are dimensioned as shown in Fig. 8-41. Dimensions for hole location should be on the circular view. Two or more identical holes are dimensioned with one note, the leader of which points *only* to the center of one of the holes, Figs. 8-45, 8-46, and 8-49.

Dimension counterbored holes with diameter and depth of the hole, and dimension countersunk holes with the diameter and the angle of the countersink as shown in Fig. 8-42. On shaft centers or countersunk holes, a standard drill and countersink may be specified, Fig. 8-43. Leaders for local notes which specify hole dimensions should be directed toward the circular view of the hole. The arrowhead should touch the outer circle and be directed toward the hole center.

Holes specified by number- or letter-size drills should include the decimal equivalent in the specification such as: *#28 (.1405) DRILL*, or *P (.3230) DRILL*.

Tapped and threaded holes are specified as shown in Chapter 12.

Coordinate dimensioning (selecting horizontal and vertical baselines or axes and orienting all dimensions from them) is standard in some industries and is preferred where greater accu-

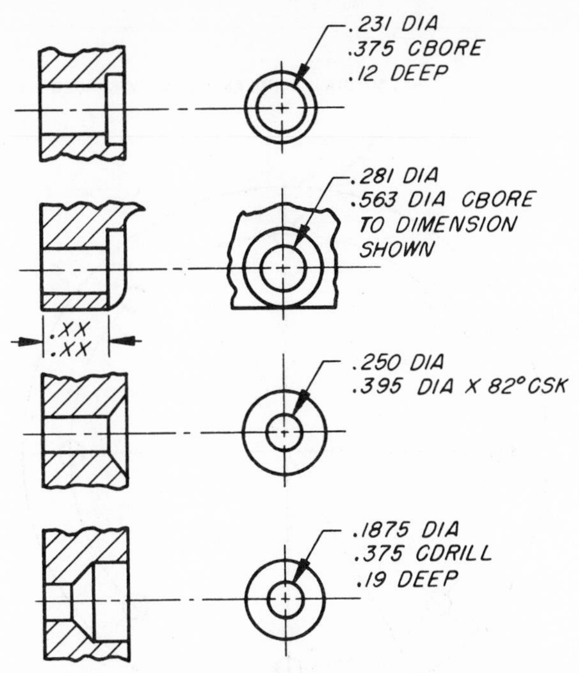

FIG. 8-42. Dimensioning Counterbored and Countersunk Holes (SAE)

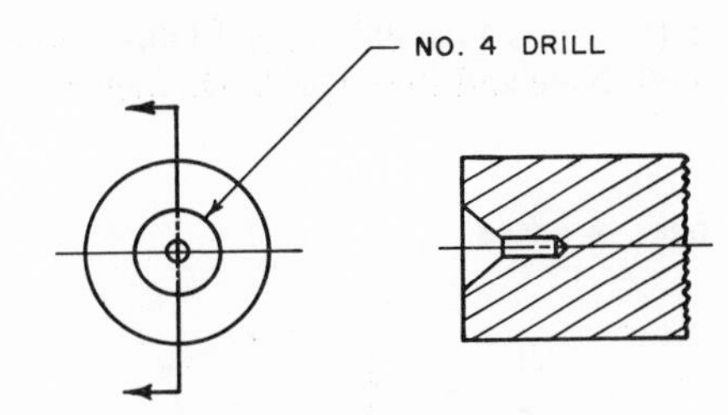

FIG. 8-43. Shaft Center (USAS)

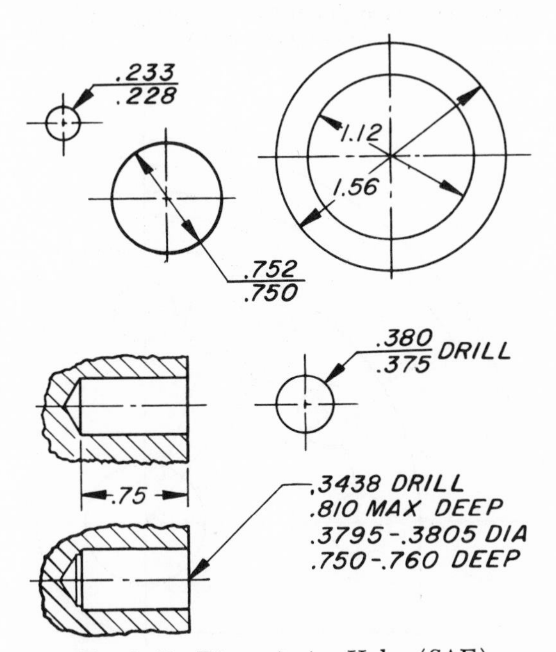

FIG. 8-41. Dimensioning Holes (SAE)

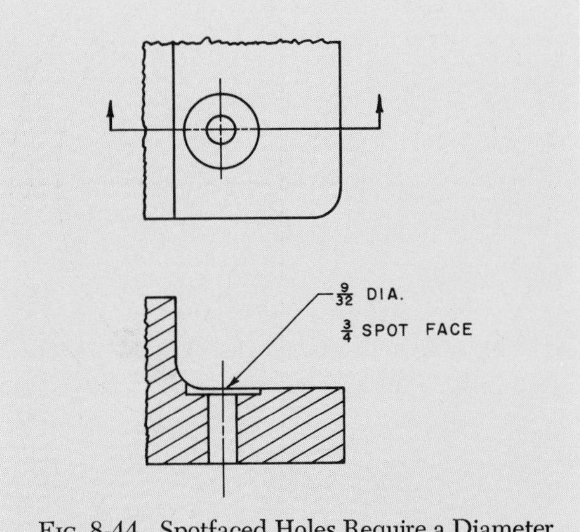

FIG. 8-44. Spotfaced Holes Require a Diameter Which May be Specified by a Local Note (USAS)

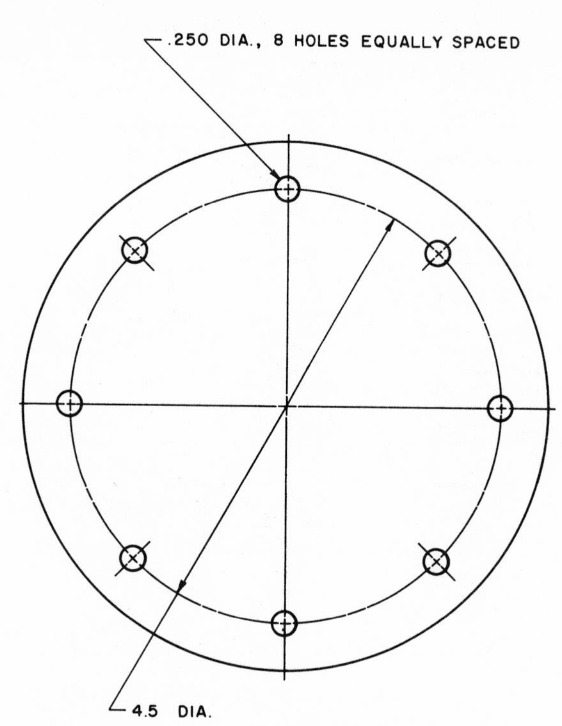

Fig. 8-45. Holes Equally Spaced Dimensioned with Note and Base-Circle Diameter

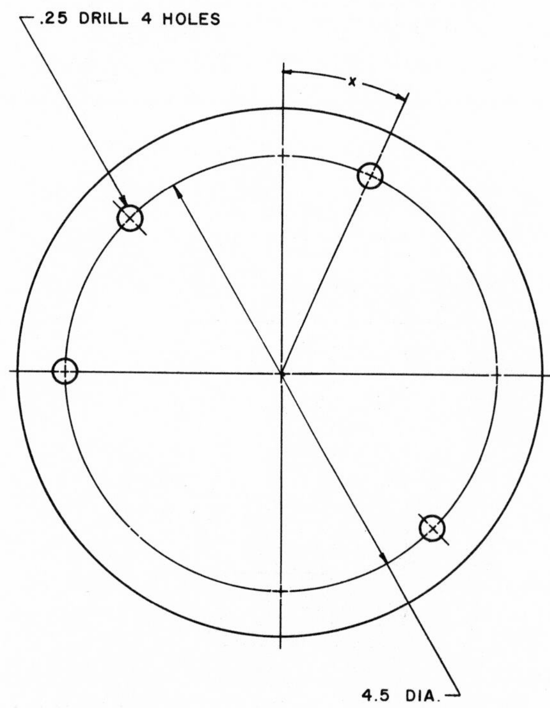

Fig. 8-46. Holes Unequally Spaced Dimensioned with a Note, Base-Circle Diameter, and Angular Measurement from One of the Center Lines

racy is required. If a circle diameter is shown, it should be clearly marked for reference by the abbreviation *REF*, Fig. 8-47.

Radial or polar coordinate dimensioning from a common baseline is used when several holes on a common base circle are located in various positions, Fig. 8-48.

Where a number of concentric circles are to be dimensioned, their diameters are shown either on the profile view or the circle view with preference given to the profile view, Fig. 8-50.

The radius of a cylinder should not be used since calipers and other measuring tools measure diameter. The diameter *(DIA.)* may be given in a note to eliminate the circle view.

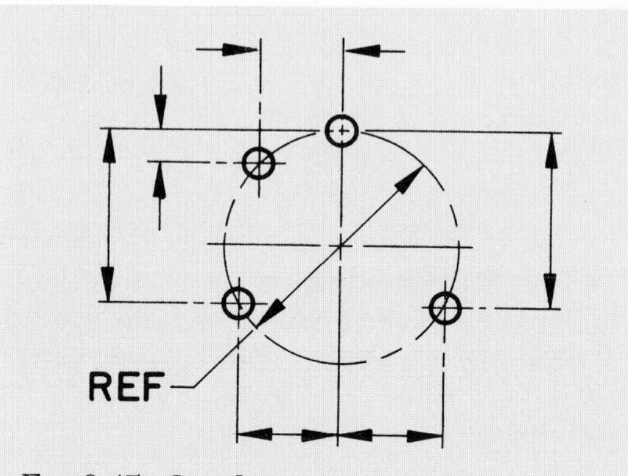

Fig. 8-47. Coordinate Dimensioning of Holes (The Martin Co.)

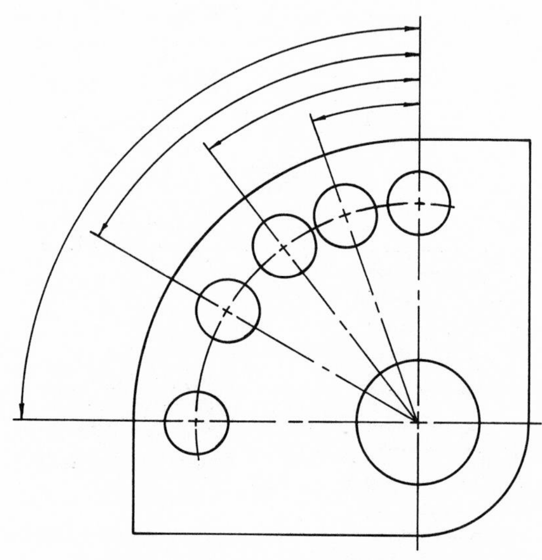
Fig. 8-48. Locating Holes by Polar Coordinates (USAS)

Slotted Holes

Slotted holes of regular shape are often used to compensate for inaccuracies in manufacturing and to provide for adjustment in operation. They are dimensioned by overall length and width, and are located by dimensions to their center line, Fig. 8-51.

Slots intended to perform a mechanical function are treated as two partial holes separated by space and are dimensioned as shown in Fig. 8-52.

Regular Curves

Regular curves are arcs of circles and are dimensioned by giving the radius. The dimension line for the radius should originate at the center, be broken for the dimension figure, and be terminated by an arrowhead touching the arc. All radial dimensions should carry the suffix letter *R*. In confined spaces the techniques shown in Fig. 8-53 are used.

A small cross is drawn at the center of a radius in cases similar to Fig. 8-54. Alternative methods for locating radii are shown in Figs. 8-55 and 8-56.

Where the center of an arc of a given radius lies outside the limits of the drawing, the radius line may be broken. The portion of the broken radius which ends with an arrow should point to the actual center for the radius, Fig. 8-57.

For rounded ends show the radius, but do not dimension it when it varies with the actual width, *a* of Fig. 8-59.

Where the hole location and radius location are subject to different requirements from the same center, dimension as shown in *b* of Fig. 8-59.

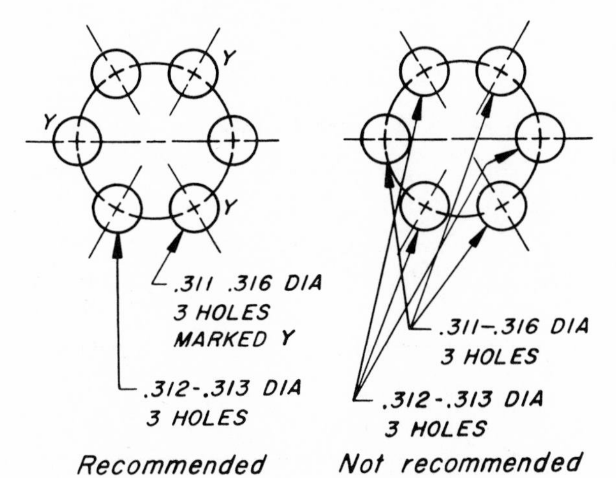

FIG. 8-49. Letter Designations Used to Avoid Long Leaders and Line Crossings (SAE)

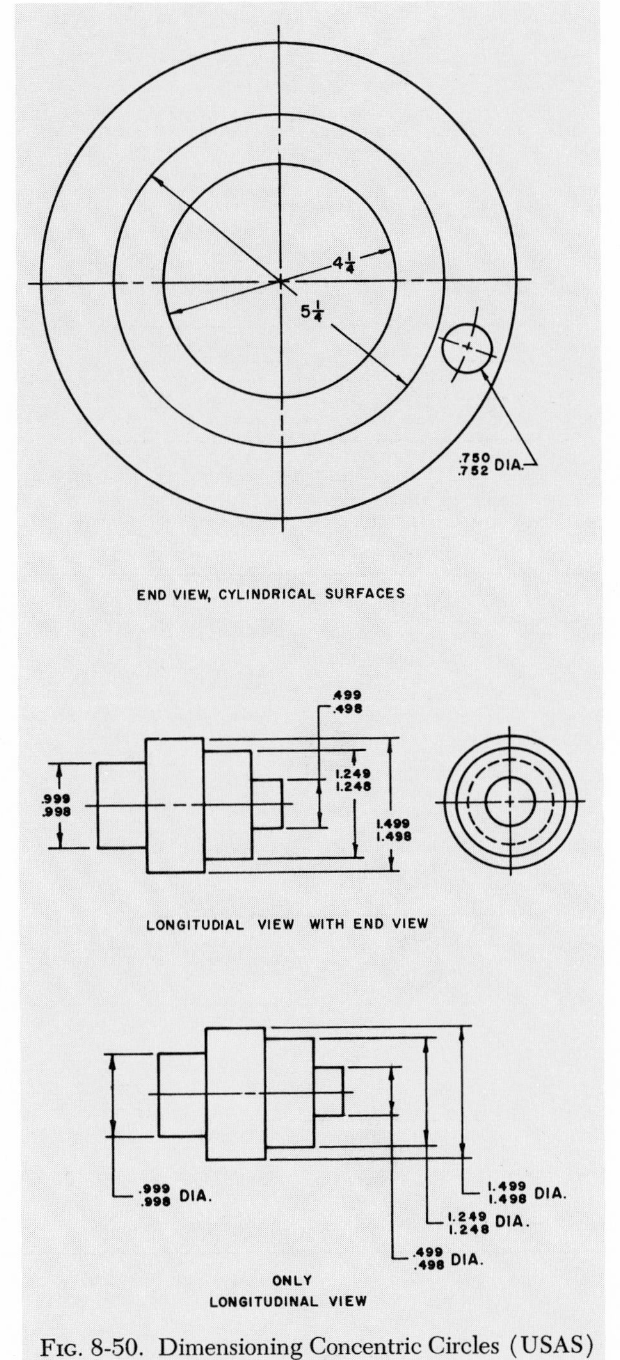

FIG. 8-50. Dimensioning Concentric Circles (USAS)

DIMENSIONING

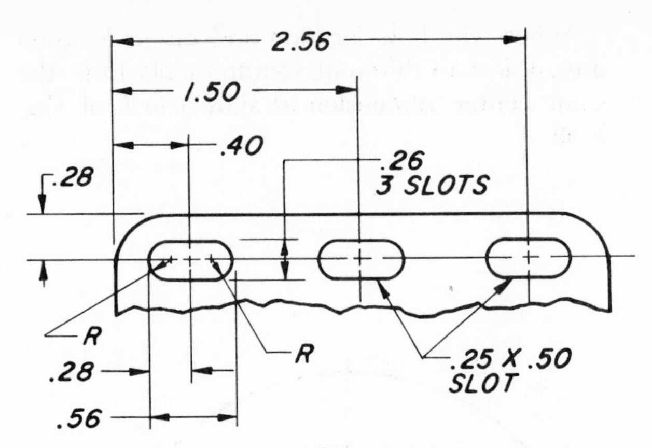

FIG. 8-51. Slotted Holes (General Motors)

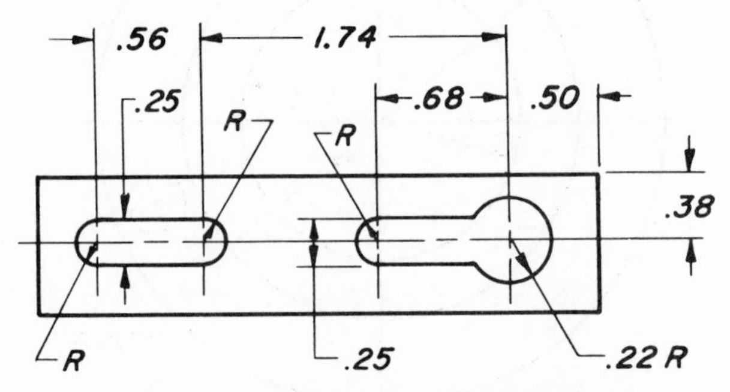

FIG. 8-52. Slotted Holes Intended to Perform a Mechanical Function (General Motors)

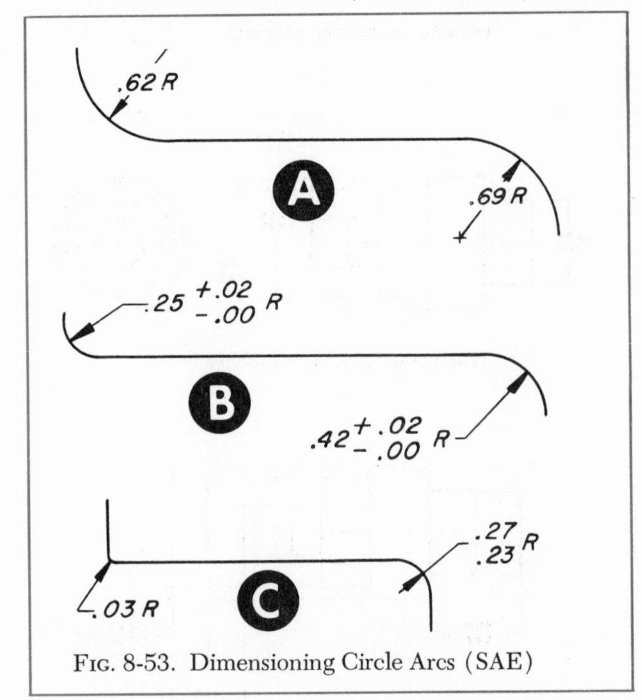

FIG. 8-53. Dimensioning Circle Arcs (SAE)

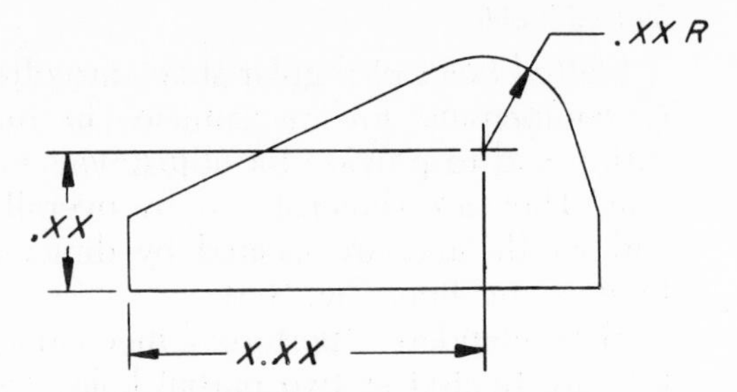

FIG. 8-54. Dimensions Given to the Center of a Radius (SAE)

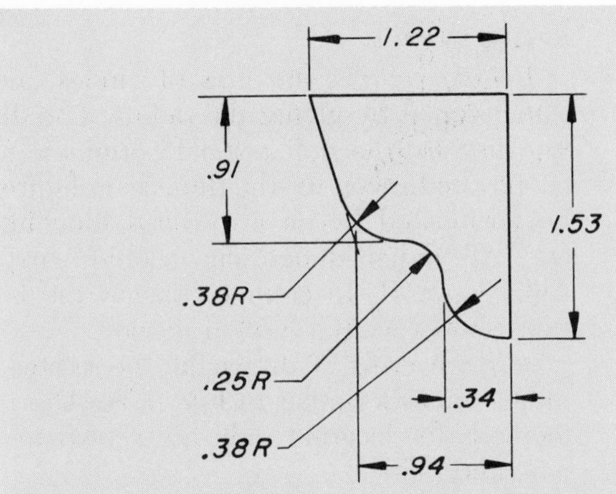

FIG. 8-55. Locating Radii by the Tangent Method (SAE)

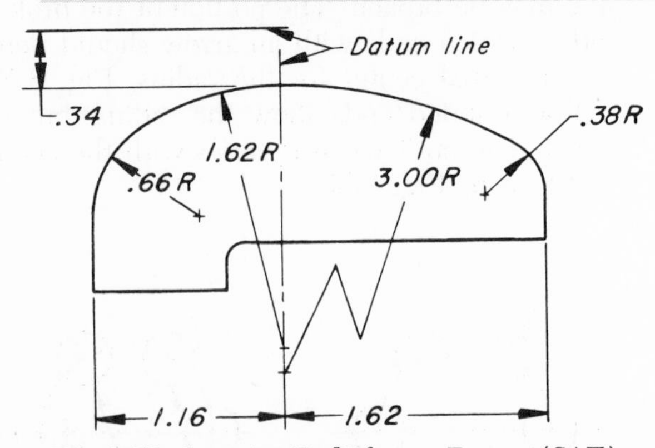

FIG. 8-56. Locating Radii from a Datum (SAE)

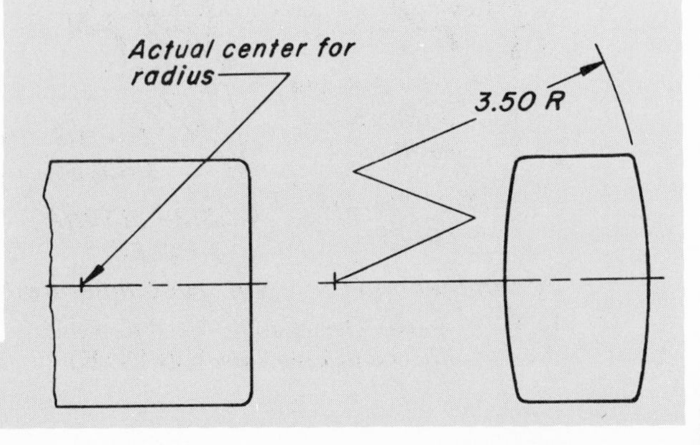

FIG. 8-57. Dimensioning a Radius with Center Off the Drawing (SAE)

Irregular Curves

Irregular curves are located from baselines or datum lines. If several coordinates are used, these should be extended to the curve outline, Fig. 8-60.

Curves may be dimensioned from numbered datum lines as shown in Fig. 8-61. This practice is not commonly used for production drawings but is used to supply information in designing

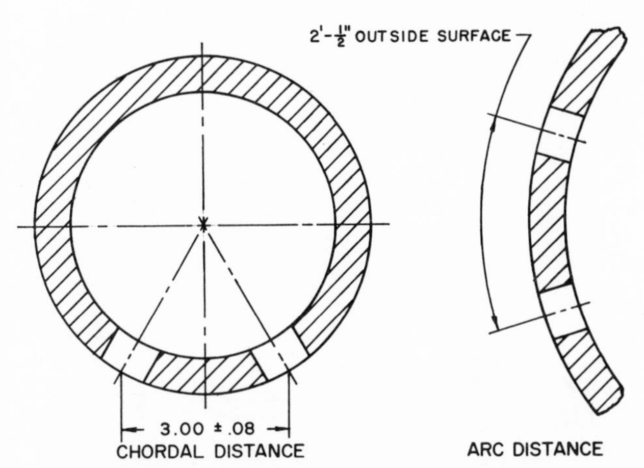

Fig. 8-58. Dimension Linear Distances Along Curved Surfaces Either as a Chordal Distance or as an Arc (USAS)

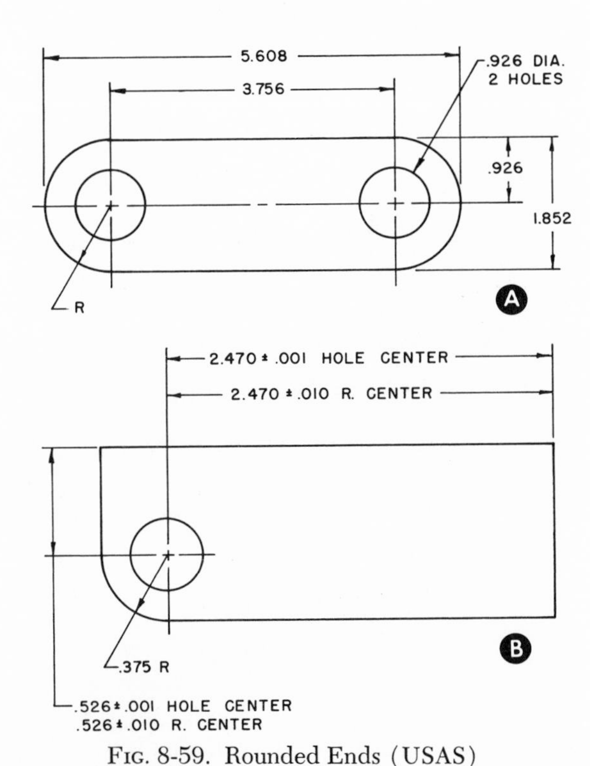

Fig. 8-59. Rounded Ends (USAS)

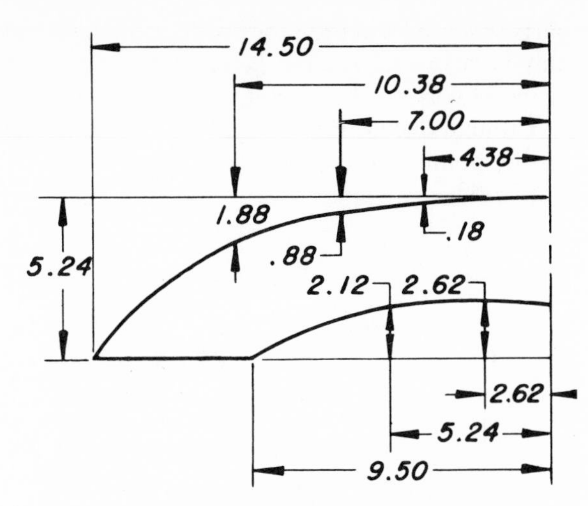

Fig. 8-60. Dimensioning a Curved Outline (General Motors)

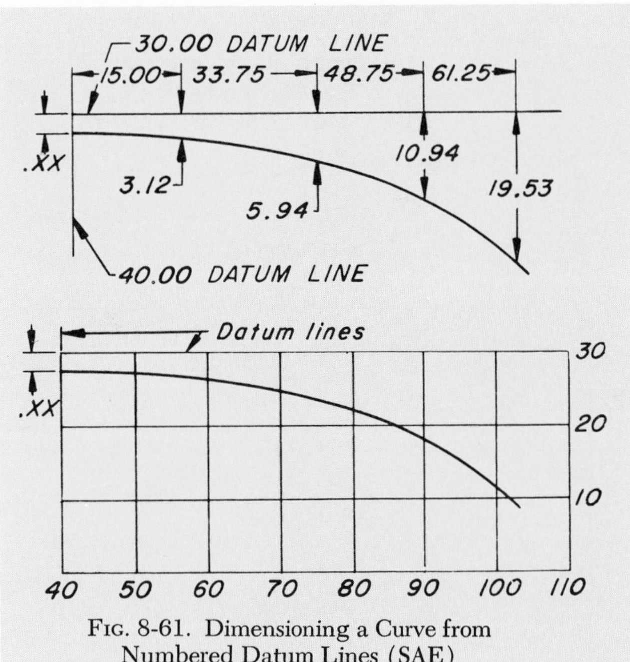

Fig. 8-61. Dimensioning a Curve from Numbered Datum Lines (SAE)

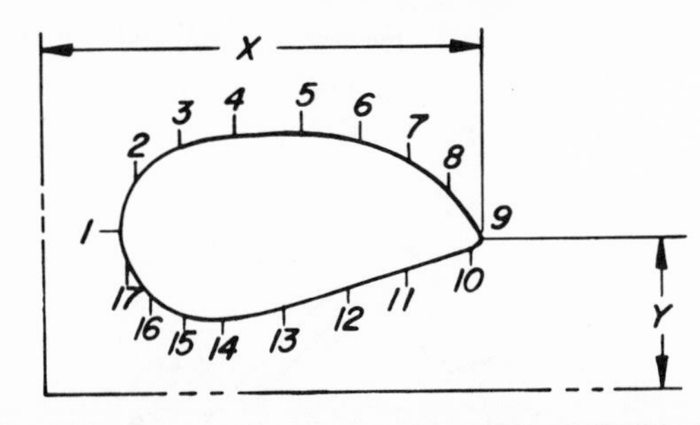

STATION	1	2	3	4	5	6	7
X	.XXX	.XXX	.XXX	.XXX	.XXX	.XXX	.XXX
Y	.XXX	.XXX	.XXX	.XXX	.XXX	.XXX	.XXX

Fig. 8-62. Tabulated Coordinates (SAE)

parts when information for production drawings may later be scaled from layouts. It is also used in woodwork to show irregular pattern layout.

Tabulated coordinates may be used to describe points which are close together as in Fig. 8-62.

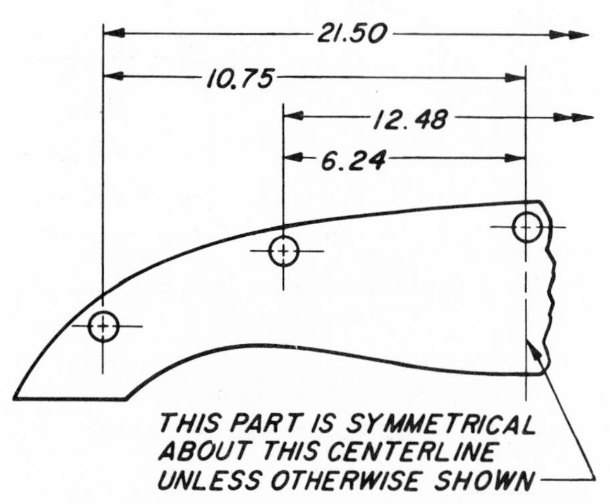

FIG. 8-63. Symmetrical Half-Parts (General Motors)

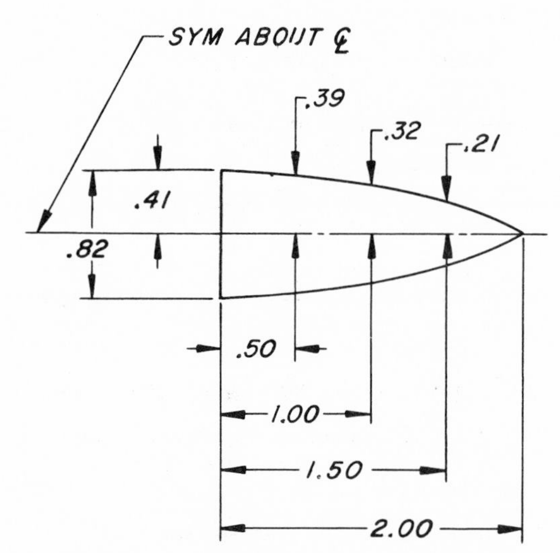

FIG. 8-64. Limited Space Dimensioning of Symmetrical Objects (SAE)

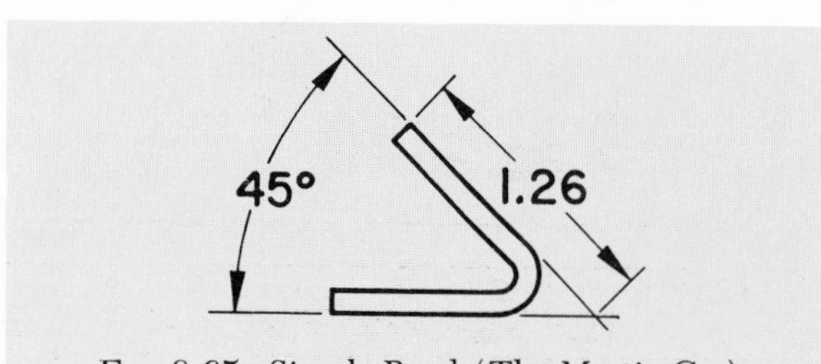

FIG. 8-65. Simple Bend (The Martin Co.)

On symmetrical parts, where only half of the part is shown, double arrows are used in conjunction with a note to fully dimension the part, Fig. 8-63.

When the symmetrical part may be shown but presents a limited space for dimensioning, only one side of the object need be dimensioned, Fig. 8-64.

Bends

Simple bend flanges are dimensioned angularly from the edge to the intersection of the two outside surfaces, Fig. 8-65.

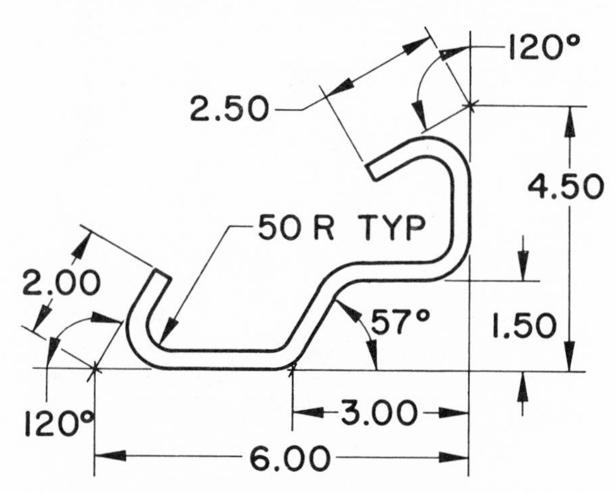

FIG. 8-66. Multiple Bends (The Martin Co.)

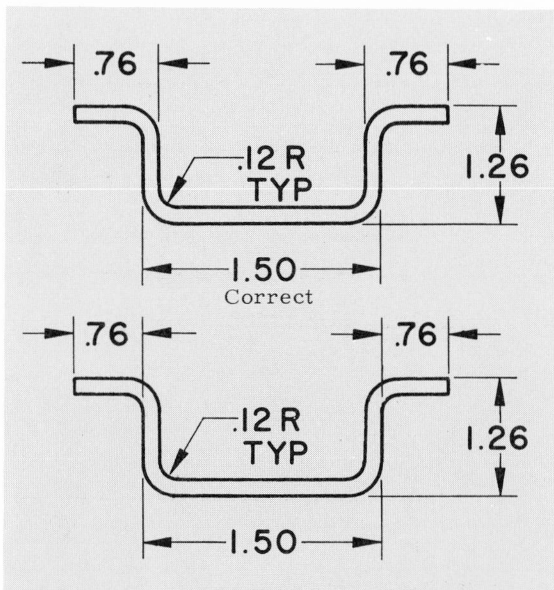

FIG. 8-67. Dimensions of Flanges Include Sheet Thickness (The Martin Co.)

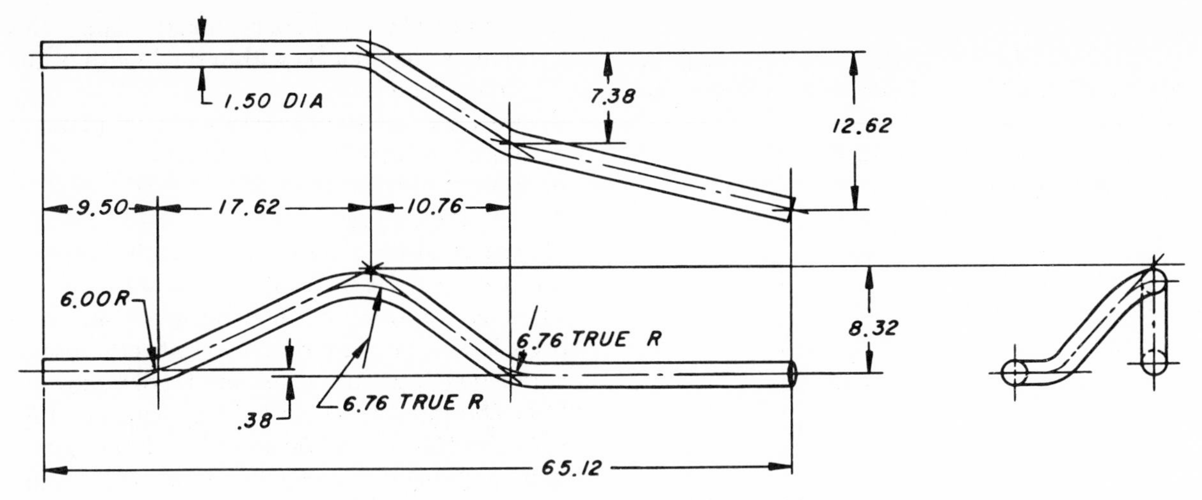

Fig. 8-68. Dimensioning Tubing (SAE)

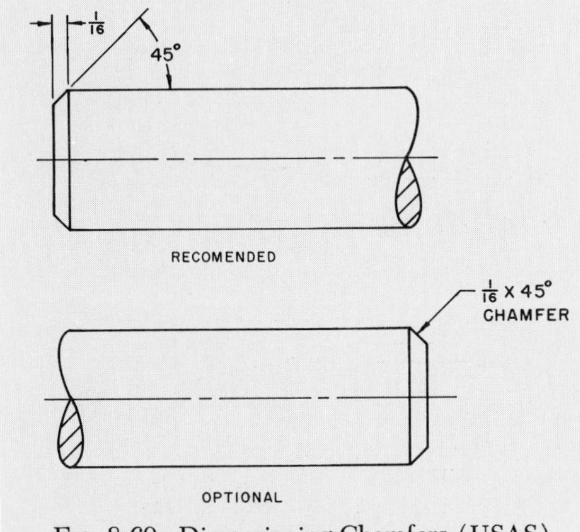

Fig. 8-69. Dimensioning Chamfers (USAS)

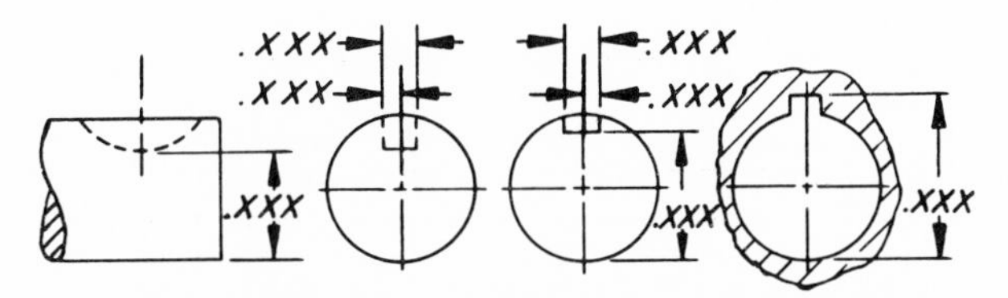

Fig. 8-70. Keys and Key Slots (SAE)

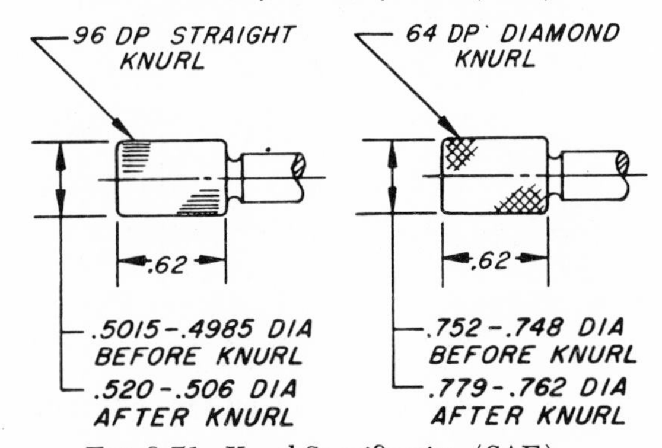

Fig. 8-71. Knurl Specification (SAE)

Multiple bends are dimensioned to the outside surfaces unless critical fits require a deviation, Fig. 8-66.

To eliminate the use of a general note or the repetition of a few dimensions, the term *typical* is used when it is not absolutely obvious that the dimension is typical. The abbreviation *TYP* is placed beside or below the dimension. It means that this dimension applies to all features that appear to be identical in size and configuration.

Flanges are dimensioned from edges and outer surfaces of the bend and include sheet thickness, Fig. 8-67.

Dimensions required for describing tubing details are shown in Fig. 8-68.

Chamfers

Chamfers (see Fig. 8-69) are dimensioned by angle and length. Forty-five degree chamfers are dimensioned by note as in Fig. 8-69.

Keys and Keyways

Key sizes and shapes are selected from established standards which give width and depth of keys and key-slots, Fig. 8-70.

Knurls

Knurls are specified by type, pitch, diameter both before and after knurling, and by the axial length of the knurl, Fig. 8-71.

DIMENSIONING

Tapers

CONICAL TAPERS[4]. Dimension conical tapers in different combinations to specify size and form:

a. diameter at each end of the taper.
b. length of the taper.
c. diameter of a cross-sectional plane; this may or may not be within the length of the tapered piece.
d. distance locating a cross-sectional plane at which a diameter is specified.
e. rate of taper.
f. included angle.

No more of these dimensions should be given than are necessary. Additional dimensions, required as information, may be given as reference dimensions. Fig. 8-72 illustrates the use of expressions that are considered adequate for dimensioning many close-fitting tapers. Fig. 8-73 illustrates an accurately dimensioned tapered plug that is not intended to mate

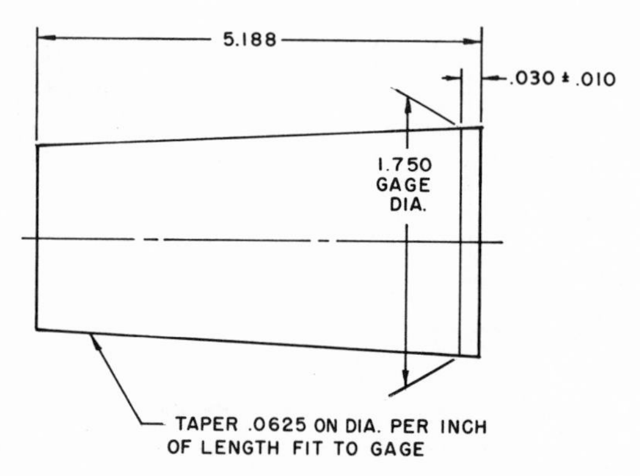

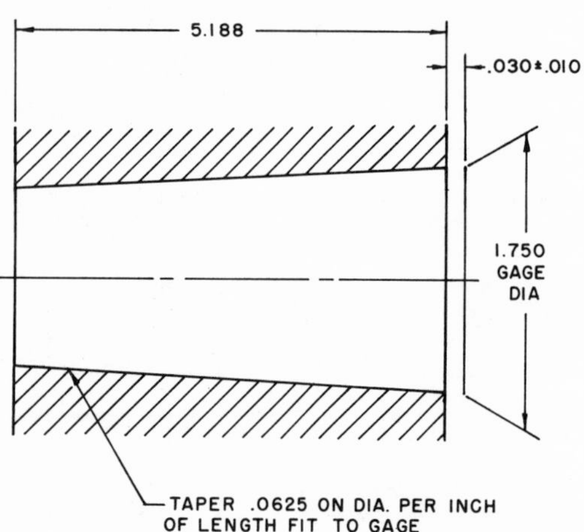

FIG. 8-72. Close-Fitting Mating Tapers (USAS)

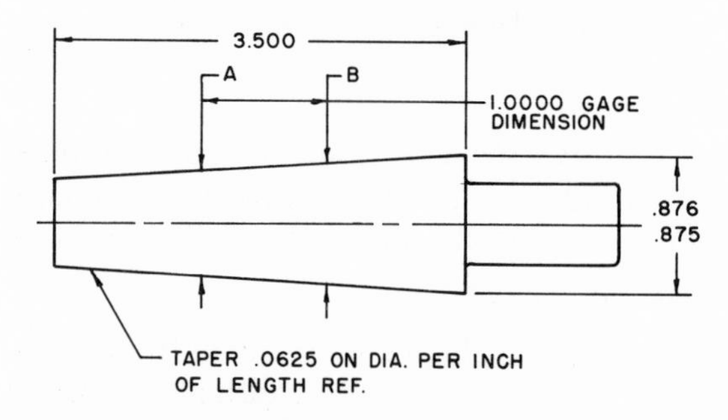

FIG. 8-73. An Accurate External Taper Not Dimensioned for a Close Fit with an Internal Taper (USAS)

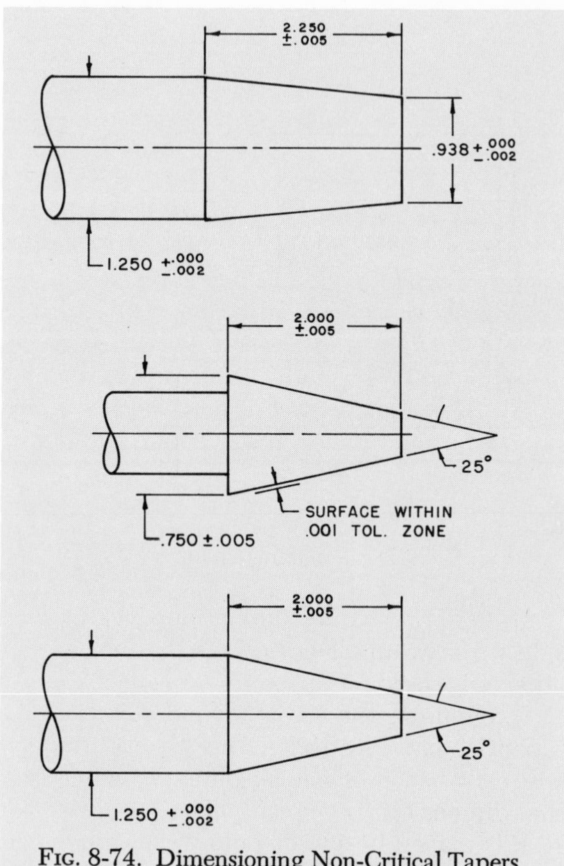

FIG. 8-74. Dimensioning Non-Critical Tapers (USAS)

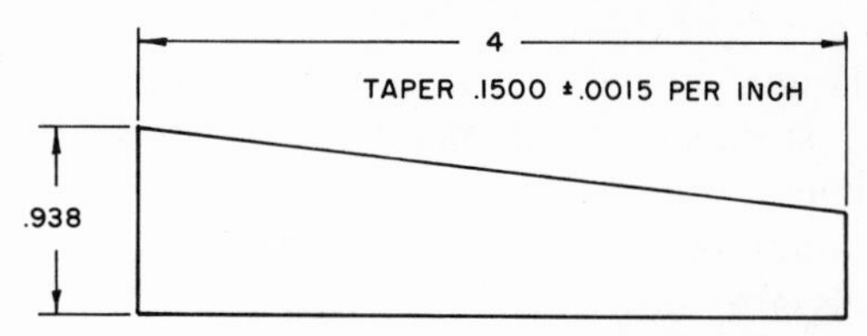

FIG. 8-75. Taper on a Flat Piece (USAS)

[4]USAS

snugly with an internal taper. Fig. 8-74 illustrates various ways of expressing less critical requirements.

MACHINE TAPERS[4] Standerd tapers are used in machine spindles, on shanks of tools, on pins, etc. For examples of standard taper dimensions, see *American Standard Machine Tapers,* USAS B5.10-1953. These standard tapers are specified on drawings by giving a diameter (usually at the large end) and the rate of taper, with a note stating the number of the taper and the name of the Standard, as: "No. 4 American Standard Taper."

FLAT TAPERS. These tapers are dimensioned by adapting the procedures stated for conical tapers, Fig. 8-75.

Chapter 8 — Problems and Projects

1. Problems 1 through 14 are drawn over a grid with 8 squares to the inch using the scale shown for each problem. Estimate the sizes to the nearest 16th of an inch. Draw or sketch the assigned problems on one-eighth inch or $\frac{1}{4}''$ grid sheets using the appropriate scale. Following the dimensioning practices in this chapter and using the fractional dimensioning system, dimension the problems carefully and completely. The exact correct dimension figures are not as important as the selection and placement of these figures.
2. Round-off the following dimension figures to three places, then to two places. Use the rules suggested in this chapter. (a) 1.0156 (b) .0312 (c) 2.0469 (d) .0625 (e) .5000 (f) .7656 (g) 9.9375 (h) .3750
3. For the following fractional dimensions, find the four-place decimal equivalents; then round them off to three places and then to two places. (a) $2\frac{5}{8}''$ (b) $8\frac{11}{16}''$ (c) $\frac{27}{32}''$ (d) $1\frac{7}{16}''$ (e) $\frac{15}{64}''$ (f) $5\frac{9}{16}''$ (g) 7″ (h) $11\frac{41}{64}''$
4. A typical drafting problem is to convert a drawing to the fractional dimensioning system. From problems 1-14 convert such problems as may be assigned you.
5. Problems 15 through 24 are drawn over a grid with 5 squares to the inch using the scale shown for each problem. Estimate the sizes to the nearest tenth of an inch. Draw or sketch the assigned problems on a grid sheet with either 5 or 10 squares to the inch using the appropriate scale. Following the dimensioning practices in this chapter and using the decimal dimensioning system, dimension the problems carefully and completely. The exact correct dimension figures are not as important as the selection and placement of these figures.
6. Of the following groups of 2-place decimals, identify the order of preference and give their metric equivalent. (a) .74, .75, .76 (b) .20, .12, .82, 1.00, .69 (c) 1.24, 3.50, 1.52, 2.19, 2.68, 1.85, 4.36 (d) 18.21, 104.72, 251.88.
7. Sketch or draw problems 15-24 and use both the decimal and the metric systems as shown in Fig. 8-2.
8. Fig. 8-81 has dimensioning errors. Make a list of those that you can find. If assigned, redraw or sketch the bird bath and dimension it correctly.

[4] USAS

DIMENSIONING

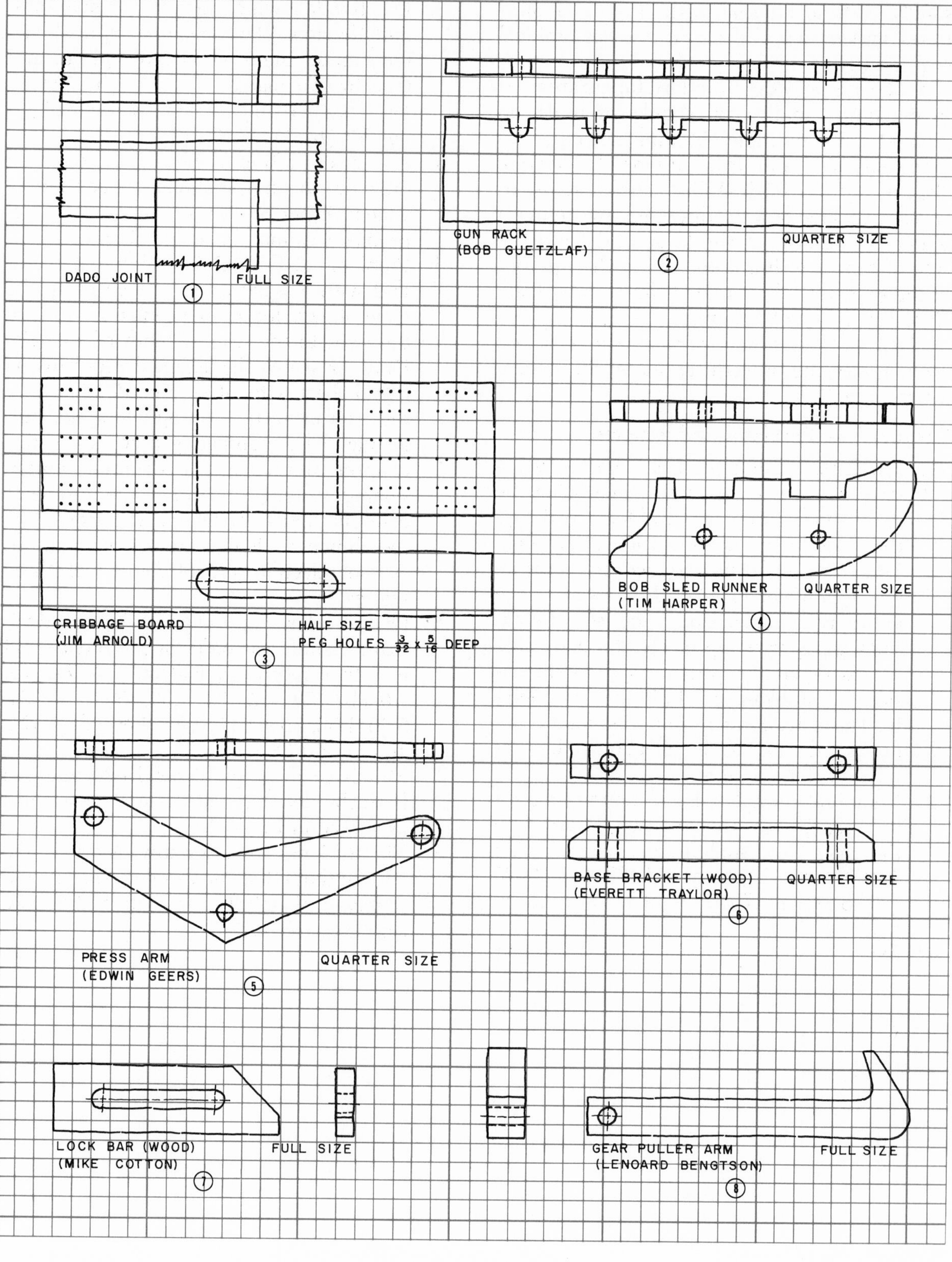

Fig. 8-76. Problems 1-8

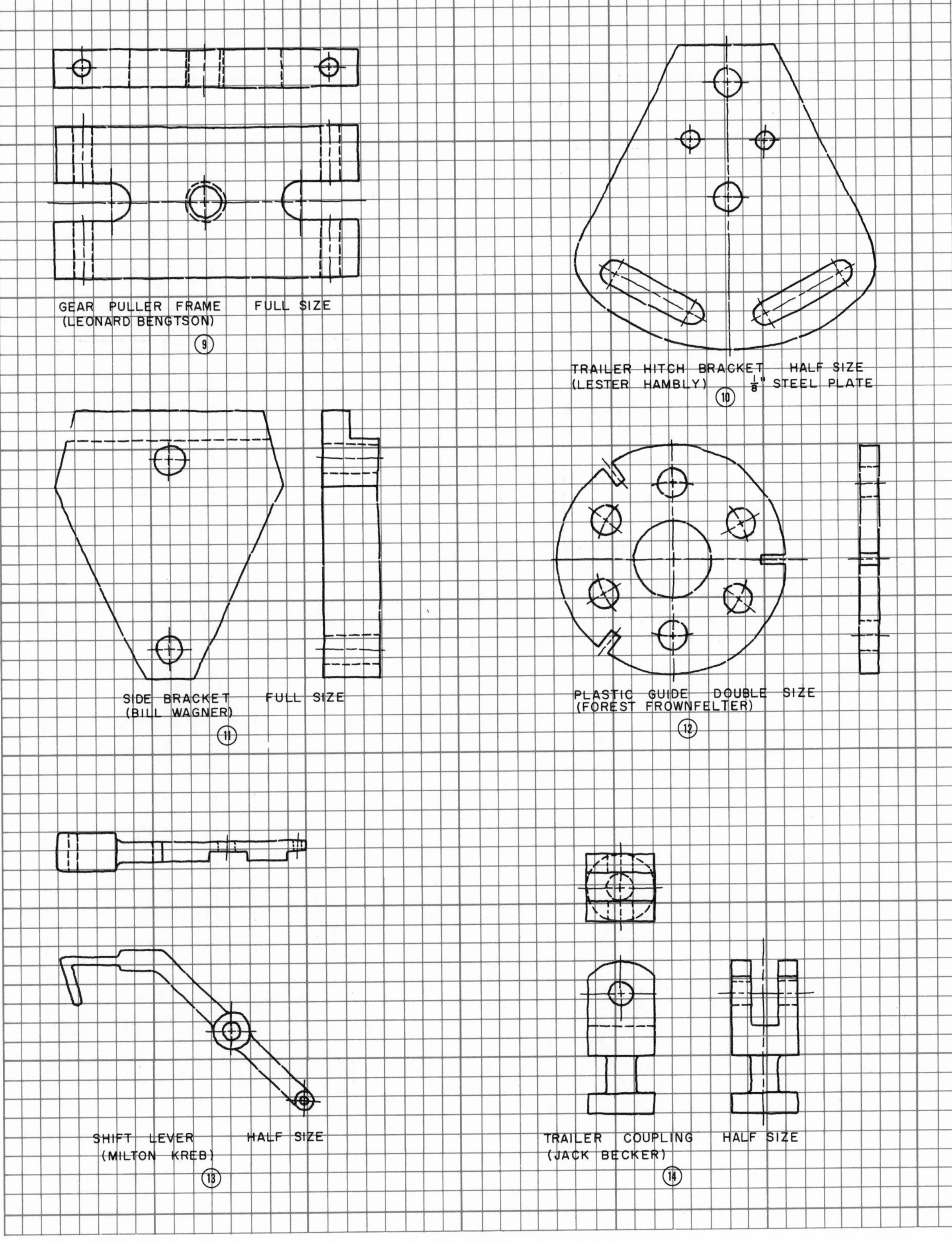

FIG. 8-77. Problems 9-14

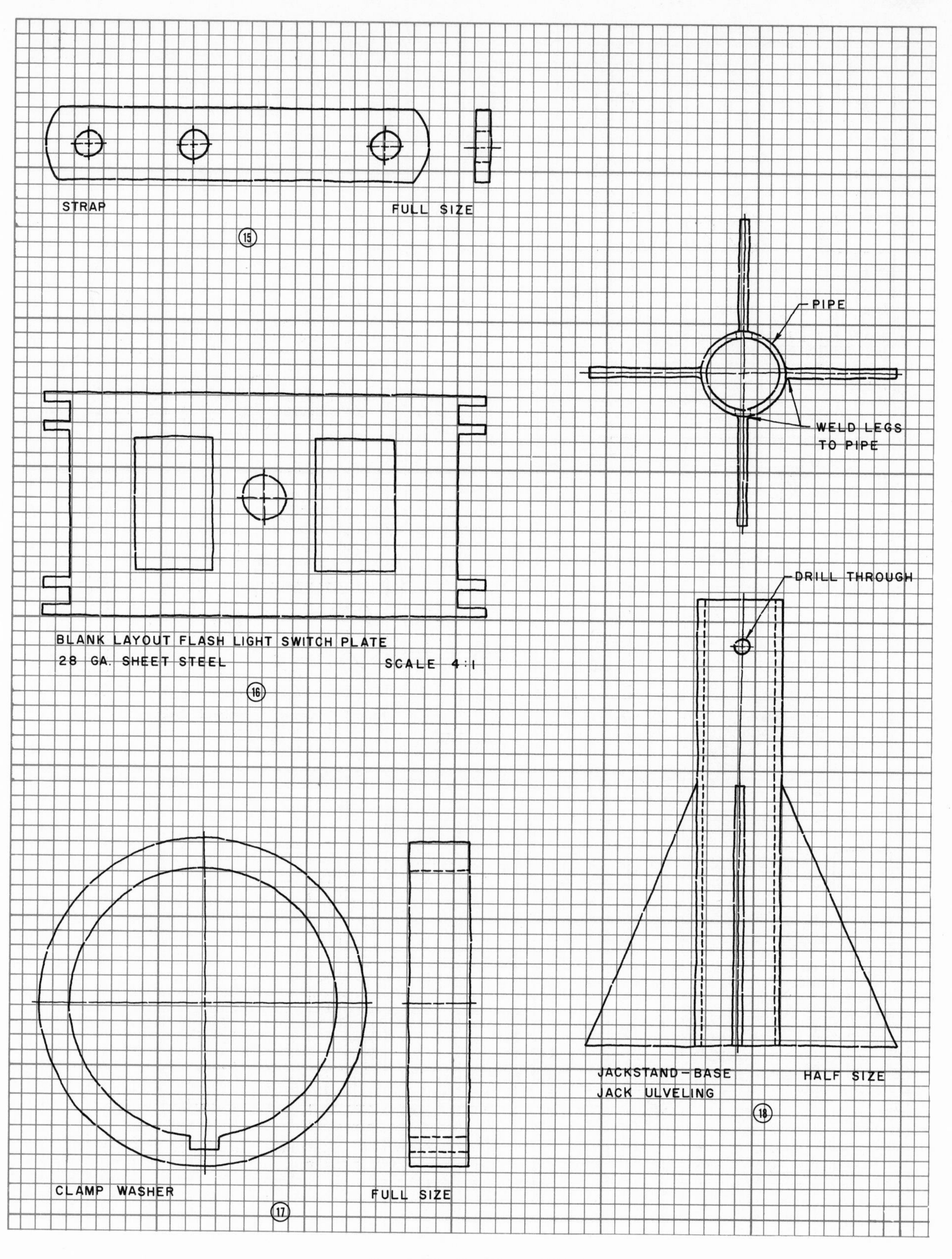

Fig. 8-78. Problems 15-18

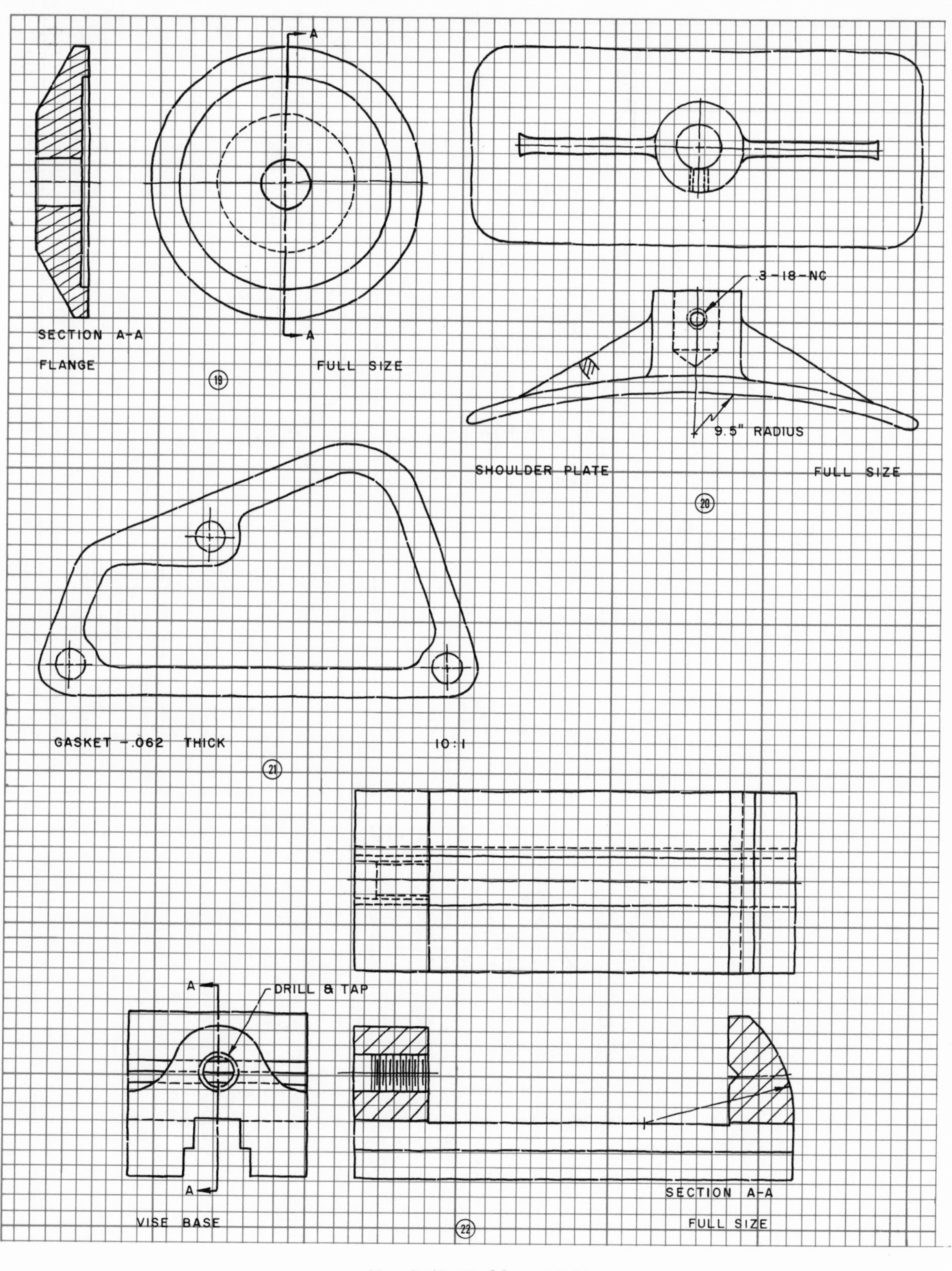

Fig. 8-79. Problems 19-22

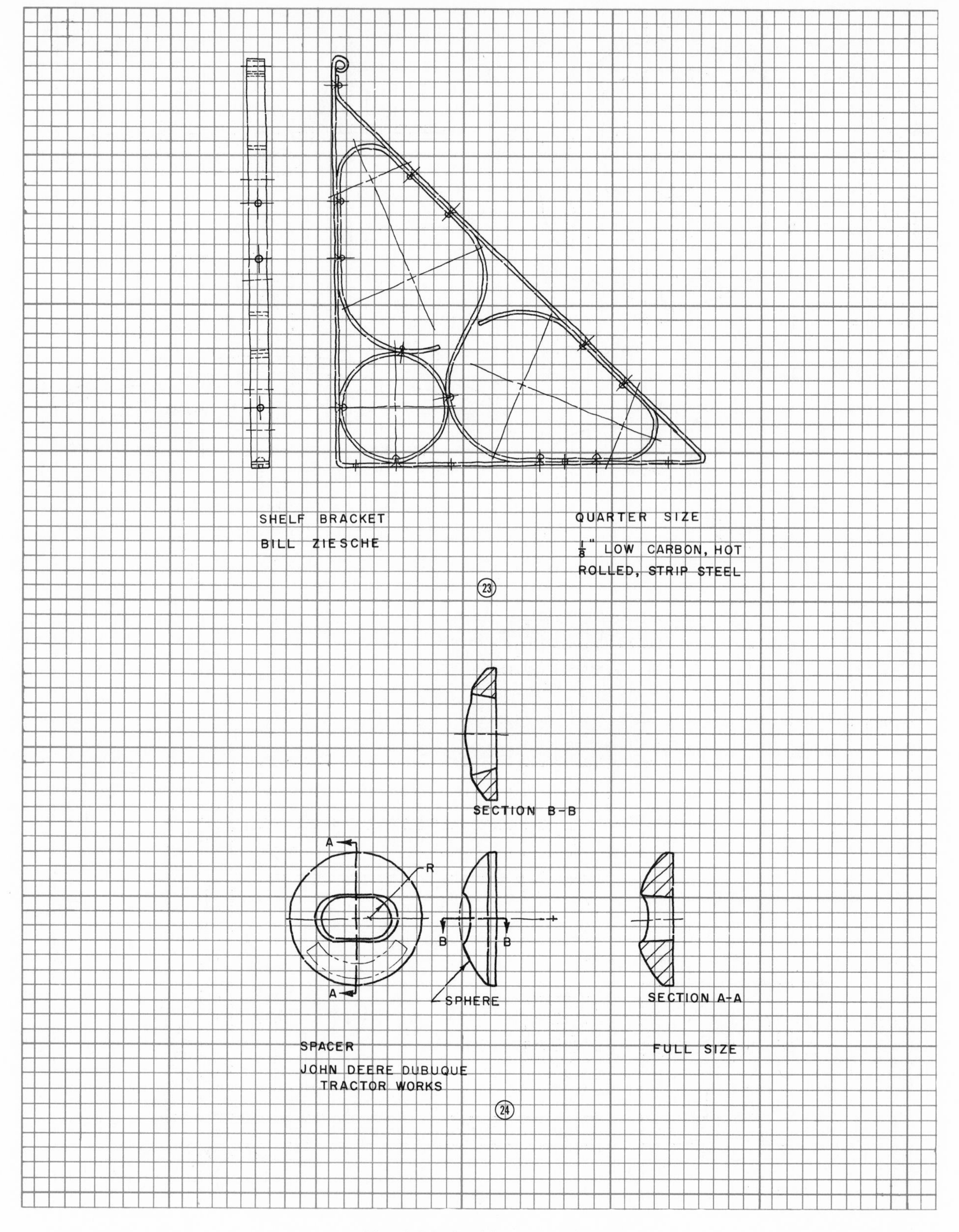

FIG. 8-80. Problems 23-24

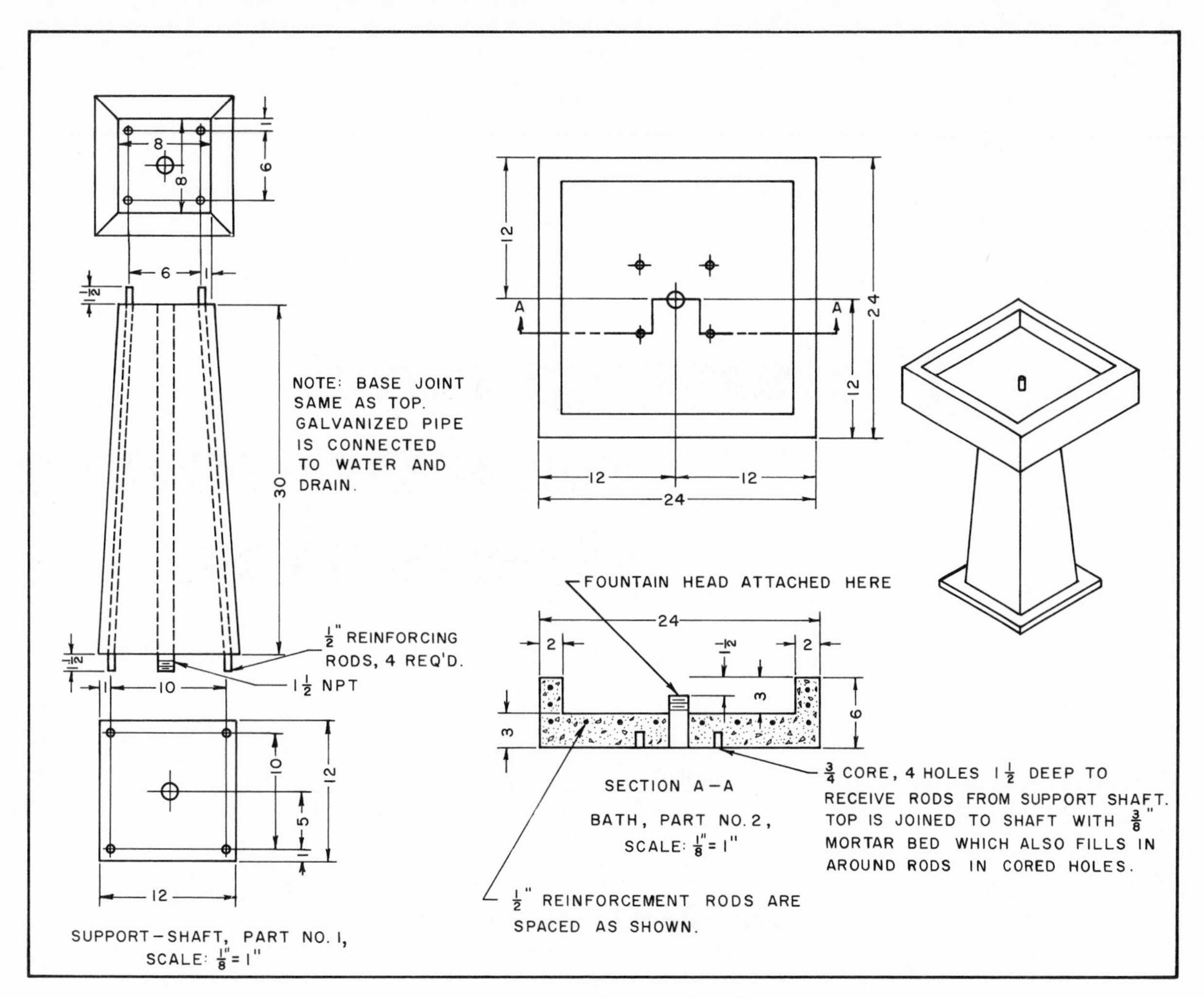

Fig. 8-81. Bird Bath
Identify the errors of dimensioning practice.

CHAPTER NINE

finishing and reproducing drawings

FINISHING
REPRODUCING

The first section of this book has identified the procedure of solving drafting problems. When the drawing is finished, it is reproduced, with the original work being carefully filed for future reference. The copies made from it are distributed as needed.

drafting media

In past years drawings were made in pencil on opaque paper. A translucent sheet was placed over it and an ink tracing was prepared; then the reproduction (generally a blueprint) was made.

With developments and improvements in both drafting media and pencils, industrial drafting room practice has changed. Today, entirely satisfactory reproductions are made from pencil used directly on the translucent sheet. In fact the proper use of special pencils with plastic leads on polyester-base films produces lines which may be mistaken for ink lines.

Kinds of Media

TRACING PAPER is a naturally translucent paper. VELLUM has been transparentized to permit faster print-making than can be done with the natural papers.

TRACING CLOTH is treated to permit use of pencil or ink and is more durable and more expensive than papers.

TRACING FILM is receptive to pencil or ink. It is "dimensionally stable"; *i.e.*, fluctuations in temperature and humidity have little effect on it. Films are among the more expensive media being used but are finding wide acceptance in industry.

GLASS CLOTH has characteristics much like tracing film and is also dimensoinally stable.

Desirable Characteristics

Translucency, surface quality and tooth, erasability, and paper strength are among the characteristics desired for drafting media.

Translucency, as used here, may not be easily observed by the eye. Translucency is related to ultraviolet-light transmission in the making of reproductions with one of the diazo printing or blueprinting processes. A good translucent paper will appear white or only slightly bluish. Papers which have a yellowish cast may not be good transmitters of ultraviolet light and may not, therefore, be as desirable as they may look. Thinness, lightness of weight, and uniformity of thickness also contribute to translucency.

SURFACE QUALITY AND TOOTH are related to the amount of graphite which can be deposited on the paper. A paper with a good tooth will wear off a sufficient graphite deposit from the pencil to give a good, dense line. Smooth-surfaced paper is more likely to smudge than paper with tooth.

Surface quality must be such that the paper does not absorb too much ink (preventing erasing) — nor too little (permitting the ink to flake-off). The paper should not pucker nor wrinkle when inked. If it does this, poor contact with the print paper may result in fuzzy spots.

ERASABILITY is important. Errors by draftsmen and students are inevitable, but more importantly, industrial drawings sooner or later are likely to be changed or revised. Good media should have the ability to withstand several erasures on the same spot without "ghosting." Ghosting occurs when the fibers in the tracing medium have been damaged by too much erasing or by too much pressure of the pencil. When crossed by a pencil, even when the graphite is removed, the ghost of the unwanted image shows in the reproduction print.

PAPER STRENGTH — repeated use in the reproduction process without smudging, wrinking, or tearing is essential. A good drafting medium should resist yellowing, curling, shrinking, and stretching. It should be free from blemishes, watermarks, dirt, specks, and oil spots. Good paper for reproduction is of uniform texture and 100% rag content. Rounded corners help to resist "dog ears" sometimes appearing during reproduction.

pencils

Factors in Selection

The best pencil for the circumstances will contribute materially to effective draftsmanship. Ordinary writing pencils do not have the desirable characteristics and should not be used to make mechanical drawings.

In selecting your drafting pencils, consider the following factors:

1. Quality and texture of the drafting medium.
2. Conditions of humidity and the like, and their effect on the drafting medium.
3. Your personal preference as a student draftsman together with a knowledge of your own characteristics and limitations.
4. Purpose and type of the drawing being prepared.
5. Anticipated method of reproduction.

Testing

Before making a selection of drafting pencils from among the many types and brands available, do some experimenting and testing. Examine pencils for the following:

1. Proper labeling and uniformity of lead gradation from one grade to the next.
2. Smoothness with no grit mixed into the lead.
3. Strength of the point.
4. Ability of the point to maintain its shape with use.
5. Straightness of wood drafting pencils and mechanical pencil leads.
6. Lines should tend not to smudge.
7. Pencil lines should be of appropriate intensity but should be erasable.

(See Table 4-3 for a sample test sheet for testing pencils.)

Pencil Techniques for Good Reproduction

Quality of reproduction is directly related to the quality of the pencil, the drafting medium, and the draftsman's understanding of these. Lines that are too light will burn out during the exposure step in reproduction. Lines that are grey will look fuzzy and indistinct rather than sharp and black. Leads in the middle and upper hardness ranges (*3H* and up) tend to be too hard for effective reproduction, and their use may damage the fibers of the drafting medium.

For best results consider these techniques:

1. All object lines, letters, and numerals should be uniform. Opaque quality is best described by the words *black, intense, medium width,* and *sharp.*
2. All other lines should be uniform and of sufficient intensity to reproduce well. Student draftsmen often make the mistake of making grey lines for fine lines and these do not reproduce well nor look well. Inspect each drawing for reproduction before leaving the board. Hold it up to the light and look at it from its back side. You will be able to tell from this whether the lines are black and whether any should be retouched.
3. Rotate the pencil slightly while drawing lines to maintain a uniform point and line weight.
4. Microfilmed drawings require an intense black line for both line work and lettering, but the lines may be just a little thinner especially for letters and numerals to avoid fill-in during reduction, enlargement, and blowback.

Simplicity and clarity are key words in describing industrial drawing. Technical drawings are made to convey ideas to others. The extent to which this objective is met depends, in part, on the quality of line work and lettering. Since one of the methods of reproducing drawings is microfilming, the effect of reduction on line work and lettering must be considered. Lines appearing close together on a drawing appear even closer on the reduction of that drawing.

Review appropriate sections of Chapter 4 for line technique and erasing technique. See Chapter 7 for lettering technique.

preparation of finished drawings

Care of Drawings During Preparation

There is a direct relationship between the care with which a drawing is prepared, its life, and its reproduction quality. The following procedures will be helpful in producing drawings with long life and high reproduction quality:

1. Keep drafting equipment and tools clean. Sponge with a solution of mild soap and lukewarm water and dry thoroughly.
2. Keep the drawing clean by covering the drawing with paper in areas where you are not working on the drawing. This will help prevent smudging and finger marks.
3. A clean piece of *back-up* paper under the drawing will help reduce dirt specks which otherwise adhere to the back of a drawing and show up later in the reproduction of it. Back-up paper preprinted with guide lines or a grid will be useful in lettering and general layout work.
4. Do not crease tracing paper nor fold it since the lines left by folding usually reproduce. Avoid dog-ears when reproducing prints by feeding the original very carefully into the machine.
5. Use *only* drafting tape for fastening tracing mediums to the drafting board. Then lift the tape off carefully to avoid tearing the corners.
6. Make erasures carefully. A soft eraser should be used to remove all traces of pencil lead. Be sure to erase the back side of the tracing paper behind erasures in order to take off any dirt or discoloring that may have occurred there.
7. When a drawing is left on a board, cover it to prevent dust and dirt from accumulating. Avoid building up layers of drawings when you are working on more than one sheet at a time.
8. Original drawings should be used and filed flat. Where flat filing is not possible, they may be filed in rolls. The core of the roll should be at least 1¼″ in diameter and several inches longer than the drawing.

9. Original drawings should *not* be used for reference purposes. It is almost always desirable to make a print for reference and to keep the original in a file.
10. Torn drawings should not be handled until the torn areas are mended with translucent mending tape.

Planning for Layout

The planning for the layout of a drawing is based upon a knowledge of whether a drawing requires one, two, three, or more views. When developing a whole page of drawings with several parts, the same principles apply. It is very important to have ample clear space between the views and to have good page balance. Preliminary planning must be done for all drawings especially removed views, section views, and auxiliary views. Such planning usually takes the form of dimensioned sketches.

Since the draftsman attempts to place views of a drawing on the page in third-angle projection, he must leave enough space between the views so that the views are easily distinguishable and yet close enough together to show the basic relationships of these views. When dimensions are added, the draftsman strives for these same things but must take into account the dimensions to be used, their placement, and the space they will occupy as he plans for the layout of his drawing.

Although the *experienced* draftsman may have enough judgment so that he does not always need to make a preliminary sketch before making the final drawing, the student draftsman should make such a sketch, Fig. 9-1. On this basis he prepares the finished drawing. He can then focus his attention on accuracy of layout, correct use of the alphabet of lines, proper visualization of parts, good dimen-

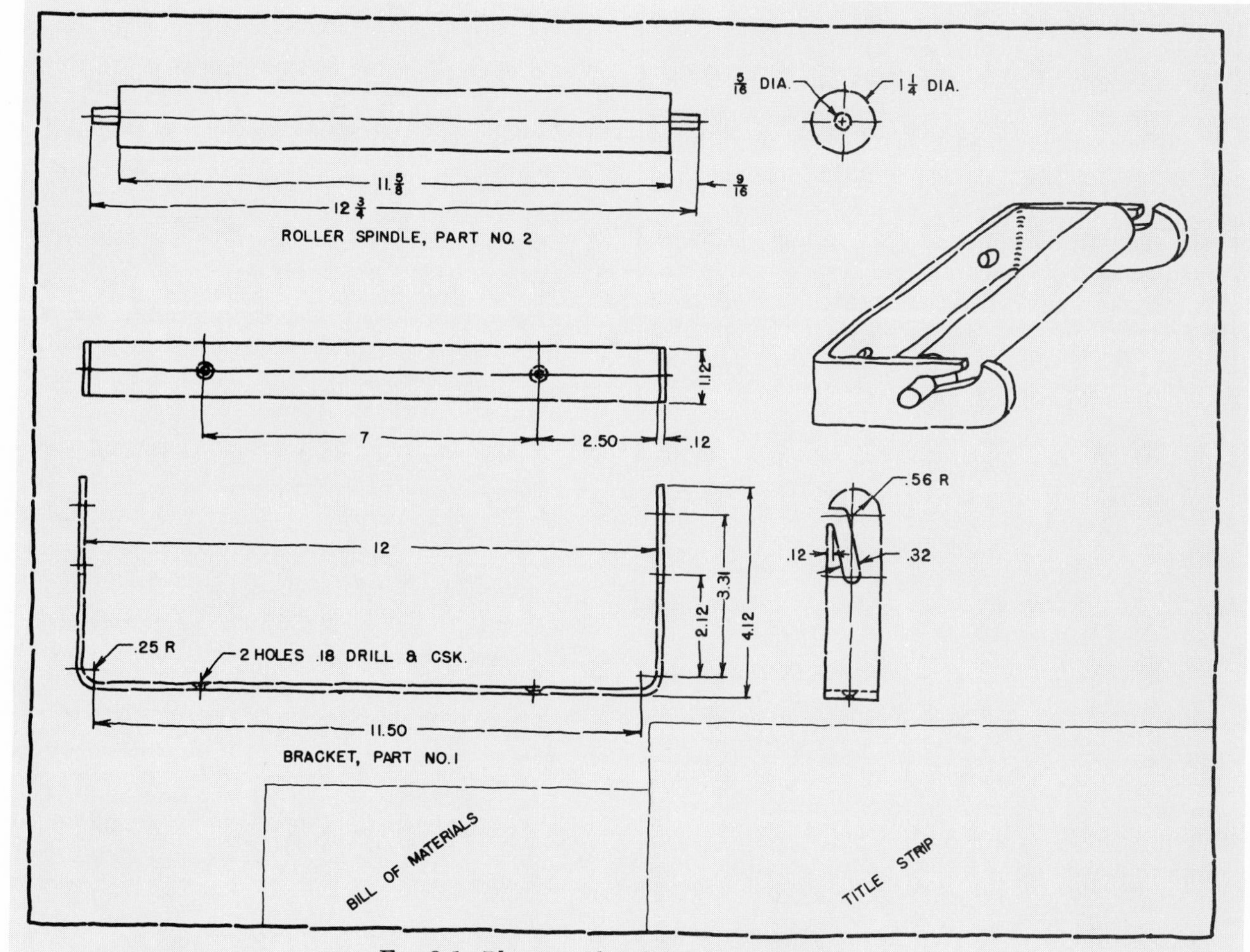

FIG. 9-1. Planning Sketch for a Towel Fixture

sioning techniques, and careful execution of information in the title strip.

For this discussion assume that a three-view pencil drawing is being developed on a reproducible tracing medium and that the border lines and a title strip are preprinted on the tracing medium. This is a typical situation in industrial drafting rooms.

Layout Procedure

1. Locate the height and width lines in the front view.
2. Block in the views. Use lightweight construction lines. If a line can be made its proper weight the first time, this should be done.
3. Layout center lines; construct circles, arcs, and irregular curves, *a* of Fig. 9-2, p. 198.
4. Layout and draw all horizontal, vertical and inclined construction lines for the remaining details.
5. Add the hidden lines full strength.
6. Darken all visible outlines, *b* of Fig. 9-2.
7. Draw extension and dimension lines. These lines must be dark enough to reproduce but definitely lighter than hidden lines.
8. Add dimension figures and notes.
9. Add section lines as appropriate. Dimensioning is done first because in some instances dimensions are located in sectioned areas. In these cases, section lines should be broken so that they do not go through the dimension figures.
10. Letter the title strip, Fig. 9-3, p. 200.
11. Check the drawing very carefully. This important step is often overlooked by the careless student. A suggested checking procedure will be covered thoroughly later in this chapter.

Inking

Inking is not used in industrial drafting as much today as in former years. Inking is done either by tracing a drawing or by applying ink directly over lines penciled on the drafting medium. Its importance to a finished drawing should not be overlooked. A black, waterproof, high-quality India ink is highly opaque. The character of ink lines is entirely in their variations of line width rather than in their opaqueness.

Procedure

The sequence of inking is determined, in part, by efficiency while waiting for ink lines to dry and, in part, by the easiest way to join ink lines together to form good tangencies and corner junctions:

1. Prepare the drawing medium for inking. Sprinkle *pounce* or other powder on the surface and rub it in. Remove the powder completely. The surface should now be ready to take ink.
2. Locate all center points and tangent points directly on the drafting medium with lightweight pencil lines.
3. Ink all circles, circle arcs, and irregular curves.
4. Ink all straight lines of the object. Do horizontal lines first, then vertical and inclined lines. Work consistently from top to bottom and from one side of the sheet to the other.
5. Ink all center, extension, and dimension lines in the same order as in the preceding step.
6. Ink the dimension figures, notes, and arrowheads.

Techniques

GENERAL:

1. Fresh ink and a clean pen make for uniformity of lines and trouble-free inking.
2. When testing ink lines, use the same kind of paper as that used for drawing.
3. Pressure on the inking instruments should be light and uniform to permit the ink to flow and to obtain uniform lines.
4. A uniform speed should be maintained when drawing lines because changes in speed result in variances in line width.
5. Center the inked lines over the pencil lines to insure proper junction.
6. Corners and intersections should not be inked unless lines previously made are dry.

RULING PEN:

7. Inking with a ruling pen is generally done with a T-square and triangles rather than with a drafting machine. The scales of the drafting machine are usually beveled, making it more difficult to keep the ink line from running under the scale.

The ruling pen should be held at a 60° angle to the paper in the direction in which the line is being drawn. It should be vertical, at a 90° angle to the paper, in relation to the edge of the T-square.

8. Excessive ink in the ruling pen causes heavier lines. Between the nibs of the pen, free-flowing ink should be filled to about one-fourth inch.
9. Always use a ruling pen with a straightedge — *never* freehand.
10. The ruling pen cannot be used satisfactorily with circle templates, ellipse templates, and the like.
11. When the pen has been set aside, even for a relatively short time, you may need to touch the pen to a piece of scratch paper to make the ink flow.

TECHNICAL FOUNTAIN PENS:

1. Inking with technical fountain pens can be done with the beveled edges of scales on drafting machines or with the straightedge of a T-square.
2. When ruling lines, technical fountain pens should be held so they are at or nearly at a 90° angle to the drafting medium. At the same time the technical fountain pen should be parallel to the face of the T-square or straightedge.
3. The newer fountain-pen types may be used either with the straightedge for drawing mechanical lines or freehand for lettering and arrows.
4. Always replace the cap when the pen is not in use.
5. If point sections do become clogged, flush with lukewarm water. Follow by soaking for 30 minutes to 8 hours in a good commercial pen cleaner. Then wipe dry.
6. The ink reservoir should be kept filled for best operation of the pen. When it is not full, the air in the ink tube can expand from the heat of the hand. This in turn may force some ink out through the "breathing" channels around the nib.
7. Use only recommended inks. A watery-type ink will tend to run out of the pen.
8. The cleaning wire in each technical fountain pen is intended to eject carbon particles and to bring the ink forward with a slight-shaking motion.
9. The use of a synthetic sponge in the cap of each drawing point section keeps the point "humidified" for a more instantaneous start. Use one drop of pen cleaner per month (water will also serve). Do not allow the sponge to dry out because this may damage pen tips.

Time studies have compared the technical fountain pen and the ruling pen. These studies indicate that the technical fountain pen saves nearly 50% of the refilling time required for the ruling pen.

Technical fountain pens are especially useful with templates of all kinds. Special compasses and adapters are available for drawing circles of any diameter with technical pens.

Drawing Numbers

Each drawing should have a number which is located in the lower right-hand corner of the title strip and in any other supplementary position required by company practice. When a print is folded face out, supplementary numbers provide identification at the upper right-hand corner. See Fig. 9-27. On drawings that will be rolled, the supplementary number should be placed on the reverse side in diagonally opposite corners.

Multiple-sheet drawings should carry the same drawing number together with a notation such as: "sheet *2* of *4*." This information should be repeated with each supplementary drawing number.

Basic Numbering Systems

THE NON-SIGNIFICANT NUMBERING SYSTEM is one in which there is no significance of the drawing number to the number of the part described. In this system, using the numeric method, a base number such as 10,000 may be selected. Drawings are numbered consecutively beyond the base number. An alphabetic-numeric method may also be used. The first drawing might be *1 A 1* which is the first available numeral letter combination. Additional numbers are formed with numeral prefixes and suffixes used in combination with letters, such as *280 C 80* or *7F 186*. (Hyphens are not used in this system.)

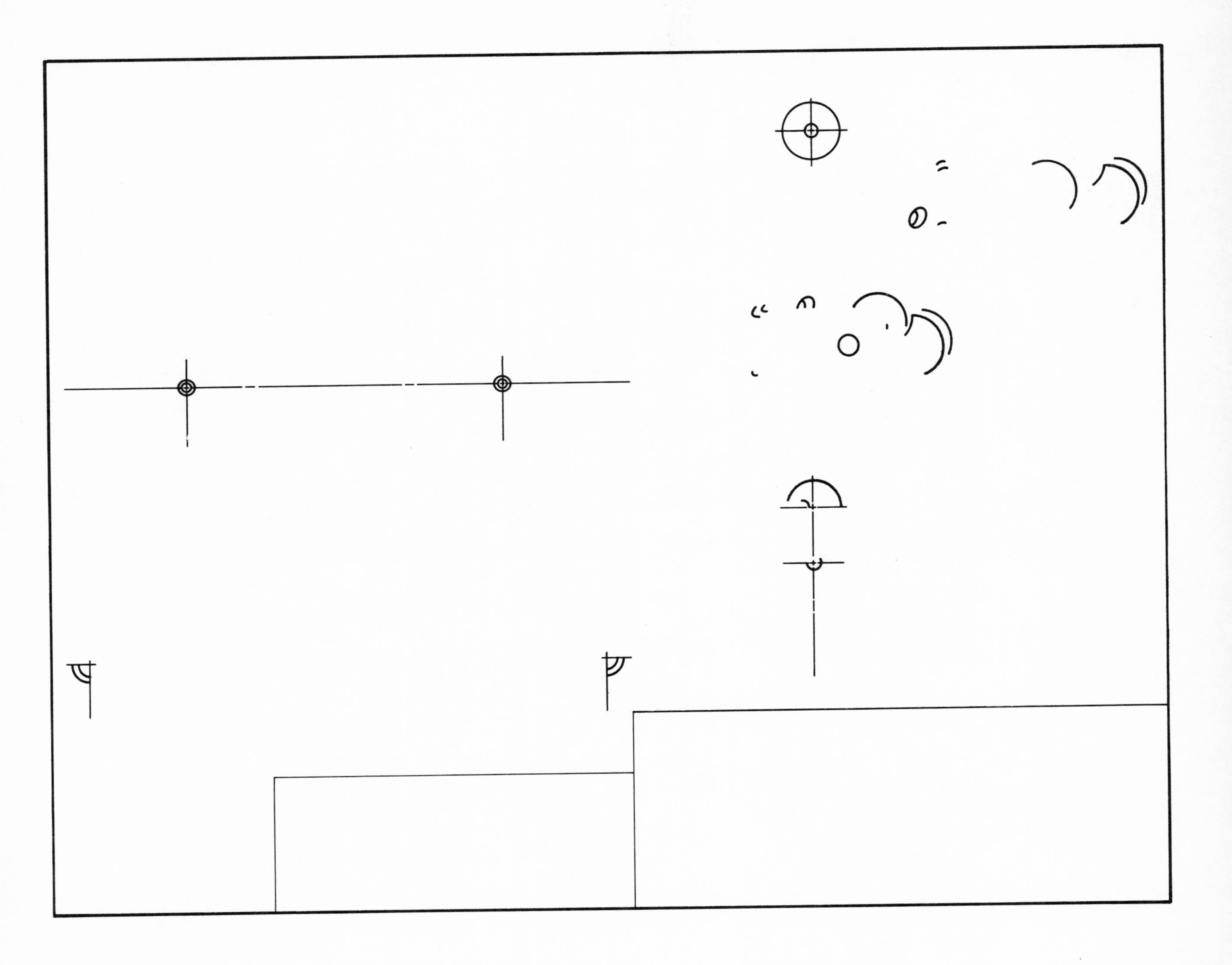

FIG. 9-2 **a**. Stages in the Completion of a Finished Drawing

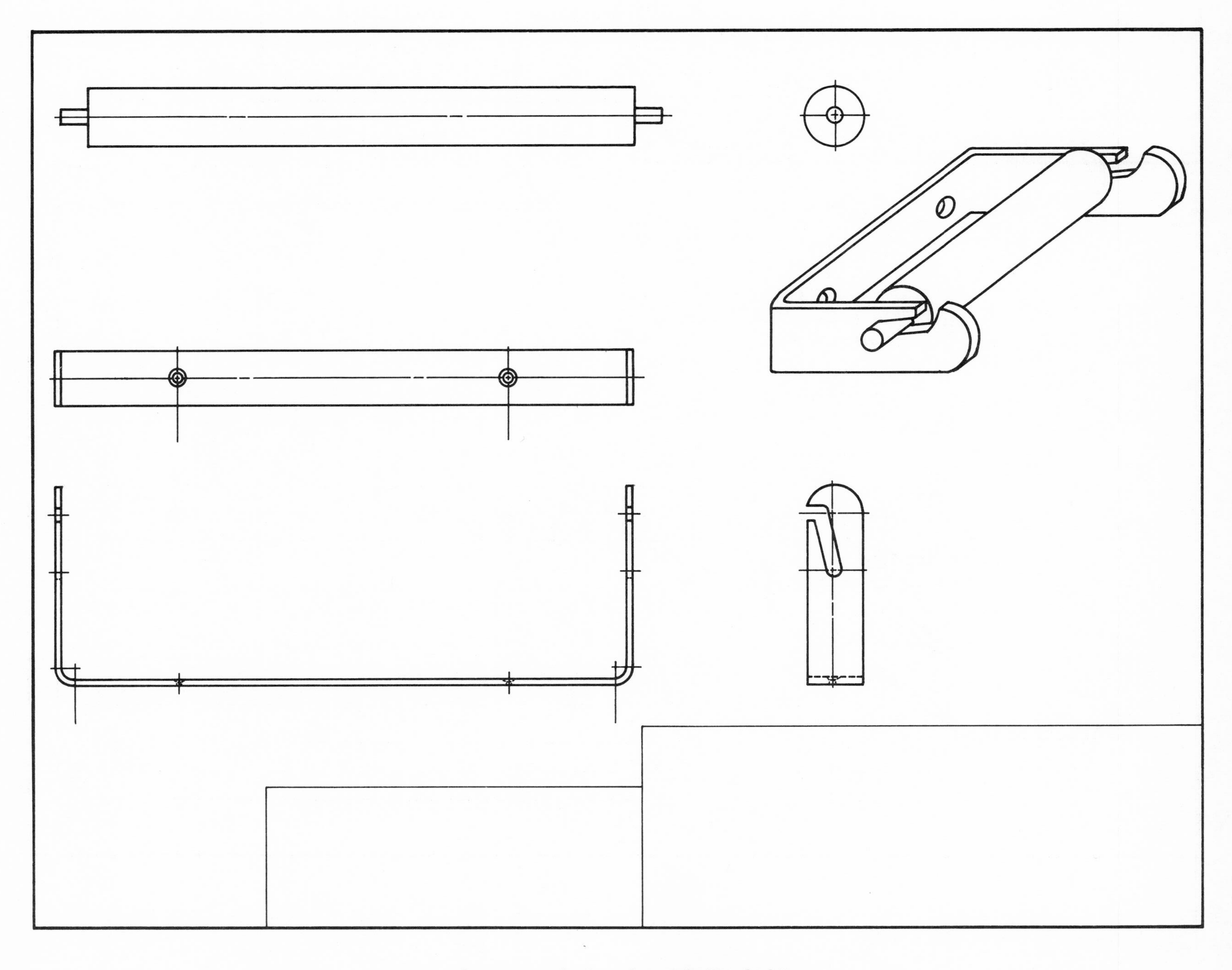

FIG. 9-2 **b**. Stages in the Completion of a Finished Drawing

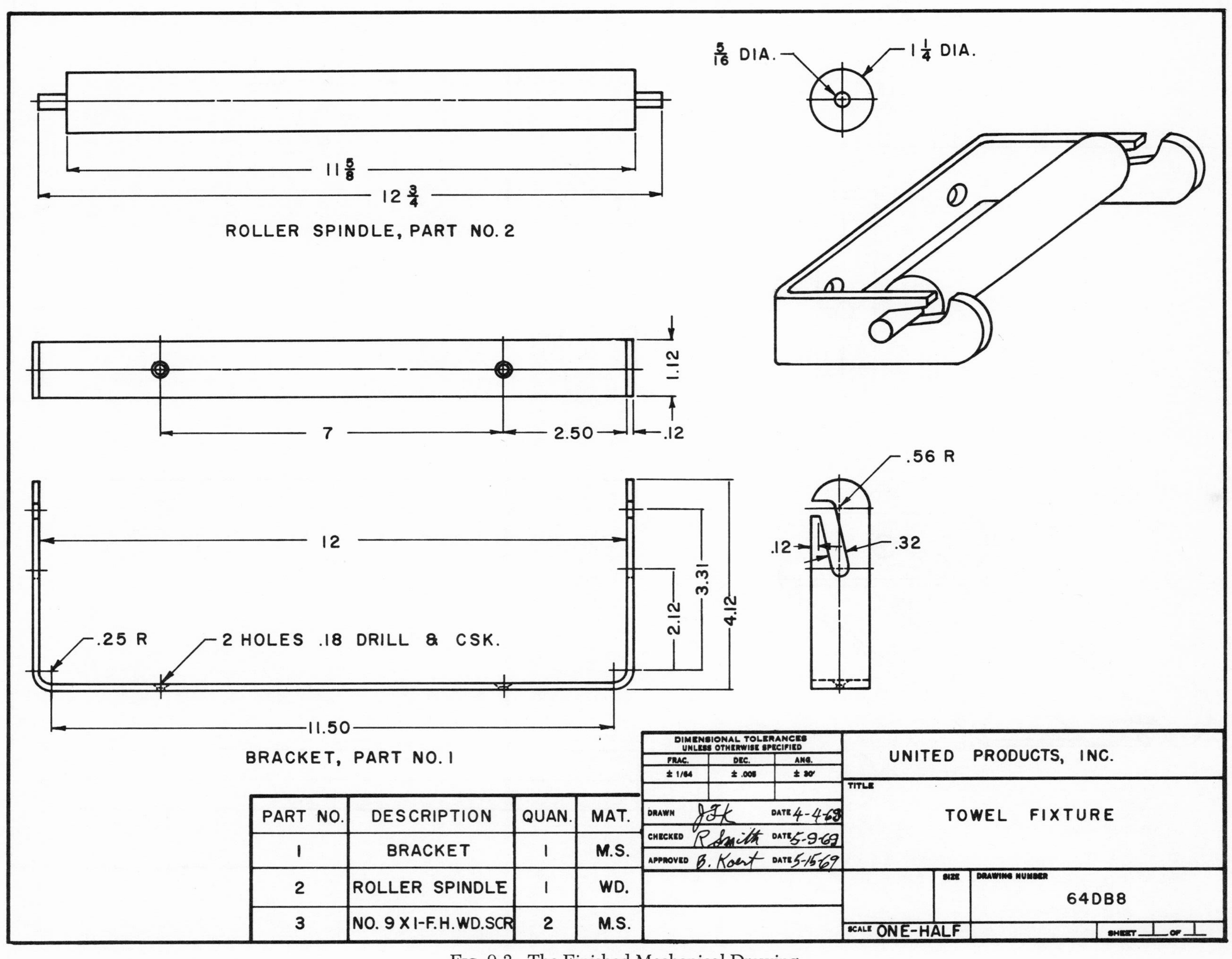

FIG. 9-3. The Finished Mechanical Drawing

THE SIGNIFICANT NUMBERING SYSTEM is one in which there is a significance of the drawing number to the part description. Hyphens are used in this system to separate the groupings clearly and distinctly. For example, the drawing number *15-8-452* might have this meaning: the first group, *15*, is the model number; the second group, *8*, is the number of cylinders; the last group, *452*, is the displacement in cubic inches. A drawing number such as *12-BG-32* in the alphabetic-numeric method means: *12 mm.* Bore, Separable-type bearing, *32 mm.* O. D.

THE SEMI-SIGNIFICANT NUMBERING SYSTEM is made up of aspects of each of the foregoing systems. One example follows: *16 F 1242-50;* where *16* is the stock class, *F* is the letter for the principal noun, *1242* is the serial number, and *50* is a subdivision of the serial number.

THE SUFFIX-NUMBERING SYSTEM is a variation of the semi-significant system. Drawing numbers in this system are composed of a significant base number, followed by a serial-type suffix number. This system may be used to identify a particular assembly with a significant number followed by the parts of the assembly each serially numbered with a suffix.

In developing a numbering system, numbers should be as short as possible to avoid errors and to permit their handling by mechanical tabulating equipment. Generally numbers should not have more than *15* characters. Fractions, decimals, and Roman numerals are not used. Certain characters of the alphabet are not used, such as: *I, O, Q, Z,* and *X*. Drawing numbers should contain no blank spaces. Only hyphens are used to separate elements.

Drawing Titles

The function of a *drawing title* is to describe an item briefly and clearly and yet to distinguish between similar titles. The title consists of a noun or noun phrase together with modifiers.

Guides for Title Making

1. Use only the singular form of the nouns, such as *bracket,* even though the plural may be needed. When the only form is plural, such as *tongs,* the plural is used.
2. Use a single rather than a compound noun where practical; *e.g.,* use *bracket* rather than *compressor bracket* if the meaning is clear.
3. Use a noun phrase when the noun is not clear. Where there are several front-frame members, use a horizontal front-frame member.
4. Use a noun or noun phrase in terms of its function, not for material or method of fabrication.
5. In assembly, subassembly, and installation drawings, assembly should appear as the last word of the noun phrase such as *Rod Assembly* or *Rod Assy.*
6. Trademark and copyrighted names are not usually used as the noun or noun phrase.
7. Primary modifiers indicate characteristics such as type, grade, or variety.
8. Secondary modifiers distinguish between similar parts.
9. The first primary modifier is separated from the noun or noun phrase by a dash. Modifiers are separated from each other by commas.
10. Abbreviations (except *Assy, Instl,* and *Subassy*) are not used in titles. Conjunctions and prepositions are not used in titles.

Drawing Title Example

1. The noun phrase is *control assy-input valve, .008 oversize, upper control assy.*
2. *Assy* is used as the last word of this phrase. A dash follows the noun phrase.
3. *Input valve* is the primary modifier.
4. *Input* precedes *valve* which it modifies. A comma follows the primary modifier.
5. *.008 oversize* is a secondary modifier. It follows the secondary modifier.
6. *Upper* is a further secondary modifier dis-differentiates by size dimension. A comma tinguishing as it does by location.
7. A properly worded title can be checked by reading it backwards such as *upper, .008 oversize, input valve control assy.*

Drafting for Microfilming

Microfilms of drawings require some changes in the standards commonly accepted for good diazo and blueprint reproduction. The latter are full-size reproductions while microfilming is a reduction of up to 30 times with later enlargement ranging to more than 50% of the original.

FINISHING
REPRODUCING

Shortcomings of Everyday Practice[1]

Shortcomings of everyday drafting practice which are not at all compatible with microfilming requirements are these:

1. Unnecessary detail.
2. Poor spacing.
3. Carelessly drawn letters and figures.
4. Faulty erasure procedures.
5. Inconsistent line weights, density, and lettering style.
6. Lack of care in handling and storage of originals.

Recommended Practices [1]

1. A minimum of *.170* height for dimensions and letters on a *D* size drawing.
2. A minimum of *.125* height for drawings *C* size and smaller.
3. Open well-rounded lettering is required.
4. *.030* is the minimum spacing between lines of lettering.
5. When lettering is typed, gothic characters should be used.
6. Decimal points should be well formed and somewhat heavier than adjacent lettering.
7. Cross-section lining should be eliminated or limited to the extremities of the sectioned area.
8. Draftsmen should be informed of the special problems involved in microfilming drawings.
9. When drawing changes are made, draftsmen should attempt to achieve the same balance between line work and background as the original.
10. Standard combinations of base materials, pencils, and erasers should be used.
11. Mechanical pencils and standard lead should be used by draftsmen.
12. Mechanical pencil sharpeners should be used to get clean, sharp linework.
13. Electric erasers should be available and used by the draftsmen.
14. Typed notes should be done on electric typewriters to insure constant pressure and clear type.
15. Develop a program requiring a smaller number of standard sizes of drawing sheets.
16. Roll drawing should be used only as a last resort.
17. All lines must be on the face of microfilm drawings.
18. Centering must be done carefully to allow for automatic processes of printing and cut sheets.

OLD	NEW	COMPARISON OF OLD AND NEW STYLE
1	1	NO CHANGE
2	2	NO CHANGE
3	3	NO CHANGE
4	4	OPEN TOP
5	5	TERMINATION OF THE LOWER PORTION AT THE CENTERLINE
6	6	STRAIGHT STEM WITH ELLIPSE
7	7	STEM AT SHARPER ANGLE
8	8	"X" SHAPED CENTER, WITH TOP EXTENSION
9	9	ELLIPSE WITH STRAIGHT STEM
0	0	NO CHANGE

Fig. 9-4. Modified Numerals for Microfilming (Caterpillar Tractor Co.)

[1]Summary of points made by Pete Scura in *Graphic Science*, July, 1963, pages 20-22.

Modified Numerals

Experience with reduction and blow-back in microfilming has suggested improvements in numerals. Sometimes small specks appear in the area of a numeral which may lead to misinterpretation. Sometimes parts of a numeral may fail to print. Carelessly formed numerals are always a problem to interpret. Effort has been made by the Caterpillar Tractor Co. of Peoria, Illinois to modify numerals to emphasize their distinctive features. Fig. 9-4 shows the present standard and the recommended modifications for microfilm use.

Because most lettering is in capital letters only and because the loss of one letter in a word is less critical than one numeral in a dimension, there is no need at the present time to modify letters for microfilming.

Preprinted Appliques for Drafting

With continuous pressure to remain competitive, drafting rooms as all other departments of industry are looking for more efficient ways of doing their work. Among the new materials leading to efficiency are the pressure-sensitive, preprinted, drafting appliques. These are now available either with or without heat-resistant backing which permits their use on standard reproduction equipment. Wax-backed appliques cannot be used in these machines.

There is now available a wide variety of commonly used units such as title blocks, symbols, notes, revision blocks, call-outs, shading media, lettering, printed circuit materials, charts, bolts, nuts, and other forms, as well as custom-made units for the individual customer. The surface can be ordered matte finish or clear. The copy can be right reading or reverse reading. Because of the clear, sharp images of lines, these appliques have good microfilming characteristics.

Procedure for Applying

Fig. 9-5.

1. Select the unit to be applied.
2. Remove the backing behind this unit.
3. Position the unit on the drawing.
4. Make the bond permanent by burnishing.

Techniques

1. The area on which the applique is to be applied must be clean to achieve good adhesion.
2. Avoid touching the pressure-sensitive back.
3. Avoid contact between the pressure-sensitive back and acetate since these are difficult to separate.
4. Tack the unit into position before final burnishing.
5. When lifting a character or symbol from the backing sheet, use the tip of the knife.
6. Use a cover sheet when burnishing to prevent smudging.
7. When placing large pieces, a straightedge or triangle may be helpful in laying the piece uniformly flat.
8. In case an air bubble appears, it may be removed by a pin prick and burnishing.
9. When burnishing use a definite pattern — starting at the top and working downward.
10. Rubber cement thinner may sometimes be used to help remove appliques from a drawing. The thinner dissolves the pressure-sensitive backing, does not stain the tracing, and dries quickly.
11. A rubber cement pickup may be used to clean an area where an applique has been removed.
12. In purchasing these materials be sure you know the shelf-life and order accordingly.

Quality Assurance in Drafting

Errors in communications to a mass-production shop may result in disastrous mistakes in a highly competitive market.

In the industrial drafting room, even though the main responsibility for accurate and complete functional drawings rests with the draftsman, checkers must review all drawings before they are released for production. Quality of drawings must be maintained 100% to be totally effective. This goal may not be reached, but management attaches enough importance on quality to pay experienced and dependable

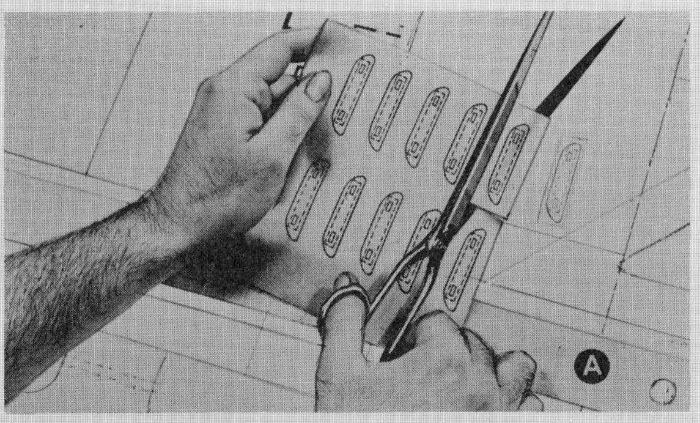

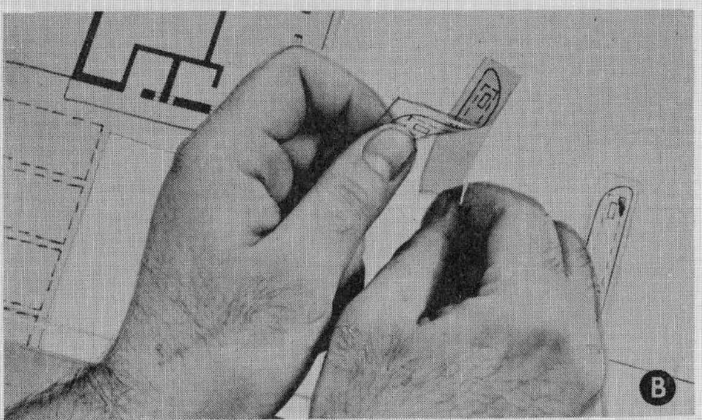

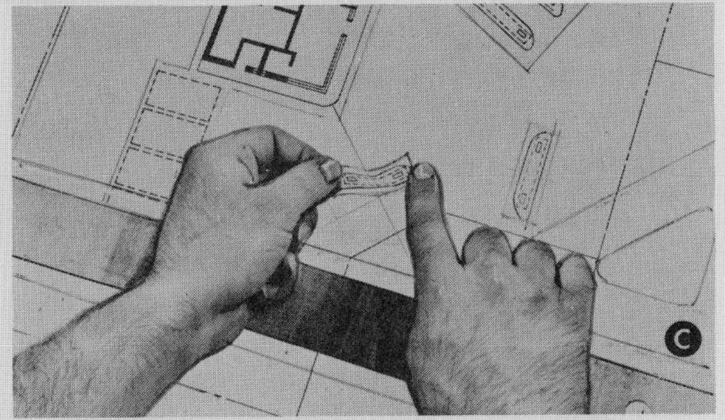

FIG. 9-5. Applying Preprinted Appliques (Eugene Dietzgen Co.)
A. Select the unit and cut it from carrier sheet.
B. Peel off the backing.
C. Position the unit on the drawing and burnish.

draftsmen for this checking service. Checking time averages about one-third of the detailing time and, of course, varies with different drawings, draftsmen, and checkers.

The work of the checker in drafting might be compared to the work of a proofreader in publishing or that of an auditor in business.

Requirements for a Good Checker

1. Experience and understanding of design and shop practice.
2. Clear thinking, the ability to evaluate effects of changes, and attention to detail.
3. Patience and understanding. (The checker becomes an important teacher for the new draftsman.)
4. Trustworthiness, faithfulness, and an ability to work with others.
5. A willingness to accept new ideas, flexibility, and adaptability to change in procedures.

Checking a Drawing

When drawings of a particular unit are completed, the checker is furnished with the original copies of the drawings, supporting layouts, sketches, calculations, and any other necessary related information. Check prints are made from the original drawings. Using a color code standardized within the industry, the checking is begun.

MAJOR AREAS CONSIDERED in this review to assure quality drawings are:

1. Design.
2. Drafting.
3. Fabrication.
4. Installation.
5. Environment.
6. Standards and Codes.

SPECIFIC QUESTIONS which should be asked under the drafting heading are these:

1. *Abbreviations.* Do abbreviations conform to the SAE Drawing Standards?
2. *Angular Relationships.* Does drawing clearly state which angular relationships are important and which may vary?
3. *Comparison.* Have parts been drawn in conformity to previous practice for similar parts?
4. *Conformance to Drawing Standards.* Does the drawing conform to applicable SAE Drawing Standards and company standards in regard to size of sheet, arrangement of views, line characteristics, scale, notes, and general appearance? Are lines and lettering distinct and dark enough to assure legible reproduction including microfilm reduction?
5. *Dimensions.* Is the part fully dimensioned and are the dimensions clearly positioned? Has true position relationship been shown where applicable? Are any dimensions repeated or shown in a manner that constitutes double dimensioning? Will dimensioning result in objectionable tolerance accumulation? Do dimensions emphasize function of design in preference to production operations or processes? Is the drawing dimensioned to avoid unnecessary shop calculations? Is the developed length required? Is stock size specified?
6. *Draft Angles and Radii.* Are proper draft angles, fillets, and corner radii specified?
7. *Drawing Numbers.* Is the correct drawing number shown in both title block and supplementary number blocks? Are necessary reference numbers or assembly numbers shown?
8. *Finish Marks.* Do finish marks appear on all applicable views?
9. *Identification.* Are part numbers, name plates, or other identification markings shown properly?
10. *Part Number Call-Outs.* Have part numbers for individual parts or subassemblies been shown on assembly drawings or the parts list?
11. *Proprietary Note.* Has a proprietary note, where required, been placed on the drawing?
12. *Revisions.* On revised drawings have revisions been properly recorded and lines damaged by erasures properly restored?
13. *Scale.* Is the drawing to scale? Is the scale shown?
14. *Security Classification.* If applicable, has a security classification, including Espionage Law notice, been properly marked on the drawing?
15. *Spelling.* Have all the words been properly spelled?

16. *Surface Relationship*. Are necessary requirements covering geometric surface relationships such as concentricity, squareness, parallelism, or others shown?
17. *Symmetrically Opposite Parts*. Is the "shown and opposite part" note with identification numbers shown? Does the drawing depict the correct part consistent with the next assembly drawing for ease of evaluating the assembly drawing?
18. *Title*. Does title definitely identify the part? Is it worded in accordance with the SAE Aero-Auto Drawing Standards and company procedure?
19. *Title Block*. Has the title block been filled in completely and information correct?
20. *Views*. Are sufficient full and sectional views shown and are they in proper relation to each other? Does cross-sectioning agree with the material symbols portrayed in the SAE Aero-Auto Drawing Standards? Are directional arrows on cutting planes properly shown? Where required, are caution notes shown when sectional views are not properly located with respect to cutting planes?
21. *Weights*. Does the weight of the part or assembly when required appear in the designated section of the title block?[2]

After the prints have been checked, they are returned to the draftsman. If enough modifications are required, the drawings are done over. If minor changes or adjustments are required, these are made on the originals. This step in the procedure is called *back drafting*. When back drafting has been completed, the checker again reviews the drawings. He repeats the whole process on redrawn work, but on changed work checks only the changes. Only when the checker knows the drawings are up to standard quality does he place his initials in the title block thus releasing the drawing for production, Figs. 9-6 and 9-7.

[2]SAE *Aerospace-Automotive Drawing Standards*. Pp. B4.02-.04.

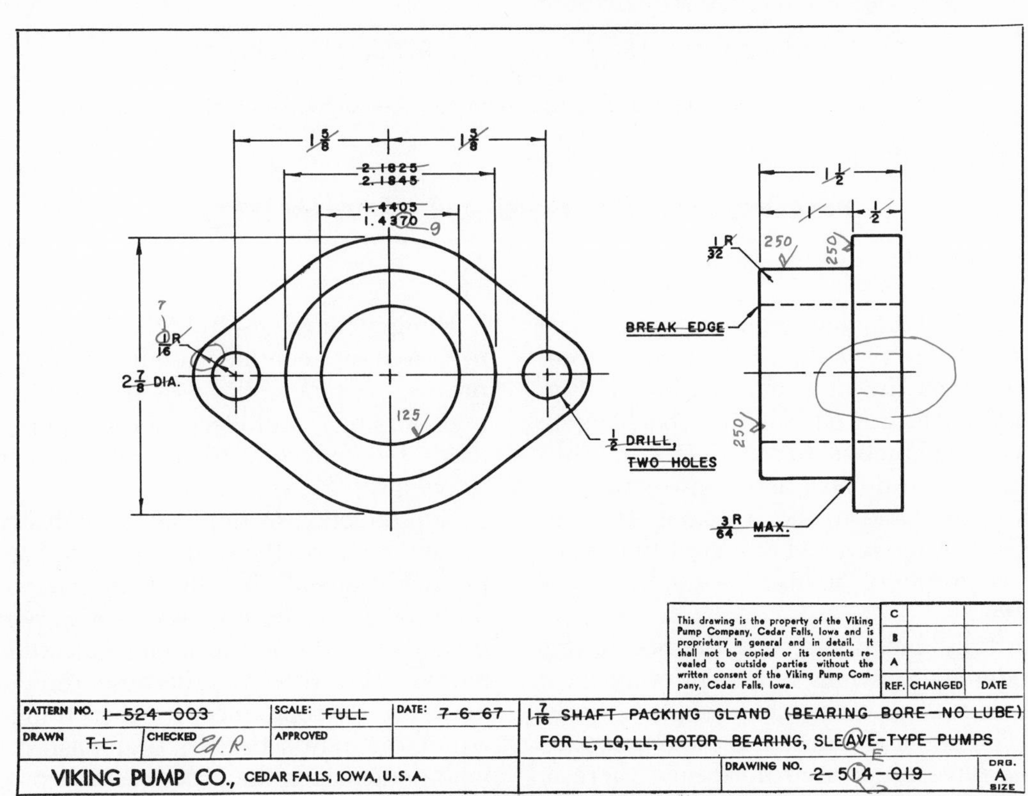

FIG. 9-6. Drawing of Packing Gland after Checking (Viking Pump Co.)
Changes are in color. Straight lines in color through various dimensions and notes mean that they have been checked and are satisfactory.

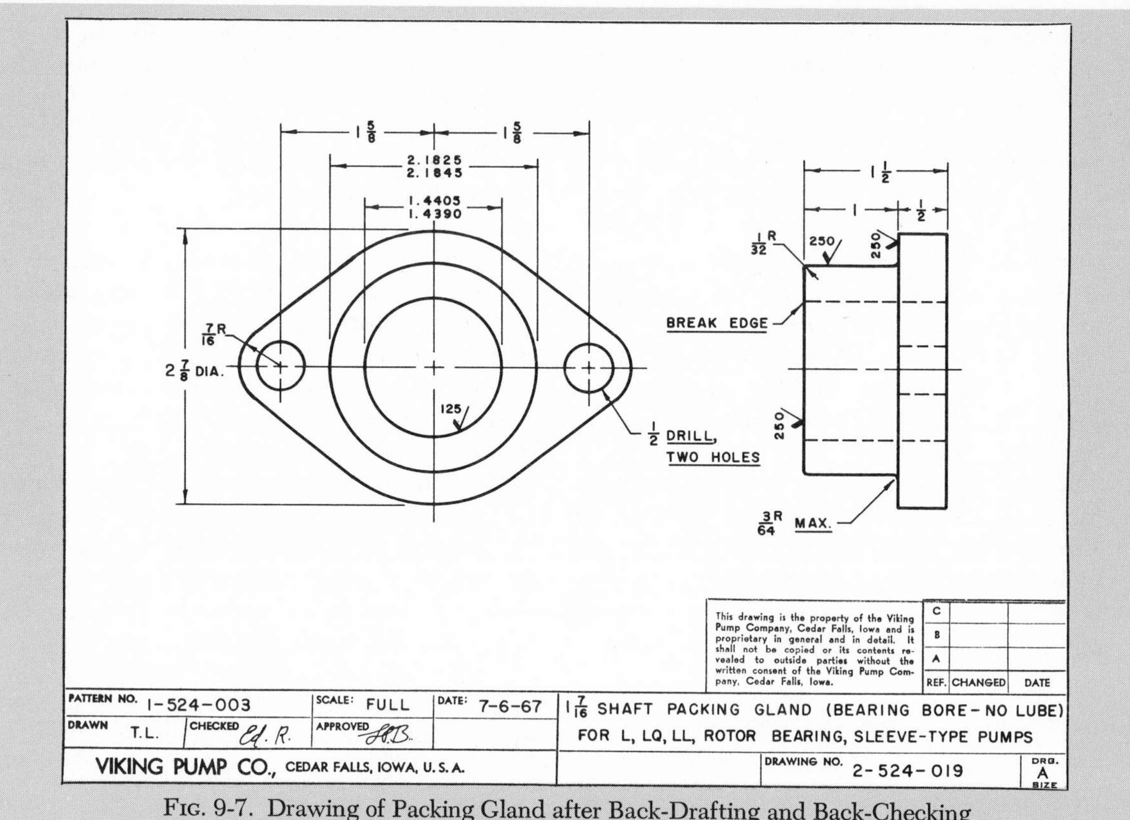

FIG. 9-7. Drawing of Packing Gland after Back-Drafting and Back-Checking (Viking Pump Co.)
All corrections have been made and print is ready for release by the drafting department.

reproductions of drawings

Most original drawings are made for the sole purpose of being reproduced. Only the reproductions of the drawing are distributed, Fig. 9-8. They go to the checker for checking, to the shop for production, to contractors and subcontractors for estimates and construction, to the serviceman, and to the customer. It is reproductions of the original drawings that serve as the language of industry — graphic communication.

Historically, blueprints were the first means of reproducing drawings. Diazo printing gave blueprinting competition shortly after World War I. The needs of industry and the processes available have progressed until now there is a variety of processes from which to choose. Reproductions are made on paper, cloth, or film. Photographic processes are becoming increasingly important.

Equipment ranges from the simple sun frame to automatic, continuous-roll machines. Offset presses, photographic equipment (including microfilming), and electrostatic equipment are used by industry to reproduce copies of drawings.

Reproduction of drawings in industry is not usually done by the draftsman. Draftsmen can profitably spend their time in more creative drafting. However, it is especially important for a student draftsman to understand the several reproduction processes because drawings are made to be reproduced. Other things being equal, the most successful draftsman is the one who understands the processes of reproduction and knows what must be done on the drawing to insure a good reproduction. Figs. 9-9 and 9-10 show how to make a sun frame and a dry diazo developing tube.

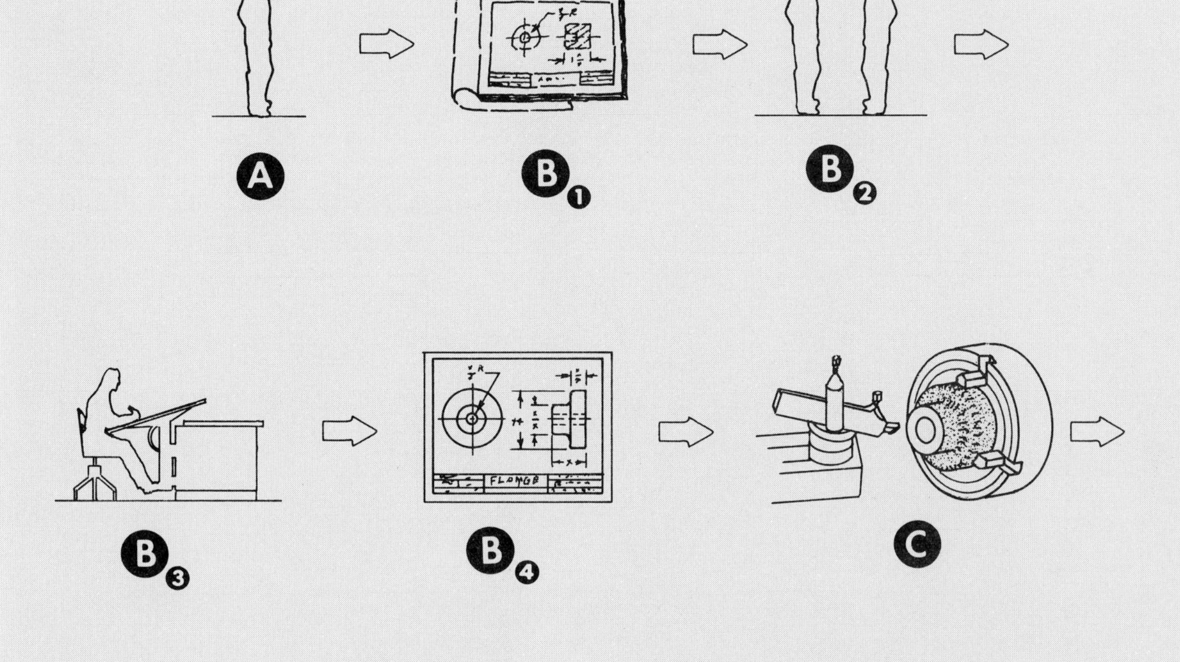

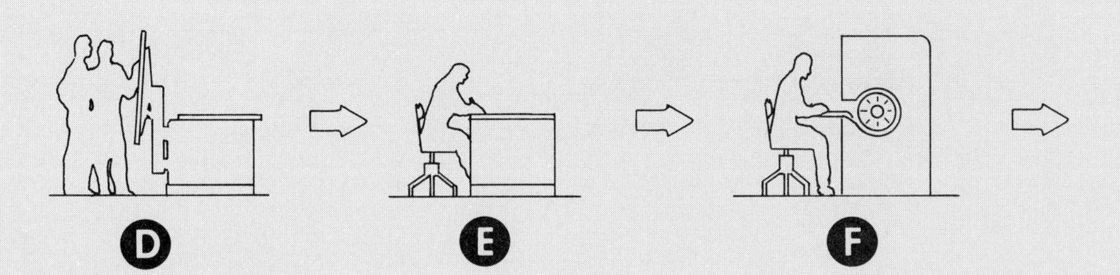

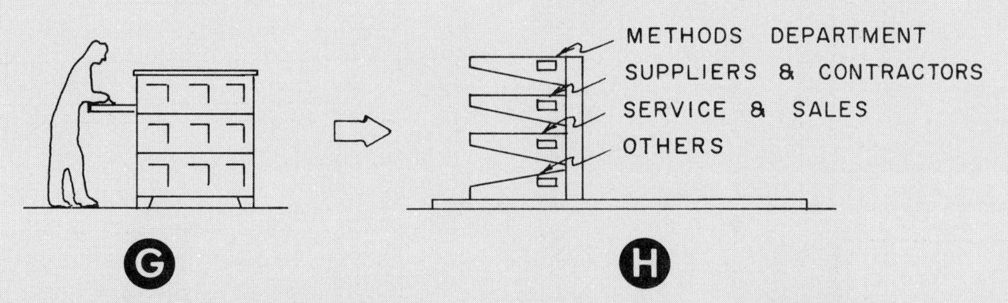

Fig. 9-8. Development and Transmittal of Ideas through Drawings and Their Reproductions

A. Someone has an idea.
B. The idea is developed.
   1. A trial sketch is made.
   2. Conferences are held.
   3. Experimental drawings are made.
   4. Reproductions of the experimental drawings are prepared.
C. A pilot model is made in the shop.
D. Further conferences are held, decisions are reached, and final drawings are prepared on the board.
E. Final drawings are checked and approved.
F. The final drawings are reproduced.
G. The final drawings are filed.
H. The reproductions are distributed.

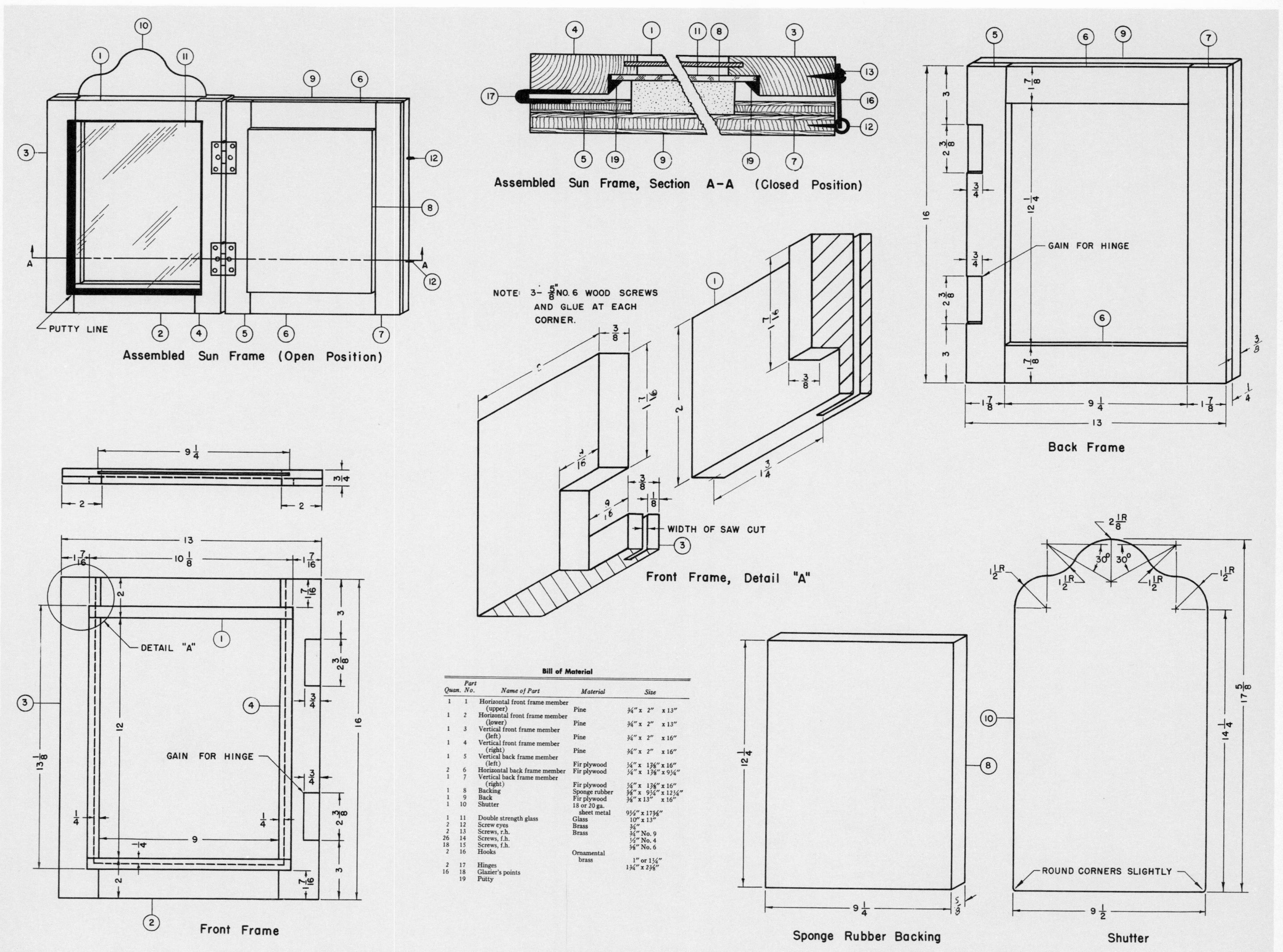

Bill of Material

Quan.	Part No.	Name of Part	Material	Size
1	1	Horizontal front frame member (upper)	Pine	¾" x 2" x 13"
1	2	Horizontal front frame member (lower)	Pine	¾" x 2" x 13"
1	3	Vertical front frame member (left)	Pine	¾" x 2" x 16"
1	4	Vertical front frame member (right)	Pine	¾" x 2" x 16"
1	5	Vertical back frame member (left)	Fir plywood	¼" x 1⅞" x 16"
2	6	Horizontal back frame member	Fir plywood	¼" x 1⅞" x 9¼"
1	7	Vertical back frame member (right)	Fir plywood	¼" x 1⅞" x 16"
1	8	Backing	Sponge rubber	⅝" x 9¼" x 12¼"
1	9	Back	Fir plywood	⅜" x 13" x 16"
1	10	Shutter	18 or 20 ga. sheet metal	9½" x 17⅝"
1	11	Double strength glass	Glass	10" x 13"
2	12	Screw eyes	Brass	¾"
2	13	Screws, r.h.	Brass	¾" No. 9
26	14	Screws, f.h.		½" No. 4
18	15	Screws, f.h.		⅝" No. 6
2	16	Hooks	Ornamental brass	1" or 1¼"
2	17	Hinges		1¾" x 2⅜"
16	18	Glazier's points		
	19	Putty		

FIG. 9-9. Sun Frame for Exposure of 8½ x 11 Drawings (*Industrial Arts and Vocational Education*, April, 1960)

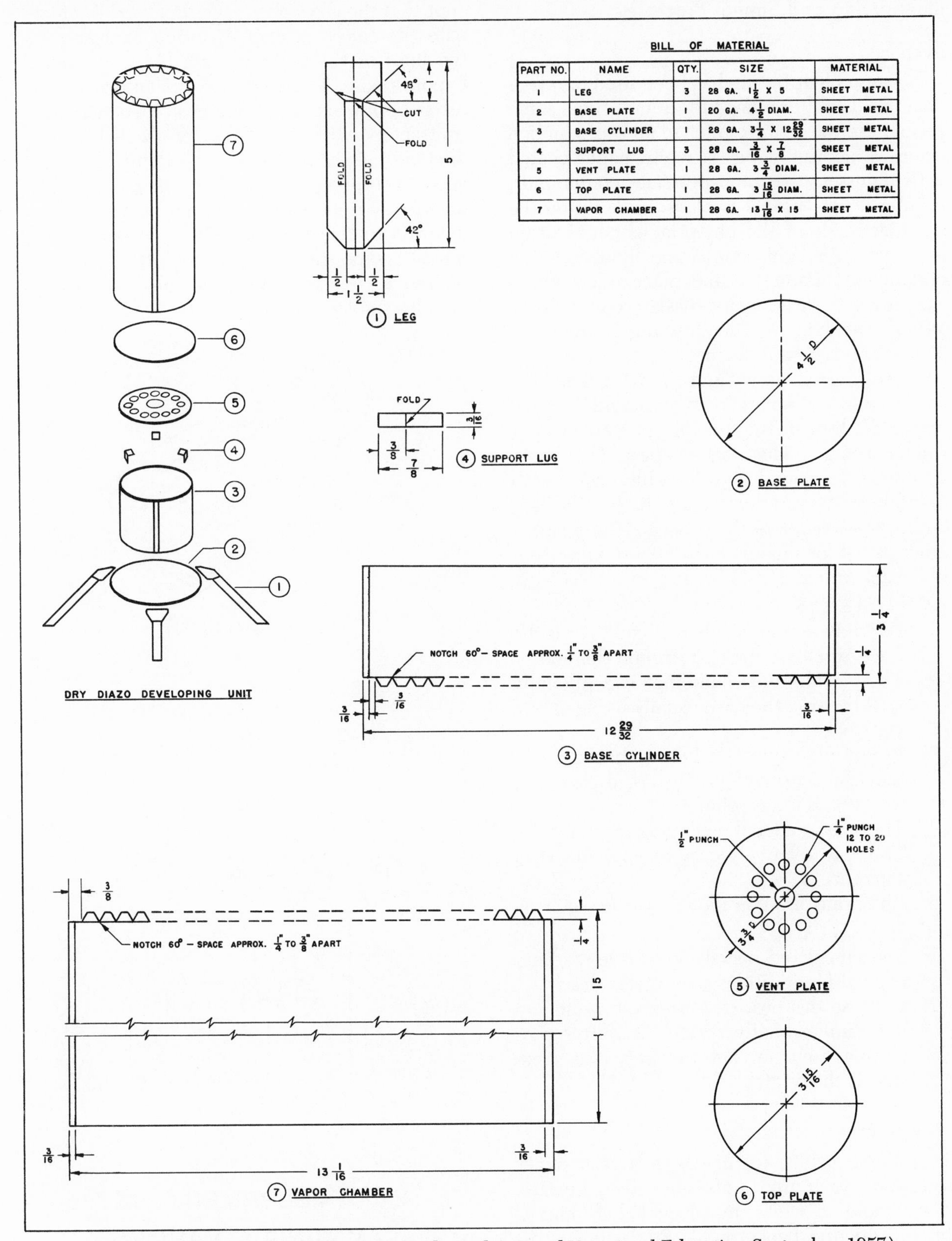

BILL OF MATERIAL

PART NO.	NAME	QTY.	SIZE	MATERIAL
1	LEG	3	28 GA. $1\frac{1}{2}$ X 5	SHEET METAL
2	BASE PLATE	1	20 GA. $4\frac{1}{2}$ DIAM.	SHEET METAL
3	BASE CYLINDER	1	28 GA. $3\frac{1}{4}$ X $12\frac{29}{32}$	SHEET METAL
4	SUPPORT LUG	3	28 GA. $\frac{3}{16}$ X $\frac{7}{8}$	SHEET METAL
5	VENT PLATE	1	28 GA. $3\frac{3}{4}$ DIAM.	SHEET METAL
6	TOP PLATE	1	28 GA. $3\frac{15}{16}$ DIAM.	SHEET METAL
7	VAPOR CHAMBER	1	28 GA. $13\frac{1}{16}$ X 15	SHEET METAL

FIG. 9-10. Dry Diazo Developing Unit (*Industrial Arts and Vocational Education,* September, 1957)

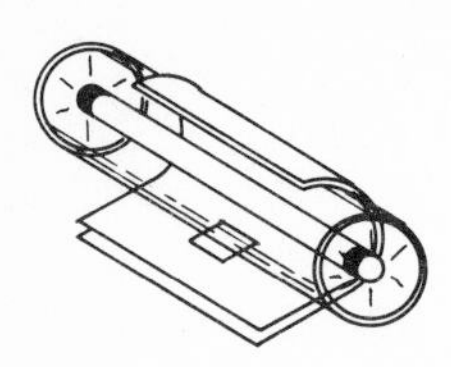

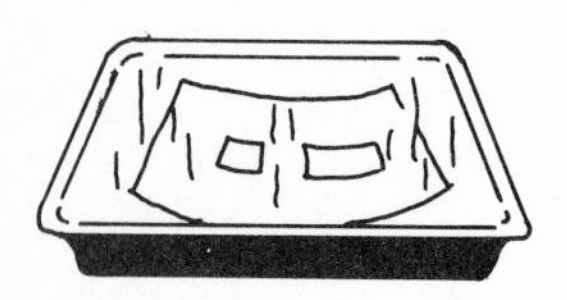

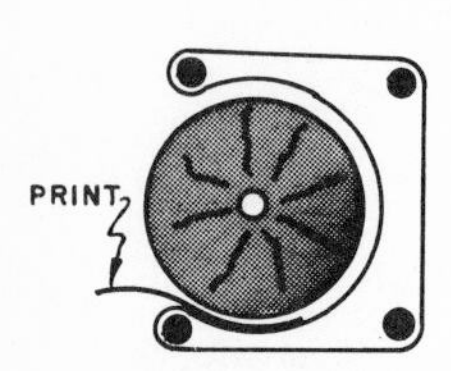

FIG. 9-11. Processing Blueprints

Blueprinting and Similar Processes

Blueprints

Because blueprinting has been used to reproduce industrial drawings for a long time, some people use the term to refer to all reproduction prints. Blueprint paper is white paper coated with light-sensitive, iron-prussiate compounds. A translucent original is placed face up on the sensitized side of the blueprint paper. During exposure to a light source, the light causes a chemical reaction to take place everywhere that it reaches the iron-prussiate compounds. Where the lines of the drawing protect the coating no reaction occurs.

Processing is shown in Fig. 9-11. The first water wash removes the sensitized coating where the lines of the drawing prevented light from causing a chemical change. The background is developed to a deep-blue color with a weak potassium-dichromate bath. Washing and drying complete the process. The result is a negative-type image — white lines on a deep-blue background.

ADVANTAGES:

1. For drawings larger than 17 x 22″, it is the least expensive method of reproduction.
2. They withstand handling exceptionally well because they are usually made of 50% rag stock.
3. Because of their dark-blue background, they stand up well under dirt, grease, and workman's fingerprints.
4. They last under direct sunlight.
5. They are relatively easy to read in direct sunlight.
6. Blueprints are considered permanent.

DISADVANTAGES:

1. Special colored pencils or erasure fluid are needed for additions and corrections.
2. Because this process is wet, the prints are not dimensionally stable, *i.e.*, after processing they are not precisely the same size as the original.

Vandyke Prints

Vandyke prints are made on a thin paper sensitized with iron salts and silver nitrate. They yield a white translucent line and a brown, opaque background. Processing is essentially the same as that for blueprinting except that the developing solution used to eliminate the salts (protected during exposure by the lines of the original) is a bath of sodium hyposulphate. The chief use of Vandykes is for second originals to provide customers and subcontractors with negatives for further reproductions. They are used for storage and are good insurance against loss of the original drawing. Prints made using the negative Vandyke reproduce positive. They are about four times as expensive as blueprints; they are considered to be permanent, but are not dimensionally stable.

FIG. 9-12. Processing Dry Diazo Prints

Blueline Prints

Blueline prints are positive prints made on blueprint paper using a Vandyke negative or photographic negative. They are especially useful when many copies can be marked for city and county departments. The cost is about 1.2 times that of blueprints.

Brownline Prints

Brownline prints are positive prints made on Vandyke paper using a Vandyke negative or photographic negative. They are used as originals to which additional lines are to be added for presentation work and the like. Cost is four times that of blueprints.

Diazo-Type Printing

Dry Diazo Prints

Diazo (dye-AZE-oh) papers are coated with light-sensitive diazo compounds together with a dyestuff component. When ammonia vapors come in contact with this coating, it is transformed into a colored dye. Dry diazo prints are processed as shown in Fig. 9-12, and are often called "whiteprints."

The original drawing (on translucent paper) is placed face up over the sensitized diazo coating. During exposure the light decomposes the coated surface except where the lines of the original protect it. Ammonia vapors then transform these lines that were protected into a dye thus producing a positive line copy of the original.

ADVANTAGES:

1. Clear background permits easy writing with pencil or pen on the print. They are especially useful as check prints.
2. They are more dimensionally stable than blueprints.
3. There are fewer steps in the printing process; thus it can be done more quickly, and the machines for processing generally take up less space.
4. Diazo has a relatively low cost; it is only 1.2 times as expensive as blueprinting.
5. Diazo is available in a wide variety of colored papers which may be opaque or translucent and in a variety of colored dyes for the line images.

DISADVANTAGES:

1. Dirt, grease, and fingerprints easily damage the prints.
2. They will not hold up well in direct sunlight or fluorescent light for long periods without fading.
3. Old tracings are difficult to reproduce without overexposure.

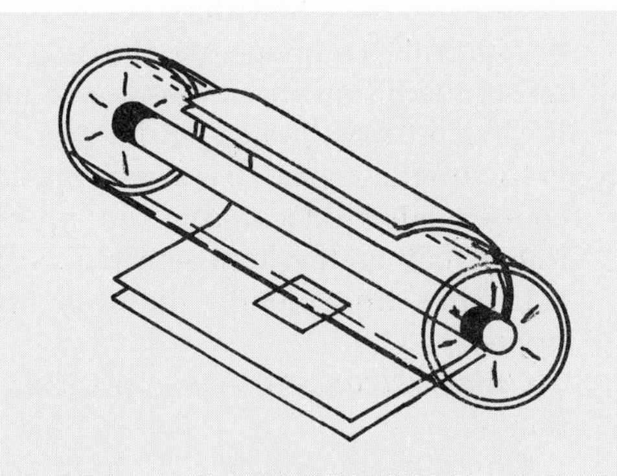

1. EXPOSURE

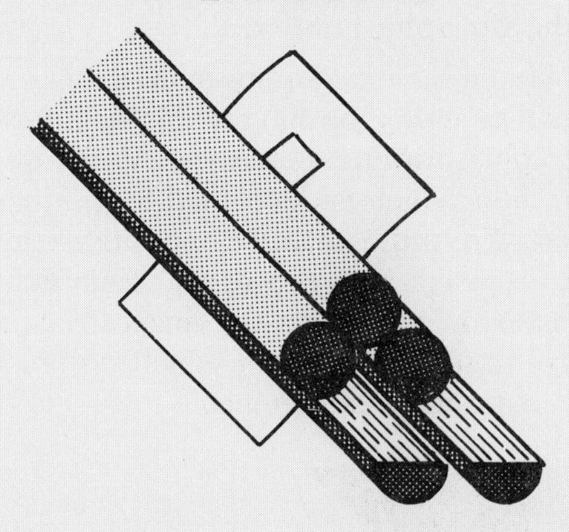

2. LIQUID DEVELOPER

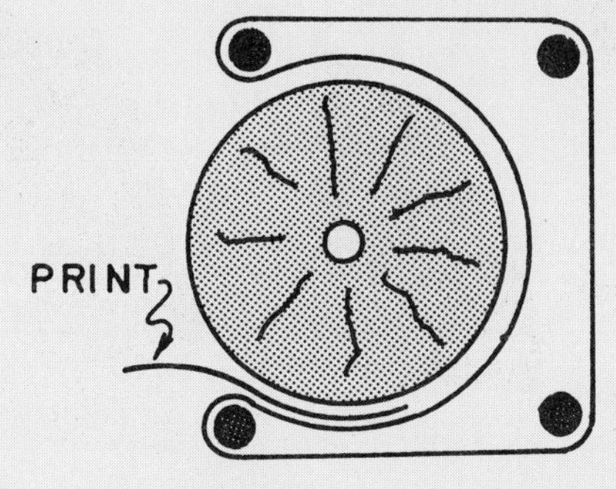

3. PRINT DRYING

FIG. 9-13. Processing Moist Diazo Prints

4. They have a tendency to reflect light in the eyes when being used out of doors.
5. Print papers made of wood pulp do not have the strength of rag-content blueprint paper.
6. Residual ammonia fumes are generally unpleasant.

Moist Diazo Prints

Moist diazo prints are very similar to the dry diazo process. Chief differences are in location of dyestuff components, the use of a liquid rather than a gas for development, and the need for a short drying step in the process. See Fig. 9-13. In the moist diazo process, the dyestuff components are located in the liquid developer rather than on the light-sensitive coating. Characteristics are generally the same for dry diazo prints.

Chief advantage — no irritating ammonia fumes.

Chief disadvantage — a drying step is required.

Photographic Printing

If you have taken personal pictures with your own camera, you have some idea of the photographic-printing processes. A picture is taken on film which is developed to produce a negative. From the negative, a positive contact print is exposed and processed. Enlargements are made by *projecting* the image from the negative to sensitized paper which is then processed to a positive enlargement.

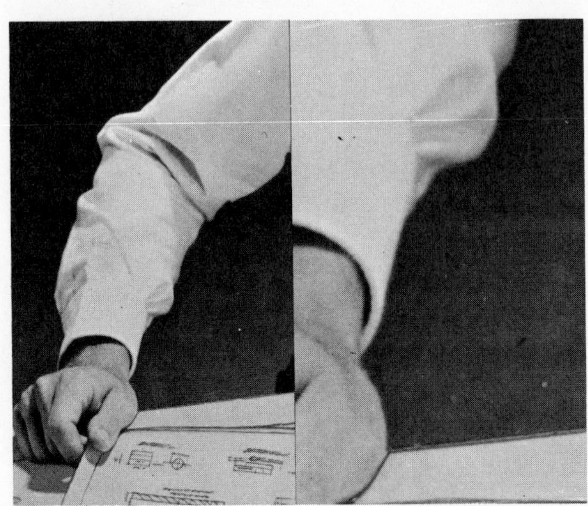

Fig. 9-14. Halftone Copy with Enlarged Area Showing Dot Structure

Very often photographic work must be done in a darkroom with controlled-light conditions. However, some photographic materials permit handling and processing under normal room light conditions.

Anything written, drawn, or printed can be copied by the professional photographer. For this reason, the photographic process is by far the most versatile of the printing processes. However, because of the use of films, chemicals, darkrooms, lenses, and the like, it is also the most expensive process.

Types of Copy

There are three basic kinds of images used in photographic processes.

LINE COPY is copy such as an inked mechanical drawing. The lines are black, the non-image area is white or clear, and there are no in-between tones of gray.

CONTINUOUS-TONE COPY is the term used to describe photographs, such as personal snapshots printed from negatives. In these there is very little, if any, pure white. The tones range from very light grey to nearly pure black. The tones are continuous to form the image. There are no continuous-tone images in this textbook.

HALFTONE COPY is that copy which consists of pure blacks and whites, but because of very small dot structures in varying patterns, it gives the appearance of tonal gradations. Reproductions of photographs in this text are halftones. Examination of these photographs with a magnifying glass shows the dot structure as illustrated in Fig. 9-14.

Most photo copying of mechanical drawings is with line copy *only*. Accordingly, the balance of the remarks in this section will deal with line copy. In photo drafting, the reproductions may be combinations of line copy and halftones from continuous-tone originals.

POSITIVES AND NEGATIVES: A *positive* copy has the black and white relationship of an original tracing — the image is black or colored and the background is white or clear. A *negative* has reverse tones, as on a blueprint — the lines are white and the background is blue. In photographic negatives, the lines are clear and the background is black. These terms should not be confused with *right-reading* (legible lettering correct left to right) and *wrong-reading* (image flopped left to right). A *reverse* usually means negative tones, and not a wrong-reading image.

Photographic films and papers may be handled under the conditions specified by the manufacturer. Many are processed only under the controlled light conditions of a photographic darkroom. Some relatively new materials may be handled under conditions of regular room light. These are especially useful in the industrial and school drafting rooms.

Photographic Processing

Processing of photographic materials is accomplished either by contact exposures or projection. Contact exposures result in same-size prints. The negative or material to be copied is placed in contact with the material on which it is to be printed. It is exposed and processed. The copies are the same size as the copy from which they were printed.

Projection exposures are those made with a lens. They may result in enlarged, same-size, or reduced-size prints. The ability to make projection prints is one of the chief advantages of the photographic process.

Steps in typical photographic processing of film are shown in Fig. 9-15. Steps in processing photographic papers are shown in Fig. 9-16.

A typical *wash-off* photographic process is shown in Fig. 9-17. A comparison of these two figures reveals the obvious advantages of the wash-off process — a smaller number of steps.

Of special use to the drafting room are the autopositive films and papers, some of which require darkroom handling and some of which may be handled under room light conditions. Depending on the type of autopositive film, it may be processed by the typical photographic process or by the wash-off process.

Microfilming

The microfilming process is photographic and may use *16mm, 35mm, 70mm* or *105mm* film. The *16mm* and *35mm* are the most popular.

Film for microfilming has extremely fine grain, high contrast, high resolution, and low photographic speed. Films come in 100′ rolls and are processed much like other photographic film, Fig. 9-18.

The chief uses of microfilming are for minimum storage area and for automatic record

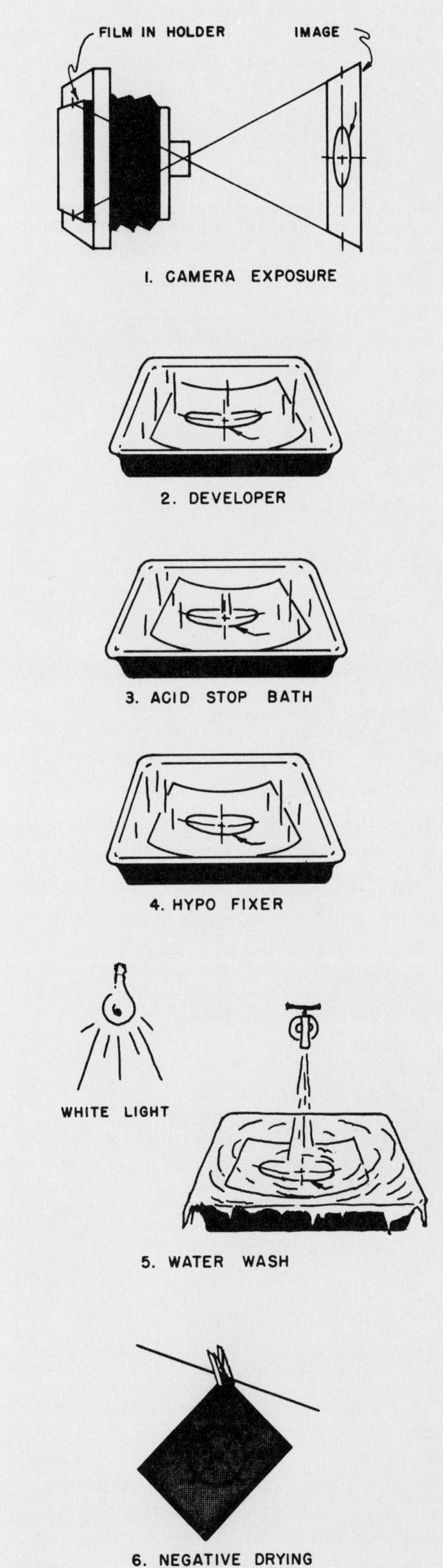

FIG. 9-15. Processing Photographic Films

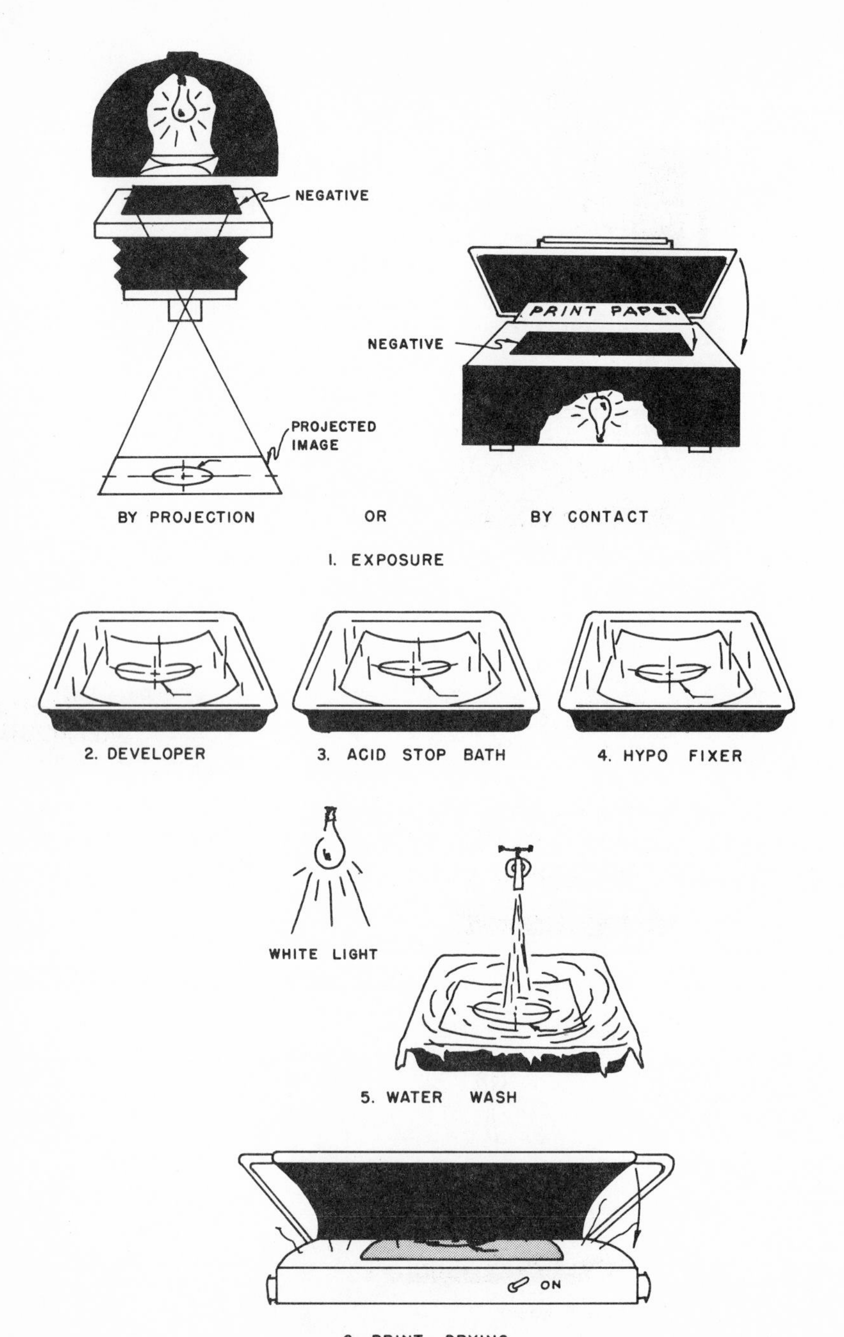

FIG. 9-16. Processing Photographic Papers

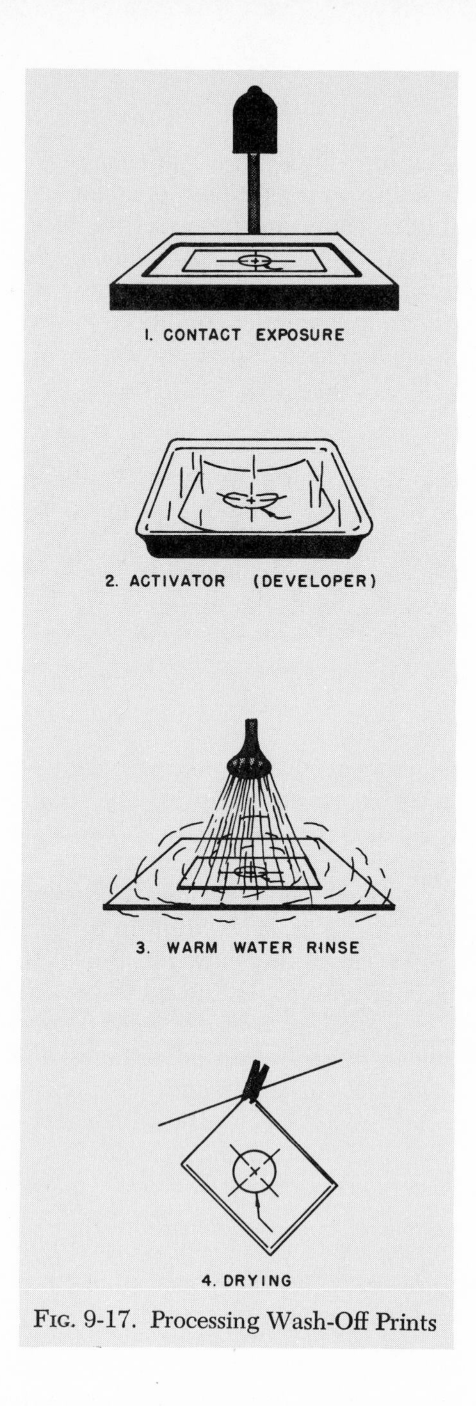

FIG. 9-17. Processing Wash-Off Prints

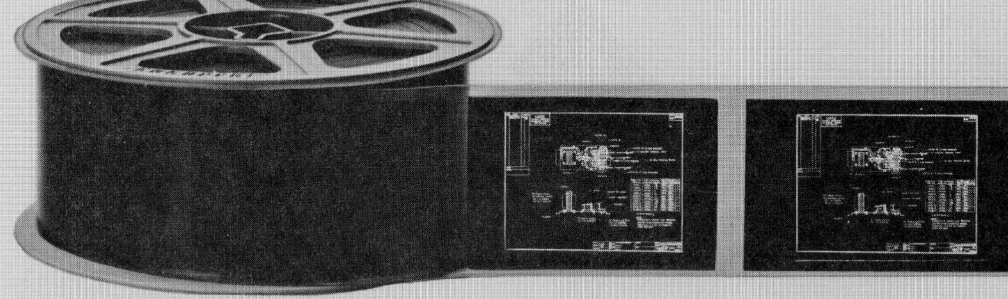

FIG. 9-18. Spool of Exposed and Developed Microfilm Images before Mounting (Recordak Co.)

handling. Cost of the film is not high, but the automatic industrial equipment is expensive. Schools can set up an illustrative microfilm unit simply by using a *35mm* camera with appropriate accessories for the reduction ratios of up to 35 to 1 and by choosing appropriate films and developers.

A microfilm center in industry will have a large file of microfilm aperture cards. Prints may be requested by engineers, supervisors, and others. They usually present the number of the drawing they want, and a copy is produced in a short time while they wait. When they are done with the reproduction, it may be destroyed. They may also put the aperture card into a reader to check a detail — a print may not be needed. See Fig. 9-20.

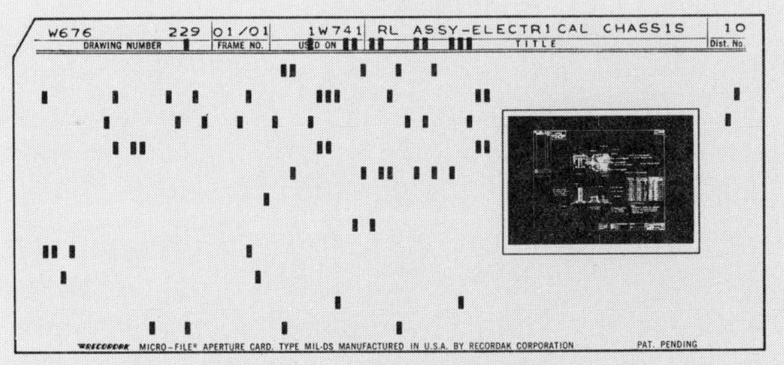

FIG. 9-19. Aperture Card with Mounted Microfilm Image (Recordak Co.)

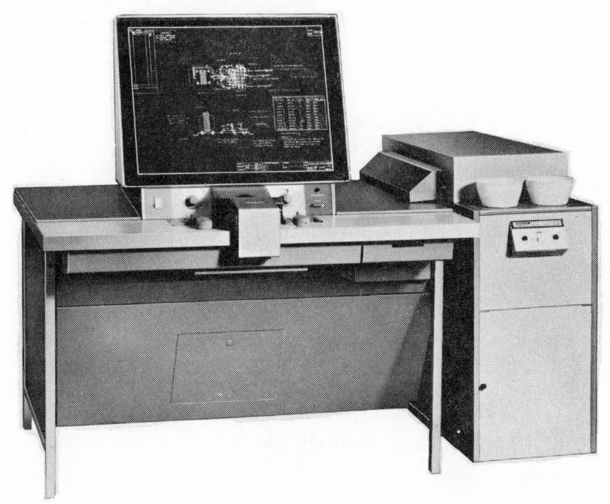

FIG. 9-20. Recordak Precision Reader-Printer with Plate Processor Accessory (Recordak Co.)

Electrostatic Printing

Electrostatic printing was in the process of development in the 1940's, and commercial equipment was introduced in the 1950's. The process is based on rather simple scientific facts: unlike charges of static electricity attract and like charges repel; depending on the molecular structure, some materials can be attracted more readily than others. The process of xerography is shown in Fig. 9-21.

Among the applications of the electrostatic processes are: copying of original documents, making of offset masters for lithographic reproduction, enlargement of microfilm, and reproduction of computer data. Automatic equipment is available.

Two of the chief advantages of the electrostatic process are that it can reproduce from opaque images and the copy is available in a very short time. It is also a dry process, can be used in daylight conditions, and utilizes unsensitized paper.

Among its disadvantages are rather expensive equipment and less image sharpness and density. Better results could be obtained with photographic processes, but it would take much longer to produce the copy.

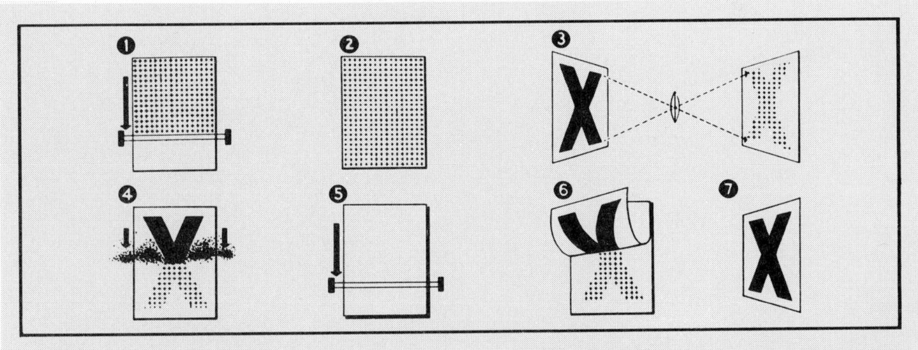

1 Surface of selenium-coated plate is electrically charged as it passes under wires.

2 Plus marks represent positively charged plate.

3 Original document is projected through camera lens. Plus marks here represent latent image retaining positive charge. Charge is drained away in areas that are exposed to light.

4 Negatively charged powder is cascaded over plate and adheres to positive image. Latent image now becomes visible.

5 Sheet of paper (or paper offset master) is placed over plate, and paper is given positive charge.

6 Positively charged paper attracts powder from plate, forming direct positive image.

7 Print or offset master is fused by heat for permanency.

FIG. 9-21. Xerography Process (Xerox Co.)

special applications of reproduction processes

As convenient and important as the basic processes for reproducing drawings are the special applications of these processes to save drafting time.

Duplicate Originals

Original drawings may be protected by making *duplicate originals* sometimes called *intermediates,* Fig. 9-22. The original drawing can then be safely filed. The duplicate original is used to take the wear-and-tear of producing the required number of copies. In some companies, other duplicate originals may be sent to branch offices or plants where they make their own reproductions, thus saving the cost of shipping large numbers of reproductions through the mails.

Several duplicate originals may be combined, so that several print copies are produced at once.

Duplicate originals can be made on appropriately sensitized translucent films and papers by blueprinting, diazo, and photographic processes.

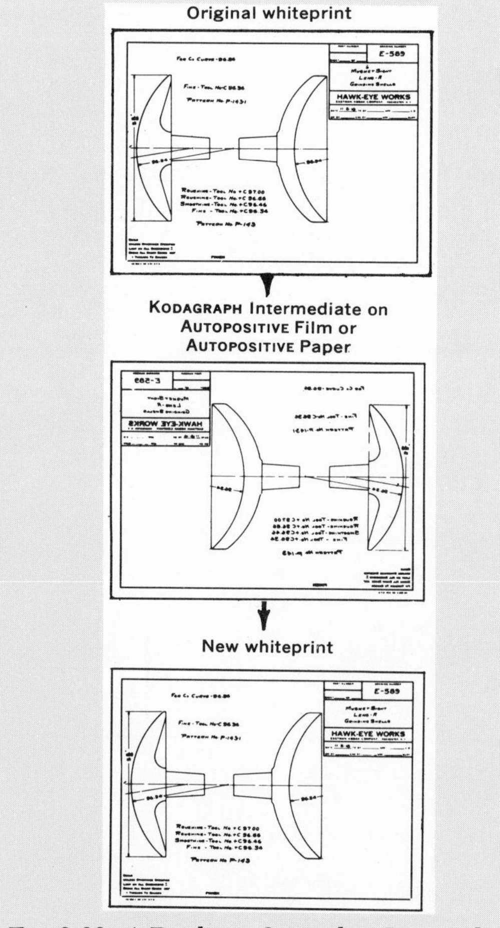

FIG. 9-22. A Duplicate Original, or Intermediate, Made on Special Film or Paper (Eastman Kodak Co.)
This is then used as an original to make copies.

Restoration of Worn Drawings

Through various combinations of continued use, aging, and possibly weak lines in the first place, original drawings often become unusable for making legible reproductions. Hours of redrafting time can be saved by making a negative on a special, high contrast film or paper. An opaquing fluid is then used to block-out any unwanted lines or any background areas which are not dense enough. This negative is used to produce either a positive or negative duplicate original from which any number of legible prints can be made, Fig. 9-23.

Another technique to restore old drawings is to make a one-half size film or paper negative of the old drawing. This will reduce the amount of opaquing needed since stains, smudges, creases, and the like tend to "drop out" in the reduction. Then, enlarge this negative into a sharp and clean duplicate original.

Either of these techniques can also be used to make a duplicate original from which a satisfactory microfilm negative can be made without redrawing.

Copying Opaque Prints

Reproduction departments frequently need copies of prints which are opaque. A translucent intermediate of these can be prepared by the *reflex* process. The sensitized reflex film is placed with the emulsion side in contact with the image side of the print to be copied. Light passes through the back side of the intermediate and the image is reflected onto it. Development of the intermediate yields a wrong-reading (reversed L to R) translucent image from which any number of copies can be exposed and printed.

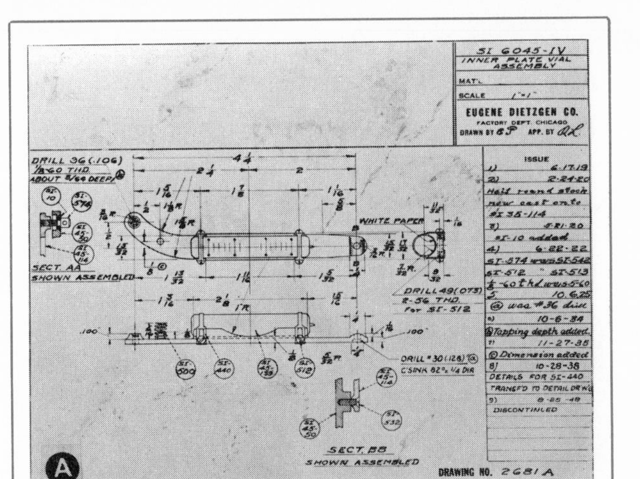

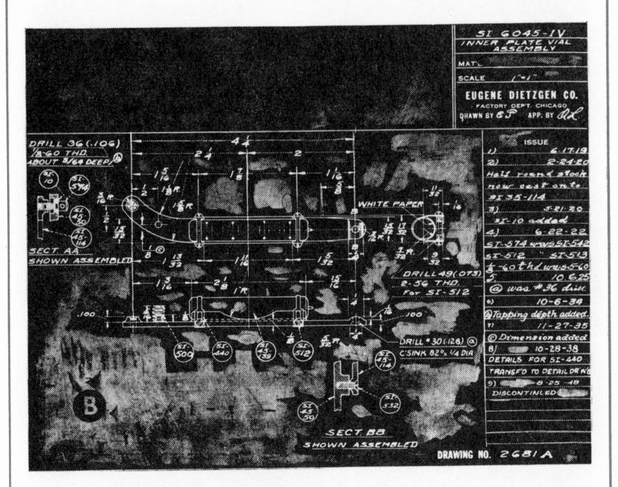

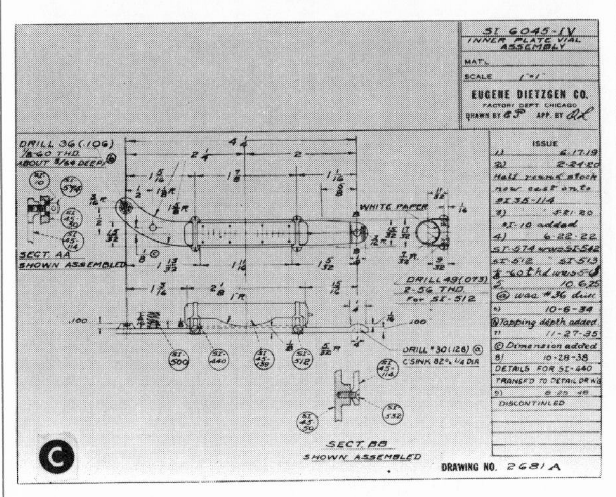

FIG. 9-23. Restoring Old Drawings (Eugene Dietzgen Co.)

A. Shopworn and stained drawing
B. Stained spots and blemishes opaqued from the negative
C. Restored drawing

Use of Intermediates to Modify Drawings

Many costly hours of tracing and redrawing can be saved in the drafting room by preparing intermediates of the original drawing and then modifying them. Sensitized paper, cloth, or film may be used. When the intermediate has been obtained, it can be modified by erasing, by eradicating fluids, by cutting out, or by adding pencil, ink, or preprinted materials, or by combining several intermediates.

You can imagine the time saved by an architect in preparing plans for a fifty-story building if one basic drawing is made and then intermediates are used for each floor plan. Appropriate detail can be given for each specific floor without redrawing the entire plan.

In the mechanical industries, small design changes may be made on an intermediate of a basic drawing which is complicated, at large savings of time and cost, Fig. 9-24.

Microfilm Blow-Backs

Duplicate full-size or half-size originals from microfilm can be obtained by using a projection-type film or paper. Changes may be made easily, as unwanted lines can be eradicated, and new lines may be added in pencil or in ink. Full-size reproductions and/or another microfilm frame can be reproduced from this blow-back as modified.

Reduced-Size Reproducibles

Reduced-size reproducibles are becoming popular because they take less space to store,

FIG. 9-24. Use of Intermediates to Make Design Changes (Eastman Kodak Co.)

distribution is less costly, and print paper costs are less. Positive or negative half-size reproducibles may be made on projection-type film or paper, Figs. 9-25 and 9-26.

Contrasting Elements

Contrasting elements may be shown on special paper by making an intermediate, drawing in the contrasting portion, and making a reproduction. The work which was reproduced as an intermediate is subdued and that which was added appears as the original, Fig. 9-27.

Dropout Intermediates

Dropout intermediates may be prepared in a similar manner. The intermediate shows the image reproduced on it. However, when a print

Original drawing

½-size negative intermediate on KODAGRAPH Fast Projection Paper

Blue-line prints

Original drawing

½-size positive intermediate on KODAGRAPH AUTOPOSITIVE Projection Film

Diazo prints

FIG. 9-25. Making Half-Size Reproducibles and Drawings (Eastman Kodak Co.)

FIG. 9-26. Easier-to-Handle Half-Size Copies of Original Drawings (Eastman Kodak Co.)

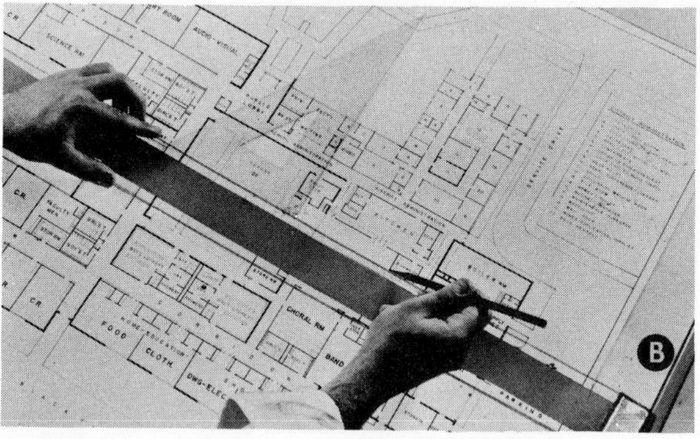

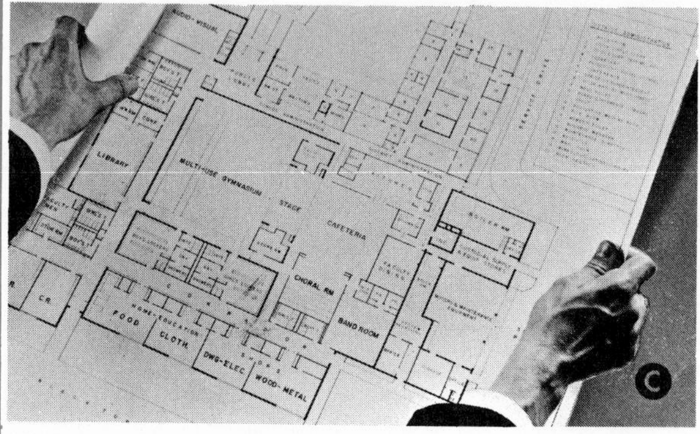

FIG. 9-27. Contrasting Elements on Special Diazo Paper (Eugene Dietzgen Co.)

A. To emphasize selected elements, prepare an intermediate with semi-opaque image.
B. Draw the new elements with ordinary pencil and ink.
C. Reproduction from the special intermediate on standard diazo materials show the drawn elements full strength.

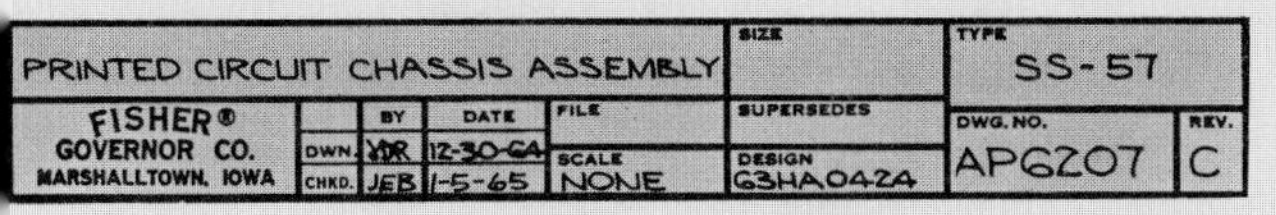

FIG. 9-28. Photograph on Drafting Film with Title Strip Ready for the Drafting to be Done (Fisher Governor Co.)

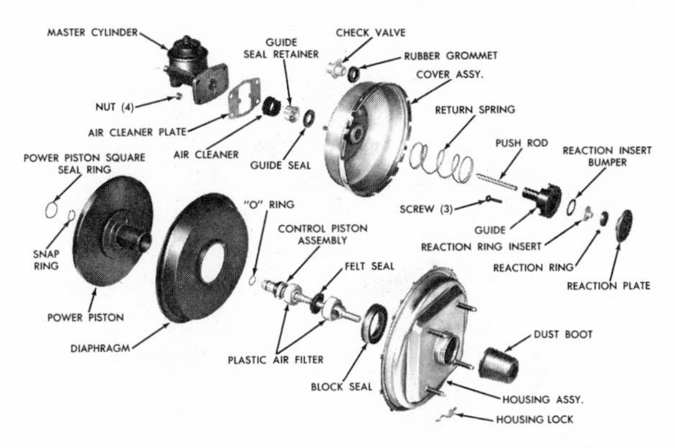

FIG. 9-30. Photo Drawing from Technical Publication (Chrysler Corp.)

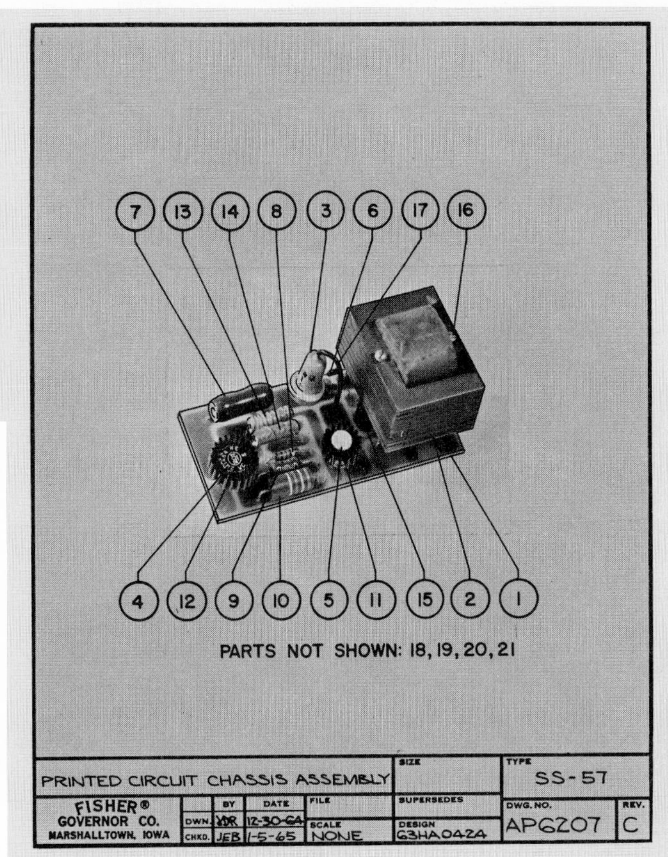

FIG. 9-29. Completed Photo Drawing (Fisher Governor Co.)

of the intermediate is made, the printed part drops out and the new line work prints full strength. This results in separate drawings in perfect register.

Photo-Drafting

Photo-drafting is a combination of photography and drafting. Although it is not a new technique, it has found favor in the 1950's and 60's as a way to reduce the amount of time required for drafting. Because photo-drafting does combine drawings and photography, many people find it easier to read than, for example, a schematic drawing.

Photo-drawings may be made only of objects that already exist. They therefore supplement rather than replace usual drafting techniques.

Photo-drafting is especially appropriate for identification diagrams and for certain assembly drawings. Fig. 9-28 shows photographs positioned on a drafting film. Fig. 9-29 shows the completed photo-drawing. See also Fig. 9-30.

Photo-drafting from models is used by some industries. An engineering model may be built just for the purpose of photo-drafting. Photographs are taken and drafting is added at considerable saving of time.

In other cases, a factory may wish to modify its facilities. Photographs of existing facilities may be taken. Draftsmen then add line work to these to show the particular modification.

Photo-drafting is a specialized field, but the draftsman should know how to make effective use of it.

drafting revision procedure

Any change made on an original is a revision. These come about through engineering change orders often referred to as *ECO*'s. The need for changes may result from a requirement noted in the field, a chance idea, or from research and development. Whatever the source, no changes can be made without proper authority nor without recording the change according to accepted company procedures.

Revisions are made by deleting, adding, redrawing, or combinations. These may take the form of *drawing amendments,* changes, changes to sepia-second originals, changes to photographed drawings, or (when sufficiently extensive) redrawing of the entire part or assembly. Crossing out information on a drawing is not recommended.

Because most drawings are subsequently revised, a revision block, usually located in the upper right-hand corner of each drawing, should appear. It should have the minimum information of symbol, zone, description, date, and approval columns, Fig. 9-31.

Revision symbols vary with company standards. SAE recommends capital letters, numerals, or letters with numeral suffixes. See Fig. 9-32. All revisions made at one time should carry the same basic revision number or letter. In addition to the revision block, the symbol of the change should be located in the field of the drawing as close to the location of the change as possible and should be encircled with a circle of about $5/16''$ diameter. Leaders may be used. The placing of symbols within the views of a drawing should be avoided. Revision symbols may be placed below the change and adjacent to the lower borderline of the drawing. Revision symbols from previous revisions are not ordinarily removed.

Descriptions should be brief but clear. When a long description is required, a note such as *see drawing change notice* may appear. In revising multiple sheet drawings, the drawing sheet numbers on which the revision applies should appear in each revision block as *see sheets 2 and 3.*

Drawing amendments are used when a minor change must be expedited. Copies of these are filed with all copies of the drawing. Periodically, drawings should be brought up to date to include all outstanding amendments.

Changes affecting the interchangeability of parts must be carefully examined and new parts numbers assigned where applicable.

REVISIONS				
SYM	ZONE	DESCRIPTION	DATE	APPROVAL

FIG. 9-31. Standard Revision Strip

REVISION AND DRAWING REFERENCE LETTER SEQUENCE

A, B, C	thru	Z	LA, LB, LC	thru	LZ
			MA, MB, MC	thru	MZ
AA, AB, AC	thru	AZ	NA, NB, NC	thru	NZ
BA, BB, BC	thru	BZ	PA, PB, PC	thru	PZ
CA, CB, CC	thru	CZ	RA, RB, RC	thru	RZ
DA, DB, DC	thru	DZ	SA, SB, SC	thru	SZ
EA, EB, EC	thru	EZ	TA, TB, TC	thru	TZ
FA, FB, FC	thru	FZ	UA, UB, UC	thru	UZ
GA, GB, GC	thru	GZ	VA, VB, VC	thru	VZ
HA, HB, HC	thru	HZ	WA, WB, WC	thru	WZ
JA, JB, JC	thru	JZ	YA, YB, YC	thru	YZ
KA, KB, KC	thru	KZ	ZA, ZB, ZC	thru	ZZ

Revision and drawing reference letters should follow in alphabetical sequence. When the single letter alphabet is exhausted, use double letter alphabet.

Letters "I", "O", "Q" and "X" should be omitted from both alphabets for revision letter use. The letters "I", "O" and "Q" should also be omitted for other drawing reference uses.

FIG. 9-32. Revision and Drawing Reference Letter Sequence (SAE)

storage of drawings and reproductions

"It is estimated that there are about 50 million new and revised engineering drawings made per year in this country by about 250,000 engineering designers and draftsmen at a cost of about two billion dollars."[3]

Filing systems for drawings and prints are designed for:

1. Safety and security.
2. Prompt retrieval.
3. Efficient filing.
4. Economy of floor space.
5. Prevention of accidents in the filing area.

Prints are stored:

1. Flat in shallow drawer files.
2. Hung in vertical files.
3. Placed in roll drawing files.
4. Folded in standard filing cabinets.
5. Photographically reduced on microfilm aperture cards.

[3]Peter G. Belitsos "Progress in Dimensioning and Tolerancing" *Graphic Science,* December, 1963, p. 28.

Prints are folded to 8½″ x 11″ letter size with the top edge folded downward so that prints will not be filed within other prints, Fig. 4-22. Prints of rolled drawings are *accordion folded* as shown for *E* and then *cross folded.* When folded with viewing side unexposed, the corner of the drawing may be folded back in the form of a triangle to permit reading of the title block.

An adequate margin of from 1″ to 1½″ is at the left of each drawing for binding. Fold marks are placed in the margin where folding is done by hand. The print-fold blueprint folding machine, introduced in 1958, allows complete automatic folding of prints. This machine provides an 8½″ x 11″ folded print packet from sheets 17″ x 22″ to 42″ x 16′ in random order.

With the tremendous volume of drawings which accumulate in the files of large industrial plants, the reduced filing space needed for microfilmed drawings is an important saving. The military now requires drawings submitted to be suitable for microfilming.

CHAPTER TEN

auxiliary projection

AUXILIARY PROJECTIONS

In Chapter 3 you studied orthographic projection as it related to the six principal or normal views, Figs. 3-4 and 3-10. These views are related in such a way that each of the principal surfaces is mutually perpendicular to the other.

Products having one or more surfaces inclined or oblique require auxiliary views to present these surfaces in their true shape. Principal views of a product with an inclined face show that face in a foreshortened manner, Fig. 10-1.

You have already learned that the view of any surface will show true shape when (1) the observer is positioned an infinite distance from the object, (2) the observer views the surface at right angles, and (3) the projection plane is parallel to the surface which is projected, Fig. 3-2 and 3-3. This principle is further illustrated in Fig. 10-2.

Correlating the Views

Auxiliary views are correlated in much the same manner as principal views. If we consider the object to be made from cardboard, a flat pattern layout would be as in Fig. 10-3. This

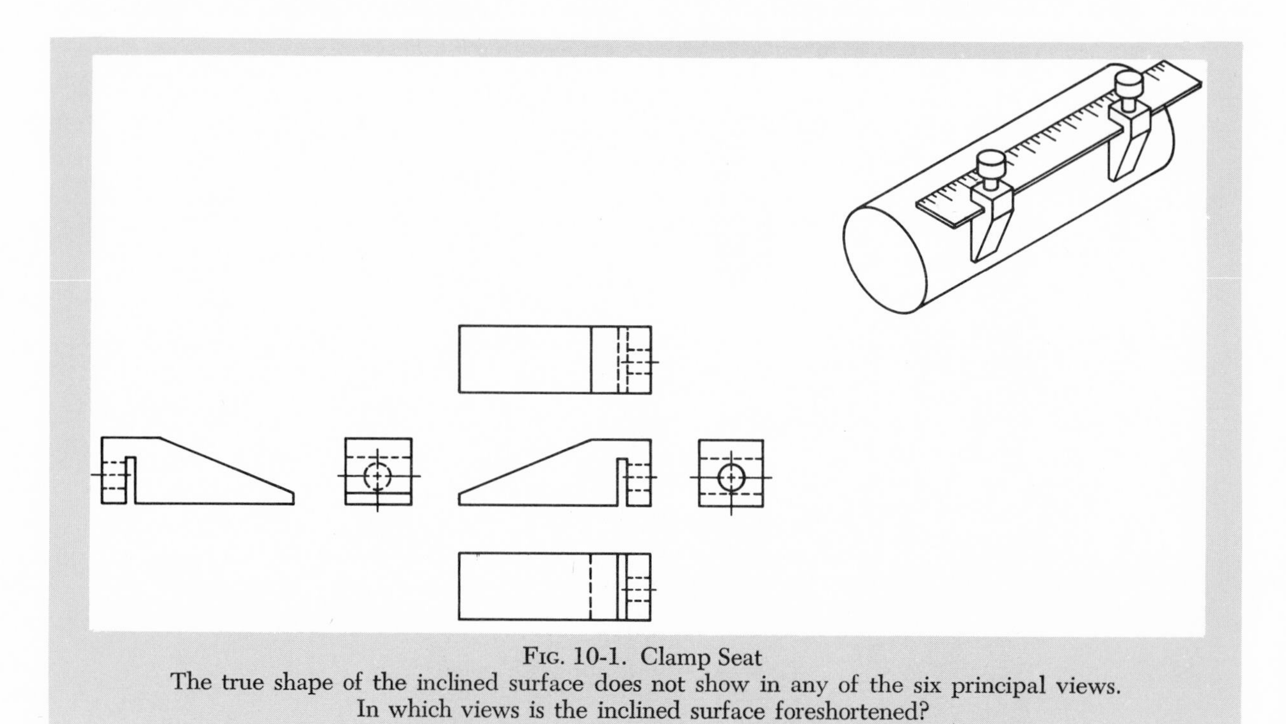

Fig. 10-1. Clamp Seat
The true shape of the inclined surface does not show in any of the six principal views.
In which views is the inclined surface foreshortened?

shows the six basic views and the auxiliary view adjacent to each other in true shape. Of course, not all of these views need dimensions to describe the object, but some space is required between views if dimensions are needed.

Consider the object placed inside a special transparent projection box, Fig. 10-4. Each face of the auxiliary projection box will be parallel to one of the faces of the object to be projected, Fig. 10-5. The auxiliary face of the projection box is parallel to the inclined face and is at a right angle to the frontal plane of projection. If these planes of the auxiliary projection box are hinged along their right-angle lines of intersection, the principal and auxiliary views on these planes can be opened flat into the plane of a piece of paper just as is done with principal views alone, Fig. 10-6. Coordination originates with the principal views and extends to auxiliary views.

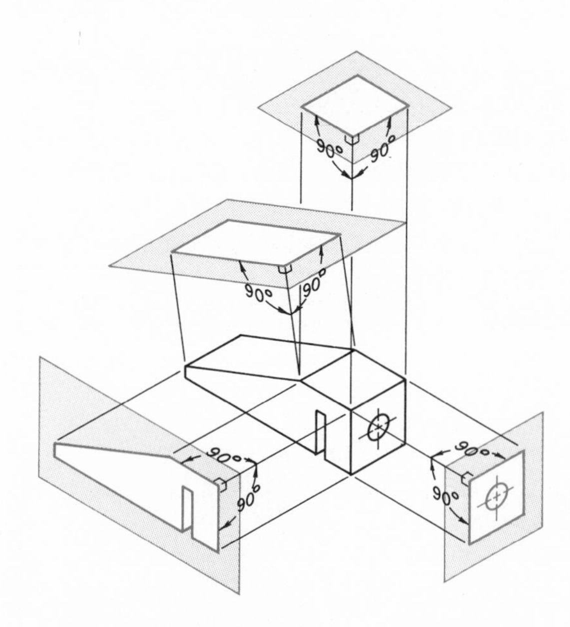

Fig. 10-2. True Surface Views on Planes Parallel to the Surface Being Projected

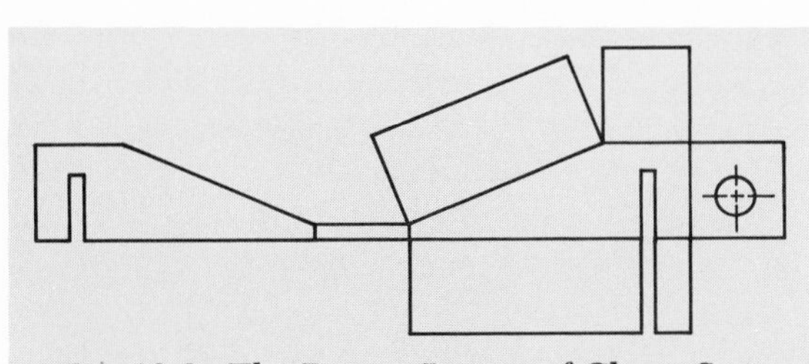
Fig. 10-3. Flat Pattern Layout of Clamp Seat

Kinds of Single Auxiliary Views

Objects with surfaces inclined to two of the three principal planes of projection, but at right angles to the other one are said to be *primary* or *single-auxiliary projections*. See Fig. 10-6.

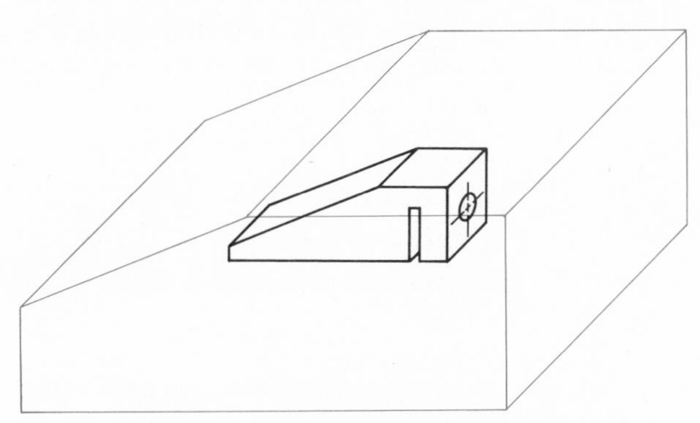
Fig. 10-4. Transparent Projection Box with Auxiliary Plane

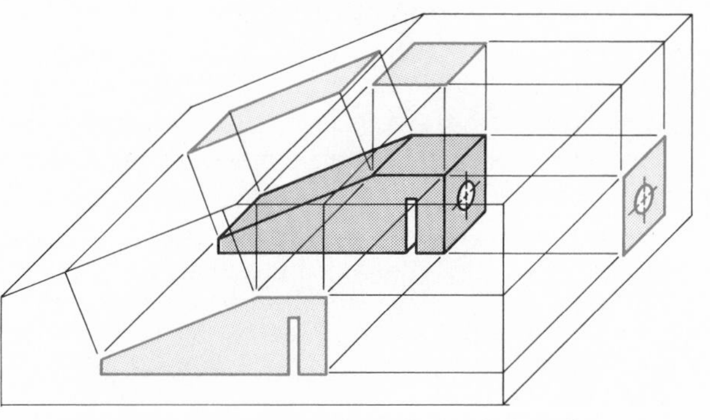
Fig. 10-5. Projection of Surfaces of the Object to the Projection Box

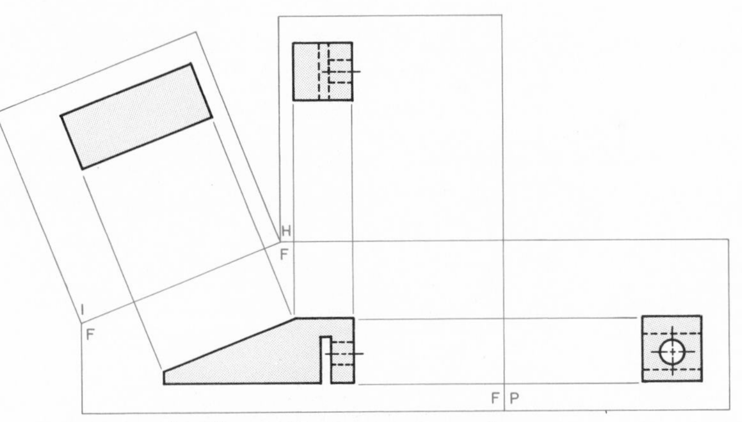

Fig. 10-6. The Planes of Projection Opened up from the Projection Box into the Flat Plane of a Piece of Paper
Note how the views are coordinated by projection lines.

Auxiliary Elevations

The auxiliary view of an object having a face perpendicular to the horizontal view but inclined to the frontal and profile views is called an *auxiliary elevation,* Fig. 10-7. These views may also be referred to as *height auxiliaries* because the principal dimension of height may always be seen in true length in an auxiliary elevation, Fig. 10-8.

Right or Left Auxiliaries

The auxiliary view of an object having a face perpendicular to the frontal plane and inclined to the horizontal and profile planes is called *a right or left auxiliary,* Fig. 10-9. These may also be referred to as *depth auxiliaries* because the principal dimension of depth may always be seen in true length in right or left auxiliary views, Fig. 10-10.

Front or Rear Auxiliaries

The auxiliary view of an object having a face perpendicular to a profile plane and inclined to the horizontal and frontal planes is called a *front* or *rear auxiliary,* Fig. 10-11. These may also be referred to as *width auxiliaries* because the

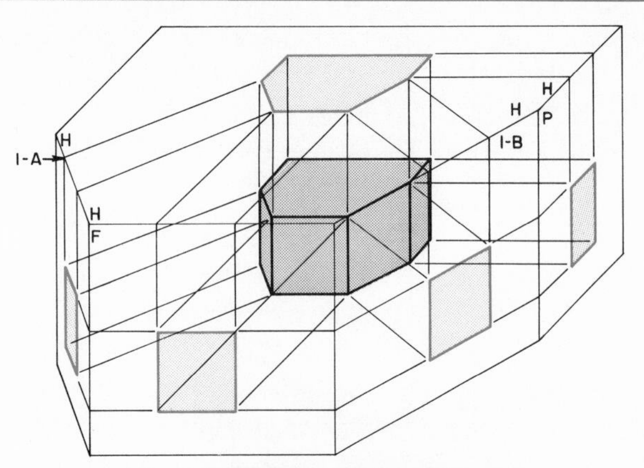

FIG. 10-7. Projection Box Showing Two Auxiliary Elevations
Note that the horizontal plane is the coordinating view and that the planes *1-A, F, 1-B* and *P* are each at right angles to *H.*

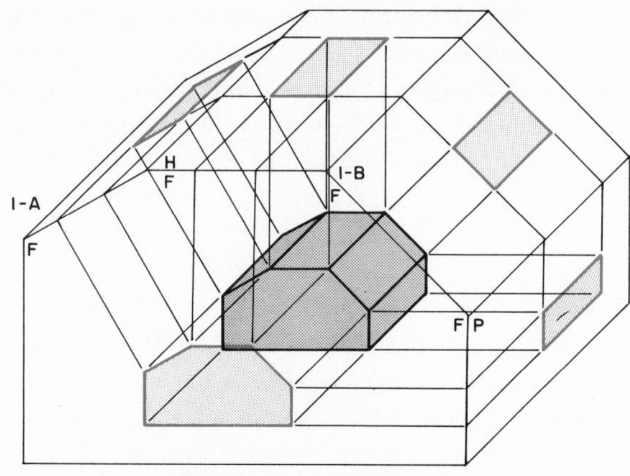

FIG. 10-9. Projection Box Showing Both Right and Left Auxiliary Views
Note that the frontal plane is the coordinating view and that *1-A, H, 1-B* and *P* are each at right angles to *F.*

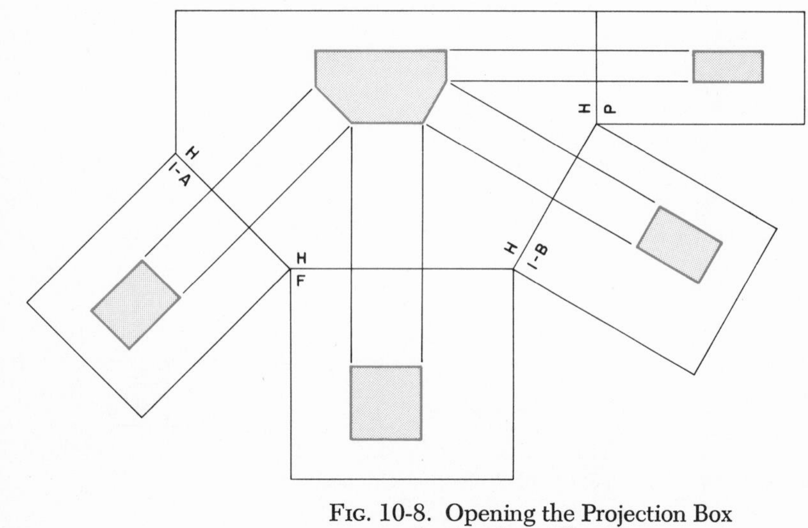

FIG. 10-8. Opening the Projection Box for Auxiliary Elevation
Note that the heigth of the object can be seen in each elevation.

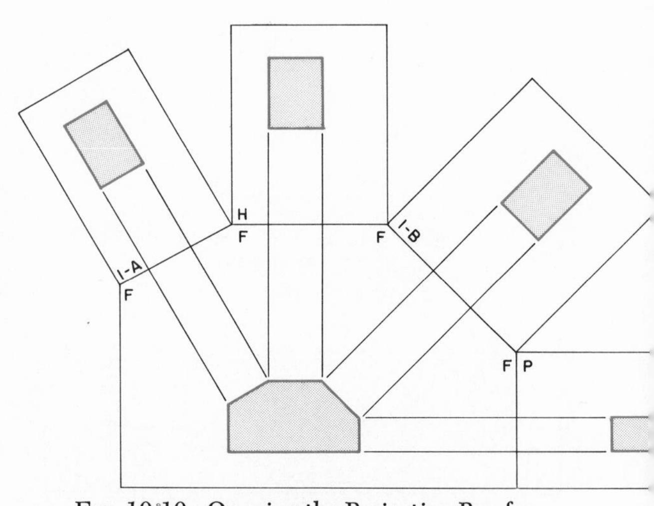

FIG. 10-10. Opening the Projection Box for Right or Left Auxiliary Views
Note that the depth of the object is seen in each auxiliary View.

principal dimension of width may always be seen in true length in front or rear auxiliary views, Fig. 10-12.

Construction of Primary Auxiliary Views

Review the section in Chapter 3 called "Elements of Visualization" before studying these paragraphs. The procedures that follow may be applied to drawing auxiliary elevations, front or rear auxiliary views, and left or right auxiliary views.

Given: two principal views with inclined surface *ABCD*, Fig. 10-13.

1. Place a reference line between the two given views, and letter the correct notation on it. This line may be, but need not be, equidistant from the two principal views. Extend projection lines from *ABCD* in the principal view, where *ABCD* appears foreshortened, to the principal view in which it appears as an edge view.
2. Establish a line of sight at right angles to the edge view of *ABCD* and place a reference line parallel to and a convenient distance away from this edge view. Letter the notation on the reference line.
3. From the edge view of *ABCD* and at right angles to it, extend projection lines through the new reference line and into the area of the auxiliary view.
4. Transfer the distance for each given point *A, B, C,* and *D* from the reference line between the given views to their positions from the reference line for the auxiliary view. What two errors do you think are commonly made by beginners in drawing this type of auxiliary view? *Hint:* How do you know which projector line to follow? From what line are all measurements taken?
5. Join the points newly located in the auxiliary view to form the true shape of surface *ABCD*.

The result is a *partial auxiliary view* of the object, Fig. 10-13. On a separate sheet of paper, sketch Fig. 10-13; then make a complete auxiliary view. What additional information does the complete auxiliary projection show? Is this information needed?

FIG. 10-11. Projection Box Showing Two Frontal Auxiliary Views
Note that the profile view is the coordinating view and that planes *H, 1-A, F* and *1-B* are each at right angles to *P*.

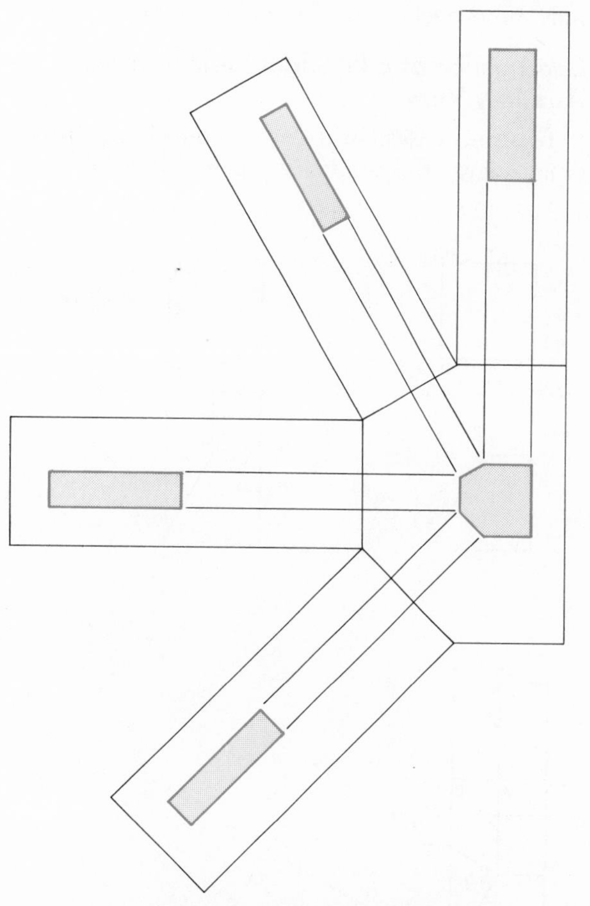

FIG. 10-12. Opening the Projection Box for Front or Rear Auxiliary Views
Note that the width of the object is seen in each auxiliary view.

The illustration in Fig. 10-13 uses an object for study which gives a right auxiliary view. On a separate sheet of paper, draw the given views of the three problems shown in Fig. 10-14. (These can be sketched on grid paper if you work carefully.) Apply the steps of procedure just presented and draw the required partial auxiliary views.

A working drawing may not have these reference lines nor the projector lines on it. These are needed only for construction of the drawing and are not needed for processing the part in the shop.

In these illustrations we have used the reference line (or edge view of the reference plane) between the views. It may be convenient to assume a reference line coincident with an edge of the object as in Fig. 10-15, or in other cases going through an object, Fig. 10-16. The latter case is used when an object is symmetrical and may be especially useful when plotting curves.

Construction of a Principal View from an Auxiliary View

In some cases, in order to complete a principal view, the auxiliary view must be constructed first from the specifications; then the principal view can be completed. Fig. 10-15 is an example. With respect to Fig. 10-15, is the complete frontal view needed? Is a partial frontal view needed? Why?

Auxiliary Half-Views and Sections

Some auxiliary views are symmetrical and can be adequately shown by a half-auxiliary view, Fig. 10-17. This saves both time and space. Observe that the *near* half-view is shown.

An auxiliary section view is shown in Chapter 5, Fig. 5-9. Auxiliary sections take the same form as regular sections such as full, half, offset, removed and the like. Because portions of the object behind the section plane may be foreshortened in auxiliary sectioning, partial auxiliary sectioned views are often used.

Secondary Auxiliary Views

A secondary auxiliary view is required to describe surfaces of objects which are inclined to all three of the principal planes of projection. The same rules apply to these as to single auxiliaries and to principal views: (1) the observer is imagined to be an infinite distance from the

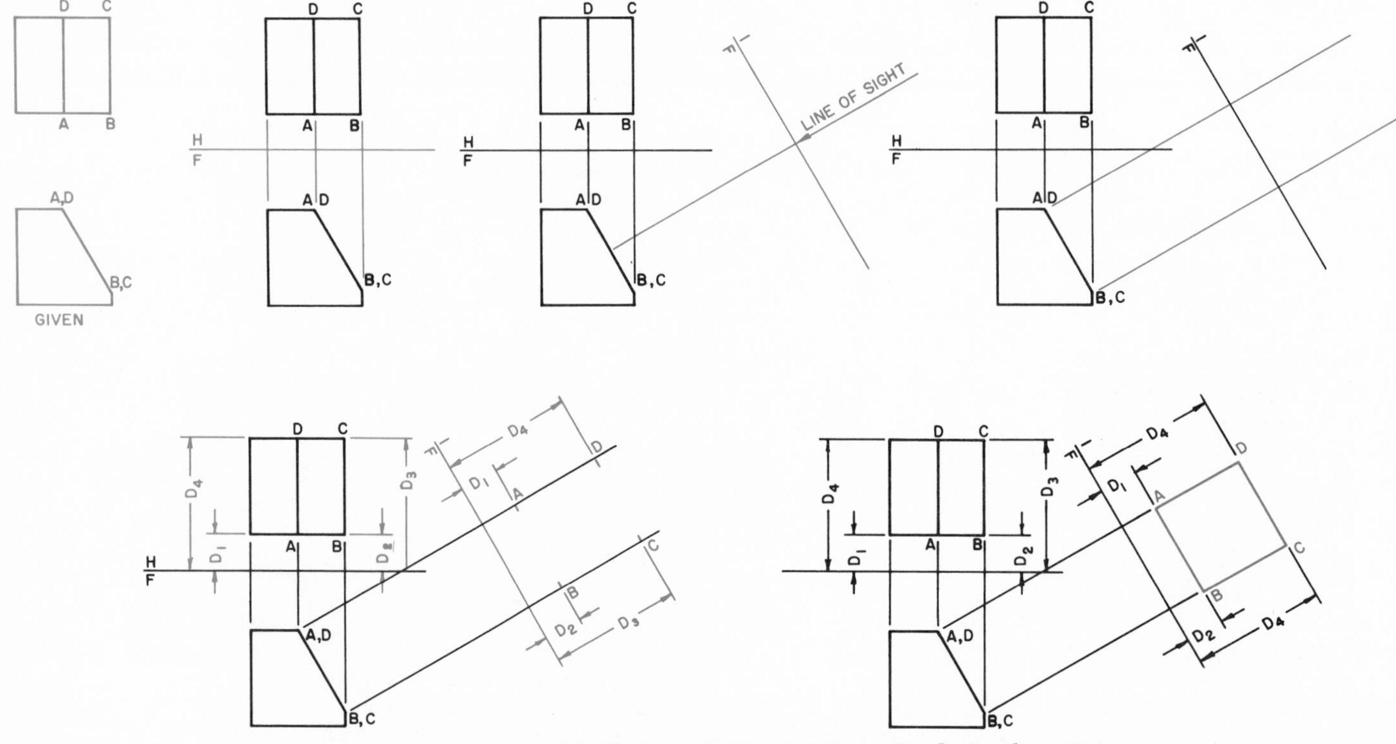

Fig. 10-13. Steps in Constructing a Single Auxiliary View

object, (2) the line of sight is at right angles to the surface to be described, (3) the projection plane is parallel to the surface and at right angles to the line of sight.

In order to coordinate an oblique view which requires secondary auxiliary projection with one or more principal views, a primary auxiliary view is required.

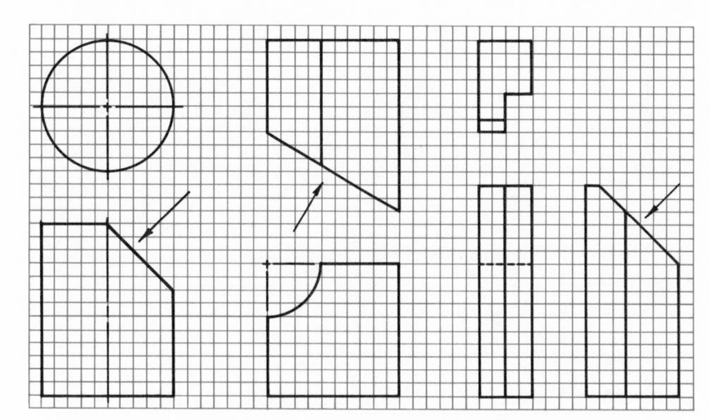

Fig. 10-14. Draw or Sketch the Given Views
Then draw or sketch a partial auxiliary view showing the shape of the inclined surface indicated by the arrow. Able students will want to draw the complete auxiliary views including all hidden lines.

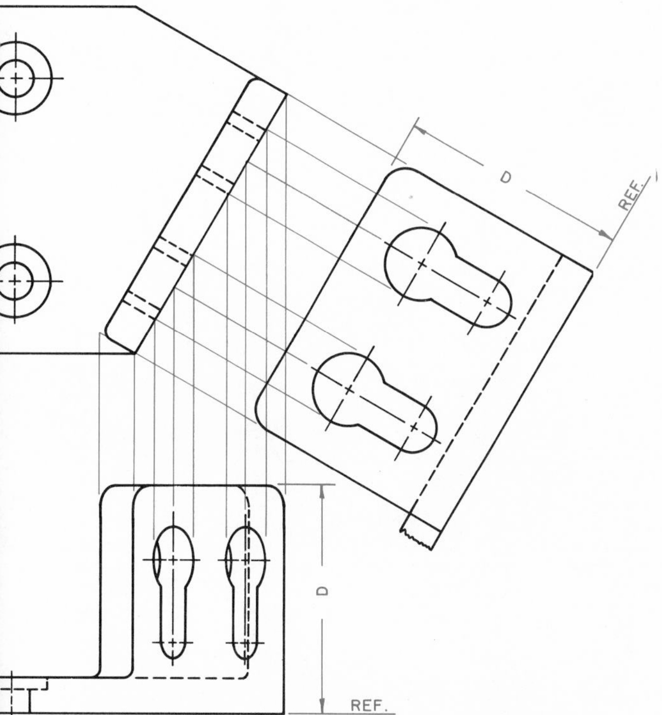

Fig. 10-15. Auxiliary View with Reference Line Coincident with the Base
Note where measurements are taken.

Given: two principal views of an object with oblique surface *ABC*, Fig. 10-18.

1. Establish and identify a reference line between the given views. Put in the projec-

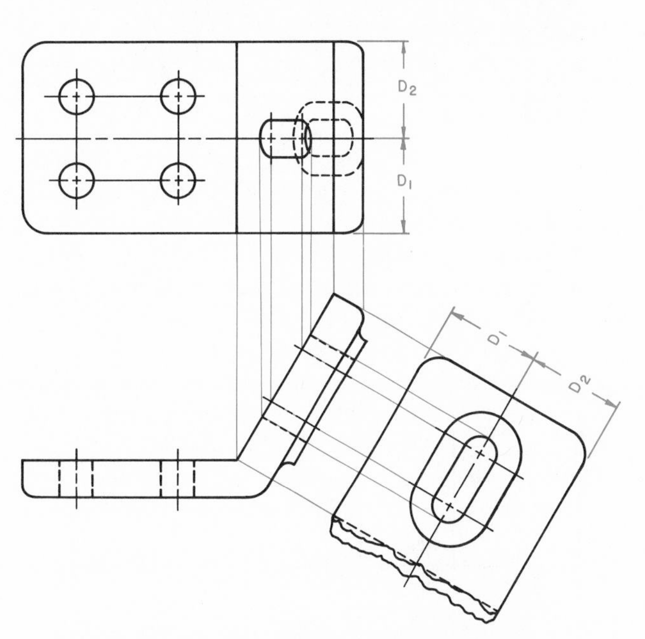

Fig. 10-16. Auxiliary View with Reference Line through the Axis of Symmetry
Note where dimensions are measured.

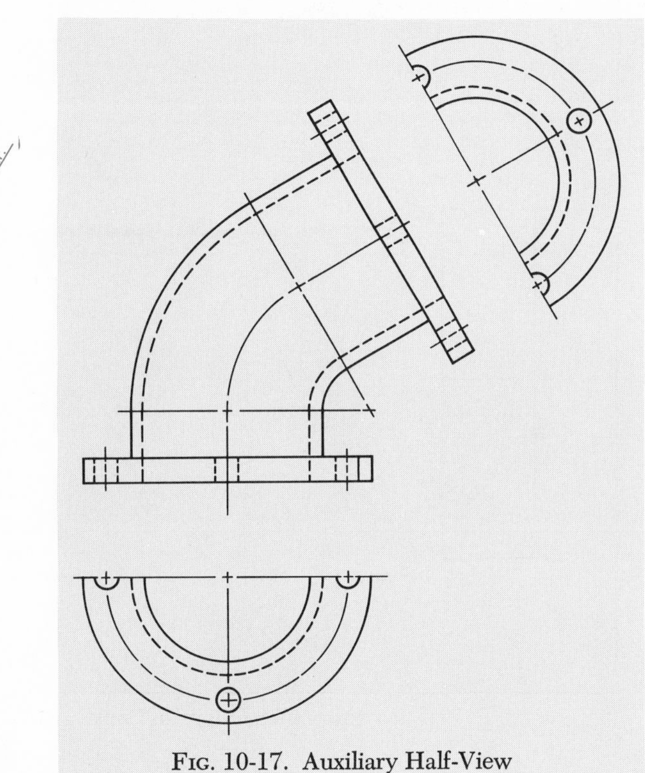

Fig. 10-17. Auxiliary Half-View

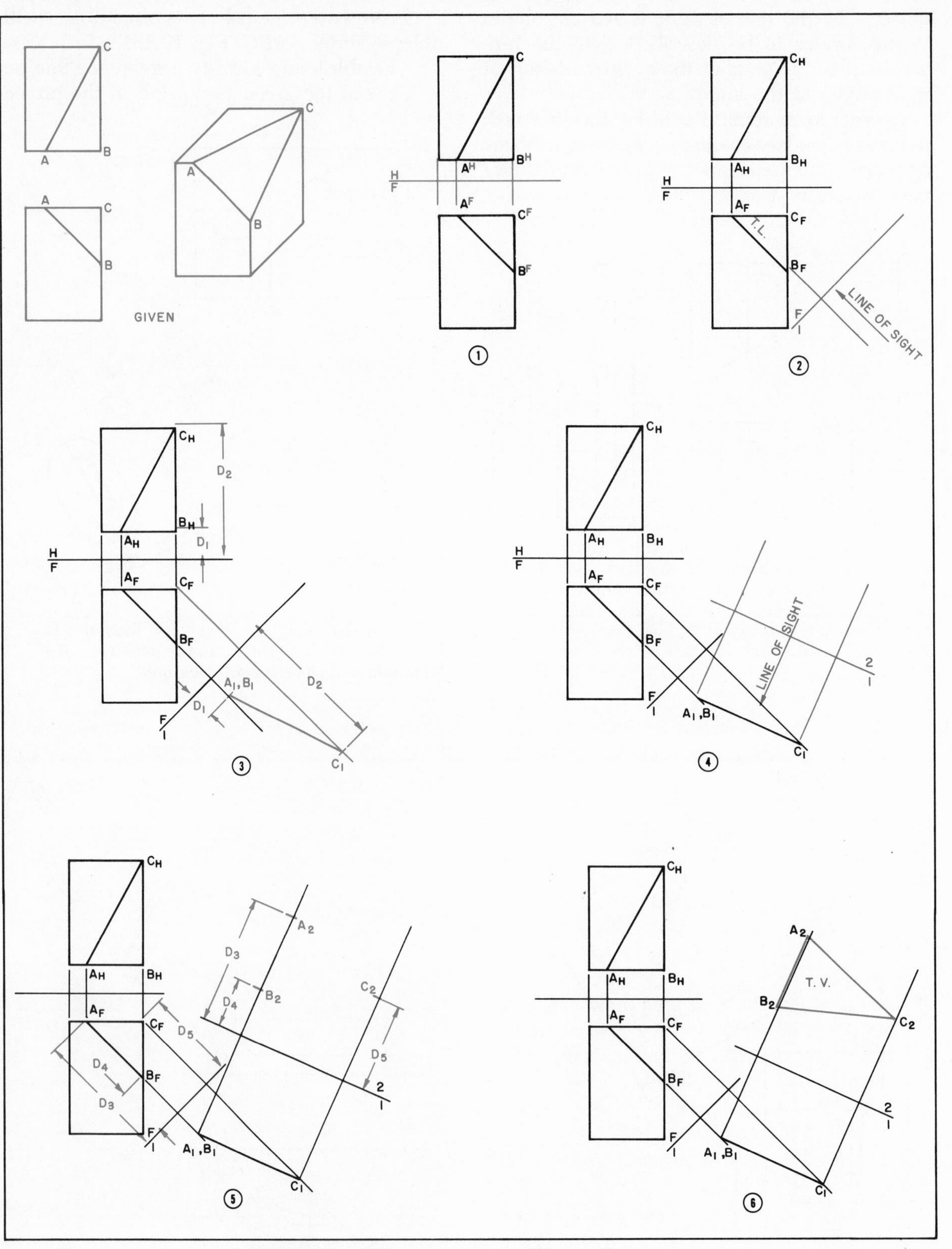

Fig. 10-18. Steps in Constructing a Double Auxiliary Projection

tor lines and the subscripts for letters indicating the plane in which they are located.

2. Find in either one of the given principal views a line lying in the oblique surface which is its true length. Extend this line to a convenient area of your paper where the first auxiliary view can be constructed. Draw and identify the reference line perpendicular to this line of sight. (Observe that in the auxiliary view you are about to construct, you will be looking at the end view of a true length line.) What is the shape of the end view of a true length line?
3. Extend projector lines from other points in the principal view into the first auxiliary view. Transfer the distance from the reference line between the two principal views to the given points, to the auxiliary view. Draw and label the first auxiliary view. (All that is needed is a partial auxiliary view showing only the oblique surface.) What is the form that the oblique surface takes in this view? Can we generalize that an auxiliary view taken from the end view of a true length line will yield an edge view of the plane in which the true length line lies?
4. Establish a line of sight at right angles to the edge view of the oblique surface. Place a reference line perpendicular to the line of sight and identify it. Extend projector lines from the edge view into the area of the secondary auxiliary view.
5. Transfer *A*, *B* and *C* to the secondary auxiliary view. Measure distances from the reference line between the first auxiliary view and the principal view. Transfer these by laying them out from the *1-2* reference line.
6. Connect the points in the secondary auxiliary view to complete the drawing for the true view of the oblique surface. What relationships of viewing had to be established before a true view of the oblique surface could be drawn?

On a separate piece of paper, draw the two given views of Fig. 10-17. Then, working with the true length line lying in the oblique surface, *as shown in the top view,* develop the needed views to show the true surface view of *ABC*. Will the true view obtained by this method be the same as that in Fig. 10-18? To gain additional experience with double auxiliary projection, solve the three problems in Fig. 10-19.

Questions on Auxiliary Projection

These questions are designed to extend your understanding of auxiliary projection.

1. Given any two principal views of an object, how many auxiliary views can be constructed off one of these principal views?
2. Which auxiliary views from question 1 will be useful views, *i.e.,* show true size of a given inclined surface?
3. Once an auxiliary view is constructed, from how many additional viewing directions could a secondary auxiliary view be constructed?
4. Is there any end to the number of successive auxiliary views that can be drawn of a given object?
5. Are any of the following statements correct? From any two adjacent views of an object an infinite number of third views can be constructed. A given view, if auxiliary, might or might not be a useful auxiliary view.

Chapter 10 — Problems and Projects

1. A table top, Fig. 10-20, has an 18″ rail under its ends. The table legs slant outward at a 10° angle and are mortised and tenoned to this rail. The tenon is ½″ deep by ⅜″ wide and 2″ long. It is centered on each end of the rail. Make a dimensioned production drawing of the rail showing the true surface layout of the tenon and the slanted face of the rail.

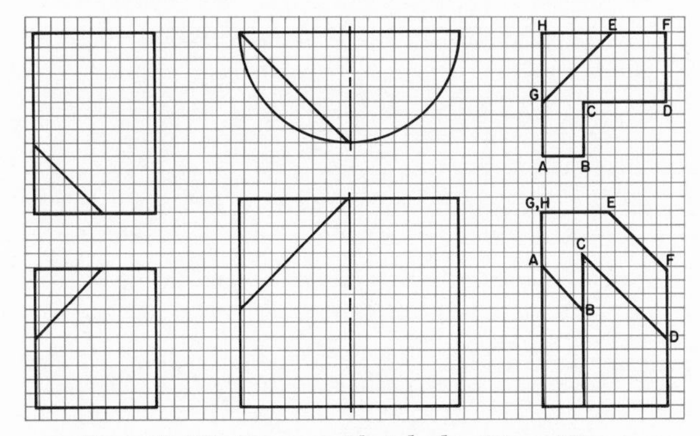

FIG. 10-19. Draw or Sketch the Given Views Then draw or sketch such views as are necessary to show the true shape of the oblique surfaces.

2. A wall-mounted bin has an observation window mounted in its inclined face, Fig. 10-21. Make a drawing showing the true shape of the inclined face and the true shape and location of the cut-out for the observation window.
3. Using a piece of steel ¼″ x 3″ x 8″, design a bracket so that the 8″ length is bent in the middle to an inclusive angle of 120°. The bracket is to hold two adjacent pieces of a hexagonal box together, Fig. 10-22. Each half of the bracket will have four ¼″ bolt-holes symmetrically spaced. Make a dimensioned production drawing of the part showing a profile view of the piece together with the necessary partial auxiliary views.
4. A stair railing slopes at a 30° angle. Vertical posts with a cross section of ¾″ x 1½″ are mounted every 6″ along the center line and are turned so that the diagonal of their cross section is aligned with the center line as shown in Fig. 10-23. Make a drawing for a sheet metal template from which you can scribe or draw the exact

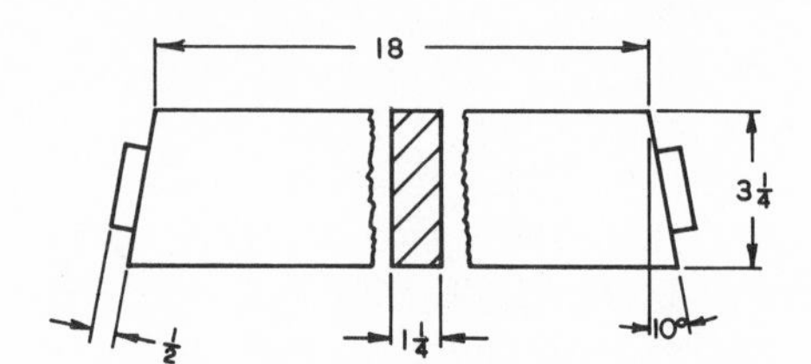

Fig. 10-20. Tabletop Rail

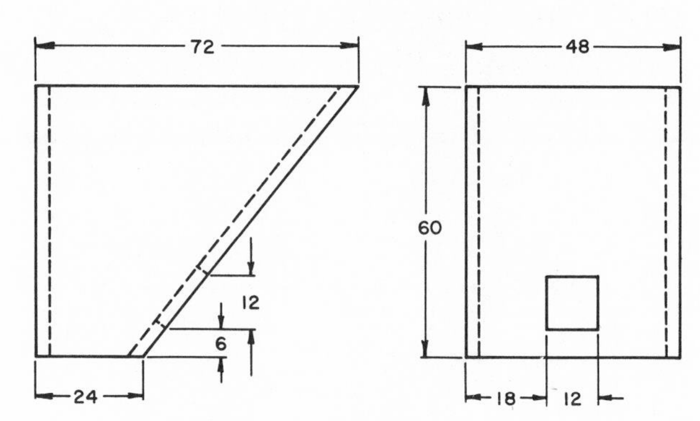

Fig. 10-21. Wall-Mounted Bin

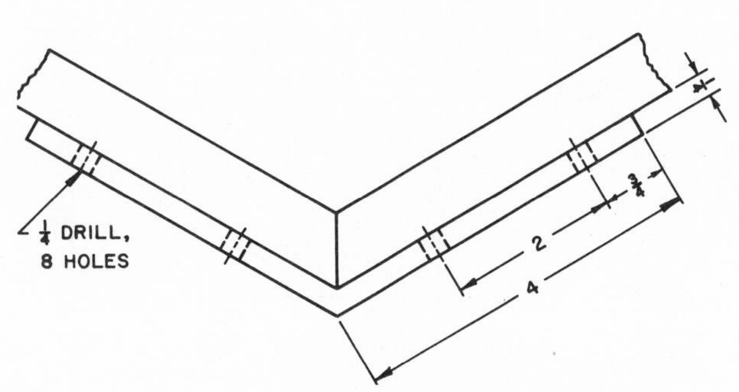

Fig. 10-22. Bracket

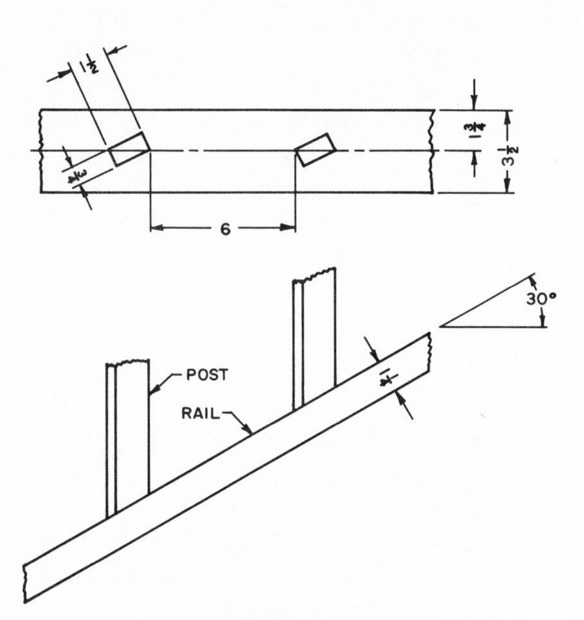

Fig. 10-23. Stair Railing Posts

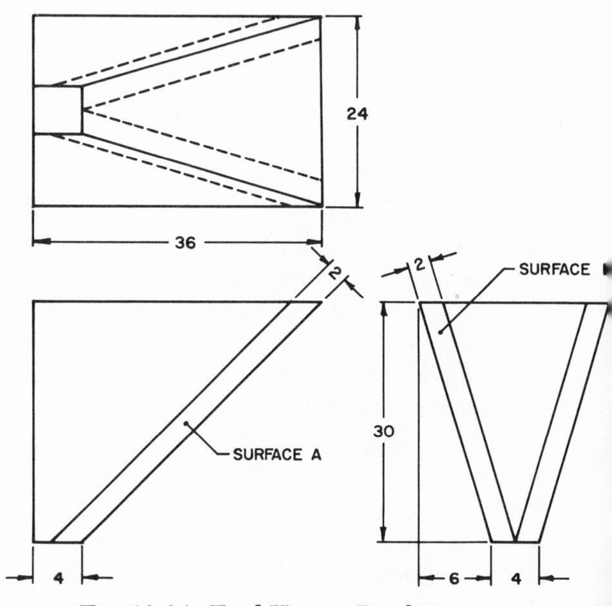

Fig. 10-24. Feed Hopper Brackets

location on the sloping railing for one post spaced correctly from an adjacent post. These posts are to be cut off with a hand saw. Make a drawing showing the angle of the hand saw cut along the ¾″ edge of the post and the angle along the 1½″ edge of the post. If a table saw were to be used, explain how it would be set to make this compound cut for the posts.

5. A feed hopper requires two angle brackets the full length of the front two corners as shown in Fig. 10-24. Make a drawing showing the true surface view of the exterior surfaces, *A* and *B*.

CHAPTER ELEVEN

tolerancing

Underlying Concepts

Interchangeability refers to the fit of mating parts — parts manufactured for the purpose of working (or functioning) together. Cast parts may have both *mating* and *non-mating* surfaces. Mating surfaces are those that fit and function with respect to other parts. Non-mating surfaces are simply exposed and require no additional machining.

Interchangeability is one of the key principles of modern industrial mass-production. When the pulley on the power steering pump of your car must be replaced, the mechanic expects with confidence that the one he gets will fit properly. He has this confidence even though the shaft on your pump is one of hundreds of thousands produced and the pulleys may or may not have been produced in the same plant.

Underlying interchangeability are two additional concepts. First, the theoretical concept that while measurement of parts to absolute values can be discussed, parts cannot be manufactured to exact size. As a practical matter, industry produces parts which vary in size. The drawing of the electric-window regulator arm in Fig. 11-1 shows that all dimensions not otherwise specified may vary plus or minus two-thousandths of an inch (± .002″) and the part will still meet all functional requirements. The hole at the left end may also vary in size, but notice that it may only vary ± .002 from the .203 dimension. In locating the center of this hole in the regulator arm with respect to the slot at its right end, the distance is 4.812 $^{+.002}_{-.001}$. This distance, 4.812, may vary from 4.811 to 4.814 and still function properly.

The second underlying concept grows out of the first: The smaller the permitted variation in size, the more expensive it will be to manufacture the parts. It is more costly to manufacture a part to ± .001 than to manufacture it to ± .002.

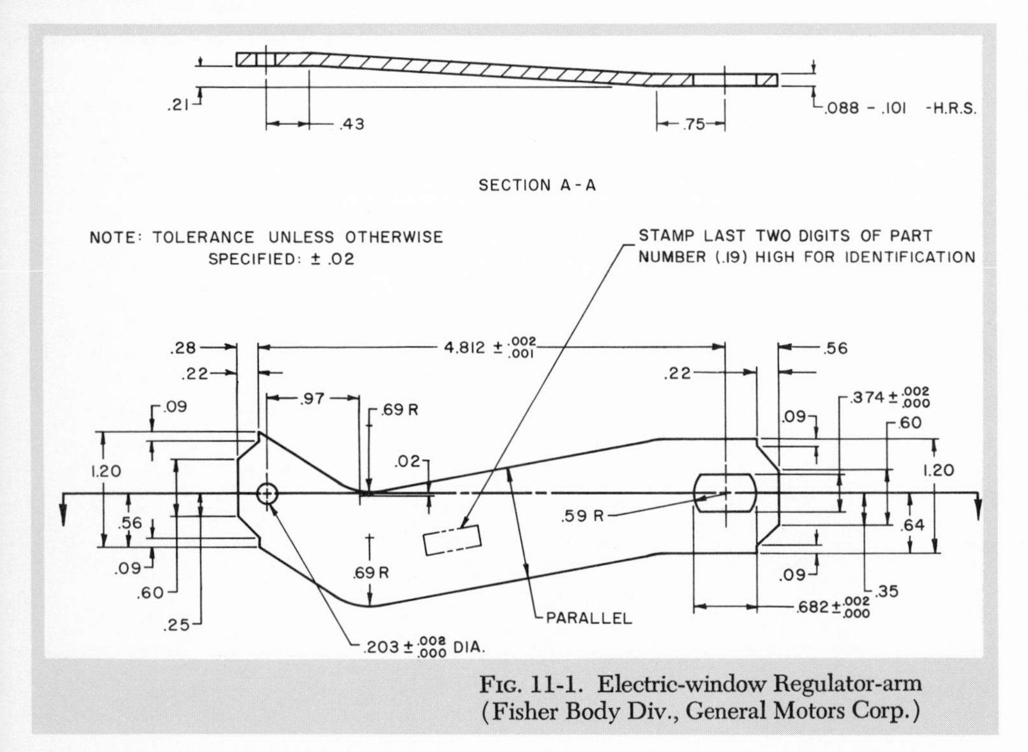

Fig. 11-1. Electric-window Regulator-arm (Fisher Body Div., General Motors Corp.)

Selective Assembly

Mating parts are often classified into several grades or sub-sets of sizes within the range of permissible sizes. Relatively large shafts (.002 oversize) are matched with relatively large holes (.002 oversize) and so on. *Selective assembly* has the advantage of reducing the cost involved in complete interchangeability of close fits. It is preferred in instances where extremely close fits are required and where it would be highly expensive to hold to complete interchangeability.

Definitions

NOMINAL DIMENSION — a dimension figure approximating actual or measured size. A 2″ x 4″ piece of lumber is more nearly 1⅝″ x 3⅝″ in measured size. The 2″ x 4″ dimension is called its nominal size. A nominal dimension is a whole number as just illustrated or the nearest common fraction as shown in Fig. 11-2.

LIMITS — the maximum and minimum sizes or dimension figures which are permitted on a specific part. Limits may be established for size, location, and form. The limits shown in Fig. 11-2 control the size. The dimension figure $4.812 \begin{smallmatrix} +.002 \\ -.001 \end{smallmatrix}$ in Fig. 11-1 controls location. Limits of form control are discussed in advanced textbooks.

Limits are considered absolute, that is, to be continued with zeros. Any variation above a specified maximum limit is not acceptable. Any variation below a specified minimum limit is not acceptable.

TOLERANCE — the total permissible variation between the limits specified. The dimension for the shaft in Fig. 11-2 is specified as $\begin{smallmatrix} +.624 \\ -.620 \end{smallmatrix}$. The difference between these limits, .004, is the tolerance for this shaft. Tolerance refers to the specifications for one dimension.

ALLOWANCE — refers to the difference between dimensions of mating parts. It is the difference between the smallest hole and the largest shaft. In Fig. 11-2 the allowance is .625 to .624, or .001. This represents the tightest fit permissible according to the specifications of the limits for the two mating parts.

BASIC SIZE — the size to which tolerances and allowances are applied to establish limits. In Fig. 11-2 the decimal equivalent of the nominal size, ⅝″ is .625″. The hole is the basis for calculations. Applying the tolerance, $\begin{smallmatrix} +.003 \\ -.000 \end{smallmatrix}$ yields the limits of .628 and .625. Application of the allowance — .001 gives the upper limit of the shaft, .624. To select basic sizes for specifying fits, choose from those shown in the technical data section, Table TD-11-1.

DESIGN SIZE — the size to which tolerances establish limits. When there is no allowance, it is the same as basic size. Note in Fig. 11-2 that the design size for the shaft is .622 and for the hole it is .625. This figure might have been dimensioned for the shaft as .625 $\begin{smallmatrix} +.001 \\ -.005 \end{smallmatrix}$ and the hole as $.625 \begin{smallmatrix} +.003 \\ -.001 \end{smallmatrix}$. This is not a practical method for the production worker since he would have to add both positive and negative numbers to obtain the limits to which he must work. Thus the actual limit dimensions are preferred on the drawings.

UNILATERAL TOLERANCES — variation in only one direction from the design size, such as $.625 \begin{smallmatrix} +.003 \\ -.000 \end{smallmatrix}$. This system is useful for close-fitting holes and shafts and is helpful to the operator as he approaches a critical size during machining.

BILATERAL TOLERANCES — variation in both directions from the design size such as the following expressions, each of which is equivalent: .625 ± .002, or $\begin{smallmatrix} .627 \\ .623 \end{smallmatrix}$ and $.625 \begin{smallmatrix} +.002 \\ -.002 \end{smallmatrix}$.

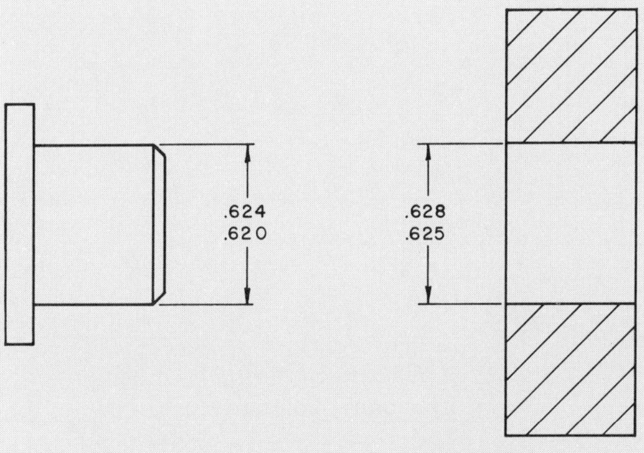

Fig. 11-2. Tolerancing for Mating Parts

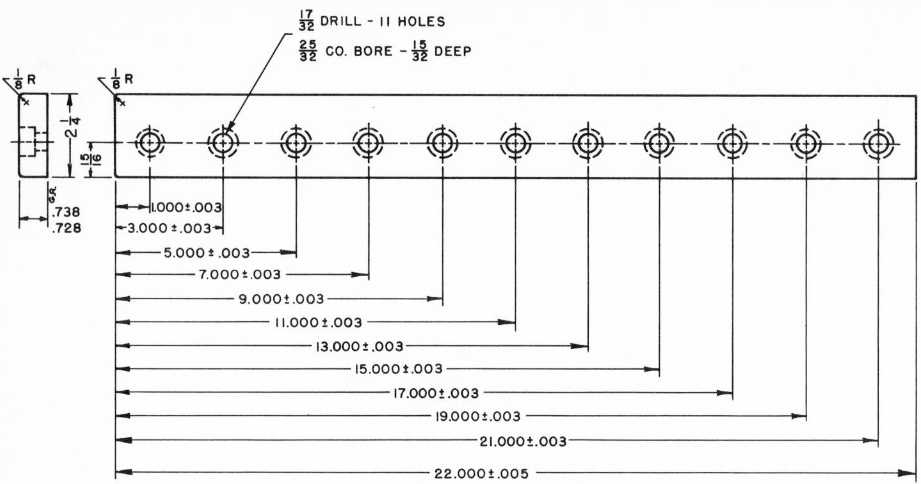

FIG. 11-3. Application of Plus and Minus Tolerancing (Gisholt Machine Co.)

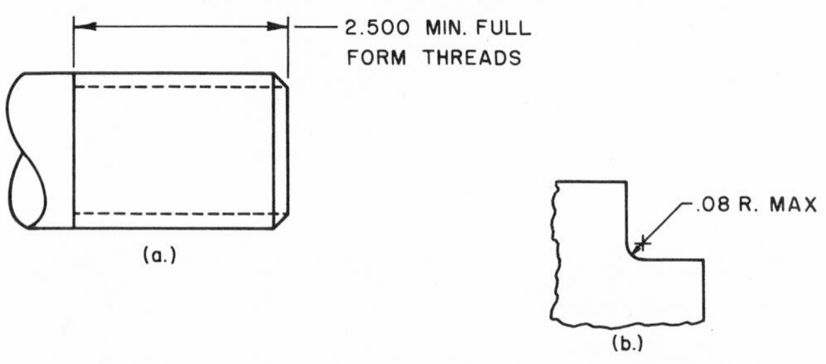

FIG. 11-4. Only One Limit May Be Important

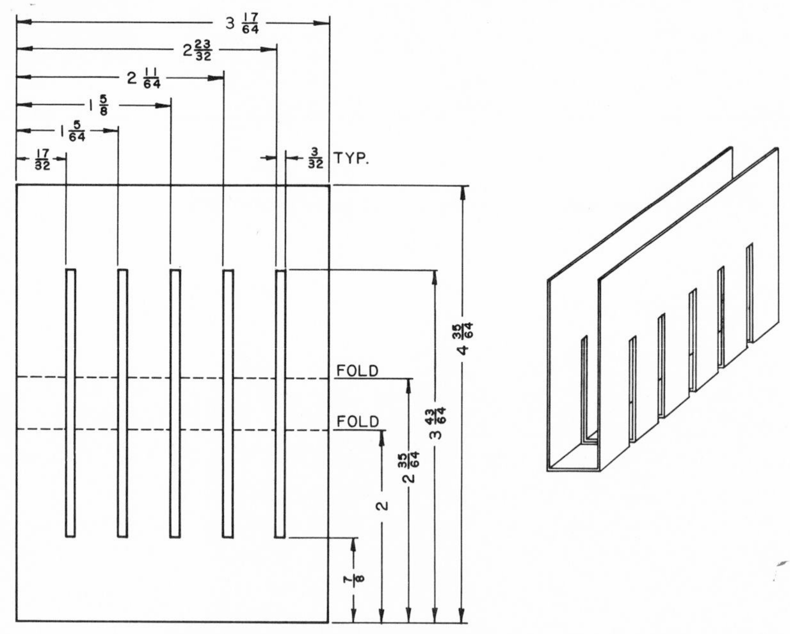

FIG. 11-5. *Cardboard Partition* Utilizes Fractional Tolerances

[1] General Motors Drafting Standards

These are used with location dimensions and where variation in either direction is permissible.

Responsibility for Tolerancing[1]

The experienced draftsman should be familiar with the various classes of fits used in the construction of mechanisms and the degree of accuracy which can be maintained commercially by the various methods of manufacture. The proper fitting of mating and adjoining parts contributes largely to the successful operation of any mechanism. Because these fits are controlled by the limits and tolerances specified on the drawings, this phase of drafting is important.

There are no rules or formulas for establishing limits and tolerances for all phases of engineering; hence the draftsman must rely on his judgment, experience, and knowledge of the persons responsible for the design. The design must therefore be analyzed carefully to determine the degree of accuracy which is essential to meet the functional requirements of each part detail. The greater the permissible limits or tolerances, the less costly the part is to produce because of reduced rejections, material costs, and less expensive tooling.

Limits or tolerances should never be specified closer than necessary either by definite specification or by the inference of any of the general notes. In certain cases it may be advisable to use closer tolerances to facilitate assembly. The necessity for this should be determined by ascertaining where the greatest saving lies—by close tolerances and shorter assembly time – or by greater tolerances and more assembly time. Investigation of current production practices is recommended as a guide in setting future limits and tolerances because in most cases they represent practical and successful manufacturing practices.

Expressing Allowable Variations

It has already been shown (Fig. 11-2) that when specifying high and low limits, the maximum limit is placed above the minimum limit. This is true for all dimensions except notes in which the minimum limit precedes the maximum, *e.g.*, .750-.752 DIA.

Specifications may take the form of those in Fig. 11-3 when the plus and minus tolerances are equal. When they are not the same, they should always take the form of the plus tolerance above the minus tolerance, *e.g.*, 4.200 $\begin{smallmatrix}+.003\\-.002\end{smallmatrix}$. When only the minimum or only the maximum limit is important, dimension as shown in Fig. 11-4.

When it is necessary to dimension with fraction tolerances, they may be applied as in Fig. 11-5.

Tolerances for angles may be expressed in degrees, minutes, or decimal parts of a degree, Fig. 11-6.

Basic Shaft and Hole Systems[2]

To specify the dimensions and tolerances of an internal and an external cylindrical surface so that they will fit together as desired, it is necessary to begin calculations by assuming either the minimum hole size or the maximum shaft size.

A basic hole system is a system of fits in which the design size of the hole is the basic size and the allowance is applied to the shaft.

A basic shaft system is a system of fits in which the design size of the shaft is the basic size and the allowance is applied to the hole.

Basic Hole System

Limits for a fit in the basic hole system are determined by (1) specifying the minimum hole size, (2) determining the maximum shaft size by subtracting the desired allowance (minimum clearance) from the minimum hole size for a clearance fit or adding the desired allowance (maximum interference) for an interference fit, and (3) adjusting the hole and shaft tolerances to obtain the desired maximum clearance or minimum interference, Fig. 11-7. Tooling economies can often be realized by calculating from the basic hole size, providing the size selected can be produced by a standard tool (reamer, broach, etc.) or gaged with a standard plug gage.

Basic Shaft System

Limits for a fit in the basic shaft system are determined by (1) specifying the maximum shaft size, (2) determining the minimum hole size by adding the desired allowance (minimum clearance) to the maximum shaft size for a clearance fit, or subtracting for an interference fit, and (3) adjusting hole and shaft tolerances to obtain the desired maximum clearance or minimum interference. See Fig. 11-8. The "basic shaft" method is recommended only if there is a particular reason for it; for example, where a standard size of shafting can be used.

[2]USAS pg. 17 (Sec. 5)

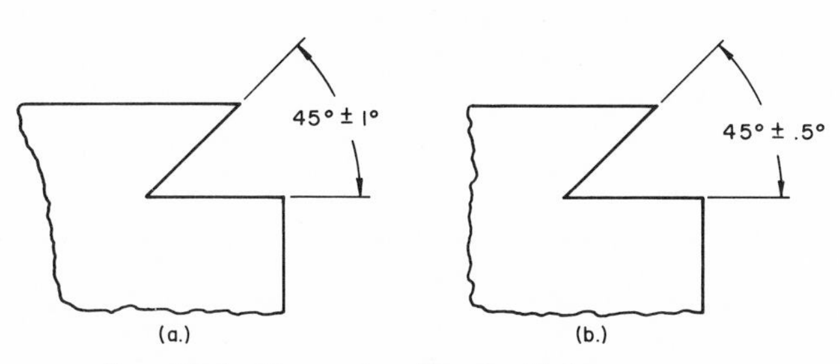

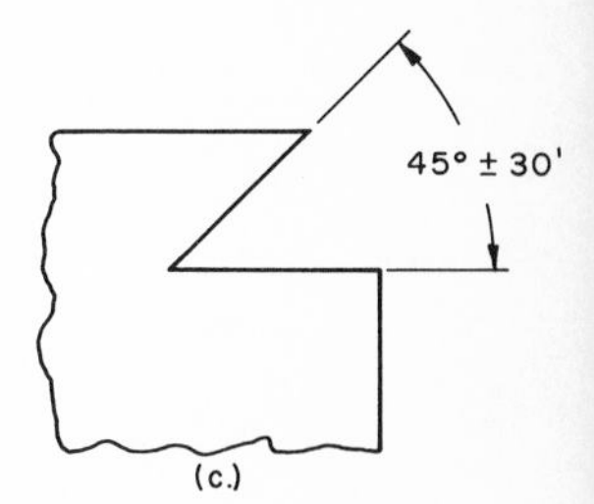

Fig. 11-6. Expressing Angular Tolerances

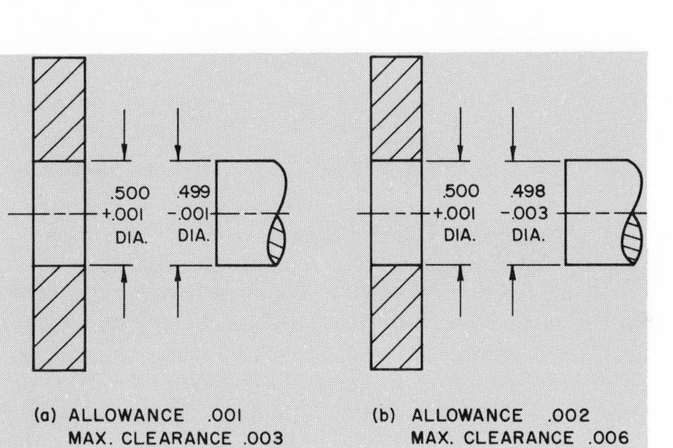

Fig. 11-7. Basic Hole System
Note that changing the fit changes the shaft size but leaves the hole size unchanged.

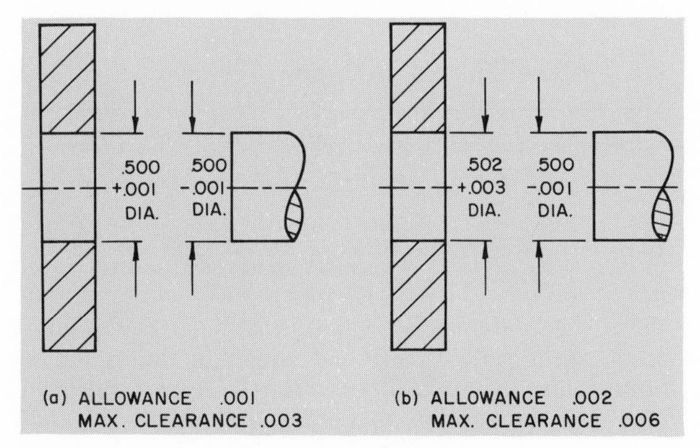

Fig. 11-8. Basic Shaft System
Note that changing the fit changes the hole size but leaves the shaft size unchanged.

Reference Dimensions

Fig. 11-9 shows an illustration with a reference dimension. It is used only for reference since to apply a tolerance to this dimension would permit two different interpretations.

Error Due to Accumulations

When several features are located in a row, such as the holes in Fig. 11-10, there is a likelihood of considerable error. The total possible variation is equal to the sum of the several maximum tolerances expressed. This type of chain dimensioning should be avoided. A datum surface such as that shown in Fig. 11-3 should be used to allow the least possible error and assure that the parts will function as intended.

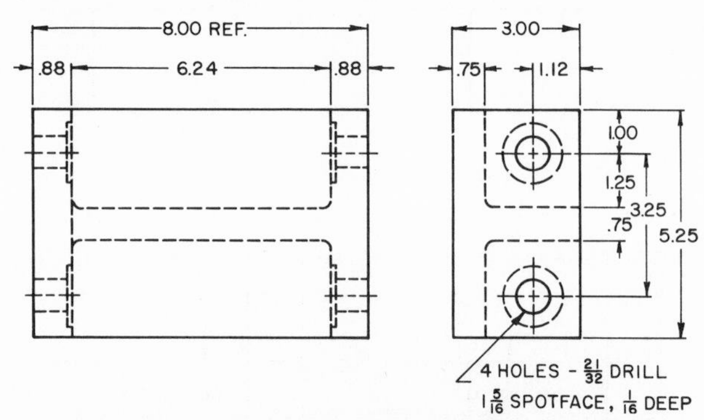

Fig. 11-9. Use of Reference (REF) Dimension to Avoid Tolerancing Confusion
If all tolerances were ± .02, what two ranges of size along the 8-inch dimension could be calculated if the "REF" were omitted?

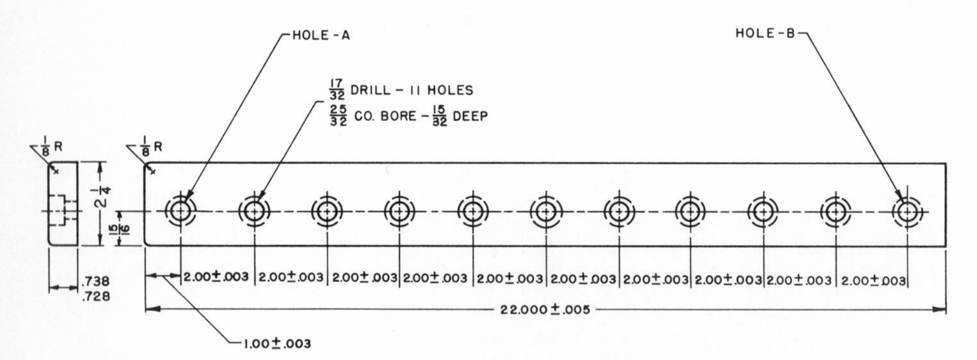

Fig. 11-10. Cumulative Error Due to Chain Dimensioning
This shows the need for datum surface dimensioning such as in Fig. 11-3. By accumulating the tolerances from hole *A* to hole *B*, what are the upper and lower limits of the position of hole *B* from hole *A*?

Standard Fits[3]

FIT is the general term used to describe the range of tightness which may result from the application of a specific combination of allowances and tolerances in the design of mating parts. Three general types of fit are clearance, transition, and interference.

A CLEARANCE FIT is one having limits of size so prescribed that an interference always results when the mating parts are assembled. The hole is always smaller than the shaft.

An INTERFERENCE FIT is one having limits of size so prescribed that an interference always results when the mating parts are assembled. The hole is always smaller than the shaft.

A TRANSITION FIT is one having limits of size so prescribed that either a clearance or an interference fit may result when mating parts are assembled.

In selecting limits of size for any application, the type of fit is determined first, based on the use or service required from the equipment being designed, and the limits of size of the mating parts are then established to insure that the desired part will be produced.

Designation of Standard Fits[4]

Standard fits are designated by means of the symbols given below to facilitate reference to classes of fit *for educational purposes.* These symbols are not shown on manufacturing drawings; instead, sizes should be specified on drawings.

The letter symbols used are as follows:

RC Running or Sliding Fit
LT Transition Fit
LC Locational Clearance Fit
LN Locational Interference Fit
FN Force or Shrink Fit

These letter symbols are used in conjunction with numbers representing the class of fit; thus *FN 4* represents a class *4* force fit.

Each of these symbols (two letters and a number) represents a complete fit for which the minimum and maximum clearance or interference and the limits of size for the mating parts are given directly in the tables.

[3]USAS B4.1-1955

[4]USAS B4.1-1955

Tables TD-11-3 through TD-11-7 in the technical data section have been developed by USAS to give a series of standard types and classes of fits on a unilateral hole basis, such that the fit produced by mating parts in any one class will produce approximately similar conditions throughout the range of sizes.

Description of Fits[4]

Running and Sliding Fits

Running and sliding fits, for which limits of clearance are given in TD11-3, are intended to provide a similar running performance with suitable lubrication allowance throughout the range of sizes. The clearances for the first two classes, used chiefly as slide fits, increase more slowly with diameter than the other classes, so that accurate location is maintained even at the expense of free relative motion.

These fits may be described briefly as follows:

RC 1 *Close sliding fits* are intended for the accurate location of parts which must assemble without perceptible play.

RC 2 *Sliding fits* are intended for accurate location, but with greater maximum clearance than class RC 1. Parts made to this fit move and turn easily but are not intended to run freely. Occasionally, RC 2 parts of larger sizes may seize with small temperature changes.

RC 3 *Precision running fits* are about the closest fits which can be expected to run freely and are intended for precision work at slow speeds and light journal pressures but are not suitable where appreciable temperature differences are likely to be encountered.

RC 4 *Close running fits* are intended chiefly for running fits on accurate machinery with moderate surface speeds and journal pressures where accurate location and minimum play are desired.

RC 5 *Medium running fits* are intended for higher running speeds, heavier journal pressures, or both.

RC 7 *Free running fits* are intended for use where accuracy is not essential, or where large temperature variations are likely to be encountered, or under both these conditions.

RC 8 and 9 *Loose running fits* are intended for use where materials such as cold-rolled shafting and tubing, made to commercial tolerances, are involved.

Locational Fits

Locational fits are fits intended to determine only the location of the mating parts; they may provide rigid or accurate location, as with interference fits, or provide some freedom of location, as with clearance fits. Accordingly they are divided into three groups: clearance fits, transition fits, and interference fits. These are more fully described as follows:

LT *Locational clearance fits* are intended for parts which are normally stationary, but which can be freely assembled or disassembled. They run from *snug fits* for parts requiring accuracy of location, through the *medium clearance fits* for parts such as spigots, to the looser *fastener fits* where freedom of assembly is of prime importance.

LT *Transition fits* are a compromise between clearance and interference fits for application where accuracy of location is important, but where either a small amount of clearance or interference is permissible.

LN *Locational interference fits* are used where accuracy of location is of prime importance and for parts requiring rigidity and alignment with no special requirements for bore pressure. Such fits are not intended for parts designed to transmit frictional loads from one part to another by virtue of the tightness of fit, as these conditions are covered by force fits.

Force Fits

Force or shrink fits constitute a special type of interference fit, normally characterized by maintenance of constant bore pressures throughout the range of sizes. The interference, therefore, varies directly with diameter. The difference between its minimum and maximum value is small enough to maintain the necessary pressure within reasonable limits.

These fits may be described briefly as follows:

FN 1 *Light drive fits* are those requiring light assembly pressures, and produce more or less permanent assemblies. They are suitable for thin sections or long fits, or in cast-iron external members.

FN 2 *Medium drive fits* are suitable for ordinary steel parts, or for shrink fits on light sections. They are about the tightest fits that can be used with high-grade cast-iron external members.

FN 3 *Heavy drive fits* are suitable for heavier steel parts or for shrink fits in medium sections.

FN 4 and 5 *Force fits* are suitable for parts which can be highly stressed or for shrink fits where the heavy pressing forces required are impractical.

Fig. 11-11 shows a graphical comparison of holes and shafts for each of the five designated classes of fit. Note that the basic size is in thousandths of an inch along the vertical axis. Note also that data in the graphs are based

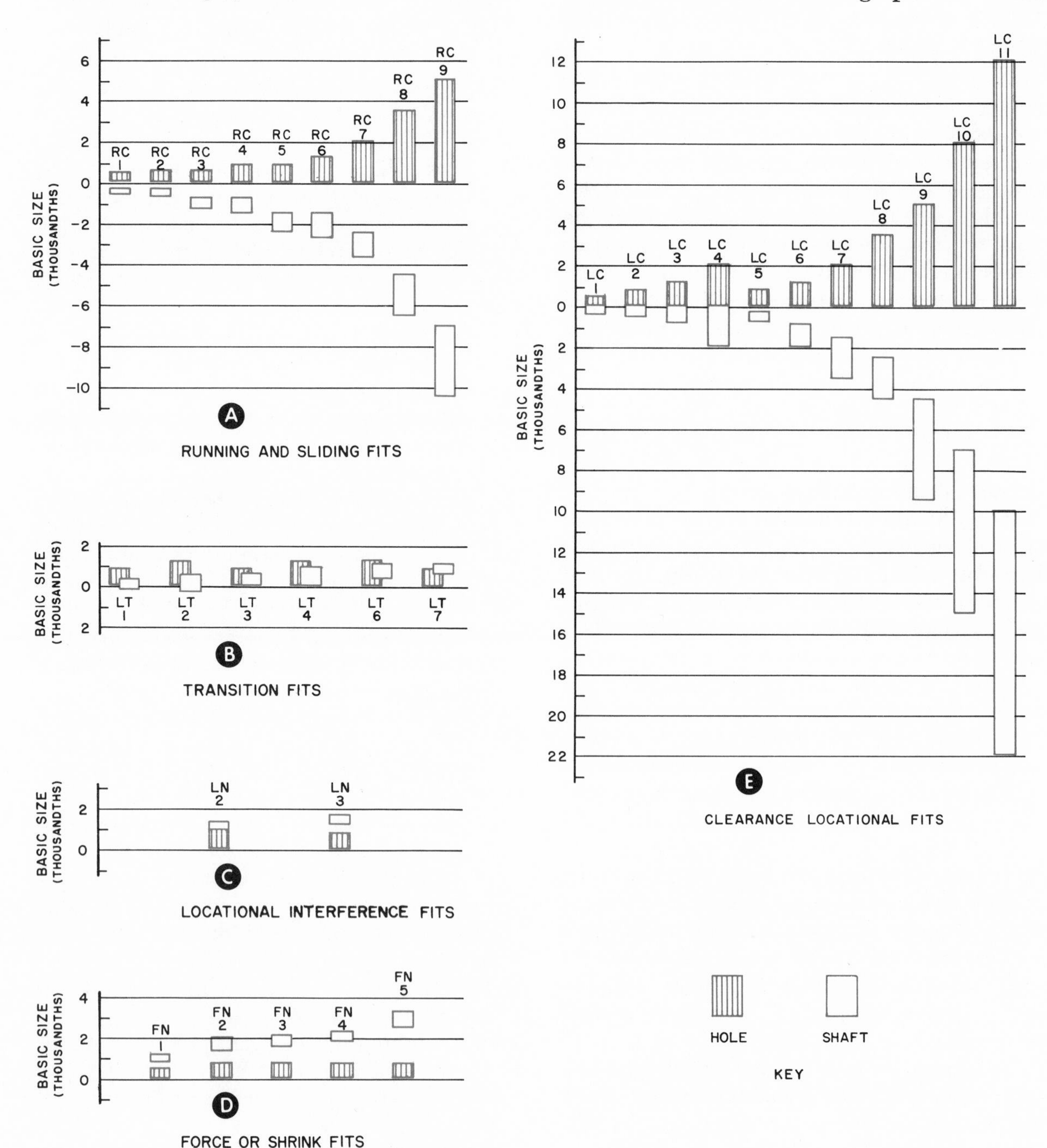

FIG. 11-11. Graphic Representation of Standard Fits with Basic Size in Thousandths of an Inch and for Diameters of One Inch (USAS B 4.1-1955)

on a diameter of one inch. These graphs should be studied to obtain a better understanding of clearance, interference, and transition as it applies to the several classes of fits. Make two similar graphs for running and sliding fits showing the relationships of the nine classes (RC-1 through RC-9, first, for nominal diameters of .04-.12 and, then, for 171.9-200 inches).

Computing Fits from a Standard Table

A nominally sized shaft and hole 1½″ diameter must fit together. They are expected to function as a part of an accurate piece of machinery with moderate speeds. Accurate location and minimum play are desired. What class of fit is appropriate? What dimension will be placed on the drawing to describe the shaft and hole?

1. Determine from the USAS standard description of fits which fit is appropriate. In this case, the running and sliding fit *4* (RC 4) meets the description.
2. Decide whether to use the basic shaft or basic hole system of dimensioning. (Most use the basic hole system.)
3. Convert the nominal size of the hole to its design size 1½″ = 1.500″.
4. Determine the tolerances for the hole and shaft from the appropriate USAS Table in the Technical Data Section Tables TD-11-3 to 7.
   a. Enter Table TD-11-3 for running and sliding fits. Enter the column heading called "Class RC 4."
   b. Locate 1½″, nominal size under the heading: "nominal size range in inches." This will fall between the 1.19-1.97 class.
   c. Read the hole and shaft limits from the table: hole = + 1.0, 0.0; shaft = — 1.0, — 2.0. Note the small type under the table title: Limits are in thousandths of an inch. The information reads: hole = + .001, + .0; shaft = — .001; — .002.
   d. Very carefully and in tabular form, apply these limits to the hole and to the shaft.

basic size of hole		1.500
high limit of hole		.001
maximum hole size	=	1.501
basic size of hole		1.500
low limit of hole		.000
minimum hole size	=	1.500
basic size of shaft		1.500
high limit of shaft		— .001
maximum shaft size	=	1.499
basic size of shaft		1.500
low limit of shaft		— .002
minimum shaft size	=	1.498

   e. The limits of clearance in the table show that for the smallest hole and largest shaft the allowance is .001; for the largest clearance space (the largest hole and the smallest shaft) .003.

Chapter 11 — Problems and Projects

1. What are the upper and lower limits of a ⅞″ shaft designed for an RC-7 fit? Also, the hole? What would these limits be if the fit were LC-7? LT-7? LN-3?
2. A common industrial problem is that of converting an old drawing dimensioned in fractions to a drawing using decimal dimensions. Fig. 11-12 is such a drawing. Redraw the gland. Dimension all figures by their upper and lower limits. Surface *A* requires an LC-3 fit; *B* requires an LC-3 fit; *C* requires an LT-1 fit. Use the tables for machining operations for the drilled hole tolerances. Angular tolerance is ± ½ degree. All dimensions not otherwise specified are ± .003.
3. Refer to the drafting instrument mast of Chapter 5, problem 13. Make a two-view drawing of this mast. Trace this so you

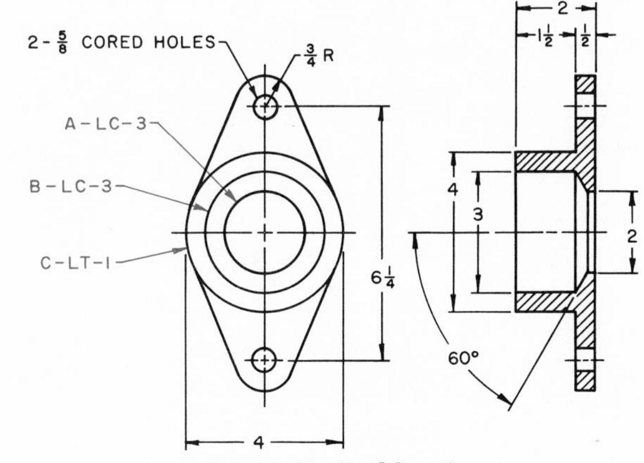

FIG. 11-12. Problem 2

TOLERANCING

have two drawings neither of which is dimensioned. Convert all dimensions to decimal inch dimensions. On one drawing place the dimensions using the basic shaft system. On the tracing, place the dimensions using the basic hole system. Diameters up to and including 1⁹⁄₃₂ require a tolerance of ± .001″; those over this size require a tolerance of .0005″. Allowance is .002″.

4. Refer to the brass compressor fitting of Chapter 5, problem 8. Convert the fractional figures to decimals. Make a drawing and dimension it using an RC-6 fit for all diameters larger than 2 inches. Use an RC-5 fit for all diameters 2″ and smaller.

CHAPTER TWELVE

fastening

There are many different ways to fasten things together. Each fastening is designed to do its job under its own peculiar set of circumstances. Three basic methods are adhesion, cohesion, and mechanical.

Adhesion is the fastening together of parts in contact with each other with an adherent or bonding agent. Such agents include a wide variety of glues, solders, plastics, and other industrial adhesives.

Cohesion is the fastening together of parts by heating the parent metal of each to a molten state and intermingling this molten metal so that upon cooling, the parts become as one piece. The welding of metals is the most common example. This may be done in some cases with the addition of a filler material and in others simply by heating the two metals.

Mechanical fastening is the joining of parts by such fasteners as rivets, nails, threaded fasteners, pins, clamps, and the like. Neither adhesion nor cohesion permits easy disassembly of parts once they have been joined together. Mechanical fasteners may or may not permit easy disassembly.

A comparison of four methods of joining metal parts under different conditions is shown in Table 12-1.

TABLE 12-1

Comparison of Joining Methods*

	Riveting	Welding	Brazing	Adhesive bonding
Preliminary Machining	P	E	P	E
With Thin Metals	P	P	F	E
Limits on Metal Combinations	F	P	P	E
Surface Preparation	E	G	F	P
Tooling	E	F	F	F
Need for Access to Joint	P	P	E	E
Heat Requirements	E	P	P	F-G
Stress Distribution	P	F-G	E	E
Sealing Function	P	F	E	G
Rate of Strength Development	E	E	E	P
Distortion of Assembly	F	P	F	E
Final Machining	G-E	F	E	E
Final Heat Treatment	E	F	F	E
Solvent Resistance	E	E	E	F
Effect of Temperature	E	E	E	P
Ease of Repair	G	P	P	F
Level of Skill Required	E	G	E	E

E-excellent; G-good; F-fair; P-poor

*Reprinted from Product Engineering, May 25, 1964. Copyright 1964 by McGraw-Hill, Inc.

FASTENING

adhesion

Theoretically, if two smooth, plane surfaces were brought into contact in a vacuum, they would adhere to each other without any bonding agent. However, in actual practice perfect plane surfaces cannot be manufactured. Even highly polished surfaces have considerable variation in their peak to valley roughness. Surfaces produced by casting and

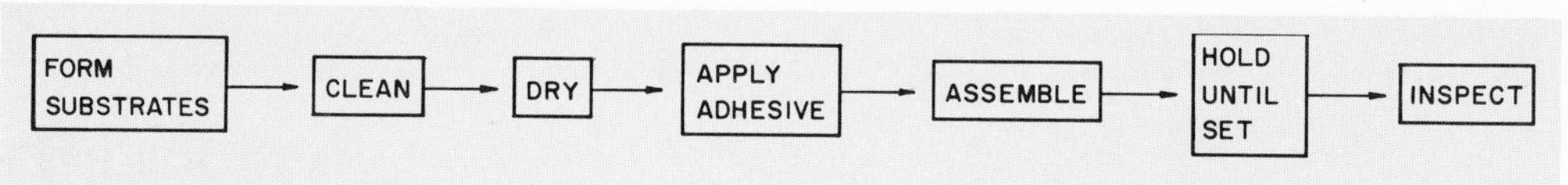

FIG. 12-1. Basic Steps in the Adhesive Bonding Process (McGraw-Hill[2])

machining actually do adhere at their various points of contact, but there are so few of these that the joint strength is very low.

Adhesives are designed to fill in the valleys in order to form a continuous layer between two adjacent surfaces. To be strong, an adhesive must solidify and desist displacement under stress.

Industrial adhesives must:

1. be in a fluid state at some step in the bonding process,
2. completely flow over the peaks and valleys of the materials being adhered,
3. set, in order to give strength.

Adhesives can be used to join almost all solid materials in about any combination or physical form. Their use in industry has given rise to very specialized personnel such as adhesive engineers and technicians. Properly bonded joints are stronger than the base materials. Certain adhesives may be attacked by fungi and/or some fluids such as acids, but in most cases they are considered quite permanent.

FASTENING

Basic steps in the adhesive bonding process are shown in Fig. 12-1.

Fig. 12-2 shows typical stress conditions of adhesive-bonded metal joints and methods of joint design which reduce possible fracture.

Table TD-12-1[1] is a guide showing adhesives used to join various materials and a table of performance, properties, and applications. These adhesives are available primarily for industrial users of adhesives and may be difficult to obtain in small quantities.

Tables TD-12-2 and TD-12-3 show common adhesives and their characteristics. These can be purchased in small containers and tubes suitable for household or school shop use.

Soldering and *brazing* are alike in that they both require heating a filler metal to join the metal parts. The application of heat must melt the filler metal but not the base metal. Surfaces of the base metal must be properly prepared for sound joints. Fluxes should be used to remove oxides and to promote flow of the metal.

Soldering is usually done at less than red heat (up to about 800° F.) and produces a weaker joint than brazing which is done at red heats (temperatures above 800° F.). Desirable practice in joint design for soldering and brazing is shown in Fig. 12-3.

Agents used in adhesive fastening are usually specified by a note on the drawing. Agents are listed in the parts list so costs can be calculated and so that they will be available at the time of assembly.

The draftsman needs some understanding of the wide range of materials available for fastening by adhesive bonding. In industrial practice a choice of adhesives may come to a draftsman as part of engineering specifications. In school shop situations the draftsman-designer may both select and specify the bonding agent to be used.

cohesion

Welding cannot take its proper place as an engineering tool unless means are provided for conveying the information from the designer to the workman. The practice of writing "to be welded throughout" or "to be completely welded" on the drawing is a means of transferring the design function from the designer to the welder. Do not expect the welder to know what strength is necessary. The absence of specifications of strength requirements is dangerous and may also be costly. In their desire to be safe, some shops use much more welding material than is necessary.

[1]TD refers to Technical Data Section
[2]Reprinted from May 25, 1964 issue of *Product Engineering*. Copyright 1964, McGraw-Hill, Inc.

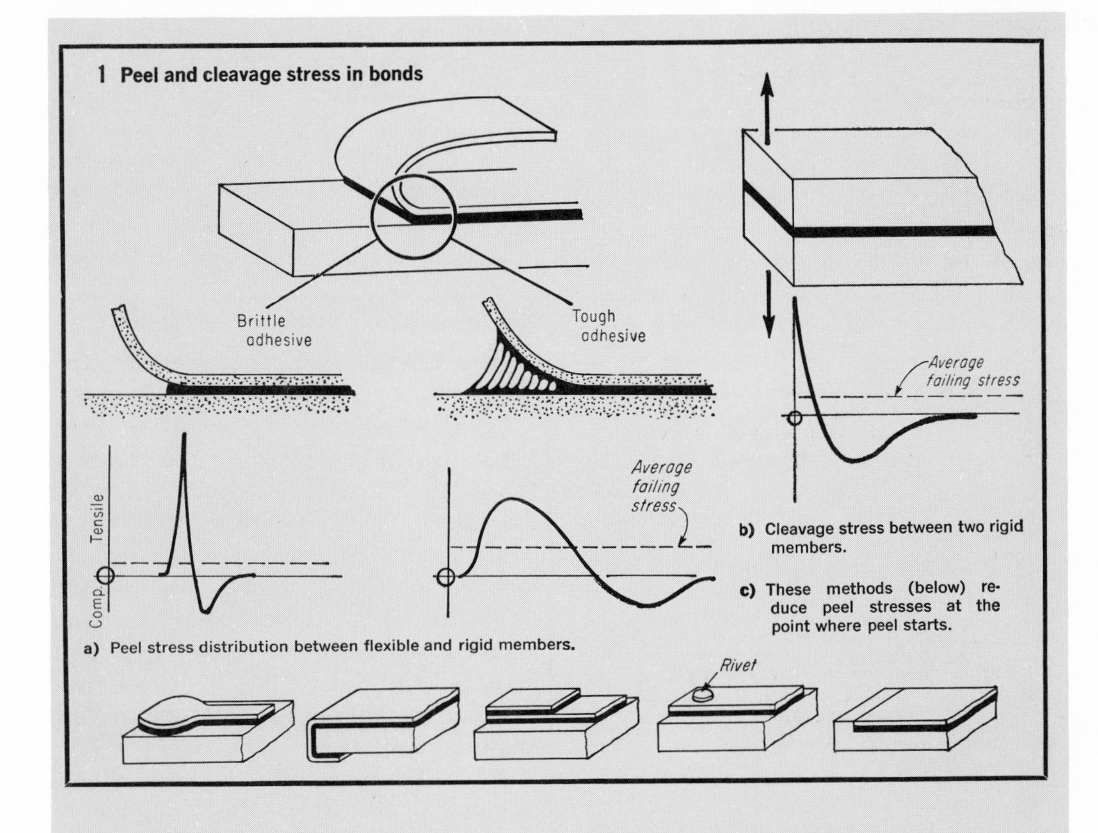

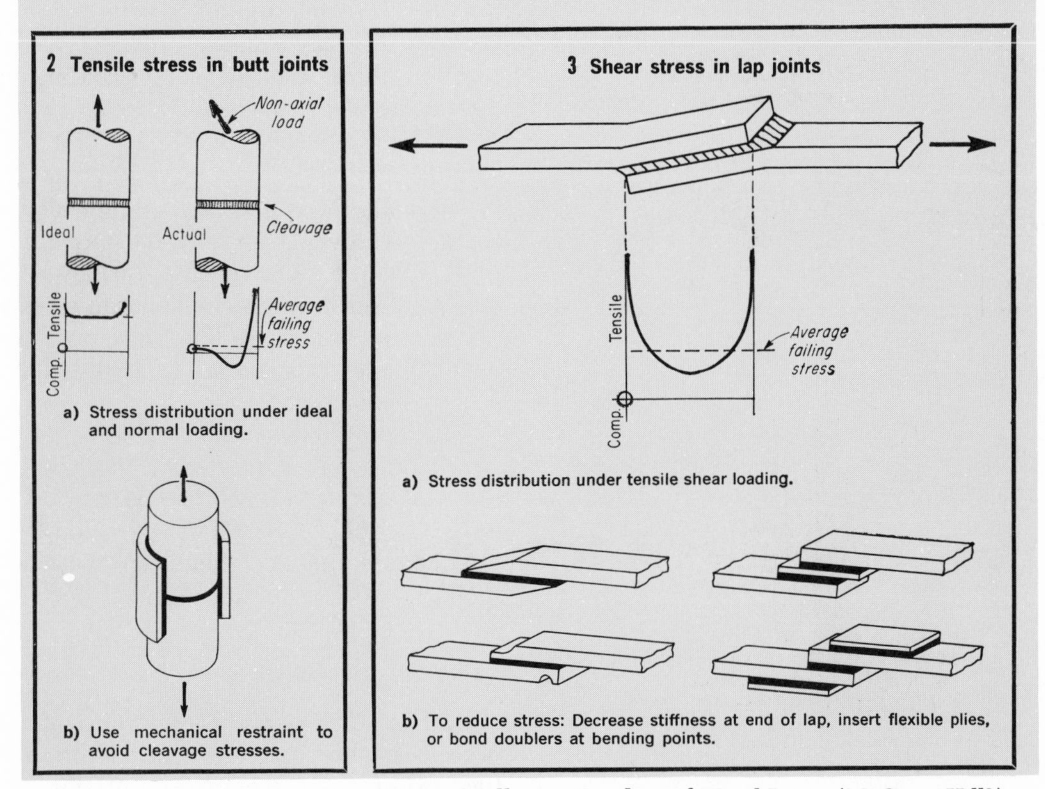

FIG. 12-2. Typical Stress Conditions of Adhesive Bonding of Metal Joints (McGraw-Hill[2])

Significance of Weld Location

Complete welding information is provided by using symbols on drawings, Fig. 12-4. Only a few symbols are needed for typical application practices. If this were done universally, everyone would be speaking the same technical language.

The use of the words *far side* and *near side* in the past has led to confusion when joints are shown in section, for all welds are an equal distance from the reader and thus "near" or "far" becomes meaningless. In the present system the *joint* is the reference point. The joint to be welded will always be identified with an "arrow side," "other side," and/or "both other sides." This information is necessary for accurate weld location in respect to the joint.

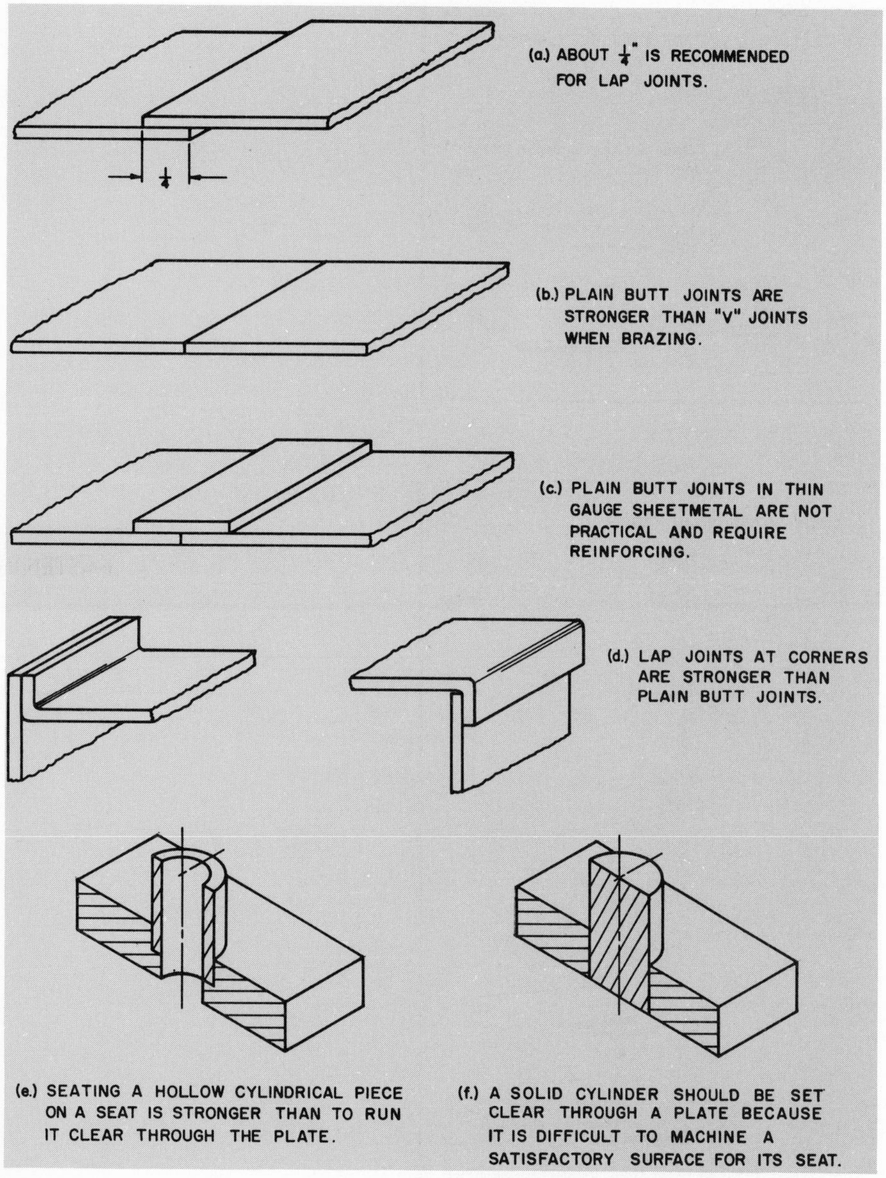

(a.) ABOUT ¼" IS RECOMMENDED FOR LAP JOINTS.

(b.) PLAIN BUTT JOINTS ARE STRONGER THAN "V" JOINTS WHEN BRAZING.

(c.) PLAIN BUTT JOINTS IN THIN GAUGE SHEETMETAL ARE NOT PRACTICAL AND REQUIRE REINFORCING.

(d.) LAP JOINTS AT CORNERS ARE STRONGER THAN PLAIN BUTT JOINTS.

(e.) SEATING A HOLLOW CYLINDRICAL PIECE ON A SEAT IS STRONGER THAN TO RUN IT CLEAR THROUGH THE PLATE.

(f.) A SOLID CYLINDER SHOULD BE SET CLEAR THROUGH A PLATE BECAUSE IT IS DIFFICULT TO MACHINE A SATISFACTORY SURFACE FOR ITS SEAT.

Fig. 12-3. Suggested Joint Design Practice for Soldering and Brazing

Location of Elements of a Welding Symbol

The *tail* of a symbol is used for designating the welding specifications, procedures, or other supplementary information to be used in the making of the weld. If a welder knows the size and type of weld, he has only part of the information necessary for making the weld. He must also know other pertinent data such as the type of process to be used, filler metal identification, or if peening or root-chipping is required. The notation indicating these data is established as required and recorded in the tail of the symbol. If notations are not used, the tail of the symbol may be omitted.[3]

Fig. 12-4 shows Standard Welding symbols as recommended by the American Welding Society. Illustrations in the tables, TD-12-4 through TD-12-10 show types of welding in pictorial form together with welding symbol application to orthographic views.

Definitions

Studying the standard welding symbols of Fig. 12-4 reveals that numerous terms are used. Most of these refer to various joints and may be seen in the technical data section. The definitions which follow are for common welding processes and are arranged alphabetically by major types.

The term *coalescence* frequently means "combining into one body." In a technical sense, it has to do with the melting of the so-called parent metal of each part and the intermingling of the two metals in a molten state such that during solidification the parts become one.

Arc Welding

In Fig. 12-5 is shown a group of welding processes wherein coalescence is produced by the heat of an electric arc or arcs, with or without the use of filler metal.

[3]American Welding Society

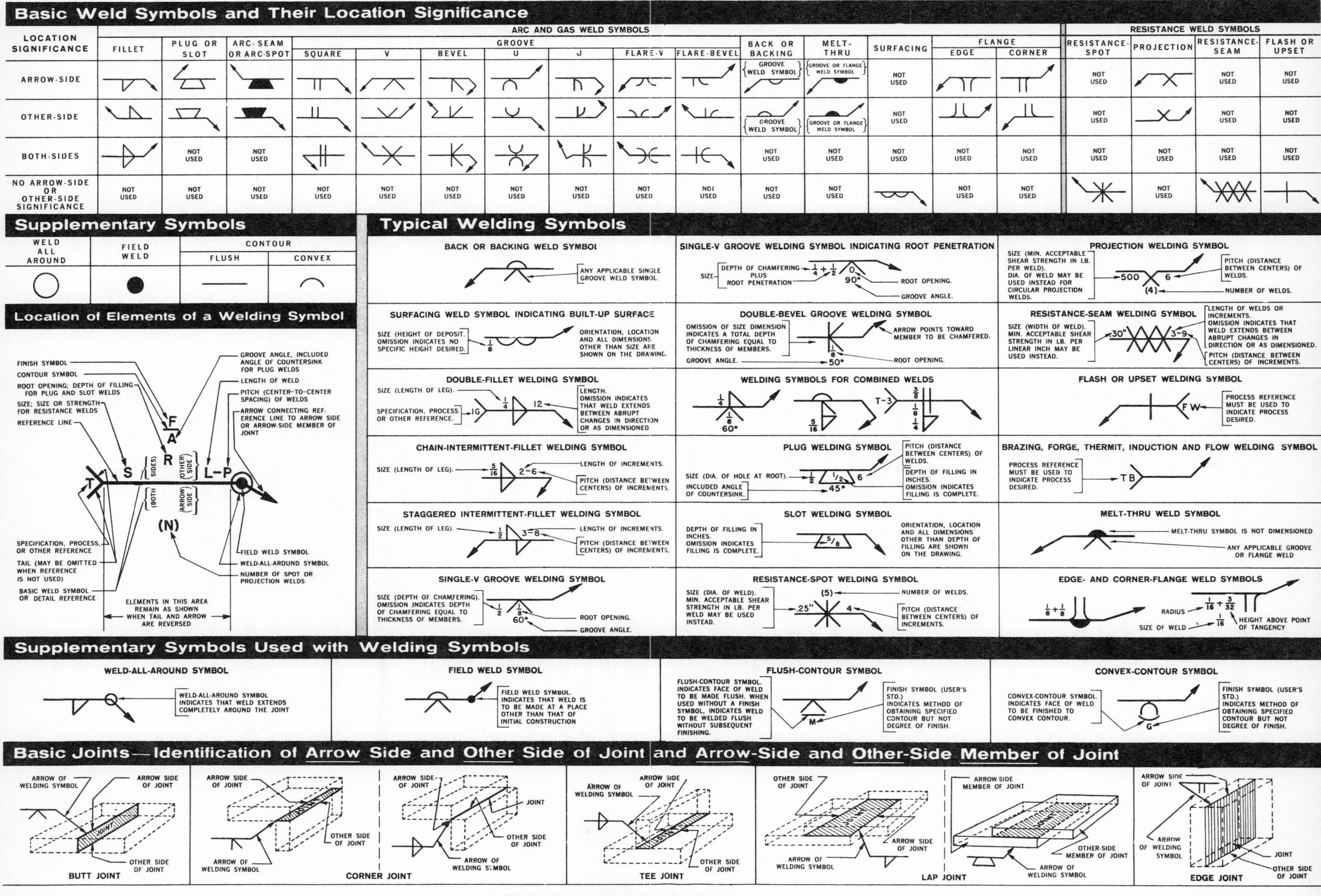

FIG. 12-4. Standard Welding Symbols (American Welding Society)

1. CARBON-ELECTRODE ARC WELDING: A group of arc welding processes which utilizes carbon electrodes.
   Carbon-Arc Welding: Coalescence is produced by the heat from an electric arc formed between a carbon electrode and the work parts. No shielding is used. Either pressure and/or filler metal may or may not be used.
   Inert-Gas Carbon-Arc Welding: A type of carbon-arc welding in which shielding is obtained from an inert gas such as helium or argon. Either pressure and/or filler metal may or may not be used.
   Shielded Carbon-Arc Welding: A type of carbon-arc welding in which shielding is obtained from the combustion of a solid material fed into the arc, or from a blanket of flux, or both.
   Twin Carbon-Arc Welding: A type of carbon-arc welding in which coalescence is produced by the heat from an electric arc maintained by two carbon electrodes rather than one. No shielding is needed. Pressure is not used, and filler metal may or may not be used.

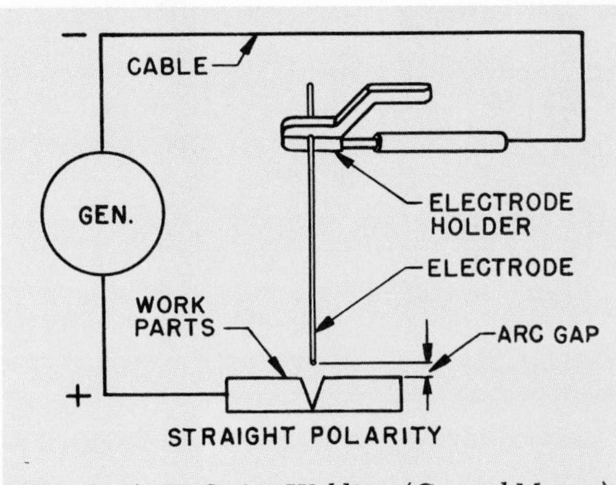

FIG. 12-5. D. C. Arc Welding (General Motors)

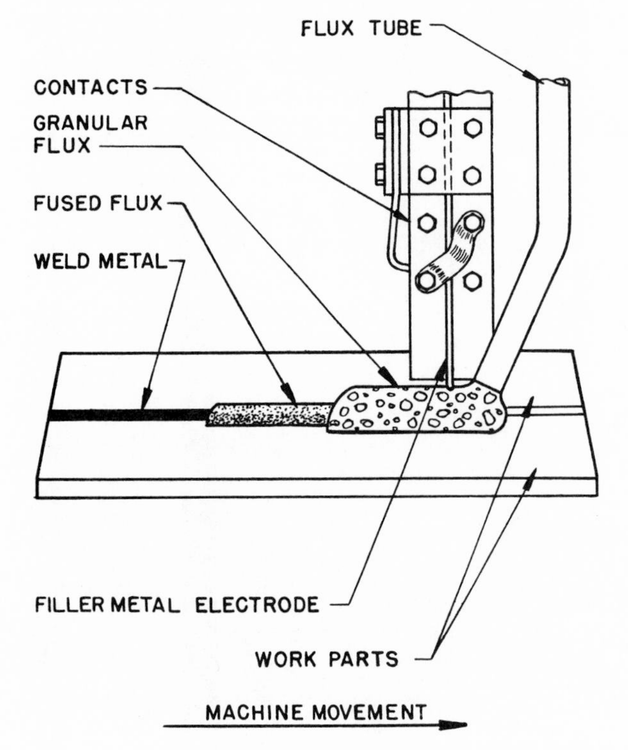

FIG. 12-6. Submerged-Arc Welding (General Motors)

2. METALLIC-ARC WELDING: A group of arc welding processes which utilizes metal electrodes.
   Atomic Hydrogen-Arc Welding: Coalescence is produced by the heat from an electric arc maintained between two metal electrodes in an atmosphere of hydrogen. Shielding is obtained from the hydrogen. Either pressure and/or filler metal may or may not be used.
   Bare Metal-Arc Welding: A type of metallic-arc welding in which the metal electrode is lightly lime-coated or bare. No shielding is used. Pressure is not used, and filler metal is obtained from the electrode.
   Inert Gas-Arc Welding: A type of metallic-arc welding in which an inert gas such as helium or argon is used for shielding. Either pressure and/or filler metal may or may not be used.
   Shielded Metal-Arc Welding: A type of metallic-arc welding in which a covered metal electrode is used. Shielding is obtained from decomposition of the electrode covering. Pressure is not used, and filler metal is obtained from the electrode.
   Stud Welding: Coalescence is produced by the heat from an electric arc or arcs formed between a metal-stud and another work part until the surfaces to be joined are properly heated and brought together under pressure. No shielding is used.
   Shielded Stud-Welding: A type of metallic stud welding in which a shield is obtained from inert gases such as helium and argon.

Submerged Arc Welding: Coalescence is produced by the heat from an electric arc or arcs formed between a bare metal electrode and the work parts. The welding is shielded by a blanket of granular, fusible material on the work. Pressure is not used, and filler metal is obtained from the electrode or from a supplementary welding rod, Fig. 12-6.

Flow Welding

Coalescence is produced by the heat from molten filler metal poured over the surfaces of the working parts until the welding temperature is attained and the required filler metal is added. The filler metal is not distributed in the joint by capillary attraction.

Forge Welding

A group of welding processes wherein coalescence is produced by heating metal pieces in a *forge furnace* and by applying pressure or *blows.*

Hammer Welding: A type of forge welding in which the blows are dealt by a hammer.
Die Welding: Pressure is applied by means of dies.
Roll Welding: Pressure is applied by means of rolls.

Gas Welding

A group of welding processes wherein coalescence is produced by heating with a *gas flame* or flames in a *gas furnace,* with or without the application of pressure and filler metal, Fig. 12-7.

Air-Acetylene Welding: A type of gas welding in which combustion of acetylene with air is obtained for the gas flame, without the use of pressure, and with or without the use of filler metal.
Oxy-acetylene Welding: A type of acetylene gas welding in which pure oxygen is used without pressure, and with or without filler metal.
Oxy-hydrogen Welding: A type of acetylene gas welding in which oxygen and hydrogen are used for combustion with or without pressure, and with or without filler metal.
Pressure Gas Welding: Coalescence is produced simultaneously over the entire area of the abutting surfaces by heating with gas flames obtained from the combustion of a fuel gas with oxygen, and with the application of pressure, without the use of filler metal.

Induction Welding

A welding process wherein coalescence is produced by the heat obtained from the resistance of the work parts to the flow of induced electric current, with or without the application of pressure.

Resistance Welding

A group of welding processes wherein coalescence is produced by the heat obtained from resistance of the work parts to the flow of electric current in a circuit and by the application of pressure.

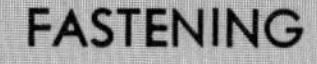

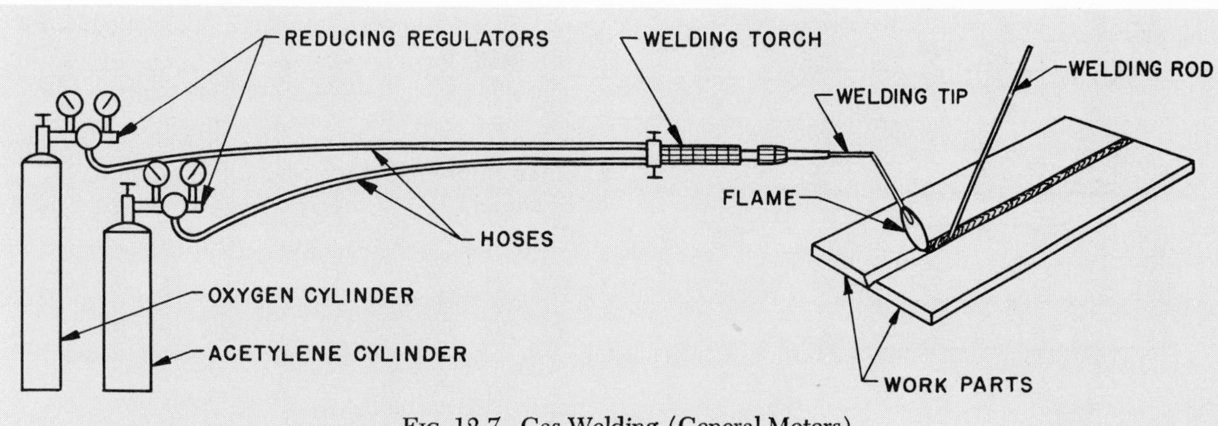

Fig. 12-7. Gas Welding (General Motors)

Flash Welding: Coalescence is produced simultaneously over the entire area of the abutting surfaces by the heat obtained from resistance to the electric current flash between the two surfaces and by the application of pressure after heating is completed. Flashing and the upsetting of the hot metal parts are accompanied by expulsion of metal from the joint, Fig. 12-8.

Projection Welding: A type of resistance welding in which the work parts are held together under pressure by electrodes. The resulting welds are localized at predetermined points by the design of the parts to be welded. The localization is usually accompanied by projections, embossments, and intersections, Fig. 12-9.

Seam Welding: A type of resistance welding in which the work parts are held together under pressure by circular electrodes. The resulting union is a series of overlapping spot welds made progressively along a joint by rotating the electrodes, Fig. 12-10.

Spot Welding: A type of resistance welding in which the work parts are held together under pressure by electrodes, and the size and shape of the individually formed welds are limited primarily by the size and contour of the electrodes, Fig. 12-11.

Upset Welding: Coalescence is produced simultaneously over the entire area of the abutting surfaces or progressively along a joint by the heat obtained from resistance to the flow of electric current through the area of contact on the surfaces. Pressure is applied before heating is started and is maintained throughout the heating period, Fig. 12-12.

Thermit Welding

A group of welding processes wherein coalescence is produced by heating with superheated liquid metal and slag resulting from a chemical reaction between a metal oxide and aluminum, with or without the application of pressure. Filler metal, when used, is obtained from the liquid metal.

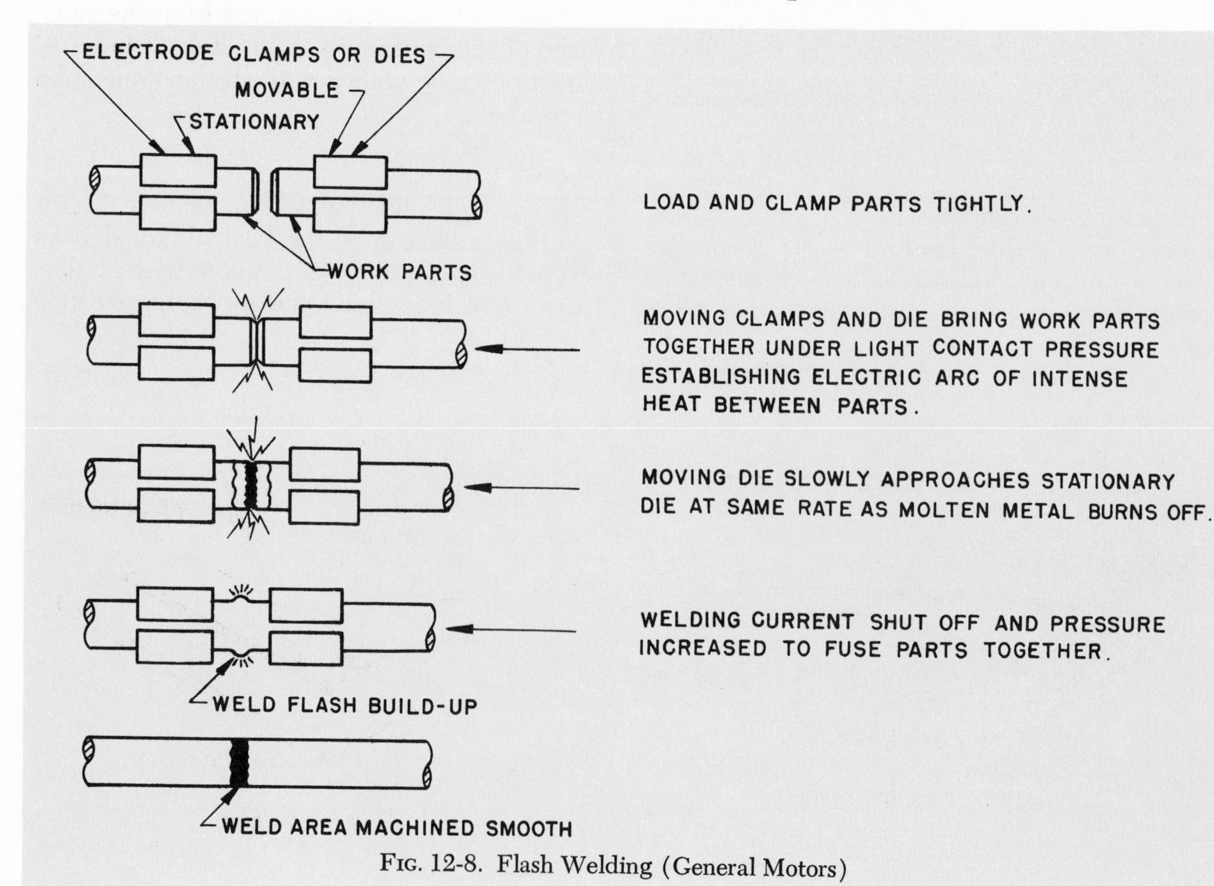

FIG. 12-8. Flash Welding (General Motors)

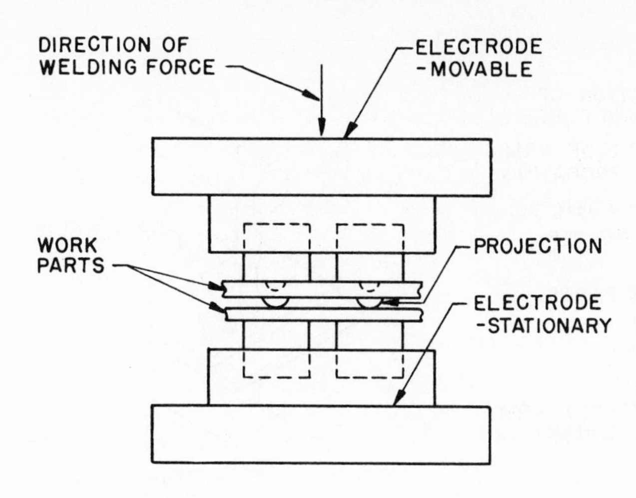

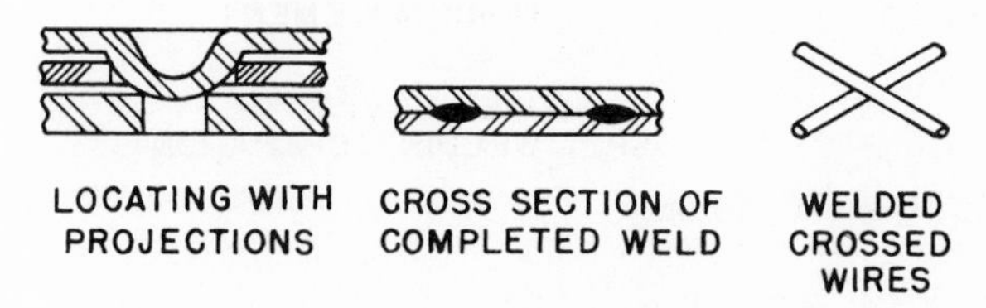

FIG. 12-9. Projection Welding (General Motors)

Non-Pressure Thermit Welding: Thermit welding without the application of pressure. Filler metal is obtained from the liquid metal.

Pressure Welding: Any welding process or method wherein pressure is used to complete the weld.

Example Symbols

Fig. 12-13 shows typical arc and gas welding symbols. Fig. 12-14 shows application of typical resistance welding symbols.

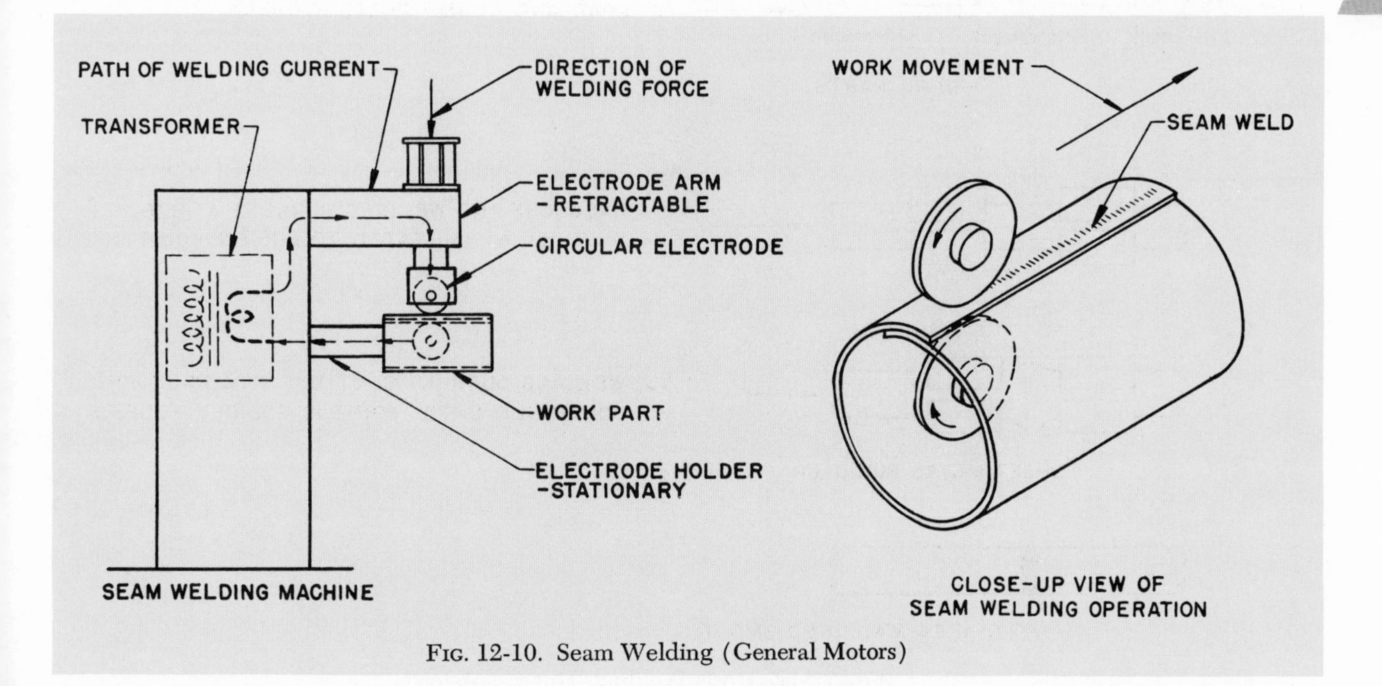

FIG. 12-10. Seam Welding (General Motors)

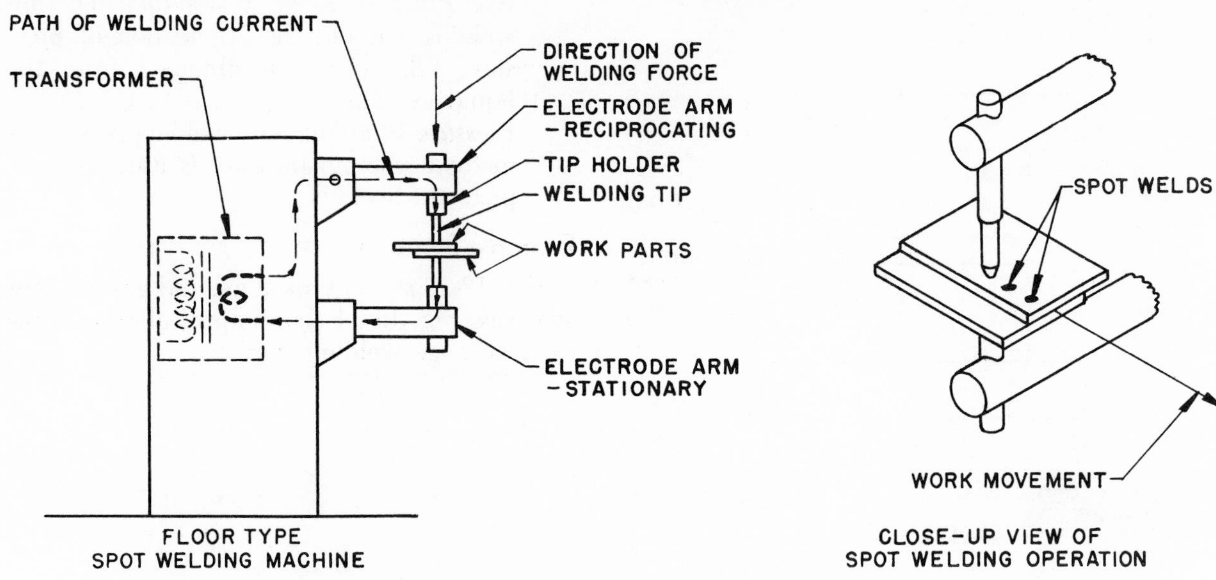

FIG. 12-11. Spot Welding (General Motors)

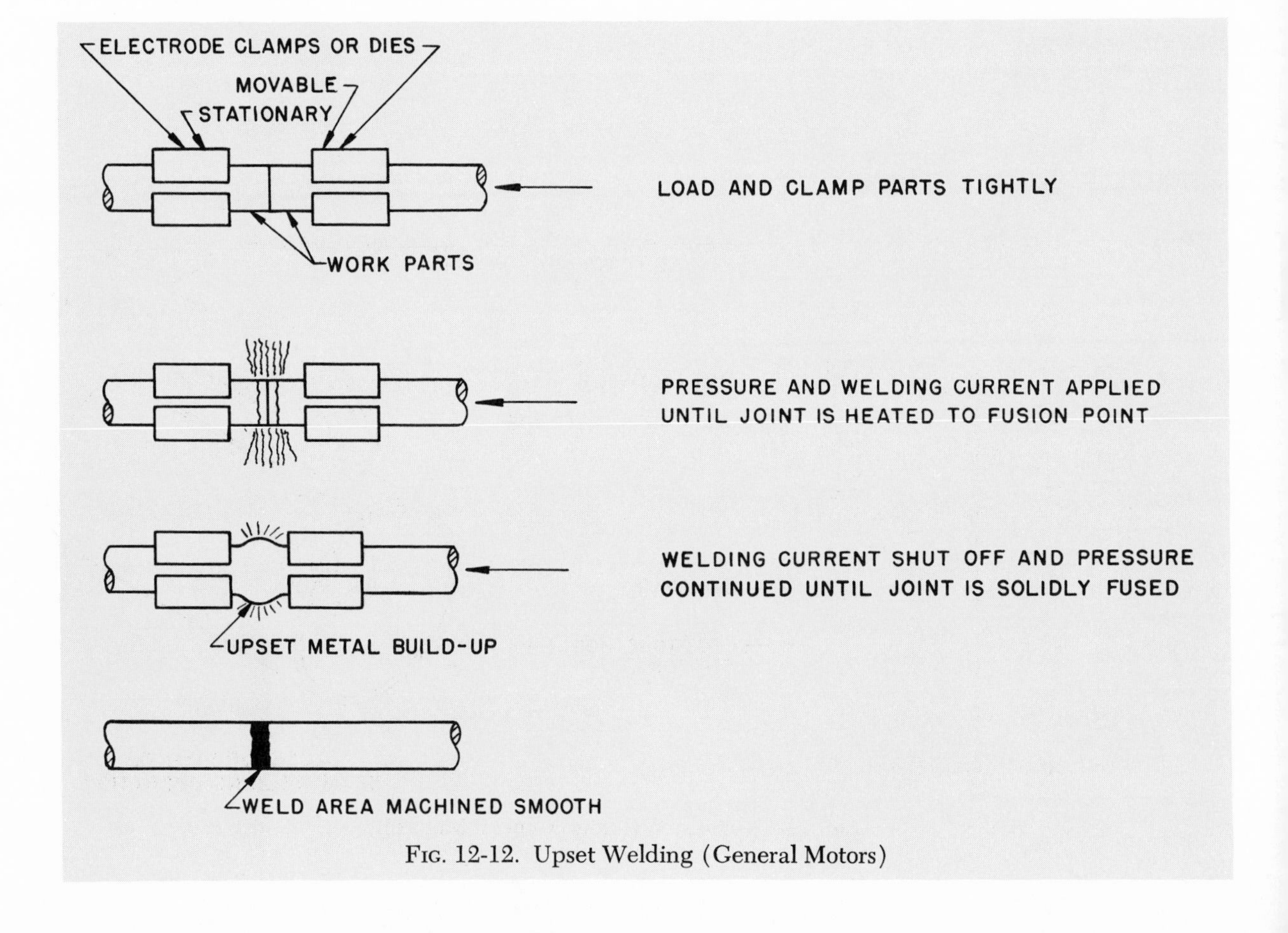

FIG. 12-12. Upset Welding (General Motors)

CONTINUOUS FILLET WELD ARROW SIDE

CONTINUOUS FILLET WELD OTHER SIDE

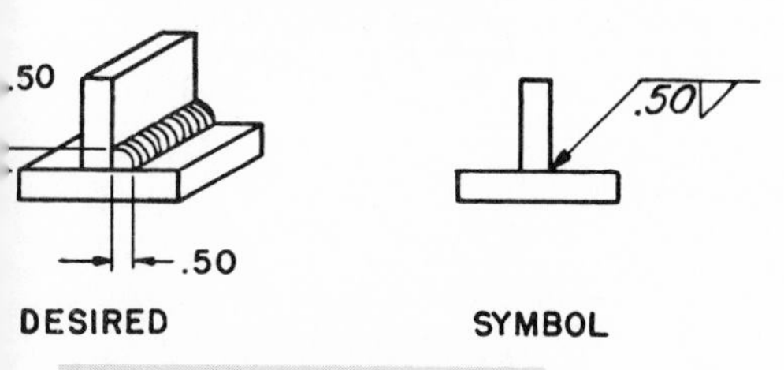

SIZE OF SINGLE FILLET WELD ARROW SIDE

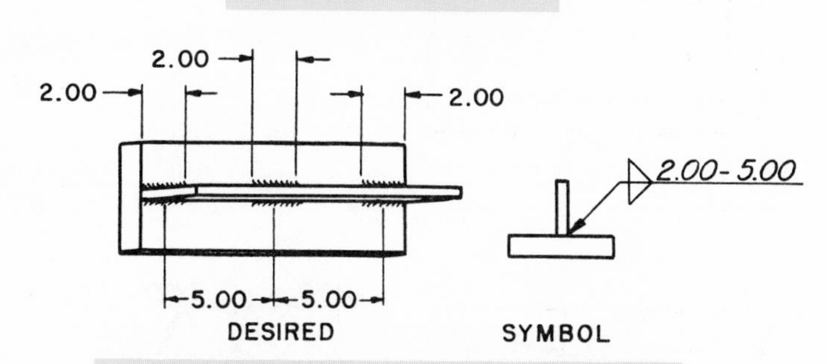

LENGTH AND PITCH OF INCREMENTS OF CHAIN INTERMITTENT FILLET WELDING — BOTH SIDES

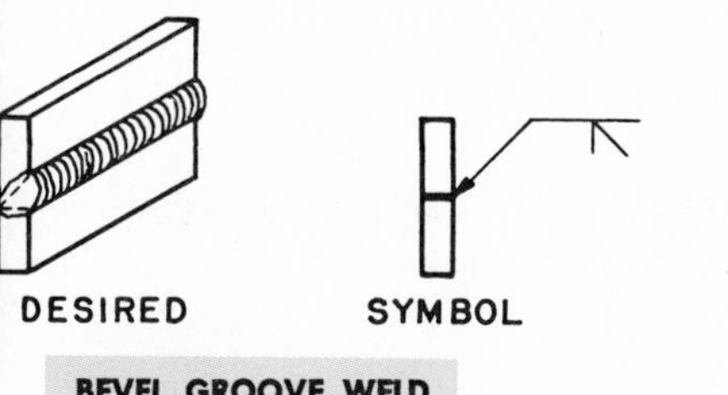

BEVEL GROOVE WELD ARROW SIDE

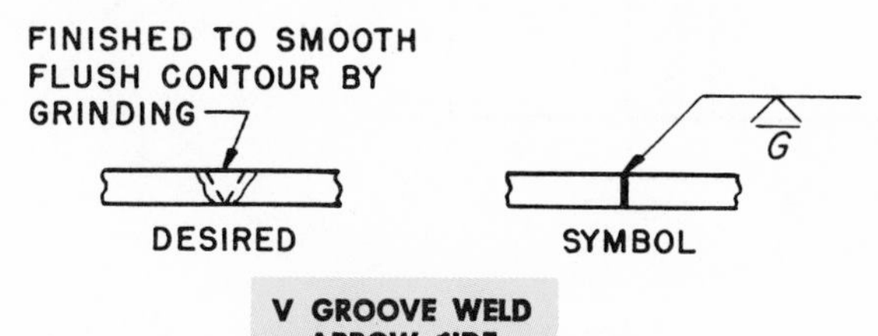

V GROOVE WELD ARROW SIDE

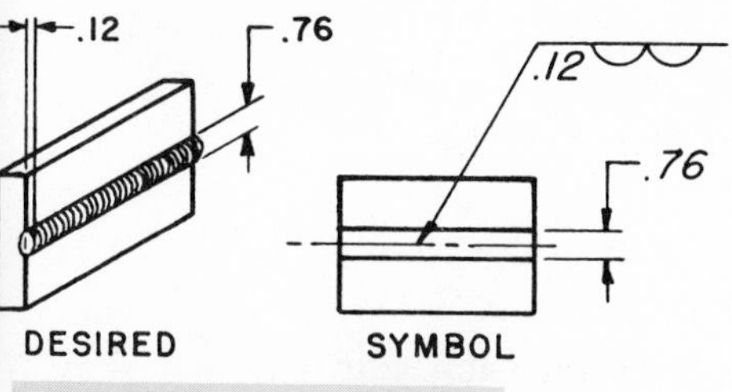
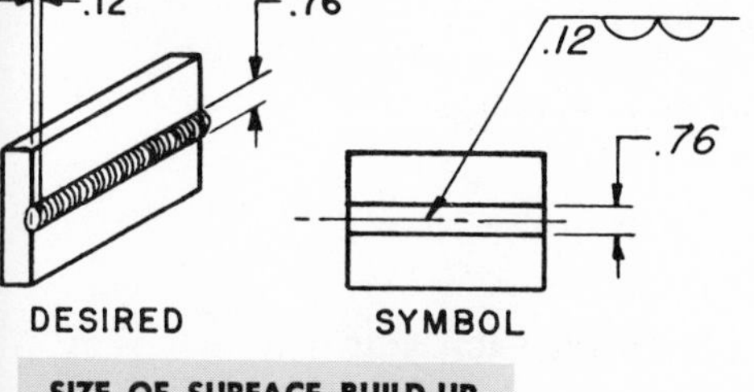

SIZE OF SURFACE BUILD-UP BY WELDING — ARROW SIDE

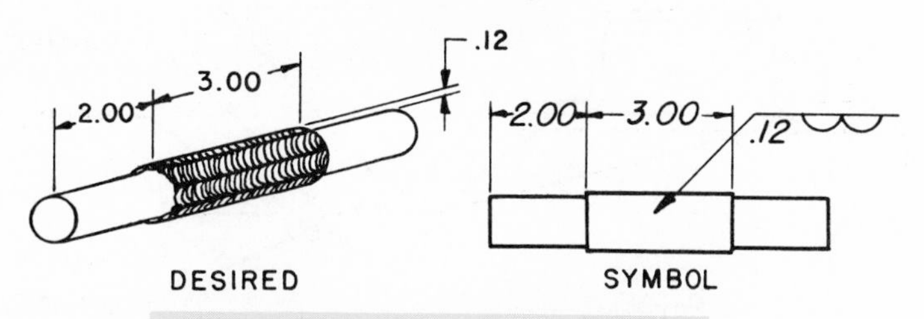

SIZE OF SURFACE BUILD-UP BY WELDING

.50 .30

.30 .50

DESIRED SYMBOL

SIZE OR DEPTH OF FILLING PLUG WELD

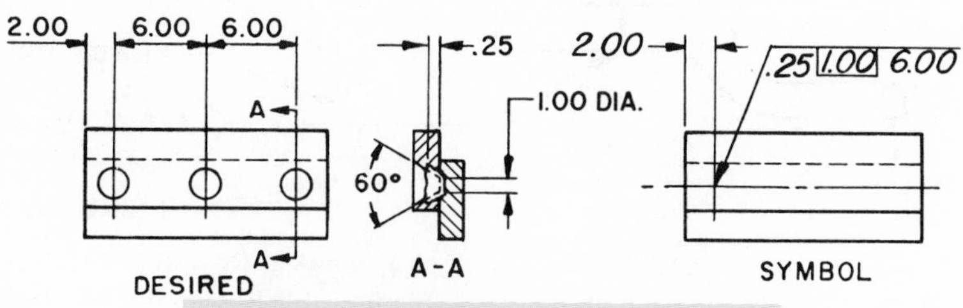

SIZE, DEPTH AND PITCH OF INCREMENTS OF CHAIN INTERMITTENT PLUG WELDING

FIG. 12-13. Typical Examples of Standard Welding Symbols for Arc and Gas Welded Joints (General Motors)

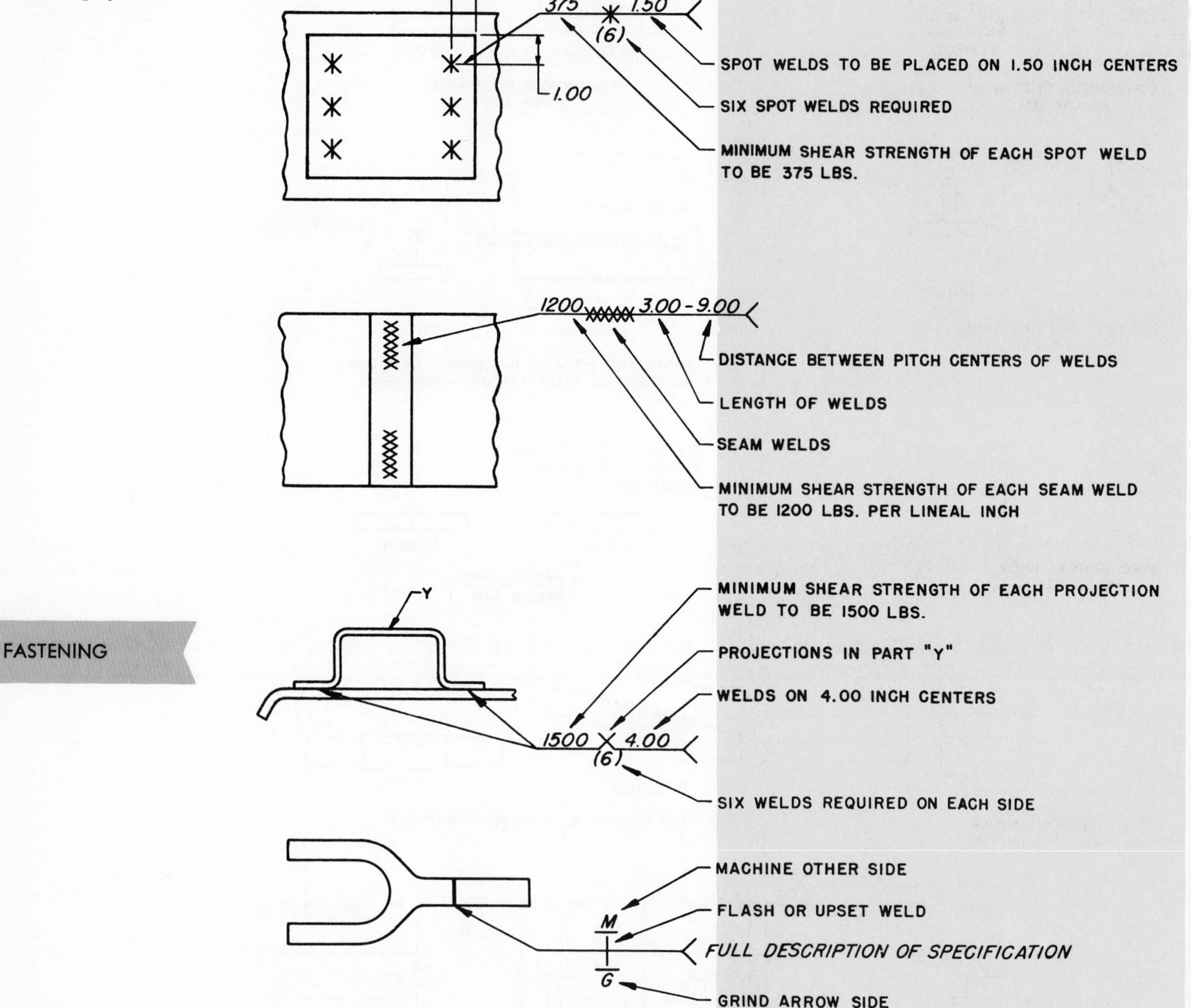

FIG. 12-14. Typical Examples of Standard Welding Symbols for Resistance Welded Joints (General Motors)

Screw Threads

The screw is one of the five simple machines. (The others are the lever, the wheel and axle, the inclined plane, and the pulley.) Screws are widely used throughout industry to transmit power, to hold parts together, and to adjust parts with relation to each other. A great deal of effort has been made over the years to standardize screw threads. The effort first came within the various countries and is now extended to the development of standards allowing international interchangeability of threaded parts. In this country we now use American Standard Threads which are called "American National Thread Forms" and whenever possible the Unified Standard Thread Forms that have been developed by the United States, Great Britain, and Canada, Fig. 12-15. Unified and American National are essentially the same thread form in this country.

Definitions[4]

Screws are either mated with a preformed internal thread or may form their own thread. They are tightened by applying torque at the head.

Screw Thread: A screw thread is a ridge, usually of uniform section, produced by forming a helical groove on the external or internal surface of a cylinder or in the form of a conical spiral on the external or internal surface of a cone or frustum of a cone. A screw thread formed on a cylinder is known as a *straight or parallel* thread to distinguish it from a *taper* screw thread which is formed on a cone or frustum of a cone, Fig. 12-16.

Thread: A thread is the portion of a screw thread encompassed by one pitch. On a single-start thread it is equal to one turn.

Single-Start Thread: The lead is equal to the pitch.

Multiple-Start Thread: The lead is an integral multiple of the pitch.

External Thread: An external thread is on a cylindrical or conical external surface.

Internal Thread: An internal thread is on a cylindrical or conical internal surface.

[4]USAS B1.7-1965

Right-Hand Thread: When viewed axially, it winds in a clockwise and receding direction. A thread is considered right-hand unless specifically indicated otherwise.

Left-Hand Thread: When viewed axially, it winds in a counterclockwise and receding direction. All left-hand threads are designated *LH*.

Thread Series: Thread series are groups of diameter-pitch combinations distinguished from each other by the number of threads per inch applied to specific diameters.

Crest: The crest is that surface of the thread which joins the flanks of the thread and is farthest from the cylinder or cone from which the thread projects.

Root: The root is that surface of the thread which joins the flanks of adjacent thread forms

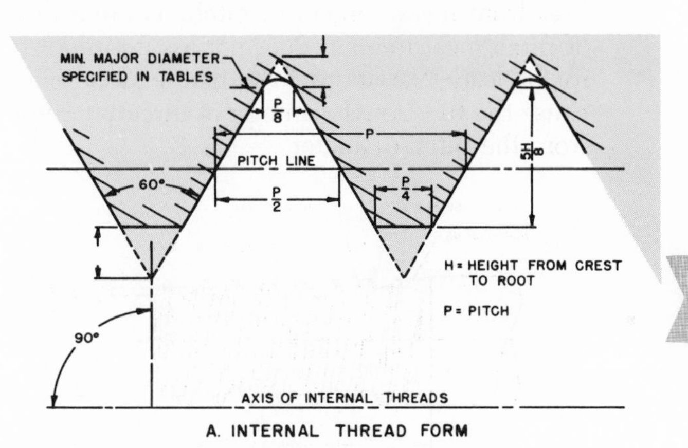

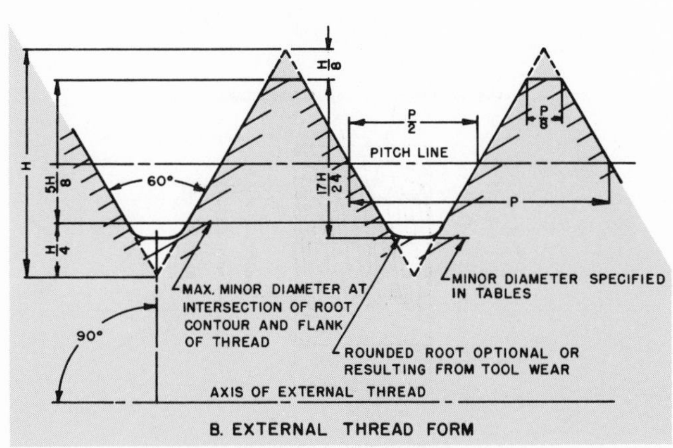

FIG. 12-15. Unified Thread Forms – Internal and External (USAS B1.1-1960)

and is identical with or immediately adjacent to the cylinder or cone from which the thread projects.

Base: The base of a thread section is that which coincides with the cylindrical or conical surface from which the thread projects.

Pitch: The pitch of a thread having uniform spacing is the distance, measured parallel to its axis, between corresponding points on adjacent thread forms in the same axial plane and on the same side of the axis. The basic pitch is equal to the lead divided by the number of thread starts.

Lead: When a threaded part is rotated about its axis with respect to a fixed mating thread, the lead is the axial distance moved by the part in relation to the amount of angular rotation. The basic lead is commonly specified as the distance to be moved in one complete rotation. It is necessary to distinguish measurement of lead from measurement of pitch, as uniformity of pitch measurement does not assure uniformity of lead. Variations in either lead or pitch cause the functional diameter of thread to differ from the pitch diameter.

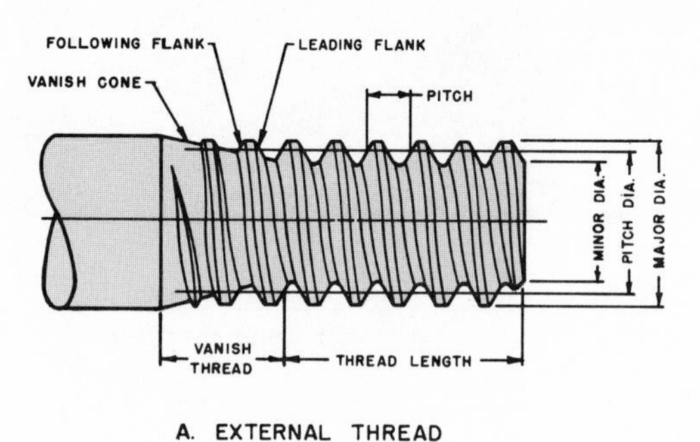

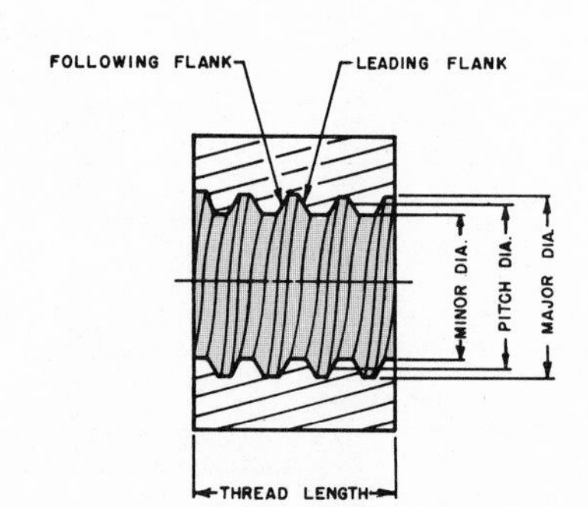

Fig. 12-16. Basic Terminology of External and Internal Threads (USAS B1.7-1965)

Threads per Inch: The number of threads per inch is the reciprocal of the pitch in inches.

Turns per Inch: The number of turns per inch is the reciprocal of the lead in inches.

Height of Thread: The height (or depth) of thread is the distance, measured radially between the major and minor cylinders or cones, respectively.

Major Diameter: On a straight thread the major diameter is that of the major cylinder. On a taper thread the major diameter at a given position on the thread axis is that of the major cone at that position, Fig. 12-16.

Minor Diameter: On a straight thread the minor diameter is that of the minor cylinder. On a taper thread the minor diameter at a given position on the thread axis is that of the minor cone at that position.

Pitch Diameter: On a straight thread the pitch diameter is the diameter of the pitch cylinder. On a taper thread, the pitch diameter at a given position on the thread axis is the diameter of the pitch cone at that position. On a single-start thread of perfect form and lead, it is also the length between intercepts of a line perpendicular to the thread axis and intersecting the thread flanks on opposite sides of the thread axis.

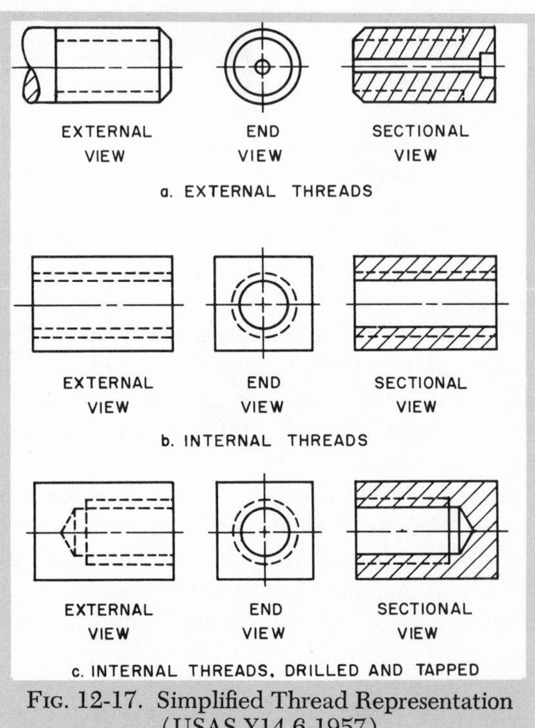

Fig. 12-17. Simplified Thread Representation (USAS Y14.6-1957)

Thread Representation

Thread forms are helical, that is, they are generated by a point moving uniformly around and up or down the surface of a cylinder or cone. To use a true projection of each helix on mechanical drawings would be very time consuming. Three systems of representation may be used depending on which best conveys the desired information to the reader and which is most efficient to draw.

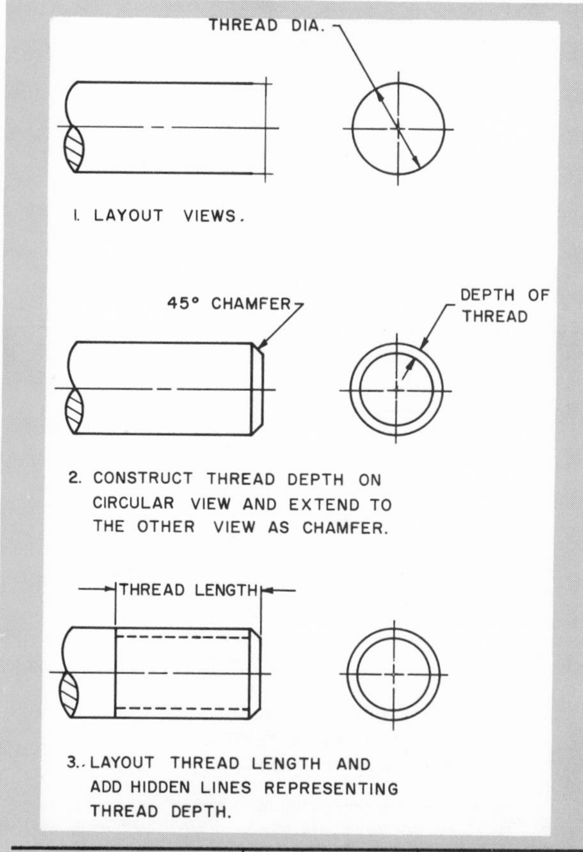

	Shaft	Hole
Nominal Size	5/8	5/8
Basic Size	——	.625
Design Size	.022	.625
Tolerance	±.002	+.003 −.000
Limits	.624 .620	.628 .625
Allowance	—.001	

FIG. 12-18. Construction of External Threads Using Simplified Representation

SIMPLIFIED REPRESENTATION: This method is the easiest to construct and the most efficient. It is the recommended method for showing screw threads on drawings and is the most commonly used by industry. The obvious disadvantage is that it looks the least realistic of the three methods. It should always be used for hidden internal threads. If there is any confusion on a drawing due to the use of simplified representation, one of the other methods should be chosen, Fig. 12-17.

SIMPLIFIED THREAD DRAFTING: The steps for drawing simplified threads are shown in Figs. 12-18 and 12-19. No attempt is made to show actual pitch nor actual thread depth.

Table 12-2 gives the recommended approximations of size, shown both in decimals and fractions. These approximations need not be measured if you can judge the distances. They are for full-size drawings. When scaling, layout the view to the appropriate scale. Then use the actual drawn size of the major diameter to

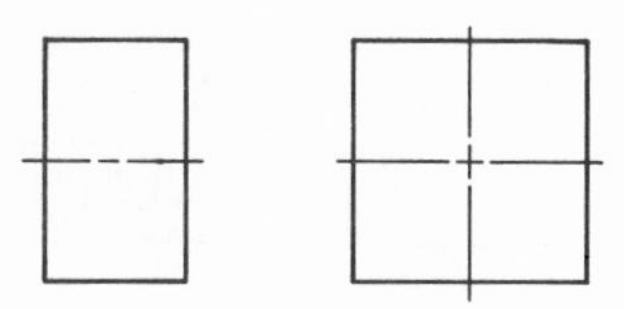

1. LAYOUT VIEWS.

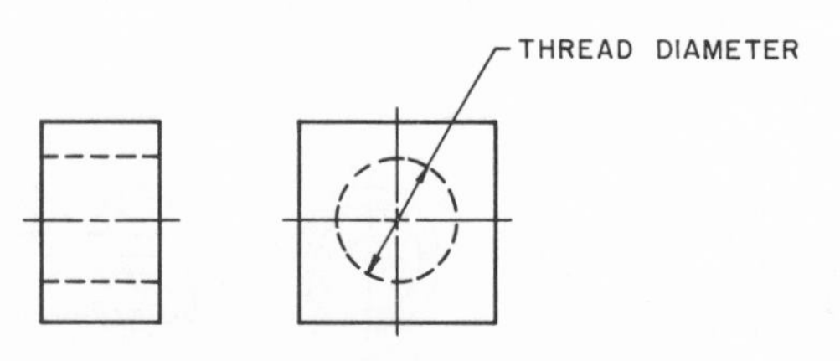

2. LOCATE THREAD DIAMETER IN CIRCLE VIEW AND TRANSFER TO THE OTHER VIEW.

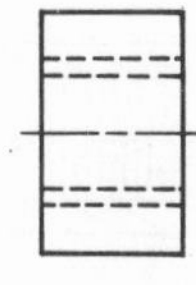
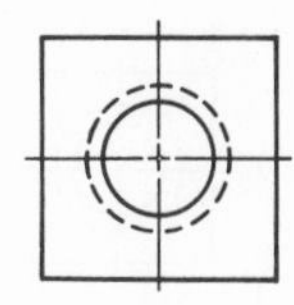

3. LOCATE THE ROOT DIAMETER IN THE CIRCLE VIEW AND TRANSFER TO COMPLETE THE CONSTRUCTION.

FIG. 12-19. Construction of Internal Threads Using Simplified Representation

enter the table. Notice that for simplified representation you will need only to enter the table.

For external threads you will need to know thread length. For internal threads going all the way through an object, the thread length is the thickness of the object. Drilled and tapped holes require thread length and the depth of the drilled hole. In actual practice, the draftsman simply notes this depth by making it extend about two and a half schematic thread pitches beyond the thread length.

Chamfers are drawn at 45° to the thread depth.

SCHEMATIC REPRESENTATION: This method, Fig. 12-20, uses two sets of lines running perpendicular to the axis of the part. The root lines are shorter and darker than the crest lines. This convention is symbolic and is easier to draw than the detailed method and is nearly as easy to read. It should not be used on hidden internal threads nor on external threads in section.

TABLE 12-2

Recommended Approximations for Pitch and Thread Depth in Drawing Simplified and Schematic Thread Symbols

Major Diameter	Pitch Approximation	Thread Depth Approximation
.19 and under ($\frac{3}{16}$)	.04 ($\frac{3}{64}$)	.02 (scant $\frac{1}{32}$)
.20 - .38 ($\frac{3}{16}$-$\frac{3}{8}$)	.06 ($\frac{1}{16}$)	.03 ($\frac{1}{32}$)
.39 - .63 ($\frac{3}{8}$-$\frac{5}{8}$)	.12 ($\frac{1}{8}$)	.06 ($\frac{1}{16}$)
.64 - .88 ($\frac{5}{8}$-$\frac{7}{8}$)	.18 ($\frac{3}{16}$)	.09 ($\frac{3}{32}$)
.89-1.00 ($\frac{7}{8}$-1)	.24 ($\frac{1}{4}$)	.12 ($\frac{1}{8}$)
1 Inch and Over	$\frac{1}{\text{No. of Threads per Inch}}$	$\frac{\text{Pitch}}{2}$

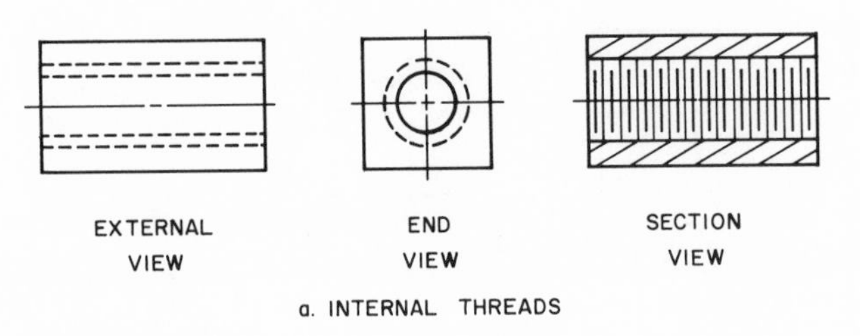

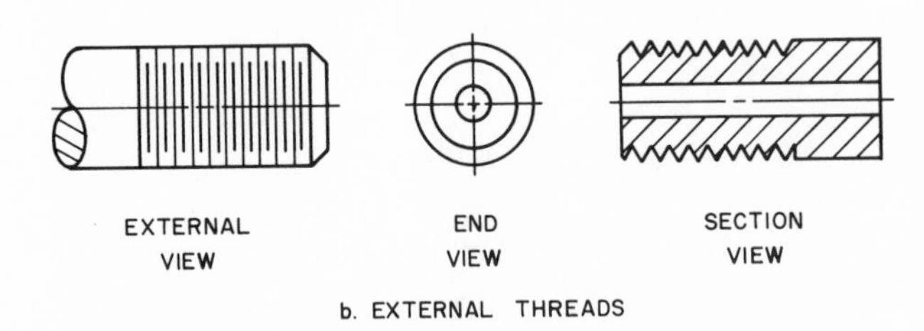

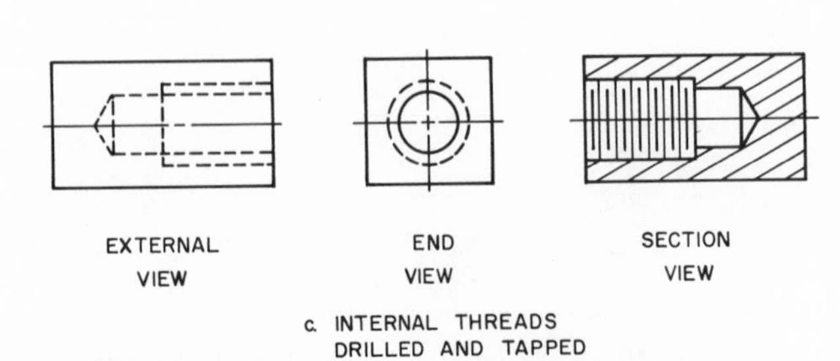

Fig. 12-20. Schematic Thread Representation

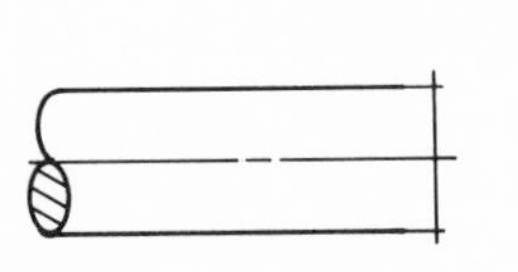
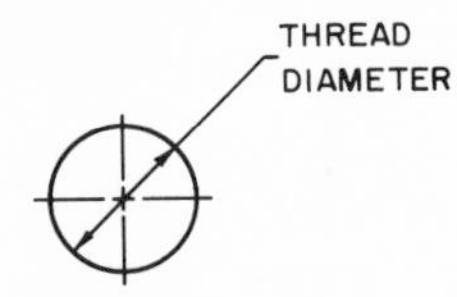

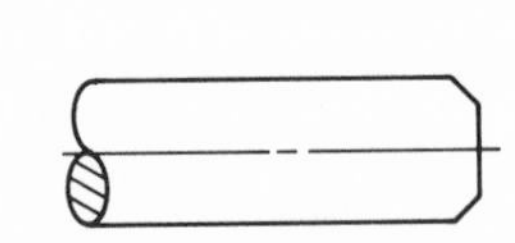
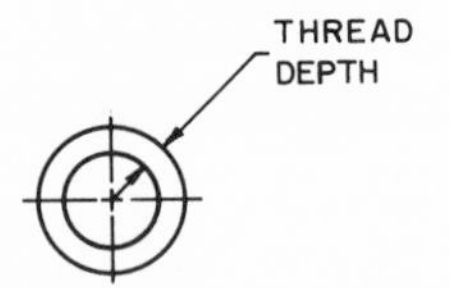

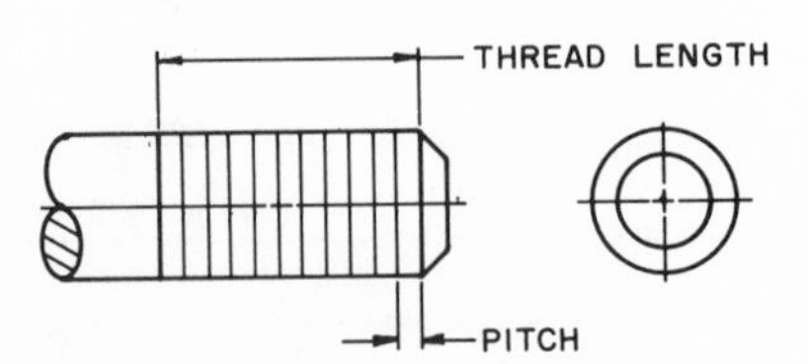

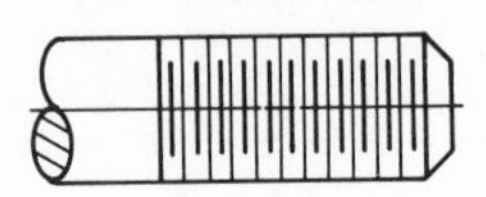

Fig. 12-21. Construction of Threads Using Schematic Rrepresentation

SCHEMATIC THREAD DRAFTING: Steps for drawing schematic threads are shown in Fig. 12-21. Enter Table 12-2 for the approximate thread depth and for the approximate pitch. The procedure for the sectional view of both internal threads and drilled and tapped holes is essentially the same as that for external simplified threads. Note that internal threads in schematic representation are just as they are in simplified representation and are drawn using that procedure.

DETAILED REPRESENTATION, Fig. 12-22, is a close approximation of the helical construction in that helixes are converted into straight lines and the crest and roots are simply shown as sharp *V's*. This method of representation is used wherever a less realistic method might tend to confuse the reader. Of the three methods of representation presented, it is the most difficult and time consuming to construct.

DETAILED THREAD DRAFTING: Steps for drawing detailed threads are shown in Fig. 12-23. The same symbol is used whether a sharp *V* is being shown or the standard flattened or rounded form. Pitch may be taken from Table TD-12-11 or may be calculated by $\frac{1}{\text{threads per inch}}$.

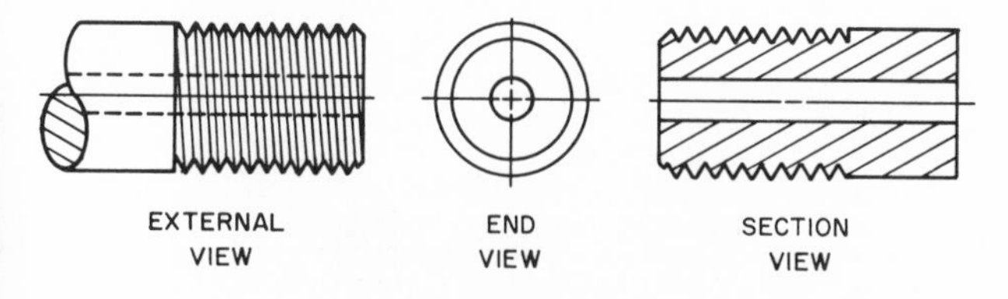

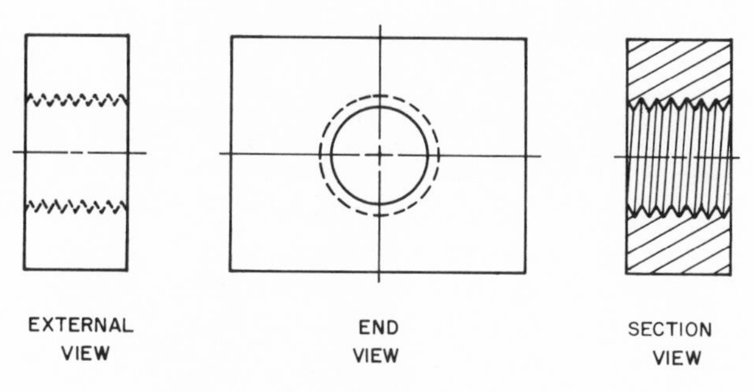

FIG. 12-22. Detailed Thread Representation

Right-hand external threads slope upward and to the left. For left-hand threads, layout the first half-pitch on the bottom of the cylin-

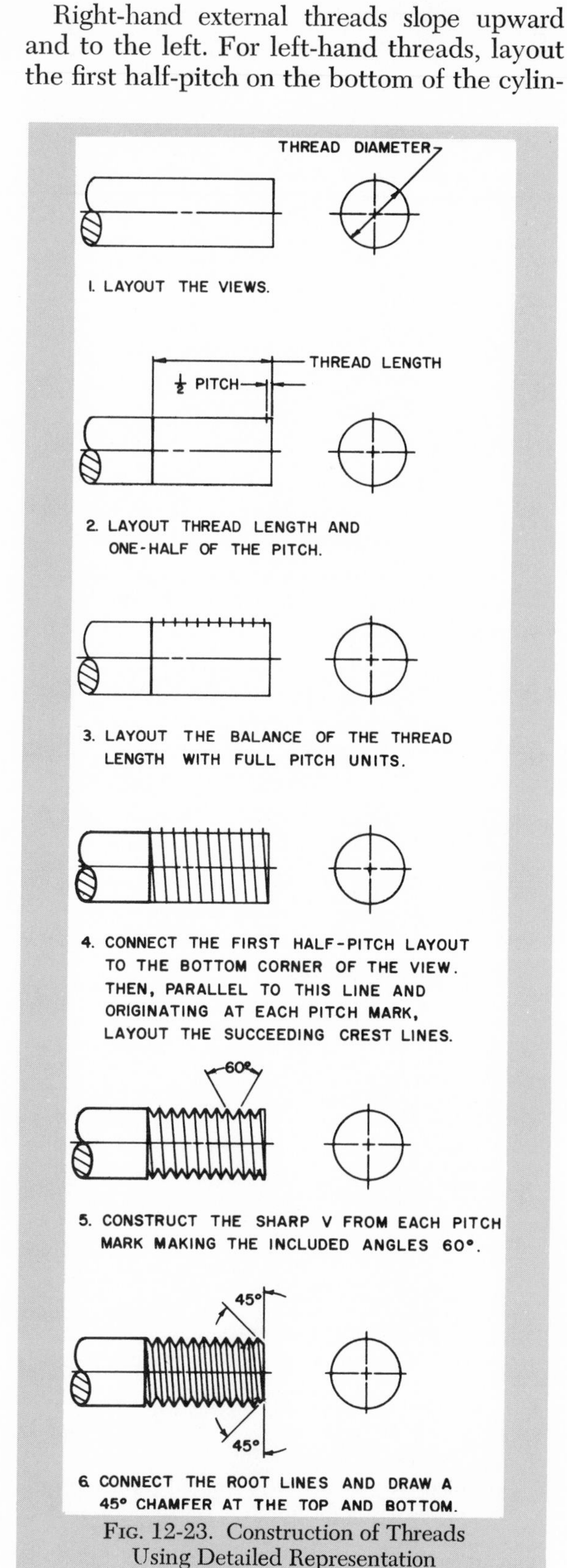

FIG. 12-23. Construction of Threads Using Detailed Representation

drical view rather than at the top as Step 2. For double threads, the crest lines are drawn from every second pitch unit. Multiple threads are laid out in multiple units of pitch marks.

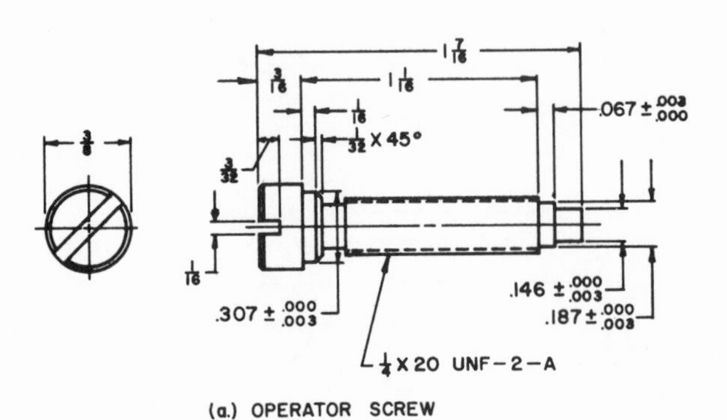

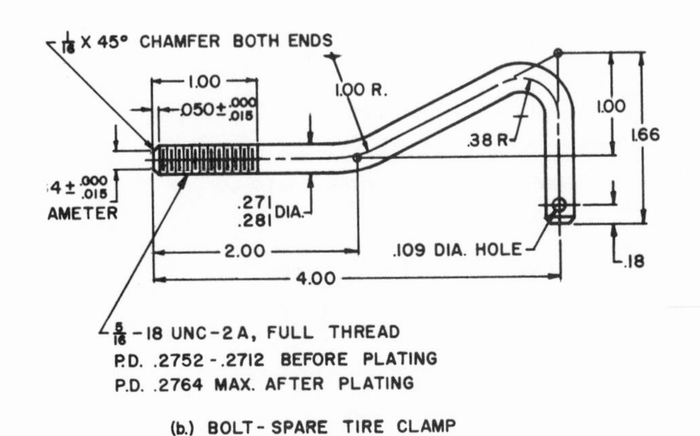

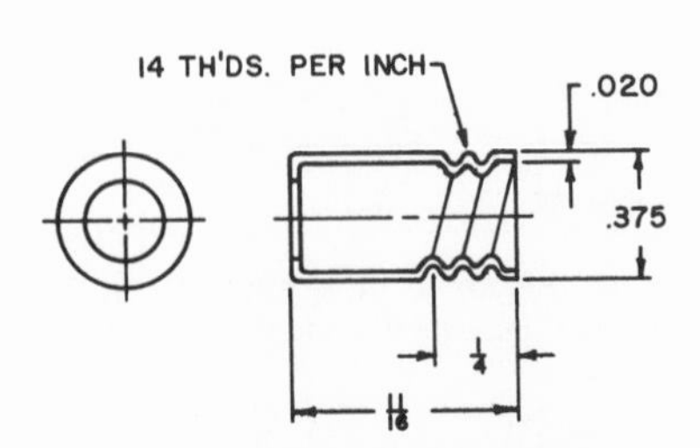

FIG. 12-24. Location of External Thread Notes for Dimensions

A. Simplified representation (Titus Mfg. Corp.)
B. Schematic representation (General Motors of Canada, Ltd.)
C. Detailed representation — rolled threads on a socket for flashlight bulb.

[5]SAE

Note in Fig. 12-22 that internal threads slope in an opposite manner to external threads. For internal threads drawn in an external view, omit the crest and root lines.

Dimensioning Threads

In addition to the usual size and shape description, threads on a drawing are dimensioned with a note. For external threads the leader for the note is directed to the profile view whether using simplified, schematic, or detailed representation, Fig. 12-24.

For internal and tapped threads the leader is directed toward the circle view, Fig. 12-25.

Thread Series[5]

Straight screw thread series are groups of diameter-pitch combinations which conform to the Unified Standard. Such threads are identified by the UN symbol and have the form and tolerances of the unified formulation.

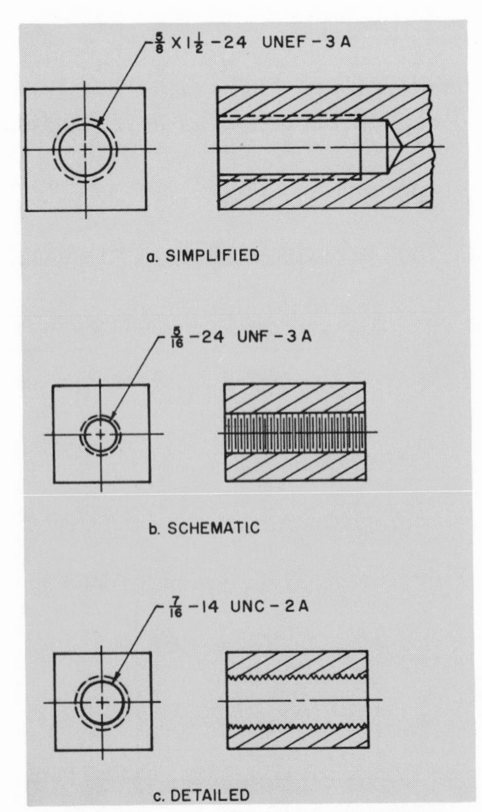

FIG. 12-25. Location of Internal Thread Notes for Dimensions

A. Simplified representation
B. Schematic representation
C. Detailed representation

COARSE THREADS: The coarse thread series, *Unified, National Coarse,* (UNC) is one of the graded pitch series, Fig. 12-26. It is used for the bulk production of screws, bolts, and nuts used in general applications and for the greater quantity of threaded parts produced by industry. Features of coarse threads are as follows:

1. Corrosion is less damaging to coarse threads because of their comparatively larger thread form for a given diameter. This is an important factor in equipment, machinery, and structures subject to constant outdoor exposure.
2. Coarse threads are less difficult to handle since they are less sensitive to damage from slight nicks, particularly in the larger sizes.
3. Coarse threads maintain stripping strength where studs or bolts are used in tapped holes in materials such as cast iron, copper alloy, and aluminum; or where both bolts and nuts are made of soft materials.

FINE THREADS: The fine thread series, UNF, is another of the graded pitch series, Fig. 12-27. It is extensively used for bolts and nuts in the automotive and aircraft industries with the higher strength materials. Features of fine threads are as follows:

1. The fine thread, having a lesser lead angle, exhibits less tendency to loosen under vibration than the coarse thread. The smaller lead angle also gives more tension for the same applied torque.
2. External threads of this series have greater tensile stress area than comparable sizes of the coarse series. The fine series is suitable where the resistance to stripping of both external and mating internal threads equals or exceeds the tensile, load carrying capacity of the externally threader member. It is also used where the length of engagement is short; where a smaller lead angle is desired; or where the wall thickness demands a fine pitch. It may also be used for threading into lower strength materials where maximum strength of the external thread is not required; otherwise the length of engagement must be selected to meet the above required strength conditions.

EXTRA-FINE THREADS: The extra-fine thread series, UNEF, is another of the graded pitch series. It is used for threaded parts which require a fine adjustment such as bearing, retaining nuts, adjusting screws, etc., and for thin walled tubing and thin nuts where the maximum number of threads is desired.

UNIFORM (CONSTANT) PITCH THREADS: When selecting threads from the uniform pitch series, UN, preference should be given, wherever possible, to the *8*, *12* and *16* series. Some uses of the various pitches are:

1. The 8 thread series above 1″ is used extensively in the utility industries for high temperature bolting in steam flange connections or as a substitute for the coarse thread series.

FASTENING

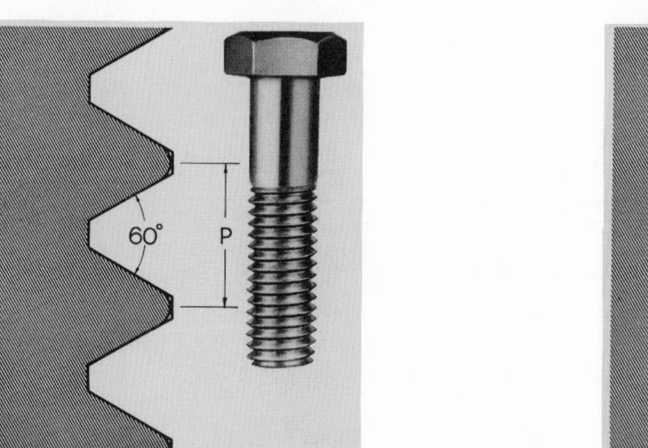

Fig. 12-26. Unified National Coarse (UNC) Thread (The H. M. Harper Co.)

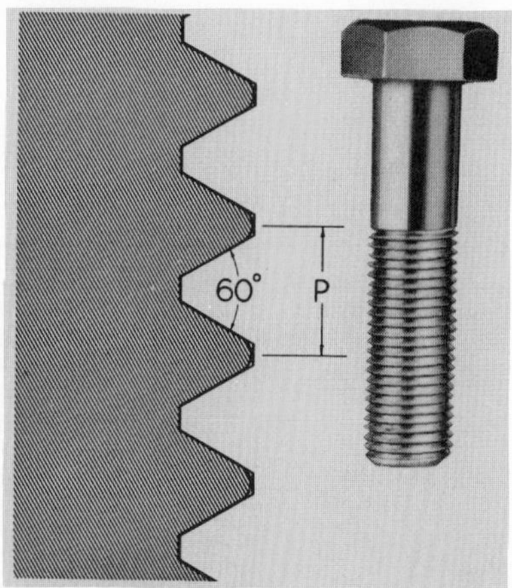

Fig. 12-27. Unified National Fine (UNF) Thread (The H. M. Harper Co.)

2. The *12* thread series is used in machine construction for thin nuts on shafts and sleeves. It also allows the specification of shoulder diameters in steps of ⅛″, which is desirable from the standpoint of good design and simplification of practice. Twelve threads per inch is the coarsest pitch in general use that will permit a threaded collar to be screwed onto a threaded shoulder and slip over the shaft, the difference in diameter between shoulder and shaft being ⅛″. It is also used as a continuation of the fine series for diameters larger than 1½″.
3. The *16* thread series is used for adjusting collars and retaining nuts, and also serves as a continuation of the extra-fine series for diameters larger than 1¹¹⁄₁₆″.
4. The *20, 28,* and *32* thread series are used for adjusting nuts, screws, and collars where a fine thread is desired.
5. The *4* and *6* thread series are used for heavy machine and structural applications.

Thread Classes

Straight screw thread classes are groups of tolerances and allowances (if applicable) which conform to the Unified Standards. Thread classes in the Unified Standard are identified by a numeral followed by the letters *A* for external threads, and *B* for internal threads. There are three classes of external threads (*1A, 2A,* and *3A*), and three classes of internal threads (*1B, 2B,* and *3B*) having slightly more tolerance than those of the same class of numeral external thread.

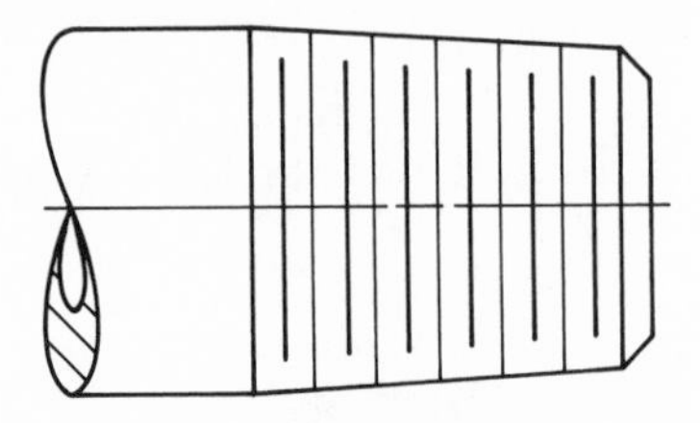

a. EXTERNAL SCHEMATIC

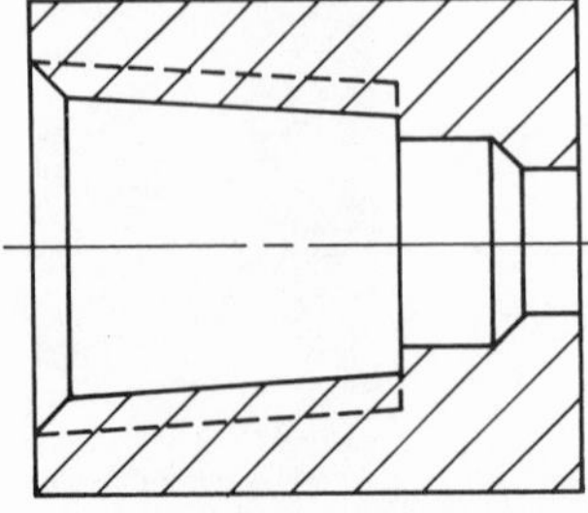

b. INTERNAL SIMPLIFIED

Fig. 12-28. Pipe Threads Shown on a Drawing Using Either Simplified or Schematic Representation

Pipe Threads

Pipe is commonly made of iron, steel, brass, copper, lead, and their alloys. It is specified by its nominal inside diameter. Interestingly enough, a given nominal inside diameter means that the outside diameter is constant for different wall thicknesses and that the inside diameters will vary. Large pipe, *12*″ in diameter and over is specified by its outside diameter and is called an *OD pipe.*

The *regular pipe thread form* is the standard for the plumbing trade. Regular pipe threads have truncated crest and root forms so that a sealer is required to prevent leakage through threaded pipe joints. See Table TD-12-12.

The *dryseal pipe thread form* is the standard for automotive, refrigeration, hydraulic tube, and pipe fittings and the like. Dryseal threads do not have clearance at the crest and root lines and therefore do not require a sealer for leakproof assemblies.

Representation of Pipe Threads on Drawings

Pipe threads are shown on the drawing just as they are for regular American Standard screw threads – by detailed, schematic, or simplified forms (Fig. 12-28). The taper is always designated as part of the thread designation so it is shown only when it is desirable to emphasize the taper. For both taper and straight forms of pipe threads, the 60° angle between the threads, the number of threads per inch, and the depth of the threads are the same. The only difference is that the taper thread is cut parallel to the axis of the taper. The taper on pipe threads is ¹⁄₁₆″ per inch of *diameter.* In showing the taper threads on a drawing, overemphasis is used. The taper is drawn ¹⁄₁₆″ per inch of *radius.*

Specifications

Threads are designated in sequential order by nominal size pipe diameter, number of threads per inch, thread form symbol if dry-seal, and thread series symbol.

Selected symbols for common thread series include:

NPT	NPSM
NPSC	NPSH
NPSL	NPTF
NPTR	NPSI

The letters in these symbols have the following meanings:

C — coupling
F — fuel and oil
H — hose coupling
I — intermediate
L — locknut
M — mechanical
N — American (National) Standard
P — pipe
R — railing fittings
S — straight
T — taper

Typical pipe thread specifications are:

¼ — 18 NPT
¼ — 18 NPT-LH
¼ — 18 DRYSEAL, NPTF
¼ — 18 DRYSEAL, NPSF
¼ — 18 NPS

Pipe threads are considered right-hand unless designated as left-hand (LH).

Threaded Fasteners

Miniature Screws

Miniature screws are used primarily in watches, instruments, and other miniature devices. By definition of the USA Standards Institute, they cover the diameter size range of from .0118″ to .0551″ or, in the metric system, from .30 to 1.40 millimeters. This is a downward extension from the American thread series which begins at number 0 for machine screws of .060 diameter and proceeds to larger diameters.

Miniature screws are standardized in four basic head types, Fig. 12-29 and Table TD-12-13. A chamfer of 45° extending to the minor diameter of the threads is standard. Thread length is a minimum of four diameters. Miniature screws equal to or shorter than four times their diameter have threads within two threads of the bearing surface of the head. Miniature screws are made of steel, stainless steel, bronze, brass, nickel-silver and other materials with finishes such as cadmium, nickel, chrome, gold, silver and other precious metals.

Not all standardized sizes are readily available. Miniature screws are specified by USAS size designation symbol from Table TD-12-13, nominal length in thousandths of an inch, followed by head type as follows:

30 UNM x 050 FIL HD

This specification is interpreted as follows: USAS size designation is 30 UNM; TD-12-13 shows that there are 318 threads per inch; nominal length is 050 thousandths, or about $3/64$″; and a fillister head is specified.

Cap Screws

Cap screws hold parts together by passing through an unthreaded hole in one piece and by being threaded into the second piece. They are used where accurate fits and good appearance are desired. They range upwards in size from ¼″ body diameter. Head styles include those shown in Fig. 12-30. For information on threads and dimensions for various types of cap screws see Tables TD-12-14 to TD-12-20.

Cap screw specifications include diameter, length, number of threads per inch, series designation, class of fit, type of head, and name of cap screw:

⅜ x 1¼ — 16 UNC — 2A HEX HD CAP SCR

Cap screw length is not standardized. Lengths in multiples of ¼″ or ⅛″ should be chosen whenever possible. When parts are assembled with cap screws, at least one thread should extend into the clearance hole.

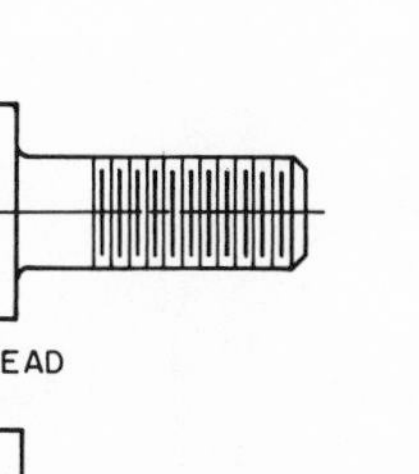

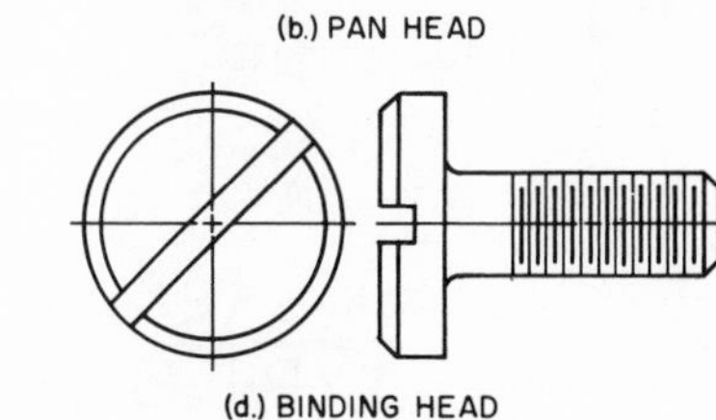

FIG. 12-29. Basic Types of American Standard Miniature Screws (USAS B18.11-1961)

Machine Screws and Nuts

Machine screws are like cap screws in that they pass through an unthreaded piece and are threaded into the second piece. They are somewhat smaller in diameter than cap screws and are used for light-duty holding jobs. Several head styles are available as shown in the tables of the TD section.

Typical machine screw specifications are:

No. 4 x ¾ – 40 UNC – 2A OVAL HEAD MACHINE SCREW

⅜ x 1 – 24 UNF – 2A SLOTTED TRUSS HEAD MACHINE SCREW

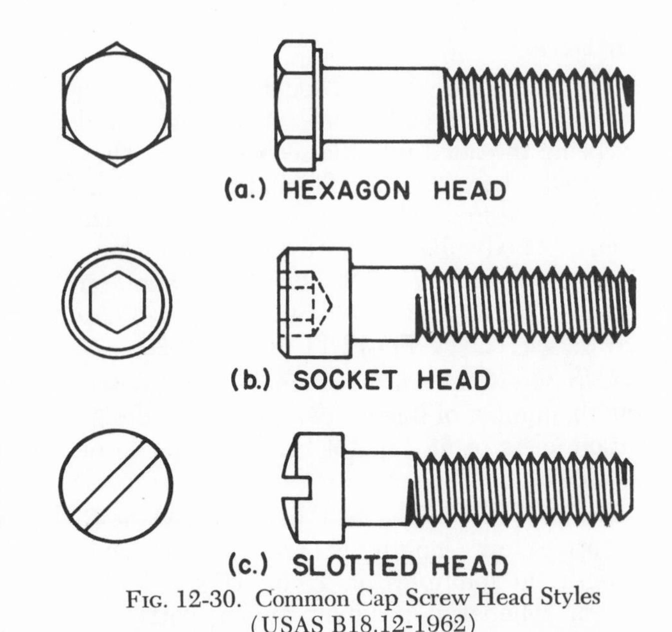

FIG. 12-30. Common Cap Screw Head Styles (USAS B18.12-1962)

USAS TYPE A

USAS TYPE B

USAS TYPE C

FIG. 12-31. Thread-Forming Tapping Screws (Harvey Hubbell Co., Inc.)

Length of machine screws is not standardized but multiples of ⅛″ or ¼″ should be chosen where possible. At least one thread of machine screws should extend into the clearance hole when assembling parts. Machine screws more than two inches long have a minimum of 1¾″ of threads.

Nuts for machine screws may be square or hexagonal. Table TD-12-25 shows the range of sizes and specifications. Typical specifications for use on a drawing are:

No. 4-40 UNC-2B HEXAGONAL MACHINE SCREW NUT

Set Screws

Set screws are designed to hold mating parts together such as a pulley on a shaft.

Slotted-headless set screws are threaded their entire length and are available in several point styles as shown in Table TD-12-26.

Square-head set screws are threaded the entire length of the body and are available in the several point sizes shown in Table TD-12-27.

Socket set screws are threaded their entire length and may be of either the hexagon-socket type or the spline-socket type. They are available in five basic point styles as shown in Table TD-12-28. Set screws may be drawn using the detailed, schematic, or simplified representation. Typical specifications are as follows:

No. 8 x ¼ – 32 UNC 3-A HEX SOCKET, CONE POINT, SET SCREW

⅝ x 1¼ – 18 UNF 3-A SQUARE HEAD, FLAT POINT, SET SCREW

Tapping Screws[6]

Tapping screws are of two basic types: *thread-forming* and *thread-cutting*. The thread-forming screws are used where large internal stresses are permissible. The thread-cutting screws are used where large internal stresses are not permissible or where excessive driving torques would be required with thread-forming screws.

Types of tapping screws may be seen in Fig. 12-31 and the TD section. Types *A*, *B*, *BP*, and *C* are thread-forming types. Type *A* is used in light sheet metal, resin impregnated plywood, asbestos compositions, and the like. They feature a gimlet point for easy starting and are the fastest driving tapping screw available.

[6]Harvey Hubbell, Inc.

Type *B* is used where the holes are easily aligned and where the flat point can enter the material easily. They are used in light and heavy sheet metal and easily deformed metals or plastics where the pilot hole can be larger than the root diameter of the screw.

Type *BP* is used in the same materials as type *B*, but because of its point it is better adapted to assemblies where holes may be slightly misaligned.

Type *C* is used where a machine screw thread is preferred over the spaced threads of types *A*, *B*, and *BP*. It may later be replaced by a machine screw. They permit assembly with standard machine screw nuts when required.

Other types in Fig. 12-32 and in the TD section are cutting screws.

Types *F*, *G*, *D* and *T* approximate machine screw threads with blunt point and tapered entering threads. They are used in aluminum, zinc, lead die castings, steel sheets and shapes, cast iron, brass, and plastics. They can be replaced by machine screws.

Types *BF*, *BG*, and *BT* have spaced threads with blunt points. They are used in plastics, die castings, metal clad and resin impregnated plywoods, asbestos, and the like. Spaced threads permit speed in assembly.

Both thread-forming and thread-cutting screws are made of the usual materials, *i.e.*, carbon steel, brass, stainless steel, aluminum, and others.

Both are available in head types shown in TD-12-33 through TD-12-40. In addition, most types of tapping screws are also available in each of the two kinds of recessed heads shown in TD-12-24. Specifications for tapping screws include number or diameter, length, number of threads per inch, type of point, type of head:

No. 8 x 3/8 — 15 TYPE A SLOTTED PAN HEAD TAPPING SCR

5/16 x 1/2 — 12 TYPE BP SLOTTED HEX WASHER TAPPING SCR

Tables in the TD section give data for purposes of specifying various tapping screws and data so if necessary, drawings can be made. For many tapping screws not included in the TD section but available in standard sizes, the reader is referred to manufacturers' catalogs and USAS B-18.6.4-1958.

Lengths are not standardized, so to find common lengths for various diameter sizes manufacturers' catalogs should be consulted. Tapping screws for some diameters are available according to the following:

Lengths from 3/16″ to 3/8″, in 1/16″ increments
Lengths from 3/8″ to 1″, in 1/8″ increments
Lengths from 1″ to 2¼″, in ¼″ increments

Wood Screws

Wood screws are manufactured in a range of sizes from ¼″ to 4″ in length, and 0 to 24 gauge in diameter. When made of steel they are bright, galvanized, blued, or plated. They are also available in aluminum, brass, bronze, cad-

FASTENING

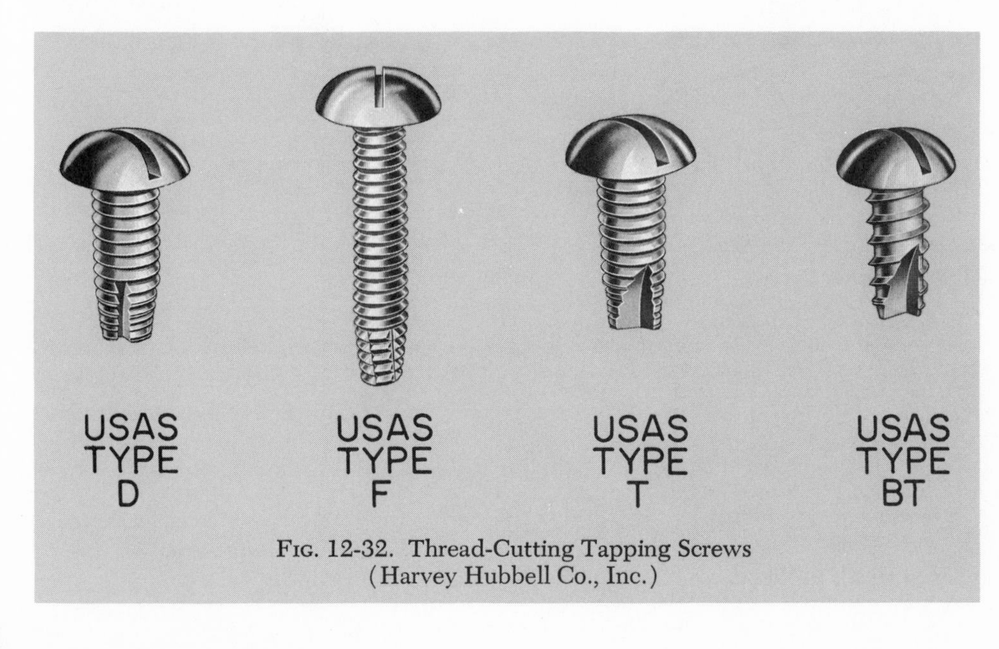

Fig. 12-32. Thread-Cutting Tapping Screws (Harvey Hubbell Co., Inc.)

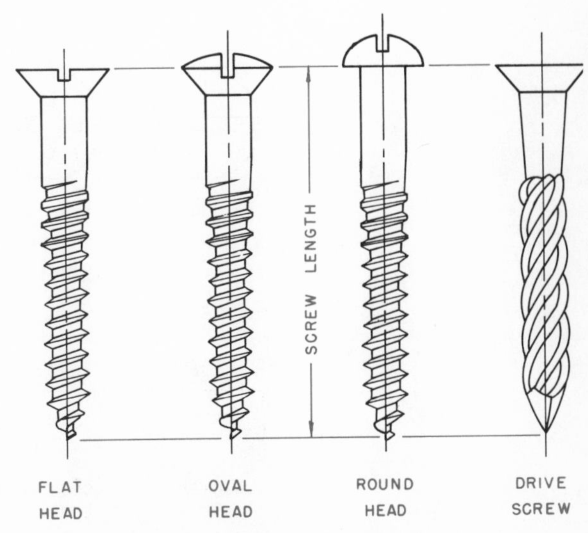

Fig. 12-33. Wood Screw Head Types

mium, and copper. They are available in four head styles, Fig. 12-33, with four basic drive types, Fig. 12-34.

To prevent splitting and to make driving easier, a shank or body hole may be drilled which is large enough for the shank of the screw. In hard woods such as maple, the shank hole should be the same size as the diameter of the shank. In soft woods such as pine, it can be about 15% smaller.

A *pilot* or *anchor* hole may be drilled in the piece into which the threaded portion of the screw is driven. The hole should be about 90% of the root diameter of the threaded portion for hard woods and about 70% for soft woods.

Flathead screws may be countersunk, counterbored, or counterbored and plugged. Oval head screws are usually countersunk. Round head screws are simply set flat against the surface, Fig. 12-35. Technical data for boring pilot and shank holes are in Table TD-12-46.

Detail drawings of common screws are not usually drawn since they are standard parts. When they are used in an assembly drawing, they are drawn as shown in Fig. 12-36.

Woodscrews are dimensioned on a drawing by a note. They are also specified in the bill of materials. Woodscrews are specified in the following sequence: length of the screw in inches, diameter of the body by gauge number, drive type, head style, head finish, material, and name as in the following examples:

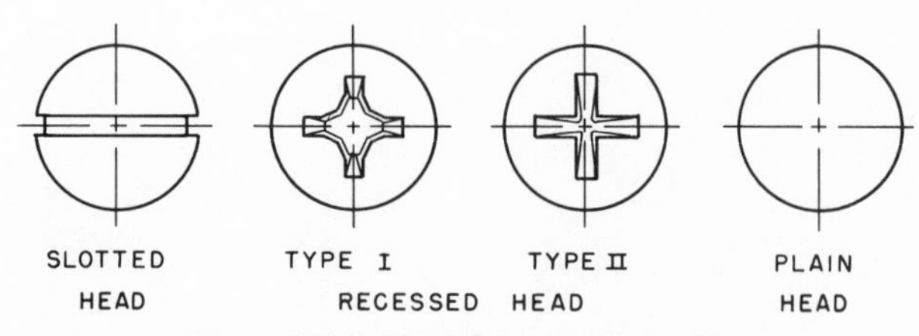

Fig. 12-34. Wood Screw Drive Types

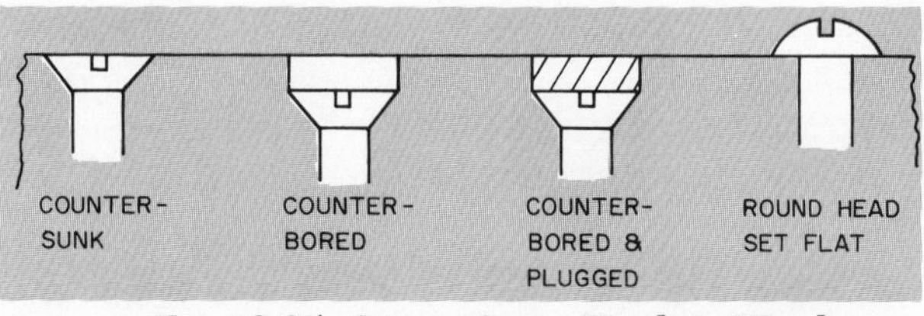

Fig. 12-35. Setting Screw Heads in Wood

1. 1¼″ – No. 8, slotted, FHB, steel, woodscrew
2. ¾″ – No. 4, Recessed, Type II, round head, brass, nickel plated, woodscrew
3. ½″ – No. 7, Plain, FH, zinc-chromate plated, steel, drive screw

In example 2, it is common to refer to the recessed head as a *Phillips head* screw.

Bolts

Bolts are inserted through unthreaded holes for assembly of parts and are tightened in place with a nut. Three basic head styles are square, hexagonal, and round. Bolts are generally unfinished except for the threaded portion.

Hexagonal bolts are regular, heavy, or structural. Common roundhead bolts are carriage, button head, and countersunk.

Thread length is measured from the end of the bolt to the last completed thread. Minimum thread length is two diameters plus ¼″ for bolts up to six inches long and two diameters plus ½″ for longer bolts.

Bolt length has not been standardized, but for those under one inch they are usually available in ⅛″ increments; those from one inch to five inches are available in ¼″ increments. Manufacturers' catalogs should be consulted for larger sizes and for special order information.

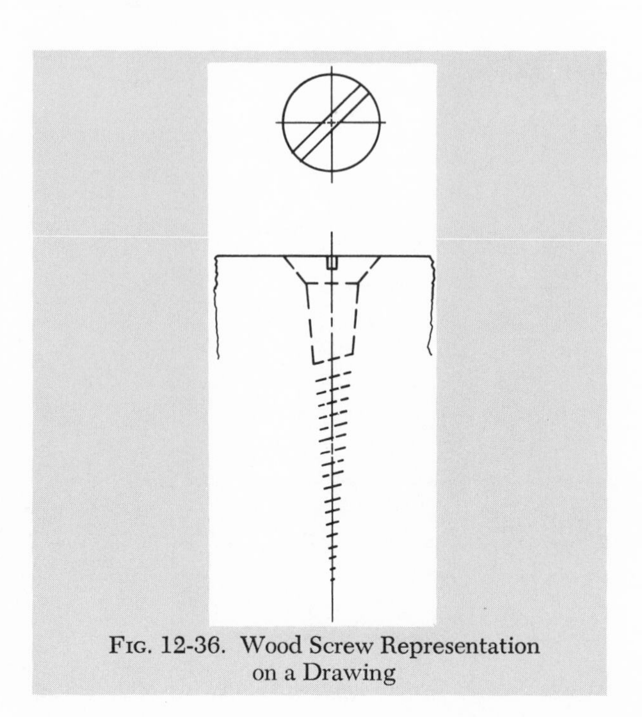
Fig. 12-36. Wood Screw Representation on a Drawing

Bolts are shown on drawings using the standard forms of thread representation: detailed, schematic, and simplified. Dimensions may be taken from the tables in the TD section. Use templates for layout.

Specifications for bolts are in the Unified National Coarse Series (UNC) and include diameter, length, number of threads per inch, series, class of fit, type of head, name.

Typical specifications for parts lists are:
⅝ x 2¼ – 11 UNC-2A SQUARE HEAD BOLT
Abbreviated form:
⅝ x 2¼ – 11 UNC-2A
Specifications for the bolt on a drawing:
⅝ x 2¼ – 11 UNC-2A
Where bolt length is shown as a dimension figure:
⅝ – 11 UNC-2A

Nuts

Nuts are square or hexagonal. The square nuts generally do not have a washer face. They are available in both regular and heavy series. Only the regular square nuts are shown in TD-12-58.

Hexagonal nuts may be with or without a washer face and are of three basic types as shown in Fig. 12-37. Of these only the standard and jam nuts are included in the TD section. Hexagonal flat nuts are those without the washer face.

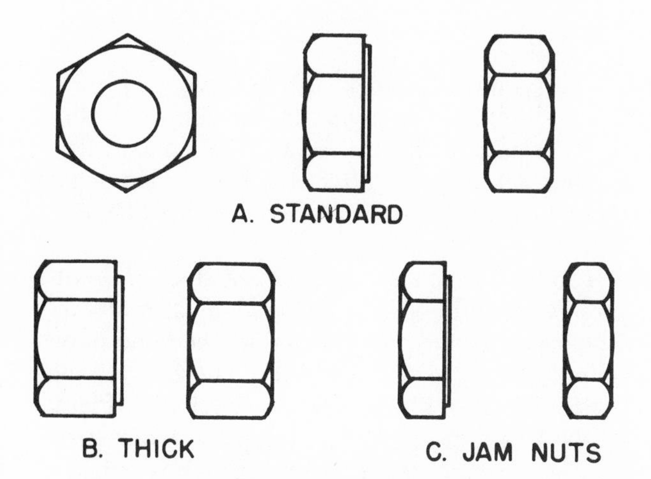

Fig. 12-37. Types of Hexagon Nuts

Slotted hexagon nuts and hexagon castle nuts are included in the TD section. Slotted nuts and castle nuts are designed for the insertion of a cotter pin when the nut is used with a drilled-shank fastener.

Machine screw nuts are designed to be used with machine screws and are either square or hexagonal. Nuts may be specified by adding the words *and nut* to a bolt or screw specification as follows:

⅝ x 2¼ – 11 UNC-2A SQ HD BOLT AND NUT

They are specified independently by nominal thread diameter, number of threads per inch, series, class of fit, and *description of nut:*

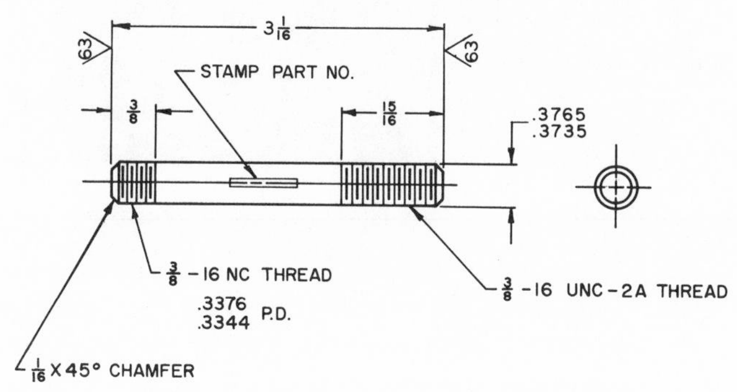

Fig. 12-38. Stud Mounting (Cherry Burrell Corp.)

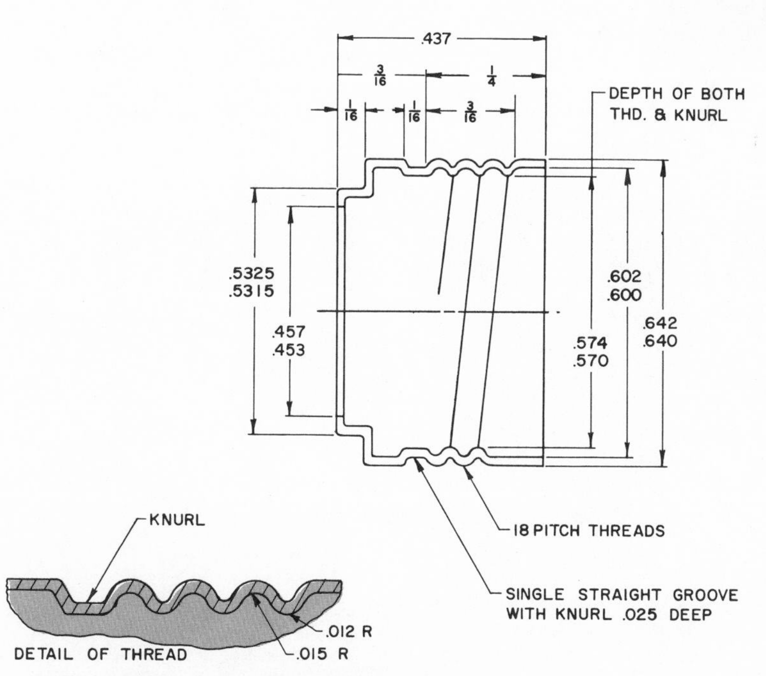

Fig. 12-39. Rolled Threads for Flashlight Bulb Receptacle

⅝ – 11 UNC-2B HEXAGONAL THICK SLOTTED NUT
or abbreviated:
⅝ – 11 UNC-2B HEX THK SLOT NUT

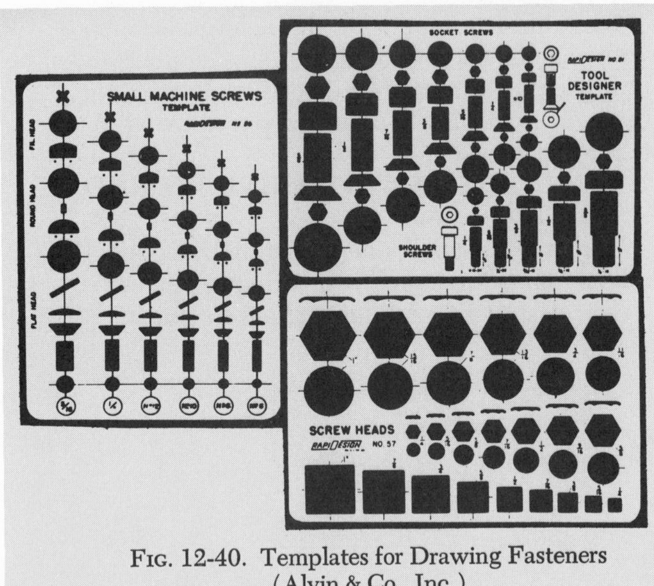

FIG. 12-40. Templates for Drawing Fasteners (Alvin & Co., Inc.)

WASHER TYPES

PLAIN WASHERS

HELICAL SPRING LOCK WASHERS

FIG. 12-41. Plain and Helical Spring Lock Washers

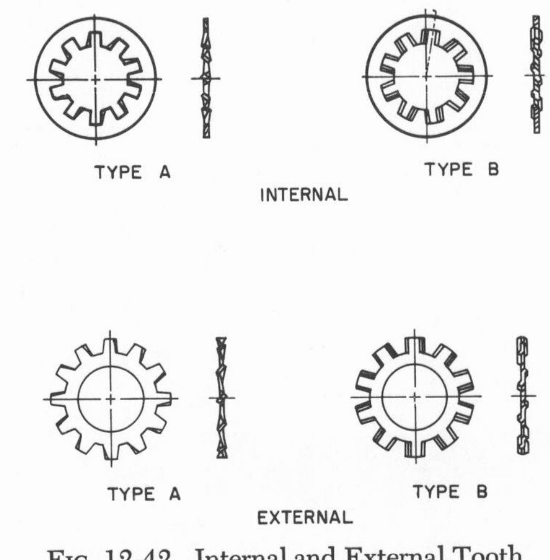

FIG. 12-42. Internal and External Tooth Lock Washers

No. 10-32 UNC-2B HEX MACH SCR NUT

Rods threaded on each end are called studs, Fig. 12-38. Threads are sometimes rolled into sheet metal such as those on light bulbs and the like, Fig. 12-39.

Thread Templates

A wide variety of templates is available to aid in drawing standard fasteners, Fig. 12-40. The standard representations for fasteners are the same whether drawn with or without templates. Templates simply outline the standard shapes more readily. Consult drafting suppliers' catalogs for the many templates available.

Unthreaded Fasteners

Washers

Plain washers, Fig. 12-41, are flat and circular with a central hole designed to fit around a bolt or screw. The USA Standards Institute lists two types: *A*, preferred sizes; and type *B*, other sizes. Some of the type *A* washers are available in narrow and wide series. The type *B* series are standardized in narrow, regular, and wide series. Only Type *A* plain washers are included in the TD section in TD-12-64.

Lockwashers, Fig. 12-41, are either of the helical-spring type or the tooth type. Helical lockwashers are either regular, extra-duty, or hi-collar type. The term *regular* replaces the older term *medium spring*. The term *extra-duty* replaces the term *extra-heavy*. Hi-collar helical spring lockwashers are for use with socket-head cap screws.

The spring type lockwashers have cross sections which are somewhat trapezoidal with the thickest part nearer the center. This makes the locking action more effective. Data relative to these lockwashers may be seen in the TD section.

Toothed lockwashers have twisted or bent projections which help grip when assembled. They are internal and external toothed and may be either type *A* or type *B*, Fig. 12-42.

SPECIFICATION OF WASHERS: Plain washers are specified by nominal washer size, narrow or wide, type, inside diameter, outside diameter, and thickness. The nominal washer size is designed to go with the same nominal bolts or screws.

⅜-W TYPE A ID .438, OD 1.000, .083 THK.

Helical-spring lockwashers are specified by nominal size and the series.

NO. 12 – REGULAR HELICAL SPG LOCK WASH

½ – HI - COLLAR HELICAL SPG LOCK WASH

Toothed lockwashers are specified by nominal size, internal or external, type *A* or *B* and name.

5/16 INTERNAL T, TYPE A, LOCK WASH

Keys

Keys are used to prevent movement between rotating parts and the shafts on which they are mounted. Various geometrical shapes are available. The *square keys, Woodruff keys* and *Pratt and Whitney keys* are among the more common types. Examples may be seen in TD-12-71, 72 and 73. *Key seats* are the slots in shafts. *Keyways* are the slots in the hub or wheel.

The square key is seated so that one-half its height is in each part. The Pratt and Whitney key is shaped like a race track, semi-circular at each end when viewed from the top. About two-thirds of the Pratt and Whitney key is seated in the key seat. The Woodruff key is semi-circular in cross section and usually the key diameter is about equal to the diameter of the shaft into which it is to be seated.

Keys are specified by number or size followed by description or name:

3/16 x 1¼ SQ KEY
No. 406 WOODRUFF KEY
No. 8 P & W KEY

Pins

Plain round pins, TD-12-74, may be used for some types of assembly. They are usually driven into position with force fits.

Taper pins may be used where parts are likely to be dismantled frequently. Taper pins are used in jig and fixture work for rapid and easy location of parts with respect to each other. Both plain and taper pins are made with chamfered ends.

Cotter pins, TD-12-75, are used to prevent cylindrical parts from moving longitudinally and with slotted and castle nuts. They are placed in a drilled hole of appropriate size and their ends are twisted or bent so they do not fall out.

Rivets

Riveting is relatively low in cost and easy to do. Parts made from different materials, as well as materials of differing thicknesses, can be easily fastened. Rivets may also be used as functional parts such as pivots, cam followers, and the like. Compared with threaded parts, they do not require lock washers, pins, or other locking devices.

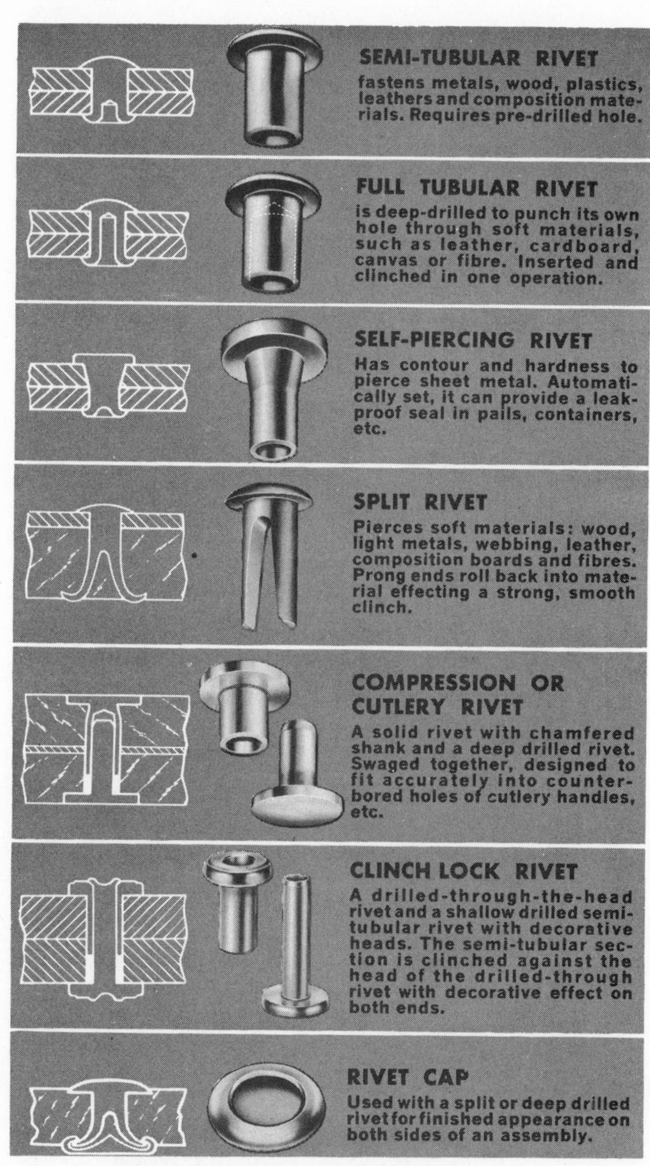

FIG. 12-43. Rivet Head Types
(Chicago Rivet and Machine Co.)

FASTENING

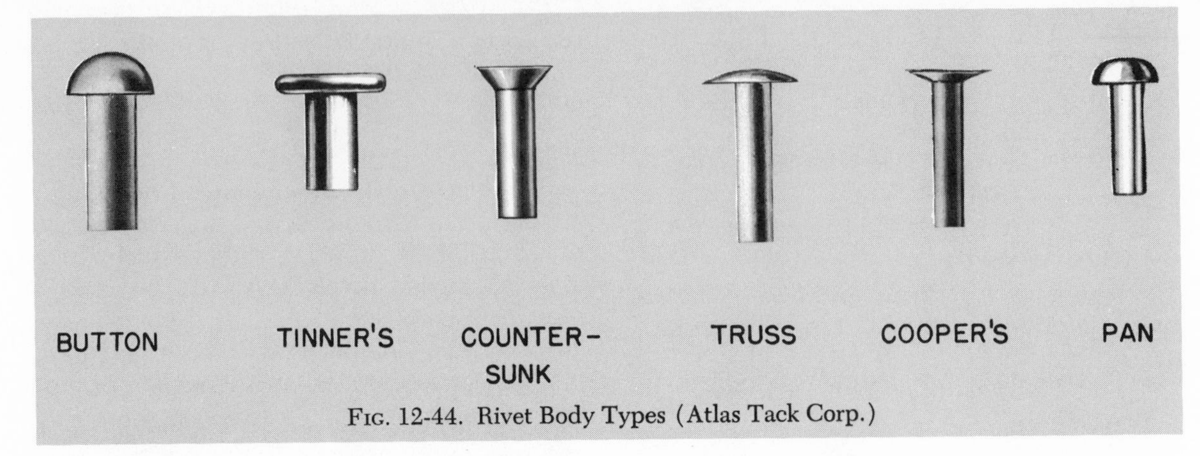

FIG. 12-44. Rivet Body Types (Atlas Tack Corp.)

Once fastened together, riveted parts cannot easily be disassembled. Threaded and welded assemblies are stronger than riveted assemblies. Riveted joints are not always air tight or water tight. Head types for rivets are shown in Fig. 12-43. Body types are shown in Fig. 12-44.

Rivet length, except for countersunk-head rivets, is measured from the underside of the head to the end of the shank. The length of a countersunk-head rivet includes the head.

For specific applications, rivet length is determined by adding the thickness of the parts to be joined and the heading or clinch allowance, Fig. 12-45. Heading allowance for solid rivets is up to two times the diameter of the rivet. Clinch allowance for semi-tubular, split, and deep hole rivets is shown in TD-12-76.

Rivets are manufactured of steel, copper, brass, aluminum, stainless steel, monel and nickel silver. Finishes include tin, copper, brass, cadmium plating, anodizing, and others.

Tinner's and cooper's rivets are sized by weight, such that each size specification is the approximate weight of 1000 rivets.

SPECIFICATIONS OF RIVETS: Rivets are specified on drawings by notes and are included in the parts list. They are specified by shank diameter, length, head type, body type, material, finish, and sometimes by weight. The following are typical specifications:

1. ¼″ x 7⁄16″, BUTTON HEAD, SEMI-TUBULAR, COPPER RIVET
2. .093″ x 172″, FLAT HEAD, SOLID, IRON, 10 OZ., TINNERS RIVET

RIVET JOINT DESIGN: The hole for the

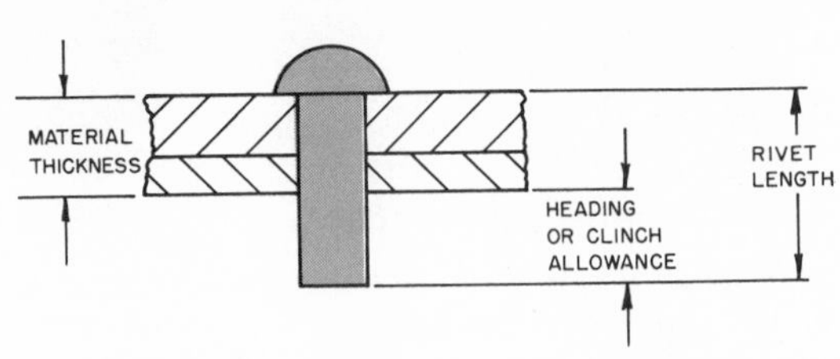

FIG. 12-45. Rivet Length Calculation

rivet should be from .003″ to .015″ larger than the diameter of the rivet. Distance between center lines for rivets is called *pitch*. The pitch for rivets should not be less than three times the diameter of the rivet. Pitch should not be more than 24 times the thickness of the metal. Rivets should not be placed closer to the edge than two times the hole diameter.

Four basic kinds of rivet joints are shown in Fig. 12-46.

Nails

The origin of nails probably dates back to the use of wood pins.

The term *penny* as it relates to nails may have had its origin through the symbol *d* which is the English symbol for pound; thus, an *8d* nail is one of such size that 1000 of them weighed one pound. Penny size has now come to indicate a definite length for a given type of nail. Some wire nails and brads are specified by wire gauge alone without reference to the penny size. The larger the wire gauge number, the smaller the diameter of the wire or nail.

Almost any shape and size nail can be obtained by special order. They are commonly available in aluminum, brass, copper, iron, steel and zinc.

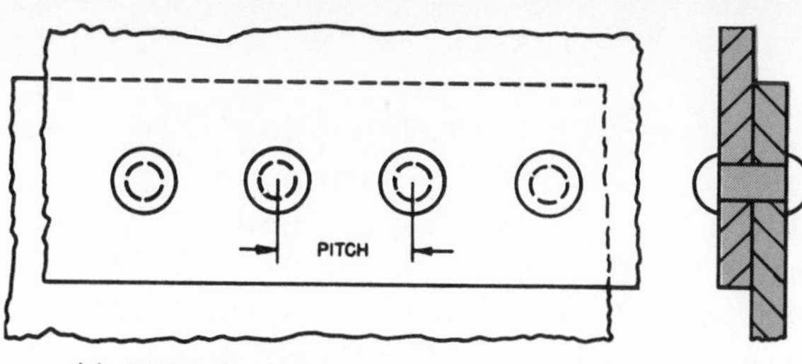

(a.) SINGLE-RIVETED LAP JOINT

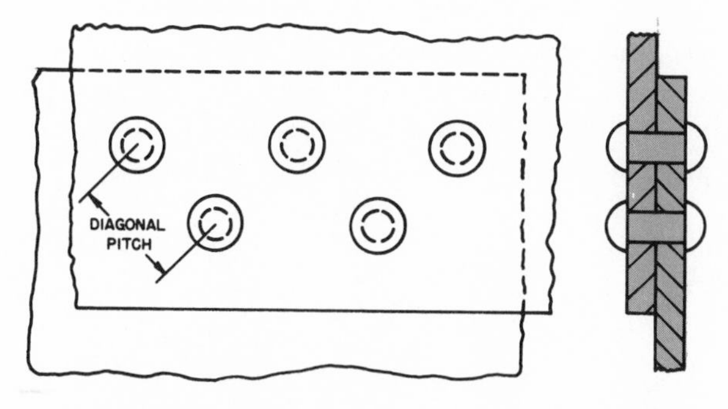

(b.) DOUBLE-RIVETED LAP JOINT

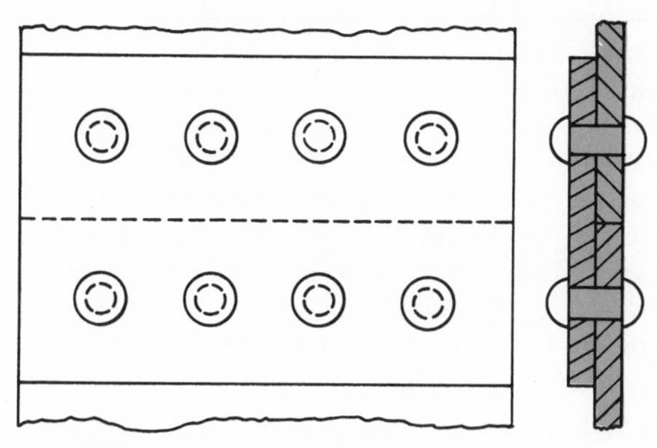

(c.) SINGLE-RIVETED BUTT JOINT

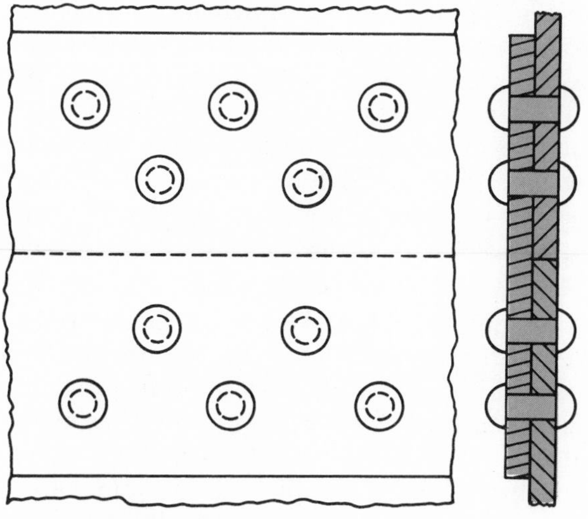

(d.) DOUBLE-RIVETED BUTT JOINT

FIG. 12-46. Rivet Joint Design

Surfaces may be smooth and bright and may be coated. Cement-coated nails, used for box and crate construction, have greater holding power than smooth nails. Zinc-coated nails protect against corrosion. Blued nails are clear and sterilized for lathers and other workers who may carry some of them in their mouths. Annealed nails are used where the points are to be clinched.

Special manufactured surfaces include *annular-threaded surface* for maximum holding power in soft woods, *spiral-threaded surface* for ease of driving and increased holding power in hardwoods, *screw-threaded surface* for ease of driving and maximum holding power, Fig. 12-47.

The basic types of nail heads are the flat, round, and countersunk heads. Many others are evolved from these, Fig. 12-48.

Nails also come in eight basic point types, Fig. 12-49. *Diamond* points are used for general-purpose work except when they are to be driven through denser woods where there

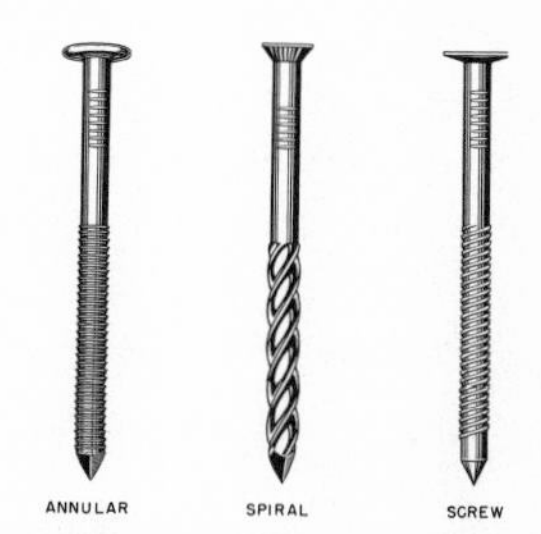

FIG. 12-47. Special Nails (Independent Nail Corp.)

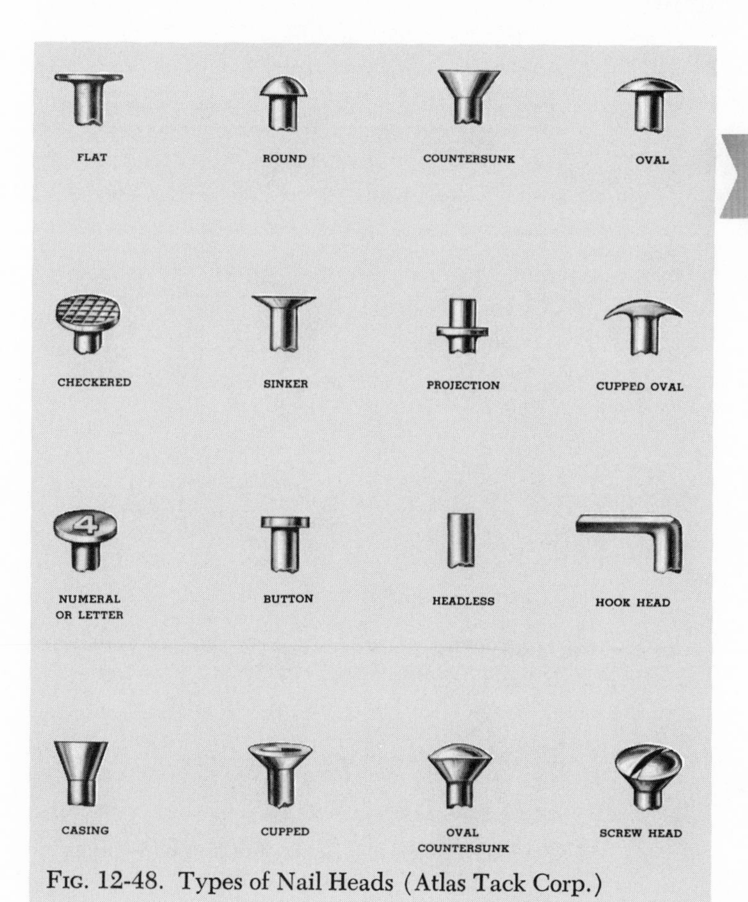

FIG. 12-48. Types of Nail Heads (Atlas Tack Corp.)

is danger of splitting. *Long-diamond* points are used where speed in nailing is desirable. The long, sharp point is helpful in setting the point before it is driven. *Blunt* points are used in dense woods where longer points cause splitting. The blunt point punches through the fibers instead of following the grain. *Chisel* points are for large spikes or nails that are to be used in hardwoods. *Round* points are used for nailing through woven materials such as carpeting to lessen the chance of breaking the fibers. *Duck-bill* points are used on small diameter nails for clinching. *Needle* points are used on reed and willow furniture and combine the advantages of a round point for non-tearing and a long point for speed. *Side* points are used in hard wood assembly to lessen the chance of splitting out and to make clinching easier.

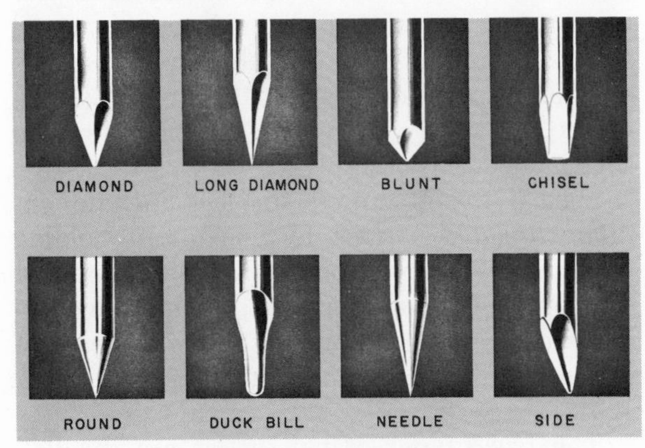

Fig. 12-49. Basic Nail Points (John Hassell Co., Inc.)

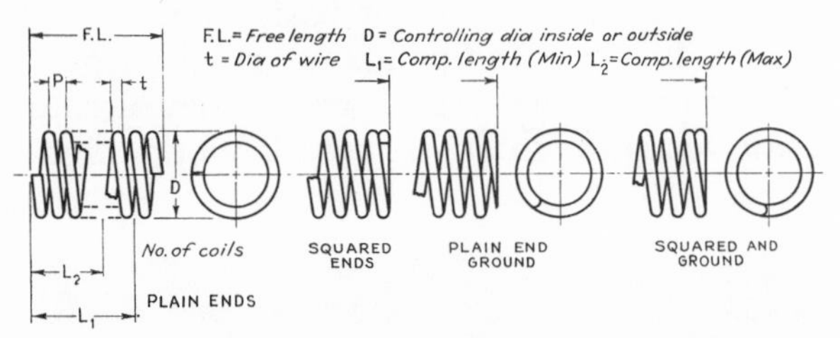

Fig. 12-50. Compression Spring (USAS Z14.1-1946)

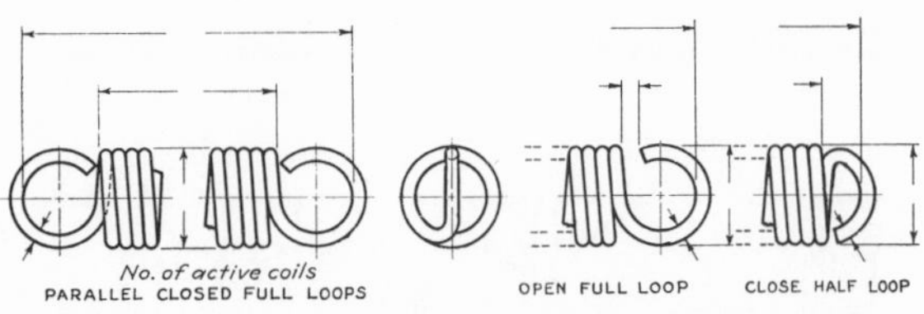

Fig. 12-51. Tension Spring (USAS Z14.1-1946)

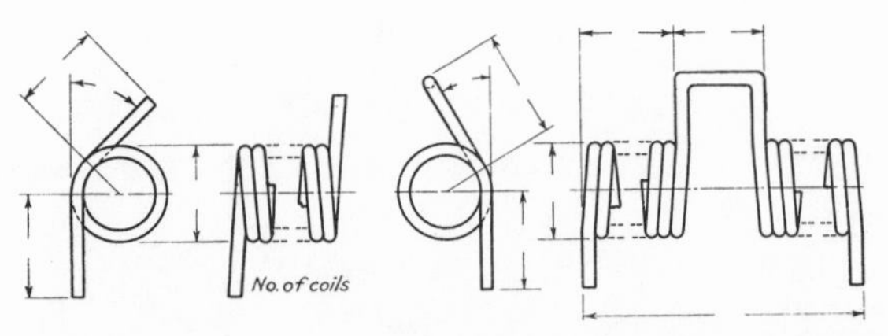

Fig. 12-52. Torsion #1 Spring (USAS Z14.1-1946)

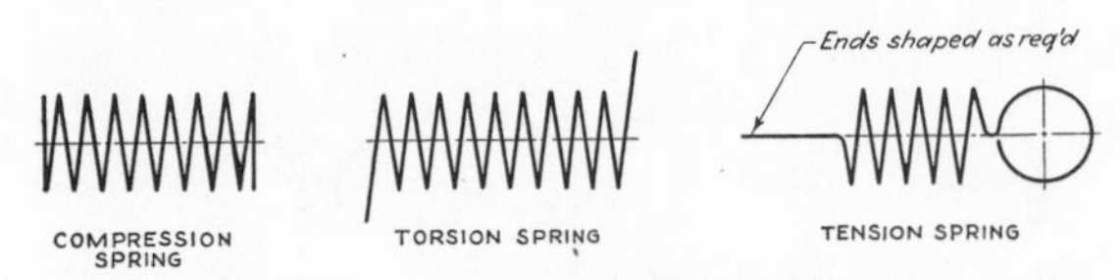

Fig. 12-53. Schematic Representation of Springs (USAS Z14.1-1946)

Common nails are general-purpose nails. *Box* nails are similar to common nails but are smaller in diameter in the same *d* size and also have a thinner head. They are used where a smaller diameter shank is less likely to produce splitting. *Finishing* nails have cupped heads for setting below the surface and are correspondingly of smaller diameter. *Casing* nails are much like finishing nails. They have longer heads for greater holding power and are of larger diameter than the same *d* size finishing nail. *Wire* nails are similar to box nails but do not go by penny size. Instead they are specified by wire gauge size and length. *Brads* are like the wire nails except for their head which is of the countersunk type like the finishing nails.

Cut tacks, double-pointed flat-wire tacks, fence staples and countersunk finishing washers may be seen in the TD section.

Nails are not usually shown on a drawing. It is left up to the judgment of the workman to select and use the right kind and quantity of nails for a given job. In a few cases it may be desirable to drill pilot holes in hard woods to prevent splitting. When nailing position or quantity is important, it may be shown on a drawing simply by the intersection of center lines and a local note.

Nails may be included in the bill of materials. Specification of nails either on the drawing or in the bill of materials is in the following sequence: Size in pennies, length in inches, wire gauge number, name of nail, finish, head style, point shape. Typical complete specifications are:

6d x 2, NO. 11½, COMMON, BRIGHT, FLATHEAD, DIAMOND POINT
4d x 1½, NO. 14, CEMENT COATED, VENEER-BOX, LARGE FLATHEAD, NEEDLE POINT
1¾, NO. 11½, BARBED, ASBESTOS SHINGLE, LARGE FLATHEADS, LONG DIAMOND POINTS

For determining the length needed for a given nail a rough rule-of-thumb is that the nail should be three times as long as the thickness of the first board it penetrates.

Springs

A mechanical spring stores energy when deflected under a load and returns the same amount of energy when released. The wires of coil springs follow a helical path somewhat like a screw thread. The three types of coil springs are compression, tension, and torsion. A compression spring is an open-coil helical spring that offers resistance to a compressive force applied axially, Fig. 12-50. A tension spring is a close-wound spring with or without initial tension that offers resistance to an axial force tending to extend its length, Fig. 12-51. Torsion springs offer resistance or exert a turning force in a plane at right angles to the chord, Fig. 12-52. Note the recommended dimensioning practice for each of these spring types.

Schematic representation may be used for springs, as shown in Fig. 12-53. Specifications for springs are quite detailed. Figs. 12-54, 12-55, and 12-56 are examples of the main types of coil springs with specifications.

Examples of other spring types with dimensions and specification data are shown in Figs. 12-57 and 12-58.

Chapter 12 — Problems and Projects

1. Make a two-view drawing of two pieces of ¼″ steel plate, one 2″ x 8″ and the other 4″ x 8″. Join these with a tee-joint centering the 2″ end along the 8″ side of the other piece. Use three fillet welds spaced 3¾″ apart on centers. The welds are ⅛″ x 1½″ and are on both sides of the tee-joint.
2. Make a two-view drawing of two pieces of metal. The base piece is ⅜″ x 8″ in diameter. The other piece is ¼″ thick and in the shape of a cylinder 6″ high with an outside diameter of 7½″. Center the cylinder over the base and weld all around the outside of the butt joint with a fillet weld.
3. Design a steel shaft 1¼″ in diameter, 4″ long, ⅛ x 45° chamfer at both ends, 6 UNC threads on the right end and 6 UNF threads on the left end. Make three drawings (all of which may be on the same A-size sheet). For the first drawing use simplified representation; the second, schematic representation; and the third, detailed representation. Dimension the shaft and use appropriate notes with leaders for specification of the threads. (See TD-12-11.)
4. Two steel plates, one of which is ½″ thick, the other ⅜″ thick, are to be held together with hex-head bolts and nuts. Make a partial sectioned drawing of the two plates with one bolt in place. You may choose or be assigned either simplified or schematic representation. (See TD-12-11, TD-12-48.)
5. A casting requires a cover plate to be fastened to it. The cover plate is of 16-gauge sheet steel. Draw a partial sectioned view showing a roundhead slotted machine screw ¾″ in length holding the parts together. Use simplified or schematic thread representation. (See TD-12-21, and TD-12-82.)
6. Make a drawing of one end of 4″ OD pipe, NPT, threaded for a distance of 3″ along this end. Use schematic representation. (See TD-12-12.)
7. Make a drawing of a compression spring made of ⅛″ diameter wire. The spring has the following characteristics: 1½″ outside diameter of spring, 16 coils, right-hand, open and ground ends, free length of 4″.
8. Make a schematic drawing of an extension spring made of 3/32 diameter wire. The spring has the following characteristics: 1″ inside diameter of spring, 12 coils, left-hand, ends parallel, single-full loop centered.

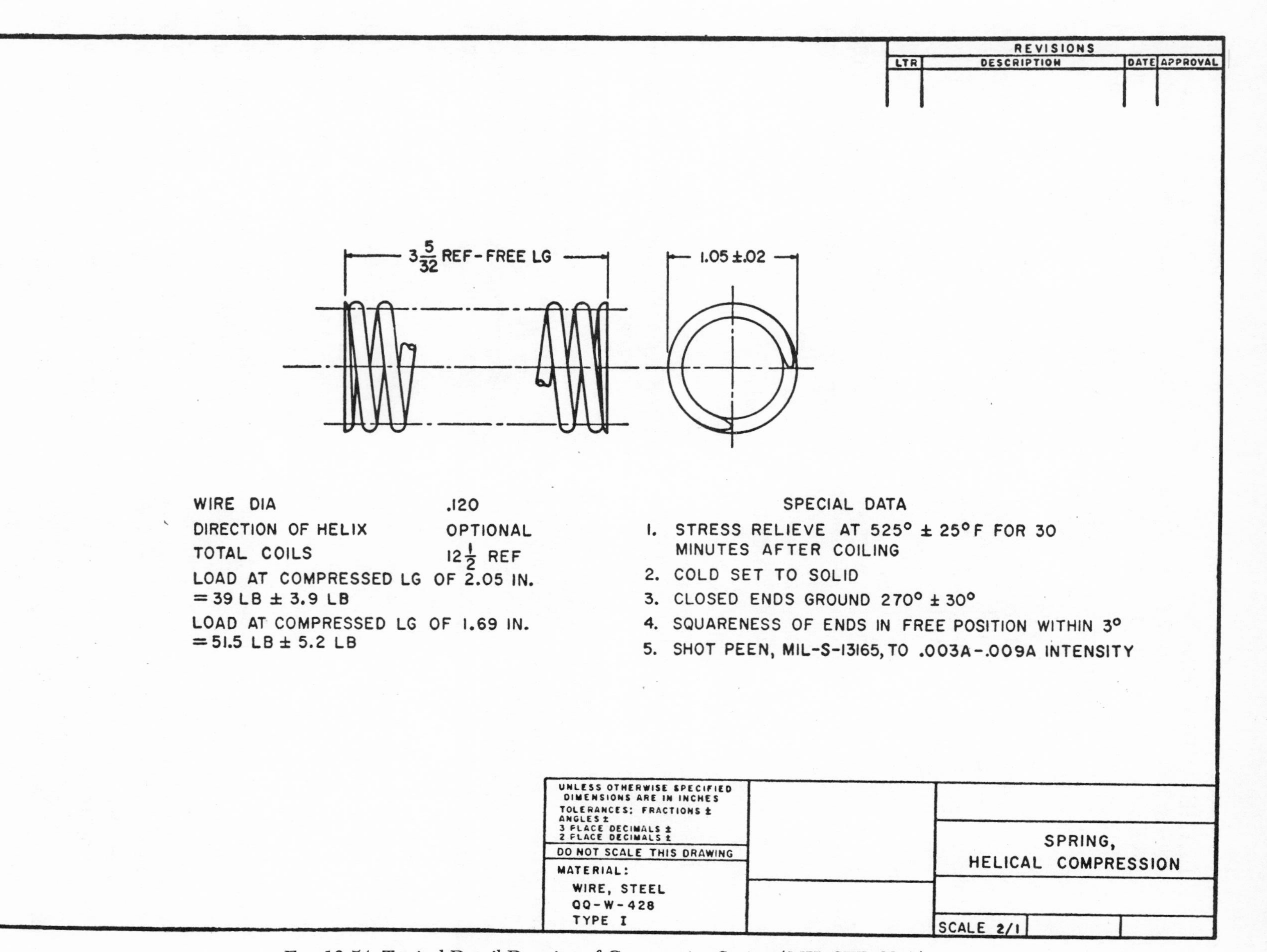

FIG. 12-54. Typical Detail Drawing of Compression Spring (MIL-STD-29 A)

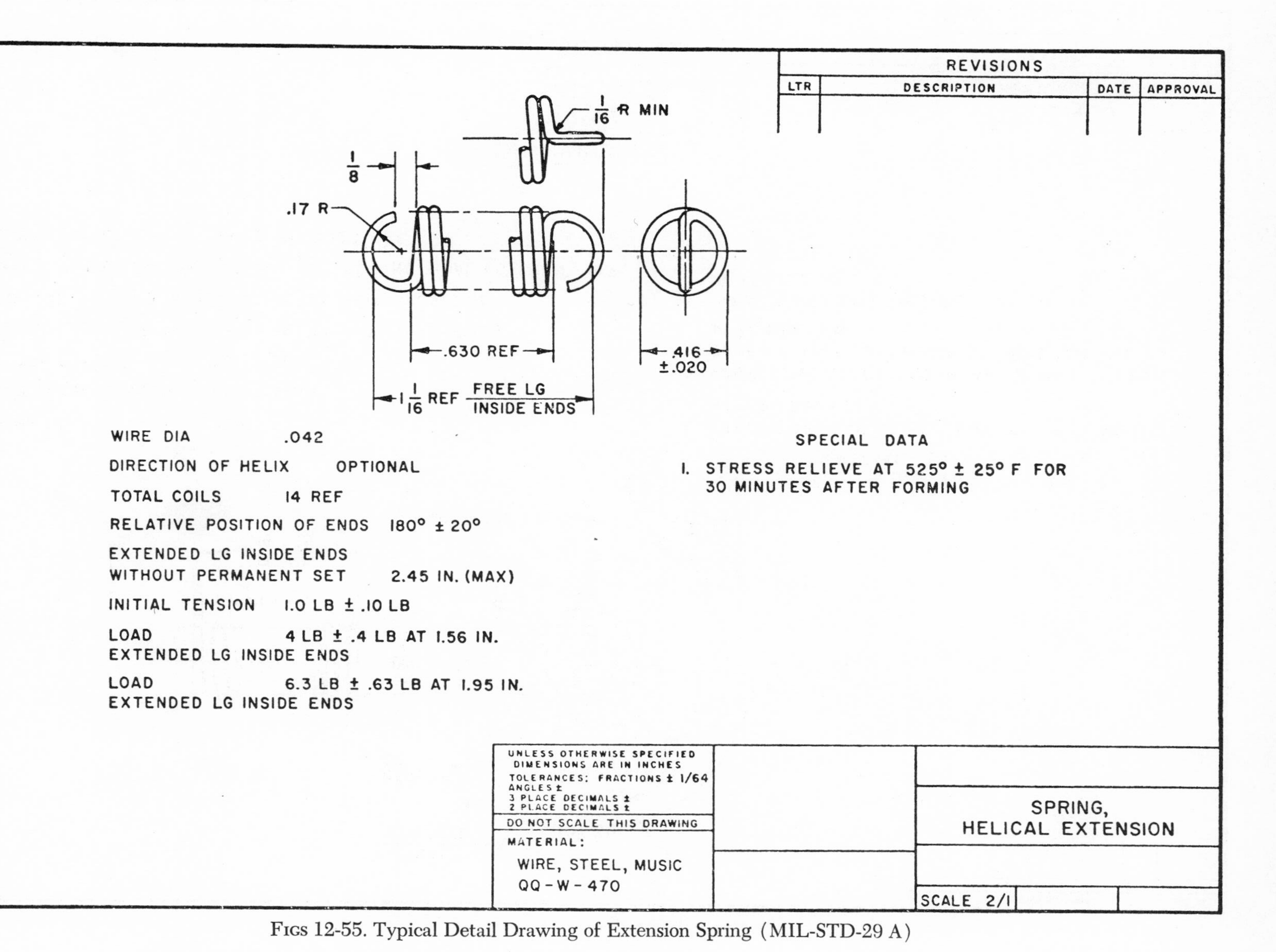

Figs 12-55. Typical Detail Drawing of Extension Spring (MIL-STD-29 A)

FASTENING

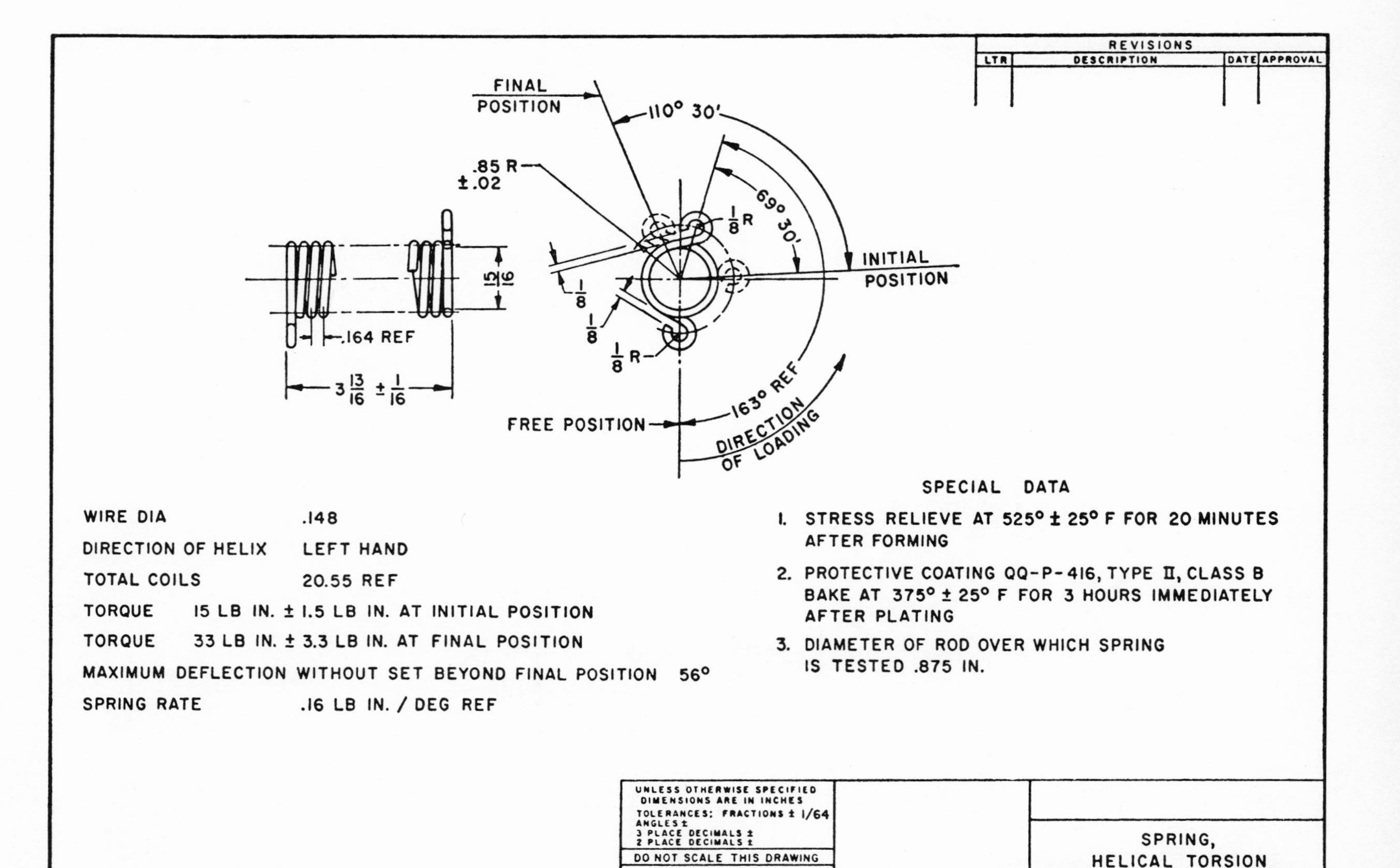

Fig. 12-56. Typical Detail Drawing of Helical Torsion Spring (MIL-STD-29 A)

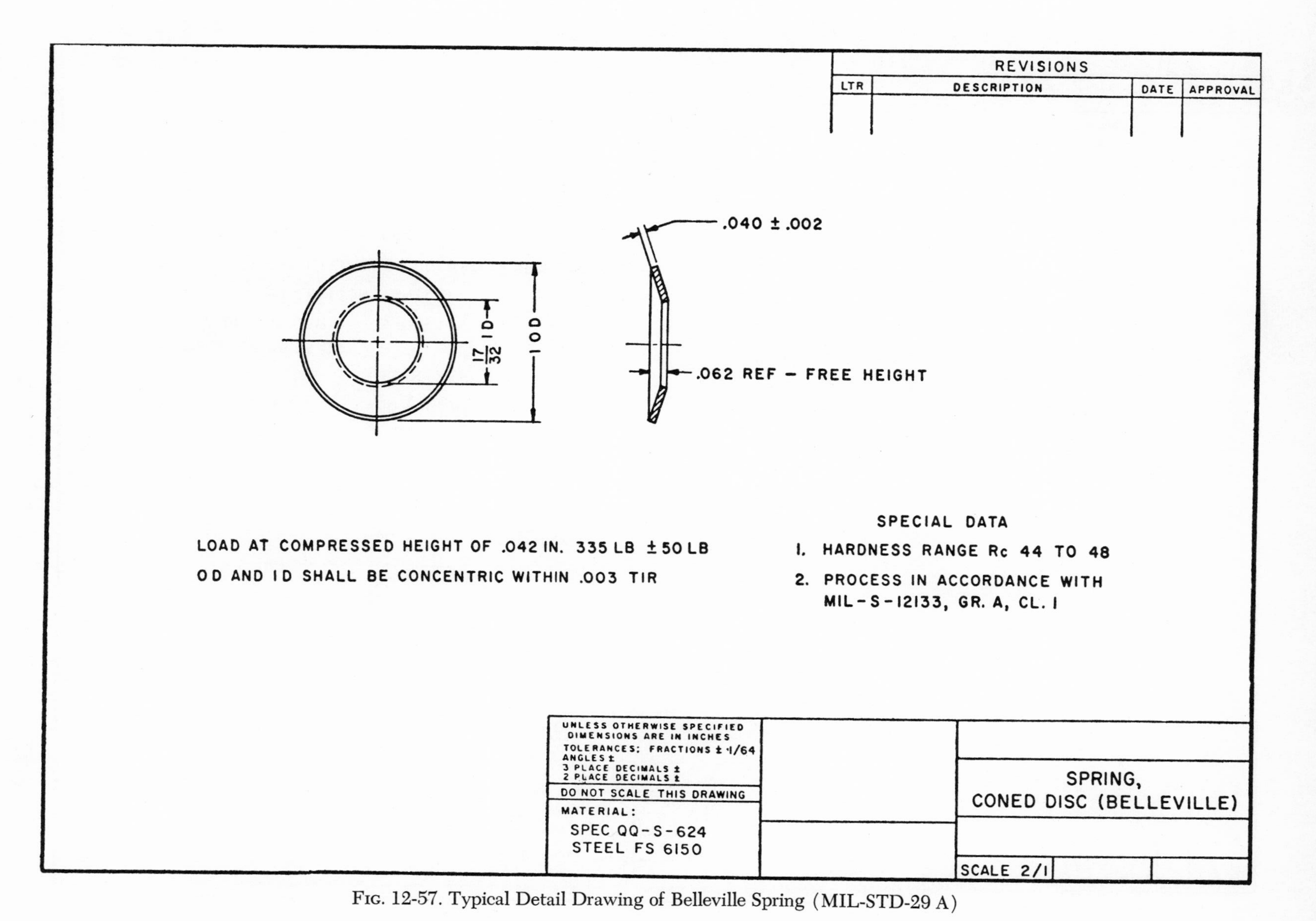

FIG. 12-57. Typical Detail Drawing of Belleville Spring (MIL-STD-29 A)

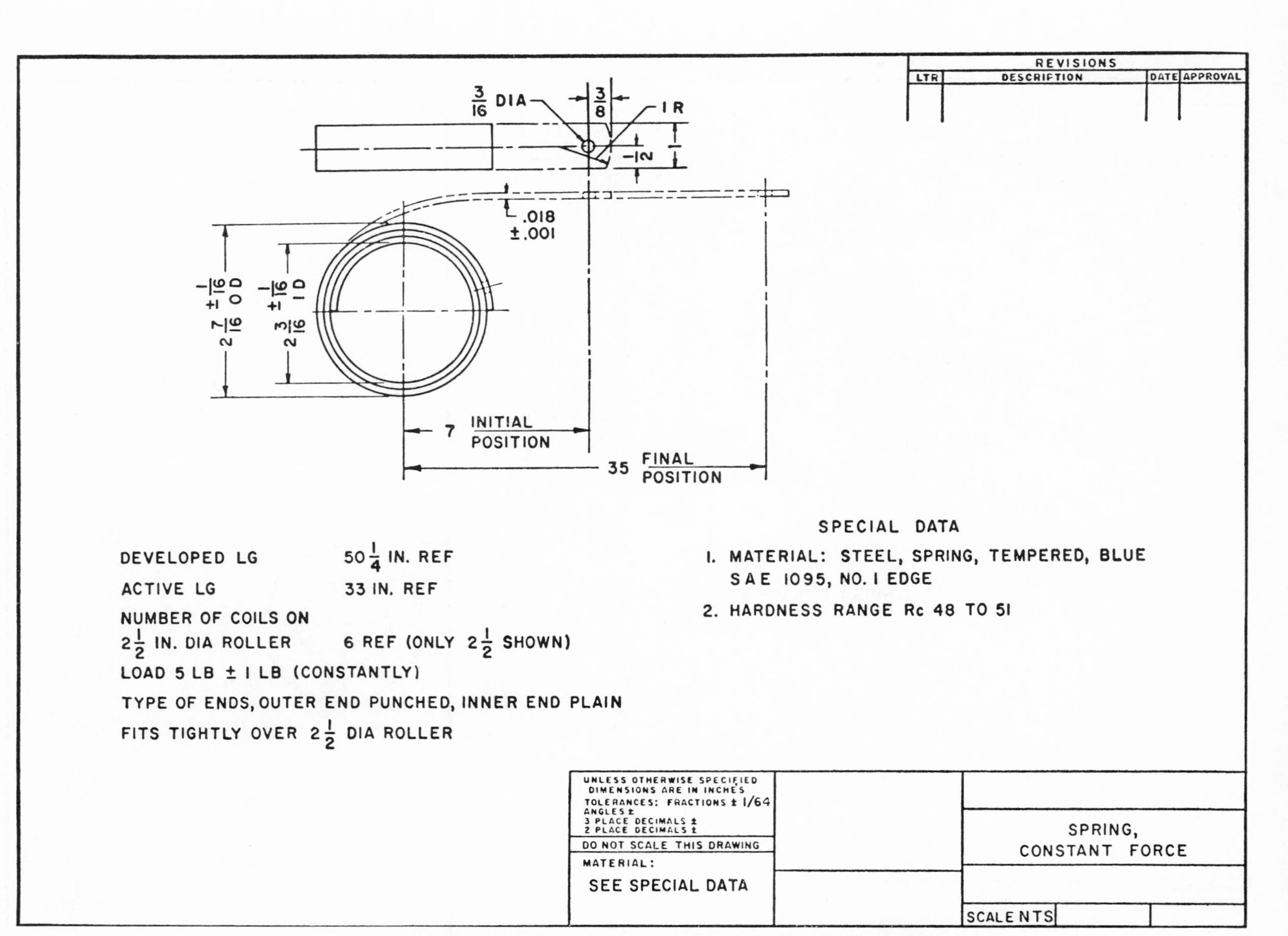

FIG. 12-58. Typical Detail Drawing of Constant Force Spring (MIL-STD-29 A)

CHAPTER THIRTEEN

product planning

Product planning is one of the most creative kinds of work to be found, Figs. 13-1 and 13-2. Large amounts of money are spent in industry for research and development. Long periods of time may be required between the conception of an idea for a product and its final manufacture.

FIG. 13-1. Sylvania Flash Cube
This product received design award in the April 1966 issue of *Materials in Design Engineering* for new use of materials in combination for effective design.

Even more time is spent on redesigning products already on the market than is spent designing new products. For example, although "new" cars come out each year, the old model automobile is simply redesigned. It takes several years of "lead" time to develop the changes, design parts, design and manufacture the tools, and then manufacture the car for introduction in early fall, Fig. 13-3. The tools of communication during this period of development include sketching and drafting.

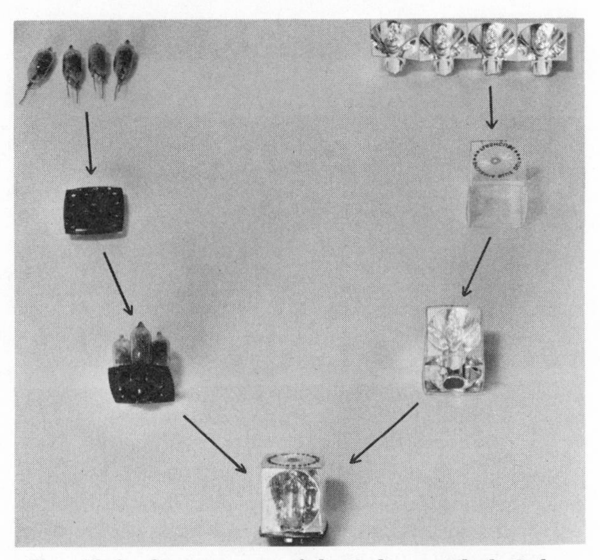

FIG. 13-2. Components of the Sylvania Flash Cube (*Materials in Design Engineering*, April, 1966)

Selection and Identification

Underlying the selection of a product for manufacturing is a need for it. Industry constantly searches for markets for the products they have and for those in various stages of development. When an industry guesses wrong about the need for a product it plans to make, trouble lies ahead. This step, then, in creating products is examined quite carefully through market analysis.

In adding to its product line, an industry attempts to answer these questions to their satisfaction:

1. Is the product related in some way to the products we already produce? Will it extend our coverage and reputation now held?
2. Is the product one which lends itself to the production facilities now used? Are expensive new machines required to produce it? Is the engineering and labor force capable of producing the product? Will it take a minimum amount of time to change over and tool-up for the initial production run?
3. Will the product meet its competition? Can it be sold at a reasonable profit? Will it have a natural obsolescence so that orderly replacement will be needed? Can the money to finance the production be obtained?

Fig. 13-3. Advanced Design Studio at G. M. Styling Staff in the General Motors Technical Center, Warren, Michigan (General Motors Corp.)
Note completed fiber glass prototype model of experimental car in foreground; full scale "seating mock-up" in center for checking on interior dimensions, seating positions, steering wheel angle, location of controls and ease of entry and exit, full size color rendering of an experimental car on rear wall; full size engineering layout at right along rear wall; and designers at work at tables along right hand side.

Students in school situations approach the planning of a product in much the same manner. A need for the product must exist. This need might have been artificially produced by the teacher directing each student to select a product, then design and produce the object. It may be a felt need for a useful purpose or for a gift, Fig. 13-4.

Answer these questions with respect to yourself and product selection:

1. Is the product of interest to me? Is it related to my needs?
2. Does the product lend itself to the school shop facilities available? Is it within my ability to complete it satisfactorily? Will it require more time than is available to me?
3. Will it be challenging? Does it have appropriate instructional content in its production? Will it meet parental and teacher approval? Will I be able to pay for the materials? Are the materials available?

When the questions relative to selection of a product for design or redesign have been answered, the problem should be identified in writing. The identification should be simple, direct, and yet stated in terms that permit an open-minded approach to the solution. This statement should be written in terms of the function that the product will serve rather than by a traditional title.

Example Product Statements

1. A corner work unit for the home draftsman — should include a drafting surface, a desk-type work surface, storage for common and specialized drafting tools and equipment, reference shelves, office-type filing space, and flat-sheet filing space, Fig. 13-5.
2. A carrying and storage drafting unit, Fig. 13-6, to contain the following:
   a. 1 pair of 6″ dividers.
   b. 1 — 6″ compasses with lengthening bar and interchangeable pen and pencil points.
   c. 1 set of 4 technical fountain pens.
   d. 1 mechanical pencil pointer.
   e. 1 combination pencil and ink eraser.
   f. 3 mechanical draftsman's pencils.
   g. 1 irregular curve.
   h. 1 erasing shield.
3. A device to hold ten standard-size books in a neat and orderly manner where they

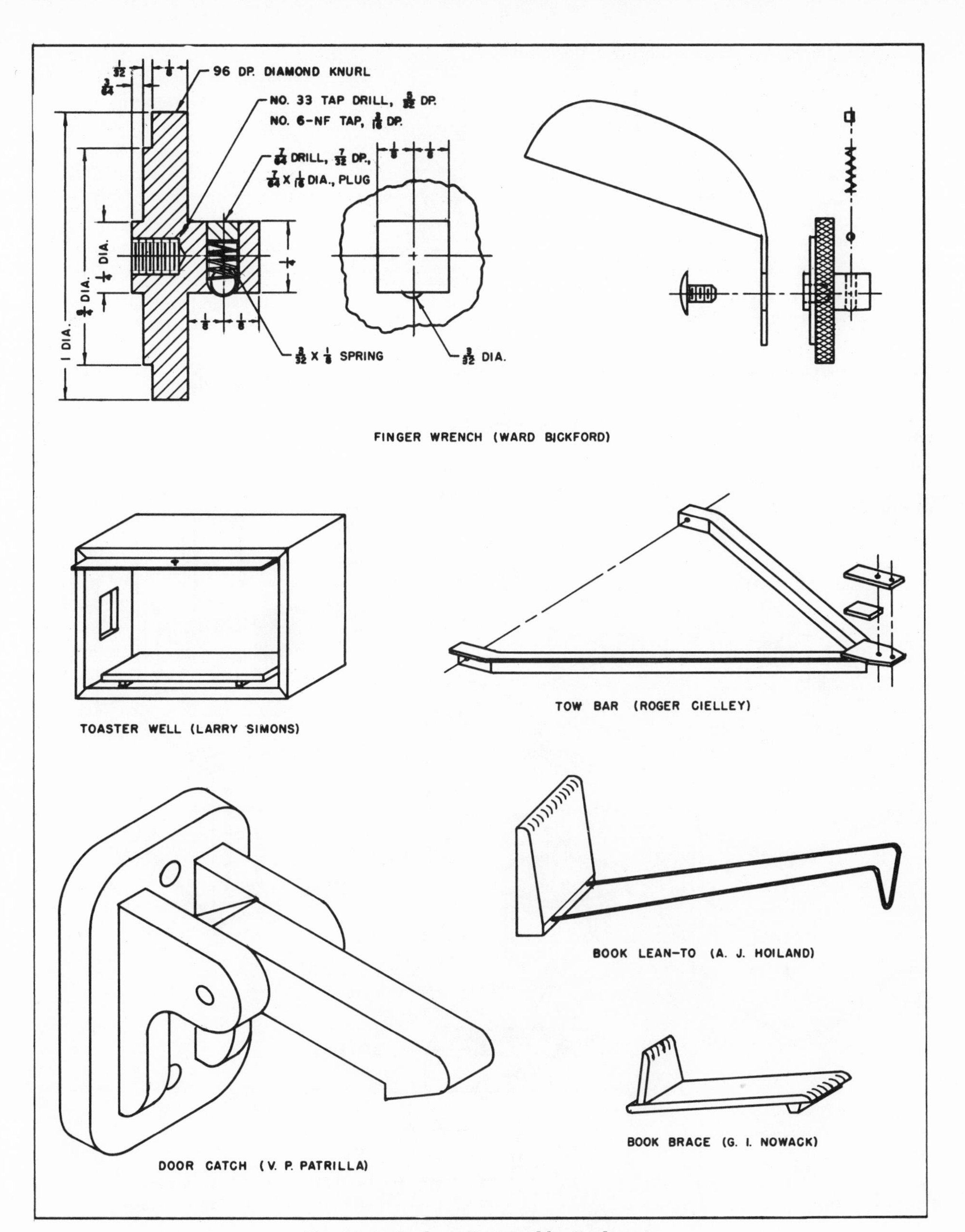

Fig. 13-4. Products Designed by Students in School Shop and Drafting Classes

will be readily accessible on a desk top, Fig. 13-4.

4. A print-making press to be constructed without any metal parts and used in humid tropical climates, Fig. 13-7.
5. A unique device to hold a bath towel, Figs. 1-32 and 1-33.
6. A portable device to hold a book and/or serve as a writing or working surface for a person confined in bed, Fig. 6-2.
7. A portable picnic device to hold cans of prepared food (such as pork and beans)

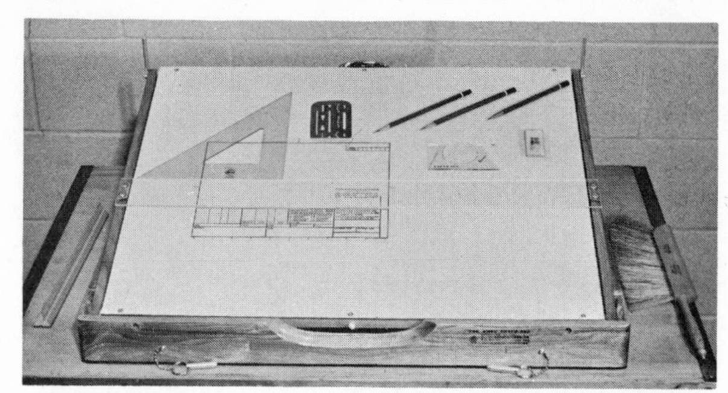

Fig. 13-6. Ames Draft-Pac in Drafting Position (Olson Mfg. Co.)

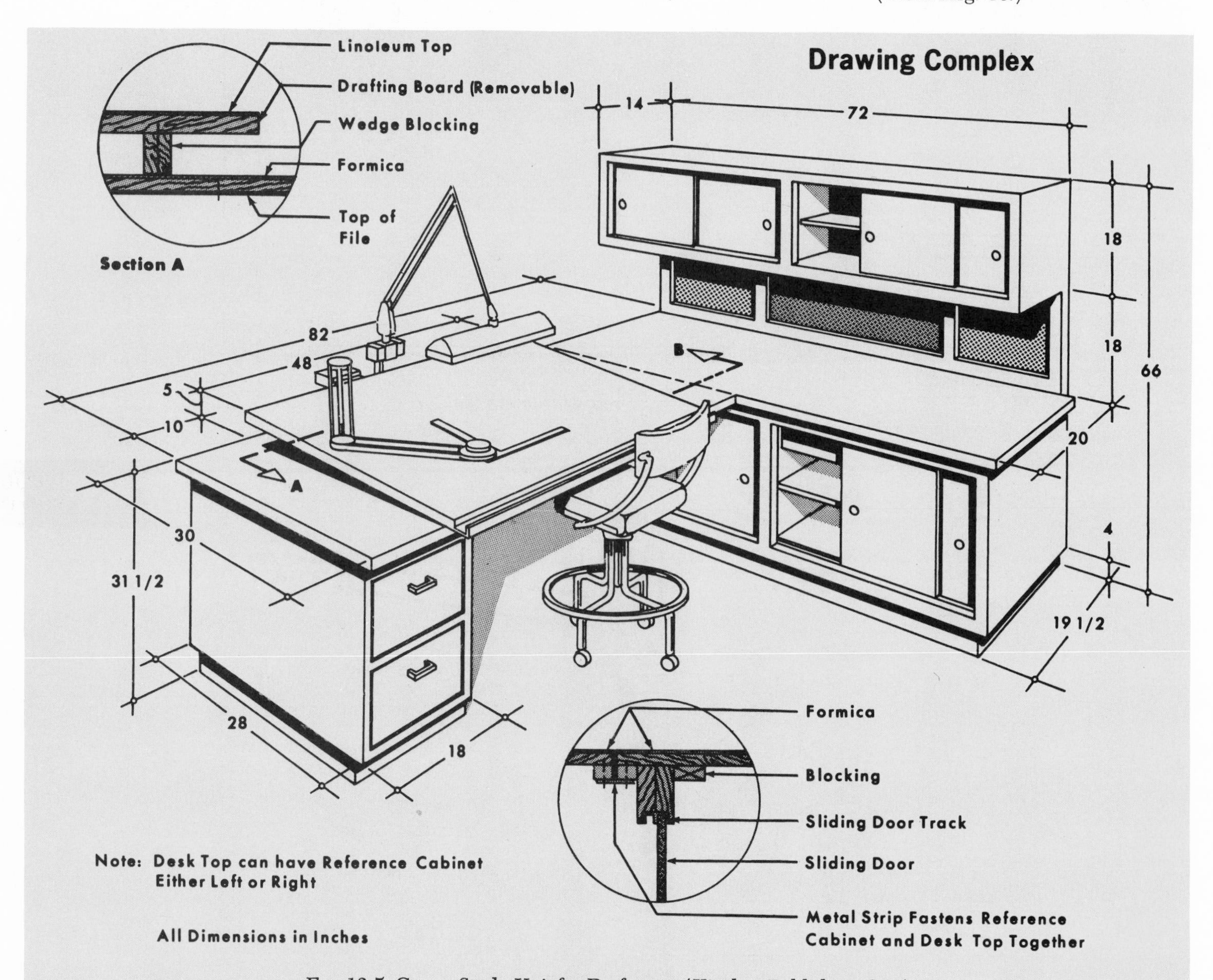

Fig. 13-5. Corner Study Unit for Draftsmen (Kinelow Publishing Co.[1])

[1]Copyright 1965, Kinelow Publishing Co., 9 Maiden Lane, New York, N.Y. Reprinted by permission of *Graphic Science,* Robert A. Harms, author.

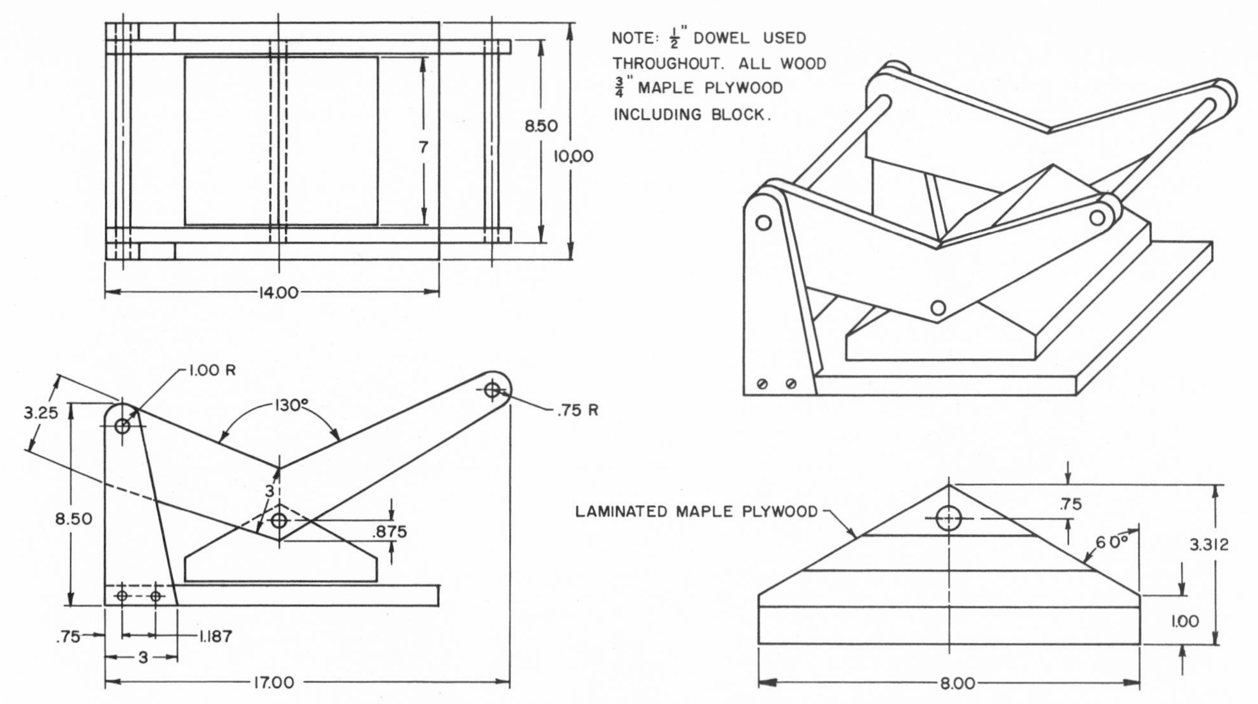

FIG. 13-7. Linoleum Block Print-Making Press (Edwin Geers)

ranging in size to 5″ in diameter and to 7″ high, while heating it over an open fire, Fig. 6-5.

Stating the problem in terms of its function permits the designer to approach the problem solution with fewer preconceived ideas of the form the project should take. For example, if problem 5, "the unique device to hold a bath towel" had been stated, "bath-towel rack," the product would probably have been an ordinary bath-towel rack or holder. However, by eliminating the conditioning word "rack," other approaches to hanging bath towels may be more freely studied. This same reasoning may be applied to design statements for most products.

FIG. 13-8. Automatic Hamburger Machine (McGraw-Hill[2])

Development of Ideas Through Analysis of Function

Function simply means the characteristic action of something or its intended use. In a product with more than one part, each has its own characteristic action or function and all must function in an integrated manner to fulfill the overall requirements of the product.

The automatic hamburger machine shown in Fig. 13-8 demonstrates an extremely functional design for producing hamburgers. The cooked patty emerges from the cooking unit at the upper right. From there it is moved to half a bun coming from the toaster in two slices. Final assembly of the hamburger may include adding a cheese slice (emerging from the cabinet in the center) or, a double hamburger (at head of assembly line in center). The top half of the

[2]Copyright 1966, McGraw-Hill, Inc. Reprinted from the June 20, 1966 issue of *Product Engineering*.

hamburger bun is added and deposited on an assembly line to be sent to the pick-up point.

In studying design problems, you must raise a number of questions and seek the best answer. Many different answers to design questions are possible, thus yielding many different solutions. How many different ways can you think of to solve this design problem: Design a device for writing? Generally the unique and simple answer produces the best product.

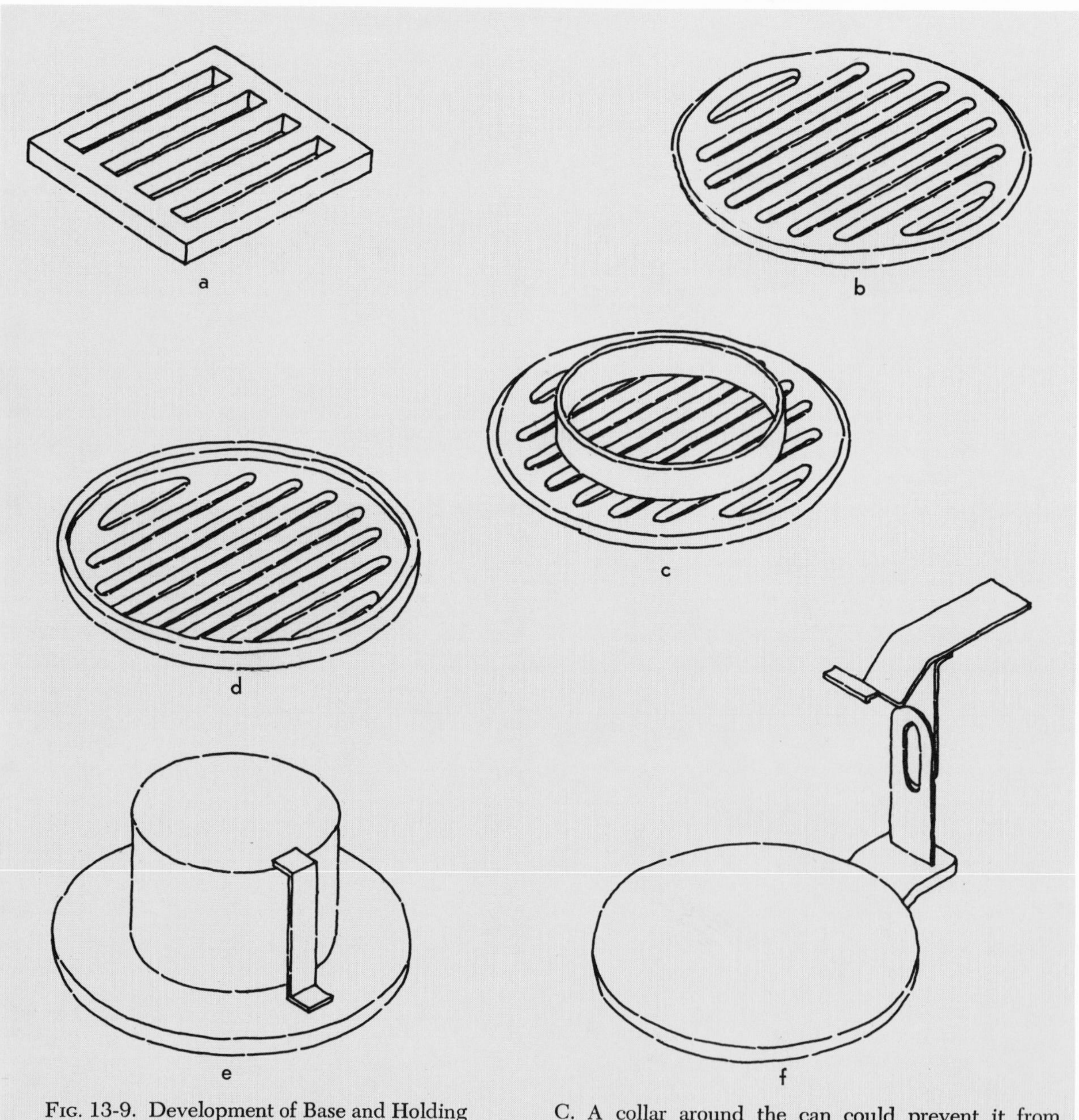

FIG. 13-9. Development of Base and Holding Mechanism for Food Warmer through Analysis of Functions

A. Ribs and slots permit heat to come through.
B. Cans are round, therefore base should be round with base diameter larger than largest can diameteı.
C. A collar around the can could prevent it from slipping off.
D. A raised edge on the casting of the base would also prevent the can from slipping.
E. A spring clip would hold the can in place.
F. A mechanical holding device would be more flexible.

For an illustration of this process, refer to statement 7 in the preceding paragraphs, to Table 13-1, and to Figs. 6-5 and 13-9.

Layout and Design Drawings

Once the preliminary analysis of the several functions has been thought through, design layouts are made. These are usually drawn quite carefully, often full-size, to enable the designer to determine how various parts function and fit with respect to each other. Layout designs do not carry the complete detail dimension of parts. Rather, they carry such dimensions as those needed to establish whether parts will work together properly.

Fig. 13-10 shows the proposed installation of an oil cooler. Note that section *A-A* shows interference of the oil cooler with the engine front support. Section *B-B* through the frame side member shows another interference. The side view indicates difficulty in assembly and removal of the short hose connection between the radiator and the oil cooler.

The interferences and assembly difficulties of the oil cooler, as shown in this layout, make it necessary to relocate or redesign this unit. While a notch in the engine support will eliminate this interference, it would not be possible to make a similar notch in the frame side member. When relocated, clearance must be provided between the side member and cooler, taking into consideration engine movements due to torque reaction. It would also be well to redesign the cooler to allow use of a longer hose for ease of assembly and removal.[3]

An example of thorough investigation to determine the largest radius counterweight that can be used in an engine is shown in Fig. 13-11. The arc described by the nose of the cam determines the counterweight radius. A relatively close clearance between the machined surfaces of the cam nose and the counterweight outside radius is permissible, because the camshaft and crankshaft

TABLE 13-1

Functional Analysis of Food Warmer (Fig. 6-5)

Statement of Function

1. The device should be such that heat will readily be transmitted to the can so that the food will be heated as quickly as possible.
2. The device should accommodate the common sizes of cans.
3. Cans placed in or on it should not readily fall off.
4. The hand-hold should be located so that it is easy to place the device over the fire and retract it without being burned.
5. It should be easily stored and transported and should be light enough in weight so that women will use it.
6. Materials appropriate to the heat of outdoor fires should be used.
7. Its cost should be reasonable and with care it should be useful over a relatively long period of time.
8. It should be strong enough to support the heaviest package likely to be placed on it.

Comments and Tentative Solutions

1. If the base is solid, heat will not be as readily transferred as when there is space for the heat to get directly to the can. The base should have slots and ribs in it, Fig. 13-9.
2. Common sizes of cans for such items as pork and beans are:

Designation	Diam.	Height	Content Weight
8 oz.	$2\frac{5}{8}''$	$3''$	8 oz.
#303	$3''$	$4\frac{7}{16}''$	1 lb.
#2	$3\frac{3}{8}''$	$4\frac{1}{2}''$	1 lb. 5 oz.
#$2\frac{1}{2}$	$4''$	$4\frac{5}{8}''$	1 lb. 15 oz.
46 oz.	$4\frac{1}{4}''$	$7''$	3 lb. 4 oz.

   Size ranges — $2\frac{5}{8}''$ to $4\frac{1}{4}''$ diam.; $3''$ to $7''$ height. Weight range — 8 oz. to 3 lbs., 4 oz.
3. Possible solutions to secure can while heating:
   a collar around the can, Fig. 13-9 (c).
   a raised edge on the casting of the base, Fig. 13-9 (d).
   a spring clip, Fig. 13-9 (e).
   a mechanical device, Fig. 13-9 (f).
4. Solutions:
   a handle which is a poor conductor of heat (wood).
   a detachable handle which will not get hot while the food is heating.
5. Device should package well, disassemble easily, store easily and transport easily.
6. Use aluminum for base; steel for holding can to base; wood for handle.
7. Use economical materials and economical methods of producing.
8. Strength of materials suitable to hold about $3\frac{1}{2}$ lbs. — check by pilot-model test.

[3] General Motors Drafting Standards Manual, p. A-145.

centers are held closely. The draftsman should question the clearance of the counterweight to the inside of the piston skirt. He should develop sections as shown at the left side of the layout to check for possible interference. By developing the line of piston skirt positions when viewed thru radial sections *1-2-3-4,* he may adopt a clearance chamfer which will not materially reduce the effectiveness of the counterweight.[4]

Note the design drawings, Figs. 13-12 and 13-13, for the upper and lower brackets of the food warmer. The size of the cans within the range selected determines the sizes of both the upper and lower brackets. Because the range is from 3″ to 7″ in height, three different sized lower brackets are required.

The clearances for the upper end of the clamp bar are determined by the shape of the cans from the top views as shown in Fig. 13-14.

Design Decisions

A fastener is needed for holding the adjustable brackets in position once the adjustment has been made. A 5/16″ diameter round-head bolt was chosen. This diameter is large enough to give strength. The round head is appropriate for use with a wing nut which is needed for ease of adjustment. The round shank will fit the contour of the rounded end of the slot in each bracket. One washer will give an adequate bearing surface and will distribute the grip of

PRODUCT PLANNING

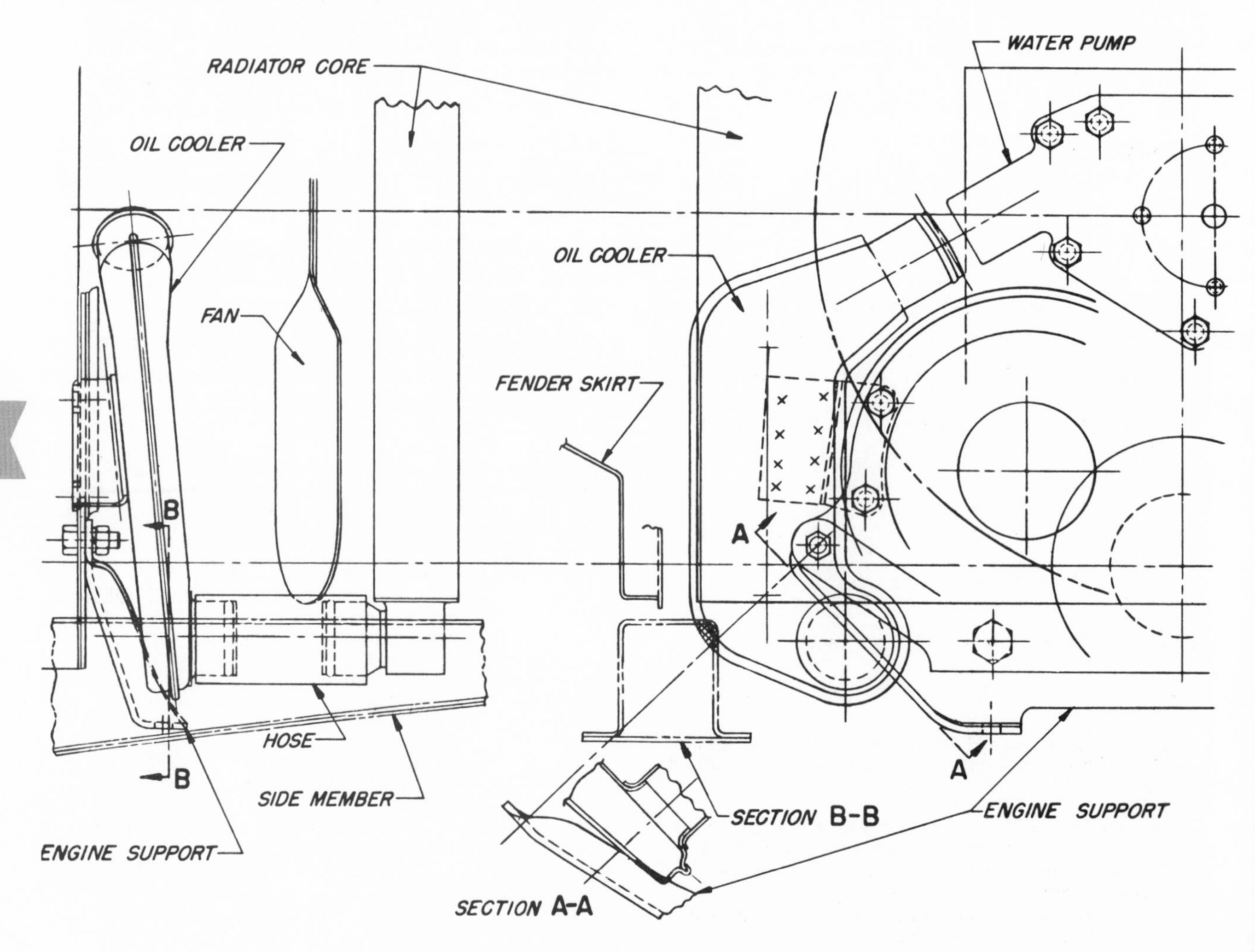

Fig. 13-10. Layout Drawing – Oil Cooler Installation (General Motors Corp.)

[4]*Ibid.,* p. A-146.

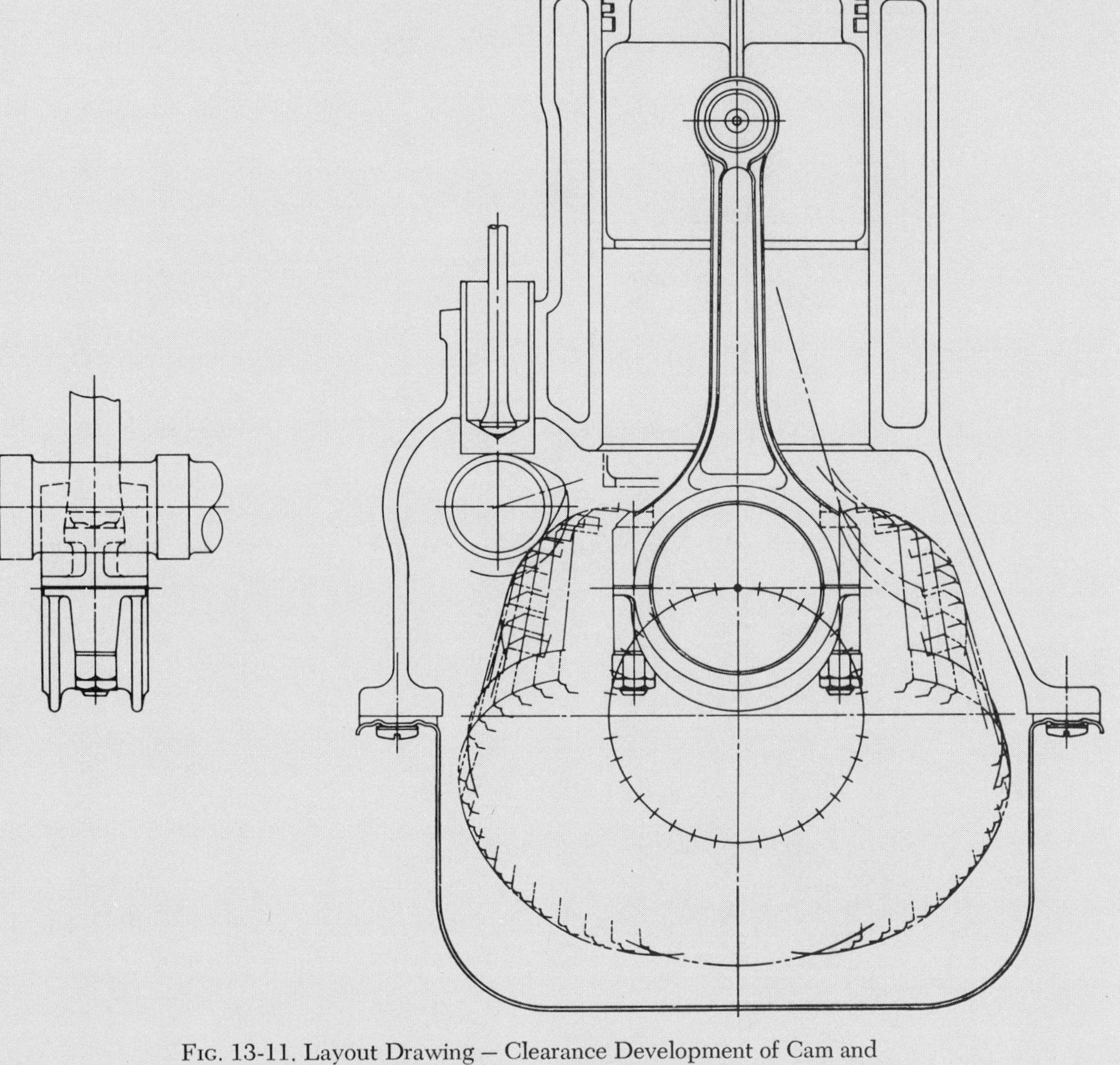

Fig. 13-11. Layout Drawing – Clearance Development of Cam and Counterweight Radius (General Motors Corp.)

fastening over a greater area of the brackets than the wing nut alone would do.

Slot size was determined on the basis of the diameter of the chosen fastening unit and the shape of the bolt near its head. An allowance of 1/32″ was made for easy insertion of the bolt into the slots and to permit easy location and adjustment of the upper and lower brackets.

The width of the brackets was determined on the basis of the strength believed necessary to hold the weight of the largest can of food. The weakest part of the bracket is the area of the slot. Use a minimum of the slot width for metal around the slot. Then choose the next

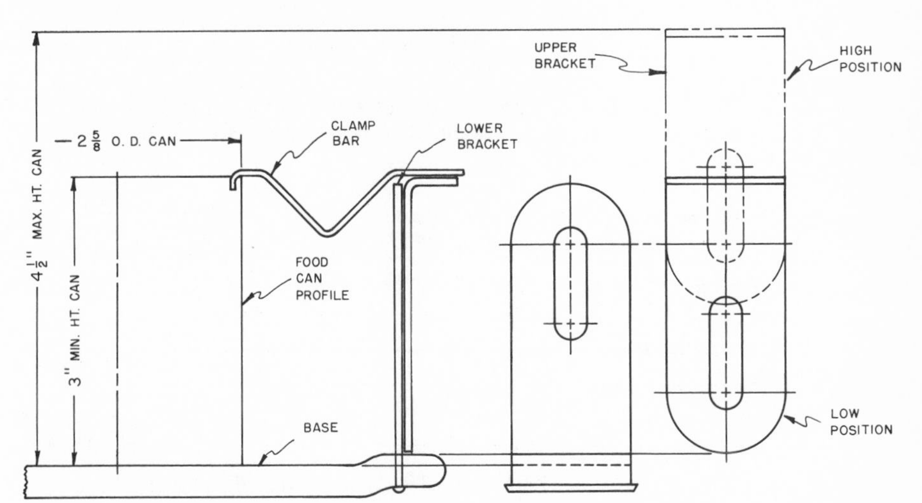

Fig. 13-12. Design Drawings to Determine Size of Upper and Lower Brackets Based on Smallest Size Can

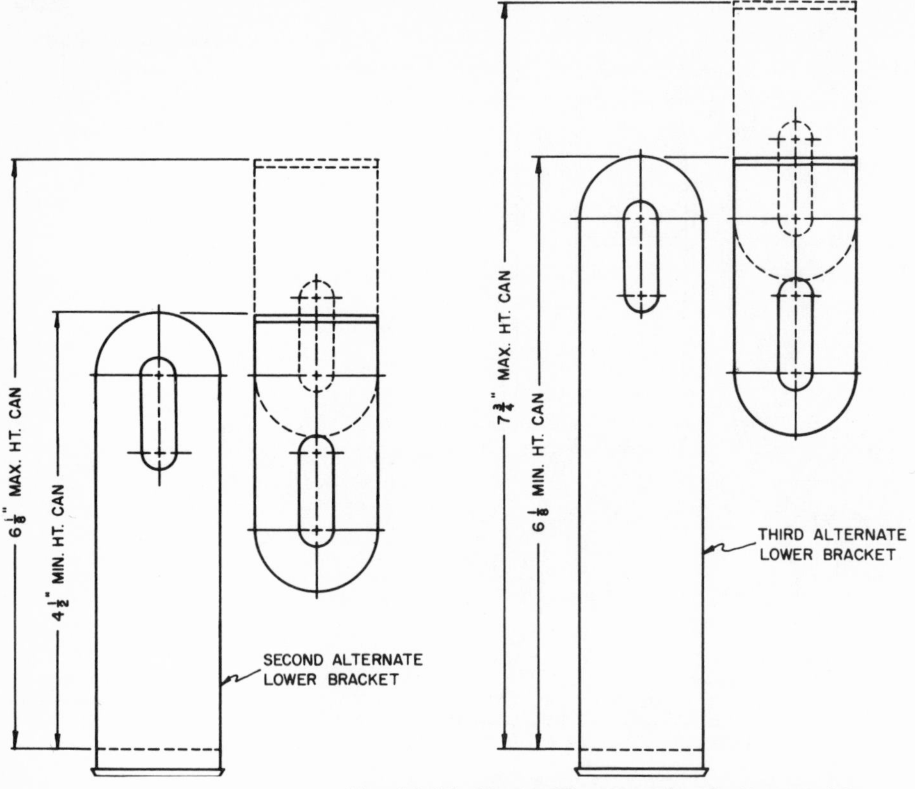

Fig. 13-13. Design Drawings for the Range of Sizes

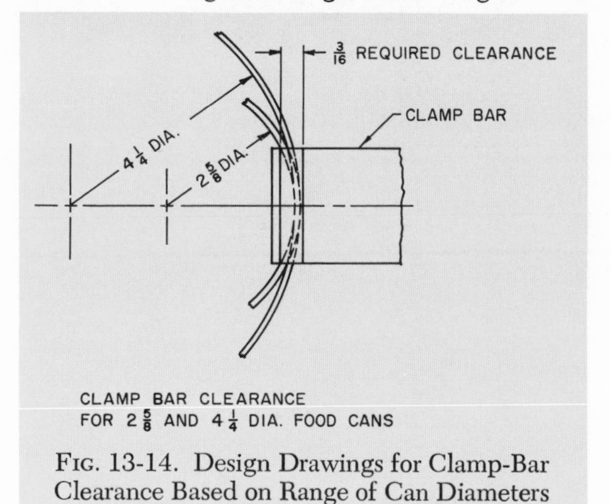

Fig. 13-14. Design Drawings for Clamp-Bar Clearance Based on Range of Can Diameters

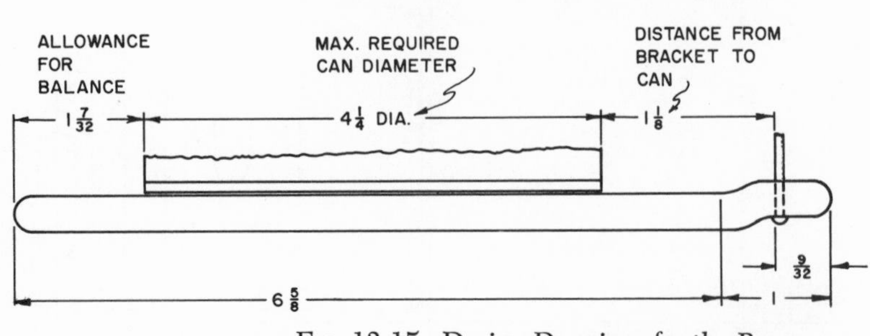

Fig. 13-15. Design Drawings for the Base

standard size width of metal. Slot width = 11/32″. Minimum allowance around the slot is 11/32″ on each side. Three times 11/32″ = 1 1/32″. The next standard size larger than this is 1⅛″ wide.

Thickness of the brackets was determined in the belief that 1/16″ would be strong enough to take the weight required and be as light in weight as possible.

The cold upset end of the lower bracket was determined on the basis of providing a bearing surface for the lower bracket and still permitting interchangeable units for the lower brackets so that different can heights could be accommodated. Blank lengths of 1/16″ oversize were allowed for the cold upset feature.

Length of the bend, and bend allowance for the upper bracket were determined on the basis of metal available for a sound spot weld to the clamp bar. Bend allowance was calculated from a standard formula:

$$BA = N\,(0.01745 \times R + 0.0078 \times T)$$

BA = bend allowance
N = number of degrees in the bend
R = radius of the bend
T = thickness of the metal

This allowance was added at the tangent of the bend.

The base piece was specified to be made from aluminum for lightness of weight and for ease of casting (possibly in a school shop). Diameter was made large enough to accommodate the largest diameter can, 4¼″, with the can in general balance on thebase, Fig. 13-15.

Thickness of the base was determined by having enough metal to provide sturdy support (5/16″). Ribs in the base bring the heat from the fire into direct contact with the can. The number of ribs was determined by an arbitrary division of the base into an equal number of spaces (8) so the ribs maintain an anticipated strength and ridgidity. The shape of the ends of the spaces in the base was determined by production requirements. Castings are stronger with rounded rather than sharp corners. The ribs were rounded at the bottom and tapered downward at 5° on each side to permit the casting to be easily removed from the form.

The lug at the base of the casting was designed to hold the lower bracket. This lug was offset upwards from the base in order to provide clearance for the cold upset end of the lower bracket. The size of the lug was determined by allowing an adequate amount of metal for strength so that the lug would not be weakened by the slot through it.

The steel knock-out core was designed so that the slot could be cast to proper size, shape, and location. See notes in Table 13-2.

Clamp bar length was determined by the bends required and the requirements of its various features, Table 13-3. Its slot width (25/64″) was determined by diameter of the handle shaft (3/8″). For quick insertion into position, a clearance of about 1/64″ should be adequate. Slot length was determined by the way the handle shaft fits, as shown in Fig. 13-16. The blank length of the slot was figured by adding the gain for three bends: 90°, .144″; 30°, .048″; and 60°, .096″ or a total of .288″ to the distance between centers of the slot as shown on the drawing of Part 5 in Fig. 6-5.

The handle diameter was judged to be comfortable in the average hand. The handle shaft should fit into the handle deeply enough for good support. The hole size to accommodate the handle shaft was specified the same size as the shaft, thus insuring a tight fit. The ferrule was back-tapered so that it would bring pressure around the handle at the handle shaft end and thus keep the handle from splitting as well as help to hold the shaft in position.

The lugs on the side of the handle shaft were formed from the shaft and should be strong enough to hold the entire unit when it is loaded. The lugs fit the "seat" in the clamp bar. The angle in the handle shaft allows a more direct and natural insertion of the shaft into its seat and permits easy retraction. A bend allowance was added to the blank length of the handle shaft to provide the angle. The length of the end of this shaft, with the lugs, extends beyond

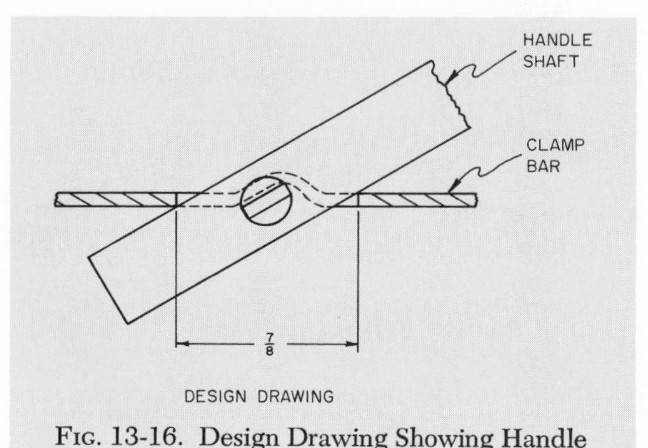

Fig. 13-16. Design Drawing Showing Handle Shaft Fitting into Clamp Bar

TABLE 13-2

Calculations for Determining Steel Knock-Out Core Specifications

Purpose: To provide a cast slot so that the three alternate lower brackets will be easily interchangeable.

Specification of bracket: #16 low carbon, hot rolled strip, SAE C-1008 .165 thick x 1.250 wide

Manufacturing variations (from Joseph T. Ryerson & Sons, Inc., data book, page 52)

1. variation from specified thickness	.004
2. additional variation at crown	.001
3. variation from specified width	.031

Allowances for class of fit: use an LC-10 fit, (TD-11-4, ± .004)

Calculations for slot size: must accommodate largest bracket

Thickness		Width	
Specified bracket thickness	.065	Width	1.250
Manufacturing variations	.005		.031
Maximum location allowance	.004		.004
Thickest bracket	.074	Widest bracket	1.285

TABLE 13-3

Clamp Bar Length Calculations*

Lip against which the can is forced	1/16″ =	.0625
90° bend-use standard formula		.144
Clearance for contour of circular cans	3/16″ =	.1875
45° bend to position clamp screw nut		.072
Space for clamp screw nut	13/16″ =	.8125
90° bend-change direction		.144
Return to desired elevation	13/16″ =	.8125
45° bend to return to desired direction		.072
Space for welding upper clamp bracket	15/16″ =	1.3125
30° bend to accommodate easy access for handle shaft		.048
Space for lugs of handle shaft	3/16″ =	.1875
90° bend to seat lugs		.144
60° bend to return clamp bar to original position		.096
Space to terminate clamp bar beyond the slot	1″ =	1.000
Blank length	53/32″ =	5.0950

*See drawings of clamp bar, Fig. 6-5.

PRODUCT PLANNING

the slot for purposes of holding it in place. Its diameter provides ample strength for lifting the loaded unit.

Basic Aesthetic Design Concepts

Aesthetics, or principles of design, are usually considered along with the planning for function. A successful product must function well, but a purely functional product will not sell as well as an *attractive* functional product.

How, then, does one make a product pleasing to observe without defeating its functional purpose? It has been implied that appropriate materials can be both functionally adequate and pleasing to the eye. Although one has never been seen, a coffee table supported by a short piece of 12″ steel I-beam would be an example of sacrificing aesthetics for function. On the other hand, a circular-picnic bench with a built-in lazy susan in the center of the table top has been invented. The idea for such a picnic table wasn't a bad one, but the choice of materials for the lazy susan was poor. The lazy susan was made from an old wagon wheel 36″ in diameter with a hub 12″ thick. The result was that the wheel blocked the line of vision of everyone sitting at the table, and it was too high and too far away for anyone to reach the food on it without standing up.

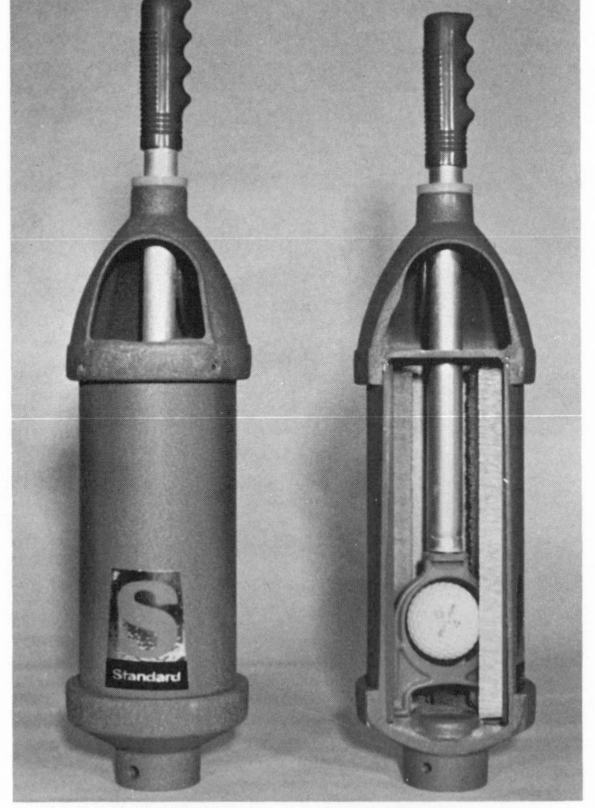

Fig. 13-17. Golf-Ball Washer (Doerfer Engineering Co.)

A sensitivity for pleasing design should be developed by all designers. The product must meet with customer approval, but designers should never compromise their ability to help the customer appreciate better design.

Before an industrial product is put on the market, careful consideration is given to its appearance and to the appearance of the package into which it is placed for shipping, display, and sale. During the last forty years, an increasing amount of attention has been given to the appearance of industrial products. It is generally accepted both by industry and the consumer that products should be functional as well as "pleasing to look at."

Even though a long thin tree branch with a piece of store string tied on it and a bent safety pin hook may be used to catch fish, more functional and more appealing equipment is available for anyone with fishing fever and a twenty-dollar bill. This may suggest that it costs money to improve the appearance of a product -- it does, but the consumer is usually willing to pay the price. In fact, more consumers are likely to buy the better-looking spin-casting outfit for fishing than are likely to make a tree-branch fishing pole. Thus the manufacturer sells more

Fig. 13-18. Dial-O-Gram Low-Form Balance (Ohaus Scale Corp.)

of his better-looking, functional, expensive product and thereby increases his profit.

An example of design improvement and larger profits is the golf ball washer shown in Fig. 13-17. This product is a redesign of a former model. Redesigning has resulted in improved styling (better looks), greater reliability, and reduced manufacturing cost.

The single-pan, low-form balance in Fig. 13-18 received a Master Designer's award from *Product Engineering*. It is both pleasing to look at and functional. The scale readings are easy to read and permit fine adjustments with a dial-type vernier scale. To insure strength and rigidity, the beam is constructed of high-strength, die-cast aluminum with ends cross braced. It uses precision sharpened knives and agate bearings to provide the utmost in accuracy.

Underlying a so-called *sensitive* design are several design principles. These principles cannot be applied with mathematical precision but rather are a matter of judgment, taste, attitude, and the like. Among the important principles are balance, proportion, rhythm, emphasis, and harmony.

Balance

The design principle of balance suggests stability. Balance can be formal and static — or informal and dynamic. Formal balance gives the impression of stateliness and dignity. Two blocks of equal size and weight placed equidistant from a fulcrum illustrates formal balance, Fig. 13-19. This principle is evidenced wherever we see objects with low centers of gravity that might be quite difficult to tip over, such as the Egyptian pyramids or a new, low-hanging racing car.

Informal or dynamic balance can be illustrated by placing two blocks of unequal size and weight at unequal distances from a fulcrum, Fig. 13-20. A hanging three-dimensional art mobile illustrates this, Fig. 13-21. In addition to the physical balance that exists, the mobile is a very interesting art form to observe because informal balance tends to be more interesting than formal balance.

The designer carefully considers whether the product he is designing evidences balance. Would you buy a car with the general shape of an old prairie schooner, Fig 13-22? Would you buy a golf club with all the weight in the handle, Fig. 13-23? There is a direct relation-

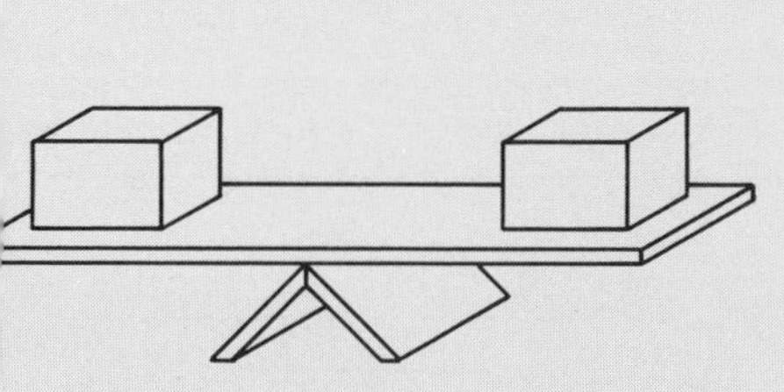

13-19. Formal Balance — Objects of Equal
ze and Weight Equidistant from Fulcrum

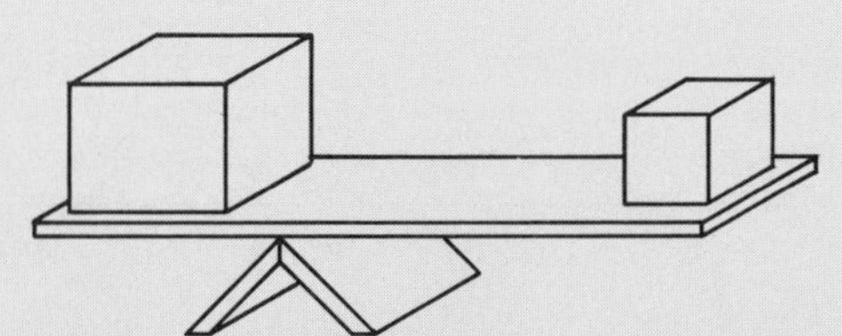

Fig. 13-20. Informal Balance — Objects of Unequal Size and Weight Placed Appropriate Distances from the Fulcrum

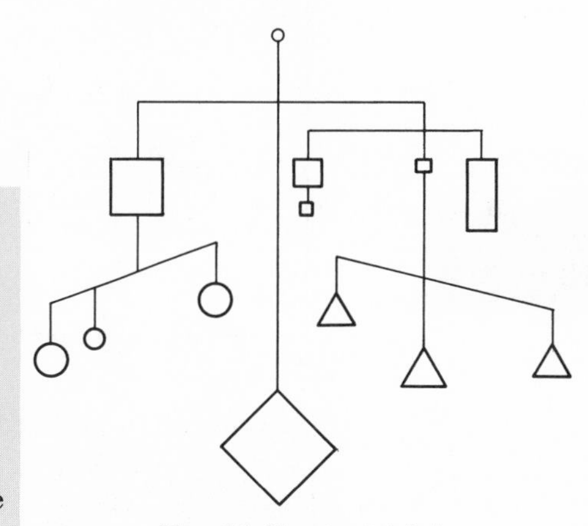

Fig. 13-21. Art Mobile

Fig. 13-22. Prairie Schooner Car

Fig. 13-23. Golf Club With Over-Weighted Handle

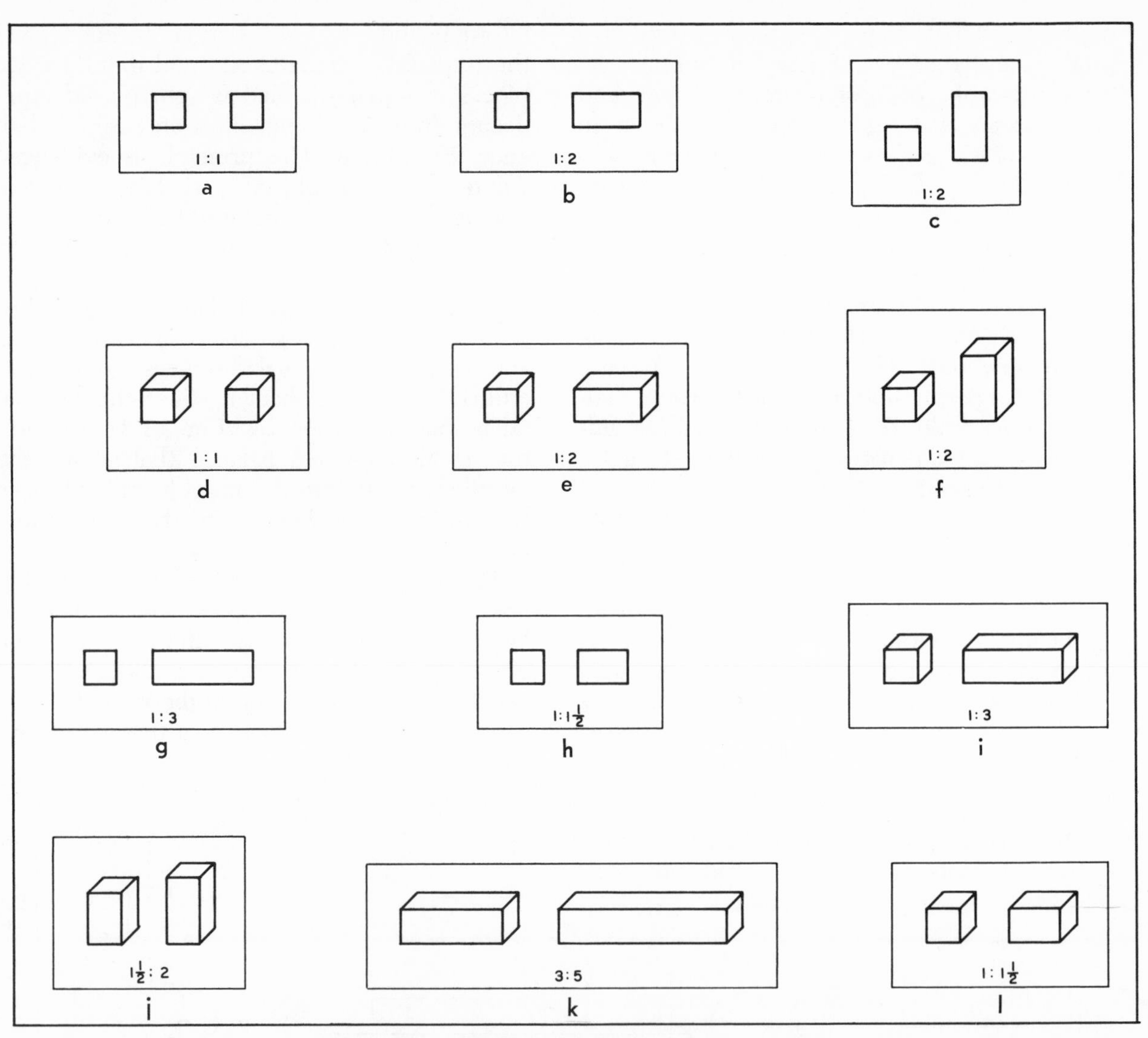

FIG. 13-24. Varying Ratios of Size

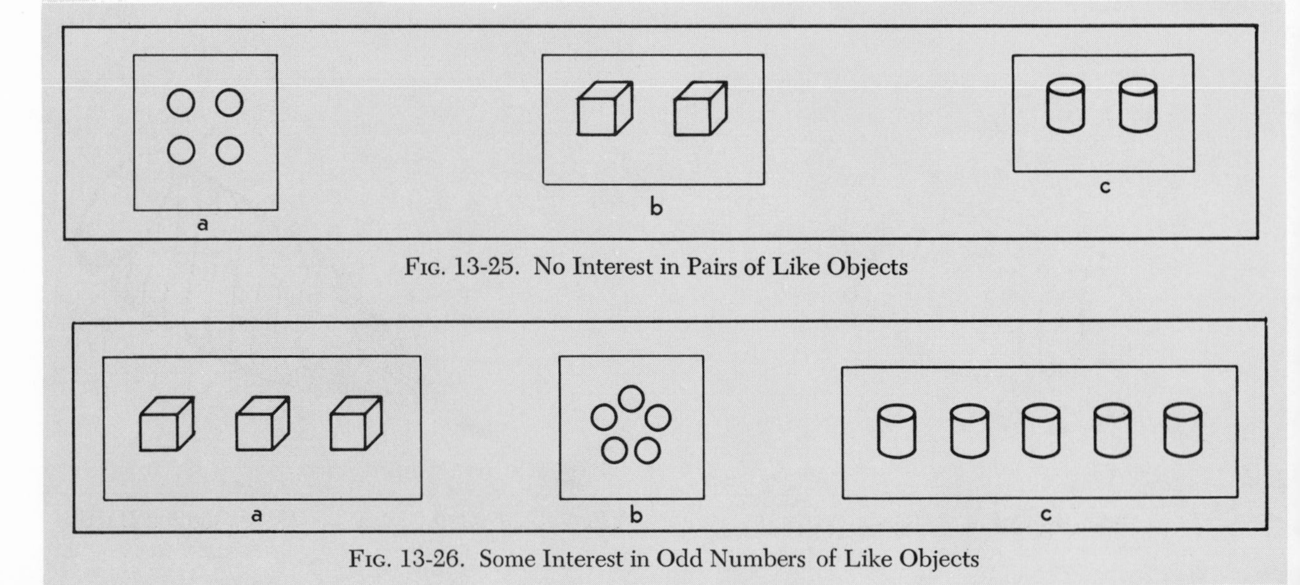

FIG. 13-25. No Interest in Pairs of Like Objects

FIG. 13-26. Some Interest in Odd Numbers of Like Objects

ship between the balance that a product exhibits, the efficiency with which its functions can be performed, and the likelihood that the consumer may buy the product.

Proportion

Proportion as a design principle may be more elusive than balance. Proportion has to do with the relationships of size and shapes in both two and three dimensions. A shape which is well proportioned from one viewing direction is not necessarily pleasing to look at from another viewing direction. Yet, in designing products, most are viewed from many angles and should exhibit sensitive proportion in all three dimensions.

When an object is pleasing to look at, it is believed to be well proportioned. Because of individual differences in people and because of different levels of understanding of good proportion, what is proportional for one person may not be well proportioned for another. Simple geometric shapes of circles or spheres and squares or cubes may hold a certain beauty for some people. To others, it might be too mechanical, too formal, and not well proportioned.

From the standpoint of construction efficiency and least cost, the best shape for a house is cubical. This is not sensitive proportion for houses and, consequently, it is quite difficult to find a house which is a true cube in shape.

Relationships of size such as 1:3, 1½:2, and 3:5 are more interesting than relationships of 1:1, 1:2, Fig. 13-24.

As products become more complex and are made up of multiple units, proportion continues to be important to appearance. Pairs of like objects of the same size are not especially interesting, Fig. 13-25. An odd number of the same object becomes more interesting, Fig. 13-26. Two objects of differing size may be placed in an interesting way. Fig. 13-27 suggests both balance and proportion. What would be the effect of interchanging the position of the large and small objects in Fig. 13-27? Try it on a piece of paper and see what it looks like. An odd number of objects, one of which is either larger or smaller, is pleasing to observe, Fig. 13-28.

Rhythm

Rhythm indicates a feeling of movement, Fig. 13-29. It may be expressed by the flow of lines and/or the repetition of design elements. Again, rhythm might be expressed by a series of equal geometrical forms, but repetition alone does not create interest. A gradual change or progression of repeated elements gives a more interesting effect.

Rhythm can exist in the changing relationship between repetitive patterns of space relations, changes in texture patterns, and changes in color.

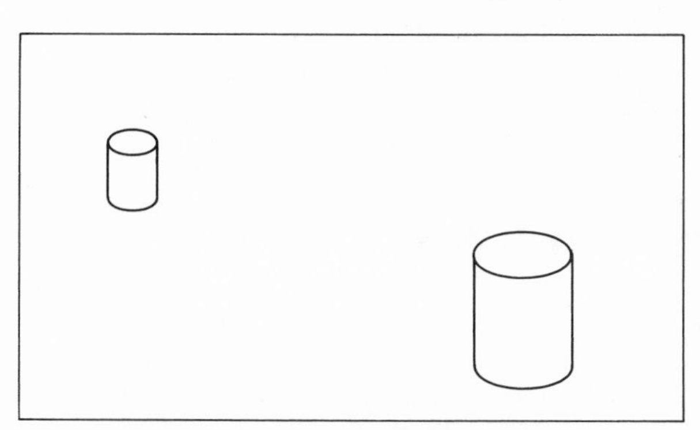

Fig. 13-27. Interesting Placement of Two Objects of Unequal Size

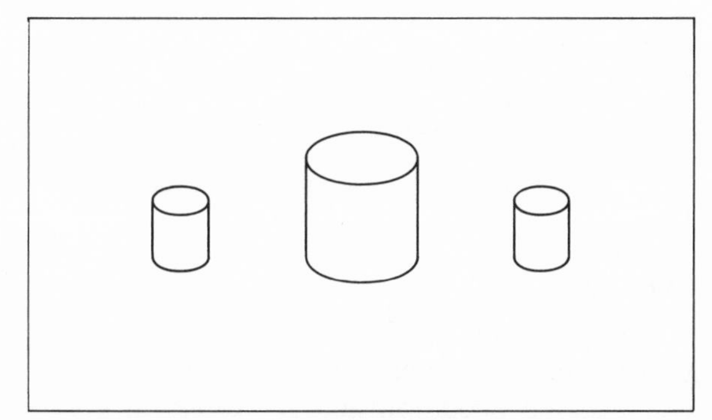

Fig. 13-28. Interesting Odd Numbers such as One Large and Two Small

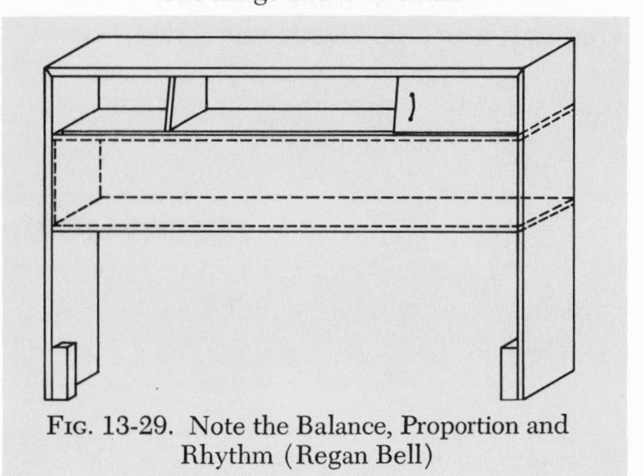

Fig. 13-29. Note the Balance, Proportion and Rhythm (Regan Bell)

FIG. 13-30. Emphasis in Advertisement Centered on the Dot

Emphasis

Emphasis permits the designer to draw attention to the important part of the design. This can also be accomplished by different treatments. Color is useful in drawing attention. An example from advertising is shown in Fig. 13-30. Lines may lead the eye to various features. Size, shape, texture, materials, and other approaches may be used to provide emphasis and to draw attention to the products.

Harmony

Harmony is the design principle relating to the general "feeling of belonging" given by the whole product, Fig. 13-8. Harmony lies somewhere between monotony and discord. Common sense, good judgment, an understanding of the desires of people, an understanding of and experience with design contributes to one's ability to apply the principles.

There are many ways in which sensitive design principles are violated. Although the two categories of violations which follow are found in commercial designs, they are most frequently found in school shop products and home workshop products.

1. Using materials that are not proportional to the strength necessary for proper function, for example: a steel hammer handle of the size and shape as the conventional well-designed wood handle, or a jewel box for men's tie clips made from ¾" solid stock. A more appropriate thickness of materials would be ⅜" or ¼" plywood or solid stock.
2. Decorating for the sake of decoration. Complicated curve forms of an ornate nature are often entirely non-functional because of the cleaning problem. This is likely to happen because wood is so easy to cut and shape. But, it may also occur in the design of wrought iron projects where, again, it is easy to bend the material.

Although the principles just discussed are by no means the only principles of design, they may be applied to design whether the problem is simple or complex, large or small, and regardless of the materials which are involved.

Those interested in a deeper understanding of sensitive design will want to study references listed in the bibliography section of this book, and especially Lindbeck's book.[5]

product description

Sketches describe products in their earliest stages of development, and are used again for studying aesthetic qualities of the product. Layout and design drawings are studies of relationships between various parts as they may function together. With technical and aesthetic problems solved and with most of the decisions

[5]John R. Lindbeck, *Design Textbook*, McKnight and McKnight Publishing Co., Bloomington, Ill., 1963.

made, the product must be described so that it can be manufactured. To bring the product from the planning stages to the finished product stage requires experimental and production types of drawings.

Experimental Drawings

Design layout studies and decisions relative to the aesthetics of the product are both a forerunner and a part of experimental drawings. Experimental drawings are both a forerunner and *may become* a part of the production drawings. Only a few of the experimental drawings ever reach the production stage. One company reported that only about one out of five of their experimental drawings reaches the production stage.

Experimental drawings are usually drawn just as completely, with just as much care, and using the same drafting techniques as production drawings. One of the chief differences between them is that the two types of drawings may carry different title blocks and the numbering systems will be sufficiently different so that each can be easily and instantly recognized by number alone.

These drawings may carry notes suggesting experimentation with forms or an alternate color or material, reflecting ideas which preliminary study alone did not show. Notes may also recommend the tryout of purchased parts from different manufacturers to see which of these actually functions best under experimental conditions.

Experimental drawings are more like drawings for custom-made products because they may be followed by making a pilot model. These models are not made on the regular production equipment. Large manufacturing companies have special shops and departments for research, experimentation, and testing. For this reason special instruction relative to the processes to be used in the manufacture of the pilot models may be included on experimental drawings.

The purpose of the pilot model is to see whether the proposed product is all that the planners had expected. What does it look like in three-dimensional form? How do the parts fit together and function as an integrated unit? What production problems may arise?

In the light of answers to these and other questions, additional experimental drawings will be prepared and possibly additional pilot models will be produced. When the intended production run is large enough to warrant it, a pilot production run is made so that all foreseeable problems can be cleared up before expensive tooling is completed.

Drawings of products made by students in classes are much more characteristic of experimental drawings than of production drawings. The product designed and made by an individual student is more characteristic of a pilot model than of a finished product. The sketches, drawings, and products made by the home craftsman are more characteristic of experimental drawings and pilot models than anything else. Almost anyone who has planned and constructed an item is anxious to point out how he would change it if he were to make another and/or how he would proceed differently if he were to construct another such article.

Production Drawings

To change experimental drawings to production drawings is not difficult. The drawing is simply reproduced on a sensitized tracing medium, the necessary drafting changes are made, a different title strip is applied and filled out, and production drawing numbers are assigned.

Terminology for various kinds of production drawings and practices and procedures are not completely standardized throughout American industry. Generally, production drawings include detail drawings completely describing the various parts of the product, assembly and/or subassembly drawings showing the relationship of the parts to the whole product, and manufacturing drawings consisting of those drawings needed to get the parts manufactured with the various production machines at the manufacturer's disposal.

Detail Drawings

A detail drawing is one which completely describes the shape, size, and location of all the geometric characteristics of a part, Fig. 13-31. Detail drawings are used in both experimental and production drawings and are usually placed on a preprinted sheet of one of the standard sizes. A detail drawing may have one, two,

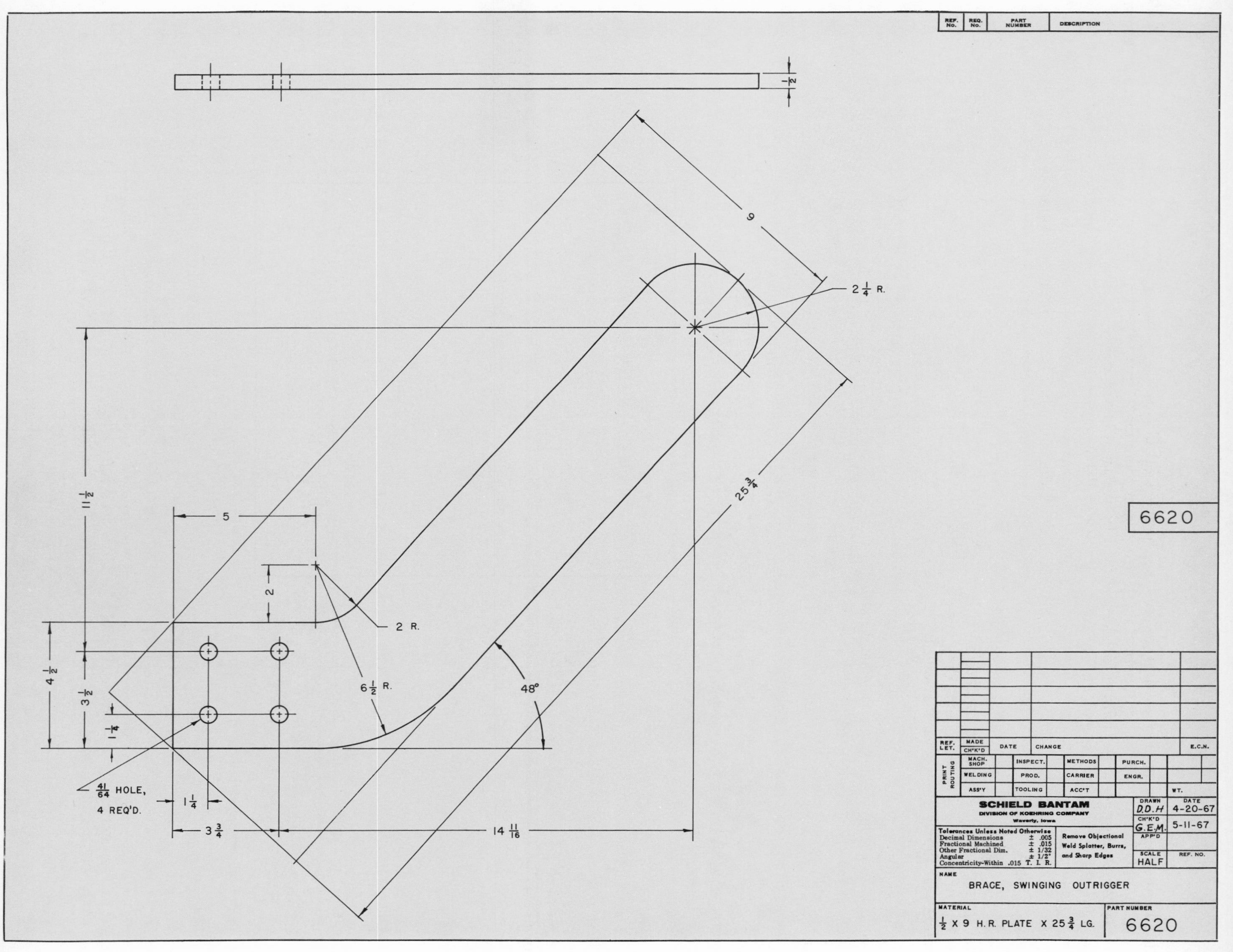

Fig. 13-31. Detail Drawing of Brace (Shield-Bantam Co.)

T20986T

INTER-FACTORY

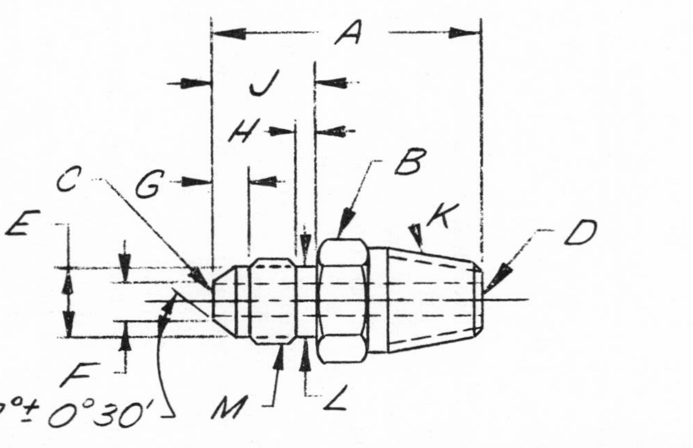

NOM TUBE OD	A	B	C	D	E	F	G	H	J	K PIPE THREAD	L	M THREAD
1/4	28,17 1.109	12,7 .50	4,36 .172	4,36 .172	9,27 .365	4,9 .193	4,9 .193	1,91 .075	13,97 .550	1/8-27NPTF	9,25 .364	7/16-20UNF-2A

DECISION	DATE	BY	CHKD
16002	3-11-64	WH	

LOCATING POINTS △ METRIC XX,X

THIRD ANGLE PROJECTION USED

⌒ FLAT & STRAIGHT ⦿ CONCENTRICITY
∠ ANGULARITY ⌖ TRUE POSITION
⊥ PERPENDICULAR ○ ROUNDNESS
∥ PARALLELISM ⌯ SYMMETRY

MAT'L REF

UNSPECIFIED TOLERANCES ARE:
MACHINE FINISH DIMENSIONS ± .02 0.5
ANGLES ± 1 DEGREE
FOR TOLERANCES NOT SPECIFIED ON DRAWING SEE DTW 301

JOHN DEERE
JOHN DEERE DUBUQUE TRACTOR WORKS
DUBUQUE, IOWA

WAS 22X18052 DRAWN WH 6-27-63 CHKD APPD SCALE NONE

MATERIAL STEEL

PURCHASE

NAME CONNECTOR

CATEGORY CODE MATERIAL CODE

T20986T

Fig. 13-32. Drafting Efficiency Achieved by Tabled Dimensions (by permission)

three, or more orthographic views — enough to completely describe it. The title block will contain the standard information, and somewhere on the detail drawing, most often in the title block, will be the part number. Usually, the necessary views for only one part are placed on one sheet of paper, although several parts may be detailed on one sheet. Because the detail drawings may be used in the shop to work from in the manufacture of the part, they are often called *working drawings.*

Where dimensions cannot conveniently be placed in confined spaces, a table may be set up to show the dimensions, Fig. 13-32.

In Fig. 13-33 the enlarged section *A* shows additional detail which could not very well be dimensioned even with the scale being four times (4x) full-size.

Assembly Drawings

Assembly drawings show relationships of parts. They may show the whole product or just a part of it, in which case they are called subassembly drawings. Basic types of assembly classifications are the projected assembly drawing, which may or may not be sectioned, and the pictorial assembly drawing, which may or may not be in exploded pictorial form.

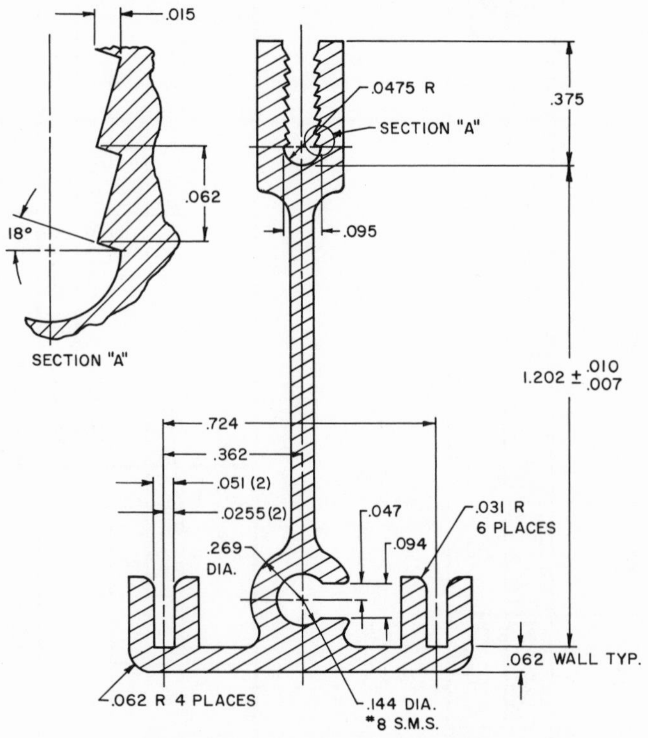

Fig. 13-34 is a projected subassembly drawing. Orthographic projection is used. All parts carry a part number for purposes of identification, and these are keyed to the parts list appearing on the drawing. The only dimensions given are those that permit the tool maker and the assembler to locate the parts in their correct relationship to one another. The welding note specifies the fastening method.

A sectioned projection subassembly drawing is shown in Fig. 13-35. The sectioning permits observation of interior detail which would not be clear without the section view. Part numbers are included for identification. These are keyed to a parts list, but the list is on a separate sheet and is not shown in the illustration.

Fig. 13-36 is a German-made sectioned subassembly drawing of a lifting spindle. The housing, part L 11313 L (Fig. 13-37) is a detail drawing completely describing the size, shape, and location of all geometrical characteristics of the housing.

An assembly drawing in pictorial form is shown in Fig. 6-2. It is accompanied by a partial sectioned assembly drawing which helps to show additional detail not visible from the pictorial form alone. The parts each bear a part number for reference and identification.

Exploded assembly drawings in pictorial form show how parts fit together. This type of assembly is often used in catalogs for easy identification and on the assembly line as an aid in the actual assembly of the product. Fig. 13-38 is a complete exploded pictorial assembly drawing. Part 13 is cut away to show how the parts relate to each other rather than to show interior detail. Leaders are placed in only two directions, thus making a much neater drawing than if they were at a wide variety of directions.

Refer back to Fig. 3-64. This example shows all of the details, together with the assembly drawing, for six different sizes of T-squares. This is accomplished by use of a table identifying the six T-square sizes and by using letters for dimensions on the drawing. This table, then, can be read for each of the various T-squares without making six separate

FIG. 13-33. Enlarged Section View "A" (Titus Metals Corp.)

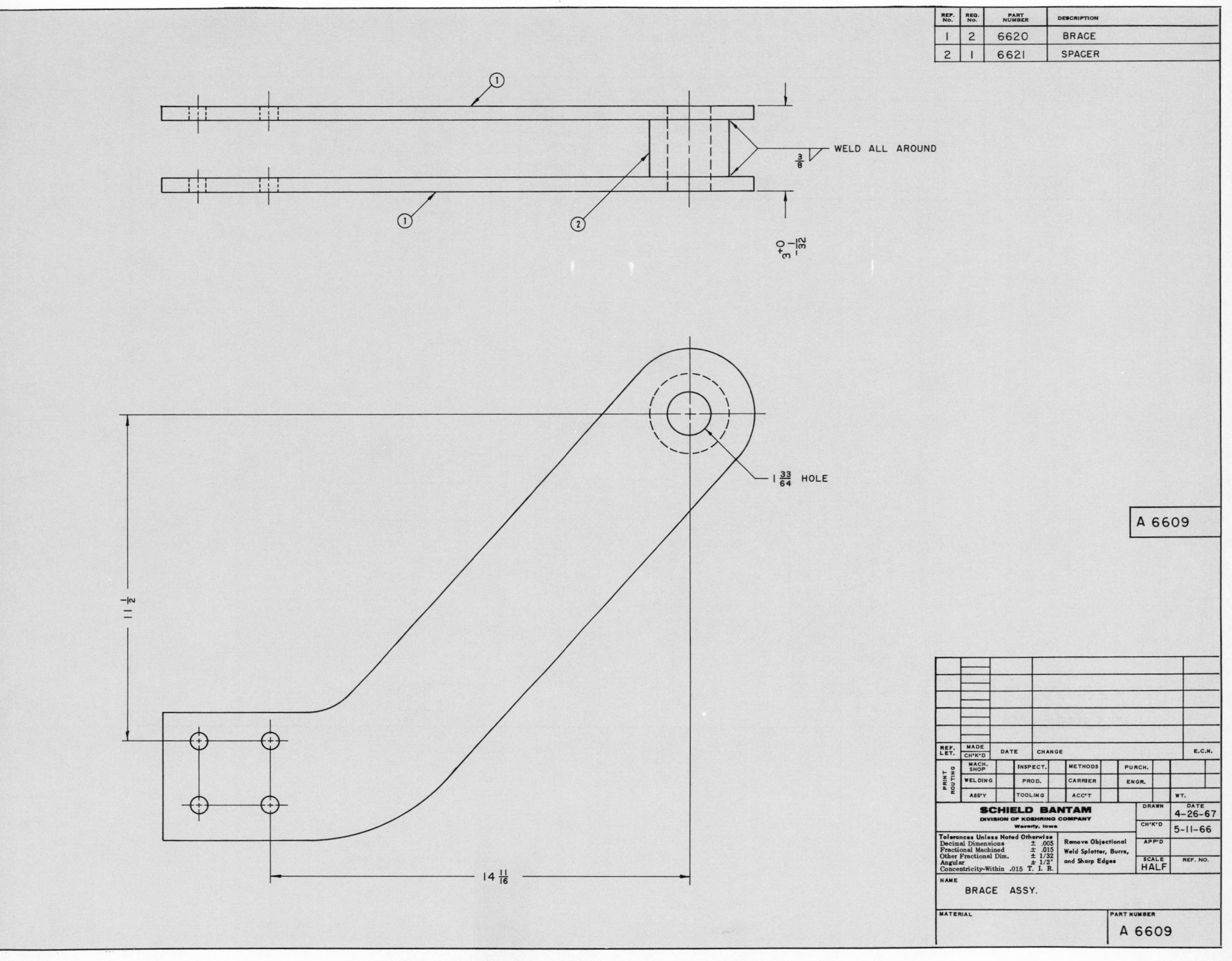

FIG. 13-34. Projected Sub-Assembly Drawing (Shield-Bantam Co.)

PRODUCT PLANNING

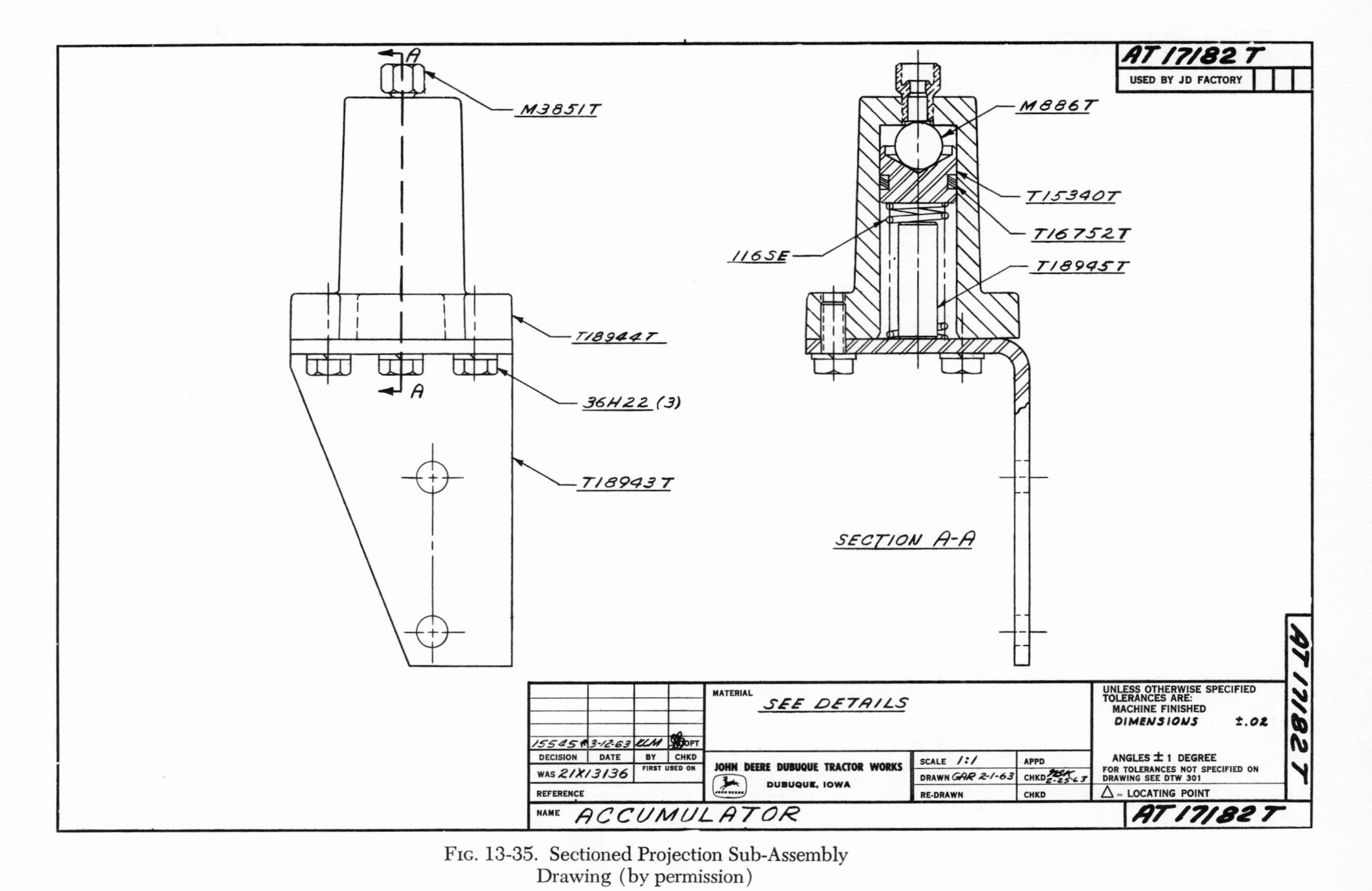

Fig. 13-35. Sectioned Projection Sub-Assembly Drawing (by permission)

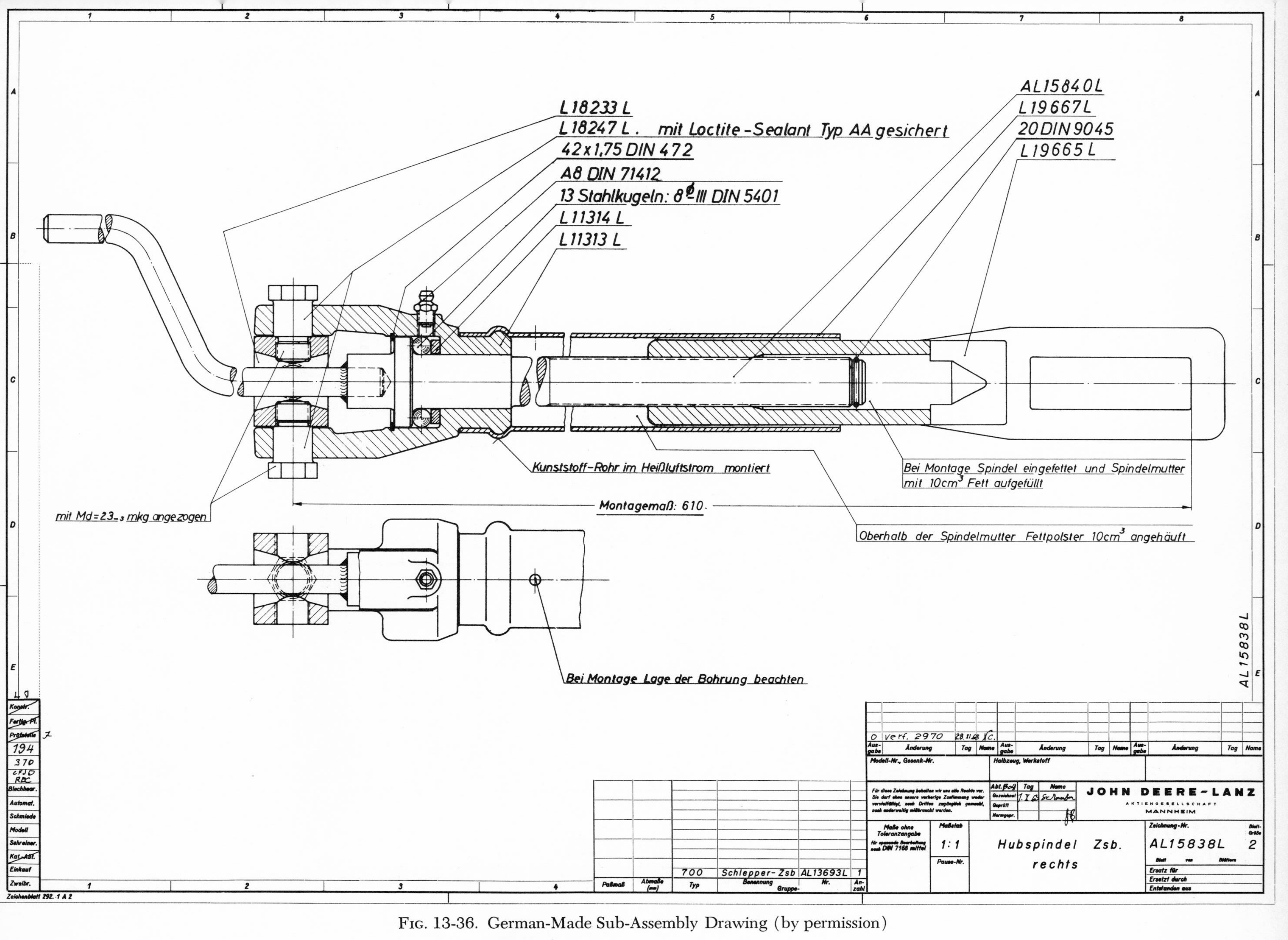

Fig. 13-36. German-Made Sub-Assembly Drawing (by permission)

PRODUCT PLANNING

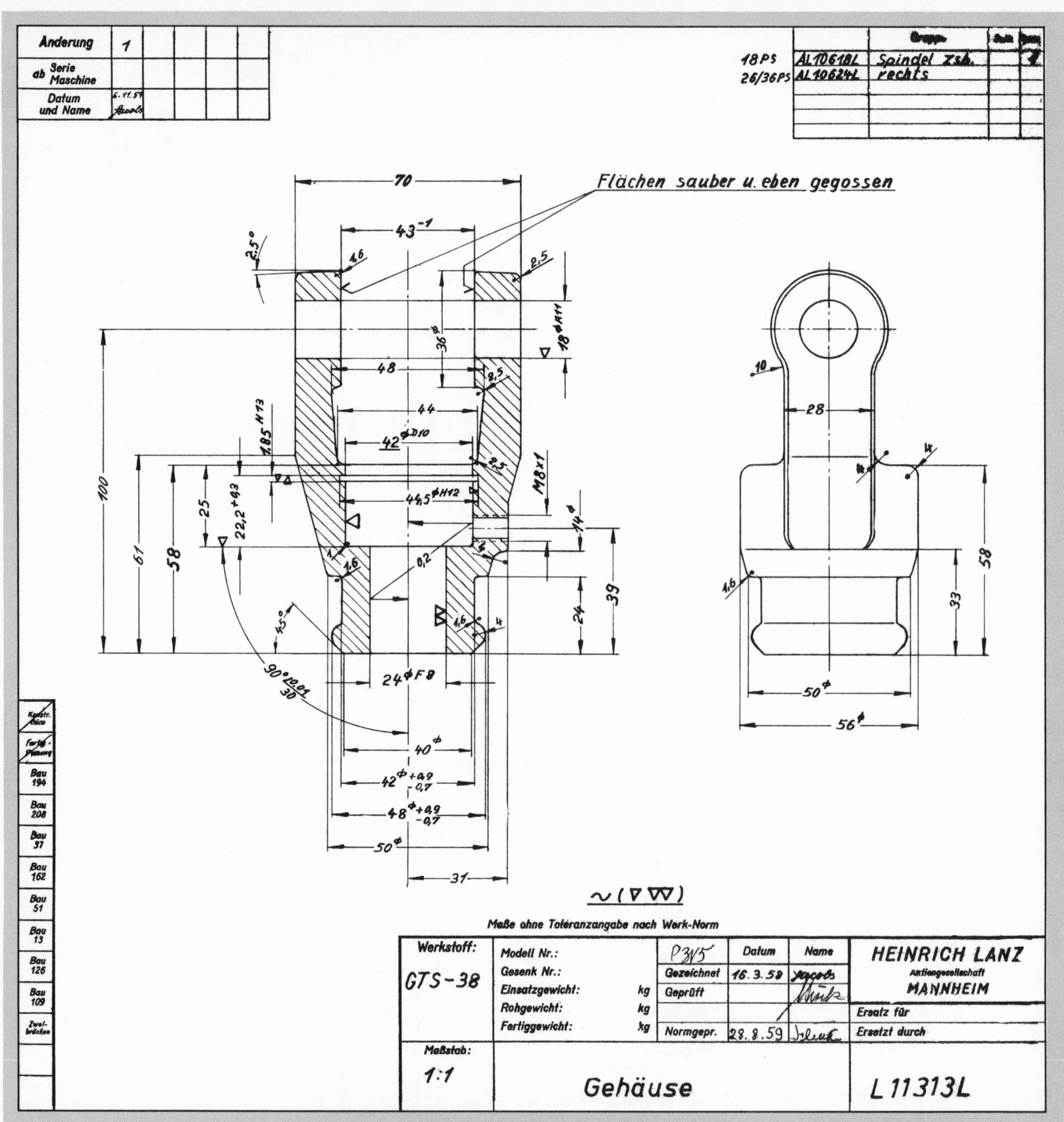

Fig. 13-37. German-Made Detail Drawing of Part No. L 11313L (by permission)

drawings. A different part number is used for each size of each part. In some cases, the same part is used to make-up more than one size T-square. The number 2-F-51 head is used on three T-squares; namely: #7051, 18″; #7052, 24″ and #7053, 30″.

Lists of Materials and Parts Lists

The *parts list* for a drawing includes the part numbers, names, and quantities required. The *list of materials* is more inclusive. It contains the part numbers, names, and quantities required plus material specification, material unit weight, and other data, Fig. 13-39. These lists itemize all the parts needed. A parts list or a materials list accompanies each assembly or subassembly drawing. Such lists may be on a separate sheet as in Tables 6-3 and 6-4 or on the drawing as already shown in Fig. 13-34. They usually occupy a position immediately above the title block in the lower right-hand corner reading upward. They may occupy some other open space on the drawing as in Fig. 3-64. In all cases the parts listed are carefully keyed to the assembly drawings and to the appropriate detail drawing. Identical parts bear the same part numbers.

Manufacturing Drawings

When the experimental drawings have been completed and the detailed drawings have been approved for production, additional drawings are required to manufacture most parts. For example, consider the detail drawing of the ¼″ flat back rotor, Fig. 13-40. Someone must decide what operations will be needed, what machines will be used, and what special tools are required to produce the rotor. The manufacturing or methods engineering department has this responsibility. It will already have done preliminary work in cost studies. Now it must identify the steps of procedure carefully and specifically and prepare the necessary paper work to insure a steady flow of these parts to the assembly line. Personnel in this department are familiar with all the machines available for use in the shop, their advantages, limitations, and general capabilities.

The forged rotor parts are purchased from a vendor. They must be machined to the specifications of Fig. 13-40. A *route sheet* is carefully prepared. This lists the operation number, description of the operation, department number, machine upon which the work is to be done, special tools needed, and the time for production, Fig. 13-41. To accompany the route sheet a blank drawing is prepared, Fig. 13-42. This shows the specific operations and their sequence as keyed to the route sheet. A stock of partially completed rotors is built up and kept on the plant floor in a storage area. Note that the route sheet of Fig. 13-41 carries the item as far as "stock point." This permits more than one finished rotor to be manufactured from this particular blank drawing. Rotors to be made from the blank drawing shown are 2-561-07, 2-561-05 and 2-561-028. Fig. 13-40 shows the finished dimensions of rotor 2-561-007. Another route sheet is prepared to bring this rotor up to the specifications required, Fig. 13-43. Notice that the finished detail drawing has a note on it that it is to be manufactured from rotor blank 2-561-994.

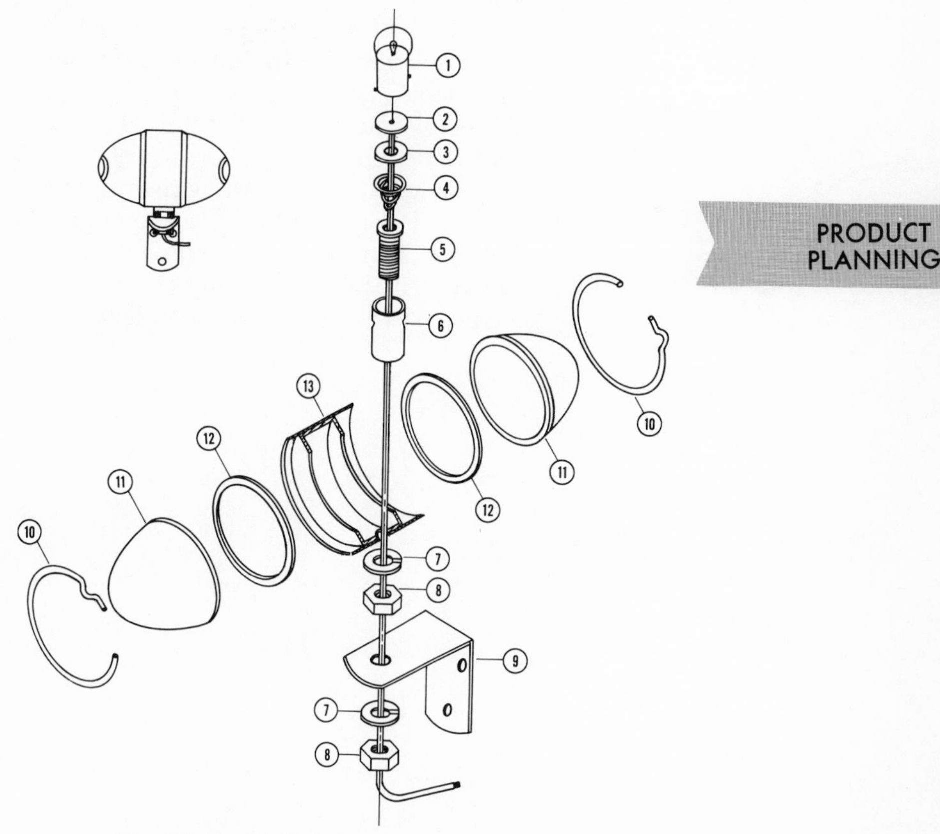

Fig. 13-38. Exploded Assembly of Double Clearance Light

Chapter 13 — Problems and Projects

1. Write problem statements, in terms of the functions to be served, for the following:
   a. A study lamp.
   b. A paper punch.
   c. Model-makers vise or hand-clamp.
   d. Outboard motor stand.
   e. A handbill advertising a local play.
   f. A key for sending Morse code.
   g. A turntable for spray finishing of model cars.
   h. Something of your choice.
2. Make a functional analysis — complete with idea, sketches, and tentative solutions — for one of the products above.
3. Study the four illustrations in Fig. 13-44, Problem 1. Decide which of the four arrangements of two shadow boxes is most pleasing to the eye. What design principles does your choice reflect?
4. Redesign the headboard, Problem 2, Fig. 13-44, for better proportion, balance, and style.
5. Problem 3 of Fig. 13-44 would not be considered sensitive design for a modern coffee table. Explain why. Redesign this coffee table and present a sketch of a more sensitive design.
6. The case for carrying drafting instruments, Problem 4, Fig. 13-44, is not functional from the standpoint of removing items from the compartments. Suggest through sketches how the interior could be redesigned so that the items put in it would be more easily accessible.
7. Suggest a rearrangement of the spacing of the shelves, Problem 5, Fig. 13-44, to make them more interesting and to give more appropriate space division.
8. The study desk, Problem 6, Fig. 13-44, is poorly designed from the standpoint of general appearance. State the principles by which its design can be improved. Make a sketch showing essentially the same study unit but with an improved aesthetic design.
9. Make a complete set of experimental drawings for the product you selected for Problem 2. Include a bill of materials and the steps of procedure for making the model.
10. Select a product suitable for mass production in a school shop situation. Write a problem statement in terms of the function of the product. Make an analysis of the function complete with sketches and tentative decisions. Prepare the experimental drawings from which the pilot model could be made. Set up a plan showing (1) the number of units to be produced, (2) the bill of materials for one unit, (3) the list of materials for the whole production run, (4) the steps of procedure to produce one object, and (5) the personnel assignments for the production run. Identify any jigs or fixtures needed and make the tool drawings for these.

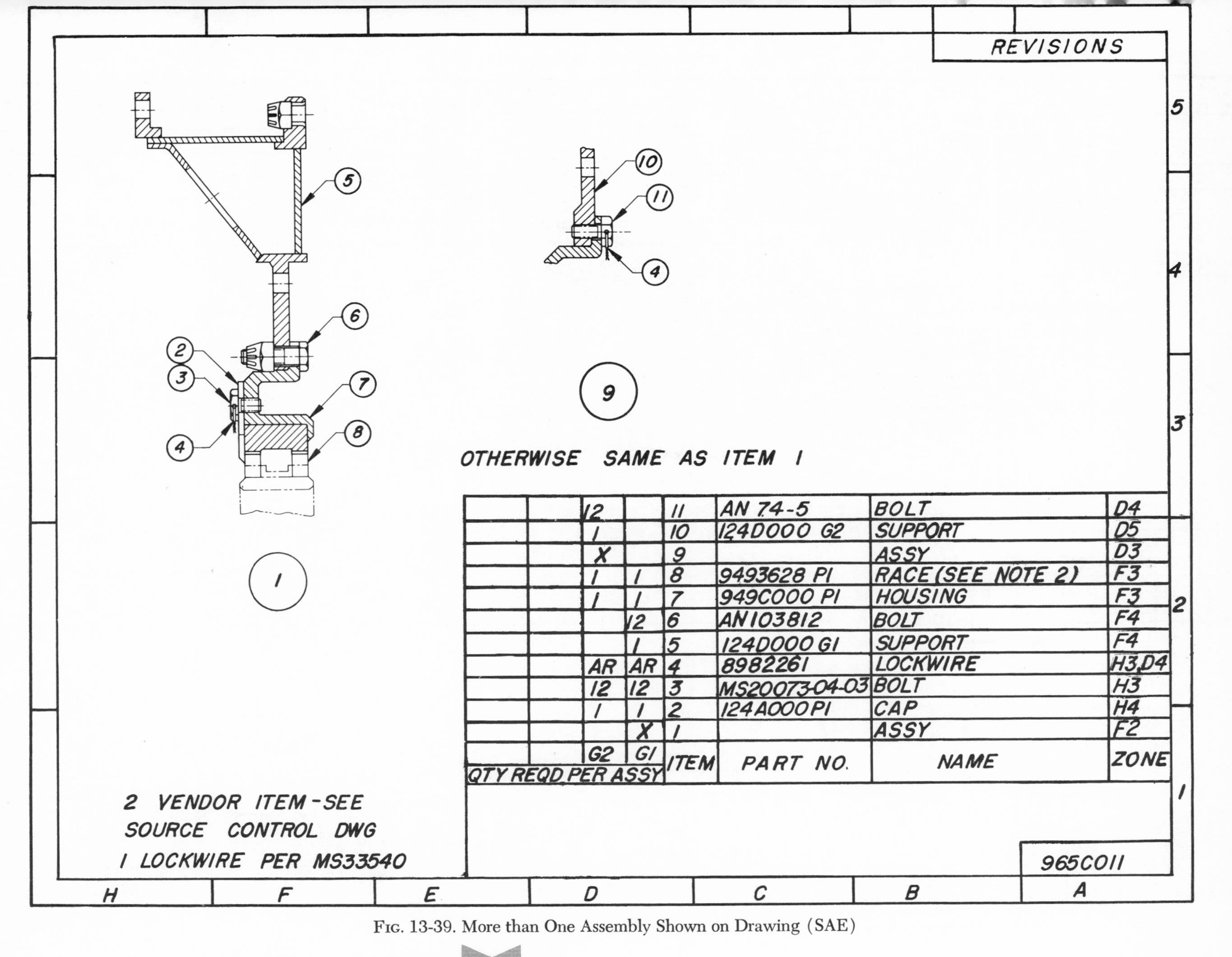

Fig. 13-39. More than One Assembly Shown on Drawing (SAE)

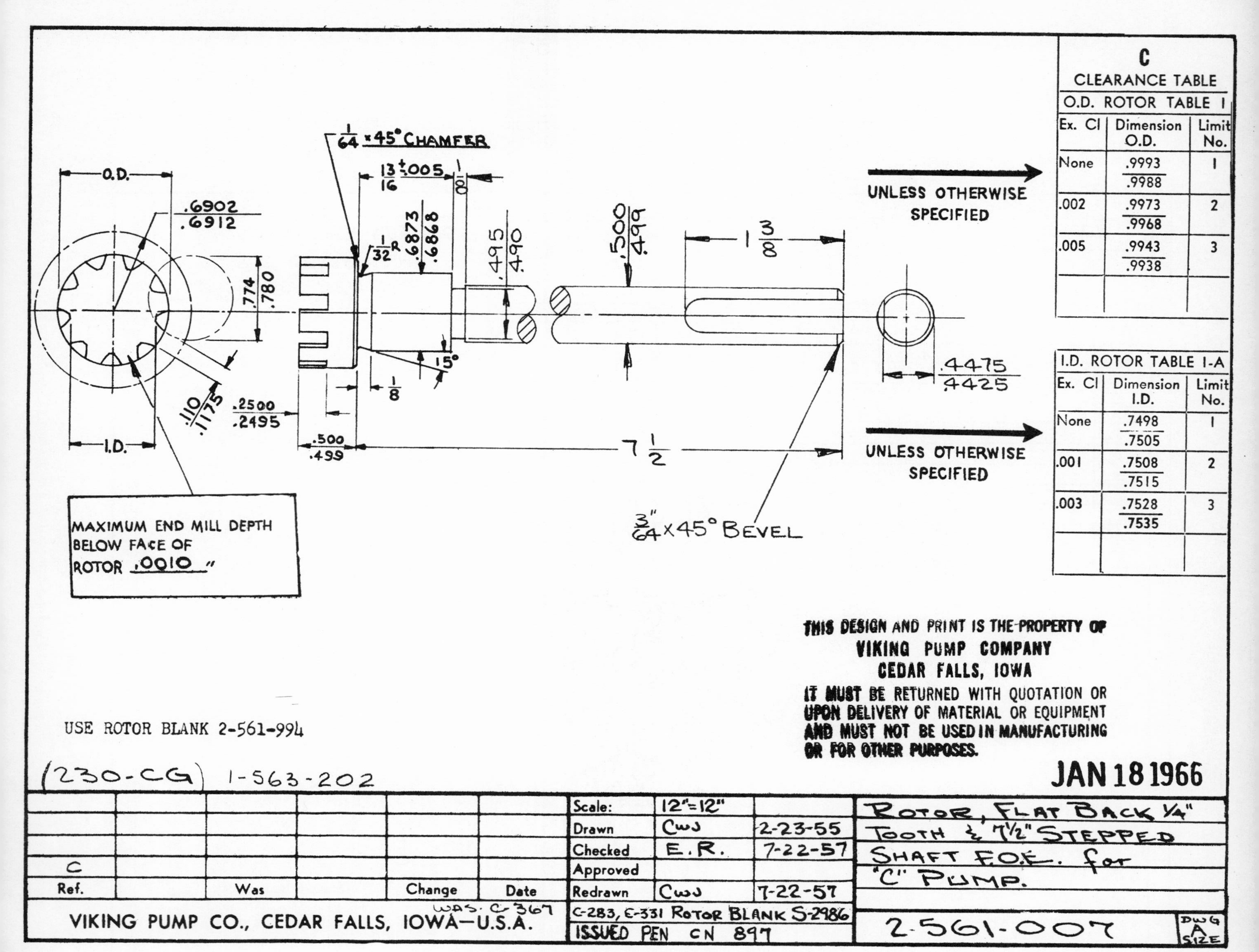

FIG. 13-40. Detail Drawing of Rotor (by permission)

CODE NO. 2-561-994-280 EFFECTIVE DATE 1-18-66

OPER. NO.	DESCRIPTION OF OPERATION		MACH.	TOOLS	STD. TIME
4	SET UP				0.1
5	CUT OFF	52	666		0.0091
9	SET UP				0.5
10	CENTER SHAFT END	52	579		0.0097
14	SET UP				1.5
15	TURN SHAFT, STEP AND UNDERCUT	52	000	TJ-985	0.0263
19	SET UP				2.8
20	TURN, BORE, FACE, FACE TEETH TO LENGTH CENTER HEAD END AND TOOL CENTER	55	448	TL-184	0.0067
24	SET UP				0.2
25	ROUGH GRIND SHAFT	53	586		0.0165
29	SET UP				0.2
30	ROUGH GRIND STEP	53	586	SG-1945	0.0138
34	SET UP				0.3
35	CUT TEETH	53	217	SG-1921, T-38, TJ-980, DG-1232	0.0275

OPER. NO.	DESCRIPTION OF OPERATION	DEPT. NO.	MACH.	TOOLS	STD. TIME
39	SET UP				0.9
40	FINISH BORE, FACE BOTTOM, FACE & BEVEL BACK	53	245	DEG-188, DG-203, TJ-991, DEG-1075, DEG-1107	0.0155
44	SET UP				0.1
45	MILL BETWEEN TEETH	53	206	XG-1202, F-124	0.0155
*	STOCK POINT				

CASTING NO. ______ PART NO. ______

CODE NUMBER	PART NAME	MATERIAL	HEAT TREAT	DWG. NO.
2-561-994-280	ROTOR BLANK, 2/3 GPM	N-1		

METHODS ENGINEERING DEPT.

FIG. 13-41. Route Sheet for Blank Drawing (Viking Pump Co.)

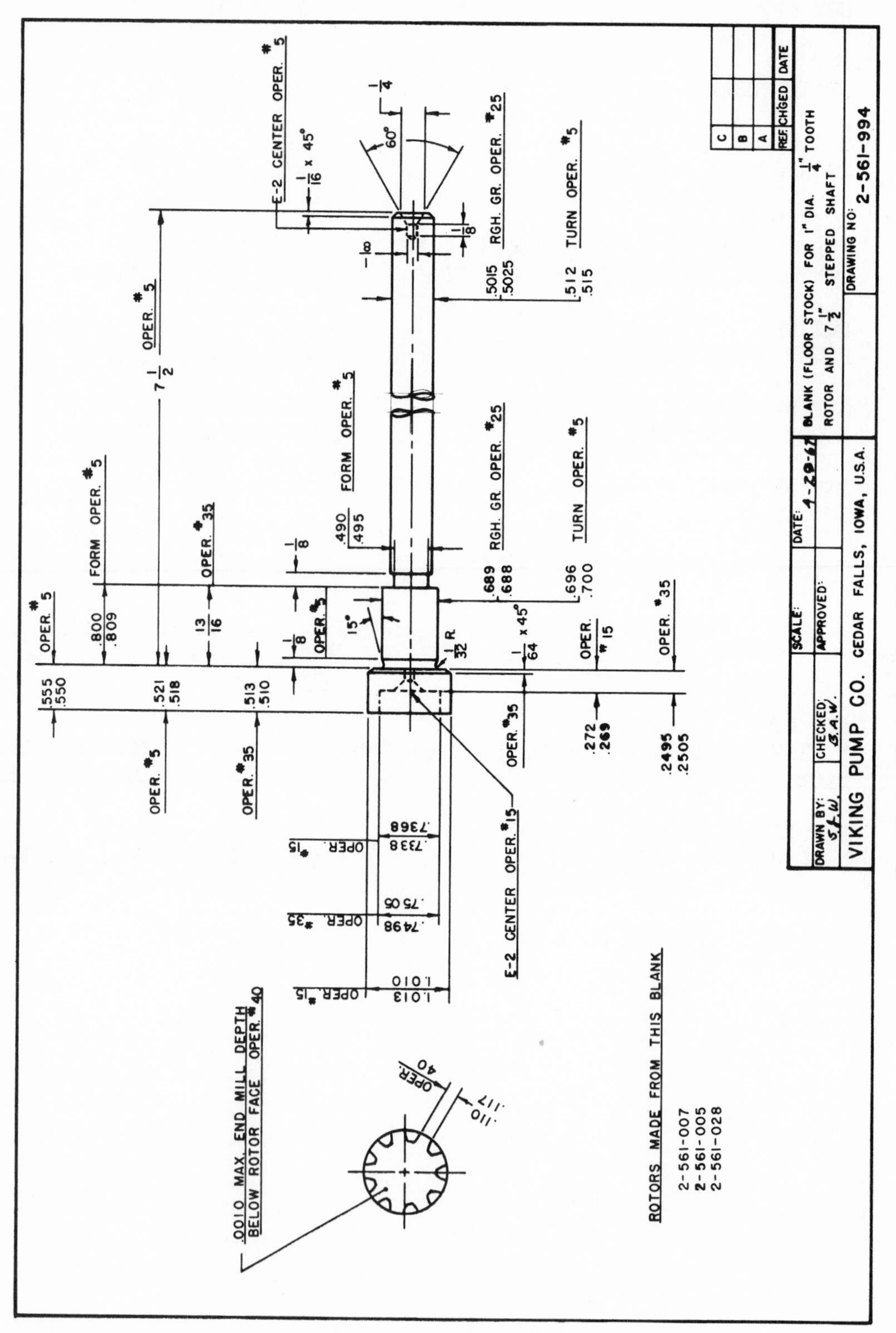

Fig. 13-42. Blank Drawing (Viking Pump Co.)

OPER. NO.	CODE NO. 2-561-007-282 DESCRIPTION OF OPERATION		MACH.	EFFECTIVE DATE 1-18-66 TOOLS	STD. TIME
	USE ROTOR BLANK 2-561-994-280				
4	SET UP				0.5
5	MILL FLAT	02	189	F-264	0.0085
9	SET UP				0.2
10	ROUGH GRIND HEAD	05	465	SG-1948	0.0116
14	SET UP				0.3
15	ROUGH GRIND ENDS OF TEETH	06	447	F-493	0.0076
20	HT-310 CYANIDE	71			
24	SET UP				0.2
25	POLISH	24	171	TJ-492	0.0074
29	SET UP				0.1
30	SPREAD TEETH & STRAIGHTEN SHAFT	24	BENCH		0.0183
34	SET UP				0.2
35	FINISH GRIND SHAFT	05	465	SG-1616	0.0156
39	SET UP				0.2
40	FINISH GRIND STEP.	05	465	SG-941	0.0113

OPER. NO.	DESCRIPTION OF OPERATION	DEPT. NO.	MACH.	TOOLS	STD. TIME
44	SET UP				0.2
45	FINISH GRIND HEAD	05	465	SG-131	0.0116
49	SET UP				0.1
50	FINISH GRIND ENDS OF TEETH	24	554	F-567	0.0097
55	DEBURR WITH WIRE WHEEL	75			
60	DRY BLAST TOOTH I.D. & FACE	75			

CASTING NO. 1-911-003-280 x 8-1/4"

PART NO. JPN

CODE NUMBER	PART NAME	MATERIAL	HEAT TREAT	DWG. NO.
2-561-007-282	ROTOR, 2/3 GPM	N-1	CYANIDED	

FIG. 13-43. Route Sheet to Finished Specifications (Viking Pump Co.)

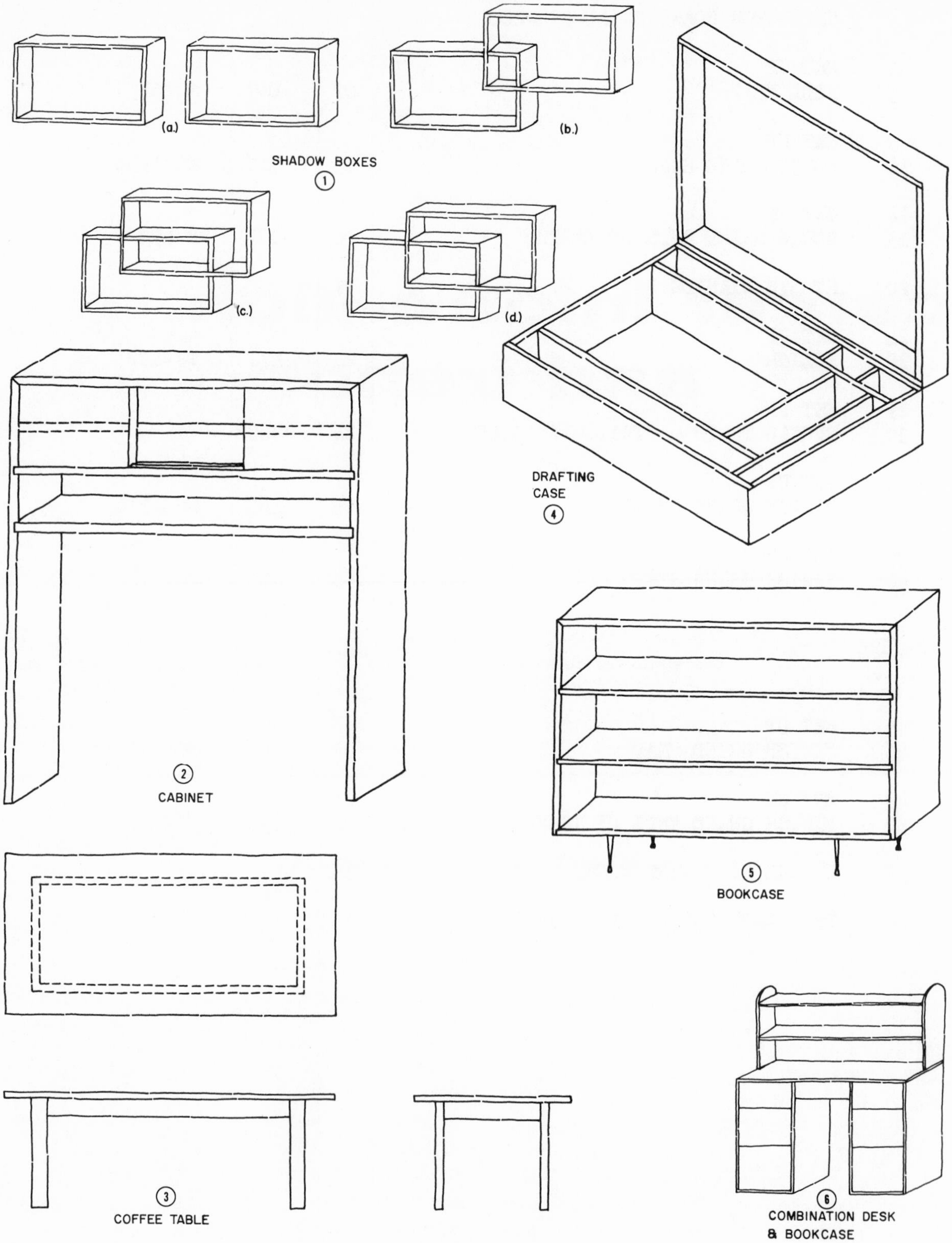

(a.)
(b.)
SHADOW BOXES
1
(c.)
(d.)
DRAFTING CASE
4
2
CABINET
5
BOOKCASE
3
COFFEE TABLE
6
COMBINATION DESK & BOOKCASE

FIG. 13-44. Problems

CHAPTER FOURTEEN

career information and trends

In Chapter 1 general information was presented on the subject of "What is Drafting?" Those paragraphs showed the usefulness of drafting to individuals from all walks of life. Later in that same chapter information was given on procedures in drafting, pointing out their contribution to the solution of problems.

Subsequent chapters have dealt with the basic techniques of the drafting language. These techniques are generally appropriate to all occupational fields of drafting, although each drafting field has its own special techniques and procedures.

This chapter provides information which will be of interest and which should help you with an overview of the field and also guide your serious study of those areas of drafting that are of most interest.

career information

Working Conditions

Working conditions for draftsmen in industry are good. Rooms are usually air-conditioned and well lighted. Drafting is a profession, and each draftsman has his own desk or work center. His equipment is modern and designed for efficiency, Fig. 13-5. Accuracy is required and work may be creative or routine and detailed. The draftsman works with other draftsmen and with engineers. It is highly important that he be able to get along well with other people. His working hours are steady, and he is not as likely to be out of work as the labor force in the shops. In most industries he has fringe benefits such as insurance, hospitalization, sick leave, pensions, paid vacations, profit sharing when available, and the like.

Among the problems of the profession are possible eyestrain from close work, back strain from poor posture at the drafting table, and a general sense of tension from urgency and pressure to complete drawings by designated times in order to meet production schedules.

Training Required

Drafting is a specialty requiring a degree of skill. High school graduation is the minimum level of schooling required for draftsmen. In high school, the prospective draftsman should take as much mathematics as he can get. He should take physics, chemistry, and English, paying particular attention to grammar and spelling. He should also take drafting and courses in shopwork to get an understanding of shop processes.

A more advantageous entry into drafting can be obtained through work in junior college, college, technical institutes, apprenticeship, or correspondence, vocational, and trade schools.

With the many changes taking place in industry today, draftsmen can expect a need for supplementary training after they are employed. This is particularly true of those with only a high school education but to some degree will hold true for all who expect to advance from their entry position.

Characteristics of Success

The author has organized several drafting conferences at which speakers from industrial drafting rooms have discussed the topic, "What We Expect of the Beginning Draftsman." Eventhough the speakers were from different industries and from different fields of specialization, there seemed to be a great deal of agreement on what they expected. Without further elaboration the following points of general agreement are presented, with no significance in the order of presentation:

1. A good draftsman must be able to work with people.
2. He must have the ability to work on problems extending over relatively long periods of time.
3. He must be willing to redraw plans when the engineer changes his mind or comes up with a new idea or approach.
4. He must meet production schedules.
5. He must understand shop processes.
6. He must have an understanding of mathematics.
7. He must know how to visualize quickly and accurately.
8. Beginners in drafting should know how to read tables and use data from engineering handbooks.
9. Student draftsmen should be acquainted with the tools, materials, and equipment commonly used in the industrial drafting rooms. This means tracing papers, polyester films, plastic-lead drafting pencils, drafting machines, and the like.
10. Beginning draftsmen must produce neat, legible lettering of appropriate size and with proper density of pencil lines.
11. The draftsman should know generally accepted standard drafting practices and be willing to learn quickly the company's drafting standards.
12. Dimensioning practice and the drawing of sectional views are among the fundamental techniques with which all draftsmen should be familiar.
13. Every draftsman should be able to sketch as a rapid means of communication.
14. Drafting employees must know scale and how to use it.
15. No matter what other characteristics a draftsman has, he must be accurate.
16. Beginning draftsmen should have a better understanding of how to layout a drawing. This includes such elementary things as which views to choose, what scale to use, and how to allow enough space on the drawing for proper dimensioning without crowding.

Advancement Opportunities

Entry Position and Orientation

Draftsmen advance on the basis of demonstrated ability, length of experience, further education, and the judgment of various supervisors. This advancement may vary from company to company but provides incentive to do good work. The new employee in large industries will undoubtedly undergo a training and orientation program designed to acquaint him with the industry, its administrative organization, its products, and the processes of manufacture. The first drafting board work he will do probably will be tracing. Emphasis will be on developing skills in lettering and line work so that efficiency will be achieved.

Junior Detailer

With experience and demonstrated ability in his position, he may be advanced to junior detailer. As such, he revises drawings, making simple changes in detail and assembly drawings. As he gains experience, he may prepare simple detail and assembly drawings.

Senior Detailer

A senior detailer or senior draftsman prepares complex detail and assembly drawings. He works with less supervision and is counted on for accuracy and good judgment. He must be good at visualization and at understanding how to project points, lines, and planes from view to view. He works from layout and design drawings, and as he gains experience he will make these drawings too.

Drafting Checker

A drafting checker has both instructional and supervisory responsibility. Several years of dependable performance in the drafting room and general acquaintance with company standards and practices are required for this position. Drawings of tracers and detailers are checked for quality of line and form as well as accuracy. (Refer to Chapter 13, p. 301.) Frequently the checker consults with engineering and manufacturing personnel. He needs to understand their requirements and to work well with them and help in the supervision of younger draftsmen.

Junior Designer

Junior designers construct layouts, work with engineering references, and prepare geometrical tolerances, clearances, and the like. They work from specifications, sketches, and notes prepared by engineers. An understanding of manufacturing processes is required and additional responsibility in supervision may be given.

Designer

Designer, senior designer, or group leader is a classification to which most draftsmen aspire. They prepare all types of layout drawings of simple and complex designs. They work closely with engineers and may frequently work from oral instructions. They assign routine drafting work to junior draftsmen and supervise their work. They are concerned with costs of production and costs of drawing preparation. They have developed considerable proficiency through experience and education in applications of mathematics and science to basic engineering problems.

Chief Draftsman

The chief draftsman is a member of the management team. He administers and coordinates all of the work in the drafting department. He is concerned with employment, employee relations, company policy, initiating standard practices, assignment of work schedules, equipment needs, budgets, and other administrative duties.

Specialties and Related Fields

At the same time as a draftsman moves through various position levels he may also develop a specialty. There are so many varied kinds of drafting work in government, business, and industry that a detailed knowledge by any one person of all phases of drafting is impossible. To some extent, any position one might hold in drafting is specialized. Many of those positions listed below require additional education beyond that required for entry into the drafting field. All of them require considerable experience to advance to positions of leadership and administration.

- *Aero-Space Drafting*
  - Aeronautical Drafting
  - Aircraft Drafting
  - Rocket and Missile Drafting
- *Architectural Drafting*
  - Commercial
  - Industrial
  - Institutional
  - Naval Architecture
- *Electrical Drafting*
  - Electro-Mechanical
  - Electronic
- *Graphic Arts*
  - Layout and Design
- *Industrial Design*
  - Automotive Styling
  - Furniture and Cabinet Design
  - Interior Decorating Layouts
  - Product Planning
- *Mechanical Drafting*
  - Forging Drawings
  - Machine Drawings
  - Pattern Shop Drawings
  - Stamping Drawings
  - Tooling Layouts
  - Welding Drawings

Patent Drawing
Piping Drafting
Heating and Air-Conditioning
Hydraulics
Plumbing
Pneumatics
Production and Technical Illustration
Structural Drafting
Concrete
Steel
Timbers
Teaching Drafting
Junior High School
High School
Vocational and Trade School
Technical Schools and Institutes
Junior Colleges
Colleges and Universities
Topographic Drafting
Cartography and Map Making
Civil Drafting
Landscaping

Seeking Additional Information

In seeking additional information don't overlook the possibility of talking to someone employed in the field in which you may have an interest. They can tell you, and are usually quite willing to do so, about the specific advantages and disadvantages of the work.

Teachers, guidance counselors, and library references may also be helpful.

Engineering societies and trade associations often are prepared to help interested young people learn more about prospective work in their fields.

The following organizations and publications may be of specific help:

American Federation of Technical Engineers, 900 F. St. N. W., Washington, D. C.

American Institute for Design and Drafting, 18465 James Couzens Highway, Detroit, Michigan

Automotive Design, Technical Data Department, Chrysler Corporation

Can I Be a Draftsman, General Motors Corporation, Detroit, Michigan

Construction, A Man's Work, General Building Contractors Assoc. Inc., 2 Penn Center Plaza, Philadelphia, Pennsylvania

Dictionary of Occupational Titles, Vols. I and II, Bureau of Employment Security, U. S. Dept. of Labor, Washington, D. C.

Mechanical Drafting and Design Technology, U. S. Office of Education, Dept. of Health, Education and Welfare, Washington, D. C.

Occupational Outlook Handbook, Current Edition, U. S. Department of Labor
a. Employment Outlook for Draftsmen
b. Employment Outlook for Architects
c. Employment Outlook for Engineers

Stylist and Engineer, Partners in Design, Technical Information Services, Chrysler Corporation

trends

Drafting is occasionally thought of as an area where very little change takes place. Nothing could be farther from the truth. Before suggesting trends that may bring about changes in the immediate and distant future for draftsmen, let us examine some recent changes in industrial drafting practice.

Changes in Recent Years

Most of the recent changes have been changes in tools, supplies or equipment and changes in emphasis, rather than changes in quality. The changes listed are not all the changes that have taken place nor have they taken place in all drafting offices. Table 14-1 should be helpful in identifying some of these significant changes.

The Present and Future

What of the future? What is going on right now that suggests what draftsmen may be doing in one, five, or even ten years in the future? There are several developments which will surely cause change.

TABLE 14-1

Changes in Drafting in Recent Years

From	To
Manila drawing paper	Tracing mediums
Tracing papers for most uses	Polyester film for some special uses
Wood encased pencils	Mechanical pencils
Ordinary carbon leads for general work on tracing papers	Special plastic leads for use on films
Ordinary erasers	Electric erasers
Ordinary erasers for carbon pencil work	Special vinyl erasers for polyester film
T-square	Parallel bar mounted on drafting table
T-square, triangles, protractor and scale	Drafting machine with base line adjustment and removable straight edges indexed with scales of different graduations
Ruling pen with adjustable nibs	Technical fountain pens with fixed size points
Mechanical lettering with small pen cups	Mechanical lettering with reservoir pens
Set of drafting instruments with three small bow instruments	Large bow instruments with interchangeable pen, pencil and divider points
Center or side adjusting thumb-screw large bow compasses	Rapid action adjusting large bow compasses
39″ high drafting tables	Standard desk-height drafting tables with auto-shift height adjustments
Drafting stools	Office type chairs
Blueprinting	Diazo printing
Storage of blue prints and white prints in large flat filing systems	Storage of microfilm copies of drawings on aperture cards
Mechanical drawing of simple geometrical configurations	Wide use of assorted templates for efficient construction of geometrical configurations
Use of fractions for most dimensioning	Use of the decimal inch for most dimensioning in the mechanical fields
Illustration of most ideas through mechanical means	Illustration of many ideas through the technical sketch
Considerable use of engineers to do drafting work	Little use of engineers to do drafting work; more use of draftsmen and drafting technicians
Complete projected geometrical delineation in mechanical form	Simplified representation of geometrical form and use of more symbols
Much dimensioning of parts without reference to base lines or datum surfaces	Much dimensioning from base lines and datum surfaces
Use of aligned system of placement of dimensioned figures	Use of unilateral system of placement of dimensioned figures
Use of templates and lofting for layout of large sheet metal parts	Use of un-dimensioned drawings on stable base materials which may then be exposed directly to sensitized surfaces of large sheet metal parts
Lettering of repetitive notes on all drawings as required	Use of preprinted, pressure-sensitive appliques for repetitive notes
Redrawing to obtain drawings which vary only in small detail	Use of sensitized intermediates and eradicators to make second originals and new drawings which vary only in small detail
Sandpaper pad or file for pointing drafting pencils	Mechanical and electrical pencil pointers
Freehand lettering most of the time	Mechanical lettering sets or long carriage typewriters for adding notes to drawings
Use of ink on tracing cloth	Pencil on tracing mediums

Need for Increased Efficiency

Trade journals continually report various ways to reduce the amount of drafting time required to produce finished manufactured products. There will be continued emphasis on finding ways to reduce this cost of engineering. To the extent that this effort is successful over the years, fewer draftsmen will be needed. However, because not enough draftsmen are available now and because of industry's need for more draftsmen to fill new positions that are created by expanding and new industry, the supply may still not meet the demand.

There will be continued developments with respect to short-cut methods and graphic symbolism to simplify drafting. This comes about slowly but progress is continually being made. The draftsman will need to read trade journals and the reports of various standards organizations in order to keep up on these developments.

Precision Dimensioning

There has been a great deal written in the early 60's on geometrical, positional, and form tolerancing. Although this is an advanced technique and not covered in these pages, information will become more standardized and additional requirements for more careful tolerancing of rockets, missiles and other items for the space age will come along. Draftsmen will be expected to be familiar with new innovations and to use them appropriately. A better understanding of fits of mating parts will be required, and draftsmen will need to understand the various manufacturing processes.

New Tools

With the endless stream of new knowledge will come additional tools, processes, and materials for manufacture. As these become available, the draftsman will need to know what they are, their advantages and limitations, and how to use and specify them.

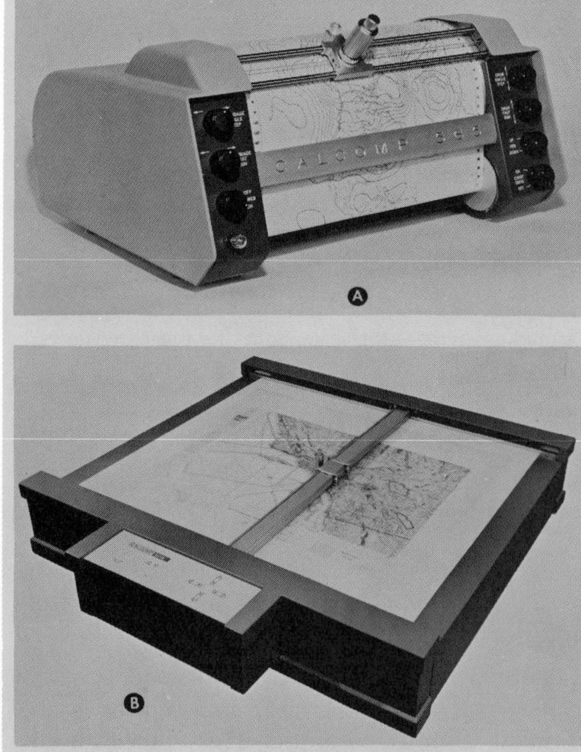

Fig. 14-1.
A. Digital Incremental Plotter, Model 565 (California Computer Products, Inc.)
B. Flatbed Plotter, Model 502 (California Computer Products, Inc.)

Standardized Practices

Continued efforts to standardize engineering and drafting practices in this country are now and will continue to be underway. In a like manner, continued effort will be made to standardize on the international level. As more and more industries in this country expand into overseas markets and develop overseas divisions and manufacturing plants, there will be increased need for international understanding. Draftsmen for some industries will need to read and understand certain drawings made in foreign countries.

As these pressures build, there will from time to time be increased efforts to cooperate on a single internationally accepted system of projection. It now appears that it would be possible at some point in the future to consider third-angle projection as the accepted standard. In the meantime, draftsmen will need some knowledge of first-angle projection and will have to be able to identify the system used on a given set of drawings and be able to read either kind.

At the same time there is increased consideration of the possibility of a universally accepted standard of measurement. It is becoming more and more apparent that the English system, even with the decimal inch, is unlikely to ever be adopted by any great number of countries now using the metric system. Although the cost to industries presently using the English system would be staggering, it also appears that with foreign trade and manufacturing there is some chance that the metric system might in the fairly distant future be the international standard of measurement. In the meantime there will be more and more need for American draftsmen to become familiar with the metric system and with converting to and from the decimal inch and the metric system.

Photography and Reproduction

The area of photography and reproduction is undergoing vast change. Terms such as *reproduction engineers* and *reprography* are already creeping into our vocabulary. Additional developments here will be forthcoming, and draftsmen will need to understand them in order to make drawings which can be reproduced satisfactorily by these new methods. The use of microfilming will be extended.

Computers

Automated drafting is already here. A number of rather expensive devices are on the market. Computers can be anticipated to have a profound influence on drafting. In the years immediately ahead, computers will likely produce pictorial drawings from orthographic views. This will facilitate a more easily understood illustration, and these will be more accurate than before. Of course, computers will reduce the time for the preparation of such drawings greatly and will eliminate mistakes.

Computers will assist in final design stages. Intermediate designs can be displayed on a television-like viewing screen. The computer can be instructed to draw circles or lines. Lines drawn on the face of the screen can be smoothed out by the computer. Design elements can be enlarged or reduced, rotated, dimensioned, or superimposed. At least some of these will become new tools both for the draftsman and the designer.

International Business Machines Corporation has an *X-Y* plotter to be used with its 1620 data processor. By correctly instructing the plotter through various commands sent to it through punched cards in the processor, drawings such as that of Figs. 14-2 and 14-3 can be produced at the rate of 300 inches per minute.

The instructions to the plotter are based on mathematical descriptions of position from known points and/or lines. Using an *X-Y* axis one might instruct the plotter to draw a rectangle such as shown in Fig. 14-4 with these directions:

Raise pen, move to X_1 Y_1 (1,1)
Lower pen, move to X_2 Y_1 (4, 1)
Leave pen down, move to X_2 Y_2 (4, 3)
Leave pen down, move to X_1 Y_2 (1, 3)
Leave pen down, move to X_1 Y_1 (1, 1)
Raise pen.

Once this information is coded and fed into the computer, it can be recalled as commanded and can be enlarged or reduced at scale. The implication seems to be that there will be little need to redraw such repetitive-parts drawings as standard fasteners, ordinary fillets and rounds, basic geometrical forms, and the like.

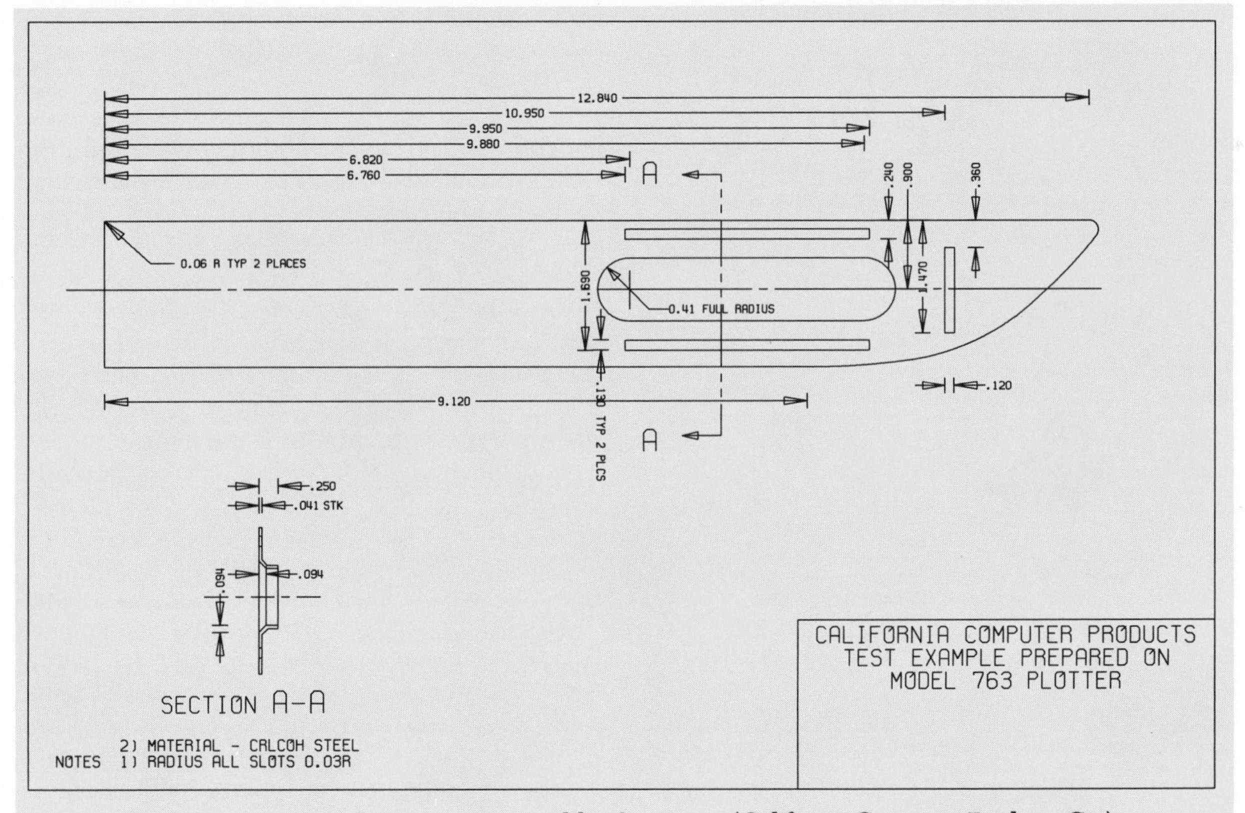

FIG. 14-2. Mechanical Drawing Executed by Computer (California Computer Products Co.)

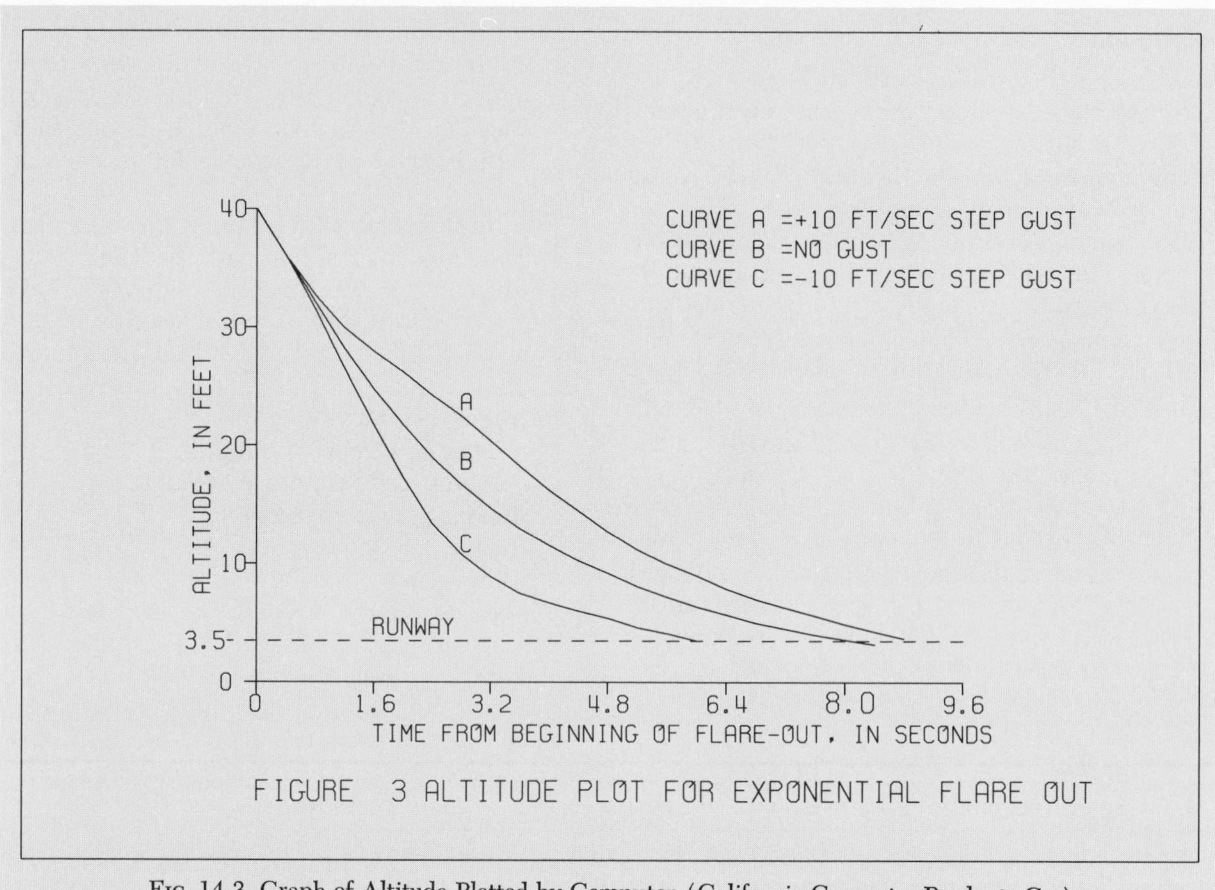

FIG. 14-3. Graph of Altitude Plotted by Computer (California Computer Products Co.)

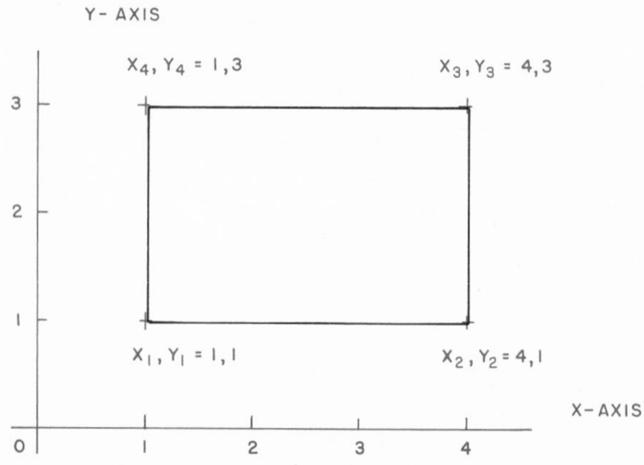

FIG. 14-4. Rectangle Showing x-y Axes from Which Dimensions May Be Taken

Other devices, even more sophisticated, are in the development process now. These will call for the draftsman to use computers, to learn to provide the machines with language they can understand, and to learn to read the computerized product.

You might test your ability now by referring to the orders given to draw a rectangle and see whether you can set up those needed to draw two principal views of the playing card holder in Fig. 3-67, Problem 5. Choose your own scale. Decide which views you want to use and how much space is needed between the views. To be useful to the computer, these instructions would have to be coded. However, just to write the commands should be instructive.

Drafting For Numerically Controlled Machines

New demands will be placed on draftsmen who make drawings of products that are later produced on numerically controlled (N/C) machines. These machines perform such operations as drilling, reaming, tapping, and milling. Instructions to these machines are contained in a coded paper type. These instructions are based on mathematical descriptions of points and path operations. For example, a hole is to be drilled at a particular point to a certain depth. A slot is cut along a particular path at

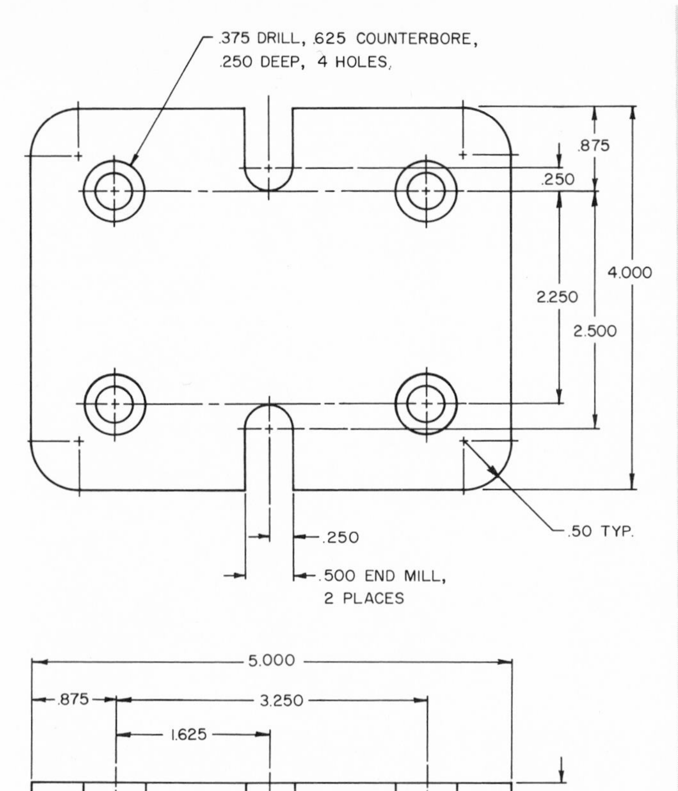

FIG. 14-5. Conventional Drawing of Base Plate

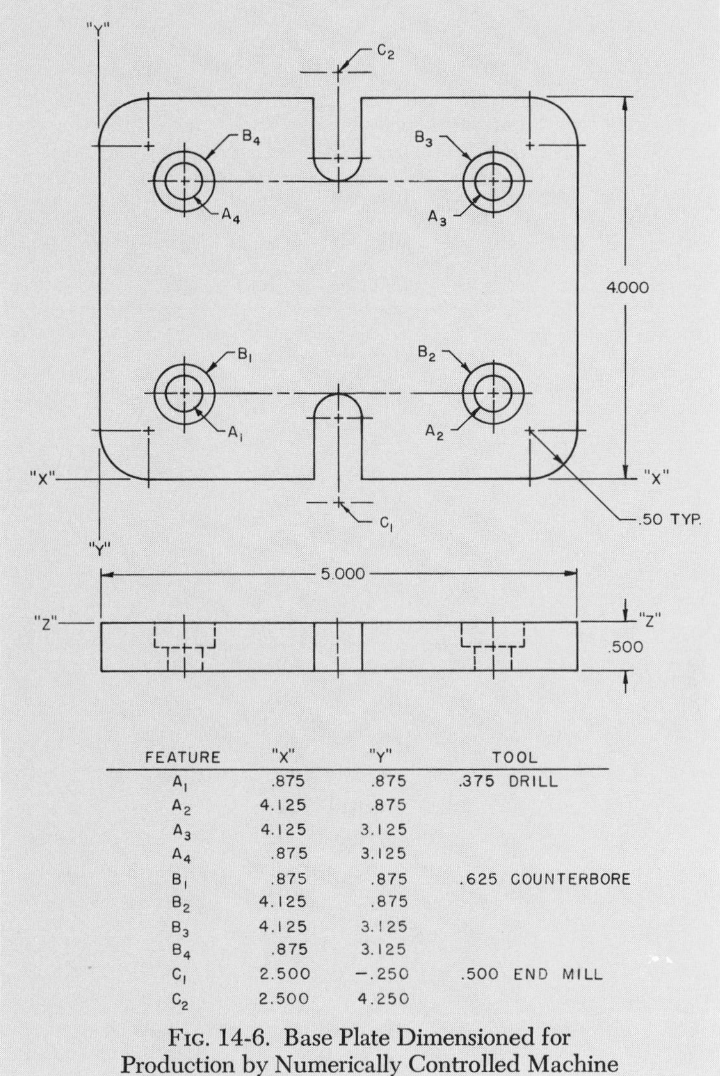

FEATURE	"X"	"Y"	TOOL
A_1	.875	.875	.375 DRILL
A_2	4.125	.875	
A_3	4.125	3.125	
A_4	.875	3.125	
B_1	.875	.875	.625 COUNTERBORE
B_2	4.125	.875	
B_3	4.125	3.125	
B_4	.875	3.125	
C_1	2.500	−.250	.500 END MILL
C_2	2.500	4.250	

FIG. 14-6. Base Plate Dimensioned for Production by Numerically Controlled Machine

a prescribed depth. Each of these can be defined mathematically. Drawings for this type of work need to be based on the cartesian coordinates. Fig. 14-5 illustrates the drawing needed to produce a base plate using standard practices, while Fig. 14-6 shows how the base plate would be dimensioned for production by numerical control. Study these illustrations and observe the use of coordinates. From these tabled dimensions, the programmer prepares information in the machine's language (Table 14-2) so the proper operation can be performed. The effect of this is not to replace the draftsman, but to require different work of him and to create new jobs in the field.

Conclusion

The effect of the several trends in the drafting field might be best summarized as:

The basic work of the draftsman will remain unchanged; he will need to visualize, to dimension, and to know symbols and the use of the basic tools. But, to this work will be added additional work involving new tools and new techniques. The draftsman will need a higher level of understandings and abilities, especially in mathematics and sciences, in order to solve the problems at hand.

Chapter 14 — Problems and Projects

1. Using the library as a reference, list the likenesses and differences between a career as an architectural and a mechanical draftsman. If both types of draftsmen are employed in or near your area, visit them and ask about working conditions, methods, responsibilities, and general rates of pay.

TABLE 14-2

Manuscript for Numerical Control

Part: Base plate, mild steel, Brinnell 150
Machine tools required: vertical mill
Operations: drilling, counterboring, end milling
Programmer: Wm. S. Miller

Sequence No.	Feature	"X"	"Y"	"Z"	Operation	Size	RPM	Feed in Ft/Min.	Instruction
1	A_1	.875	.875	.100	Drill	.375	1,200	120	Drill through Z axis to —.700
2	A_2	4.125	.875	.100					
3	A_3	4.125	3.125	.100					
4	A_4	.875	3.125	.100					
5	B_1	.875	.875	.100	Counter-bore	.625	725	120	Counterbore on Z axis to —.250
6	B_2	4.125	.875	.100					
7	B_3	4.125	3.125	.100					
8	B_4	.875	3.125	.100					
9	C_1	2.500	—.250	—.600	End mill	.500	600	120	End mill to .625 on Y
10	C_2	2.500	4.250	—.600					End mill to 3.375 on Y

CAREERS
TRENDS

2. How do the potential earnings of a drafting teacher compare with those of a professional draftsman? Compare their employment conditions.
3. Keep a record of the job opportunities for draftsmen appearing in the "want ads" of your newspaper over a period of one month.
4. Make a list of the jobs appearing in the "want ads" for which the applicant should have the ability to read drawings.
5. Why is it so important that a draftsman be able to get along with other people? Is this an important characteristic for most occupations?
6. Assume that you are a draftsman working for an employer who has some characteristics which are difficult for you to understand and to put up with. Aside from quitting, explain how you might try to make conditions easier.
7. Explain why a draftsman needs to be able to make technical sketches.
8. Make up an organization chart showing normal paths of advancement for a draftsman.
9. What opportunities for draftsmen are there in government service? In military service?
10. Use the items in Table 14-1 as a check list to make two lists, one showing older practices still used in your school drafting room, and the other showing the newer practices used.
11. Make a list of trade and maufacturing journals with which a draftsman should be familiar. You might wish to ask a draftsman this question.
12. Develop a set of directions for instructing a computer plotter to draw:
    a. A five-pointed star within a circle 5″ in diameter.
    b. A hexagon within a circle 4″ in diameter.
    c. The layout for a plain white envelope (your choice of size; use an envelope as a sample).
    d. The three views of a rectangular prism measuring 1″ x 1½″ x 3″.
    e. The three views of a rectangular prism measuring 2″ x 4″ x 8″ (choose an appropriate scale to get this on an 8½″ x 11″ sheet).
13. Redraw Problems 9-14, Chapter 8, and dimension so that they could be processed by numerically controlled machines.
14. Make a list of the special types of work that may be required of draftsmen who work with computer plotters and numerically controlled machines.

technical data section

TD-4-1

Construct a Line Through a Given Point and Parallel to a Given Line

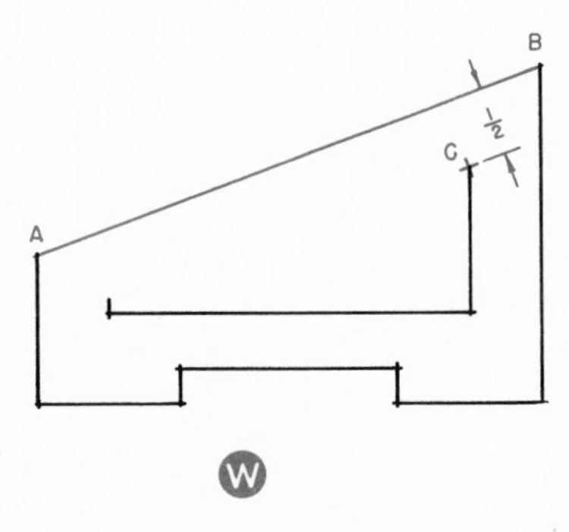

Given: Line AB and the location of point C

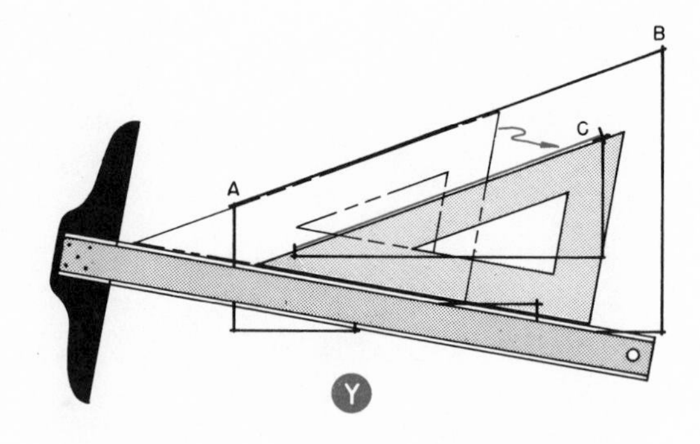

T-square and triangle procedure

1. Align triangle with AB.
2. Place T-square along edge of triangle and hold.
3. Move triangle along edge of T-square to point C as shown by arrow and draw required line.

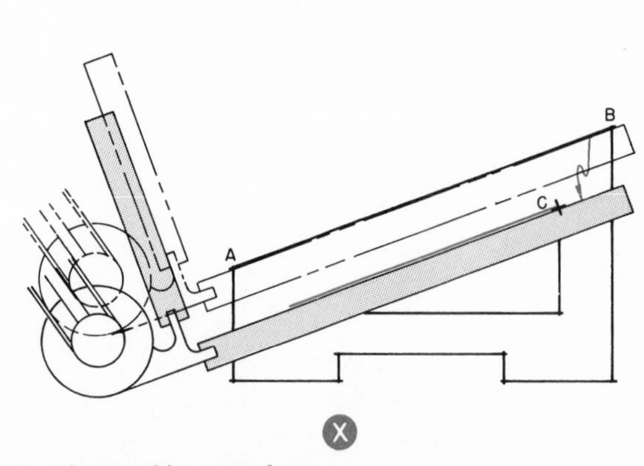

Drafting machine procedure

1. Align horizontal scale with given line AB.
2. Move the machine so that the horizontal scale is aligned with point C as shown by arrow and draw required line.

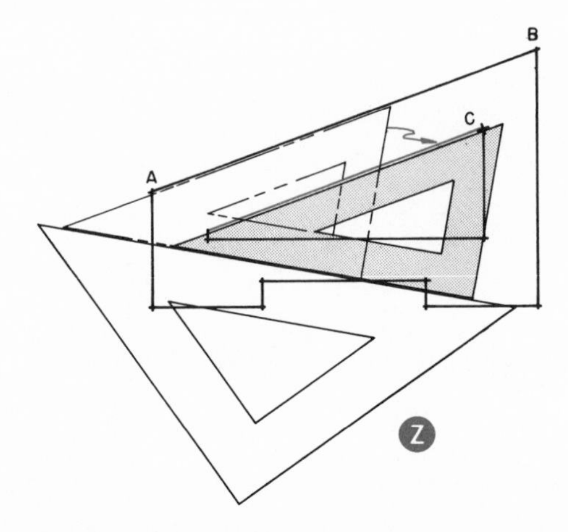

Two-triangle procedure

1. Align triangle with AB.
2. Place other triangle as a straightedge and hold.
3. Move first triangle along straightedge to point C as shown by arrow and draw required line.

TD-4-2

Construct a Line Through a Given Point and Perpendicular to a Given Line

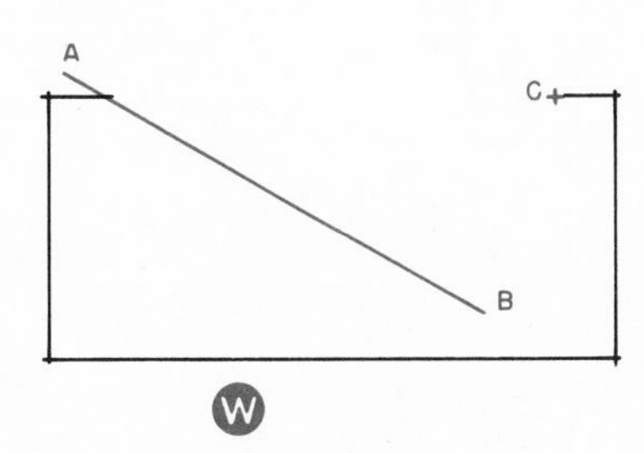

Given: Line *AB* and the location of point *C*

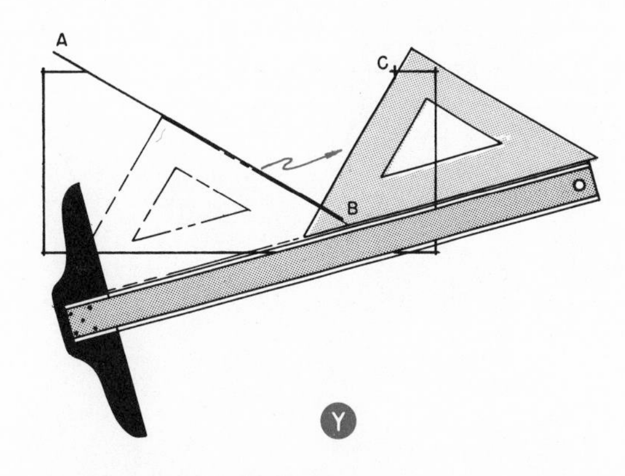

T-square and triangle procedure

1. Align triangle with *AB* so that one leg is coincident with *AB* and a second leg is at right angles to *AB*.
2. Place T-square along hypotenuse of triangle.
3. Move the triangle in direction of the arrow along edge of T-square to point *C* and draw required line.

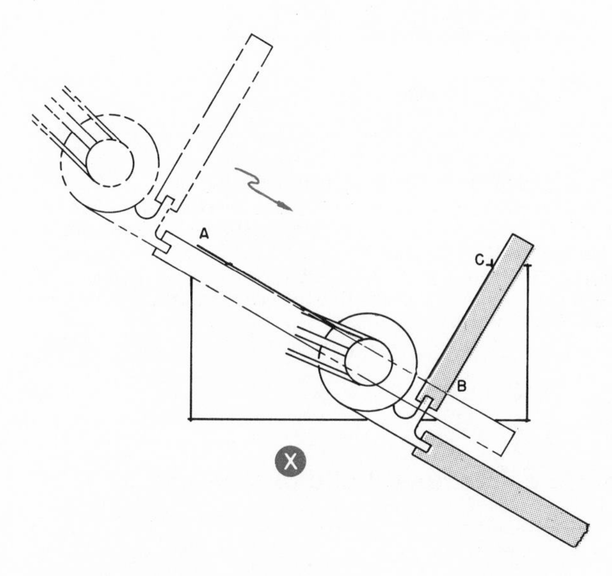

Drafting machine procedure

1. Align horizontal scale with given line *AB*.
2. Move the machine (as shown by the arrow) so that the vertical scale is aligned with point *C* and draw the required line.

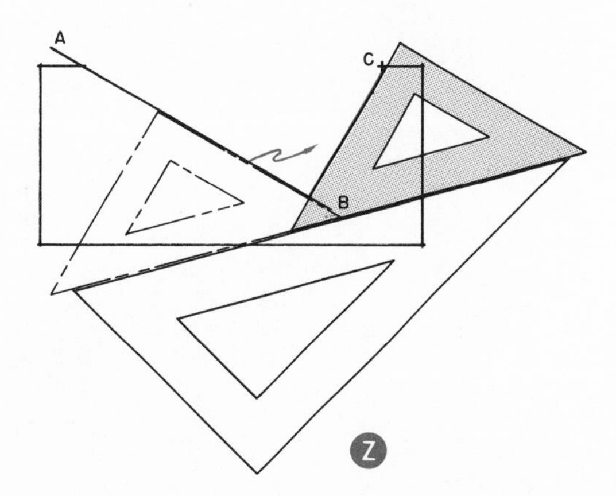

Two-triangle procedure

1. Align triangle with *AB* so that one leg is coincident with *AB* and the second leg is at right angles to *AB*.
2. Place hypotenuse of second triangle along hypotenuse of first triangle as a straightedge and hold.
3. Move first triangle as shown by arrow to point *C* and draw required line.

TD-4-3

Construct a Perpendicular Bisector of a Straight Line

A B

GIVEN

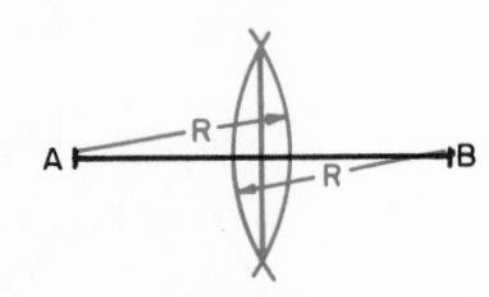

Given: Line AB

TD-4-4

Construct a Bisector of an Arc

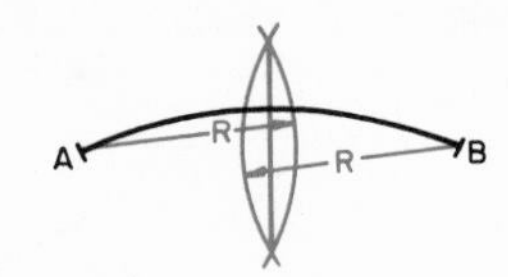

Given: Arc AB

TD-4-5

Construct a Bisector of an Angle

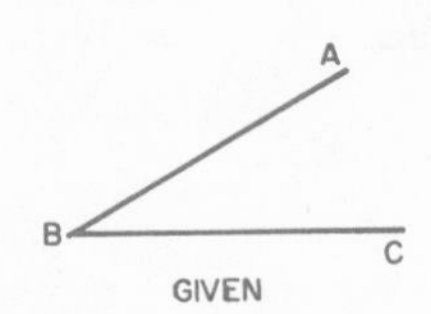

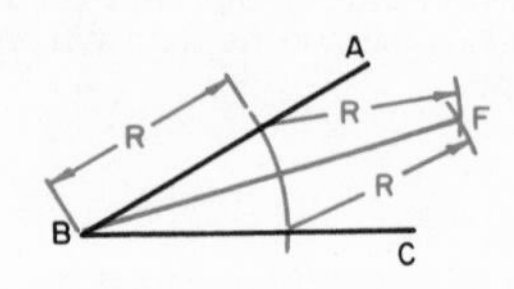

Given: Angle ABC

TD-4-6

Divide a Line (or Space) into an Equal Number of Divisions

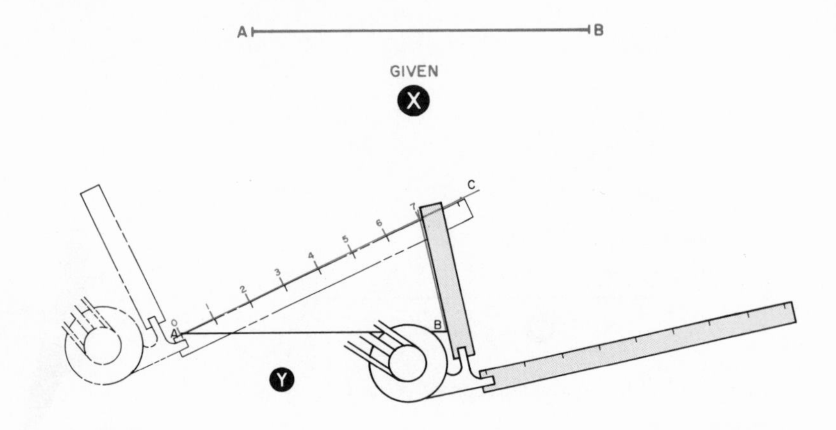

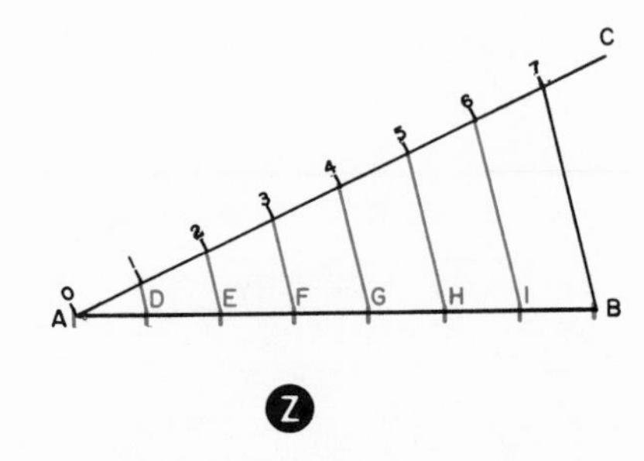

Given: Line AB to be divided into 7 equal parts (Drawing X)

1. Construct a line at any angle from A. With A as the origin, layout 7 equal units of any convenient length. Align scale with last of the 7 unit marks and point B. (Drawing Y)
2. Draw successive lines parallel to **7**-B and through each of the unit marks to line AB to divide the given line into the required number of equal divisions. (Drawing Z)

TD-4-7

Divide a Line into a Prescribed Ratio of Divisions

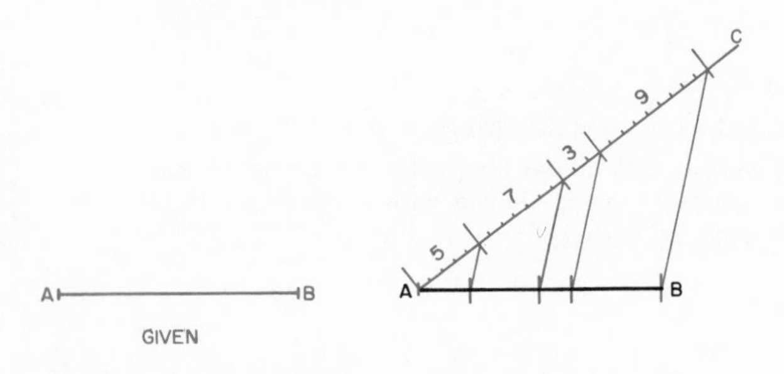

Given: Line AB to be divided into the ratio 5:7:3:9

TD-4-8

Locate the Center of a Circle (or Circle Arc)

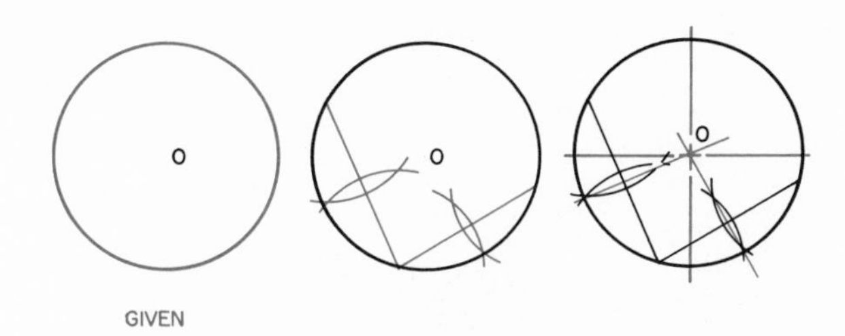

Given: Circle *O*

TD-4-9

Construct a Circle Through Three Given Points

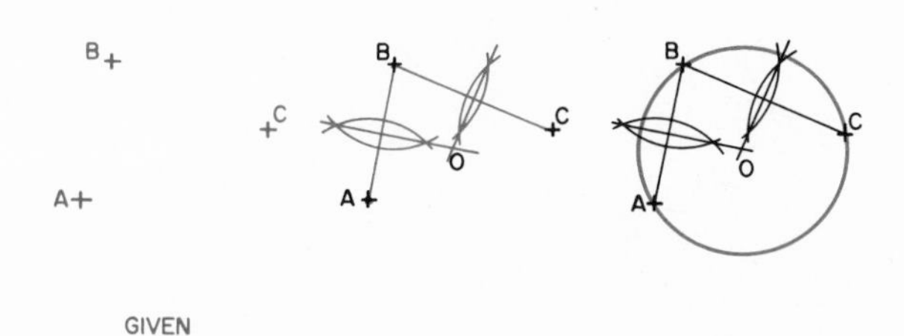

Given: Points *A*, *B*, *C*

TD-4-10

Construct a Triangle with Three Given Sides

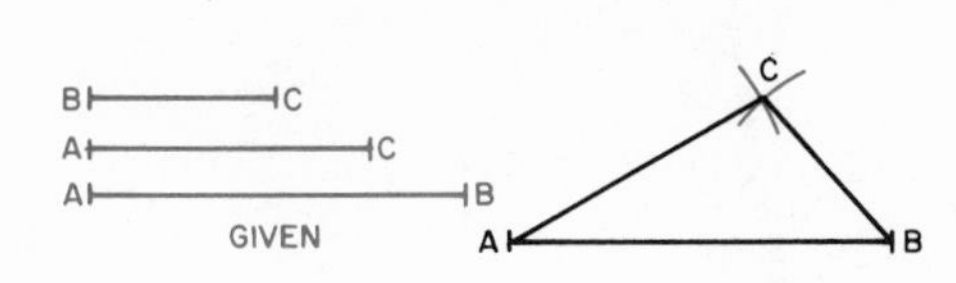

Given: Sides *BC*, *AC*, and *AB*

TD-4-11

Construct a Square with One Given Side

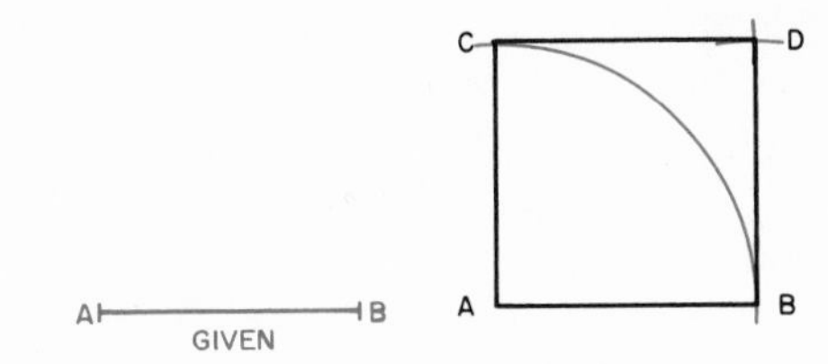

Given: Side *AB*

TD-4-12

Construct a Hexagon with One Given Width Across the Corners

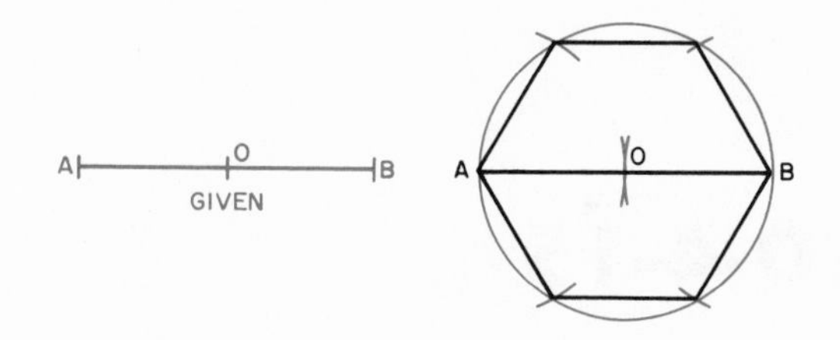

Given: Width across corners *AB*

TD-4-13

Construct-a Hexagon with One Given Width Across the Flats

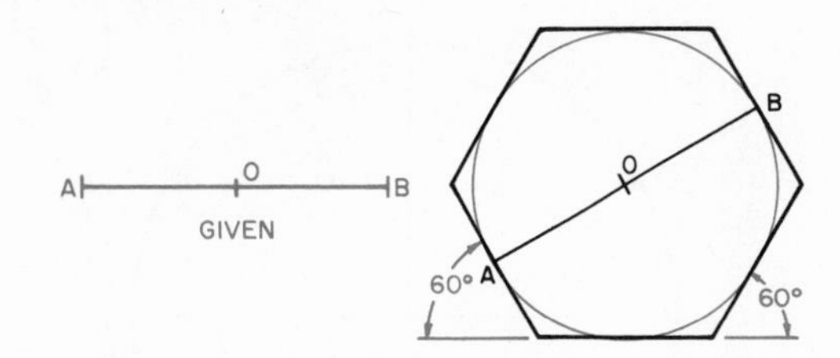

Given: Width across flats *AB*

A point of tangency has the property of being located on the circumference of an arc so that a straight line through the tangent point is perpendicular to the radius of the arc at the point of tangency.

TD-4-14

Construct a Point on a Circle Arc

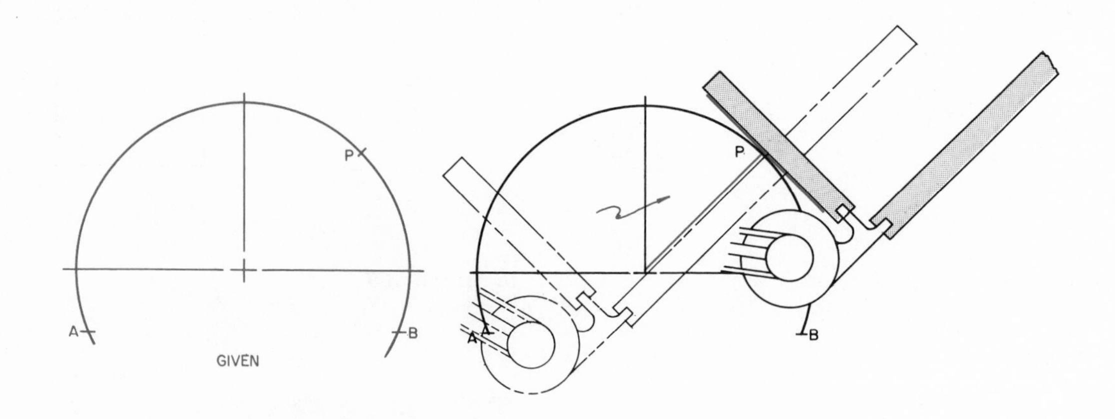

Given: Arc AB and point P on its circumference

TD-4-15

Construct a Tangent to a Circle Arc from a Point Not on the Arc

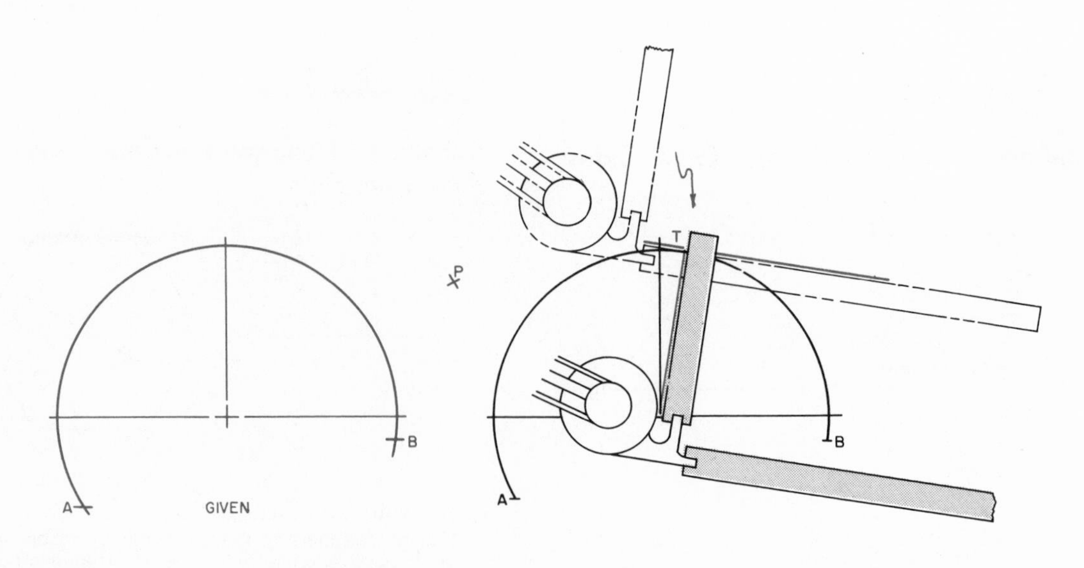

Given: Arc AB and point P

TD-4-16

Construct a Line Tangent to Two Given Circle Arcs

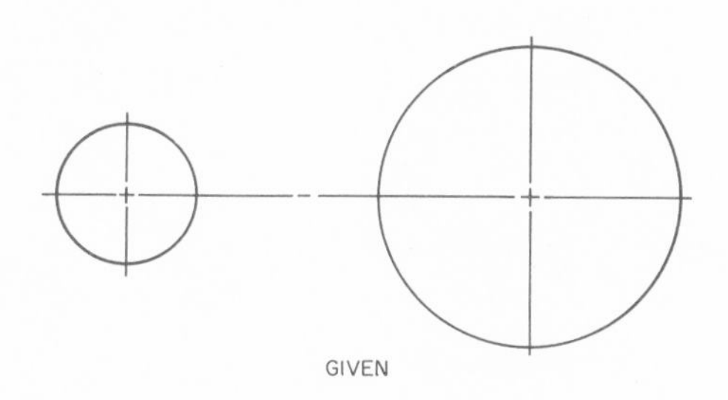

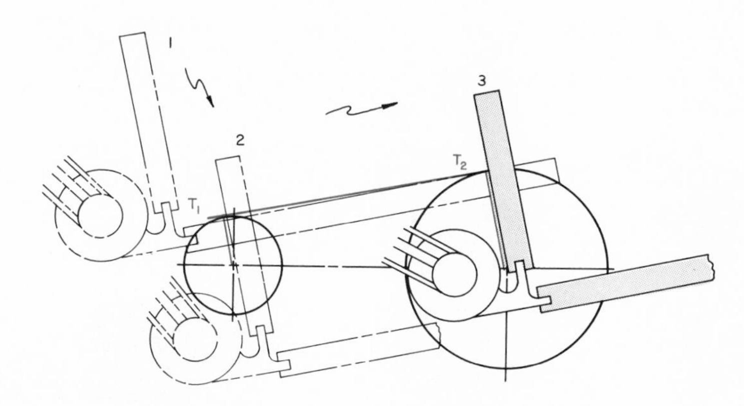

TD-4-17

Construct a Circle Arc of Given Radius Tangent to Two Lines at Right Angles to Each Other

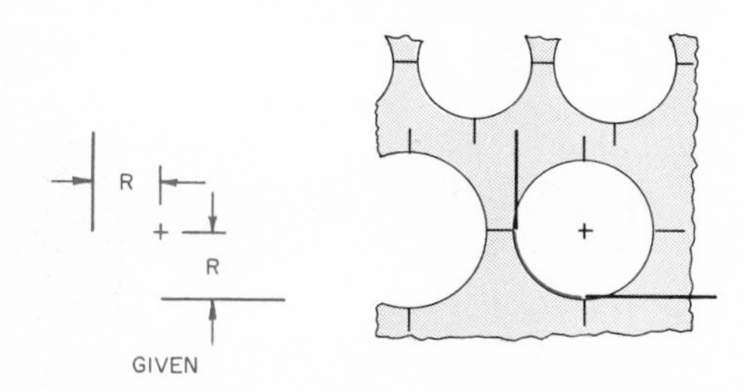

TD-4-18

Construct a Circle Arc of Given Radius Tangent to Two Lines not at Right Angles to Each Other

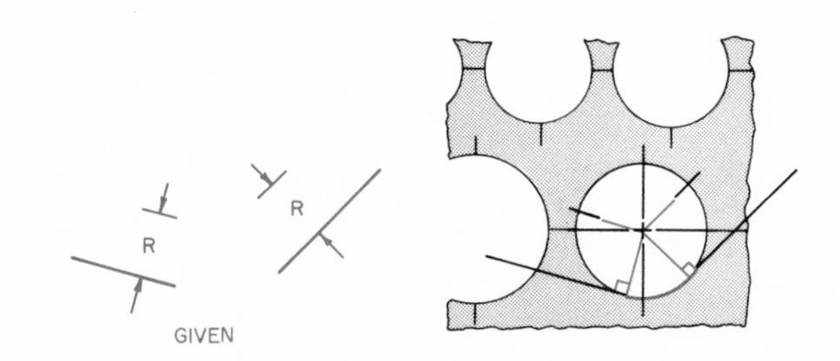

TD-4-19

Construct an Arc of Given Radius Tangent to Two Given Arcs

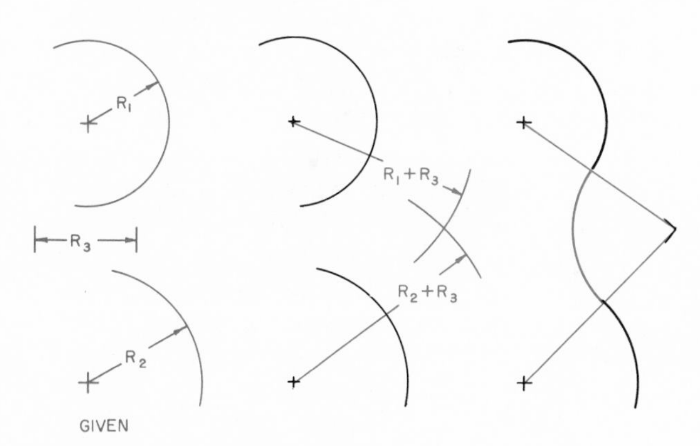

TECHNICAL DATA

TD-4-20

Construct a Line a Given Distance from an Irregular Curve and Parallel to It

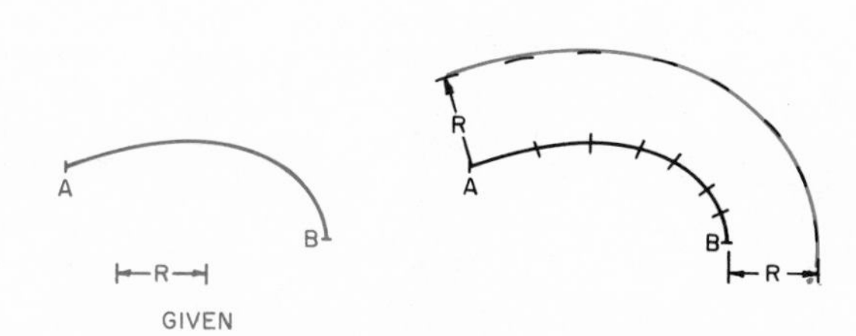

TD-4-21

Layout the Length of a Circle Arc Along a Straight Line (Rectify a Circle Arc)

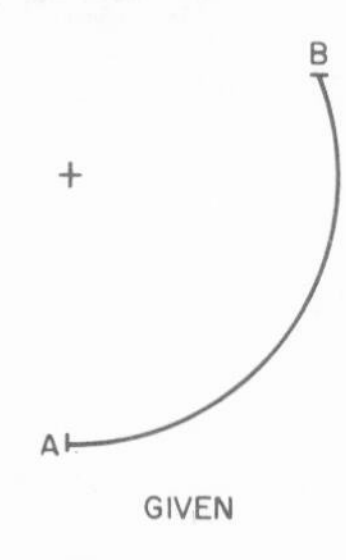

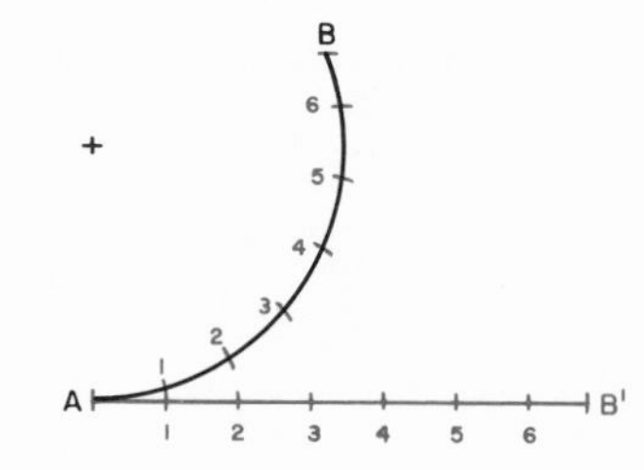

TD-4-22

Areas of Plane Figures (Hyatt Bearings Division, General Motors Corporation)

Nomenclature

a, b, c, d	— Lengths of Sides
A	— Area
d, d_1, d_2	— Diameters
e, f	— Lengths of Diagonals
h	— Vertical Height or Altitude
l, l_1, l_2	— Length of Arc
L	— Lateral Length or Slant Height
n	— Number of Sides
θ	— Number of Degrees of Arc
p	— Perimeter
r, r_1, r_2, R	— Radii

1. RIGHT TRIANGLE

$p = a + b + c$

$c^2 = a^2 + b^2$

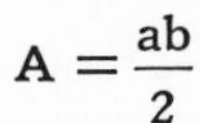

$b = \sqrt{c^2 - a^2}$

$A = \frac{ab}{2}$

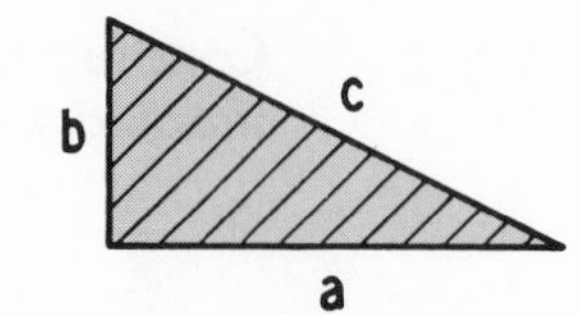

2. EQUILATERAL TRIANGLE

$p = 3a$

$h = \frac{a}{2}\sqrt{3} = .866\,a$

$A = a^2\frac{\sqrt{3}}{4} = .433\,a^2$

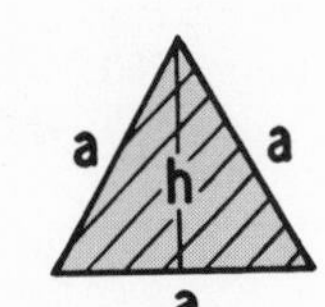

3. GENERAL TRIANGLE

Let $s = \frac{a + b + c}{2}$

$p = a + b + c$

$h = \frac{2}{a}\sqrt{s(s-a)(s-b)(s-c)}$

$A = \frac{ah}{2}$

$A = \sqrt{s(s-a)(s-b)(s-c)}$

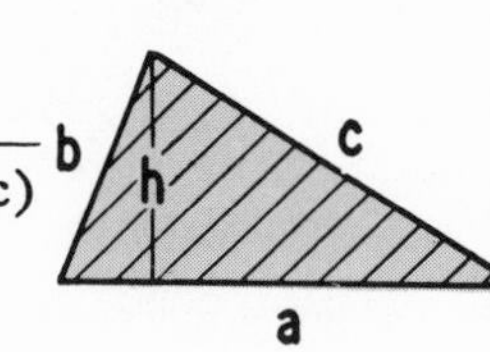

4. SQUARE

$a = b$

$p = 4a$

$A = a^2 = .5e^2$

$e = a\sqrt{2} = 1.414\,a$

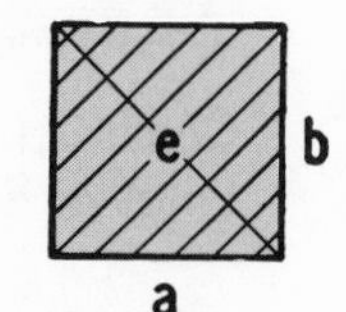

5. RECTANGLE

$p = 2(a + b)$

$e = \sqrt{a^2 + b^2}$

$b = \sqrt{e^2 - a^2}$

$A = ab$

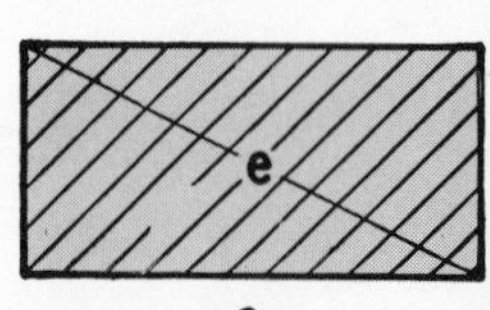

TD-4-22 (con't.)

Areas of Plane Figures (Hyatt Bearings Division, General Motors Corporation)

6. GENERAL PARALLELOGRAM OR RHOMBOID; AND RHOMBUS

Rhomboid—opposite sides parallel

$p = 2(a + b)$

$e^2 + f^2 = 2(a^2 + b^2)$

$A = ah$

Rhombus—opposite sides parallel and all sides equal

$a = b$

$p = 4a = 4b$

$e^2 + f^2 = 4a^2$

$A = ah = \frac{ef}{2}$

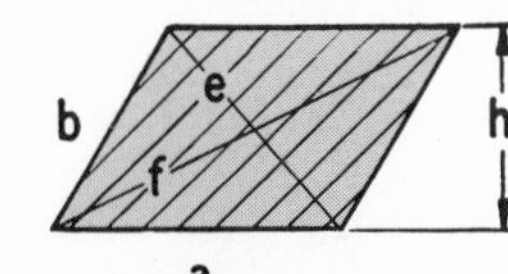

7. TRAPEZOID

$p = a + b + c + d$

$A = \frac{(a + b)}{2} h$

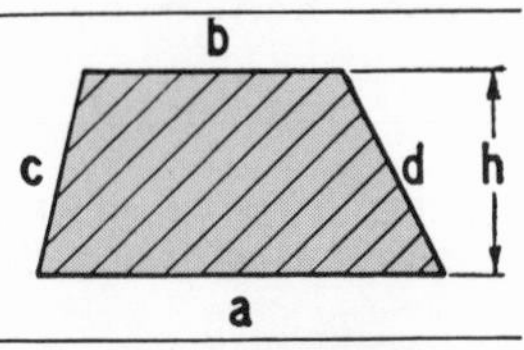

8. TRAPEZIUM

$p = a + b + c + d$

A = Sum of Areas of two major triangles

$A = \frac{(h_1 + h_2) g + fh_1 + jh_2}{2}$

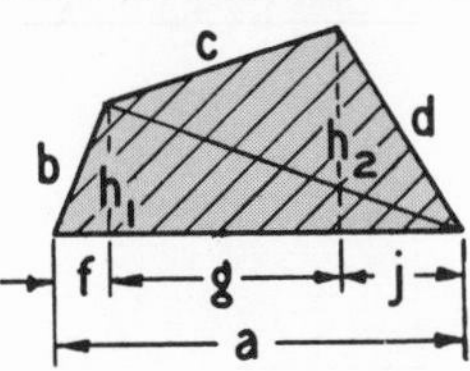

9. REGULAR POLYGON

Let n = number of sides

$p = na$

$a = 2\sqrt{R^2 - r^2}$

$A = \frac{nar}{2} = \frac{na}{2}\sqrt{R^2 - \frac{a^2}{4}}$

$= n \times$ Area of each triangle

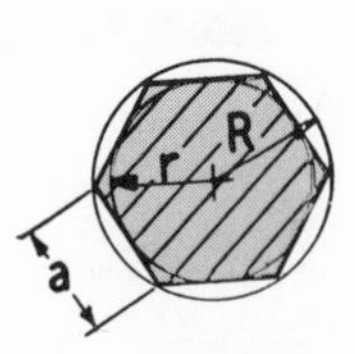

10. CIRCLE

$p = 2\pi r = \pi d = 3.1416d$

$A = \pi r^2 = \frac{\pi d^2}{4} = .7854d^2$

$= \frac{p^2}{4\pi} = .07958p^2$

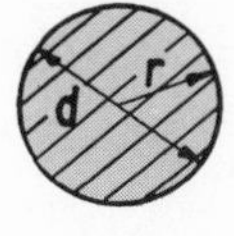

11. HOLLOW CIRCLE or ANNULUS

$A = \frac{\pi}{4}(d_2^2 - d_1^2) = .7854\,(d_2^2 - d_1^2)$

$= \pi\,(r_2^2 - r_1^2)$

$= \pi \frac{d_1 + d_2}{2}(r_2 - r_1)$

$= \pi\,(r_1 + r_2)\,(r_2 - r_1)$

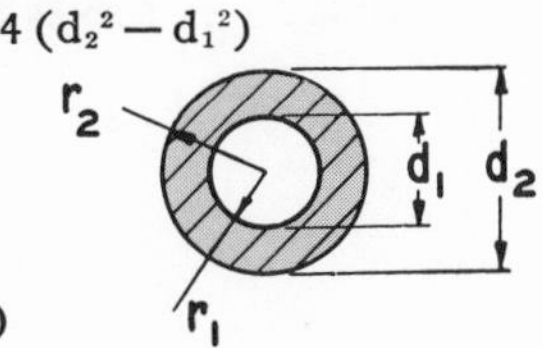

12. SECTOR of CIRCLE

$l = \frac{\pi r \theta}{180} = \frac{r\theta}{57.3} = .01745 r\theta$

$= \frac{2A}{r}$

$A = \frac{\pi \theta r^2}{360} = .008727\theta r^2$

$= \frac{lr}{2}$

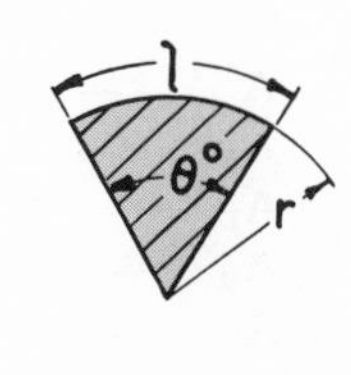

13. SEGMENT of CIRCLE

for $\theta < 90°$

$A = \frac{r^2}{2}\left(\frac{\pi\theta}{180} - \sin\theta\right)$

for $\theta > 90°$

$A = \frac{r^2}{2}\left(\frac{\pi\theta}{180} - \sin(180 - \theta)\right)$

for chord rise, etc., see "Properties of Circle"

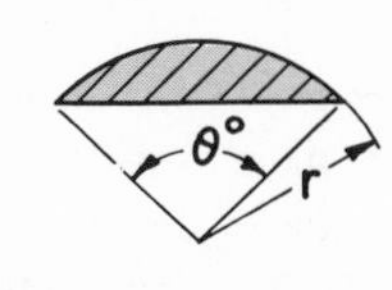

14. SECTOR of HOLLOW CIRCLE

$A = \frac{\pi\theta\,(r_2^2 - r_1^2)}{360}$

$A = \frac{r_1 - r_2}{2}(l_1 + l_2)$

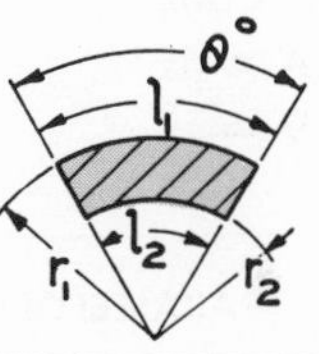

15. FILLET

$A = .215r^2$

or approximately

$A = \frac{r^2}{5}$

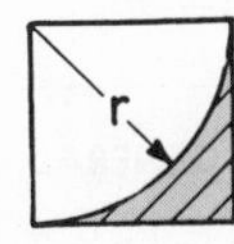

16. ELLIPSE

$p = \pi(a + b)$ approximately

$= \pi[1.5(a + b) - \sqrt{ab}]$ more nearly

$A = \pi ab$

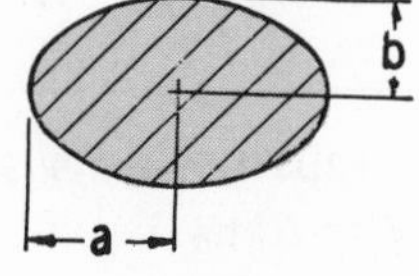

17. PARABOLA

$A = \frac{2}{3}ab$

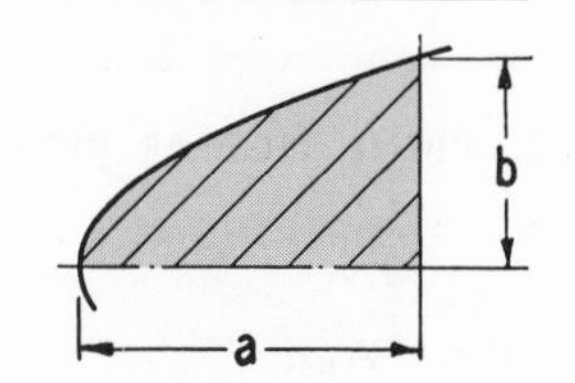

TD-4-23

Volume of Solids (Hyatt Bearings Division, General Motors Corporation)

Nomenclature

a, b, c, d	—	Lengths of Sides
C	—	Length of Chord
A	—	Total Area
A_B	—	Area of Base
A_L	—	Area of Lateral or Convex Surfaces
A_R	—	Area of Right Section
A_T	—	Area of Top Section
h, h_1, h_2	—	Vertical Height or Altitude
h_G	—	Vertical Distance between Centers of Gravity of Areas
L, L_1, L_2	—	Lateral Length or Slant Height
L_G	—	Slant Height between Centers of Gravity of Areas
p	—	Perimeter
p_B	—	Perimeter of Base
p_R	—	Perimeter of Right Section
r, r_1	—	Radii
V	—	Volume

18. CUBE

$A = 6a^2$

$V = a^3$

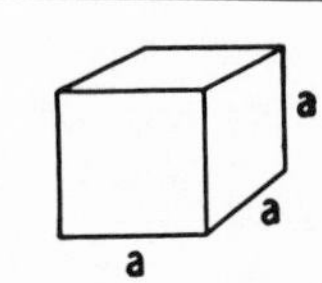

19. PARALLELOPIPED

$A = 2(ab + bc + ac)$

$V = abc$

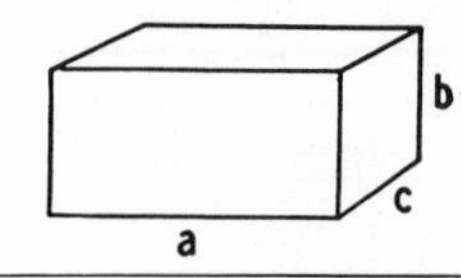

20. GENERAL PRISM AND RIGHT REGULAR PRISM

$A_L = p_R L = p_B h$

$A = A_L + 2A_B$

$V = A_R \times L = A_B h$

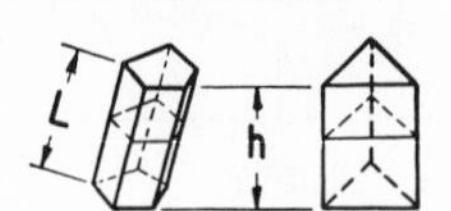

21. FRUSTUM of PRISM

$V = A_B h_G$

$V = A_R L_G$

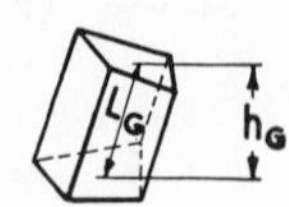

22. RIGHT REGULAR PYRAMID or CONE

$A_L = \frac{1}{2} p_B L$

$V = \frac{1}{3} A_B h$

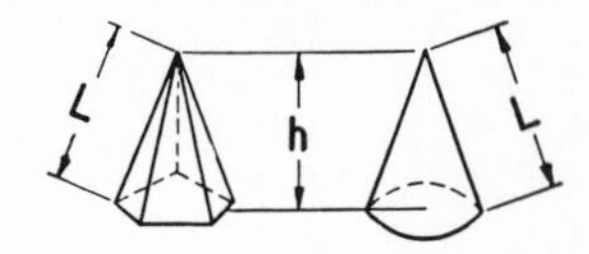

23. GENERAL PYRAMID or CONE

$V = \frac{1}{3} A_B h$

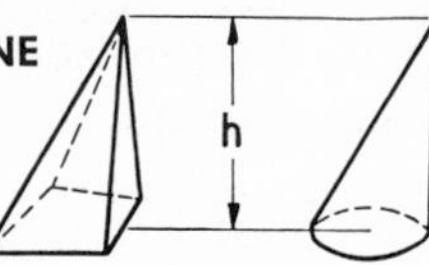

24. FRUSTUM of RIGHT REGULAR PYRAMID or CONE

$A_L = \frac{1}{2} L (p_B + p_T)$

$A = A_L + A_B + A_T$

$V = \frac{1}{3} h (A_B + A_T + \sqrt{A_B A_T})$

25. FRUSTUM of GENERAL PYRAMID or CONE (PARALLEL ENDS)

$V = \frac{1}{3} h (A_B + A_T + \sqrt{A_B A_T})$

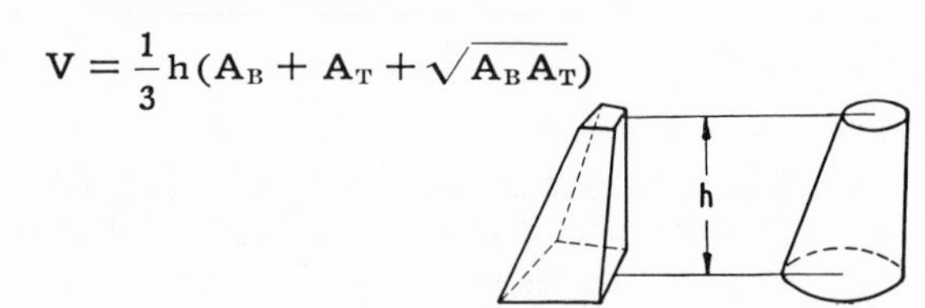

26. RIGHT CIRCULAR CYLINDER

$A_L = 2\pi r h$

$A = 2\pi r (r + h)$

$V = \pi r^2 h$

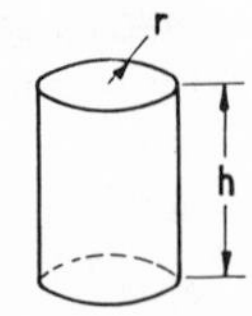

27. GENERAL CYLINDER (ANY CROSS SECTION)

$A_L = p_B h = p_R L$

$A = A_L + 2A_B$

$V = A_B h = A_R L$

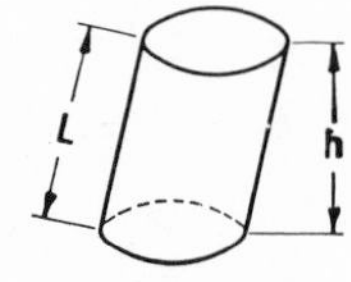

28. FRUSTUM of GENERAL CYLINDER

$V = \frac{1}{2} A_R (L_1 + L_2)$

$V = A_B h_G$

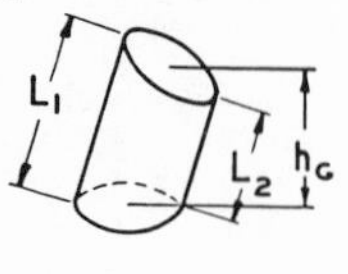

TD-4-23 (con't.)

Volume of Solids (Hyatt Bearings Division, General Motors Corporation)

29. FRUSTUM of RIGHT CIRCULAR CYLINDER

$A_L = \pi r (h_1 + h_2)$

$A_T = \pi r \sqrt{r^2 + \left(\frac{h_1 - h_2}{2}\right)^2}$

$A_B = \pi r^2$

$A = A_L + A_T + A_B$

$V = \frac{\pi r^2}{2} (h_1 + h_2)$

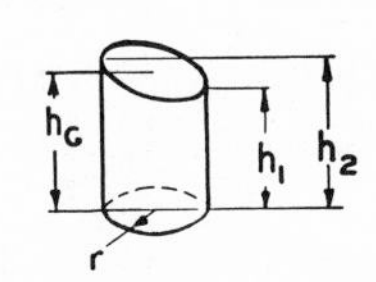

30. SPHERE

$A = 4\pi r^2 = 12.566r^2$

$V = \frac{4}{3} \pi r^3 = 4.189r^3$

31. SPHERICAL SECTOR

$A = \frac{\pi r}{2} (4h + C)$

$V = \frac{2}{3} \pi r^2 h = 2.0944r^2 h$

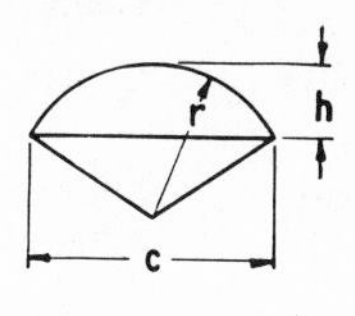

32. SPHERICAL SEGMENT

$A_T = 2\pi rh = \frac{\pi}{4} (4h^2 + C^2)$

$V = \frac{\pi}{3} h^2(3r - h) = \frac{\pi}{24} h(3C^2 + 4h^2)$

33. SPHERICAL ZONE

$A_L = 2\pi rh$

$A = \frac{\pi}{4} (8rh + a^2 + b^2)$

$V = \frac{\pi h}{24} (3C^2 + 3b^2 + 4h^2)$

34. TORUS

$A = 4\pi^2 r r_1$

$V = 2\pi^2 r^2 r_1$

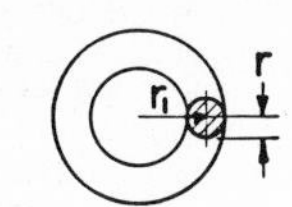

TD-6-1

Characteristics and Uses of Various Woods

Wood	Selected Characteristics	Representative Uses
Ash	Coarse grained, heavy, hard, resistant to shock	Athletic goods, interior and cabinet work, oars, handles
Balsa	Extremely light in weight	Insulation, life preservers
Butternut	Coarse grained, light, soft, easily worked, takes high polish	Interior finish
Cedar	Compact, brittle, easily worked, resistant to decay, low strength	Linings for vermin-proof closets and chests, posts, sills, pencils, fencing, shingles
Chestnut	Coarse grained, moderately light, moderate strength, easily worked, weather resistant	Core stock for veneer panels, heavy construction, interior finish, railroad ties, telegraph poles, caskets
Cypress	Close grained, light, hard, brittle, durable, easily worked, takes high polish, resistant to moisture	Interior finish, cabinet work, building construction, docks, trestles
Douglas Fir	Strong, hard, durable, difficult to work	Construction, fuel, sash, doors, railroad car construction, wood pipe, tanks
Elm	Close grained, hard, heavy, tough, high shock resistance, difficult to work, warps during drying	Wagon and ship building, bridge timbers, sills, furniture, boxes, barrels, panels
Gum	Close grained, moderately hard, tough, tends to warp and shrink in seasoning, not resistant to weather	Furniture, pulpwood, veneer, cooperage, furniture, interior trim
Hemlock	Coarse grain, uneven in texture, light, soft, brittle, splits easily, not durable under exposure	Crates, packing cases
Hickory	Heaviest, hardest, strongest and toughest of American woods, extremely flexible, shrinks considerably during drying	Ladder rungs, bows, bent work, dowels, gym apparatus
Lignum Vitae	Very heavy, hard, resinous difficult to work	Small turnings, tool handles, pulley sheaves
Locust	Close grained, strong, heavy, hard, high in shock resistance	Mine timbers and equipment, posts, turnings
Mahogany	Brittle, resistant to dry rot and worms	Interior finish, furniture, hand rails, patterns
Maple	Fine grained, uniform texture, heavy, hard, strong, not resistant to water	Flooring, interior finish, furniture veneers, pulpwood, boxes, woodenware
Oak	Close grained, heavy, hard, strong, tough, takes high polish	Framed structures, interior finish, furniture, woodenware, shipbuilding, railroad ties and cars, agricultural implements
Palmetto	Light wood, durable under water	Piling
White Pine	Straight grained, low strength, soft, easily worked	Interior finish, patterns, shade and map rollers, toys
Yellow Pine	Coarse grained, hard, strong, durable if dry and well ventilated.	Heavy framing, timbers, subflooring, sheeting, cooperage
Norway Pine	Coarse grained, hard, light, compact	All purposes of construction
Poplar	Close and straight grain, soft, brittle, shrinks excessively when drying, warps and twists, easily worked	General carpentry work
Redwood	Coarse grained, brittle, light, soft, easily worked, durable when in contact with soil	Railroad ties, fence posts, telegraph poles
Spruce	Medium strength, light, soft, fine grain, low in resistance to shock	Structural purposes, aircraft construction, general construction, framing, piles, other submerged construction, pulpwood, piano sounding boards.
Tamarack	Coarse in texture, intermediate weight	Telegraph poles, railway ties, shipbuilding, pulpwood, fuel, boxes, crates
Walnut	Coarse grain, hard, heavy, strong	Interior finish, cabinet work, gunstocks

TD-6-2

Characteristics and Uses of Various Metals

Metal	Selected Characteristics	Representative Uses
Cast Iron (gray iron)	Refined pig iron containing relatively high percent of carbon, cheap, easily machined to a smooth surface, brittle, grainy structure	Machine tool frames and bases, used where bulk and inertia are important
Malleable Iron (white iron)	Relatively tough and strong cast iron, can be hammered into different shapes without cracking, high shock resistance	Farm tools, railroad equipment
Wrought Iron	Tough, malleable, high ductility, easily forged or welded	Pipe, sheet metal, ornamental metalwork, rivets, bolts
Carbon Steel	Manufactured metal, somewhere between wrought iron and cast iron in carbon content, it is graded by the carbon content	Machine tools, pipe, sheet metal, gears, forgings, hand tools
Nickel Steel	Great strength, toughness, high elastic limit, good ductility, resistant to corrosion	Propeller shafts, axles, gears, bolts, studs, keys, wire cables, armor plate, incandescent light-bulb wires
Chromium Steel	Combines hardness with high strength and elastic limit, erosion resistant	Bearings, armor piercing projectiles, tableware, auto parts and trim, instruments, airplane engine, valves
Chrome-Nickel Steel	Tough, ductile, good tensile strength, elastic, high endurance	Forged axles, connecting rods, springs, machine parts
Molybdenum Steel	Especially resistant to repeated stress, high hardness and tensile strength, good machineability	Fine wire, transmission gears and mainshafts, high grade machinery
Tungsten Steel	High magnetic reluctance, shock resistant, wear resistant	Cutting tools, permanent magnets, dies, electrical measuring instruments, cam rolls
Vanadium Steel	High tensile strength, high elastic limit, good ductility, light, tough, withstands great shock	Springs, locomotive forgings, gears
Chrome-Vanadium Steel	Extremely good tensile strength, elastic limit, endurance limit, ductility	Drop forged parts, springs, shafting, pins, connecting rods, stainless steel
Manganese Steel	Resistant to wear, very high ductility, moderate tensile strength	Teeth of digging machinery, bridge construction, railroad rails, gears, axles
High Speed Steel	Retains hardness during long periods at relatively high temperatures	High production metalworking tools, cold chisels, drills
Copper	Very malleable and ductile, excellent conductor of electricity	Generators, motors, bus bars, wires, condensers, cooking utensils, evaporators, art metal work, radiator cores, wire, sheets, strips, bars, plates, seamless tubes, castings, screen, wire cloth, bolts
Brass	Corrosion resistant, hard, strong, not readily welded, easily machined, produced in a range of from hard to soft	Water pump impellers, battery terminals, musical instruments, hardware items, fittings for gas, oil, and water lines
Bronze	High heat conductivity, not readily welded, easily machined, produced in a range of from hard to soft, generally harder than brass and lasts longer	Piston rings, statues, bells, bushings, bullet jackets, propeller shafts
Zinc	Low tensile strength, hard, brittle, extremely low resonance	Galvanized protective coatings, sound apparatus, roofing, sheets, canning jar covers
Aluminum	Very ductile and malleable, soft, easily cast, does not rust, light in weight	Cooking utensils, electrical cable, wrapping, airplane frames, furniture, boats, ornamental work, structural members
Lead	Soft, weak, malleable, low ductility	Pipes, storage batteries, solder, paint, cover for electrical cables, toys, weights
Tin	Very malleable, highly resistant to corrosion, low strength, soft	Tin plate for cans, solder, alloyed with copper and other metals
Nickel	Ductile, hard, magnetic	Plating to improve appearance, propellers, alloyed with other metals to increase strength

TD-6-3

Characteristics and Uses of Materials Other than Wood and Metal

Material	Selected Characteristics	Representative Uses
Cork	Resistant to liquid penetration, prolonged compression yields little deformity, resilient, high coefficient of friction	Seals, gaskets, cushioning, floats, insulation, tool handles, life preservers
Rubber	Softens when heated, becomes brittle when cooled, plastic, tacky, soluble in coal tar or petroleum solvents	Machinery mountings, bumpers, springs, lining of tanks, absorption of vibration, tires
Ceramics	Generally brittle; strong corrosion, heat and wear resistance; wide range of characteristics depending on manufacture and materials used	Tips for machine tool bits; glassware; dishes; electrical insulators; electronic, industrial, machine, and structural applications; missile components
Thermoplastics	Can be reheated and reformed, properties vary and depend on chemistry of manufacture	Toothbrushes, tool handles, spectacle frames, steering wheels, combs, phonograph records, airplane windows, adhesives in safety glass
Thermosetting Plastics	Cannot be reformed, properties depend on chemistry of manufacture	Gears, rollers, industrial parts, kitchen counter tops
Paper	Properties of paper depend upon the chemistry of manufacture	Gaskets, publishing, boxes, cartons
Leather	Hides of different animals exhibit different properties	Shoes, craft work, industrial belts

TD-7-1

Vertical Single-Stroke Gothic Characters

Study the proportions of each character.

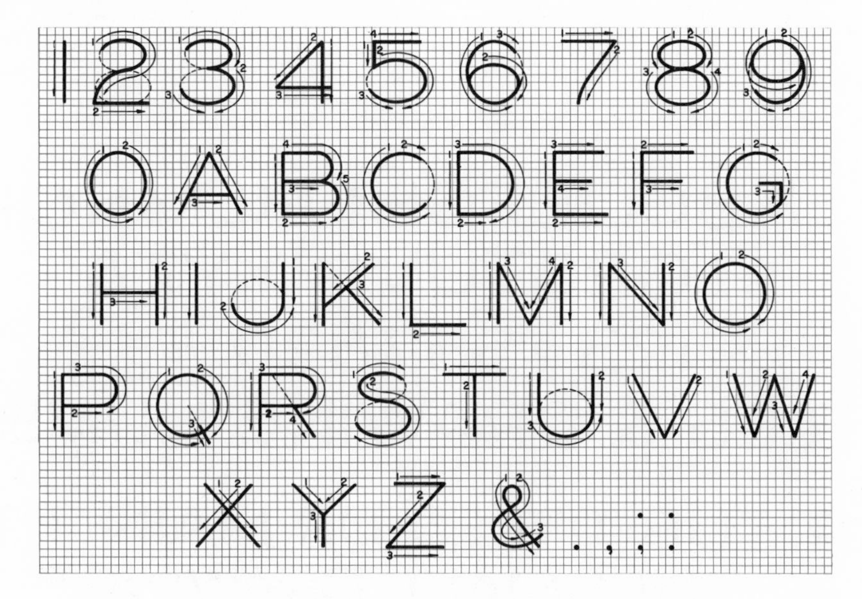

TD-7-2

Inclined Single-Stroke Gothic Characters

Study the proportions of each character.

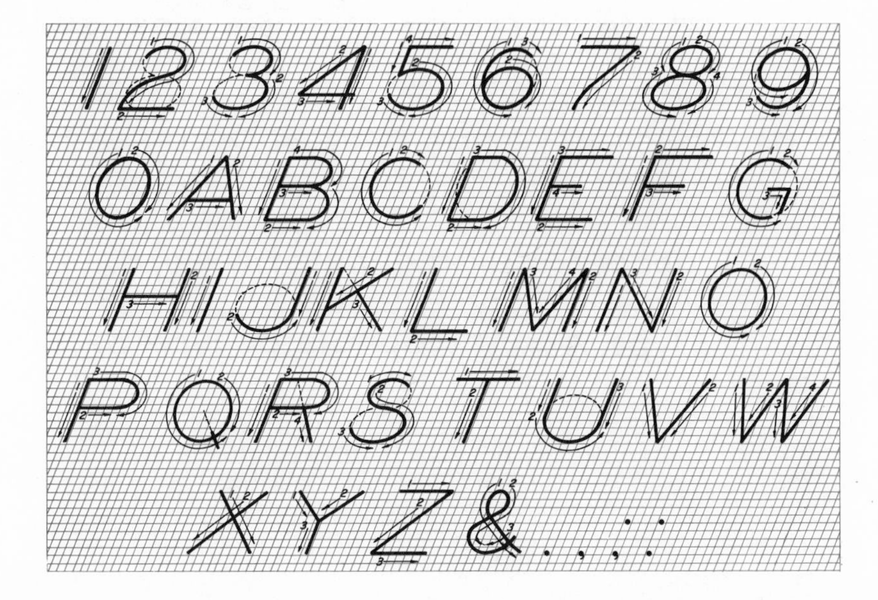

TD-7-3A

Vertical USAS Alphabet

TYPE 1 ABCDEFGHIJKLMNOP
QRSTUVWXYZ&
1234567890 $\frac{1}{2}$ $\frac{3}{4}$ $\frac{5}{8}$
TITLES & DRAWING NUMBERS

TYPE 2
FOR SUB-TITLES OR MAIN TITLES
ON SMALL DRAWINGS

TYPE 3 ABCDEFGHIJKLMNOPQRSTUVWXYZ&
1234567890 $\frac{1}{2}$ $\frac{3}{4}$ $\frac{5}{8}$ $\frac{9}{32}$
FOR HEADINGS AND PROMINENT NOTES

TYPE 4 ABCDEFGHIJKLMNOPQRSTUVWXYZ&
1234567890 $\frac{1}{2}$ $\frac{3}{4}$ $\frac{5}{8}$ $\frac{23}{64}$
FOR BILLS OF MATERIAL, DIMENSIONS & GENERAL NOTES

TYPE 5
OPTIONAL TYPE SAME AS TYPE 4 BUT USING TYPE 3 FOR FIRST LETTER OF PRINCIPAL WORDS. MAY BE USED FOR SUB-TITLES AND NOTES ON THE BODY OF DRAWINGS.

TYPE 6 abcdefghijklmnopqrstuvwxyz
Type 6 may be used in place of
Type 4 with capitals of Type 3.

TECHNICAL DATA

TD-7-3B

Inclined USAS Alphabet

TYPE 1

ABCDEFGHIJKLMNOP
QRSTUVWXYZ&
1234567890 $\frac{1}{2}$ $\frac{3}{4}$ $\frac{5}{8}$ $\frac{7}{16}$
TO BE USED FOR MAIN TITLES
& DRAWING NUMBERS

5
2

TYPE 2

ABCDEFGHIJKLMNOPQR
STUVWXYZ&
1234567890 $\frac{13}{64}$ $\frac{5}{8}$ $\frac{1}{2}$
TO BE USED FOR SUB-TITLES

TYPE 3

ABCDEFGHIJKLMNOPQRSTUVWXYZ&
1234567890 $\frac{1}{2}$ $\frac{3}{4}$ $\frac{5}{8}$ $\frac{7}{16}$
FOR HEADINGS AND PROMINENT NOTES

TYPE 4

ABCDEFGHIJKLMNOPQRSTUVWXYZ&
1234567890 $\frac{1}{2}$ $\frac{1}{4}$ $\frac{3}{8}$ $\frac{5}{16}$ $\frac{7}{32}$ $\frac{1}{8}$
FOR BILLS OF MATERIAL, DIMENSIONS & GENERAL NOTES

TYPE 5

OPTIONAL TYPE SAME AS TYPE 4 BUT USING TYPE 3 FOR FIRST LETTER OF PRINCIPAL WORDS. MAY BE USED FOR SUB-TITLES & NOTES ON THE BODY OF DRAWINGS.

TYPE 6

abcdefghijklmnopqrstuvwxyz
Type 6 may be used in place of
Type 4 with capitals of Type 3

TD-7-3C

Vertical SAE Alphabet

.350

ABCDEFGHIJKLMNOPQRST
UVWXYZ& OR ₵-1234567890

.240

ABCDEFGHIJKLMNOPQRSTUVWX
YZ& OR ₵-1234567890

.175

ABCDEFGHIJKLMNOPQRSTUVWXYZ& OR ₵
1234567890

.140

ABCDEFGHIJKLMNOPQRSTUVWXYZ& OR ₵ – 1234567890

.120

ABCDEFGHIJKLMNOPQRSTUVWXYZ& OR ₵ – 1234567890

TD-7-3D

Inclined SAE Alphabet

TD-7-3E

Vertical (MIL-STD) Alphabet

.20 LETTERS:

ABCDEFGHIJKLMNOPQRSTUVWXYZ

1234567890 $\frac{1}{2}$ $\frac{3}{4}$ $\frac{5}{8}$ $\frac{7}{16}$ .06 MIN

LOOK .06 MIN SPACING ROUND LETTERS

HILL .12 MAX SPACING STRAIGHT BACK LETTERS

.18 LETTERS:

ABCDEFGHIJKLMNOPQRSTUVWXYZ

1234567890 $\frac{1}{2}$ $\frac{3}{4}$ $\frac{5}{8}$ $\frac{7}{16}$ .06 MIN

LOOK .06 MIN SPACING ROUND LETTERS

HILL .10 MAX SPACING STRAIGHT BACK LETTERS

.14 LETTERS:

ABCDEFGHIJKLMNOPQRSTUVWXYZ

1234567890 $\frac{1}{2}$ $\frac{3}{4}$ $\frac{5}{8}$ $\frac{7}{16}$ .03 MIN

LOOK .06 MIN SPACING ROUND LETTERS

HILL .10 MAX SPACING STRAIGHT BACK LETTERS

.12 LETTERS:

ABCDEFGHIJKLMNOPQRSTUVWXYZ

1234567890 $\frac{1}{2}$ $\frac{3}{4}$ $\frac{5}{8}$ $\frac{7}{16}$ .03 MIN

LOOK .06 MIN SPACING ROUND LETTERS

HILL .10 MAX SPACING STRAIGHT BACK LETTERS

Inclined (MIL-STD) Alphabet

.20 LETTERS:

ABCDEFGHIJKLMNOPQRSTUVWXYZ

1234567890 $\frac{1}{2}$ $\frac{3}{4}$ $\frac{5}{8}$ $\frac{7}{16}$ .06 M

LOOK — .06 MIN SPACING ROUND LETTERS

HILL — .12 MAX SPACING STRAIGHT BACK LETTERS

.18 LETTERS:

ABCDEFGHIJKLMNOPQRSTUVWXYZ

1234567890 $\frac{1}{2}$ $\frac{3}{4}$ $\frac{5}{8}$ $\frac{7}{16}$ .06 MIN

LOOK — .06 MIN SPACING ROUND LETTERS

HILL — .10 MAX SPACING STRAIGHT BACK LETTERS

.14 LETTERS:

ABCDEFGHIJKLMNOPQRSTUVWXYZ

1234567890 $\frac{1}{2}$ $\frac{3}{4}$ $\frac{5}{8}$ $\frac{7}{16}$ .03 MIN

LOOK — .06 MIN SPACING ROUND LETTERS

HILL — .10 MAX SPACING STRAIGHT BACK LETTERS

.12 LETTERS:

ABCDEFGHIJKLMNOPQRSTUVWXYZ

1234567890 $\frac{1}{2}$ $\frac{3}{4}$ $\frac{5}{8}$ $\frac{7}{16}$ .03 MIN

LOOK — .06 MIN SPACING ROUND LETTERS

HILL — .10 MAX SPACING STRAIGHT BACK LETTERS

TD-7-4

Application of Military Standard Letters and Numerals
(MIL-STD-1B, July 9, 1963)

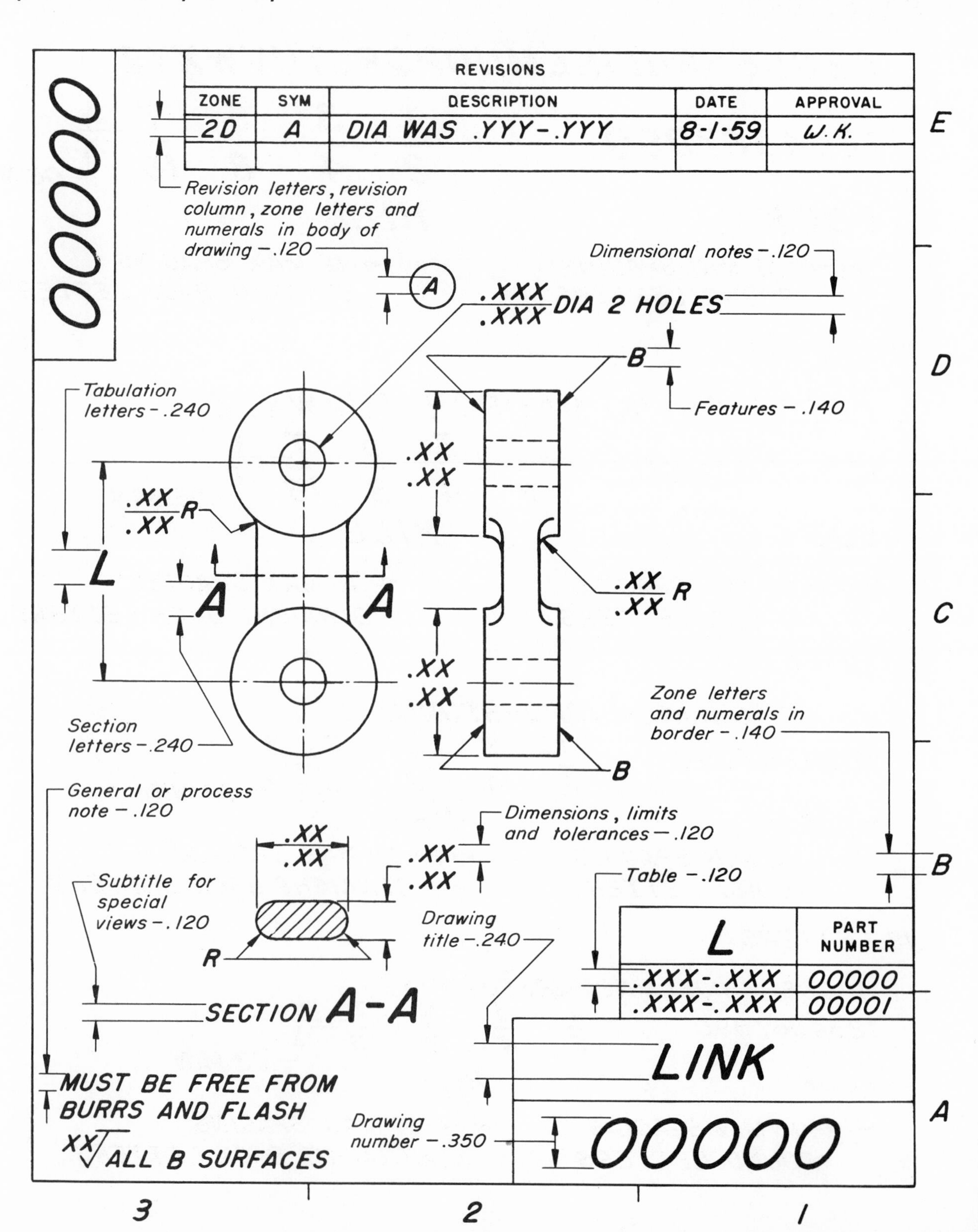

TD-8-1

Preferred Two-Place Decimals and Their Metric Equivalents (Deere & Company)

Order of Preference					Order of Preference				
1	2	3	4	Millimeter Equivalent	1	2	3	4	Millimeter Equivalent
		.02		.508			.52		13.208
			.03	.762				.53	13.462
		.04		1.016			.54		13.716
			.05	1.270				.55	13.970
	.06			1.524		.56			14.224
		.08		2.032			.58		14.732
			.09	2.286				.59	14.986
.10				2.540	.60				15.240
	.12			3.048		.62			15.748
		.14		3.556			.64		16.256
			.15	3.810				.65	16.510
		.16		4.064			.66		16.764
	.18			4.572		.68			17.272
			.19	4.826				.69	17.526
.20				5.080	.70				17.780
		.22		5.588			.72		18.288
	.24			6.096		.74			18.796
			.25	6.350				.75	19.050
		.26		6.604			.76		19.304
		.28		7.112			.78		19.812
.30				7.620	.80				20.320
			.31	7.874				.81	20.574
	.32			8.128		.82			20.828
		.34		8.636			.84		21.336
			.35	8.890				.85	21.590
		.36		9.144			.86		21.844
			.37	9.398				.87	22.098
	.38			9.652		.88			22.352
.40				10.160	.90				22.860
			.41	10.414				.91	23.114
		.42		10.668			.92		23.368
	.44			11.176		.94			23.876
			.45	11.430				.95	24.130
		.46		11.684			.96		24.384
			.47	11.938				.97	24.638
		.48		12.192			.98		24.892
.50				12.700	1.00				25.400

TD-8-2

Conversion of Fractions to Decimals (SAE)

32nds	64ths	To 4 Places	To 3 Places	To 2 Places	32nds	64ths	To 4 Places	To 3 Places	To 2 Places
	1/64	.0156	.016	.02		33/64	.5156	.516	.52
1/32		.0312	.031	.03	17/32		.5312	.531	.53
	3/64	.0469	.047	.05		35/64	.5469	.547	.55
1/16		.0625	.062	.06	9/16		.5625	.562	.56
	5/64	.0781	.078	.08		37/64	.5781	.578	.58
3/32		.0938	.094	.09	19/32		.5938	.594	.59
	7/64	.1094	.109	.11		39/64	.6094	.609	.61
1/8		.1250	.125	.12	5/8		.6250	.625	.62
	9/64	.1406	.141	.14		41/64	.6406	.641	.64
5/32		.1562	.156	.16	21/32		.6562	.656	.66
	11/64	.1719	.172	.17		43/64	.6719	.672	.67
3/16		.1875	.188	.19	11/16		.6875	.688	.69
	13/64	.2031	.203	.20		45/64	.7031	.703	.70
7/32		.2188	.219	.22	23/32		.7188	.719	.72
	15/64	.2344	.234	.23		47/64	.7344	.734	.73
1/4		.2500	.250	.25	3/4		.7500	.750	.75
	17/64	.2656	.266	.27		49/64	.7656	.766	.77
9/32		.2812	.281	.28	25/32		.7812	.781	.78
	19/64	.2969	.297	.30		51/64	.7969	.797	.80
5/16		.3125	.312	.31	13/16		.8125	.812	.81
	21/64	.3281	.328	.33		53/64	.8281	.828	.83
11/32		.3438	.344	.34	27/32		.8438	.844	.84
	23/64	.3594	.359	.36		55/64	.8594	.859	.86
3/8		.3750	.375	.38	7/8		.8750	.875	.88
	25/64	.3906	.391	.39		57/64	.8906	.891	.89
13/32		.4062	.406	.41	29/32		.9062	.906	.91
	27/64	.4219	.422	.42		59/64	.9219	.922	.92
7/16		.4375	.438	.44	15/16		.9375	.938	.94
	29/64	.4531	.453	.45		61/64	.9531	.953	.95
15/32		.4688	.469	.47	31/32		.9688	.969	.97
	31/64	.4844	.484	.48		63/64	.9844	.984	.98
1/2		.5000	.500	.50	1		1.0000	1.000	1.00

TD-11-1

Preferred Basic Sizes for Specifying Fits of Mating Parts (USAS B4.1-1955)

Fractions	Decimals	Two-Place Decimals
...	0.0100	...
...	0.0125	...
1/64	0.015625	...
...	0.0200	...
...	0.0250	...
1/32	0.03125	...
...	0.0400	0.04
...	0.0500	...
...	...	0.06
1/16	0.0625	...
...	0.0800	...
3/32	0.09375	...
...	0.1000	0.10
1/8	0.1250	...
...	...	0.15
5/32	0.15625	...
3/16	0.1875	...
...	...	0.20
1/4	0.2500	0.25
...	...	0.30
5/16	0.3125	...
...	...	0.35
3/8	0.3750	...
...	...	0.40
7/16	0.4375	...
1/2	0.5000	0.50
9/16	0.5625	...
...	...	0.60
5/8	0.6250	...
11/16	0.6875	...
...	...	0.70
3/4	0.7500	0.75
...	...	0.80
7/8	0.8750	...
...	...	0.90
1	1.0000	1.0
...	...	1.1
1 1/8	1.1250	...
...	...	...
1 1/4	1.2500	1.25
1 3/8	1.3750	...
...	...	1.40
1 1/2	1.5000	1.50
1 5/8	1.6250	...
1 3/4	1.7500	1.75
1 7/8	1.8750	...
2	2.0000	2.0
2 1/8	2.1250	...
2 1/4	2.2500	2.25
2 3/8	2.3750	...
2 1/2	2.5000	2.5
2 5/8	2.6250	...
2 3/4	2.7500	2.75
2 7/8	2.8750	...
3	3.0000	3.0
3 1/4	3.2500	3.25
3 1/2	3.5000	3.5
3 3/4	3.7500	3.75
4	4.0000	4.0
4 1/4	4.2500	4.25
4 1/2	4.5000	4.5
4 3/4	4.7500	4.75
5	5.0000	5.0
5 1/4	5.2500	5.25
5 1/2	5.5000	5.5
5 3/4	5.7500	5.75
6	6.0000	6.0
6 1/2	6.5000	6.5
7	7.0000	7.0
7 1/2	7.5000	7.5
8	8.0000	8.0
8 1/2	8.5000	8.5
9	9.0000	9.0
9 1/2	9.5000	9.5
10	10.0000	10.0
10 1/2	10.5000	10.5
11	11.0000	11.0
11 1/2	11.5000	11.5
12	12.0000	12.0
12 1/2	12.5000	12.5
13	13.0000	13.0
13 1/2	13.5000	13.5
14	14.0000	14.0
14 1/2	14.5000	14.5
15	15.0000	15.0
15 1/2	15.5000	15.5
16	16.0000	16.0
16 1/2	16.5000	16.5
17	17.0000	17.0
17 1/2	17.5000	17.5
18	18.0000	18.0
18 1/2	18.5000	18.5
19	19.0000	19.0
19 1/2	19.5000	19.5
20	20.0000	20.0
20 1/2	20.5000	...
21	21.0000	...

TECHNICAL DATA

TD-11-2

Standard Tolerances with Machining Processes Normally Expected to Produce Work within Tolerances Indicated by Various Grades of Production Difficulty (USAS B4.1-1955)

Tolerance values are in thousandths of an inch.

Nominal Size Range Inches Over To	Grade 4	Grade 5	Grade 6	Grade 7	Grade 8	Grade 9	Grade 10	Grade 11	Grade 12	Grade 13
0.04- 0.12	0.15	0.20	0.25	0.4	0.6	1.0	1.6	2.5	4	6
0.12- 0.24	0.15	0.20	0.3	0.5	0.7	1.2	1.8	3.0	5	7
0.24- 0.40	0.15	0.25	0.4	0.6	0.9	1.4	2.2	3.5	6	9
0.40- 0.71	0.2	0.3	0.4	0.7	1.0	1.6	2.8	4.0	7	10
0.71- 1.19	0.25	0.4	0.5	0.8	1.2	2.0	3.5	5.0	8	12
1.19- 1.97	0.3	0.4	0.6	1.0	1.6	2.5	4.0	6	10	16
1.97- 3.15	0.3	0.5	0.7	1.2	1.8	3.0	4.5	7	12	18
3.15- 4.73	0.4	0.6	0.9	1.4	2.2	3.5	5	9	14	22
4.73- 7.09	0.5	0.7	1.0	1.6	2.5	4.0	6	10	16	25
7.09- 9.85	0.6	0.8	1.2	1.8	2.8	4.5	7	12	18	28
9.85- 12.41	0.6	0.9	1.2	2.0	3.0	5.0	8	12	20	30
12.41- 15.75	0.7	1.0	1.4	2.2	3.5	6	9	14	22	35
15.75- 19.69	0.8	1.0	1.6	2.5	4	6	10	16	25	40
19.69- 30.09	0.9	1.2	2.0	3	5	8	12	20	30	50
30.09- 41.49	1.0	1.6	2.5	4	6	10	16	25	40	60
41.49- 56.19	1.2	2.0	3	5	8	12	20	30	50	80
56.19- 76.39	1.6	2.5	4	6	10	16	25	40	60	100
76.39-100.9	2.0	3	5	8	12	20	30	50	80	125
100.9- 131.9	2.5	4	6	10	16	25	40	60	100	160
131.9- 171.9	3	5	8	12	20	30	50	80	125	200
171.9- 200	4	6	10	16	25	40	60	100	160	250

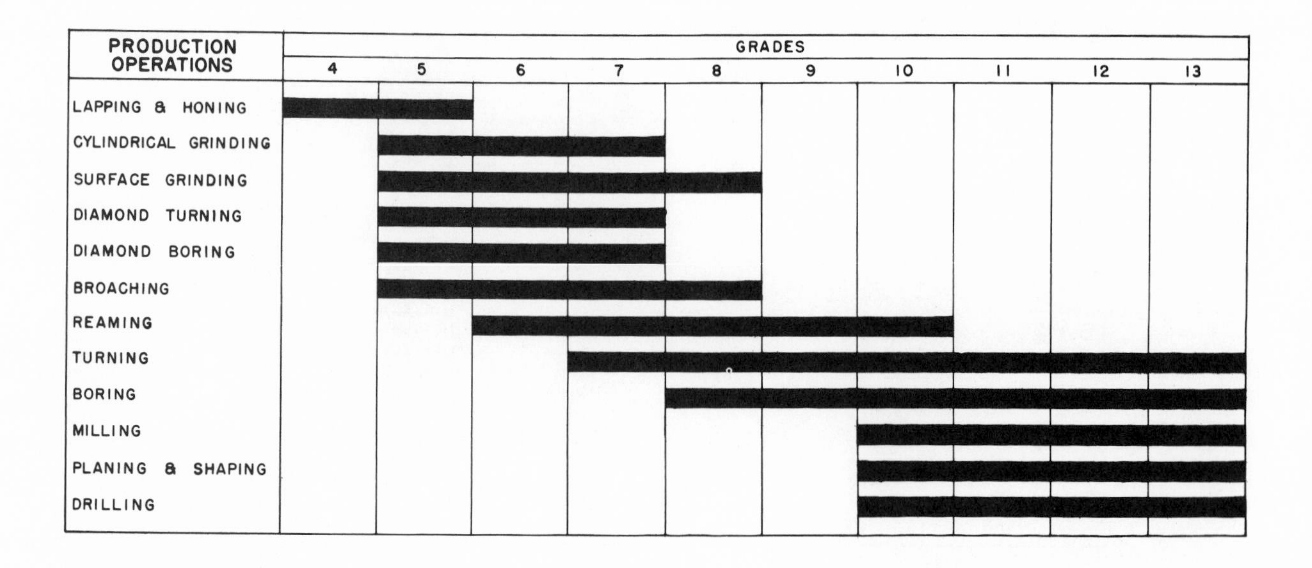

TD-11-3

Running and Sliding Fits (USAS B4.1-1955)

Limits are in thousandths of an inch.

Limits for hole and shaft are applied algebraically to the basic size to obtain the limits of size for the parts.

Date in **bold face** are in accordance with ABC agreements.

Symbols H5, g5, etc., are Hole and Shaft designations used in ABC System.

83.1 *Running and Sliding Fits.* Running and sliding fits, for which limits of clearance are given here, are intended to provide a similar running performance, with suitable lubrication allowance, throughout the range of sizes. The clearances for the first two classes, used chiefly as slide fits, increase more slowly with diameter than the other classes, so that accurate location is maintained even at the expense of free relative motion.

RC 1 *Close sliding fits* are intended for the accurate location of parts which must assemble without perceptible play.

RC 2 *Sliding fits* are intended for accurate location, but with greater maximum clearance than class RC 1. Parts made to this fit move and turn easily but are not intended to run freely, and in the larger sizes may seize with small temperature changes.

RC 3 *Precision running fits* are about the closest fits which can be expected to run freely, and are intended for precision work at slow speeds and light journal pressures, but are not suitable where appreciable temperature differences are likely to be encountered.

RC 4 *Close running fits* are intended chiefly for running fits on accurate machinery with moderate surface speeds and journal pressures, where accurate location and minimum play are desired.

	Class RC 1			Class RC 2			Class RC 3			Class RC 4		
Nominal Size Range	Limits of	Standard Limits		Limits of	Standard Limits		Limits of	Standard Limits		Limits of	Standard Limits	
Inches Over To	Clearance	Hole H5	Shaft g4	Clearance	Hole H6	Shaft g5	Clearance	Hole H6	Shaft f6	Clearance	Hole H7	Shaft f7
0.04– 0.12	**0.1** **0.45**	**+0.2** **0**	**− 0.1** **− 0.25**	**0.1** **0.55**	**+ 0.25** **0**	**− 0.1** **− 0.3**	**0.3** **0.8**	**+ 0.25** **0**	**− 0.3** **− 0.55**	**0.3** **1.1**	**+ 0.4** **0**	**− 0.3** **− 0.7**
0.12– 0.24	**0.15** **0.5**	**+0.2** **0**	**− 0.15** **− 0.3**	**0.15** **0.65**	**+ 0.3** **0**	**− 0.15** **− 0.35**	**0.4** **1.0**	**+ 0.3** **0**	**− 0.4** **− 0.7**	**0.4** **1.4**	**+ 0.5** **0**	**− 0.4** **− 0.9**
0.24– 0.40	**0.2** **0.6**	**+0.25** **0**	**− 0.2** **− 0.35**	**0.2** **0.85**	**+ 0.4** **0**	**− 0.2** **− 0.45**	**0.5** **1.3**	**+ 0.4** **0**	**− 0.5** **− 0.9**	**0.5** **1.7**	**+ 0.6** **0**	**− 0.5** **− 1.1**
0.40– 0.71	**0.25** **0.75**	**+0.3** **0**	**− 0.25** **− 0.45**	**0.25** **0.95**	**+ 0.4** **0**	**− 0.25** **− 0.55**	**0.6** **1.4**	**+ 0.4** **0**	**− 0.6** **− 1.0**	**0.6** **2.0**	**+ 0.7** **0**	**− 0.6** **− 2.0**
0.71– 1.19	**0.3** **0.95**	**+0.4** **0**	**− 0.3** **− 0.55**	**0.3** **1.2**	**+ 0.5** **0**	**− 0.3** **− 0.7**	**0.8** **1.8**	**+ 0.5** **0**	**− 0.8** **− 1.3**	**0.8** **2.4**	**+ 0.8** **0**	**− 0.8** **− 1.6**
1.19– 1.97	**0.4** **1.1**	**+0.4** **0**	**− 0.4** **− 0.7**	**0.4** **1.4**	**+ 0.6** **0**	**− 0.4** **− 0.8**	**1.0** **2.2**	**+ 0.6** **0**	**− 1.0** **− 1.6**	**1.0** **3.0**	**+ 1.0** **0**	**− 1.0** **− 2.0**
1.97– 3.15	**0.4** **1.2**	**+0.5** **0**	**− 0.4** **− 0.7**	**0.4** **1.6**	**+ 0.7** **0**	**− 0.4** **− 0.9**	**1.2** **2.6**	**+ 0.7** **0**	**− 1.2** **− 1.9**	**1.2** **3.6**	**+ 1.2** **0**	**− 1.2** **− 2.4**
3.15– 4.73	**0.5** **1.5**	**+0.6** **0**	**− 0.5** **− 0.9**	**0.5** **2.0**	**+ 0.9** **0**	**− 0.5** **− 1.1**	**1.4** **3.2**	**+ 0.9** **0**	**− 1.4** **− 2.3**	**1.4** **4.2**	**+ 1.4** **0**	**− 1.4** **− 2.8**
4.73– 7.09	**0.6** **1.8**	**+0.7** **0**	**− 0.6** **− 1.1**	**0.6** **2.3**	**+ 1.0** **0**	**− 0.6** **− 1.3**	**1.6** **3.6**	**+ 1.0** **0**	**− 1.6** **− 2.6**	**1.6** **4.8**	**+ 1.6** **0**	**− 1.6** **− 3.2**
7.09– 9.85	**0.6** **2.0**	**+0.8** **0**	**− 0.6** **− 1.2**	**0.6** **2.6**	**+ 1.2** **0**	**− 0.3** **− 1.4**	**2.0** **4.4**	**+ 1.2** **0**	**− 2.0** **− 3.2**	**2.0** **5.6**	**+ 1.8** **0**	**− 2.0** **− 3.8**
9.85– 12.41	0.8 2.3	**+0.9** **0**	− 0.8 − 1.4	0.8 2.9	**+ 1.2** **0**	− 0.8 − 1.7	2.5 4.9	**+ 1.2** **0**	− 2.5 − 3.7	2.5 6.5	**+ 2.0** **0**	− 2.5 − 4.5
12.41– 15.75	1.0 2.7	**+1.0** **0**	− 1.0 − 1.7	1.0 3.4	**+ 1.4** **0**	− 1.0 − 2.0	3.0 5.8	**+ 1.4** **0**	− 3.0 − 4.4	3.0 7.4	**+ 2.2** **0**	− 3.0 − 5.2
15.75– 19.69	1.2 3.0	**+1.0** **0**	− 1.2 − 2.0	1.2 3.8	**+ 1.6** **0**	− 1.2 − 2.2	4.0 7.2	**+ 1.6** **0**	− 4.0 − 5.6	4.0 9.0	**+ 2.5** **0**	− 4.0 − 6.5
19.69– 30.09	1.6 3.7	+1.2 0	− 1.6 − 2.5	1.6 4.8	+ 2.0 0	− 1.6 − 2.8	5.0 9.0	+ 2.0 0	− 5.0 − 7.0	5.0 11.0	+ 3.0 0	− 5.0 − 8.0
30.09– 41.49	2.0 4.6	+1.6 0	− 2.0 − 3.0	2.0 6.1	+ 2.5 0	− 2.0 − 3.6	6.0 11.0	+ 2.5 0	− 6.0 − 8.5	6.0 14.0	+ 4.0 0	− 6.0 −10.0
41.49– 56.19	2.5 5.7	+2.0 0	− 2.5 − 3.7	2.5 7.5	+ 3.0 0	− 2.5 − 4.5	8.0 14.0	+ 3.0 0	− 8.0 −11.0	8.0 18.0	+ 5.0 0	− 8.0 −13.0
56.19– 76.39	3.0 7.1	+2.5 0	− 3.0 − 4.6	3.0 9.5	+ 4.0 0	− 3.0 − 5.5	10.0 18.0	+ 4.0 0	−10.0 −14.0	10.0 22.0	+ 6.0 0	−10.0 −16.0
76.39–100.9	4.0 9.0	+3.0 0	− 4.0 − 6.0	4.0 12.0	+ 5.0 0	− 4.0 − 7.0	12.0 22.0	+ 5.0 0	−12.0 −17.0	12.0 28.0	+ 8.0 0	−12.0 −20.0
100.9 –131.9	5.0 11.5	+4.0 0	− 5.0 − 7.5	5.0 15.0	+ 6.0 0	− 5.0 − 9.0	16.0 28.0	+ 6.0 0	−16.0 −22.0	16.0 36.0	+10.0 0	−16.0 −26.0
131.9 –171.9	6.0 14.0	+5.0 0	− 6.0 − 9.0	6.0 19.0	+ 8.0 0	− 6.0 −11.0	18.0 34.0	+ 8.0 0	−18.0 −26.0	18.0 42.0	+12.0 0	−18.0 −30.0
171.9 –200	8.0 18.0	+6.0 0	− 8.0 −12.0	8.0 24.0	+10.0 0	− 8.0 −12.0	22.0 42.0	+10.0 0	−22.0 −32.0	22.0 54.0	+16.0 0	−22.0 −38.0

TD-11-3 (con't.)

Running and Sliding Fits (USAS B4.1-1955)

RC 5) RC 6) *Medium running fits* are intended for higher running speeds, or heavy journal pressures, or both.

RC 7 *Free running fits* are intended for use where accuracy is not essential, or where large temperature variations are likely to be encountered, or under both these conditions.

RC 8) RC 9) *Loose running fits* are intended for use where materials such as cold-rolled shafting and tubing, made to commercial tolerances, are involved.

	Class RC 5			Class RC 6			Class RC 7			Class RC 8			Class RC 9		
Nominal Size Range Inches Over To	Limits of Clearance	Standard Limits Hole H7	Standard Limits Shaft e7	Limits of Clearance	Standard Limits Hole H8	Standard Limits Shaft c8	Limits of Clearance	Standard Limits Hole H9	Standard Limits Shaft d8	Limits of Clearance	Standard Limits Hole H10	Standard Limits Shaft c9	Limits of Clearance	Standard Limits Hole H11	Standard Limits Shaft
0.04– 0.12	**0.6** **1.4**	**+ 0.4** **0**	**− 0.6** **− 1.0**	**0.6** **1.8**	**+ 0.6** **0**	**− 0.6** **− 1.2**	**1.0** **2.6**	**+ 1.0** **0**	**− 1.0** **− 1.6**	**2.5** **5.1**	**+ 1.6** **0**	**− 2.5** **− 3.5**	4.0 8.1	**+ 2.5** **0**	− 4.0 − 5.6
0.12– 0.24	**0.8** **1.8**	**+ 0.5** **0**	**− 0.8** **− 1.3**	**0.8** **2.2**	**+ 0.7** **0**	**− 0.8** **− 1.5**	**1.2** **3.1**	**+ 1.2** **0**	**− 1.2** **− 1.9**	**2.8** **5.8**	**+ 1.8** **0**	**− 2.8** **− 4.0**	4.5 9.0	**+ 3.0** **0**	− 4.5 − 6.0
0.24– 0.40	**1.0** **2.2**	**+ 0.6** **0**	**− 1.0** **− 1.6**	**1.0** **2.8**	**+ 0.9** **0**	**− 1.0** **− 1.9**	**1.6** **3.9**	**+ 1.4** **0**	**− 1.6** **− 2.5**	**3.0** **6.6**	**+ 2.2** **0**	**− 3.0** **− 4.4**	5.0 10.7	**+ 3.5** **0**	− 5.0 − 7.2
0.40– 0.71	**1.2** **2.6**	**+ 0.7** **0**	**− 1.2** **− 1.9**	**1.2** **3.2**	**+ 1.0** **0**	**− 1.2** **− 2.2**	**2.0** **4.6**	**+ 1.6** **0**	**− 2.0** **− 3.0**	**3.5** **7.9**	**+ 2.8** **0**	**− 3.5** **− 5.1**	6.0 12.8	**+ 4.0** **0**	− 6.0 − 8.8
0.71– 1.19	**1.6** **3.2**	**+ 0.8** **0**	**− 1.6** **− 2.4**	**1.6** **4.0**	**+ 1.2** **0**	**− 1.6** **− 2.8**	**2.5** **5.7**	**+ 2.0** **0**	**− 2.5** **− 3.7**	**4.5** **10.0**	**+ 3.5** **0**	**− 4.5** **− 6.5**	7.0 15.5	**+ 5.0** **0**	− 7.0 − 10.5
1.19– 1.97	**2.0** **4.0**	**+ 1.0** **0**	**− 2.0** **− 3.0**	**2.0** **5.2**	**+ 1.6** **0**	**− 2.0** **− 3.6**	**3.0** **7.1**	**+ 2.5** **0**	**− 3.0** **− 4.6**	**5.0** **11.5**	**+ 4.0** **0**	**− 5.0** **− 7.5**	8.0 18.0	**+ 6.0** **0**	− 8.0 − 12.0
1.97– 3.15	**2.5** **4.9**	**+ 1.2** **0**	**− 2.5** **− 3.7**	**2.5** **6.1**	**+ 1.8** **0**	**− 2.5** **− 4.3**	**4.0** **8.8**	**+ 3.0** **0**	**− 4.0** **− 5.8**	**6.0** **13.5**	**+ 4.5** **0**	**− 6.0** **− 9.0**	9.0 20.5	**+ 7.0** **0**	− 9.0 − 13.5
3.15– 4.73	**3.0** **5.8**	**+ 1.4** **0**	**− 3.0** **− 4.4**	**3.0** **7.4**	**+ 2.2** **0**	**− 3.0** **− 5.2**	**5.0** **10.7**	**+ 3.5** **0**	**− 5.0** **− 7.2**	**7.0** **15.5**	**+ 5.0** **0**	**− 7.0** **− 10.5**	10.0 24.0	**+ 9.0** **0**	− 10.0 − 15.0
4.73– 7.09	**3.5** **6.7**	**+ 1.6** **0**	**− 3.5** **− 5.1**	**3.5** **8.5**	**+ 2.5** **0**	**− 3.5** **− 6.0**	**6.0** **12.5**	**+ 4.0** **0**	**− 6.0** **− 8.5**	**8.0** **18.0**	**+ 6.0** **0**	**− 8.0** **− 12.0**	12.0 28.0	**+ 10.0** **0**	− 12.0 − 18.0
7.09– 9.85	**4.0** **7.6**	**+ 1.8** **0**	**− 4.0** **− 5.8**	**4.0** **9.6**	**+ 2.8** **0**	**− 4.0** **− 6.8**	**7.0** **14.3**	**+ 4.5** **0**	**− 7.0** **− 9.8**	**10.0** **21.5**	**+ 7.0** **0**	**− 10.0** **− 14.5**	15.0 34.0	**+ 12.0** **0**	− 15.0 − 22.0
9.85– 12.41	5.0 9.0	**+ 2.0** **0**	− 5.0 − 7.0	5.0 11.0	**+ 3.0** **0**	− 5.0 − 8.0	8.0 16.0	**+ 5.0** **0**	− 8.0 − 11.0	**12.0** **25.0**	**+ 8.0** **0**	**− 12.0** **− 17.0**	18.0 38.0	**+ 12.0** **0**	− 18.0 − 26.0
12.41– 15.75	6.0 10.4	**+ 2.2** **0**	− 6.0 − 8.2	6.0 13.0	**+ 3.5** **0**	− 6.0 − 9.5	10.0 19.5	**+ 6.0** **0**	− 10.0 − 13.5	**14.0** **29.0**	**+ 9.0** **0**	**− 14.0** **− 20.0**	22.0 45.0	**+ 14.0** **0**	− 22.0 − 31.0
15.75– 19.69	8.0 13.0	**+ 2.5** **0**	− 8.0 −10.5	8.0 16.0	**+ 4.0** **0**	− 8.0 −12.0	12.0 22.0	**+ 6.0** **0**	− 12.0 − 16.0	**16.0** **32.0**	**+10.0** **0**	**− 16.0** **− 22.0**	25.0 51.0	**+ 16.0** **0**	− 25.0 − 35.0
19.69– 30.09	10.0 16.0	+ 3.0 0	−10.0 −13.0	10.0 20.0	+ 5.0 0	−10.0 −15.0	16.0 29.0	+ 8.0 0	− 16.0 − 21.0	20.0 40.0	+12.0 0	− 20.0 − 28.0	30.0 62.0	+ 20.0 0	− 30.0 − 42.0
30.09– 41.49	12.0 20.0	+ 4.0 0	−12.0 −16.0	12.0 24.0	+ 6.0 0	−12.0 −18.0	20.0 36.0	+10.0 0	− 20.0 − 26.0	25.0 51.0	+16.0 0	− 25.0 − 35.0	40.0 81.0	+ 25.0 0	− 40.0 − 56.0
41.49– 56.19	16.0 26.0	+ 5.0 0	−16.0 −21.0	16.0 32.0	+ 8.0 0	−16.0 −24.0	25.0 45.0	+12.0 0	− 25.0 − 33.0	30.0 62.0	+20.0 0	− 30.0 − 42.0	50.0 100	+ 30.0 0	− 50.0 − 70.0
56.19– 76.39	20.0 32.0	+ 6.0 0	−20.0 −26.0	20.0 40.0	+10.0 0	−20.0 −30.0	30.0 56.0	+16.0 0	− 30.0 − 40.0	40.0 81.0	+25.0 0	− 40.0 − 56.0	60.0 125	+ 40.0 0	− 60.0 − 85.0
76.39–100.9	25.0 41.0	+ 8.0 0	−25.0 −33.0	25.0 49.0	+12.0 0	−25.0 −37.0	40.0 72.0	+20.0 0	− 40.0 − 52.0	50.0 100	+30.0 0	− 50.0 − 70.0	80.0 160	+ 50.0 0	− 80.0 −110
100.9 –131.9	30.0 50.0	+10.0 0	−30.0 −40.0	30.0 62.0	+16.0 0	−30.0 −46.0	50.0 91.0	+25.0 0	− 50.0 − 66.0	60.0 125	+40.0 0	− 60.0 − 85.0	100 200	+ 60.0 0	−100 −140
131.9 –171.9	35.0 59.0	+12.0 0	−35.0 −47.0	35.0 75.0	+20.0	−35.0 −55.0	60.0 110.0	+30.0 0	− 60.0 − 80.0	80.0 160	+50.0 0	− 80.0 −110	130 260	+ 80.0 0	−130 −180
171.9 –200	45.0 77.0	+16.0 0	−45.0 −61.0	45.0 95.0	+25.0 0	−45.0 −70.0	80.0 145.0	+40.0 0	− 80.0 −105.0	100 200	+60.0 0	−100 −140	150 310	+100 0	−150 −210

TD-11-4

Clearance Locational Fits (USAS B4.1-1955)

Limits are in thousandths of an inch.
Limits for hole and shaft are applied algebraically, to the basic size to obtain the limits of size for the parts.
Data in **bold face** are in accordance with ABC agreements.
Symbols H6, h5, etc., are Hole and Shaft designations used in ABC System.

8.3.2 *Locational Fits.* Locational fits are fits intended to determine only the location of the mating parts; they may provide rigid or accurate location, as with interference fits, or provide some freedom of location, as with clearance fits. Accordingly they are divided into three groups: clearance fits, transition fits, and interference fits.

LC *Locational clearance fits* are intended for parts which are normally stationary, but which can be freely assembled or disassembled. They run from snug fits for parts requiring accuracy of location, through the medium clearance fits for parts such as spigots, to the looser fastener fits where freedom of assembly is of prime importance.

	Class LC 1			Class LC 2			Class LC 3			Class LC 4			Class LC 5		
Nominal Size Range	Limits of	Standard Limits		Limits of	Standard Limits		Limits of	Standard Limits		Limits of	Standard Limits		Limits of	Standard Limits	
Inches Over To	Clearance	Hole H6	Shaft h5	Clearance	Hole H7	Shaft h6	Clearance	Hole H8	Shaft h7	Clearance	Hole H9	Shaft h9	Clearance	Hole H7	Shaft g6
0.04– 0.12	0 0.45	+ 0.25 − 0	+ 0 − 0.2	0 0.65	+ 0.4 − 0	+ 0 − 0.25	0 1	+ 0.6 − 0	+ 0 − 0.4	0 2.0	+ 1.0 − 0	+ 0 − 1.0	0.1 0.75	+ 0.4 − 0	− 0.1 − 0.35
0.12– 0.24	0 0.5	+ 0.3 − 0	+ 0 − 0.2	0 0.8	+ 0.5 − 0	+ 0 − 0.3	0 1.2	+ 0.7 − 0	+ 0 − 0.5	0 2.4	+ 1.2 − 0	+ 0 − 1.2	0.15 0.95	+ 0.5 − 0	− 0.15 − 0.45
0.24– 0.40	0 0.65	+ 0.4 − 0	+ 0 − 0.25	0 1.0	+ 0.6 − 0	+ 0 − 0.4	0 1.5	+ 0.9 − 0	+ 0 − 0.6	0 2.8	+ 1.4 − 0	+ 0 − 1.4	0.2 1.2	+ 0.6 − 0	− 0.2 − 0.6
0.40– 0.71	0 0.7	+ 0.4 − 0	+ 0 − 0.3	0 1.1	+ 0.7 − 0	+ 0 − 0.4	0 1.7	+ 1.0 − 0	+ 0 − 0.7	0 3.2	+ 1.6 − 0	+ 0 − 1.6	0.25 1.35	+ 0.7 − 0	− 0.25 − 0.65
0.71– 1.19	0 0.9	+ 0.5 − 0	+ 0 − 0.4	0 1.3	+ 0.8 − 0	+ 0 − 0.5	0 2	+ 1.2 − 0	+ 0 − 0.8	0 4	+ 2.0 − 0	+ 0 − 2.0	0.3 1.6	+ 0.8 − 0	− 0.3 − 0.8
1.19– 1.97	0 1.0	+ 0.6 − 0	+ 0 − 0.4	0 1.6	+ 1.0 − 0	+ 0 − 0.6	0 2.6	+ 1.6 − 0	+ 0 − 1	0 5	+ 2.5 − 0	+ 0 − 2.5	0.4 2.0	+ 1.0 − 0	− 0.4 − 1.0
1.97– 3.15	0 1.2	+ 0.7 − 0	+ 0 − 0.5	0 1.9	+ 1.2 − 0	+ 0 − 0.7	0 3	+ 1.8 − 0	+ 0 − 1.2	0 6	+ 3 − 0	+ 0 − 3	0.4 2.3	+ 1.2 − 0	− 0.4 − 1.1
3.15– 4.73	0 1.5	+ 0.9 − 0	+ 0 − 0.6	0 2.3	+ 1.4 − 0	+ 0 − 0.9	0 3.6	+ 2.2 − 0	+ 0 − 1.4	0 7	+ 3.5 − 0	+ 0 − 3.5	0.5 2.8	+ 1.4 − 0	− 0.5 − 1.4
4.73– 7.09	0 1.7	+ 1.0 − 0	+ 0 − 0.7	0 2.6	+ 1.6 − 0	+ 0 − 1.0	0 4.1	+ 2.5 − 0	+ 0 − 1.6	0 8	+ 4 − 0	+ 0 − 4	0.6 3.2	+ 1.6 − 0	− 0.6 − 1.6
7.09– 9.85	0 2.0	+ 1.2 − 0	+ 0 − 0.8	0 3.0	+ 1.8 − 0	+ 0 − 1.2	0 4.6	+ 2.8 − 0	+ 0 − 1.8	0 9	+ 4.5 − 0	+ 0 − 4.5	0.6 3.6	+ 1.8 − 0	− 0.6 − 1.8
9.85– 12.41	0 2.1	+ 1.2 − 0	+ 0 − 0.9	0 3.2	+ 2.0 − 0	+ 0 − 1.2	0 5	+ 3.0 − 0	+ 0 − 2.0	0 10	+ 5 − 0	+ 0 − 5	0.7 3.9	+ 2.0 − 0	− 0.7 − 1.9
12.41– 15.75	0 2.4	+ 1.4 − 0	+ 0 − 1.0	0 3.6	+ 2.2 − 0	+ 0 − 1.4	0 5.7	+ 3.5 − 0	+ 0 − 2.2	0 12	+ 6 − 0	+ 0 − 6	0.7 4.3	+ 2.2 − 0	− 0.7 − 2.1
15.75– 19.69	0 2.6	+ 1.6 − 0	+ 0 − 1.0	0 4.1	+ 2.5 − 0	+ 0 − 1.6	0 6.5	+ 4 − 0	+ 0 − 2.5	0 12	+ 6 − 0	+ 0 − 6	0.8 4.9	+ 2.5 − 0	− 0.8 − 2.4
19.69– 30.09	0 3.2	+ 2.0 − 0	+ 0 − 1.2	0 5.0	+ 3 − 0	+ 0 − 2	0 8	+ 5 − 0	+ 0 − 3	0 16	+ 8 − 0	+ 0 − 8	0.9 5.9	+ 3.0 − 0	− 0.9 − 2.9
30.09– 41.49	0 4.1	+ 2.5 − 0	+ 0 − 1.6	0 6.5	+ 4 − 0	+ 0 − 2.5	0 10	+ 6 − 0	+ 0 − 4	0 20	+10 − 0	+ 0 −10	1.0 7.5	+ 4.0 − 0	− 1.0 − 3.5
41.49– 56.19	0 5.0	+ 3.0 − 0	+ 0 − 2.0	0 8.0	+ 5 − 0	+ 0 − 3	0 13	+ 8 − 0	+ 0 − 5	0 24	+12 − 0	+ 0 −12	1.2 9.2	+ 5.0 − 0	− 1.2 − 4.2
56.19– 76.39	0 6.5	+ 4.0 − 0	+ 0 − 2.5	0 10	+ 6 − 0	+ 0 − 4	0 16	+10 − 0	+ 0 − 6	0 32	+16 − 0	+ 0 −16	1.2 11.2	+ 6.0 − 0	− 1.2 − 5.2
76.39–100.9	0 8.0	+ 5.0 − 0	+ 0 − 3.0	0 13	+ 8 − 0	+ 0 − 5	0 20	+12 − 0	+ 0 − 8	0 40	+20 − 0	+ 0 −20	1.4 14.4	+ 8.0 − 0	− 1.4 − 6.4
100.9 –131.9	0 10.0	+ 6.0 − 0	+ 0 − 4.0	0 16	+10 − 0	+ 0 − 6	0 26	+16 − 0	+ 0 −10	0 50	+25 − 0	+ 0 −25	1.6 17.6	+10.0 − 0	− 1.6 − 7.6
131.9 –171.9	0 13.0	+ 8.0 − 0	+ 0 − 5.0	0 20	+12 − 0	+ 0 − 8	0 32	+20 − 0	+ 0 −12	0 60	+30 − 0	+ 0 −30	1.8 21.8	+12.0 − 0	− 1.8 − 9.8
171.9 –200	0 16.0	+10.0 − 0	+ 0 − 6.0	0 26	+16 − 0	+ 0 −10	0 41	+25 − 0	+ 0 −16	0 80	+40 − 0	+ 0 −40	1.8 27.8	+16.0 − 0	− 1.8 −11.8

TD-11-4 (con't.)

Clearance Locational Fits (USAS B4.1-1955)

Nominal Size Range Inches Over To	Class LC 6 Limits of Clearance	Class LC 6 Standard Limits Hole H8	Class LC 6 Standard Limits Shaft f8	Class LC 7 Limits of Clearance	Class LC 7 Standard Limits Hole H9	Class LC 7 Standard Limits Shaft e9	Class LC 8 Limits of Clearance	Class LC 8 Standard Limits Hole H10	Class LC 8 Standard Limits Shaft d9
0.04– 0.12	0.3 1.5	+ 0.6 − 0	− 0.3 − 0.9	0.6 2.6	+ 1.0 − 0	− 0.6 − 1.6	1.0 3.6	+ 1.6 − 0	− 1.0 − 2.0
0.12– 0.24	0.4 1.8	+ 0.7 − 0	− 0.4 − 1.1	0.8 3.2	+ 1.2 − 0	− 0.8 − 2.0	1.2 4.2	+ 1.8 − 0	− 1.2 − 2.4
0.24– 0.40	0.5 2.3	+ 0.9 − 0	− 0.5 − 1.4	1.0 3.8	+ 1.4 − 0	− 1.0 − 2.4	1.6 5.2	+ 2.2 − 0	− 1.6 − 3.0
0.40– 0.71	0.6 2.6	+ 1.0 − 0	− 0.6 − 1.6	1.2 4.4	+ 1.6 − 0	− 1.2 − 2.8	2.0 6.4	+ 2.8 − 0	− 2.0 − 3.6
0.71– 1.19	0.8 3.2	+ 1.2 − 0	− 0.8 − 2.0	1.6 5.6	+ 2.0 − 0	− 1.6 − 3.6	2.5 8.0	+ 3.5 − 0	− 2.5 − 4.5
1.19– 1.97	1.0 4.2	+ 1.6 − 0	− 1.0 − 2.6	2.0 7.0	+ 2.5 − 0	− 2.0 − 4.5	3.0 9.5	+ 4.0 − 0	− 3.0 − 5.5
1.97– 3.15	1.2 4.8	+ 1.8 − 0	− 1.2 − 3.0	2.5 8.5	+ 3.0 − 0	− 2.5 − 5.5	4.0 11.5	+ 4.5 − 0	− 4.0 − 7.0
3.15– 4.73	1.4 5.8	+ 2.2 − 0	− 1.4 − 3.6	3.0 10.0	+ 3.5 − 0	− 3.0 − 6.5	5.0 13.5	+ 5.0 − 0	− 5.0 − 8.5
4.73– 7.09	1.6 6.6	+ 2.5 − 0	− 1.6 − 4.1	3.5 11.5	+ 4.0 − 0	− 3.5 − 7.5	6 16	+ 6 − 0	− 6 −10
7.09– 9.85	2.0 7.6	+ 2.8 − 0	− 2.0 − 4.8	4.0 13.0	+ 4.5 − 0	− 4.0 − 8.5	7 18.5	+ 7 − 0	− 7 −11.5
9.85– 12.41	2.2 8.2	+ 3.0 − 0	− 2.2 − 5.2	4.5 14.5	+ 5.0 − 0	− 4.5 − 9.5	7 20	+ 8 − 0	− 7 − 12
12.41– 15.75	2.5 9.5	+ 3.5 − 0	− 2.5 − 6.0	5 17	+ 6 − 0	− 5 −11	8 23	+ 9 − 0	− 8 −14
15.75– 19.69	2.8 10.8	+ 4.0 − 0	− 2.8 − 6.8	5 17	+ 6 − 0	− 5 −11	9 25	+10 − 0	− 9 −15
19.69– 30.09	3.0 13.0	+ 5.0 − 0	− 3.0 − 8.0	6 22	+ 8 − 0	− 6 −14	10 30	+12 − 0	−10 −18
30.09– 41.49	3.5 15.5	+ 6.0 − 0	− 3.5 − 9.5	7 27	+10 − 0	− 7 −17	12 38	+16 − 0	−12 −22
41.49– 56.19	4.0 20.0	+ 8.0 − 0	− 4.0 −12.0	8 32	+12 − 0	− 8 −20	14 46	+20 − 0	−14 −26
56.19– 76.39	4.5 24.5	+10.0 − 0	− 4.5 −14.5	9 41	+16 − 0	− 9 −25	16 57	+25 − 0	−16 −32
76.39–100.9	5 29	+12 − 0	− 5 −17	10 50	+20 − 0	−10 −30	18 68	+30 − 0	−18 −38
100.9 –131.9	6 38	+16 − 0	− 6 −22	12 62	+25 − 0	−12 −27	20 85	+40 − 0	−20 −45
131.9 –171.9	7 47	+20 − 0	− 7 −27	14 74	+30 − 0	−14 −44	25 105	+50 − 0	−25 −55
171.9 –200	7 57	+25 − 0	− 7 −32	14 94	+40 − 0	−14 −54	25 125	+60 − 0	−25 −65

Nominal Size Range Inches Over To	Class LC 9 Limits of Clearance	Class LC 9 Standard Limits Hole H11	Class LC 9 Standard Limits Shaft c11	Class LC 10 Limits of Clearance	Class LC 10 Standard Limits Hole H12	Class LC 10 Standard Limits Shaft	Class LC 11 Limits of Clearance	Class LC 11 Standard Limits Hole H13	Class LC 11 Standard Limits Shaft
0.04– 0.12	2.5 7.5	+ 2.5 − 0	− 2.5 − 5.0	4 12	+ 4 − 0	− 4 − 8	5 17	+ 6 − 0	− 5 − 11
0.12– 0.24	2.8 8.8	+ 3.0 − 0	− 2.8 − 5.8	4.5 14.5	+ 5 − 0	− 4.5 − 9.5	6 20	+ 7 − 0	− 6 − 13
0.24– 0.40	3.0 10.0	+ 3.5 − 0	− 3.0 − 6.5	5 17	+ 6 − 0	− 5 − 11	7 25	+ 9 − 0	− 7 − 16
0.40– 0.71	3.5 11.5	+ 4.0 − 0	− 3.5 − 7.5	6 20	+ 7 − 0	− 6 − 13	8 28	+ 10 − 0	− 8 − 18
0.71– 1.19	4.5 14.5	+ 5.0 − 0	− 4.5 − 9.5	7 23	+ 8 − 0	− 7 − 15	10 34	+ 12 − 0	− 10 − 22
1.19– 1.97	5 17	+ 6 − 0	− 5 − 11	8 28	+ 10 − 0	− 8 − 18	12 44	+ 16 − 0	− 12 − 28
1.97– 3.15	6 20	+ 7 − 0	− 6 − 13	10 34	+ 12 − 0	− 10 − 22	14 50	+ 18 − 0	− 14 − 32
3.15– 4.73	7 25	+ 9 − 0	− 7 − 16	11 39	+ 14 − 0	− 11 − 25	16 60	+ 22 − 0	− 16 − 38
4.73– 7.09	8 28	+ 10 − 0	− 8 − 18	12 44	+ 16 − 0	− 12 − 28	18 68	+ 25 − 0	− 18 − 43
7.09– 9.85	10 34	+ 12 − 0	− 10 − 22	16 52	+ 18 − 0	− 16 − 34	22 78	+ 28 − 0	− 22 − 50
9.85– 12.41	12 36	+ 12 − 0	− 12 − 24	20 60	+ 20 − 0	− 20 − 40	28 88	+ 30 − 0	− 28 − 58
12.41– 15.75	14 42	+ 14 − 0	− 14 − 28	22 66	+ 22 − 0	− 22 − 44	30 100	+ 35 − 0	− 30 − 65
15.75– 19.69	16 48	+ 16 − 0	− 16 − 32	25 75	+ 25 − 0	− 25 − 50	35 115	+ 40 − 0	− 35 − 75
19.69– 30.09	18 58	+ 20 − 0	− 18 − 38	28 88	+ 30 − 0	− 28 − 58	40 140	+ 50 − 0	− 40 − 90
30.09– 41.49	20 70	+ 25 − 0	− 20 − 45	30 110	+ 40 − 0	− 30 − 70	45 165	+ 60 − 0	− 45 −105
41.49– 56.19	25 85	+ 30 − 0	− 25 − 55	40 140	+ 50 − 0	− 40 − 90	60 220	+ 80 − 0	− 60 −140
56.19– 76.39	30 110	+ 40 − 0	− 30 − 70	50 170	+ 60 − 0	− 50 −110	70 270	+100 − 0	− 70 −170
76.39–100.9	35 135	+ 50 − 0	− 35 − 85	50 210	+ 80 − 0	− 50 −130	80 330	+125 − 0	− 80 −205
100.9 –131.9	40 160	+ 60 − 0	− 40 −100	60 260	+100 − 0	− 60 −160	90 410	+160 − 0	− 90 −250
131.9 –171.9	50 210	+ 80 − 0	− 50 −130	80 330	+125 − 0	− 80 −205	100 500	+200 − 0	−100 −300
171.9 –200	50 250	+100 − 0	− 50 −150	90 410	+160 − 0	− 90 −250	125 625	+250 − 0	−125 −375

TD-11-5

Transition Locational Fits (USAS B4.1-1955)

Limits are in thousandths of an inch.

Limits for hole and shaft are applied algebraically to the basic size to obtain the limits of size for the mating parts.

Data in **bold face** are in accordance with ABC agreements.

"Fits" represents the maximum interference (minus values) and the maximum clearance (plus values).

Symbols H7, j6, etc., are Hole and Shaft designations used in the ABC System.

LT *Transition fits* are a compromise between clearance and interference fits, for application where accuracy of location is important, but either a small amount of clearance or interference is permissible.

	Class LT 1			Class LT 2			Class LT 3			Class LT 4			Class LT 6			Class LT 7		
Nominal Size Range	Fit	Standard Limits		Fit	Standard Limits		Fit	Standard Limits		Fit	Standard Limits		Fit	Standard Limits		Fit	Standard Limits	
Inches Over To		Hole H7	Shaft j6		Hole H8	Shaft j7		Hole H7	Shaft k6		Hole H8	Shaft k7		Hole H8	Shaft m7		Hole H7	Shaft n6
0.04– 0.12	−0.15 +0.5	+0.4 −0	+0.15 −0.1	−0.3 +0.7	+0.6 −0	+0.3 −0.1							−0.55 +0.45	+0.6 −0	+0.55 +0.15	−0.5 +0.15	+0.4 −0	+0.5 +0.25
0.12– 0.24	−0.2 +0.6	+0.5 −0	+0.2 −0.1	−0.4 +0.8	+0.7 −0	+0.4 −0.1							−0.7 +0.5	+0.7 −0	+0.7 +0.2	−0.6 +0.2	+0.5 −0	+0.6 +0.3
0.24– 0.40	−0.3 +0.7	+0.6 −0	+0.3 −0.1	−0.4 +1.1	+0.9 −0	+0.4 −0.2	−0.5 +0.5	+0.6 −0	+0.5 +0.1	−0.7 +0.8	+0.9 −0	+0.7 +0.1	−0.8 +0.7	+0.9 −0	+0.8 +0.2	−0.8 +0.2	+0.6 −0	+0.8 +0.4
0.40– 0.71	−0.3 +0.8	+0.7 −0	+0.3 −0.1	−0.5 +1.2	+1.0 −0	+0.5 −0.2	−0.5 +0.6	+0.7 −0	+0.5 +0.1	−0.8 +0.9	+1.0 −0	+0.8 +0.1	−1.0 +0.7	+1.0 −0	+1.0 +0.3	−0.9 +0.2	+0.7 −0	+0.9 +0.5
0.71– 1.19	−0.3 +1.0	+0.8 −0	+0.3 −0.2	−0.5 +1.5	+1.2 −0	+0.5 −0.3	−0.6 +0.7	+0.8 −0	+0.6 +0.1	−0.9 +1.1	+1.2 −0	+0.9 +0.1	−1.1 +0.9	+1.2 −0	+1.1 +0.3	−1.1 +0.2	+0.8 −0	+1.1 +0.6
1.19– 1.97	−0.4 +1.2	+1.0 −0	+0.4 −0.2	−0.6 +2.0	+1.6 −0	+0.6 −0.4	−0.7 +0.9	+1.0 −0	+0.7 +0.1	−1.1 +1.5	+1.6 −0	+1.1 +0.1	−1.4 +1.2	+1.6 −0	+1.4 +0.4	−1.3 +0.3	+1.0 −0	+1.3 +0.7
1.97– 3.15	−0.4 +1.5	+1.2 −0	+0.4 −0.3	−0.7 +2.3	+1.8 −0	+0.7 −0.5	−0.8 +1.1	+1.2 −0	+0.8 +0.1	−1.3 +1.7	+1.8 −0	+1.3 +0.1	−1.7 +1.3	+1.8 −0	+1.7 +0.5	−1.5 +0.4	+1.2 −0	+1.5 +0.8
3.15– 4.73	−0.5 +1.8	+1.4 −0	+0.5 −0.4	−0.8 +2.8	+2.2 −0	+0.8 −0.6	−1.0 +1.3	+1.4 −0	+1.0 +0.1	−1.5 +2.1	+2.2 −0	+1.5 +0.1	−1.9 +1.7	+2.2 −0	+1.9 +0.5	−1.9 +0.4	+1.4 −0	+1.9 +1.0
4.73– 7.09	−0.6 +2.0	+1.6 −0	+0.6 −0.4	−0.9 +3.2	+2.5 −0	+0.9 −0.7	−1.1 +1.5	+1.6 −0	+1.1 +0.1	−1.7 +2.4	+2.5 −0	+1.7 +0.1	−2.2 +1.9	+2.5 −0	+2.2 +0.6	−2.2 +0.4	+1.6 −0	+2.2 +1.2
7.09– 9.85	−0.7 +2.3	+1.8 −0	+0.7 −0.5	−1.0 +3.6	+2.8 −0	+1.0 −0.8	−1.4 +1.6	+1.8 −0	+1.4 +0.2	−2.0 +2.6	+2.8 −0	+2.0 +0.2	−2.4 +2.2	+2.8 −0	+2.4 +0.6	−2.6 +0.4	+1.8 −0	+2.6 +1.4
9.85– 12.41	−0.7 +2.6	+2.0 −0	+0.7 −0.6	−1.0 +4.0	+3.0 −0	+1.0 −1.0	−1.4 +1.8	+2.0 −0	+1.4 +0.2	−2.2 +2.8	+3.0 −0	+2.2 +0.2	−2.8 +2.2	+3.0 −0	+2.8 +0.8	−2.6 +0.6	+2.0 −0	+2.6 +1.4
12.41– 15.75	−0.7 +2.9	+2.2 −0	+0.7 −0.7	−1.2 +4.5	+3.5 −0	+1.2 −1.0	−1.6 +2.0	+2.2 −0	+1.6 +0.2	−2.4 +3.3	+3.5 −0	+2.4 +0.2	−3.0 +2.7	+3.5 −0	+3.0 +0.8	−3.0 +0.6	+2.2 −0	+3.0 +1.6
15.75– 19.69	−0.8 +3.2	+2.5 −0	+0.8 −0.7	−1.3 +5.2	+4.0 −0	+1.3 −1.2	−1.8 +2.3	+2.5 −0	+1.8 +0.2	−2.7 +3.8	+4.0 −0	+2.7 +0.2	−3.4 +3.1	+4.0 −0	+3.4 +0.9	−3.4 +0.7	+2.5 −0	+3.4 +1.8

TD-11-6

Interference Locational Fits (USAS B4.1-1955)

Limits are in thousandths of an inch.

Limits for hole and shaft are applied algebraically to the basic size to obtain the limits of size for the parts.

Data in **bold face** are in accordance with ABC agreements.

Symbols H7, p6, etc., are Hole and Shaft designations used in ABC system.

LN *Locational interference fits* are used where accuracy of location is of prime importance, and for parts requiring rigidity and alignment with no special requirements for bore pressure. Such fits are not intended for parts designed to transmit frictional loads from one part to another by virtue of the tightness of fit, as these conditions are covered by force fits.

Nominal Size Range Inches	Class LN 2			Class LN 3		
	Limits of Interference	Standard Limits		Limits of Interference	Standard Limits	
Over To		Hole H7	Shaft p6		Hole H7	Shaft r6
0.04– 0.12	**0** **0.65**	**+ 0.4** **− 0**	**+ 0.65** **+ 0.4**	**0.1** **0.75**	**+ 0.4** **− 0**	**+ 0.75** **+ 0.5**
0.12– 0.24	**0** **0.8**	**+ 0.5** **− 0**	**+ 0.8** **+ 0.5**	**0.1** **0.9**	**+ 0.5** **− 0**	**+ 0.9** **+ 0.6**
0.24– 0.40	**0** **1.0**	**+ 0.6** **− 0**	**+ 1.0** **+ 0.6**	**0.2** **1.2**	**+ 0.6** **− 0**	**+ 1.2** **+ 0.8**
0.40– 0.71	**0** **1.1**	**+ 0.7** **− 0**	**+ 1.1** **+ 0.7**	**0.3** **1.4**	**+ 0.7** **− 0**	**+ 1.4** **+ 1.0**
0.71– 1.19	**0** **1.3**	**+ 0.8** **− 0**	**+ 1.3** **+ 0.8**	**0.4** **1.7**	**+ 0.8** **− 0**	**+ 1.7** **+ 1.2**
1.19– 1.97	**0** **1.6**	**+ 1.0** **− 0**	**+ 1.6** **+ 1.0**	**0.4** **2.0**	**+ 1.0** **− 0**	**+ 2.0** **+ 1.4**
1.97– 3.15	**0.2** **2.1**	**+ 1.2** **− 0**	**+ 2.1** **+ 1.4**	**0.4** **2.3**	**+ 1.2** **− 0**	**+ 2.3** **+ 1.6**
3.15– 4.73	**0.2** **2.5**	**+ 1.4** **− 0**	**+ 2.5** **+ 1.6**	**0.6** **2.9**	**+ 1.4** **− 0**	**+ 2.9** **+ 2.0**
4.73– 7.09	**0.2** **2.8**	**+ 1.6** **− 0**	**+ 2.8** **+ 1.8**	**0.9** **3.5**	**+ 1.6** **− 0**	**+ 3.5** **+ 2.5**
7.09– 9.85	**0.2** **3.2**	**+ 1.8** **− 0**	**+ 3.2** **+ 2.0**	**1.2** **4.2**	**+ 1.8** **− 0**	**+ 4.2** **+ 3.0**
9.85– 12.41	**0.2** **3.4**	**+ 2.0** **− 0**	**+ 3.4** **+ 2.2**	**1.5** **4.7**	**+ 2.0** **− 0**	**+ 4.7** **+ 3.5**
12.41– 15.75	**0.3** **3.9**	**+ 2.2** **− 0**	**+ 3.9** **+ 2.5**	**2.3** **5.9**	**+ 2.2** **− 0**	**+ 5.9** **+ 4.5**
15.75– 19.69	**0.3** **4.4**	**+ 2.5** **− 0**	**+ 4.4** **+ 2.8**	**2.5** **6.6**	**+ 2.5** **− 0**	**+ 6.6** **+ 5.0**
19.69– 30.09	0.5 5.5	+ 3 − 0	+ 5.5 + 3.5	4 9	+ 3 − 0	+ 9 + 7
30.09– 41.49	0.5 7.0	+ 4 − 0	+ 7.0 + 4.5	5 11.5	+ 4 − 0	+11.5 + 9
41.49– 56.19	1 9	+ 5 − 0	+ 9 + 6	7 15	+ 5 − 0	+15 +12
56.19– 76.39	1 11	+ 6 − 0	+11 + 7	10 20	+ 6 − 0	+20 +16
76.39–100.9	1 14	+ 8 − 0	+14 + 9	12 25	+ 8 − 0	+25 +20
100.9 –131.9	2 18	+10 − 0	+18 +12	15 31	+10 − 0	+31 +25
131.9 –171.9	4 24	+12 − 0	+24 +16	18 38	+12 − 0	+38 +30
171.9 –200	4 30	+16 − 0	+30 +20	24 50	+16 − 0	+50 +40

TD-11-7

Force and Shrink Fits (USAS B4.1-1955)

Limits are in thousandths of an inch.
Limits for hole and shaft are applied algebraically to the basic size to obtain the limits of size for the parts.
Data in **bold face** are in accordance with ABC agreements.
Symbols H7, s6, etc., are Hole and Shaft designations used in ABC System.

8.3.3 *Force Fits*. Force or shrink fits constitute a special type of interference fit, normally characterized by maintenance of constant bore pressures throughout the range of sizes. The interference therefore varies almost directly with diameter, and the difference between its minimum and maximum value is small, to maintain the resulting pressures within reasonable limits.

These fits may be described briefly as follows:

FN 1 *Light drive fits* are those requiring light assembly pressures, and produce more or less permanent assemblies. They are suitable for thin sections or long fits, or in cast-iron external members.

FN 2 *Medium drive fits* are suitable for ordinary steel parts, or for shrink fits on light sections. They are about the tightest fits that can be used with high-grade cast-iron external members.

FN 3 *Heavy drive fits* are suitable for heavier steel parts or for shrink fits in medium sections.

FN 4) Force fits are suitable for parts which can be
FN 5) highly stressed, or for shrink fits where the heavy pressing forces required are impractical.

	Class FN 1			Class FN 2			Class FN 3			Class FN 4			Class FN 5		
Nominal Size Range	Limits of	Standard Limits		Limits of	Standard Limits		Limits of	Standard Limits		Limits of	Standard Limits		Limits of	Standard Limits	
Inches Over To	Interference	Hole H6	Shaft	Interference	Hole H7	Shaft s6	Interference	Hole H7	Shaft t6	Interference	Hole H7	Shaft u6	Interference	Hole H7	Shaft x7
12.41– 13.98	3.1	**+ 1.4**	+ 5.5	**5.8**	**+ 2.2**	**+ 9.4**	**7.8**	**+ 2.2**	**+ 11.4**	**13.8**	**+ 2.2**	**+ 17.4**	**19.8**	**+ 2.2**	**+ 24.2**
	5.5	**− 0**	+ 4.5	**9.4**	**− 0**	**+ 8.0**	**11.4**	**− 0**	**+ 10.0**	**17.4**	**− 0**	**+ 16.0**	**24.2**	**− 0**	**+ 22.0**
13.98– 15.75	3.6	**+ 1.4**	+ 6.1	**5.8**	**+ 2.2**	**+ 9.4**	**9.8**	**+ 2.2**	**+ 13.4**	**15.8**	**+ 2.2**	**+ 19.4**	**22.8**	**+ 2.2**	**+ 27.2**
	6.1	**− 0**	+ 5.0	**9.4**	**− 0**	**+ 8.0**	**13.4**	**− 0**	**+ 12.0**	**19.4**	**− 0**	**+ 18.0**	**27.2**	**− 0**	**+ 25.0**
15.75– 17.72	4.4	**+ 1.6**	+ 7.0	**6.5**	**+ 2.5**	**+ 10.6**	**9.5**	**+ 2.5**	**+ 13.6**	**17.5**	**+ 2.5**	**+ 21.6**	**25.5**	**+ 2.5**	**+ 30.5**
	7.0	**− 0**	+ 6.0	**10.6**	**− 0**	**+ 9.0**	**13.6**	**− 0**	**+ 12.0**	**21.6**	**− 0**	**+ 20.0**	**30.5**	**− 0**	**+ 28.0**
17.72– 19.69	4.4	**+ 1.6**	+ 7.0	**7.5**	**+ 2.5**	**+ 11.6**	**11.5**	**+ 2.5**	**+ 15.6**	**19.5**	**+ 2.5**	**+ 23.6**	**27.5**	**+ 2.5**	**+ 32.5**
	7.0	**− 0**	+ 6.0	**11.6**	**− 0**	**+ 10.0**	**15.6**	**− 0**	**+ 14.0**	**23.6**	**− 0**	**+ 22.0**	**32.5**	**− 0**	**+ 30.0**
19.69– 24.34	6.0	+ 2.0	+ 9.2	9.0	+ 3.0	+ 14.0	15.0	+ 3.0	+ 20.0	22.0	+ 3.0	+ 27.0	32.0	+ 3.0	+ 38.0
	9.2	− 0	+ 8.0	14.0	− 0	+ 12.0	20.0	− 0	+ 18.0	27.0	− 0	+ 25.0	38.0	− 0	+ 35.0
24.34– 30.09	7.0	+ 2.0	+10.2	11.0	+ 3.0	+ 16.0	17.0	+ 3.0	+ 22.0	27.0	+ 3.0	+ 32.0	37.0	+ 3.0	+ 43.0
	10.2	− 0	+ 9.0	16.0	− 0	+ 14.0	22.0	− 0	+ 20.0	32.0	− 0	+ 30.0	43.0	− 0	+ 40.0
30.09– 35.47	7.5	+ 2.5	+11.6	14.0	+ 4.0	+ 20.5	21.0	+ 4.0	+ 27.5	31.0	+ 4.0	+ 37.5	46.0	+ 4.0	+ 54.0
	11.6	− 0	+10.0	20.5	− 0	+ 18.0	27.5	− 0	+ 25.0	37.5	− 0	+ 35.0	54.0	− 0	+ 50.0
35.47– 41.49	9.5	+ 2.5	+13.6	16.0	+ 4.0	+ 22.5	24.0	+ 4.0	+ 30.5	36.0	+ 4.0	+ 43.5	56.0	+ 4.0	+ 64.0
	13.6	− 0	+12.0	22.5	− 0	+ 20.0	30.5	− 0	+ 28.0	43.5	− 0	+ 40.0	64.0	− 0	+ 60.0
41.49– 48.28	11.0	+ 3.0	+16.0	17.0	+ 5.0	+ 25.0	30.0	+ 5.0	+ 38.0	45.0	+ 5.0	+ 53.0	65.0	+ 5.0	+ 75.0
	16.0	− 0	+14.0	25.0	− 0	+ 22.0	38.0	− 0	+ 35.0	53.0	− 0	+ 50.0	75.0	− 0	+ 70.0
48.28– 56.19	13.0	+ 3.0	+18.0	20.0	+ 5.0	+ 28.0	35.0	+ 5.0	+ 43.0	55.0	+ 5.0	+ 63.0	75.0	+ 5.0	+ 85.0
	18.0	− 0	+16.0	28.0	− 0	+ 25.0	43.0	− 0	+ 40.0	63.0	− 0	+ 60.0	85.0	− 0	+ 80.0
56.19– 65.54	14.0	+ 4.0	+20.5	24.0	+ 6.0	+ 34.0	39.0	+ 6.0	+ 49.0	64.0	+ 6.0	+ 74.0	94.0	+ 6.0	+106
	20.5	− 0	+18.0	34.0	− 0	+ 30.0	49.0	− 0	+ 45.0	74.0	− 0	+ 70.0	106	− 0	+100
65.54– 76.39	18.0	+ 4.0	+24.5	29.0	+ 6.0	+ 39.0	44.0	+ 6.0	+ 54.0	74.0	+ 6.0	+ 84.0	114	+ 6.0	+126
	24.5	− 0	+22.0	39.0	− 0	+ 35.0	54.0	− 0	+ 50.0	84.0	− 0	+ 80.0	126	− 0	+120
76.39– 87.79	20.0	+ 5.0	+28.0	32.0	+ 8.0	+ 45.0	52.0	+ 8.0	+ 65.0	82.0	+ 8.0	+ 95.0	132	+ 8.0	+148
	28.0	− 0	+25.0	45.0	− 0	+ 40.0	65.0	− 0	+ 60.0	95.0	− 0	+ 90.0	148	− 0	+140
87.79–100.9	23.0	+ 5.0	+31.0	37.0	+ 8.0	+ 50.0	62.0	+ 8.0	+ 75.0	92.0	+ 8.0	+105	152	+ 8.0	+168
	31.0	− 0	+28.0	50.0	− 0	+ 45.0	75.0	− 0	+ 70.0	105	− 0	+100	168	− 0	+160
100.9– 115.3	24.0	+ 6.0	+34.0	40.0	+10.0	+ 56.0	70.0	+10.0	+ 86.0	110	+10.0	+126	170	+10.0	+190
	34.0	− 0	+30.0	56.0	− 0	+ 50.0	86.0	− 0	+ 80.0	126	− 0	+120	190	− 0	+180
115.3 –131.9	29.0	+ 6.0	+39.0	50.0	+10.0	+ 66.0	80.0	+10.0	+ 96.0	130	+10.0	+146	190	+10.0	+210
	39.0	− 0	+35.0	66.0	− 0	+ 60.0	96.0	− 0	+ 90.0	146	− 0	+140	210	− 0	+200
131.9 –152.2	37.0	+ 8.0	+50.0	58.0	+12.0	+ 73.0	88.0	+12.0	+108	148	+12.0	+168	208	+12.0	+232
	50.0	− 0	+45.0	78.0	− 0	+ 70.0	108	− 0	+100	168	− 0	+160	232	− 0	+220
152.2 –171.9	42.0	+ 8.0	+55.0	68.0	+12.0	+ 88.0	108	+12.0	+128	168	+12.0	+188	238	+12.0	+262
	55.0	− 0	+50.0	88.0	− 0	+ 80.0	128	− 0	+120	188	− 0	+170	262	− 0	+250
171.9 –200	50.0	+10.0	+66.0	74.0	+16.0	+100	124	+16.0	+150	184	+16.0	+210	284	+16.0	+316
	66.0	− 0	+60.0	100	− 0	+ 90.0	150	− 0	+140	210	− 0	+200	316	− 0	+300

TD-11-7 (con't.)

Force and Shrink Fits (USAS B4.1-1955)

	Class FN 1			Class FN 2			Class FN 3			Class FN 4			Class FN 5		
Nominal Size Range	Limits of	Standard Limits		Limits of	Standard Limits		Limits of	Standard Limits		Limits of	Standard Limits		Limits of	Standard Limits	
Inches Over To	Inter-ference	Hole H6	Shaft	Inter-ference	Hole H7	Shaft s6	Inter-ference	Hole H7	Shaft t6	Inter-ference	Hole H7	Shaft u6	Inter-ference	Hole H7	Shaft x7
0.04– 0.12	0.05 0.5	+0.25 −0	+0.5 +0.3	0.2 0.85	+0.4 −0	+0.85 +0.6				0.3 0.95	+0.4 −0	+ 0.95 + 0.7	0.5 1.3	+0.4 −0	+ 1.3 + 0.9
0.12– 0.24	0.1 0.6	+0.3 −0	+0.6 +0.4	0.2 1.0	+0.5 −0	+1.0 +0.7				0.4 1.2	+0.5 −0	+ 1.2 + 0.9	0.7 1.7	+0.5 −0	+ 1.7 + 1.2
0.24– 0.40	0.1 0.75	+0.4 −0	+0.75 +0.5	0.4 1.4	+0.6 −0	+1.4 +1.0				0.6 1.6	+0.6 −0	+ 1.6 + 1.2	0.8 2.0	+0.6 −0	+ 2.0 + 1.4
0.40– 0.56	0.1 0.8	+0.4 −0	+0.8 +0.5	0.5 1.6	+0.7 −0	+1.6 +1.2				0.7 1.8	+0.7 −0	+ 1.8 + 1.4	0.9 2.3	+0.7 −0	+ 2.3 + 1.6
0.56– 0.71	0.2 0.9	+0.4 −0	+0.9 +0.6	0.5 1.6	+0.7 −0	+1.6 +1.2				0.7 1.8	+0.7 −0	+ 1.8 + 1.4	1.1 2.5	+0.7 −0	+ 2.5 + 1.8
0.71– 0.95	0.2 1.1	+0.5 −0	+1.1 +0.7	0.6 1.9	+0.8 −0	+1.9 +1.4				0.8 2.1	+0.8 −0	+ 2.1 + 1.6	1.4 3.0	+0.8 −0	+ 3.0 + 2.2
0.95– 1.19	0.3 1.2	+0.5 −0	+1.2 +0.8	0.6 1.9	+0.8 −0	+1.9 +1.4	0.8 2.1	+0.8 −0	+ 2.1 + 1.6	1.0 2.3	+0.8 −0	+ 2.3 + 1.8	1.7 3.3	+0.8 −0	+ 3.3 + 2.5
1.19– 1.58	0.3 1.3	+0.6 −0	+1.3 +0.9	0.8 2.4	+1.0 −0	+2.4 +1.8	1.0 2.6	+1.0 −0	+ 2.6 + 2.0	1.5 3.1	+1.0 −0	+ 3.1 + 2.5	2.0 4.0	+1.0 −0	+ 4.0 + 3.0
1.58– 1.97	0.4 1.4	+0.6 −0	+1.4 +1.0	0.8 2.4	+1.0 −0	+2.4 +1.8	1.2 2.8	+1.0 −0	+ 2.8 + 2.2	1.8 3.4	+1.0 −0	+ 3.4 + 2.8	3.0 5.0	+1.0 −0	+ 5.0 + 4.0
1.97– 2.56	0.6 1.8	+0.7 −0	+1.8 +1.3	0.8 2.7	+1.2 −0	+2.7 +2.0	1.3 3.2	+1.2 −0	+ 3.2 + 2.5	2.3 4.2	+1.2 −0	+ 4.2 + 3.5	3.8 6.2	+1.2 −0	+ 6.2 + 5.0
2.56– 3.15	0.7 1.9	+0.7 −0	+1.9 +1.4	1.0 2.9	+1.2 −0	+2.9 +2.2	1.8 3.7	+1.2 −0	+ 3.7 + 3.0	2.8 4.7	+1.2 −0	+ 4.7 + 4.0	4.8 7.2	+1.2 −0	+ 7.2 + 6.0
3.15– 3.94	0.9 2.4	+0.9 −0	+2.4 +1.8	1.4 3.7	+1.4 −0	+3.7 +2.8	2.1 4.4	+1.4 −0	+ 4.4 + 3.5	3.6 5.9	+1.4 −0	+ 5.9 + 5.0	5.6 8.4	+1.4 −0	+ 8.4 + 7.0
3.94– 4.73	1.1 2.6	+0.9 −0	+2.6 +2.0	1.6 3.9	+1.4 −0	+3.9 +3.0	2.6 4.9	+1.4 −0	+ 4.9 + 4.0	4.6 6.9	+1.4 −0	+ 6.9 + 6.0	6.6 9.4	+1.4 −0	+ 9.4 + 8.0
4.73– 5.52	1.2 2.9	+1.0 −0	+2.9 +2.2	1.9 4.5	+1.6 −0	+4.5 +3.5	3.4 6.0	+1.6 −0	+ 6.0 + 5.0	5.4 8.0	+1.6 −0	+ 8.0 + 7.0	8.4 11.6	+1.6 −0	+11.6 +10.0
5.52– 6.30	1.5 3.2	+1.0 −0	+3.2 +2.5	2.4 5.0	+1.6 −0	+5.0 +4.0	3.4 6.0	+1.6 −0	+ 6.0 + 5.0	5.4 8.0	+1.6 −0	+ 8.0 + 7.0	10.4 13.6	+1.6 −0	+13.6 +12.0
6.30– 7.09	1.8 3.5	+1.0 −0	+3.5 +2.8	2.9 5.5	+1.6 −0	+5.5 +4.5	4.4 7.0	+1.6 −0	+ 7.0 + 6.0	6.4 9.0	+1.6 −0	+ 9.0 + 8.0	10.4 13.6	+1.6 −0	+13.6 +12.0
7.09– 7.88	1.8 3.8	+1.2 −0	+3.8 +3.0	3.2 6.2	+1.8 −0	+6.2 +5.0	5.2 8.2	+1.8 −0	+ 8.2 + 7.0	7.2 10.2	+1.8 −0	+10.2 + 9.0	12.2 15.8	+1.8 −0	+15.8 +14.0
7.88– 8.86	2.3 4.3	+1.2 −0	+4.3 +3.5	3.2 6.2	+1.8 −0	+6.2 +5.0	5.2 8.2	+1.8 −0	+ 8.2 + 7.0	8.2 11.2	+1.8 −0	+11.2 +10.0	14.2 17.8	+1.8 −0	+17.8 +16.0
8.86– 9.85	2.3 4.3	+1.2 −0	+4.3 +3.5	4.2 7.2	+1.8 −0	+7.2 +6.0	6.2 9.2	+1.8 −0	+ 9.2 + 8.0	10.2 13.2	+1.8 −0	+13.2 +12.0	14.2 17.8	+1.8 −0	+17.8 +16.0
9.85– 11.03	2.8 4.9	+1.2 −0	+4.9 +4.0	4.0 7.2	+2.0 −0	+7.2 +6.0	7.0 10.2	+2.0 −0	+10.2 + 9.0	10.2 13.2	+2.0 −0	+13.2 +12.0	16.0 20.0	+2.0 −0	+20.0 +18.0
11.03– 12.41	2.8 4.9	+1.2 −0	+4.9 +4.0	5.0 8.2	+2.0 −0	+8.2 +7.0	7.0 10.2	+2.0 −0	+10.2 + 9.0	12.0 15.2	+2.0 −0	+15.2 +14.0	18.0 22.0	+2.0 −0	+22.0 +20.0

TD-11-8

Drilled and Punched Hole Tolerances (GMC)

Drill Size Range		Tolerance	
Smallest	Largest	Plus	Minus
.0135 (#80)	.042 (#58)	.003	.002
.043 (#57)	.093	.004	.002
.0935 (#42)	.156	.005	.002
.1562	.2656	.006	.002
.266 (H)	.4219	.007	.002
.4375	.6094	.008	.002
.625	.750	.009	.002
.7656	.8437	.009	.003
.8594	2.000	.010	.003

Tolerances from Basic Dimensions by Diameter or Stock Size for Various Machining Operations (GMC)

Diameter or Stock Size		to .250	.251 to .500	.501 to .750	.751 to 1.000	1.001 to 2.000	2.001 to 4.000
Drilling		See "Limits & Tolerances"					
Reaming	Hand	±.0005	±.0005	±.0010	±.0010	±.0020	±.0030
	Machine	±.0010	±.0010	+.0010 −.0015	+.0010 −.0020	±.0020	±.0030
Turning			±.0010	±.0010	±.0010	±.0020	±.0030
Boring			±.0010	±.0010	±.0015	±.0020	±.0030
Automatic Screw Machine	Internal	Same as in Drilling, Reaming or Boring					
	External Forming	±.0015	±.0020	±.0020	±.0025	±.0025	±.0030
	External Shaving	±.0010	±.0010	±.0010	±.0010	±.0015	±.0020
	Shoulder Location, Turning	±.0050	±.0050	±.0050	±.0050	±.0050	±.0050
	Shoulder Location, Forming	±.0015	±.0015	±.0015	±.0015	±.0015	±.0015
Milling (Single Cut)	Straddle Milling	±.0020	±.0020	±.0020	±.0020	±.0020	±.0020
	Slotting (Width)	±.0015	±.0015	±.0020	±.0020	±.0020	±.0025
	Face Milling	±.0020	±.0020	±.0020	±.0020	±.0020	±.0020
	End Milling (Slot Widths)	±.0020	±.0025	±.0025	±.0025		
	Hollow Milling		±.0060	±.0080	±.0100		
Broaching	Internal	±.0005	±.0005	±.0005	±.0005	±.0010	±.0015
	Surface (Thickness)		±.0010	±.0010	±.0010	±.0015	±.0015
Precision Boring	Diameter	+.0005 −.0000	+.0005 −.0000	+.0005 −.0000	+.0005 −.0000	+.0005 −.0000	+.0010 −.0000
	Shoulder Depth	±.0010	±.0010	±.0010	±.0010	±.0010	±.0010
Hobbing		±.0005	±.0010	±.0010	±.0010	±.0015	±.0020
Honing		+.0005 −.0000	+.0005 −.0000	+.0005 −.0000	+.0005 −.0000	+.0008 −.0000	+.0010 −.0000
Shaping (Gear)		±.0005	±.0010	±.0010	±.0010	±.0015	±.0020
Burnishing		±.0005	±.0005	±.0005	±.0005	±.0008	±.0010
Grinding	Cylindrical (External)	+.0000 −.0005	+.0000 −.0005	+.0000 −.0005	+.0000 −.0005	+.0000 −.0005	+.0000 −.0005
	Cylindrical (Internal)		+.0005 −.0000	+.0005 −.0000	+.0005 −.0000	+.0005 −.0000	+.0005 −.0000
	Centerless	+.0000 −.0005	+.0000 −.0005	+.0000 −.0005	+.0000 −.0005	+.0000 −.0005	+.0000 −.0005
	Surface (Thickness)	+.0000 −.0020	+.0000 −.0020	+.0000 −.0030	+.0000 −.0030	+.0000 −.0040	+.0000 −.0050

TD-12-1

Industrial Adhesives — Performance, Properties, and Uses (3M Company)*

		Performance		
		Performance Temperature Range	Resistance	
3M Product Identification	Comments		H_2O	Oil
3M Brand "FASTBOND" 30 Contact Cement	Non-flammable in wet state, changes color when dry, high initial strength, for plastic laminates	−30° to 220°F.	Good	Excellent
3M Brand Insulation Adhesive 33	Fast tack, long open time, retains some tackiness, principally used for lightweight insulation	−20° to 250°F.	Good	Poor
3M Brand Insulation Adhesive 34	Fast tack, long open time, almost invisible when applied, principally used for paper, cardboard and insulation	−20° to 250°F.	Good	Poor
3M Brand Insulation Adhesive 35	Non-flammable in wet state, fast tack, long open time, principally used for low density insulation	−20° to 250°F.	Good	Poor
3M Brand Spray Adhesive 77	A high solids, unique adhesive that develops quick, aggressive tack, provided in an aerosol container that really works	−20° to 250°F.	Good	Poor
3M Brand Adhesive EC-226	Fast drying, develops tough and rubbery bonds, versatile in use, used for bonding rubber sheet	−20° to 180°F.	Good	Poor
3M Brand Adhesive EC-321	Long bonding range, excellent heat resistance, used to bond low density insulating materials to wood and painted metal	−35° to 300°F.	Excellent	Poor
3M Brand Adhesive EC-847	Fast drying, resists some plasticizers, high strength, general purpose, excellent for bonding nitrile rubber	−40° to 250°F.	Excellent	Excellent
3M Brand Adhesive EC-871	Non-flammable during application, good wet strength, for bonding porous and non-porous materials	−65° to 200°F.	Good	Poor
3M Brand Adhesive EC-959	High immediate strength, permanently flexible, general purpose mastic, used for metal to glass and ceramics	−65° to 200°F.	Excellent	Poor
3M Brand Adhesive EC-971	Will bond only to itself when dry, very high strength, used to bond porous sheet materials and leather to wood	−40° to 200°F.	Excellent	Excellent
3M Brand Adhesive EC-1099	Fast drying, used to bond plastic sheet, glass, cloth and rubber, bonds leather, vinyls and fiber gaskets to metal and wood	−40° to 250°F.	Excellent	Excellent
3M Brand Adhesive EC-1300	High tack, high immediate bond strength, outstanding oil resistance, primarily used to bond weatherstrip to metal	−5° to 300°F.	Excellent	Good
3M Brand Adhesive EC-1357	High initial strength, heat and solvent reactivatable, principally a contact type adhesive, used for sandwich panel assembly	−20° to 220°F.	Excellent	Good
3M Brand Adhesive EC-1870	Fast drying, high immediate bond strength, water resistant, a good general purpose adhesive outstanding for bonding fabrics	−10° to 175°F.	Excellent	Poor
"SCOTCH-WELD" Brand Structural Adhesive EC-1258 B/A	An equal mix, two-part epoxy resin based adhesive, general purpose structural use, good adhesion to most surfaces	−70° to 160°F.	Excellent	Excellent
3M Brand Adhesive EC-2210	Dries tack free, high initial strength, principally used for bonding plastic laminates	−30° to 220°F.	Excellent	Good
"SCOTCH-WELD" Brand Structural Adhesive EC-2214	A one-part structural adhesive, cures possible as low as 225°F., excellent for bonding structural plastics	−70° to 225°F.	Excellent	Excellent
"SCOTCH-WELD" Brand Structural Adhesive EC-2216 B/A	A two-part structural adhesive that withstands severe shock and vibration, excellent for metal and/or plastic bonding	−93° to 350°F.	Excellent	Excellent
3M Brand Vinyl Adhesive 2262	Quick tack, non-staining, dries clear, excellent for bonding vinyl extrusions to wood and metal, resists plasticizers	−30° to 180°F.	Fair	Excellent
3M Brand Panel Adhesive PA-2318	Long bonding range, high temperature resistance, passes ASTM-D-1037 Cycle tests, for laminating and sandwich panel assembly	−30° to 220°F.	Excellent	Excellent
3M Brand Adhesive EC-4475	A crystal clear adhesive that will bond to almost anything. Good for vinyls. Develops good immediate tack and holding strength	0° to 200°F.	Excellent	Excellent

*Before using, user should test to determine suitability under his situation.

Properties				Application						
				Method					Bonding Range	
Color	Consistency	Solvent or Vehicle	Solids % by weight	Brush	Spray	Roller	Flow	Trowel	One Coat	Two Coats
Green	Thin Syrup	Water	50%	X	X				to 10 minutes	10 minutes to 2 hours
Red & Black	Light Gel	Petroleum Naphtha	32%	X	X	X			to 5 minutes	to 4 hours
Clear	Medium Thin Liquid	Petroleum Naphtha	32%	X	X	X			to 5 minutes	to 4 hours
Blue	Medium Thin Liquid	Chlorinated Hydrocarbon	19%	X	X	X			to 7 minutes	to 4 hours
Clear	Medium Thin Liquid	Petroleum Naphtha	31%		X				to 10 minutes	to 4 hours
Black	Medium Syrup	Petroleum Naphtha	50%	X	X		X		to 5 minutes	5 to 90 minutes
Black	Soft Paste	Water	70%		X	X		X	to 10 minutes	to 30 minutes
Brown	Medium Syrup	Acetone	37%	X			X	X	3 to 10 minutes	10 to 30 minutes
Cream	Thin Paste	Water	55%	X	X		X		3 to 5 minutes	—
Light Cream	Heavy Paste	Petroleum Naphtha	62%					X	5 to 20 minutes	—
Brown	Thin Pasty Liquid	Water	50%	X	X	X			to 5 minutes	1 to 4 hours
Light Tan	Thin Syrup	Acetone	32%	X				X	3 to 5 minutes	5 to 15 minutes
Yellow	Thin Syrup	Solvent Blend	37%	X	X	X			to 1 minute	to 4 minutes
Gray-Green	Thin Syrup	Solvent Blend	25%	X	X				2 to 10 minutes	5 to 45 minutes
Amber	Thin Syrup	Petroleum Naphtha	27%	X	X				to 5 minutes	5 to 10 minutes
Light Grey	Heavy Liquid	None	100%				X	X	8 hours	—
Yellow	Thin Syrup	MEK and Petroleum Naphtha	22%	X				X	to 10 minutes	10 minutes to 2 hours
Aluminum	Paste	None	100%				X	X	280°F. for 40 minutes	—
Light Grey	Soft Paste	None	100%				X	X	8 hours	—
Clear	Thin Syrup	Solvent Blend	25%	X		X		X	—	3 to 8 minutes
Green	Thin Syrup	Solvent Blend	18%	X					to 10 minutes	10 to 120 minutes
Water Clear	Thin Syrup	Ketone	40%				X		to 5 minutes	5 to 15 minutes

TECHNICAL DATA

TD-12-2

Common Adhesives — Their Characteristics and Uses (The Franklin Glue Company)

Adhesive Type	Temperature in Room	Preparing Adhesive	How to Apply	Clamping Time at 70°		Application		Advantages
				Hard wood	Soft wood	Uses	Cautions	
Liquid Hide	Sets best above 70°; can be used in colder room if glue is warmer.	Ready to use.	Spread thin coat on both surfaces; let get tacky before joining.	2 hours	3 hours	Furniture work and wherever a tough, lasting wood-to-wood bond is needed. A favorite for cabinet work and general wood gluing.	It is not waterproof; do not use for outdoor furniture or for boat building.	Very strong. Rawhide tough and does not become brittle; easy to use, light in color, resists heat and mold. Has good filling qualities, so gives strength even in poorly fitted joints.
White Liquid Resin	Any temperature above 60°, the warmer the better.	Ready to use.	Spread on and clamp at once.	1 hour	1½ hours	An all-around household glue for mending and furniture making and repair. Excellent for model work, paper, leather and small assemblies.	Not sufficiently moisture-resistant for anything to be exposed to weather. Not so strong and lasting as Liquid Hide Glue for fine furniture work.	Always ready to use at any temperature. Non-staining, clean and white. Recommended for work where good clamping is not possible.
Resorcinol	Must be 70° or warmer. Will set faster at 90°.	Mix 3 parts of powder to 4 parts of liquid catalyst.	Apply thin coat to both surfaces. Use within 8 hours after mixing.	16 hours	16 hours	For any work that may be exposed to soaking; outdoor furniture, boats, wooden sinks.	Not good for work that must be done at temperatures below 70°. Because of dark color and mixing, not often used unless waterproof quality is needed.	Very strong, as well as waterproof. Works better with poor joints than many glues do.
Powdered Resin	Must be 70° or warmer. Will set faster at 90°.	Mix 2 parts of powder with ½ to 1 part of water.	Apply thin coat to both surfaces. Use within 4 hours after mixing.	16 hours	16 hours	For woodworking and general gluing where considerable moisture resistance is wanted.	Do not use with oily woods or with joints that are not closely fitted and tightly clamped. Must be mixed for each use.	Very strong, although brittle if joint fits poorly. Light colored, almost waterproof.
Powdered Casein	Any temperature above freezing, the warmer the better.	Stir together equal parts by volume of glue and water. Wait 10 minutes, then stir again.	Apply thin coat to both surfaces. Use within 8 hours after mixing.	2 hours	3 hours	Will do most woodworking jobs and is especially desirable with oily woods; teak, lemon, yew.	Not moisture resistant enough for outdoor furniture. Will stain acid woods such as redwood. Must be mixed for each use.	Strong, fairly water-resistant, works in cool locations, fills poor joints well.
Flake or Powdered Animal	Must be 70° or warmer. Keep work warm.	For each ounce of glue, add 1½ ounces of water for soft wood; 2 ounces of water for hard wood.	Apply heavy coat at 140° to both surfaces. Assemble rapidly.	1 hour	1½ hours	Good for quantity woodworking jobs that justify the time and trouble of mixing and heating the glue.	Too much trouble to use for small jobs or most home shop work. Not waterproof.	Same advantages as Liquid Hide Glue but must be mixed, heated, kept hot, used at high temperatures.
Aliphatic Resin	Any temperature above 35°.	Ready to use.	Spread on and clamp at once.	1 hour	1½ hours	Resistance to cold flow — especially good for edge glued panels. Better than average solvent resistance. Not affected by most lacquers, sealers, or solvents.	Not sufficiently moisture resistant to be exposed to the weather.	Very strong, non-staining, easy to use, and quick setting.

TD-12-3

Common Weldwood Adhesives — Characteristics and Uses (United States Plywood Corporation)

Adhesive	Applications	Packaged Form	Clamping	Setting Time	Water Resistance
Epoxy Glue	Heavy duty household repairs; china, glass, metals, plastics, porcelain Concrete to concrete, wood, masonry Metal to metal, wood, masonry	Resin and Hardener; easily mixed	Not required	Hardens overnight	Waterproof
Contact Cement	Light duty, household repairs, china, glass, metals, plastics, procelain Plastic laminates to plywood or particle board Leather to leather, wood	Liquid; ready-mixed for use	Not required	Bonds on contact (when dry)	High
White Glue	Light assembly, interior wood cabinets, built-ins, furniture Paper to paper, fabric, cardboard Canvas, cork or felt to wood	Liquid; ready-mixed for use	Moderate pressure	20-30 minutes	Moderate
Plastic-Resin Glue	Heavy assembly interior wood cabinets, built-ins, furniture Hardboard to wood	Powder; mixes quickly with water	Required	5-6 hours	Very high
Resorcinol Glue	Exterior wood, outdoor furniture, sports equipment, wood to wood, cork, canvas Boats (wood)	Liquid and Powder; easily mixed	Required	8-10 hours	100% waterproof

TD-12-4

Application of Fillet, Plug, and Slot-Welding Symbols (American Welding Society)

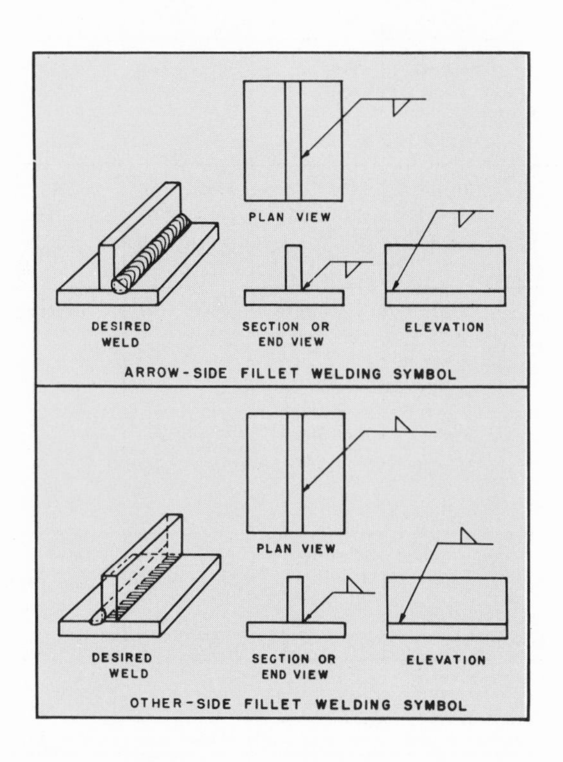

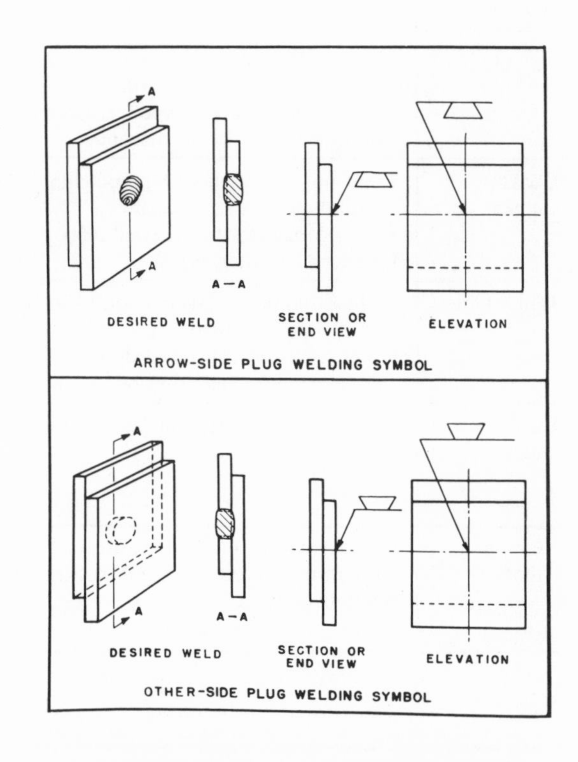

JOINT "A"
JOINT "B"
DESIRED WELD
SECTION OR END VIEW
ELEVATION
BOTH-SIDES FILLET WELDING SYMBOL FOR ONE JOINT

JOINT "A"
JOINT "B"
DESIRED WELD
SECTION OR END VIEW
ELEVATION
BOTH-SIDES FILLET WELDING SYMBOL FOR TWO JOINTS

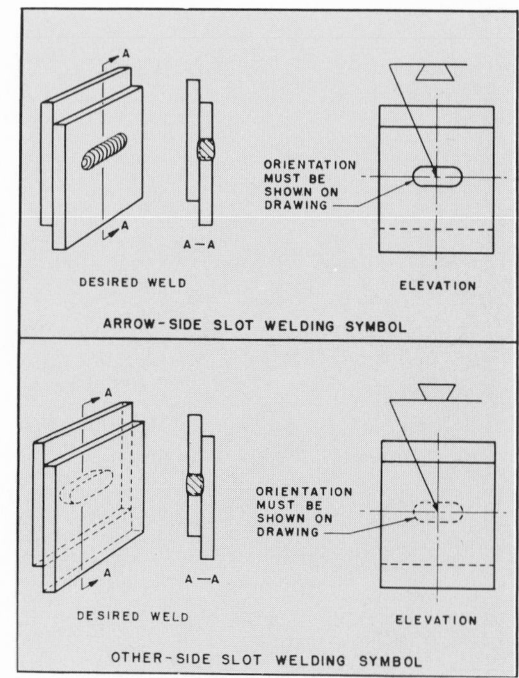

TD-12-5

Application of Arc-Spot, Arc-Seam, Square-Groove, and V-Groove Welding Symbols (American Welding Society)

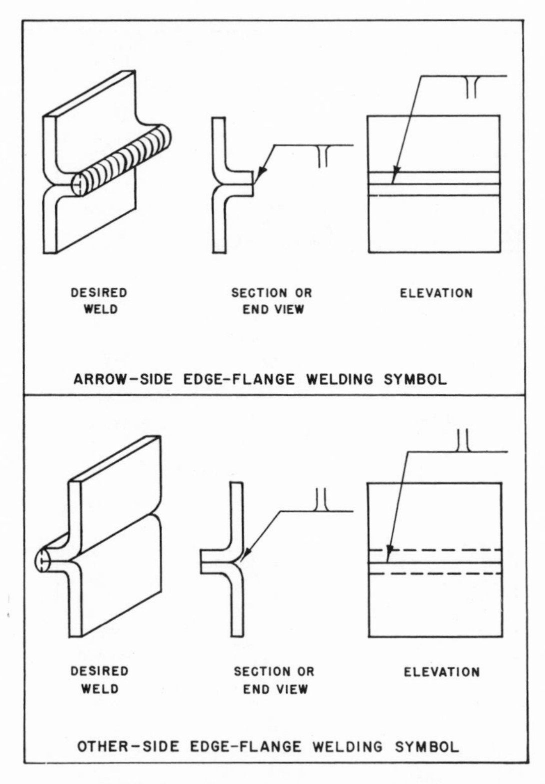

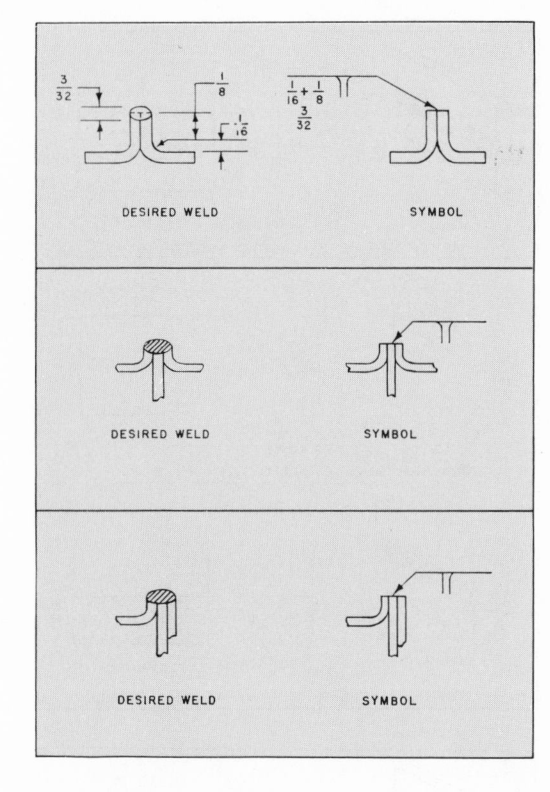

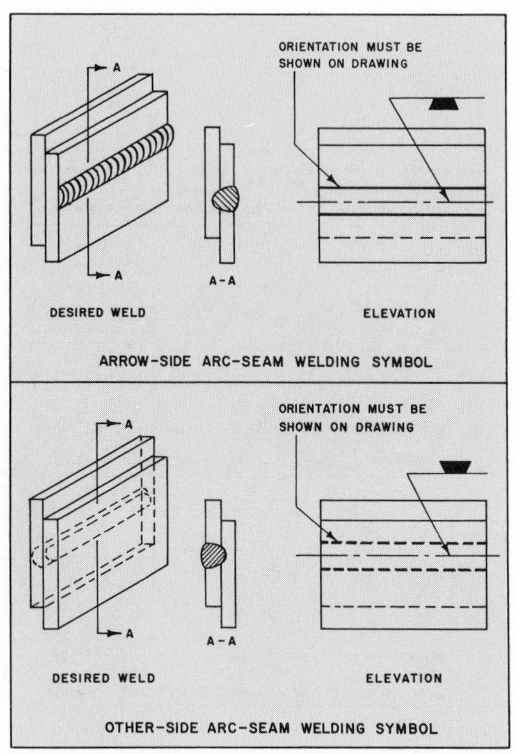

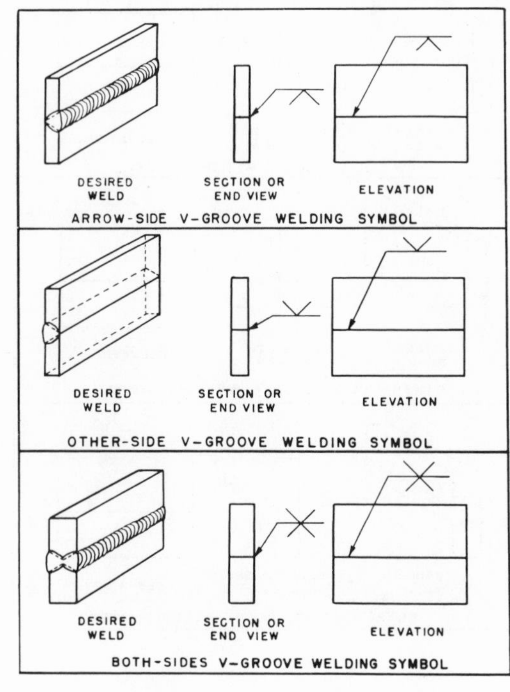

TD-12-6

Application of Bevel-Groove, U-Groove, J-Groove, and Flare-V-Groove Welding Symbols (American Welding Society)

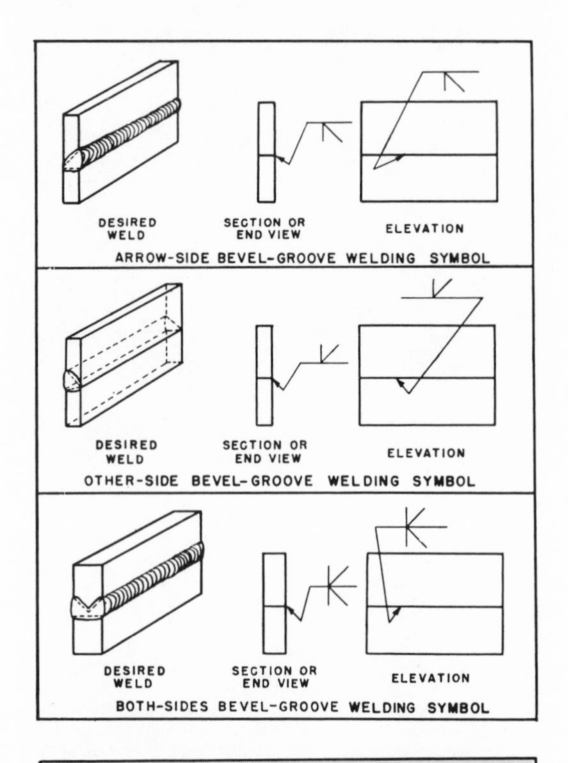

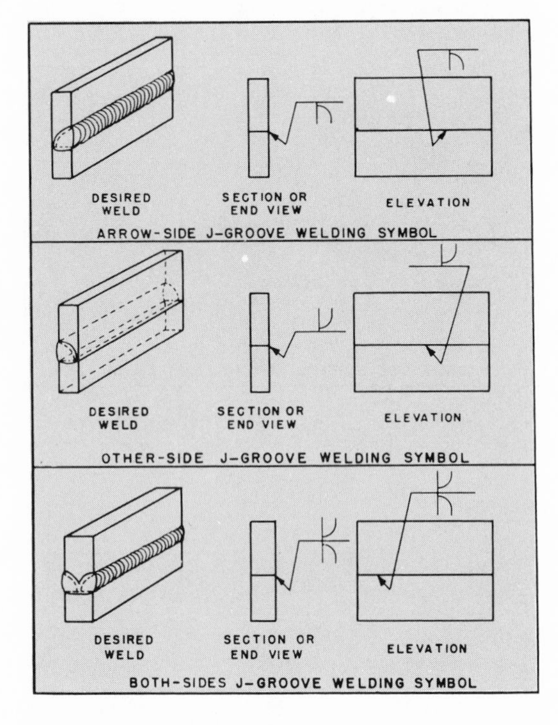

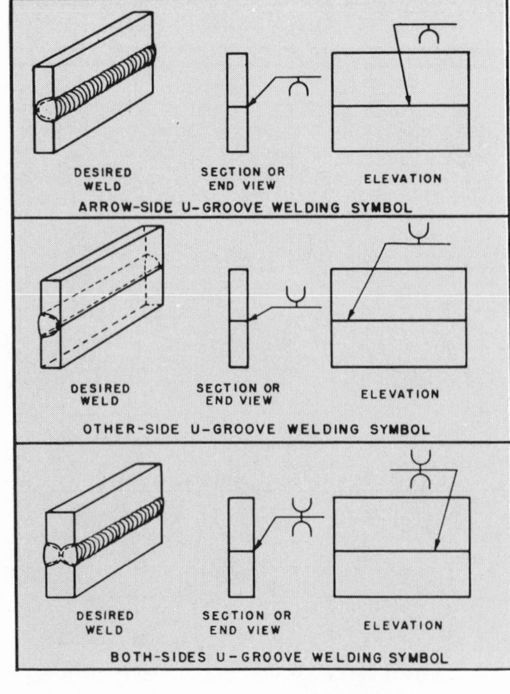

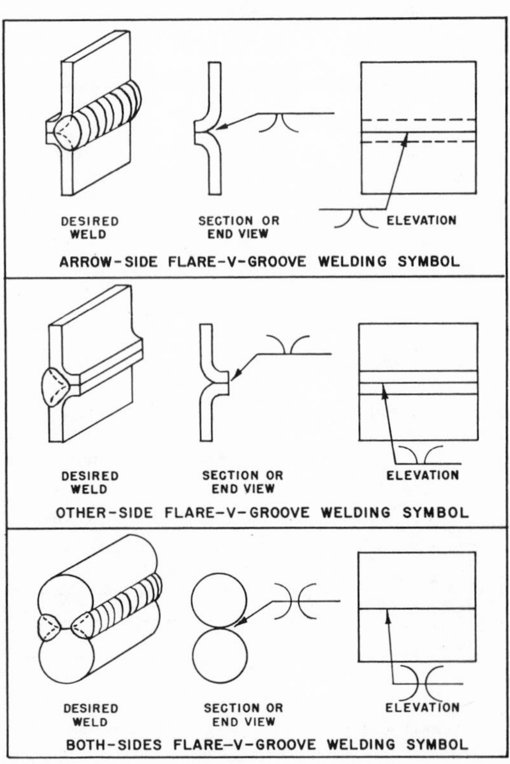

TECHNICAL DATA

TD-12-7

Application of Flare-Bevel-Groove, Back-Weld, Melt-Through, and Surface-Weld Welding Symbols (American Welding Society)

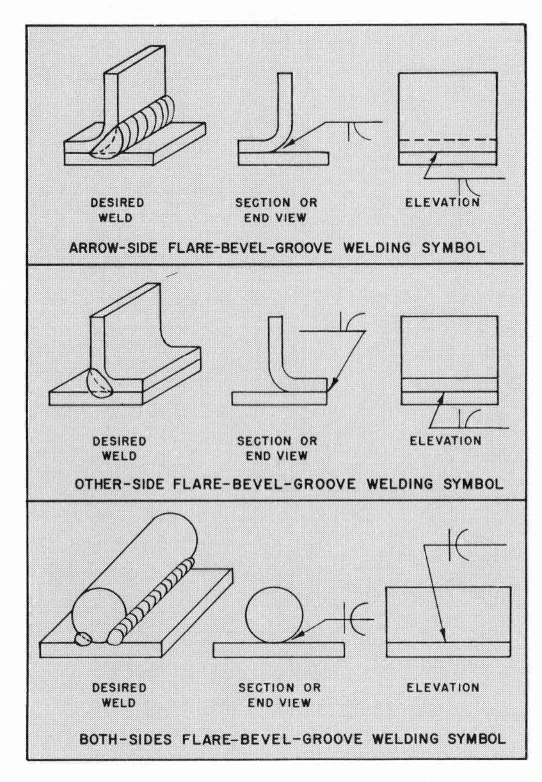

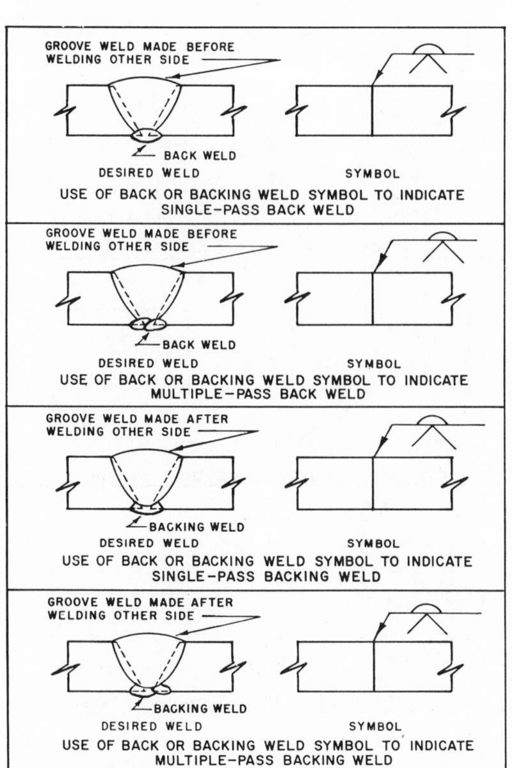

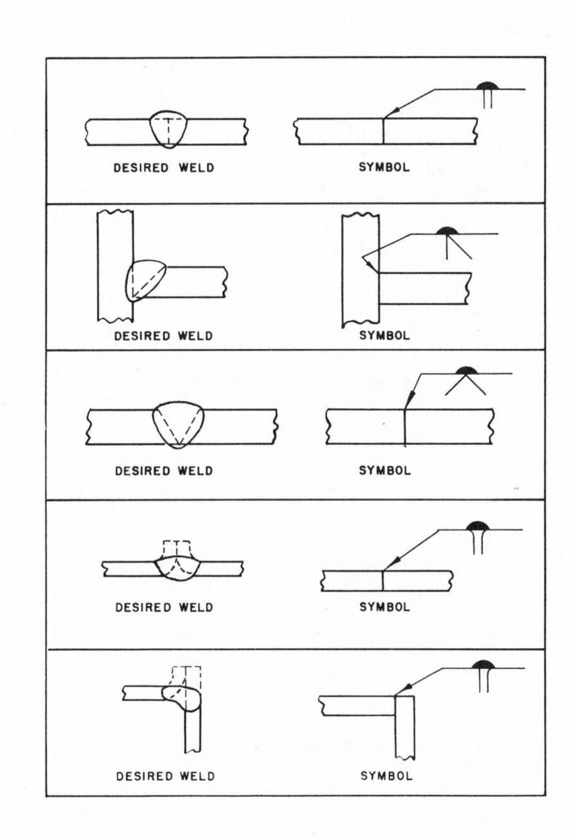

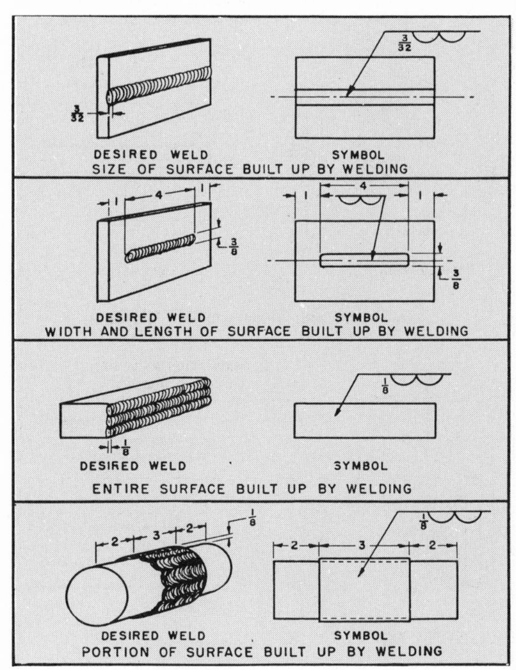

TECHNICAL DATA

TD-12-8

Application of Edge-Flange, Corner-Flange, Resistance-Spot and Resistance-Seam Welding Symbols (American Welding Society)

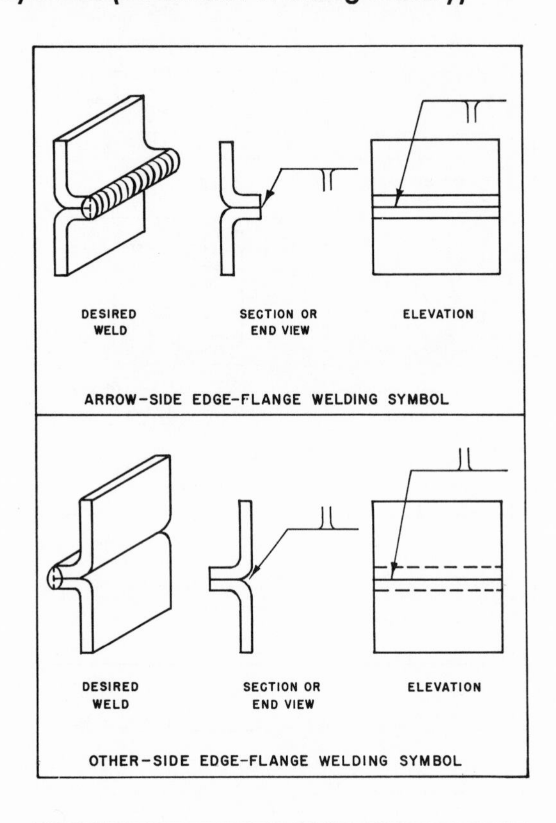

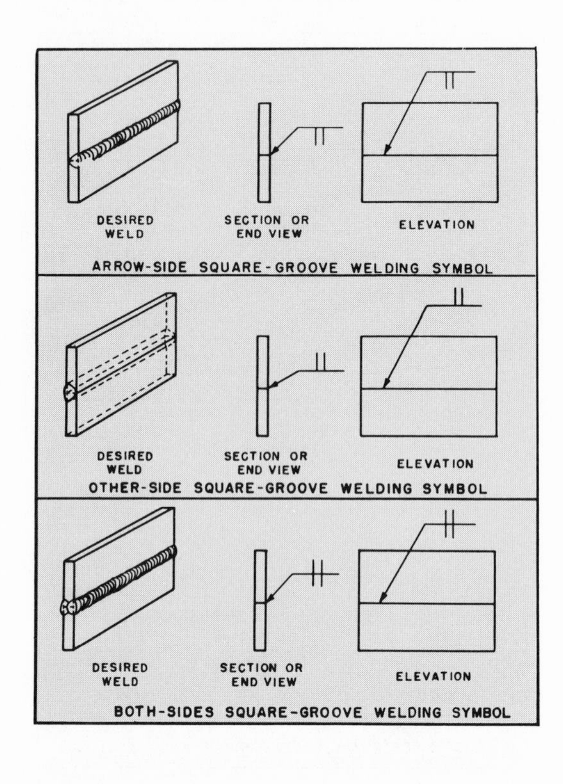

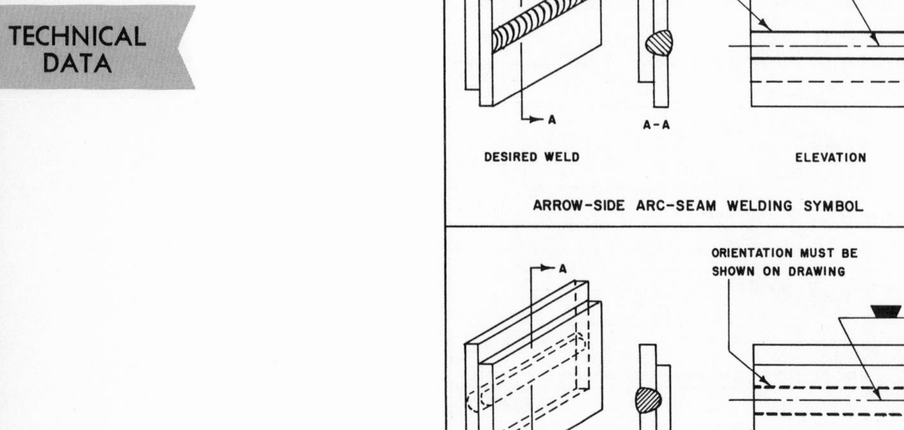

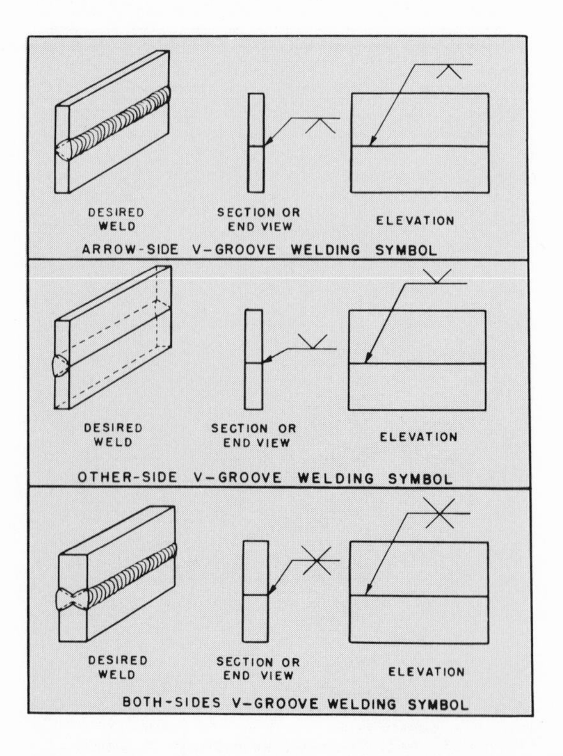

TD-12-9

Application of Projection, Flash, and Upset Welding Symbols and Dimensioning Fillet Welds (American Welding Society)

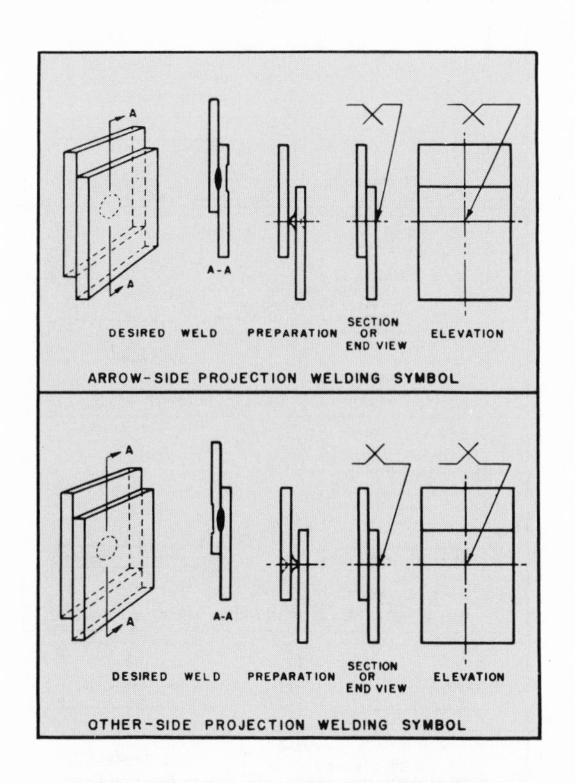

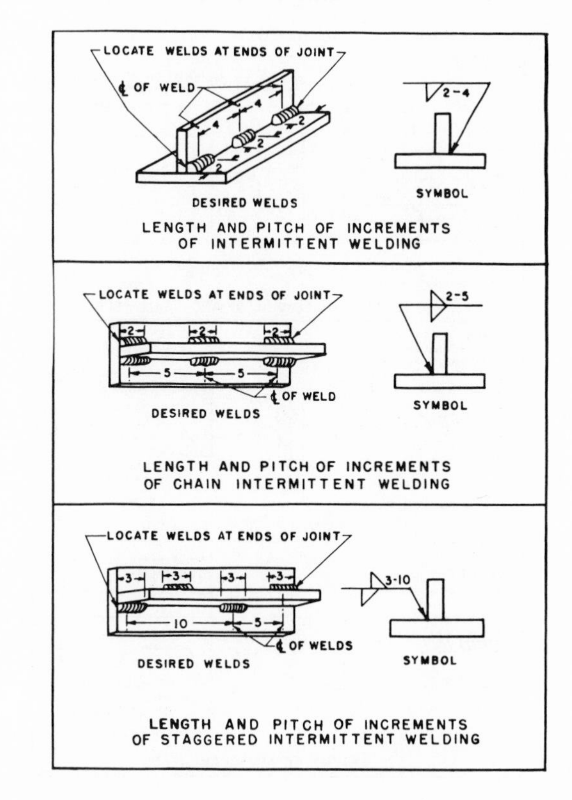

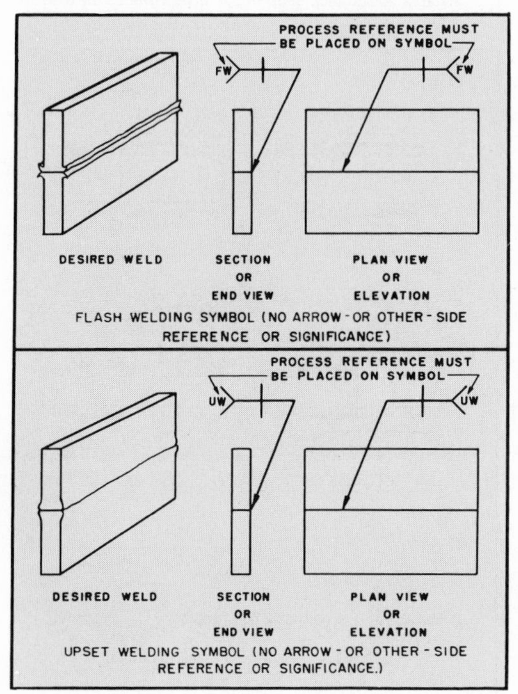

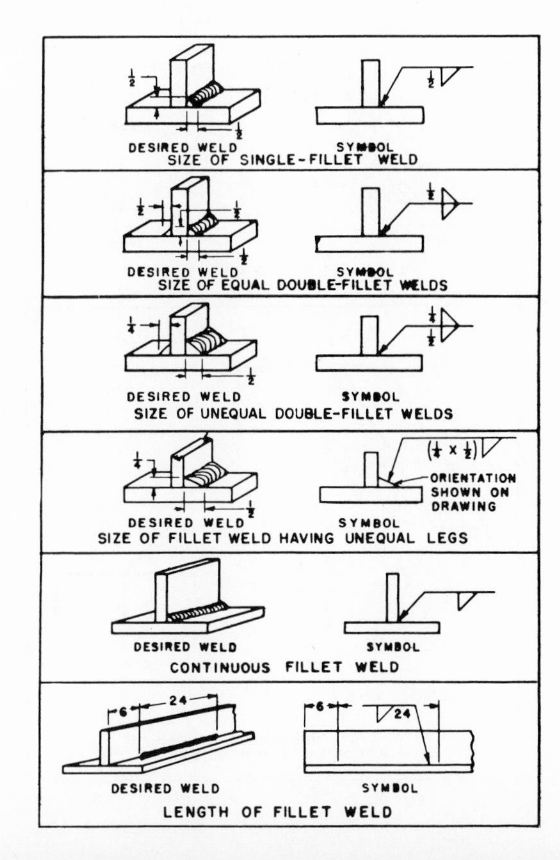

TD-12-10

Application of Dimensions for Arc-Seam, Fillet, Groove, and Resistance-Spot Welds and Application of Brazing Symbols (American Welding Society)

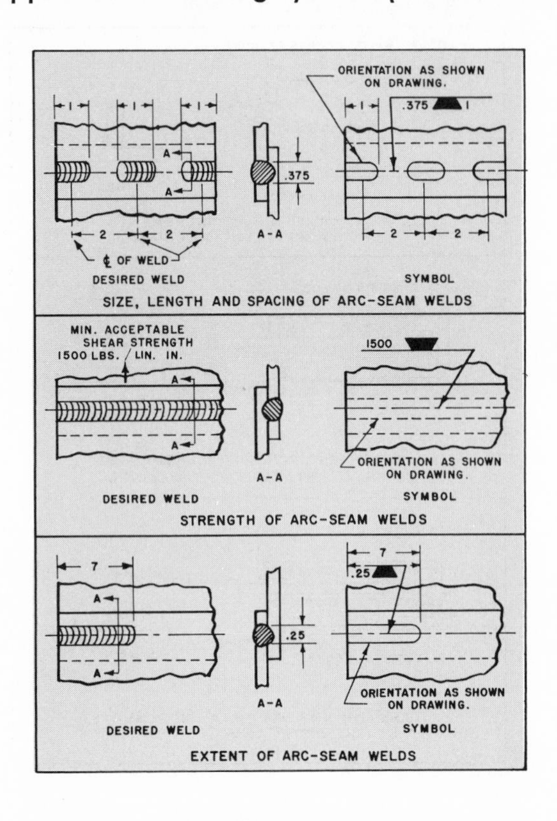

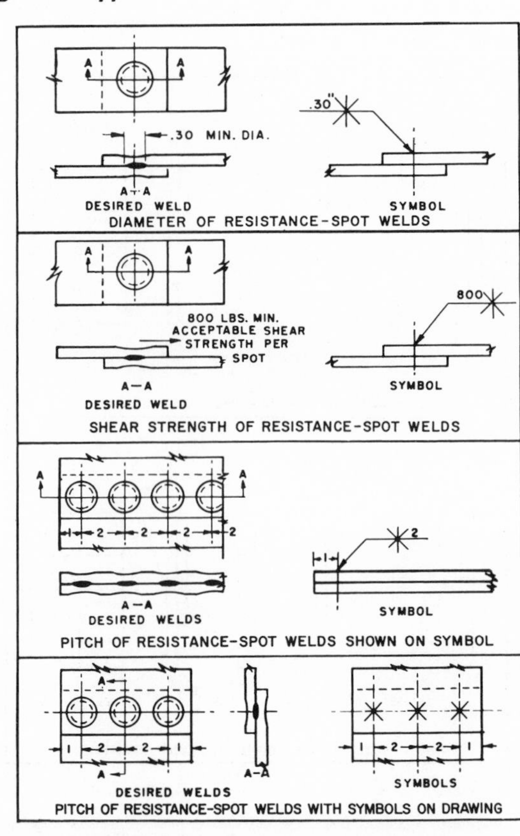

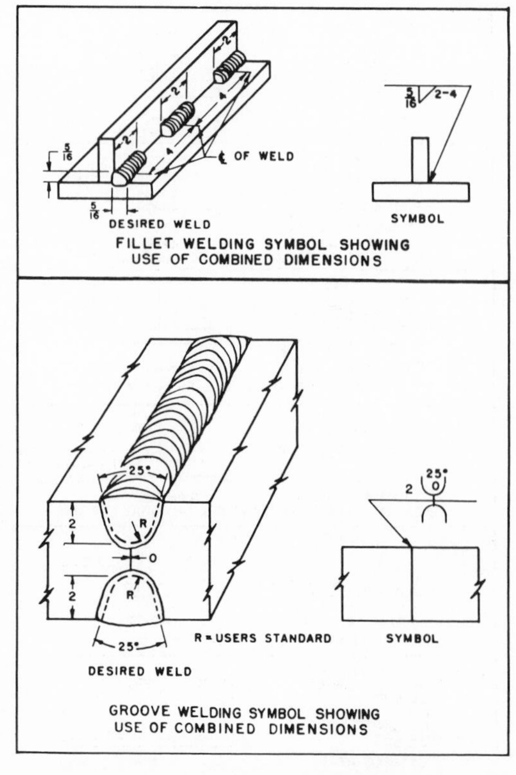

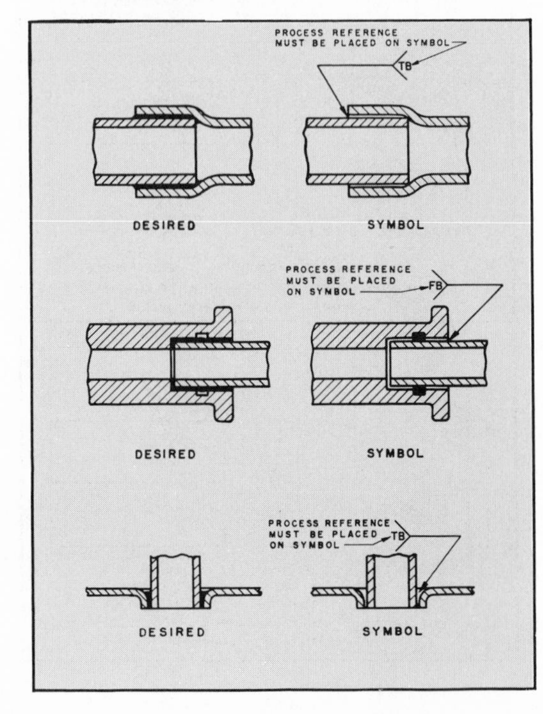

TECHNICAL DATA

TD-12-11

Unified Screw Thread Standard Series (SAE)

Nominal Size Preferred	Nominal Size Secondary	Basic Major (Nominal) Diameter	Graded Pitch Series: Coarse UNC	Fine UNF	Extra-Fine UNEF	Constant Pitch Series: 4 UN	6 UN	8 UN	12 UN	16 UN	20 UN	28 UN	32 UN	Nominal Size
			Threads Per Inch											
0		0.0600	—	80	—	—	—	—	—	—	—	—	—	0
	1	0.0730	64	72	—	—	—	—	—	—	—	—	—	1
2		0.0860	56	64	—	—	—	—	—	—	—	—	—	2
	3	0.0990	48	56	—	—	—	—	—	—	—	—	—	3
4		0.1120	40	48	—	—	—	—	—	—	—	—	—	4
5		0.1250	40	44	—	—	—	—	—	—	—	—	—	5
6		0.1380	32	40	—	—	—	—	—	—	—	—	UNC	6
8		0.1640	32	36	—	—	—	—	—	—	—	—	UNC	8
10		0.1900	24	32	—	—	—	—	—	—	—	—	UNF	10
	12	0.2160	24	28	32	—	—	—	—	—	—	UNF	UNEF	12
1/4		0.2500	20	28	32	—	—	—	—	—	UNC	UNF	UNEF	1/4
5/16		0.3125	18	24	32	—	—	—	—	—	20	28	UNEF	5/16
3/8		0.3750	16	24	32	—	—	—	—	UNC	20	28	UNEF	3/8
7/16		0.4375	14	20	28	—	—	—	—	16	UNF	UNEF	32	7/16
1/2		0.5000	13	20	28	—	—	—	—	16	UNF	UNEF	32	1/2
9/16		0.5625	12	18	24	—	—	—	UNC	16	20	28	32	9/16
5/8		0.6250	11	18	24	—	—	—	12	16	20	28	32	5/8
	11/16	0.6875	—	—	24	—	—	—	12	16	20	28	32	11/16
3/4		0.7500	10	16	20	—	—	—	12	UNF	UNEF	28	32	3/4
	13/16	0.8125	—	—	20	—	—	—	12	16	UNEF	28	32	13/16
7/8		0.8750	9	14	20	—	—	—	12	16	UNEF	28	32	7/8
	15/16	0.9375	—	—	20	—	—	—	12	16	UNEF	28	32	15/16
1		1.0000	8	12	20	—	—	UNC	UNF	16	UNEF	28	32	1
	1 1/16	1.0625	—	—	18	—	—	8	12	16	20	28	—	1 1/16
1 1/8		1.1250	7	12	18	—	—	8	UNF	16	20	28	—	1 1/8
	1 3/16	1.1875	—	—	18	—	—	8	12	16	20	28	—	1 3/16
1 1/4		1.2500	7	12	18	—	—	8	UNF	16	20	28	—	1 1/4
	1 5/16	1.3125	—	—	18	—	—	8	12	16	20	28	—	1 5/16
1 3/8		1.3750	6	12	18	—	UNC	8	UNF	16	20	28	—	1 3/8
	1 7/16	1.4375	—	—	18	—	6	8	12	16	20	28	—	1 7/16
1 1/2		1.5000	6	12	18	—	UNC	8	UNF	16	20	28	—	1 1/2
	1 9/16	1.5625	—	—	18	—	6	8	12	16	20	—	—	1 9/16
1 5/8		1.6250	—	—	18	—	6	8	12	16	20	—	—	1 5/8
	1 11/16	1.6875	—	—	18	—	6	8	12	16	20	—	—	1 11/16
1 3/4		1.7500	5	—	—	—	6	8	12	16	20	—	—	1 3/4
	1 13/16	1.8125	—	—	—	—	6	8	12	16	20	—	—	1 13/16
1 7/8		1.8750	—	—	—	—	6	8	12	16	20	—	—	1 7/8
	1 15/16	1.9375	—	—	—	—	6	8	12	16	20	—	—	1 15/16
2		2.0000	4 1/2	—	—	—	6	8	12	16	20	—	—	2
	2 1/8	2.1250	—	—	—	—	6	8	12	16	20	—	—	2 1/8
2 1/4		2.2500	4 1/2	—	—	—	6	8	12	16	20	—	—	2 1/4
	2 3/8	2.3750	—	—	—	—	6	8	12	16	20	—	—	2 3/8
2 1/2		2.5000	4	—	—	UNC	6	8	12	16	20	—	—	2 1/2
	2 5/8	2.6250	—	—	—	4	6	8	12	16	20	—	—	2 5/8
2 3/4		2.7500	4	—	—	UNC	6	8	12	16	20	—	—	2 3/4
	2 7/8	2.8750	—	—	—	4	6	8	12	16	20	—	—	2 7/8
3		3.0000	4	—	—	UNC	6	8	12	16	20	—	—	3
	3 1/8	3.1250	—	—	—	4	6	8	12	16	—	—	—	3 1/8
3 1/4		3.2500	4	—	—	UNC	6	8	12	16	—	—	—	3 1/4
	3 3/8	3.3750	—	—	—	4	6	8	12	16	—	—	—	3 3/8
3 1/2		3.5000	4	—	—	UNC	6	8	12	16	—	—	—	3 1/2
	3 5/8	3.6250	—	—	—	4	6	8	12	16	—	—	—	3 5/8
3 3/4		3.7500	4	—	—	UNC	6	8	12	16	—	—	—	3 3/4
	3 7/8	3.8750	—	—	—	4	6	8	12	16	—	—	—	3 7/8
4		4.0000	4	—	—	UNC	6	8	12	16	—	—	—	4
	4 1/8	4.1250	—	—	—	4	6	8	12	16	—	—	—	4 1/8
4 1/4		4.2500	—	—	—	4	6	8	12	16	—	—	—	4 1/4
	4 3/8	4.3750	—	—	—	4	6	8	12	16	—	—	—	4 3/8
4 1/2		4.5000	—	—	—	4	6	8	12	16	—	—	—	4 1/2
	4 5/8	4.6250	—	—	—	4	6	8	12	16	—	—	—	4 5/8
4 3/4		4.7500	—	—	—	4	6	8	12	16	—	—	—	4 3/4
	4 7/8	4.8750	—	—	—	4	6	8	12	16	—	—	—	4 7/8
5		5.0000	—	—	—	4	6	8	12	16	—	—	—	5
	5 1/8	5.1250	—	—	—	4	6	8	12	16	—	—	—	5 1/8
5 1/4		5.2500	—	—	—	4	6	8	12	16	—	—	—	5 1/4
	5 3/8	5.3750	—	—	—	4	6	8	12	16	—	—	—	5 3/8
5 1/2		5.5000	—	—	—	4	6	8	12	16	—	—	—	5 1/2
	5 5/8	5.6250	—	—	—	4	6	8	12	16	—	—	—	5 5/8
5 3/4		5.7500	—	—	—	4	6	8	12	16	—	—	—	5 3/4
	5 7/8	5.8750	—	—	—	4	6	8	12	16	—	—	—	5 7/8
6		6.0000	—	—	—	4	6	8	12	16	—	—	—	6

TD-12-12

Basic Dimensions, American Standard Taper Pipe Thread, NPT (USAS B2.1-1960)[1]

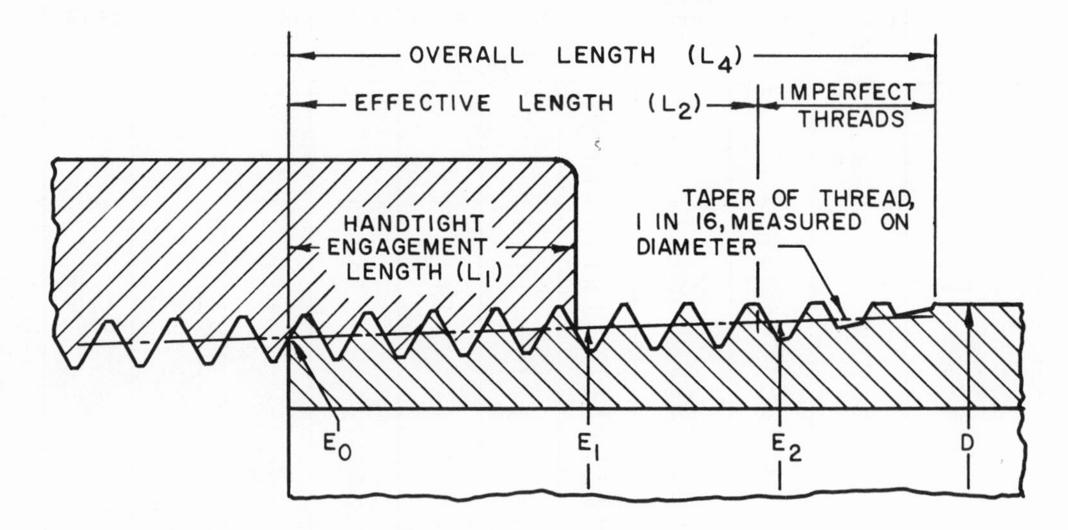

Nominal Pipe Size	Outside Diameter of Pipe, D	Threads per Inch, n	Pitch of Thread, p	Pitch Diameter at Beginning of External Thread, E_0	Handtight Engagement: Length, L_1, In.	Handtight Engagement: Length, L_1, Thds	Handtight Engagement: Diam, E_1	Effective Thread, External: Length, L_2, In.	Effective Thread, External: Length, L_2, Thds	Effective Thread, External: Diam, E_2	Length L_4: Overall Length External Thread L_4
1	2	3	4	5	6	7	8	9	10	11	
1/16	0.3125	27	0.03704	0.27118	0.160	4.32	0.28118	0.2611	7.05	0.28750	.3896
1/8	0.405	27	0.03704	0.36351	0.1615	4.36	0.37360	0.2639	7.12	0.38000	.3924
1/4	0.540	18	0.05556	0.47739	0.2278	4.10	0.49163	0.4018	7.23	0.50250	.5946
3/8	0.675	18	0.05556	0.61201	0.240	4.32	0.62701	0.4078	7.34	0.63750	.6006
1/2	0.840	14	0.07143	0.75843	0.320	4.48	0.77843	0.5337	7.47	0.79179	.7815
3/4	1.050	14	0.07143	0.96768	0.339	4.75	0.98887	0.5457	7.64	1.00179	.7935
1	1.315	11½	0.08696	1.21363	0.400	4.60	1.23863	0.6828	7.85	1.25630	.9845
1¼	1.660	11½	0.08696	1.55713	0.420	4.83	1.58338	0.7068	8.13	1.60130	1.0085
1½	1.900	11½	0.08696	1.79609	0.420	4.83	1.82234	0.7235	8.32	1.84130	1.0252
2	2.375	11½	0.08696	2.26902	0.436	5.01	2.29627	0.7565	8.70	2.31630	1.0582
2½	2.875	8	0.12500	2.71953	0.682	5.46	2.76216	1.1375	9.10	2.79062	1.5712
3	3.500	8	0.12500	3.34062	0.766	6.13	3.38850	1.2000	9.60	3.41562	1.6337
3½	4.000	8	0.12500	3.83750	0.821	6.57	3.88881	1.2500	10.00	3.91562	1.6837
4	4.500	8	0.12500	4.33438	0.844	6.75	4.38712	1.3000	10.40	4.41562	1.7337
5	5.563	8	0.12500	5.39073	0.937	7.50	5.44929	1.4063	11.25	5.47862	1.8400
6	6.625	8	0.12500	6.44609	0.958	7.66	6.50597	1.5125	12.10	6.54062	1.9462
8	8.625	8	0.12500	8.43359	1.063	8.50	8.50003	1.7125	13.70	8.54062	2.1462
10	10.750	8	0.12500	10.54531	1.210	9.68	10.62094	1.9250	15.40	10.66562	2.3587
12	12.750	8	0.12500	12.53281	1.360	10.88	12.61781	2.1250	17.00	12.66562	2.5587
14 OD	14.000	8	0.12500	13.77500	1.562	12.50	13.87262	2.2500	18.90	13.91562	2.6837
16 OD	16.000	8	0.12500	15.76250	1.812	14.50	15.87575	2.4500	19.60	15.91562	2.8837
18 OD	18.000	8	0.12500	17.75000	2.000	16.00	17.87500	2.6500	21.20	17.91562	3.0837
20 OD	20.000	8	0.12500	19.73750	2.125	17.00	19.87031	2.8500	22.80	19.91562	3.2837
24 OD	24.000	8	0.12500	23.71250	2.375	19.00	23.86094	3.2500	26.00	23.91562	3.6837

[1]The basic dimensions of the American Standard Taper Pipe Thread are given in inches to four or five decimal places. While this implies a greater degree of precision than is ordinarily attained, these dimensions are the basis of gage dimensions and are so expressed for the purpose of eliminating errors in computations.

TD-12-13

Unified Miniature Screws (USAS B18.11-1961)

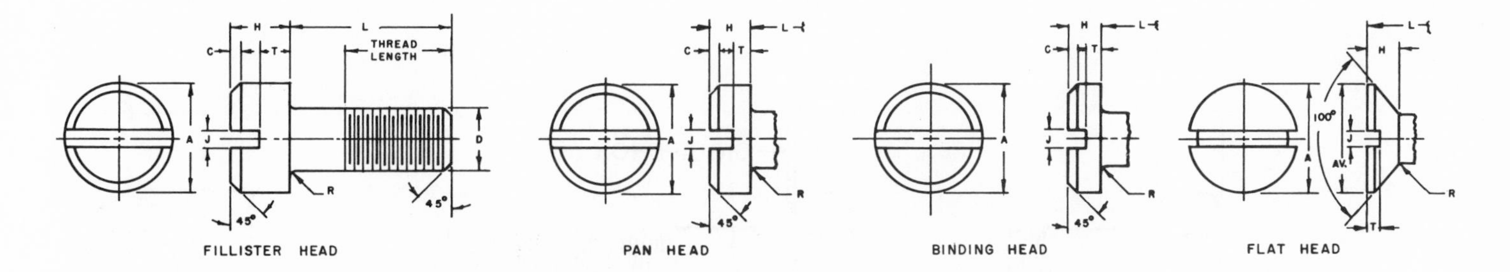

Size Designation	Thds per Inch	D Basic Major Dia	C Cham-fer	Fillister Head Dimensions (Max.)						Pan Head Dimensions (Max.)				
				L Length Range[1]	A Head Dia	H Head Hgt	J Slot Width	T Slot Depth	R Ra-dius	A Head Dia	B Head Hgt	J Slot Width	T Slot Depth	R Ra-dius
30 UNM	318	0.0118	0.002	.020-.120	0.021	0.012	0.004	0.006	0.002	0.025	0.010	0.005	0.005	0.002
35 UNM	282	0.0138	0.002	.025-.160	0.023	0.014	0.004	0.007	0.002	0.029	0.011	0.005	0.006	0.002
40 UNM	254	0.0157	0.002	.025-.160	0.025	0.016	0.005	0.008	0.002	0.033	0.012	0.006	0.006	0.002
45 UNM	254	0.0177	0.002	.032-.200	0.029	0.018	0.005	0.009	0.002	0.037	0.014	0.006	0.007	0.002
50 UNM	203	0.0197	0.003	.032-.200	0.033	0.020	0.006	0.010	0.002	0.041	0.016	0.008	0.008	0.002
55 UNM	203	0.0217	0.003	.040-.250	0.037	0.022	0.006	0.011	0.002	0.045	0.018	0.008	0.009	0.002
60 UNM	169	0.0236	0.004	.040-.250	0.041	0.025	0.008	0.012	0.003	0.051	0.020	0.010	0.010	0.003
70 UNM	145	0.0276	0.004	.050-.320	0.045	0.028	0.008	0.014	0.003	0.056	0.022	0.010	0.011	0.003
80 UNM	127	0.0315	0.005	.050-.320	0.051	0.032	0.010	0.016	0.004	0.062	0.025	0.012	0.012	0.004
90 UNM	113	0.0354	0.005	.060-.400	0.056	0.036	0.010	0.018	0.004	0.072	0.028	0.012	0.014	0.004
100 UNM	102	0.0394	0.006	.060-.400	0.062	0.040	0.012	0.020	0.005	0.082	0.032	0.016	0.018	0.005
110 UNM	102	0.0433	0.006	.080-.500	0.072	0.045	0.012	0.022	0.005	0.092	0.036	0.016	0.018	0.005
120 UNM	102	0.0472	0.008	.080-.500	0.082	0.050	0.016	0.025	0.006	0.103	0.040	0.020	0.020	0.006
140 UNM	85	0.0551	0.008	.100-.600	0.092	0.055	0.016	0.028	0.006	0.113	0.045	0.020	0.022	0.006

Size Designation	Thds per Inch	D Basic Major Dia	C Cham-fer	Binding Head Dimensions (Max.)					Flat Head Dimensions (Max.)					
				A Head Dia	H Head Hgt	J Slot Width	T Slot Depth	R Ra-dius	A Head Dia	H Head Hgt	J Slot Width	T Slot Depth	R Ra-dius	L Length Range[1] (Flat Head Only)
30 UNM	318	0.0118	0.002						0.023	0.007	0.004	0.004	0.005	.025-.160
35 UNM	282	0.0138	0.002						0.025	0.007	0.004	0.004	0.005	.032-.200
40 UNM	254	0.0157	0.002	0.041	0.010	0.006	0.005	0.004	0.029	0.008	0.005	0.005	0.006	.032-.200
45 UNM	254	0.0177	0.002	0.045	0.011	0.006	0.006	0.004	0.033	0.009	0.005	0.005	0.006	.040-.250
50 UNM	203	0.0197	0.003	0.051	0.012	0.008	0.006	0.004	0.037	0.011	0.006	0.006	0.008	.040-.250
55 UNM	203	0.0217	0.003	0.056	0.014	0.008	0.007	0.004	0.041	0.012	0.006	0.006	0.008	.050-.320
60 UNM	169	0.0236	0.004	0.062	0.016	0.010	0.008	0.006	0.045	0.013	0.008	0.008	0.010	.050-.320
70 UNM	145	0.0276	0.004	0.072	0.018	0.010	0.009	0.006	0.051	0.014	0.008	0.008	0.010	.060-.400
80 UNM	127	0.0315	0.005	0.082	0.020	0.012	0.010	0.008	0.056	0.016	0.010	0.010	0.012	.060-.400
90 UNM	113	0.0354	0.005	0.092	0.022	0.012	0.011	0.008	0.062	0.017	0.010	0.010	0.012	.080-.500
100 UNM	102	0.0394	0.006	0.103	0.025	0.016	0.012	0.010	0.072	0.019	0.012	0.012	0.016	.080-.500
110 UNM	102	0.0433	0.006	0.113	0.028	0.016	0.014	0.010	0.082	0.022	0.012	0.012	0.016	.100-.600
120 UNM	102	0.0472	0.008	0.124	0.032	0.020	0.016	0.012	0.092	0.025	0.016	0.016	0.020	.100-.600
140 UNM	85	0.0551	0.008	0.144	0.036	0.020	0.018	0.012	0.103	0.027	0.016	0.016	0.020	.120-.600

[1]Desired lengths within these ranges are any of the tabled values in either of the "length range" columns.

TD-12-14

Hex-Head Cap Screws (USAS B18.2.1-1965)

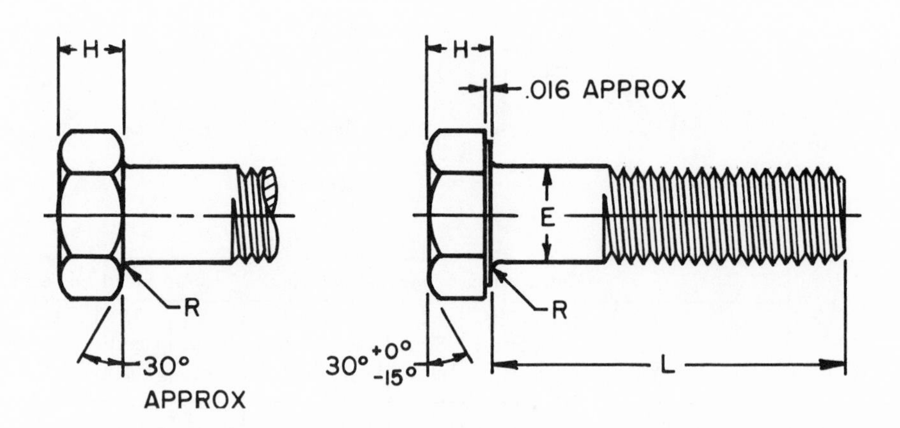

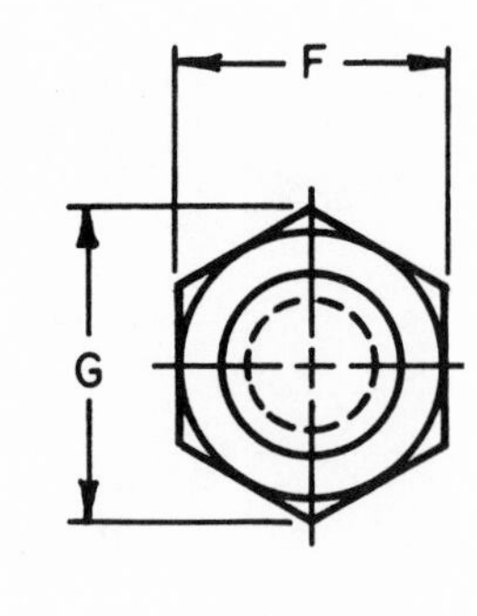

Nominal Size or Basic Product Dia. in Inches		Max. Body Dia. E	Basic Width Across Flats F	Max. Width Across Corners G	Basic Height H	Max. Radius of Fillet R
1/4	0.2500	0.2500	7/16	0.505	5/32	0.025
5/16	0.3125	0.3125	1/2	0.577	13/64	0.025
3/8	0.3750	0.3750	9/16	0.650	15/64	0.025
7/16	0.4375	0.4375	5/8	0.722	9/32	0.025
1/2	0.5000	0.5000	3/4	0.866	5/16	0.025
9/16	0.5625	0.5625	13/16	0.938	23/64	0.045
5/8	0.6250	0.6250	15/16	1.083	25/64	0.045
3/4	0.7500	0.7500	1 1/8	1.299	15/32	0.045
7/8	0.8750	0.8750	1 5/16	1.516	35/64	0.065
1	1.0000	1.0000	1 1/2	1.732	39/64	0.095
1 1/8	1.1250	1.1250	1 11/16	1.949	11/16	0.095
1 1/4	1.2500	1.2500	1 7/8	2.165	25/32	0.095
1 3/8	1.3750	1.3750	2 1/16	2.382	27/32	0.095
1 1/2	1.5000	1.5000	2 1/4	2.598	15/16	0.095
1 3/4	1.7500	1.7500	2 5/8	3.031	1 3/32	0.095
2	2.0000	2.0000	3	3.464	1 7/32	0.095
2 1/4	2.2500	2.2500	3 3/8	3.897	1 3/8	0.095
2 1/2	2.5000	2.5000	3 3/4	4.330	1 17/32	0.095
2 3/4	2.7500	2.7500	4 1/8	4.763	1 11/16	0.095
3	3.0000	3.0000	4 1/2	5.196	1 7/8	0.095

TD-12-15

Hexagon- and Spline-Socket Head Cap Screws (USAS B18.3-1961)

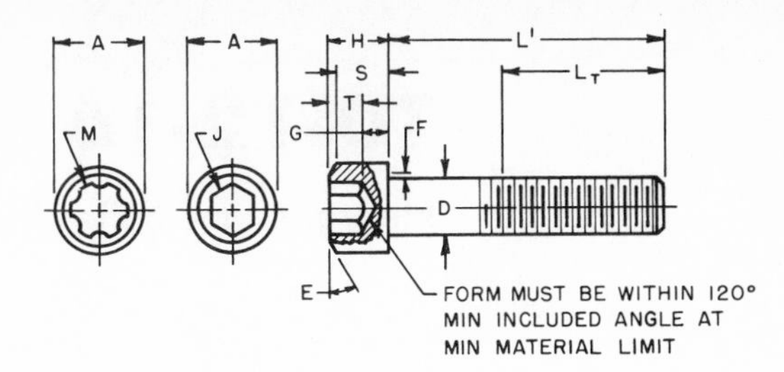

[1]Standard Lengths

	D	A	H	S	M	J	T	G	F	L_T
Nominal Size	Body Diameter	Head Diameter	Head Height	Head Side Height	Spline Socket Size	Hexagon Socket Size	Key Engagement	Wall Thickness	Fillet	Basic Thread Length
	Max.	Max.	Max.	Min.	Nom.	Nom.	Min.	Min.	Max.	
0	0.0600	0.096	0.060	0.054	0.062	0.050	0.025	0.019	0.007	0.500
1	0.0730	0.118	0.073	0.066	0.074	1/16	0.031	0.023	0.007	0.625
2	0.0860	0.140	0.086	0.077	0.098	5/64	0.038	0.028	0.008	0.625
3	0.0990	0.161	0.099	0.089	0.098	5/64	0.044	0.032	0.008	0.625
4	0.1120	0.183	0.112	0.101	0.115	3/32	0.051	0.036	0.009	0.750
5	0.1250	0.205	0.125	0.112	0.115	3/32	0.057	0.040	0.010	0.750
6	0.1380	0.226	0.138	0.124	0.137	7/64	0.064	0.044	0.010	0.750
8	0.1640	0.270	0.164	0.148	0.173	9/64	0.077	0.052	0.012	0.875
10	0.1900	5/16	0.190	0.171	0.188	5/32	0.090	0.061	0.014	0.875
1/4	0.2500	3/8	1/4	0.225	0.221	3/16	0.120	0.080	0.014	1.000
5/16	0.3125	15/32	5/16	0.281	0.298	1/4	0.151	0.100	0.017	1.125
3/8	0.3750	9/16	3/8	0.337	0.380	5/16	0.182	0.120	0.020	1.250
7/16	0.4375	21/32	7/16	0.394	0.463	3/8	0.213	0.140	0.023	1.375
1/2	0.5000	3/4	1/2	0.450	0.463	3/8	0.245	0.160	0.026	1.500
5/8	0.6250	15/16	5/8	0.562	0.604	1/2	0.307	0.200	0.032	1.750
3/4	0.7500	1 1/8	3/4	0.675	0.631	5/8	0.370	0.240	0.039	2.000
7/8	0.8750	1 5/16	7/8	0.787	0.709	3/4	0.432	0.280	0.044	2.250
1	1.0000	1 1/2	1	0.900	0.801	3/4	0.495	0.320	0.050	2.500
1 1/8	1.1250	1 11/16	1 1/8	1.012	....	7/8	0.557	0.360	0.055	2.812
1 1/4	1.2500	1 7/8	1 1/4	1.125	....	7/8	0.620	0.400	0.060	3.125
1 3/8	1.3750	2 1/16	1 3/8	1.237	....	1	0.682	0.440	0.065	3.437
1 1/2	1.5000	2 1/4	1 1/2	1.350	....	1	0.745	0.480	0.070	3.750
1 3/4	1.7500	2 5/8	1 3/4	1.575	....	1 1/4	0.870	0.560	0.080	4.375
2	2.0000	3	2	1.800	....	1 1/2	0.995	0.640	0.090	5.000
2 1/4	2.2500	3 3/8	2 1/4	2.025	....	1 3/4	1.120	0.720	0.100	5.625
2 1/2	2.5000	3 3/4	2 1/2	2.250	....	1 3/4	1.245	0.800	0.110	6.250
2 3/4	2.7500	4 1/8	2 3/4	2.475	....	2	1.370	0.880	0.120	6.875
3	3.0000	4 1/2	3	2.700	....	2 1/4	1.495	0.960	0.130	7.500
3 1/4	3.2500	4 7/8	3 1/4	2.925	....	2 1/4	1.620	1.040	0.140	8.125
3 1/2	3.5000	5 1/4	3 1/2	3.150	....	2 3/4	1.745	1.120	0.150	8.750
3 3/4	3.7500	5 5/8	3 3/4	3.375	....	2 3/4	1.870	1.200	0.160	9.375
4	4.0000	6	4	3.600	....	3	1.995	1.280	0.170	10.000

Nominal Screw Size	Nominal Screw Length	Standard Length Increment
0 to 1 inch inclusive	1/8 thru 1/4	1/16
	1/4 thru 1	1/8
	1 thru 3 1/2	1/4
	3 1/2 thru 7	1/2
	7 thru 10	1
Over 1 inch	1 thru 7	1/2
	7 thru 10	1
	over 10	2

TD-12-16

Hexagon- and Spline-Socket Flat Head Cap Screws (USAS B18.3-1961)

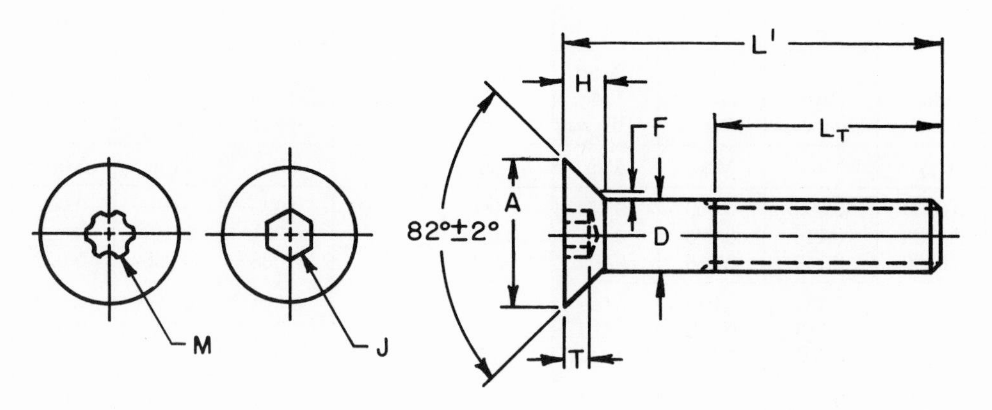

[1]Standard Lengths

Nominal Size	D	A	H	M	J	T	F	L_T
	Body Diameter	Head Diameter	Head Height	Spline Socket Size	Hexagon Socket Size	Key Engagement	Fillet	Basic Thread Length
	Max.	Max.	Reference	Nom.	Nom.	Min.	Max.	
0	0.0600	0.138	0.044	0.050	0.035	0.025	0.006	0.500
1	0.0730	0.168	0.054	0.062	0.050	0.031	0.007	0.625
2	0.0860	0.197	0.064	0.062	0.050	0.038	0.009	0.625
3	0.0990	0.226	0.073	0.074	1/16	0.044	0.010	0.625
4	0.1120	0.255	0.083	0.074	1/16	0.055	0.011	0.750
5	0.1250	0.281	0.090	0.098	5/64	0.061	0.012	0.750
6	0.1380	0.307	0.097	0.098	5/64	0.066	0.014	0.750
8	0.1640	0.359	0.112	0.115	3/32	0.076	0.016	0.875
10	0.1900	0.411	0.127	0.149	1/8	0.087	0.019	0.875
1/4	0.2500	0.531	0.161	0.188	5/32	0.111	0.025	1.000
5/16	0.3125	0.656	0.198	0.221	3/16	0.135	0.031	1.125
3/8	0.3750	0.781	0.234	0.256	7/32	0.159	0.037	1.250
7/16	0.4375	0.844	0.234	0.298	1/4	0.159	0.044	1.375
1/2	0.5000	0.937	0.251	0.380	5/16	0.172	0.050	1.500
5/8	0.6250	1.188	0.324	0.463	3/8	0.220	0.050	1.750
3/4	0.7500	1.438	0.396	0.463	3/8	0.270	0.050	2.000

Nominal Screw Length	Standard Length Increment
1/8 thru 1/4	1/16
1/4 thru 1	1/8
1 thru 3 1/2	1/4
3 1/2 thru 6	1/2

TECHNICAL DATA

TD-12-17

Hexagon- and Spline-Socket Button Head Cap Screws (USAS B18.3-1961)

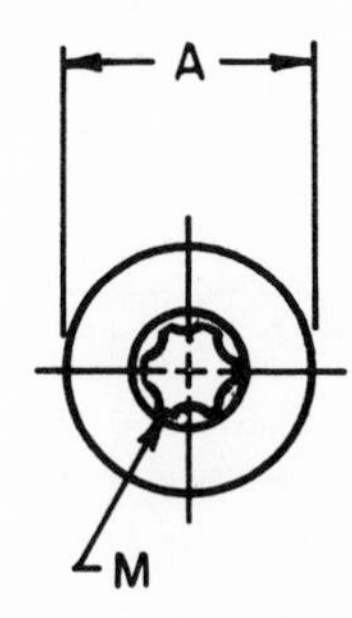

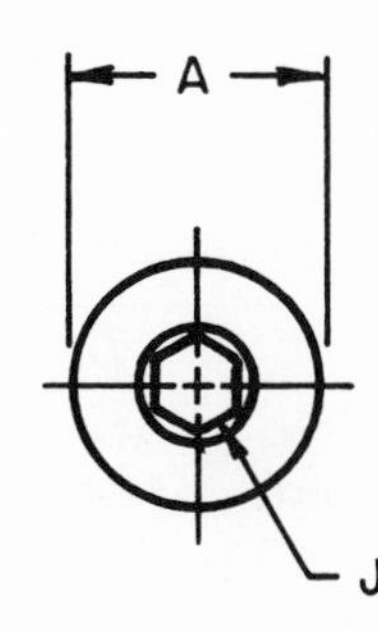

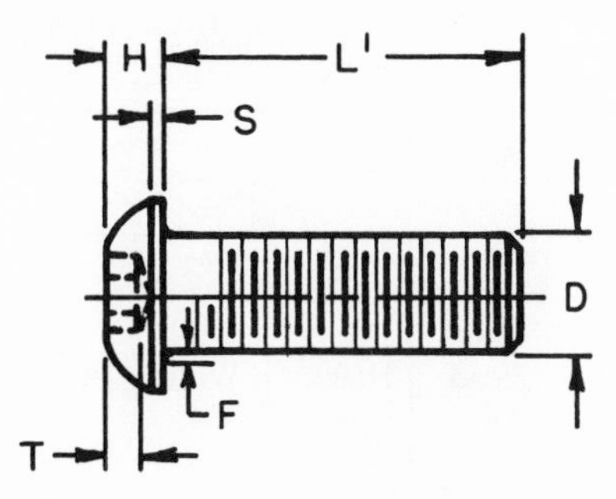

[1]Standard Lengths

Nominal Size	D	A	H	S	M	J	T	F	L
	Screw Diameter	Head Diameter	Head Height	Head Side Height	Spline Socket Size	Hexagon Socket Size	Key Engagement	Fillet	Standard Length
	Basic	Max.	Max.	Ref.	Nom.	Nom.	Min.	Max.	Max.
0	0.0600	0.114	0.032	0.010	0.050	0.035	0.020	0.010	1/2
1	0.0730	0.139	0.039	0.010	0.062	0.050	0.028	0.010	1/2
2	0.0860	0.164	0.046	0.010	0.062	0.050	0.028	0.010	1/2
3	0.0990	0.188	0.052	0.010	0.074	1/16	0.035	0.010	1/2
4	0.1120	0.213	0.059	0.015	0.074	1/16	0.035	0.010	1/2
5	0.1250	0.238	0.066	0.015	0.098	5/64	0.044	0.010	1/2
6	0.1380	0.262	0.073	0.015	0.098	5/64	0.044	0.010	5/8
8	0.1640	0.312	0.087	0.015	0.115	3/32	0.052	0.015	3/4
10	0.1900	0.361	0.101	0.020	0.149	1/8	0.070	0.015	1
1/4	0.2500	0.437	0.132	0.031	0.188	5/32	0.087	0.020	1
5/16	0.3125	0.547	0.166	0.031	0.221	3/16	0.105	0.020	1
3/8	0.3750	0.656	0.199	0.031	0.256	7/32	0.122	0.020	1 1/4
1/2	0.5000	0.875	0.265	0.046	0.380	5/16	0.175	0.030	2
5/8	0.6250	1.000	0.331	0.062	0.463	3/8	0.210	0.030	2

Nominal Screw Length	Standard Length Increment
1/8 thru 1/4	1/16
1/4 thru 1	1/8
1 thru 2	1/4

TD-12-18

Flat Head Cap Screws (USAS B18.6.2-1956)

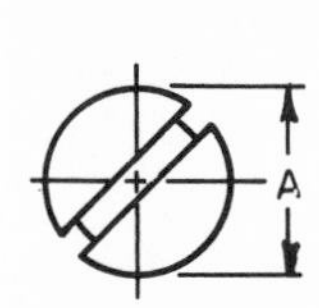

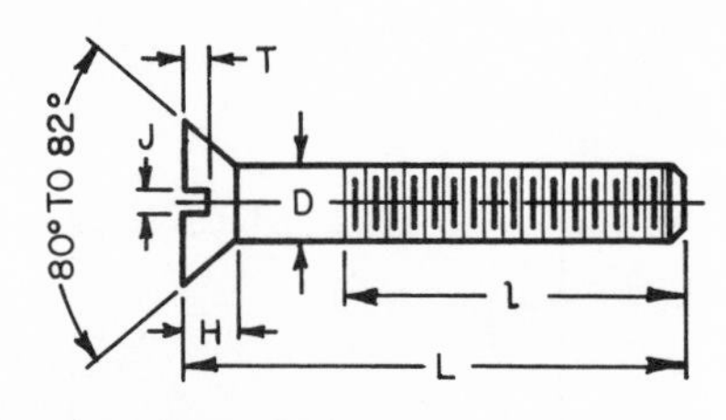

	D	A	H	J	T
Nominal Size	Max. Body Dia.	Max. Head Dia.	Max. Height of Head	Max. Width of Slot	Max. Depth of Slot
¼	0.250	0.500	0.140	0.075	0.068
5/16	0.3125	0.625	0.177	0.084	0.086
⅜	0.375	0.750	0.210	0.094	0.103
7/16	0.4375	0.8125	0.210	0.094	0.103
½	0.500	0.875	0.210	0.106	0.103
9/16	0.5625	1.000	0.244	0.118	0.120
⅝	0.625	1.125	0.281	0.133	0.137
¾	0.750	1.375	0.352	0.149	0.171
⅞	0.875	1.625	0.423	0.167	0.206
1	1.000	1.875	0.494	0.188	0.240
1⅛	1.125	2.062	0.529	0.196	0.257
1¼	1.250	2.312	0.600	0.211	0.291
1⅜	1.375	2.562	0.665	0.226	0.326
1½	1.500	2.812	0.742	0.258	0.360

TD-12-19

Round Head Cap Screws (USAS B18.6.2-1956)

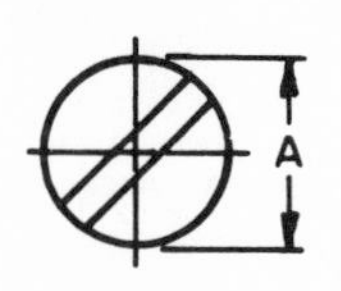

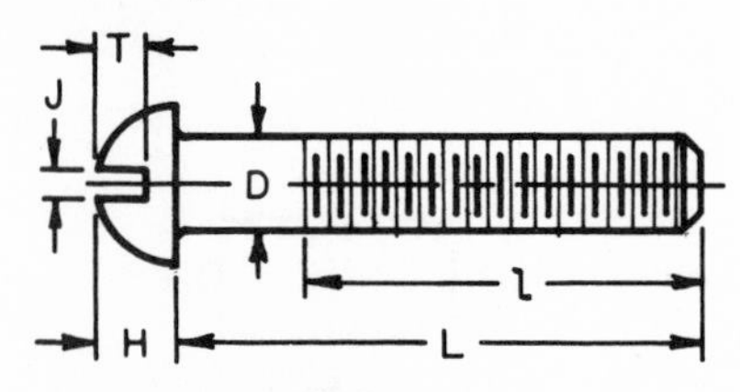

	D	A	H	J	T
Nominal Size	Max. Body Dia.	Max. Head Dia.	Max. Height of Head	Max. Width of Slot	Max. Depth of Slot
¼	0.250	0.437	0.191	0.075	0.117
5/16	0.3125	0.562	0.245	0.084	0.151
⅜	0.375	0.625	0.273	0.094	0.168
7/16	0.4375	0.750	0.328	0.094	0.202
½	0.500	0.812	0.354	0.106	0.218
9/16	0.5625	0.937	0.409	0.118	0.252
⅝	0.625	1.000	0.437	0.133	0.270
¾	0.750	1.250	0.546	0.149	0.338

TECHNICAL DATA

Fillister Head Cap Screws (USAS B18.6.2-1956)

	D	A	H	O	J	T
Nominal Size	Max. Body Dia.	Max. Head Dia.	Max. Height of Head	Max, Total Height of Head	Max. Width of Slot	Max. Depth of Slot
¼	0.250	0.375	0.172	0.216	0.075	0.097
5/16	0.3125	0.437	0.203	0.253	0.084	0.115
⅜	0.375	0.562	0.250	0.314	0.094	0.142
7/16	0.4375	0.625	0.297	0.368	0.094	0.168
½	0.500	0.750	0.328	0.413	0.106	0.193
9/16	0.5625	0.812	0.375	0.467	0.118	0.213
⅝	0.625	0.875	0.422	0.521	0.133	0.239
¾	0.750	1.000	0.500	0.612	0.149	0.283
⅞	0.875	1.125	0.594	0.720	0.167	0.334
1	1.000	1.312	0.656	0.803	0.188	0.371

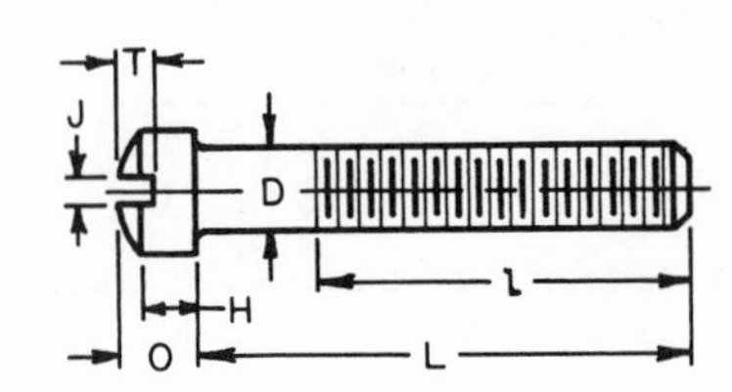

TD-12-21

Slotted Machine Screws — Flat, Oval, Round Fillister, and Truss Head Styles (USAS B18.6.3-1962)

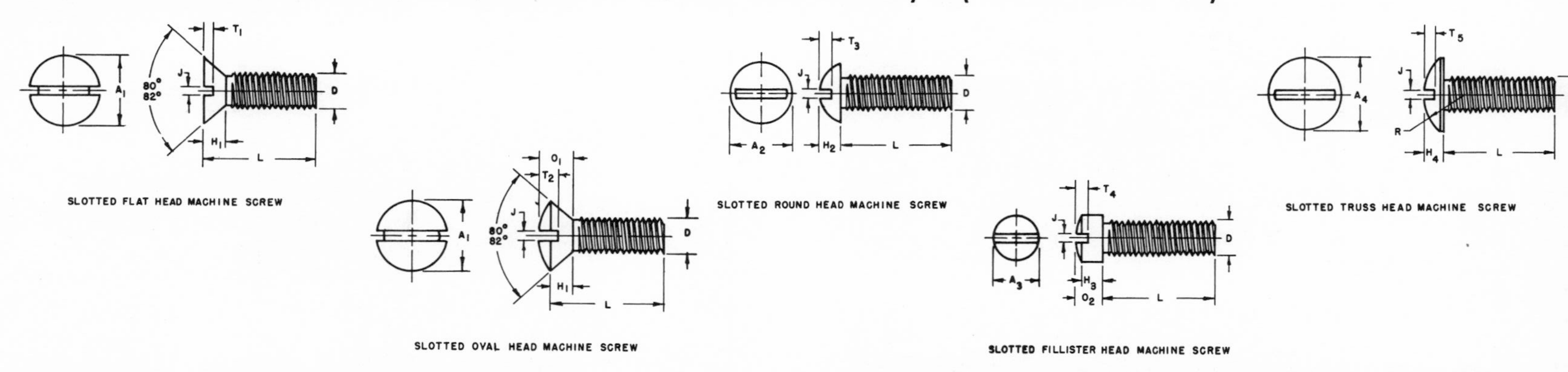

Nominal Size	Basic Dia. of Screw	Max. Head Diameter				Max. Head Height				Max. Total Head Height		Max. Width of Slot	Max. Depth of Slot					Max. Radius
	D	A_1	A_2	A_3	A_4	H_1	H_2	H_3	H_4	O_1	O_2	J	T_1	T_2	T_3	T_4	T_5	R
0	0.0600	0.119	0.113	0.096	0.131	0.035	0.053	0.045	0.037	0.056	0.059	0.023	0.015	0.030	0.039	0.025	0.022	0.087
1	0.0730	0.146	0.138	0.118	0.164	0.043	0.061	0.053	0.045	0.068	0.071	0.026	0.019	0.038	0.044	0.031	0.027	0.107
2	0.0860	0.172	0.162	0.140	0.194	0.051	0.069	0.062	0.053	0.080	0.083	0.031	0.023	0.045	0.048	0.037	0.031	0.129
3	0.0990	0.199	0.187	0.161	0.226	0.059	0.078	0.070	0.061	0.092	0.095	0.035	0.027	0.052	0.053	0.043	0.036	0.151
4	0.1120	0.225	0.211	0.183	0.257	0.067	0.086	0.079	0.069	0.104	0.107	0.039	0.030	0.059	0.058	0.048	0.040	0.169
5	0.1250	0.252	0.236	0.205	0.289	0.075	0.095	0.088	0.078	0.116	0.120	0.043	0.034	0.067	0.063	0.054	0.045	0.191
6	0.1380	0.279	0.260	0.226	0.321	0.083	0.103	0.096	0.086	0.128	0.132	0.048	0.038	0.074	0.068	0.060	0.050	0.211
8	0.1640	0.332	0.309	0.270	0.384	0.100	0.120	0.113	0.102	0.152	0.156	0.054	0.045	0.088	0.077	0.071	0.058	0.254
10	0.1900	0.385	0.359	0.313	0.448	0.116	0.137	0.130	0.118	0.176	0.180	0.060	0.053	0.103	0.087	0.083	0.068	0.283
12	0.2160	0.438	0.408	0.357	0.511	0.132	0.153	0.148	0.134	0.200	0.205	0.067	0.060	0.117	0.096	0.094	0.077	0.336
1/4	0.2500	0.507	0.472	0.414	0.573	0.153	0.175	0.170	0.150	0.232	0.237	0.075	0.070	0.136	0.109	0.109	0.087	0.375
5/16	0.3125	0.635	0.590	0.518	0.698	0.191	0.216	0.211	0.183	0.290	0.295	0.084	0.088	0.171	0.132	0.137	0.106	0.457
3/8	0.3750	0.762	0.708	0.622	0.823	0.230	0.256	0.253	0.215	0.347	0.355	0.094	0.106	0.206	0.155	0.164	0.124	0.538
7/16	0.4375	0.812	0.750	0.625	0.948	0.223	0.328	0.265	0.248	0.345	0.368	0.094	0.103	0.210	0.196	0.170	0.142	0.619
1/2	0.5000	0.875	0.813	0.750	1.073	0.223	0.355	0.297	0.280	0.354	0.412	0.106	0.103	0.216	0.211	0.190	0.161	0.701
9/16	0.5625	1.000	0.938	0.812	1.198	0.260	0.410	0.336	0.312	0.410	0.466	0.118	0.120	0.250	0.242	0.214	0.179	0.783
5/8	0.6250	1.125	1.000	0.875	1.323	0.298	0.438	0.375	0.345	0.467	0.521	0.133	0.137	0.285	0.258	0.240	0.196	0.863
3/4	0.7500	1.375	1.250	1.000	1.573	0.372	0.547	0.441	0.410	0.578	0.612	0.149	0.171	0.353	0.320	0.281	0.234	1.024

TD-12-22

Slotted Machine Screws — Pan and Binding Head Styles (USAS B18.6.3-1962)

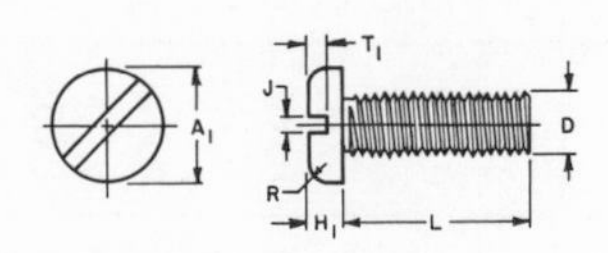
SLOTTED PAN HEAD MACHINE SCREW

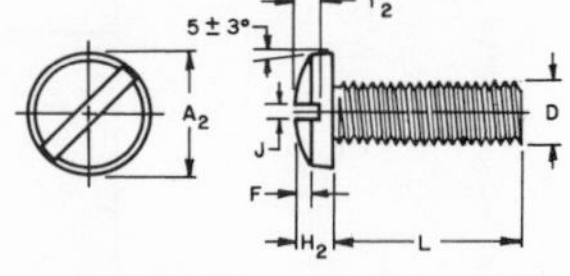
SLOTTED BINDING HEAD MACHINE SCREW

Nominal Size	Basic Diameter of Screw	Max. Head Diameter		Max. Head Height		Max. Height of Oval	Max. Width of Slot	Max. Depth of Slot		Max. Head Radius
	D	A_1	A_2	H_1	H_2	F	J	T_1	T_2	R
0	0.0600	0.116		0.039			0.023	0.022		0.020
1	0.0730	0.142		0.046			0.026	0.027		0.025
2	0.0860	0.167	0.181	0.053	0.050	0.018	0.031	0.031	0.030	0.035
3	0.0990	0.193	0.208	0.060	0.059	0.022	0.035	0.036	0.036	0.037
4	0.1120	0.219	0.235	0.068	0.068	0.025	0.039	0.040	0.042	0.042
5	0.1250	0.245	0.263	0.075	0.078	0.029	0.043	0.045	0.048	0.044
6	0.1380	0.270	0.290	0.082	0.087	0.032	0.048	0.050	0.053	0.046
8	0.1640	0.322	0.344	0.096	0.105	0.039	0.054	0.058	0.065	0.052
10	0.1900	0.373	0.399	0.110	0.123	0.045	0.060	0.068	0.077	0.061
12	0.2160	0.425	0.454	0.125	0.141	0.052	0.067	0.077	0.089	0.078
¼	0.2500	0.492	0.513	0.144	0.165	0.061	0.075	0.087	0.105	0.087
5/16	0.3125	0.615	0.641	0.178	0.209	0.077	0.084	0.106	0.134	0.099
⅜	0.3750	0.740	0.769	0.212	0.253	0.094	0.094	0.124	0.163	0.143

TD-12-23

Machine Screws — Plain and Slotted Hex and Hex-Washer Head Styles (USAS B18.6.3-1962)

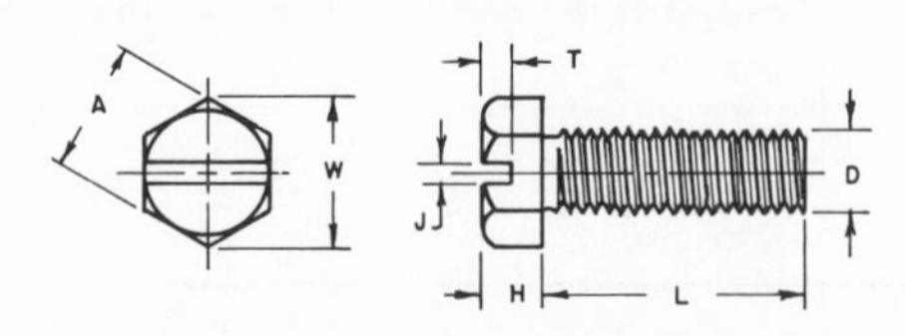
PLAIN AND SLOTTED HEX HEAD MACHINE SCREW

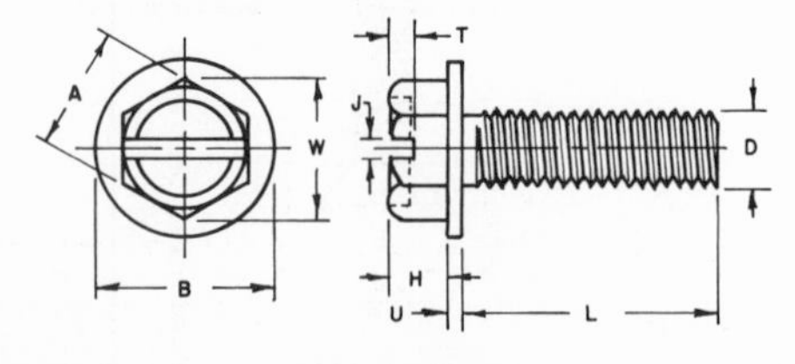
PLAIN AND SLOTTED HEX WASHER HEAD MACHINE SCREW

Nominal Size	Basic Diameter of Screw	Max. Width Across Flats	Min, Width Across Corners	Max. Head Height	Max. Width of Slot	Max. Depth of Slot	Max. Washer Diameter	Max. Washer Thickness
	D	A	W	H	J	T	B	U
2	0.0860	0.125	0.134	0.050	....	....	0.166	0.016
3	0.0990	0.125	0.134	0.055	....	....	0.177	0.016
4	0.1120	0.187	0.202	0.060	0.039	0.042	0.243	0.019
5	0.1250	0.187	0.202	0.070	0.043	0.049	0.260	0.025
6	0.1380	0.250	0.272	0.093	0.048	0.053	0.328	0.025
8	0.1640	0.250	0.272	0.110	0.054	0.074	0.348	0.031
10	0.1900	0.312	0.340	0.120	0.060	0.080	0.414	0.031
12	0.2160	0.312	0.340	0.155	0.067	0.103	0.432	0.039
¼	0.2500	0.375	0.409	0.190	0.075	0.111	0.520	0.050
5/16	0.3125	0.500	0.545	0.230	0.084	0.134	0.676	0.055
⅜	0.3750	0.562	0.614	0.295	0.094	0.168	0.780	0.063

Unless otherwise specified, hex washer head machine screws are not slotted.

TD-12-24

Cross Recess Machine Screws — Type I and Type II* Available in Seven Head Styles

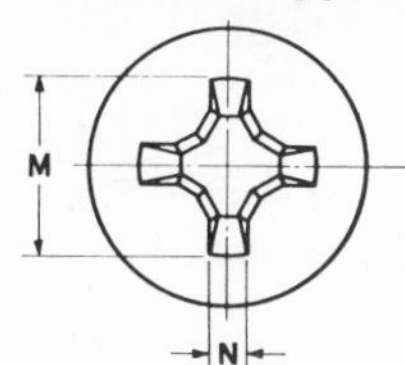

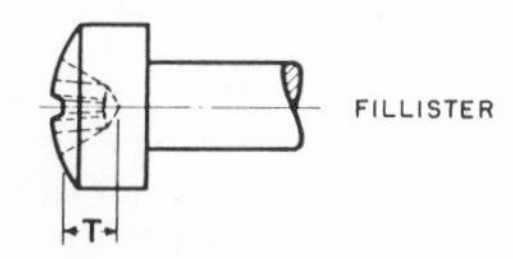

This type of recess has a large center opening, tapered wings, and blunt bottom, with all edges relieved or rounded.

TYPE I

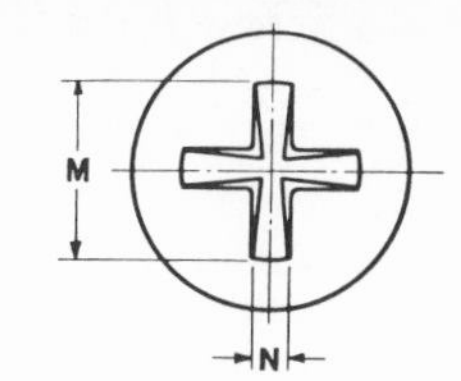

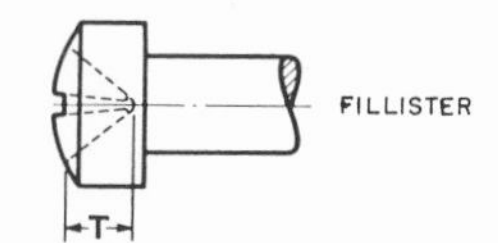

This type of recess consists of two intersecting slots with parallel sides converging to a slightly truncated apex at bottom of recess.

TYPE II

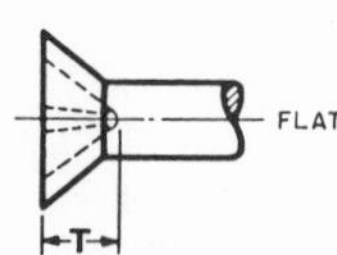

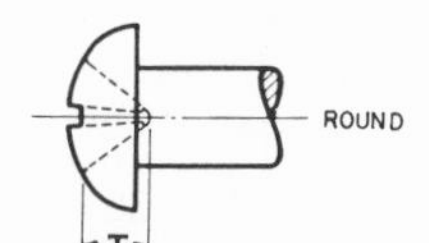

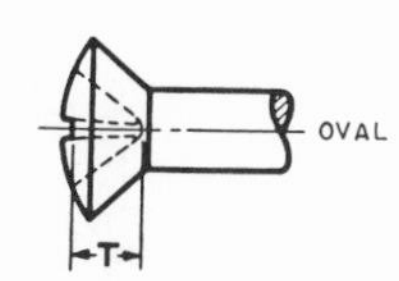

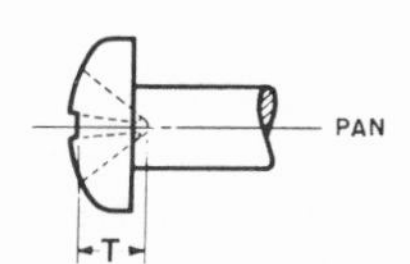

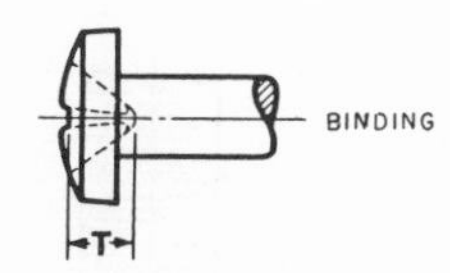

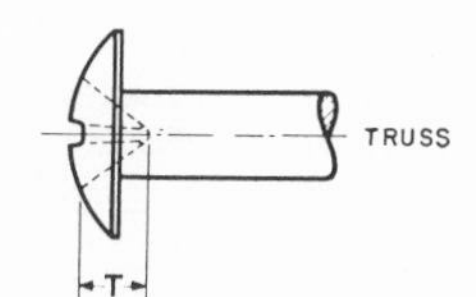

HEAD STYLES

Type I					Type II			
Nominal Size	Max. Diameter of Recess	Max. Depth of Recess	Min. Width of Recess	Size of Driver	Nominal Size	Max. Diameter of Recess	Max. Depth of Recess	Min. Width of Recess
	M	T	N			M	T	N
0	.07	.04	.01	0	0	.07	.04	.02
1	.07	.04	.01	0	1	.09	.05	.02
2	.10	.06	.02	1	2	.10	.06	.02
3	.11	.07	.02	1	3	.12	.07	.03
4	.12	.08	.02	1	4	.14	.08	.03
5	.15	.07	.03	2	5	.15	.09	.03
6	.17	.09	.03	2	6	.17	.10	.03
8	.18	.11	.03	2	8	.20	.12	.04
10	.20	.12	.03	2	10	.24	.13	.04
12	.26	.14	.03	3	12	.27	.16	.05
¼	.28	.16	.04	3	¼	.31	.18	.05
5/16	.32	.20	.04	4	5/16	.39	.23	.07
⅜	.39	.23	.06	4	⅜	.47	.28	.08
7/16	.41	.26	.07	4	7/16	.47	.28	.08
½	.44	.28	.07	4	½	.56	.34	.09
9/16	.46	.30	.08	4	9/16	.61	.37	.10
⅝	.57	.34	.08	5	⅝	.61	.37	.10
¾	.62	.39	.08	5	¾	.61	.37	.10

*For more detailed information and for three place decimal figures see USAS B18.6.3-1962.

TECHNICAL DATA

TD-12-25

Square and Hexagon Machine Screw Nuts (USAS B18.6.3-1962)

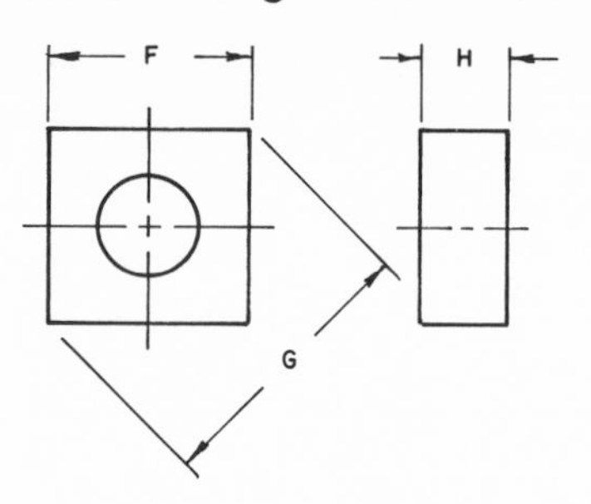

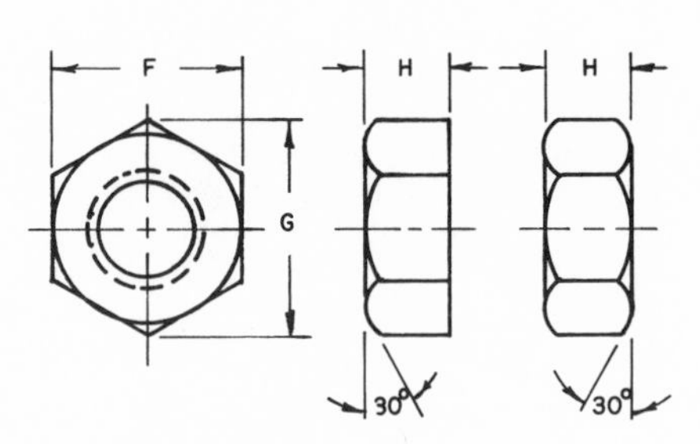

Nominal Size	Major Diameter of Thread	F Width Across Flats	G Max. Width Across Corners		H Nominal Thickness
	Basic	Basic	Square	Hex	
0	0.0600	5/32	0.221	0.180	3/64
1	0.0730	5/32	0.221	0.180	3/64
2	0.0860	3/16	0.265	0.217	1/16
3	0.0990	3/16	0.265	0.217	1/16
4	0.1120	1/4	0.354	0.289	3/32
5	0.1250	5/16	0.442	0.361	7/64
6	0.1380	5/16	0.442	0.361	7/64
8	0.1640	11/32	0.486	0.397	1/8
10	0.1900	3/8	0.530	0.433	1/8
12	0.2160	7/16	0.619	0.505	5/32
1/4	0.2500	7/16	0.619	0.505	3/16
5/16	0.3125	9/16	0.795	0.650	7/32
3/8	0.3750	5/8	0.884	0.722	1/4

TD-12-26

Slotted Headless Set Screws (USAS B18.6.2-1956)

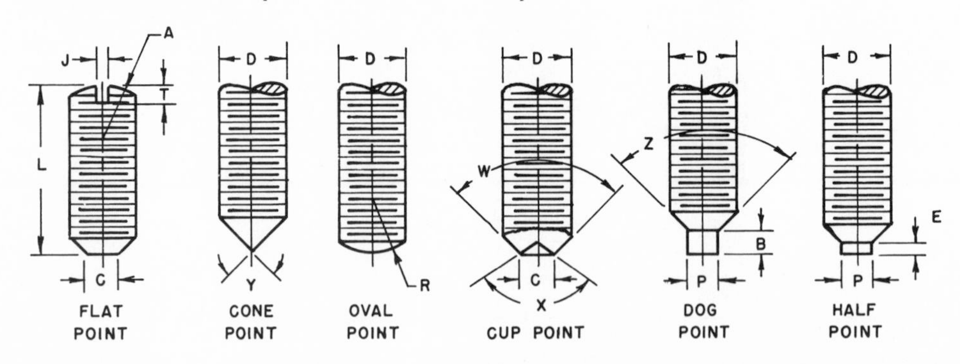

D Nominal Size		A Radius of Headless Crown	J Width of Slot	T Depth of Slot	R Oval Point Radius	C Max. Dia. of Cup and Flat Points	P Max. Dia. of Dog Point	B Length of Dog Point Full	E Length of Dog Point Half
5	0.125	0.125	0.023	0.031	0.094	0.067	0.083	0.060	0.030
6	0.138	0.138	0.025	0.035	0.109	0.074	0.092	0.070	0.035
8	0.164	0.164	0.029	0.041	0.125	0.087	0.109	0.080	0.040
10	0.190	0.190	0.032	0.048	0.141	0.102	0.127	0.090	0.045
12	0.216	0.216	0.036	0.054	0.156	0.115	0.144	0.110	0.055
1/4	0.250	0.250	0.045	0.063	0.188	0.132	0.156	0.125	0.063
5/16	0.3125	0.313	0.051	0.078	0.234	0.172	0.203	0.156	0.078
3/8	0.375	0.375	0.064	0.094	0.281	0.212	0.250	0.188	0.094
7/16	0.4375	0.438	0.072	0.109	0.328	0.252	0.297	0.219	0.109
1/2	0.500	0.500	0.081	0.125	0.375	0.291	0.344	0.250	0.125
9/16	0.5625	0.563	0.091	0.141	0.422	0.332	0.391	0.281	0.140
5/8	0.625	0.625	0.102	0.156	0.469	0.371	0.469	0.313	0.156
3/4	0.750	0.750	0.129	0.188	0.563	0.450	0.563	0.375	0.188

TD-12-27

Square Head Set Screws and Points (USAS B18.32-1956)

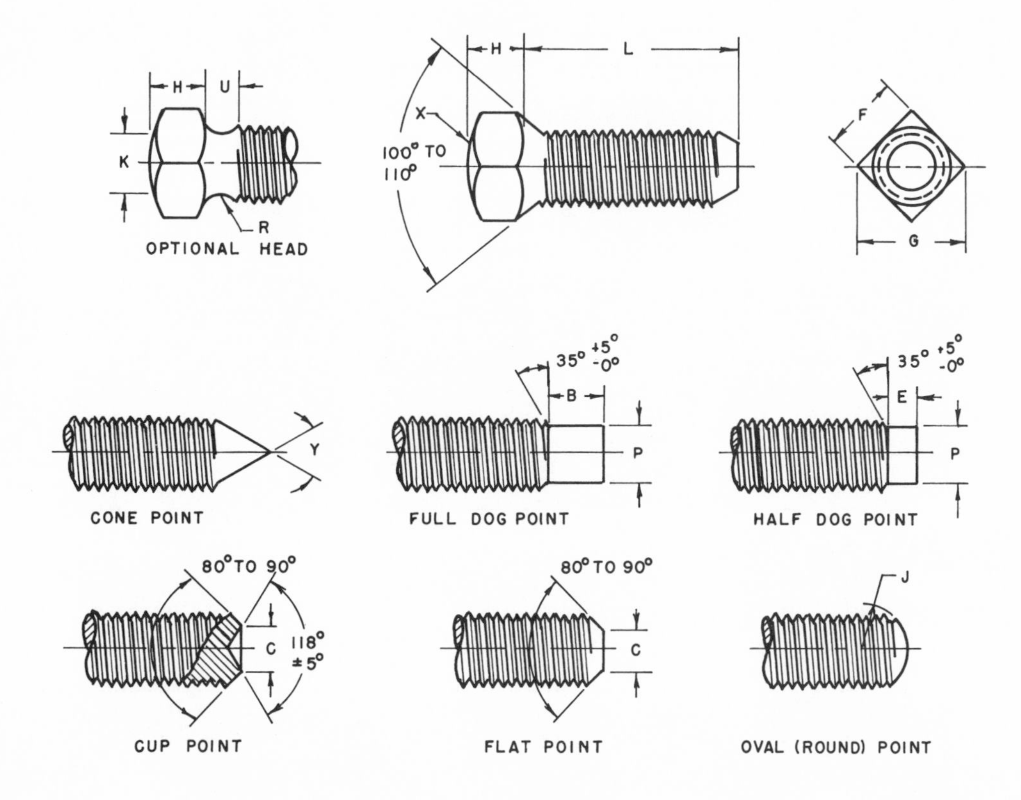

Nominal Size		F Width Across Flats (Max.)	G Width Across Corners	H Height of Head (Nominal)	K Dia. of Neck Relief (Max.)	X Radius of Head	R Radius of Neck Relief	U Width of Neck Relief	C Dia. of Cup and Flat Points	J Oval (Rd) Point Radius	Full Dog, Half Dog, and Pivot Point: P Dia. (Max.)	B Full Dog and Pvt.	E Half Dog
#10	0.190	0.1875	0.247	9/64	0.145	15/32	0.027	0.083	3/32	0.141	0.127	0.090	0.045
#12	0.216	0.216	0.292	5/32	0.162	35/64	0.029	0.091	7/64	0.156	0.144	0.110	0.055
1/4	0.250	0.250	0.331	3/16	0.185	5/8	0.032	0.100	1/8	0.188	0.156	0.125	0.063
5/16	0.3125	0.3125	0.415	15/64	0.240	25/32	0.036	0.111	11/64	0.234	0.203	0.156	0.078
3/8	0.3750	0.375	0.497	9/32	0.294	15/16	0.041	0.125	13/64	0.281	0.250	0.188	0.094
7/16	0.4375	0.4375	0.581	21/64	0.345	1 3/32	0.046	0.143	16/64	0.328	0.297	0.219	0.109
1/2	0.500	0.500	0.665	3/8	0.400	1 1/4	0.050	0.154	9/32	0.375	0.344	0.250	0.125
9/16	0.5625	0.5625	0.748	27/64	0.454	1 13/32	0.054	0.167	5/16	0.422	0.391	0.281	0.140
5/8	0.6250	0.625	0.833	15/32	0.507	1 9/16	0.059	0.182	23/64	0.469	0.469	0.313	0.156
3/4	0.750	0.750	1.001	9/16	0.620	1 7/8	0.065	0.200	7/16	0.563	0.563	0.375	0.188
7/8	0.875	0.875	1.170	21/32	0.731	2 3/16	0.072	0.222	33/64	0.656	0.656	0.438	0.219
1	1.000	1.000	1.337	3/4	0.838	2 1/2	0.081	0.250	19/32	0.750	0.750	0.500	0.250
1 1/8	1.125	1.125	1.505	27/32	0.939	2 13/16	0.092	0.283	43/64	0.844	0.844	0.562	0.281
1 1/4	1.250	1.250	1.674	15/16	1.064	3 1/8	0.092	0.283	3/4	0.938	0.938	0.625	0.312
1 3/8	1.375	1.375	1.843	1 1/32	1.159	3 7/16	0.109	0.333	53/64	1.031	1.031	0.688	0.344
1 1/2	1.500	1.500	2.010	1 1/8	1.284	3 3/4	0.109	0.333	29/32	1.125	1.125	0.750	0.375

TD-12-28

Socket Cap, Shoulder and Set Screws (USAS B18.3-1961)

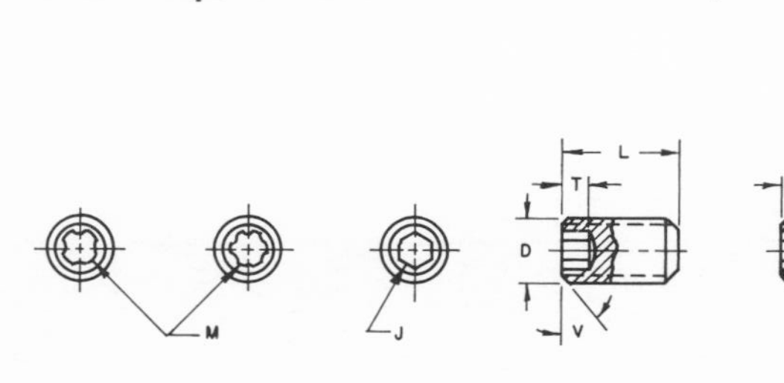

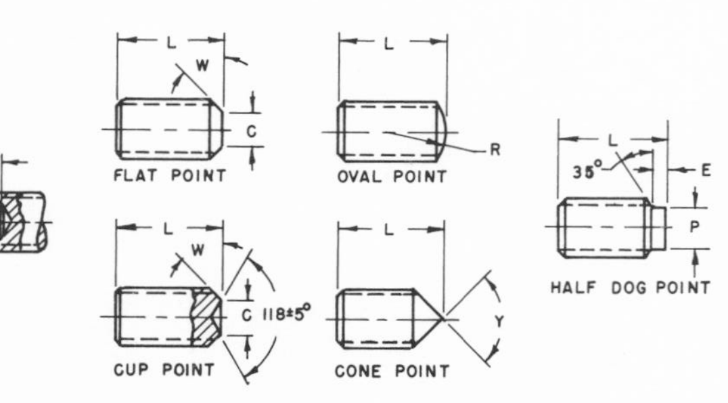

Standard Lengths for Set Screws

Nominal Screw Length	Standard Length Increment
1/16 thru 3/16*	1/32
1/8 thru 1/2	1/16
1/2 thru 1	1/8
1 thru 2	1/4
2 thru 6	1/2
6 and longer	1

*Applicable only to sizes 0 to 3 inclusive

	D	J	M	T	C	R	Y	P	E	B			
								Half Dog Point		Shortest Nominal Length To Which Column T Applies			
Nominal Size	Basic Screw Diameter	Hexagon Socket Size	Spline Socket Size	Key Engage-ment	Cup and Flat Point Diameters (Max.)	Oval Point Radius	Cone Point Angle 90° ±2° For These Lengths and Over; 118° ±2° For Shorter Lengths	Diameter (Max.)	Length (Max.)	Cup, Flat & Oval Point	118° Cone Point	90° Cone Point	Half Dog Point
0	0.0600	0.028	0.035	0.022	0.033	3/64	5/64	0.040	0.017	1/16	1/16	5/64	5/64
1	0.0730	0.035	0.035	0.028	0.040	0.055	3/32	0.049	0.021	5/64	5/64	3/32	3/32
2	0.0860	0.035	0.050	0.028	0.047	1/16	7/64	0.057	0.024	3/32	3/32	7/64	7/64
3	0.0990	0.050	0.050	0.040	0.054	5/64	1/8	0.066	0.027	3/32	7/64	1/8	1/8
4	0.1120	0.050	0.062	0.040	0.061	0.084	5/32	0.075	0.030	7/64	1/8	9/64	1/8
5	0.1250	1/16	0.074	0.050	0.067	3/32	3/16	0.083	0.033	1/8	9/64	5/32	9/64
6	0.1380	1/16	0.074	0.050	0.074	7/64	3/16	0.092	0.038	9/64	5/32	11/64	5/32
8	0.1640	5/64	0.098	0.062	0.087	1/8	1/4	0.109	0.043	5/32	11/64	13/64	3/16
10	0.1900	3/32	0.115	0.075	0.102	9/64	1/4	0.127	0.049	3/16	13/64	1/4	7/32
1/4	0.2500	1/8	0.149	0.100	0.132	3/16	5/16	5/32	0.067	1/4	17/64	5/16	19/64
5/16	0.3125	5/32	0.188	0.125	0.172	15/64	3/8	13/64	0.082	5/16	21/64	25/64	23/64
3/8	0.3750	3/16	0.221	0.150	0.212	9/32	7/16	1/4	0.099	3/8	25/64	15/32	27/64
7/16	0.4375	7/32	0.256	0.175	0.252	21/64	1/2	19/64	0.114	7/16	29/64	35/64	31/64
1/2	0.5000	1/4	0.298	0.200	0.291	3/8	9/16	11/32	0.130	1/2	33/64	39/64	35/64
5/8	0.6250	5/16	0.380	0.250	0.371	15/32	3/4	15/32	0.164	5/8	41/64	41/64	43/64
3/4	0.7500	3/8	0.463	0.300	0.450	9/16	7/8	9/16	0.196	3/4	49/64	29/32	51/64
7/8	0.8750	1/2	0.604	0.400	0.530	21/32	1	21/32	0.227	7/8	55/64	1 1/16	59/64
1	1.0000	9/16	0.631	0.450	0.609	3/4	1 1/8	3/4	0.260	1	1 1/64	1 13/64	1 3/32
1 1/8	1.1250	9/16	0.709	0.450	0.689	27/32	1 1/4	27/32	0.291	1 1/8	1 9/64	1 23/64	1 3/16
1 1/4	1.2500	5/8	0.801	0.500	0.767	15/16	1 1/2	15/16	0.323	1 1/4	1 1/4	1 1/2	1 5/16
1 3/8	1.3750	5/8	0.869	0.500	0.848	1 1/32	1 5/8	1 1/32	0.354	1 3/8	1 3/8	1 21/32	1 7/16
1 1/2	1.5000	3/4	0.970	0.600	0.926	1 1/8	1 3/4	1 1/8	0.385	1 1/2	1 1/2	1 51/64	1 9/16
1 3/4	1.7500	1	1.275	0.800	1.086	1 5/16	2	1 5/16	0.448	1 3/4	1 45/64	2 3/32	1 13/16
2	2.0000	1	1.275	0.800	1.244	1 1/2	2 1/4	1 1/2	0.510	2	1 31/32	2 25/64	2 5/64

TD-12-29

Designation of Types of Tapping Screws and Metallic Drive Screws (USAS B18.6.4-1958)

Type	USAS	Manuf.	Federal
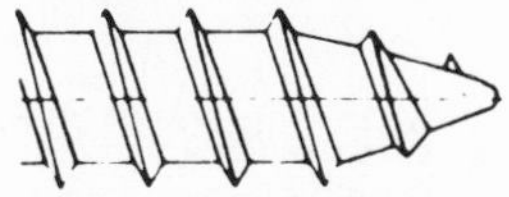	A	A	A
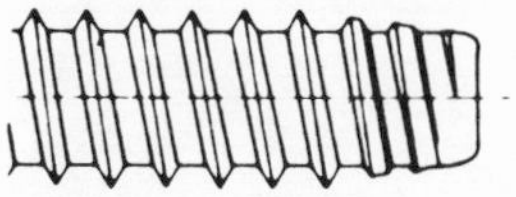	B	B or Z	B
	BP	BP or ZP	BP
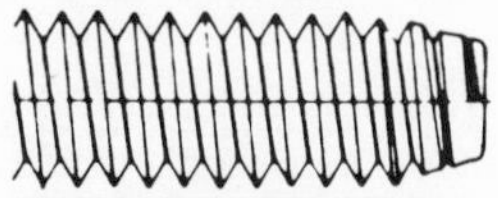	C	C	C
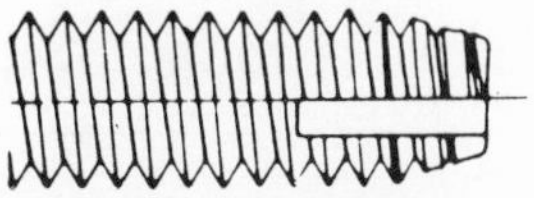	D	1	CS Alt. #1
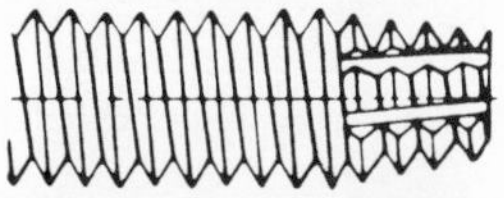	F	F	CF
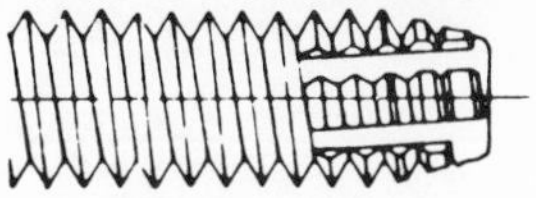	F	F	CF
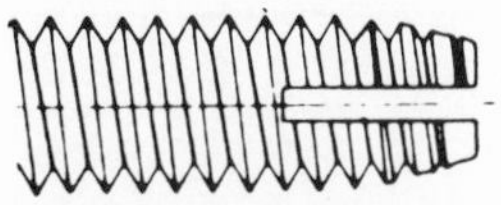	G	G	CS Alt. #2
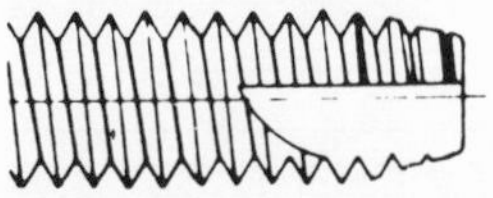	T	23	CG
	BF	FZ	BF
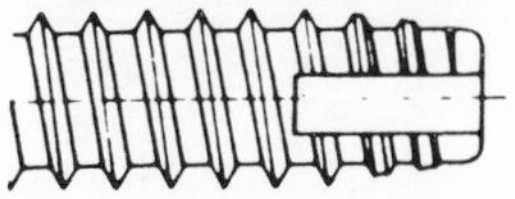	BG	H	BG
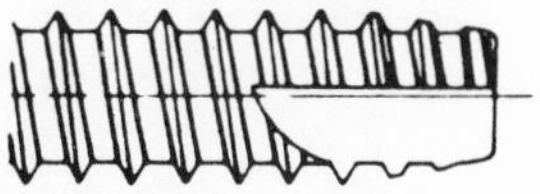	BT	25	BG

TD-12-30

Dimensions of Thread-Forming Tapping Screws — Types A, B and BP (USAS B18.6.4-1958)

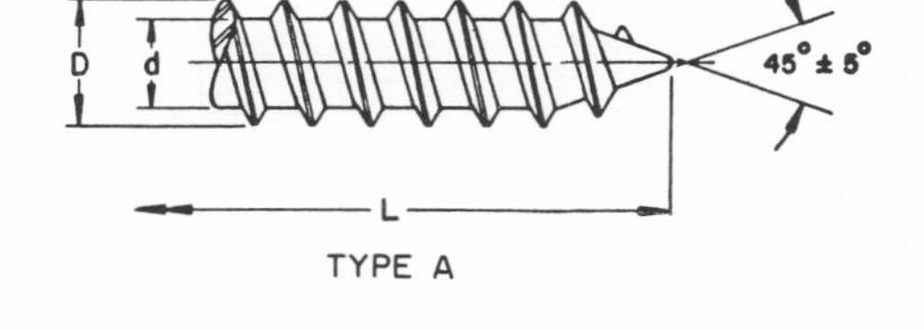

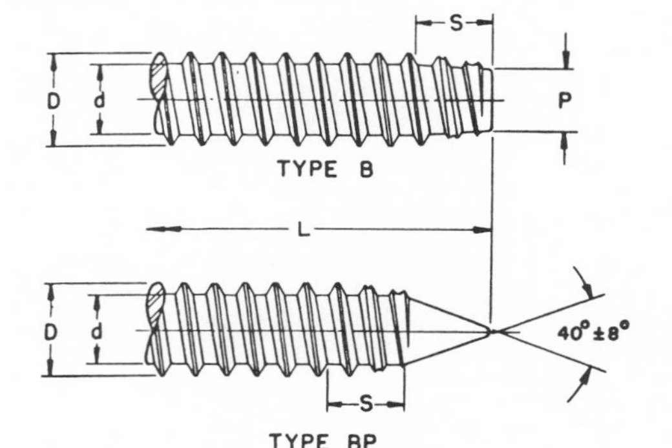

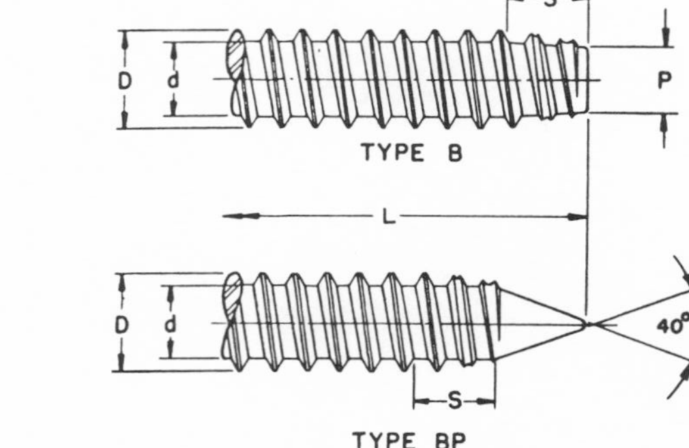

Type A

Standard Screws		D			d		L	
		Major Diameter			Minor Diameter		Special Lengths	
Screw Size	Threads per inch	Basic	Max.	Min.	Max.	Min.	90°	C'sk.
0	40	0.060	0.060	0.057	0.042	0.039	1/8	3/16
1	32	0.073	0.075	0.072	0.051	0.048	1/8	3/16
2	32	0.086	0.088	0.084	0.061	0.056	5/32	3/16
3	28	0.099	0.101	0.097	0.076	0.071	3/16	7/32
4	24	0.112	0.114	0.110	0.083	0.078	3/16	1/4
5	20	0.125	0.130	0.126	0.095	0.090	3/16	1/4
6	18	0.138	0.141	0.136	0.102	0.096	1/4	5/16
7	16	0.151	0.158	0.152	0.114	0.108	5/16	3/8
8	15	0.164	0.168	0.162	0.123	0.116	3/8	7/16
10	12	0.190	0.194	0.188	0.133	0.126	3/8	1/2
12	11	0.216	0.221	0.215	0.162	0.155	7/16	9/16
14	10	0.242	0.254	0.248	0.185	0.178	1/2	5/8
16	10	0.268	0.280	0.274	0.197	0.189	9/16	3/4
18	9	0.294	0.306	0.300	0.217	0.209	5/8	13/16
20	9	0.320	0.333	0.327	0.234	0.226	11/16	13/16
24	9	0.372	0.390	0.383	0.291	0.282	3/4	1

Type B and Type BP

Standard Screws		D			d		P		L	
		Major Diameter			Minor Diameter		Point Diameter			
Screw Size	Threads per inch	Basic	Max.	Min.	Max.	Min.	Max.	Min.	90°	C'sk.
0	48	0.060	0.060	0.057	0.036	0.033	0.031	0.027	5/64	1/8
1	42	0.073	0.075	0.072	0.049	0.046	0.044	0.040	5/64	5/32
2	32	0.086	0.088	0.084	0.064	0.060	0.058	0.054	7/64	3/16
3	28	0.099	0.101	0.097	0.075	0.071	0.068	0.063	9/64	7/32
4	24	0.112	0.114	0.110	0.086	0.082	0.079	0.074	3/16	1/4
5	20	0.125	0.130	0.126	0.094	0.090	0.087	0.082	3/16	1/4
6	20	0.138	0.139	0.135	0.104	0.099	0.095	0.089	1/4	5/16
7	19	0.151	0.154	0.149	0.115	0.109	0.105	0.099	5/16	3/8
8	18	0.164	0.166	0.161	0.122	0.116	0.112	0.106	5/16	7/16
10	16	0.190	0.189	0.183	0.141	0.135	0.130	0.123	3/8	1/2
12	14	0.216	0.215	0.209	0.164	0.157	0.152	0.145	7/16	9/16
1/4	14	0.250	0.246	0.240	0.192	0.185	0.179	0.171	1/2	5/8
5/16	12	0.3125	0.315	0.308	0.244	0.236	0.230	0.222	1/2	5/8
3/8	12	0.375	0.380	0.371	0.309	0.299	0.293	0.285	1/2	5/8
7/16	10	0.4375	0.440	0.431	0.359	0.349	0.343	0.335	5/8	3/4
1/2	10	0.500	0.504	0.495	0.423	0.413	0.407	0.399	5/8	3/4

TD-12-31

Dimensions of Thread-Forming Tapping Screws, Type C and Thread-Cutting Tapping Screws, Types D, F, G and T (USAS B18.6.4-1958)

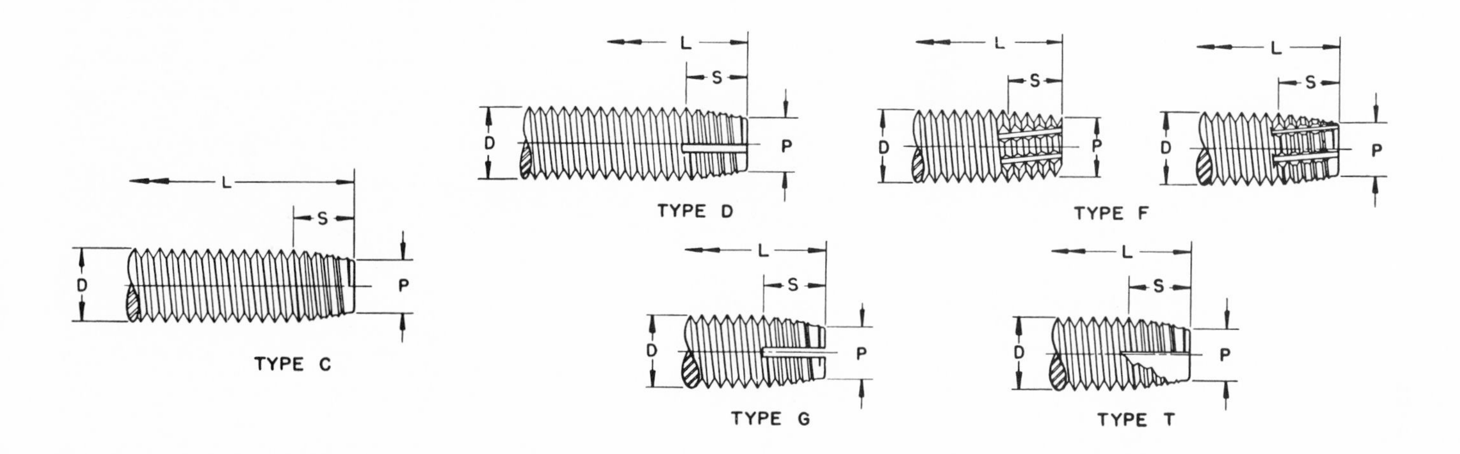

Thread Forming Type C						
		D			P	
		Major Diameter			Point Diameter	
Screw Size	Threads per inch	Basic	Max.	Min.	Max.	Min.
2	56	0.0860	0.0860	0.0820	0.067	0.061
2	64	0.0860	0.0860	0,0822	0,070	0.064
3	48	0.0990	0.0990	0.0946	0.077	0.070
3	56	0.0990	0.0990	0.0950	0.080	0.074
4	40	0.1120	0.1120	0.1072	0.086	0.077
4	48	0.1120	0.1120	0.1076	0.090	0.083
5	40	0.1250	0.1250	0.1202	0.099	0.090
5	44	0.1250	0.1250	0.1204	0.101	0.093
6	32	0.1380	0.1380	0.1326	0.106	0.095
6	40	0.1380	0.1380	9.1332	0.112	0.103
8	32	0.1640	0.1640	0.1586	0.132	0.121
8	36	0.1640	0.1640	0.1590	0.135	0.125
10	24	0.1900	0.1900	0.1834	0.147	0.133
10	32	0.1900	0.1900	0.1846	0.158	0.147
12	24	0.2160	0.2160	0.2094	0.173	0.159
12	28	0.2160	0.2160	0.2098	0.179	0.167
1/4	20	0.2500	0.2500	0.2428	0.198	0.181
1/4	28	0.2500	0.2500	0.2438	0.213	0.201
5/16	18	0.3125	0.3125	0.3043	0.255	0.236
5/16	24	0.3125	0.3125	0.3059	0.269	0.255
3/8	16	0.3750	0.3750	0.3660	0.310	0.289
3/8	24	0.3750	0.3750	0.3684	0.332	0.318

Thread Cutting Types D, F, G, and T						
		D			P	
		Major Diameter			Point Diameter	
Screw Size	Threads per inch	Basic	Max.	Min.	Max.	Min.
2	56	0.0860	0.0860	0.0820	0.067	0.061
2	64	0.0860	0.0860	0.0822	0.070	0.064
3	48	0.0990	0.0990	0.0946	0.077	0.070
3	56	0.0990	0.0990	0.0950	0.080	0.074
4	40	0.1120	0.1120	0.1072	0.086	0.077
4	48	0.1120	0.1120	0.1076	0.090	0.083
5	40	0.1250	0.1250	0.1202	0.099	0.090
5	44	0.1250	0.1250	0.1204	0.101	0.093
6	32	0.1380	0.1380	0.1326	0.106	0.095
6	40	0.1380	0.1380	0.1332	0.112	0.103
8	32	0.1640	0.1640	0.1586	0.132	0.121
8	36	0.1640	0.1640	0.1590	0.135	0.125
10	24	0.1900	0.1900	0.1834	0.147	0.133
10	32	0.1900	0.1900	0.1846	0.158	0.147
12	24	0.2160	0.2160	0.2094	0.173	0.159
12	28	0.2160	0.2160	0.2098	0.179	0.167
1/4	20	0.2500	0.2500	0.2428	0.198	0.181
1/4	28	0.2500	0.2500	0.2438	0.213	0.201
5/16	18	0.3125	0.3125	0.3043	0.255	0.236
5/16	24	0.3125	0.3125	0.3059	0.269	0.255
3/8	16	0.3750	0.3750	0.3660	0.310	0.289
3/8	24	0.3750	0.3750	0.3684	0.332	0.318

TD-12-32

Dimensions of Thread-Cutting Tapping Screws, Types BF, BG, BT, and Metallic Drive Screws, Type U (USAS B18.6.4-1958)

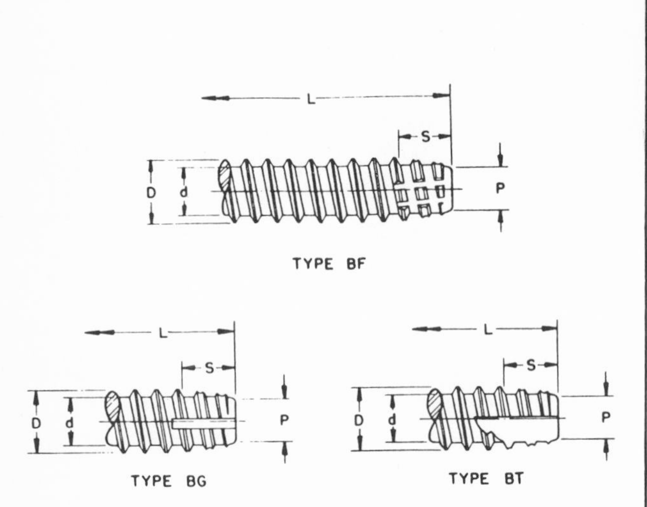

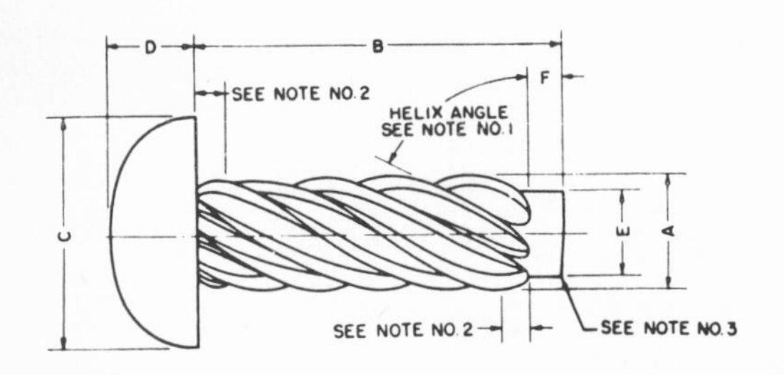

Thread Cutting Screws Types BF, BG, and BT

Screw Size	Threads per inch	D Major Diameter Basic	D Major Diameter Max.	D Major Diameter Min.	d Minor Diameter Max.	d Minor Diameter Min.	P Point Diameter Max.	P Point Diameter Min.	L (Special Taper Length S for these lengths and under shall be 1½ to 2 times the pitch of the thread) 90°	L C'sk.
0	48	0.060	0.060	0.057	0.036	0.033	0.031	0.027	5/64	1/8
1	42	0.073	0.075	0.072	0.049	0.046	0.044	0.040	5/64	5/32
2	32	0.086	0.088	0.084	0.064	0.060	0.058	0.054	7/64	3/16
3	28	0.099	0.101	0.097	0.075	0.071	0.068	0.063	9/64	7/32
4	24	0.112	0.114	0.110	0.086	0.082	0.079	0.074	3/16	1/4
5	20	0.125	0.130	0.126	0.094	0.090	0.087	0.082	3/16	1/4
6	20	0.138	0.139	0.135	0.104	0.099	0.095	0.089	1/4	5/16
7	19	0.151	0.154	0.149	0.115	0.109	0.105	0.099	5/16	3/8
8	18	0.164	0.166	0.161	0.122	0.116	0.112	0.106	5/16	7/16
10	16	0.190	0.189	0.183	0.141	0.135	0.130	0.123	3/8	1/2
12	14	0.216	0.215	0.209	0.164	0.157	0.152	0.145	7/16	9/16
1/4	14	0.250	0.246	0.240	0.192	0.185	0.179	0.171	1/2	5/8
5/16	12	0.3125	0.315	0.308	0.244	0.236	0.230	0.222	1/2	5/8
3/8	12	0.375	0.380	0.371	0.309	0.299	0.293	0.285	1/2	5/8
7/16	10	0.4375	0.440	0.431	0.359	0.349	0.343	0.335	5/8	3/4
1/2	10	0.500	0.504	0.495	0.423	0.413	0.407	0.399	5/8	3/4

Metallic Drive Screws Type U

Screw Size	A Outside Diameter Max.	A Outside Diameter Min.	E Pilot Diameter Max.	E Pilot Diameter Min.	C Head Diameter Max.	C Head Diameter Min.	D Head Height Max.	D Head Height Min.	Number of Threads Starts	Use Drill Size No. Size	Use Drill Size Dec. Eqiv.
00	0.060	0.057	0.049	0.046	0.099	0.090	0.034	0.026	6	55	0.052
0	0.075	0.072	0.063	0.060	0.127	0.118	0.049	0.041	6	51	0.067
2	0.100	0.097	0.083	0.080	0.162	0.146	0.069	0.059	8	44	0.086
4	0.116	0.112	0.096	0.092	0.211	0.193	0.086	0.075	7	37	0.104
6	0.140	0.136	0.116	0.112	0.260	0.240	0.103	0.091	7	31	0.120
7	0.154	0.150	0.126	0.122	0.285	0.264	0.111	0.099	8	29	0.136
8	0.167	0.162	0.136	0.132	0.309	0.287	0.120	0.107	8	27	0.144
10	0.182	0.177	0.150	0.146	0.359	0.334	0.137	0.123	8	20	0.161
12	0.212	0.206	0.177	0.173	0.408	0.382	0.153	0.139	8	11	0.191
14	0.242	0.236	0.202	0.198	0.457	0.429	0.170	0.155	9	2	0.221
5/16	0.315	0.309	0.272	0.267	0.590	0.557	0.216	0.198	11	M	0.295
3/8	0.378	0.371	0.334	0.329	0.708	0.670	0.256	0.237	12	T	0.358

All dimensions are given in inches.

B	Screw Length	1/8″	3/16″	1/4″	5/16″	3/8″	1/2″	5/8″	3/4″	1″ and over
F	Pilot Length	3/64	3/64	3/64	3/64	1/16	1/16	5/64	5/64	1/8

TD-12-33

Dimensions of Slotted Flat Head Tapping Screws, Type A (USAS B18.6.4-1958)

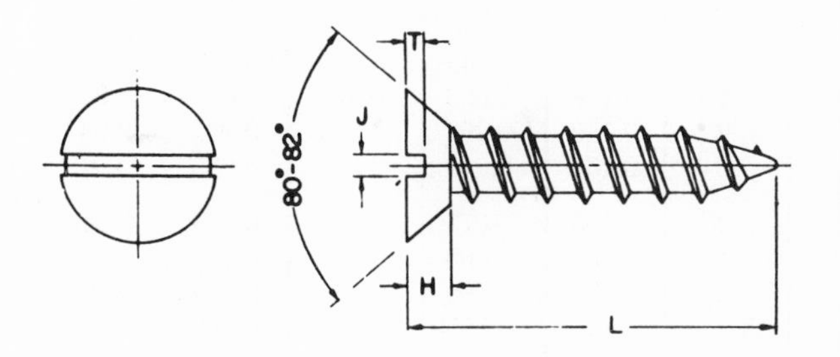

	A	H	J	T
Nominal Size	Max. Head Diameter	Head Height Ref.	Max. Width of Slot	Max. Depth of Slot
0	0.119	0.035	0.023	0.015
1	0.146	0.043	0.026	0.019
2	0.172	0.051	0.031	0.023
3	0.199	0.059	0.035	0.027
4	0.225	0.067	0.039	0.030
5	0.252	0.075	0.043	0.034
6	0.279	0.083	0.048	0.038
7	0.305	0.091	0.048	0.041
8	0.332	0.100	0.054	0.045
10	0.385	0.116	0.060	0.053
12	0.438	0.132	0.067	0.060
14	0.491	0.148	0.075	0.068
16	0.544	0.164	0.075	0.075
18	0.597	0.180	0.084	0.083
20	0.650	0.196	0.084	0.090
24	0.756	0.228	0.094	0.105

TD-12-34

Dimensions of Slotted Oval Head Tapping Screws, Type A (USAS B18.6.4-1958)

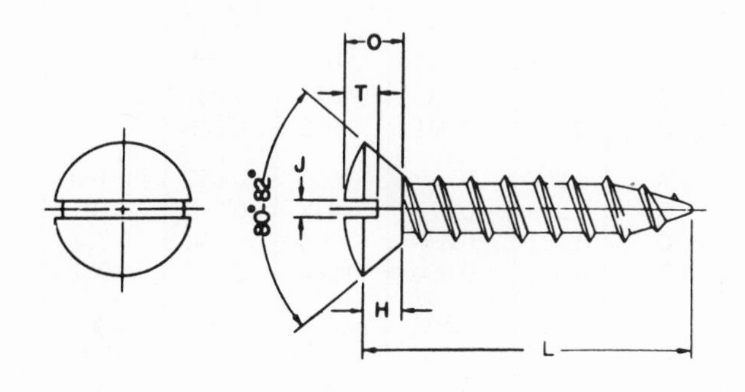

	A	H	O	J	T
Nominal Size	Max. Head Dia.	Side Height Ref.	Total Height of Head	Max. Width of Slot	Max. Depth of Slot
0	0.119	0.035	0.056	0.023	0.030
1	0.146	0.043	0.068	0.026	0.038
2	0.172	0.051	0.080	0.031	0.045
3	0.199	0.059	0.092	0.035	0.052
4	0.225	0.067	0.104	0.039	0.059
5	0.252	0.075	0.116	0.043	0.067
6	0.279	0.083	0.128	0.048	0.074
7	0.305	0.091	0.140	0.048	0.081
8	0.332	0.100	0.152	0.054	0.088
10	0.385	0.116	0.176	0.060	0.103
12	0.438	0.132	0.200	0.067	0.117
14	0.491	0.148	0.224	0.075	0.132
16	0.544	0.164	0.248	0.075	0.146
18	0.597	0.180	0.272	0.084	0.160
20	0.650	0.196	0.296	0.084	0.175
24	0.756	0.228	0.344	0.094	0.204

TD-12-35

Dimensions of Slotted Fillister Head Tapping Screws, Type A (USAS B18.6.4-1958)

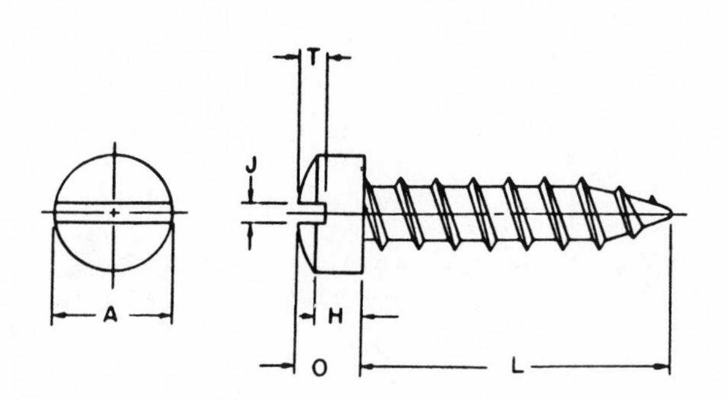

	A	H	O	J	T
Nominal Size	Max. Head Dia.	Max. Side Height of Head	Total Height of Head	Max. Width of Slot	Max. Depth of Slot
0	0.096	0.045	0.059	0.023	0.025
1	0.118	0.053	0.071	0.026	0.031
2	0.140	0.062	0.083	0.031	0.037
3	0.161	0.070	0.095	0.035	0.043
4	0.183	0.079	0.107	0.039	0.048
5	0.205	0.088	0.120	0.043	0.054
6	0.226	0.096	0.132	0.048	0.060
7	0.248	0.105	0.144	0.048	0.065
8	0.270	0.113	0.156	0.054	0.071
10	0.313	0.130	0.180	0.060	0.083
12	0.357	0.148	0.205	0.067	0.094
14	0.400	0.165	0.230	0.075	0.105

TD-12-36

Dimensions of Slotted Truss Head Tapping Screws, Type A (USAS B18.6.4-1958)

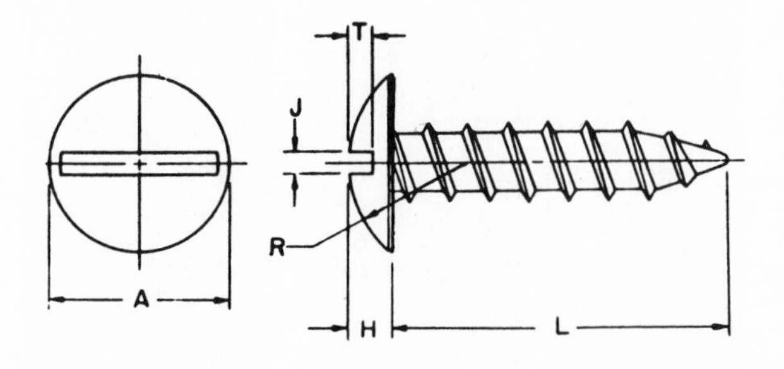

	A	H	J	T	R
Nominal Size	Max. Head Dia.	Max. Height of Head	Max. Width of Slot	Max. Depth of Slot	Radius
0	0.131	0.037	0.023	0.022	0.087
1	0.164	0.045	0.026	0.027	0.107
2	0.194	0.053	0.031	0.031	0.129
3	0.226	0.061	0.035	0.036	0.151
4	0.257	0.069	0.039	0.040	0.169
5	0.289	0.078	0.043	0.045	0.191
6	0.321	0.086	0.048	0.050	0.211
7	0.352	0.094	0.048	0.054	0.231
8	0.384	0.102	0.054	0.058	0.254
10	0.448	0.118	0.060	0.068	0.283
12	0.511	0.134	0.067	0.077	0.336
14	0.557	0.146	0.075	0.085	0.375
16	0.609	0.159	0.075	0.093	0.410
18	0.661	0.173	0.084	0.100	0.446
20	0.713	0.186	0.084	0.108	0.484
24	0.817	0.213	0.094	0.123	0.557

TD-12-37

Dimensions of Slotted Hex-Head Tapping Screws, Type A (USAS B18.6.4-1958)

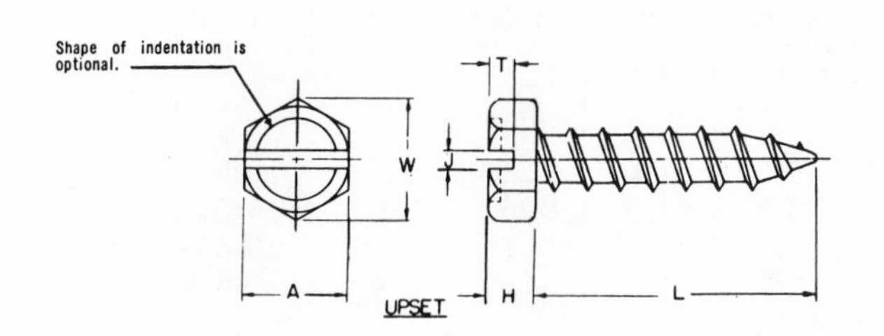

	A	W	H	J	T
Nominal Size	Max. Width Across Flats	Min. Width Across Corners	Max. Height of Head	Max. Width of Slot	Max. Depth of Slot
1	0.125	0.134	0.050	....	....
2	0.125	0.134	0.050	....	....
3	0.187	0.202	0.055	....	....
4	0.187	0.202	0.060	0.039	0.036
5	0.187	0.202	0.070	0.043	0.042
6	0.250	0.272	0.093	0.048	0.046
7	0.250	0.272	0.093	0.048	0.054
8	0.250	0.272	0.110	0.054	0.066
10	0.312	0.340	0.120	0.060	0.072
12	0.312	0.340	0.155	0.067	0.093
14	0.375	0.409	0.190	0.075	0.101
20	0.500	0.545	0.230	0.084	0.122
24	0.562	0.614	0.295	0.094	0.156

TD-12-38

Dimensions of Slotted Round Head Tapping Screws, Types B and BD (USAS B18.6.4-1958)

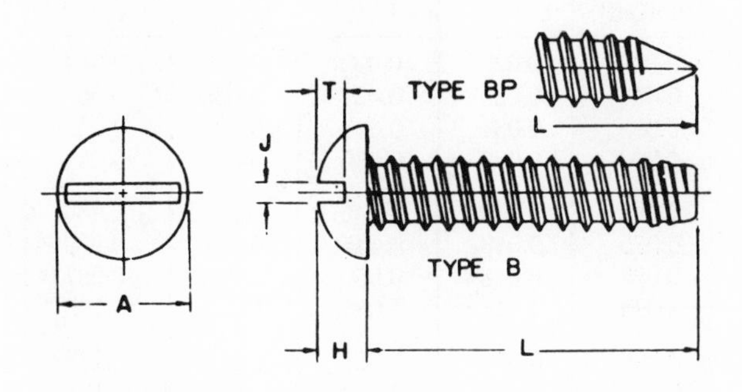

	A	H	J	T
Nominal Size	Max. Head Diameter	Max. Height of Head	Max. Width of Slot	Max. Depth of Slot
0	0.113	0.053	0.023	0.039
1	0.138	0.061	0.026	0.044
2	0.162	0.069	0.031	0.048
3	0.187	0.078	0.035	0.053
4	0.211	0.086	0.039	0.058
5	0.236	0.095	0.043	0.063
6	0.260	0.103	0.048	0.068
7	0.285	0.111	0.048	0.072
8	0.309	0.120	0.054	0.077
10	0.359	0.137	0.060	0.087
12	0.408	0.153	0.067	0.096
¼	0.472	0.175	0.075	0.109
5⁄16	0.590	0.216	0.084	0.132
⅜	0.708	0.256	0.094	0.155
7⁄16	0.750	0.328	0.094	0.196
½	0.813	0.355	0.106	0.211

TD-12-39

Dimensions of Slotted Hex Washer Head Tapping Screws, Type A (USAS B18.6.4-1958)

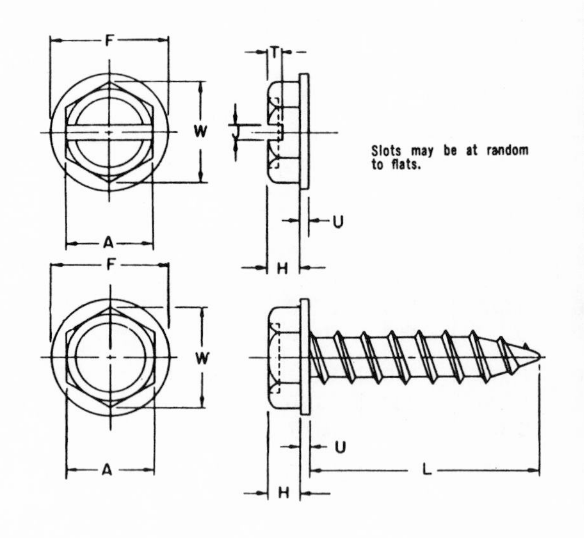

	A	W	H	F	U	J	T
Nominal Size	Width Across Flats	Min. Width Across Corners	Height of Head	Dia. of Washer	Thickness of Washer	Width of Slot	Depth of Slot
2	0.125	0.134	0.050	0.166	0.016	.....	.....
3	0.125	0.134	0.055	0.177	0.016	.....	.....
4	0.187	0.202	0.060	0.243	0.019	0.039	0.042
5	0.187	0.202	0.070	0.260	0.025	0.043	0.049
6	0.250	0.272	0.093	0.328	0.025	0.048	0.053
7	0.250	0.272	0.093	0.328	0.029	0.048	0.062
8	0.250	0.272	0.110	0.348	0.031	0.054	0.074
10	0.312	0.340	0.120	0.414	0.031	0.060	0.080
12	0.312	0.340	0.155	0.432	0.039	0.067	0.103
14	0.375	0.409	0.190	0.520	0.050	0.075	0.111
20	0.500	0.545	0.230	0.676	0.055	0.084	0.134
24	0.562	0.614	0.295	0.780	0.063	0.094	0.168

TD-12-40

Dimensions of Slotted Pan Head Tapping Screws, Types B and BD (USAS B18.6.4-1958)

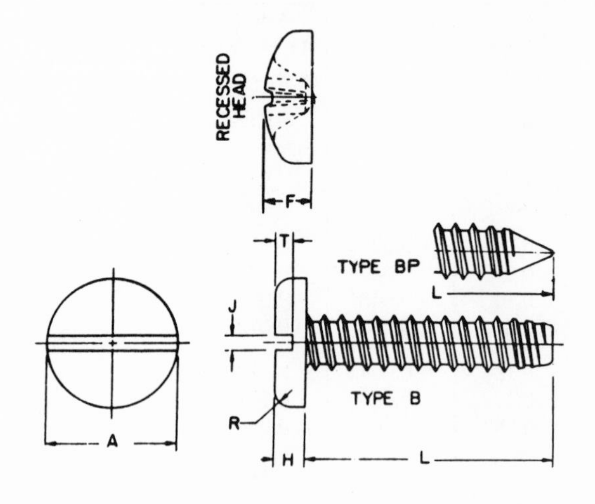

	A	H	J	T	R	F
Nominal Size	Max. Head Diameter	Max. Height of Head (Slotted)	Max. Width of Slot	Max. Depth of Slot	Radius	Max. Height of Head (Recessed)
0	0.116	0.039	0.023	0.022	0.020	0.044
1	0.142	0.046	0.026	0.027	0.025	0.053
2	0.167	0.053	0.031	0.031	0.035	0.062
3	0.193	0.060	0.035	0.036	0.037	0.071
4	0.219	0.068	0.039	0.040	0.042	0.080
5	0.245	0.075	0.043	0.045	0.044	0.089
6	0.270	0.082	0.048	0.050	0.046	0.097
7	0.296	0.089	0.048	0.054	0.049	0.106
8	0.322	0.096	0.054	0.058	0.052	0.115
10	0.373	0.110	0.060	0.068	0.061	0.133
12	0.425	0.125	0.067	0.077	0.078	0.151
1/4	0.492	0.144	0.075	0.087	0.087	0.175
5/16	0.615	0.178	0.084	0.106	0.099	0.218
3/8	0.740	0.212	0.094	0.124	0.143	0.261

TD-12-41

Approximate Hole Sizes for Steel Tapping Screws, Type A (USAS B18.6.4-1958)

In Sheet Metal Steel, Stainless Steel, Monel,® Brass, Aluminum				
		Pierced or Extruded Hole	Drilled or Clean Punched Hole	
Screw Size	Metal Thickness	Hole Required	Hole Required	Drill Size No.
4	0.015	....	0.086	44
	0.018	....	0.086	44
	0.024	0.098	0.093	42
	0.030	0.098	0.093	42
	0.036	0.098	0.098	40
6	0.015	....	0.099	39
	0.018	....	0.099	39
	0.024	0.111	0.099	39
	0.030	0.111	0.101	38
	0.036	0.111	0.106	36
7	0.015	....	0.104	37
	0.018	....	0.104	37
	0.024	0.120	0.110	35
	0.030	0.120	0.113	33
	0.036	0.120	0.116	32
	0.048	0.120	0.120	31
8	0.018	....	0.113	33
	0.024	0.136	0.113	33
	0.030	0.136	0.116	32
	0.036	0.136	0.120	31
	0.048	0.142	0.128	30
10	0.018	....	0.128	30
	0.024	0.157	0.128	30
	0.030	0.157	0.128	30
	0.036	0.157	0.136	29
	0.048	0.157	0.149	25
12	0.024	....	0.147	26
	0.030	0.185	0.149	25
	0.036	0.185	0.152	24
	0.048	0.185	0.157	22
14	0.024	....	0.180	15
	0.030	0.209	0.189	12
	0.036	0.209	0.191	11
	0.048	0.209	0.196	9

In Plywood (Resin Impregnated) Compreg, Pregwood, Etc.					
				Penetration in Blind Holes	
Screw Size	Hole Required	Drill Size No.	Min. Matl. Thick.	Min.	Max.
4	0.098	40	3/16	1/4	3/4
6	0.110	35	3/16	1/4	3/4
7	0.128	30	1/4	5/16	3/4
8	0.140	28	1/4	5/16	3/4
10	0.169	18	5/16	3/8	1
12	0.189	12	5/16	3/8	1
14	0.228	1	7/16	1/2	1

In Asbestos Compositions Transite, Ebony Asbestos, Etc.					
				Penetration in Blind Holes	
Screw Size	Hole Required	Drill Size No.	Min. Matl. Thick.	Min.	Max.
4	0.093	42	3/16	1/4	3/4
6	0.106	36	3/16	1/4	3/4
7	0.125	1/8	1/4	5/16	3/4
8	0.136	29	1/4	5/16	3/4
10	0.161	20	5/16	3/8	1
12	0.185	13	5/16	3/8	1
14	0.213	3	7/16	1/2	1

TD-12-42

Approximate Hole Sizes for Steel Tapping Screws, Type B (USAS B18.6.4-1958)

Steel, Stainless Steel, Monel,® Brass					Aluminum								
		Pierced or Extruded Hole	Drilled or Clean-Punched Hole		Pierced or Extruded Hole	Drilled or Clean-Punched Hole		In Castings of Aluminum, Zinc, White Metal, Etc.		In Bakelite, Durez and Other Plastics		In Slate, Ebony Asbestos, Etc.	
Screw Size	Metal Thickness	Hole Required	Hole Required	Drill Size No.	Hole Required	Hole Required	Drill Size No.	Dia. Hole Required	Drill Size	Dia. Hole Required	Drill Size	Dia. Hole Required	Drill Size
	0.015		0.063	52									
	0.018		0.063	52									
	0.024		0.067	51		0.063	52						
2	0.030		0.070	50		0.063	52	.078	No. 47	.078	No. 47	.076	No. 48
	0.036		0.073	49		0.063	52						
	0.048		0.073	49		0.067	51						
	0.060		0.076	48		0.070	50						
	0.015	0.086	0.086	44									
	0.018	0.086	0.086	44									
	0.024	0.098	0.089	43	0.086								
	0.030	0.098	0.093	42	0.086	0.086	44						
4	0.036	0.098	0.093	42	0.086	0.086	44	.104	No. 37	.099	No. 39	.101	No. 38
	0.048		0.096	41	0.086	0.086	44						
	0.060		0.099	39		0.089	43						
	0.075		0.101	38		0.089	43						
	0.105					0.093	42						
	0.015	0.111	0.104	37									
	0.018	0.111	0.104	37									
	0.024	0.111	0.106	36	0.111								
	0.030	0.111	0.106	36	0.111	0.104	37						
	0.036	0.111	0.110	35	0.111	0.104	37						
6	0.048		0.111	34	0.111	0.104	37	.128	No. 30	.128	No. 30	.120	No. 31
	0.060		0.116	32		0.106	36						
	0.075		0.120	31		0.110	35						
	0.105		0.128	30		0.111	34						
	0.128 to 0.250					0.120	31						
	0.018	0.136											
	0.024	0.136	0.116	32	0.136								
	0.030	0.136	0.120	31	0.136	0.116	32						
	0.036	0.136	0.120	31	0.136	0.120	31						
	0.048	0.136	0.128	30	0.136	0.128	30						
	0.060		0.136	29		0.136	29						
8	0.075		0.140	28		0.140	28	.152	No. 24	.149	No. 25	.147	No. 26
	0.105		0.149	25		0.147	26						
	0.125		0.149	25		0.147	26						
	0.135		0.152	24		0.149	25						
	0.162 to 0.375					0.152	24						

TD-12-42 (con't.)

Approximate Hole Sizes for Steel Tapping Screws, Type B (USAS B18.6.4-1958)

Steel, Stainless Steel, Monel,® Brass					Aluminum								
		Pierced or Ex-truded Hole	Drilled or Clean-Punched Hole		Pierced or Ex-truded Hole	Drilled or Clean-Punched Hole		In Castings of Aluminum, Zinc, White Metal, Etc.		In Bakelite, Durez and Other Plastics		In Slate, Ebony Asbestos, Etc.	
Screw Size	Metal Thick-ness	Hole Re-quired	Hole Re-quired	Drill Size No.	Hole Re-quired	Hole Re-quired	Drill Size No.	Dia. Hole Re-quired	Drill Size	Dia. Hole Re-quired	Drill Size	Dia. Hole Re-quired	Drill Size
	0.018	0.157											
	0.024	0.157	0.144	27	0.157								
	0.030	0.157	0.144	27	0.157								
	0.036	0.157	0.147	26	0.157	0.144	27						
	0.048	0.157	0.152	24	0.157	0.144	27						
	0.060		0.152	24		0.144	27						
10	0.075		0.157	22		0.147	26	.177	No. 16	.177	No. 16	.166	No. 19
	0.105		0.161	20		0.147	26						
	0.125		0.169	18		0.154	23						
	0.135		0.169	18		0.154	23						
	0.164		0.173	17		0.159	21						
	0.200 to 0.375					0.166	19						
	0.024	0.185	0.166	19									
	0.030	0.185	0.166	19									
	0.036	0.185	0.166	19									
	0.048	0.185	0.169	18		0.161	20						
	0.060		0.177	16		0.166	19						
12	0.075		0.182	14		0.173	17	.199	No. 8	.199	No. 8	.196	No. 9
	0.105		0.185	13		0.180	15						
	0.125		0.196	9		0.182	14						
	0.135		0.196	9		0.182	14						
	0.164		0.201	7		0.189	12						
	0.200 to 0.375					0.196	9						
	0.030	0.209	0.185	13									
	0.036	0.209	0.185	13									
	0.048	0.209	0.191	11									
	0.060		0.199	8		0.199	8						
	0.075		0.204	6		0.201	7						
	0.105		0.209	4		0.204	6						
14	0.125		0.228	1		0.209	4	.234	15/64	.234	15/64	.228	No. 1
	0.135		0.228	1		0.209	4						
	0.164		0.234	15/64"		0.213	3						
	0.187		0.234	15/64"		0.213	3						
	0.194		0.234	15/64"		0.221	2						
	0.200 to 0.375					0.228	1						

TD-12-43

Hole Sizes Recommended for Tapping Screws, Type C (USAS B18.6.4-1958)

Screw Size	Sheet Metal Gauge	Decimal Thick-ness	Hole Diameter	Drill Size	Screw Size	Sheet Metal Gauge	Decimal Thick-ness	Hole Diameter	Drill Size
No. 4-40 .112 in.	No. 20	0.037	0.093	42	No. 12-24 .216 in.	No. 20	0.037	0.189	12
	No. 18	0.048	0.093	42		No. 18	0.048	0.1935	10
	No. 16	0.062	0.093	41		No. 16	0.062	0.1935	10
	No. 14	0.075	0.0995	39		No. 14	0.075	0.199	8
	No. 12	0.015	0.101	38		No. 12	0.105	0.199	8
	No. 10	0.134	0.101	38		No. 10	0.134	0.199	8
No. 6-32 .138 in.	No. 20	0.037	0.113	33	No. ¼-20 .250 in.	No. 20	0.037	0.221	2
	No. 18	0.048	0.116	32		No. 18	0.048	0.221	2
	No. 16	0.062	0.1160	32		No. 16	0.062	0.2280	1
	No. 14	0.075	0.122	3.1 m.m.		No. 14	0.075	0.234	A
	No. 12	0.105	0.125	⅛		No. 12	0.105	0.234	A
	No. 10	0.134	0.125	⅛		No. 10	0.134	0.236	6 m.m.
No. 8-32 .164 in.	No. 20	0.037	0.136	29	No. ¼-28	No. 20	0.037	0.224	5.7 m.m.
	No. 18	0.048	0.144	27		No. 18	0.048	0.228	1
	No. 16	0.062	0.144	27		No. 16	0.062	0.232	5.9 m.m.
	No. 14	0.075	0.147	26		No. 14	0.075	0.234	A
	No. 12	0.105	0.1495	25		No. 12	0.105	0.238	B
	No. 10	0.134	0.1495	25		No. 10	0.134	0.238	B
No. 10-24 .190 in.	No. 20	0.037	0.154	23	No. 5/16-18	No. 20	0.037	0.290	L
	No. 18	0.048	0.161	20		No. 18	0.048	0.290	L
	No. 16	0.062	0.166	19		No. 16	0.062	0.290	L
	No. 14	0.075	0.1695	18		No. 14	0.075	0.295	M
	No. 12	0.105	0.173	17		No. 12	0.105	0.295	M
	No. 10	0.134	0.177	16		No. 10	0.134	0.295	M
No. 10-32 .190 in.	No. 20	0.037	0.1695	18					
	No. 18	0.048	0.1695	18					
	No. 16	0.062	0.1695	18					
	No. 14	0.075	0.1730	17					
	No. 12	0.105	0.177	16					
	No. 10	0.134	0.177	16					

TECHNICAL DATA

Approximate Hole Sizes for Steel Thread Cutting Screws, Types D, F, G, and T (USAS B18.6.4-1958)

Screw Size	Stock Thickness in Inches										
	0.050	0.060	0.083	0.109	0.125	0.140	3/16	¼	5/16	⅜	½
	In Steel										
2-56	0.0730	0.0730	0.0730	0.0730	0.0760	0.0760	......	......	......	......	......
3-48	0.0810	0.0810	0.0820	0.0860	0.0860	0.0860	0.0890	......	......	......	......
4-40	0.0890	0.0890	0.0935	0.0960	0.0980	0.0980	0.1015	......	......	......	......
5-40	0.1060	0.1060	0.1060	0.1065	0.1094	0.1100	0.1160	0.1160	......	......	......
6-32	0.1100	0.1130	0.1160	0.1160	0.1160	0.1200	0.1250	0.1250	......	......	......
8-32	0.1360	0.1405	0.1405	0.1440	0.1440	0.1470	0.1495	0.1495	0.1495	......	......
10-24	0.1520	0.1540	0.1610	0.1610	0.1660	0.1695	0.1730	0.1730	0.1730	0.1730	......
10-32	0.1590	0.1660	0.1660	0.1695	0.1695	0.1695	0.1770	0.1770	0.1770	0.1770	......
12-24	......	0.1800	0.1820	0.1875	0.1910	0.1910	0.1990	0.1990	0.1990	0.1990	0.1990
¼-20	......	......	0.2130	0.2188	0.2210	0.2210	0.2280	0.2280	0.2280	0.2280	0.2280
¼-28	......	......	0.2210	0.2280	0.2280	0.2340	0.2344	0.2344	0.2344	0.2344	0.2344
5/16-18	......	......	......	0.2770	0.2770	0.2813	0.2900	0.2900	0.2900	0.2900	0.2900

TD-12-44 (con't.)

Approximate Hole Sizes for Steel Thread Cutting Screws, Types D, F, G, and T (USAS B18.6.4-1958)

Screw Size	Stock Thickness in Inches										
	0.050	0.060	0.083	0.109	0.125	0.140	3/16	1/4	5/16	3/8	1/2
5/16-24	......	......	......	0.2900	0.2900	0.2900	0.2950	0.2950	0.2950	0.2950	0.2950
3/8-16	......	......	......	......	0.3390	0.3390	0.3480	0.3580	0.3580	0.3580	0.3580
3/8-24	......	......	......	......	0.3480	0.3480	0.3580	0.3580	0.3580	0.3580	0.3580
In Aluminum											
2-56	0.0700	0.0730	0.0730	0.0730	0.0730	0.0730	......	......	......	......	......
3-48	0.0781	0.0810	0.0820	0.0820	0.0820	0.0860	0.0860	......	......	......	......
4-40	0.0890	0.0890	0.0890	0.0935	0.0935	0.0938	0.0980	......	......	......	......
5-40	0.1015	0.1015	0.1040	0.1040	0.1065	0.1065	0.1100	0.1130	......	......	......
6-32	0.1094	0.1094	0.1110	0.1130	0.1160	0.1160	0.1200	0.1250	......	......	......
8-32	0.1360	0.1360	0.1360	0.1405	0.1405	0.1440	0.1470	0.1495	0.1495	......	......
10-24	0.1495	0.1520	0.1540	0.1570	0.1590	0.1610	0.1660	0.1719	0.1730	0.1730	......
10-32	0.1610	0.1610	0.1610	0.1660	0.1660	0.1660	0.1719	0.1770	0.1770	0.1770	......
12-24	......	0.1770	0.1800	0.1820	0.1850	0.1875	0.1910	0.1990	0.1990	0.1990	0.1990
1/4-20	......	......	0.2055	0.2090	0.2130	0.2130	0.2210	0.2280	0.2280	0.2280	0.2280
1/4-28	......	......	0.2188	0.2210	0.2210	0.2210	0.2280	0.2344	0.2344	0.2344	0.2344
5/16-18	......	......	......	0.2660	0.2720	0.2720	0.2810	0.2900	0.2900	0.2900	0.2900
5/16-24	......	......	......	0.2810	0.2812	0.2812	0.2900	0.2950	0.2950	0.2950	0.2950
3/8-16	......	......	......	......	0.3281	0.3320	0.3390	0.3480	0.3480	0.3480	0.3480
3/8-24	......	......	......	......	0.3438	0.3438	0.3480	0.3580	0.3580	0.3580	0.3580
In Cast Iron											
2-56	0.0760	0.0760	0.0760	0.0781	0.0781	0.0781	......	......	......	......	......
3-48	0.0890	0.0890	0.0890	0.0890	0.0890	0.0935	0.0935	......	......	......	......
4-40	0.0995	0.0995	0.1015	0.1015	0.1015	0.1015	0.1040	......	......	......	......
5-40	0.1110	0.1110	0.1130	0.1130	0.1160	0.1160	0.1160	0.1160	......	......	......
6-32	0.1200	0.1200	0.1250	0.1250	0.1250	0.1250	0.1285	0.1285	......	......	......
8-32	0.1470	0.1495	0.1495	0.1495	0.1495	0.1495	0.1540	0.1540	0.1540	......	......
10-24	0.1695	0.1695	0.1719	0.1730	0.1730	0.1730	0.1770	0.1770	0.1770	0.1770	......
10-32	0.1730	0.1730	0.1770	0.1770	0.1770	0.1770	0.1800	0.1800	0.1800	0.1800	......
12-24	......	0.1960	0.1990	0.1990	0.1990	0.1990	0.2031	0.2040	0.2040	0.2040	0.2040
1/4-20	......	......	0.2280	0.2280	0.2280	0.2280	0.2344	0.2344	0.2344	0.2344	0.2344
1/4-28	......	......	0.2340	0.2344	0.2344	0.2344	0.2380	0.2380	0.2380	0.2380	0.2380
5/16-18	......	......	......	0.2900	0.2900	0.2900	0.2950	0.2950	0.2950	0.2950	0.2950
5/16-24	......	......	......	0.2950	0.2950	0.2950	0.3020	0.3020	0.3020	0.3020	0.3020
3/8-16	......	......	......	......	0.3480	0.3480	0.3480	0.3480	0.3480	0.3480	0.3480
3/8-24	......	......	......	......	0.3580	0.3580	0.3580	0.3580	0.3580	0.3580	0.3580

Types D, F and T

In Plastics

	Phenol Formaldehyde				Cellulose Acetate, Cellulose Nitrate, Acrylic Resins, Styrene Resins			
			Depth of Penetration				Depth of Penetration	
Screw Size	Hole Required	Drill Size No.	Min.	Max.	Hole Required	Drill Size No.	Min.	Max.
2-56	0.0781	5/64	7/32	3/8	0.0760	48	7/32	3/8
3-48	0.0890	43	7/32	3/8	0.0860	44	7/32	3/8
4-40	0.098	40	1/4	5/16	0.093	42	1/4	5/16
5-40	0.1130	33	1/4	7/16	0.1100	35	1/4	7/16
6-32	0.116	32	1/4	5/16	0.116	32	1/4	5/16
8-32	0.144	27	5/16	1/2	0.144	27	5/16	1/2
10-24	0.161	20	3/8	1/2	0.161	20	3/8	1/2
10-32	0.166	19	3/8	1/2	0.166	19	3/8	1/2
1/4-20	0.228	1	3/8	5/8	0.228	1	3/8	1

TD-12-45

Approximate Hole Sizes for Steel Thread-Cutting Screws, Types BF, BG, and BT (USAS B18.6.4-1958)

In Zinc and Aluminum Die Castings										
Screw Size	Stock Thickness in Inches									
	0.060	0.083	0.109	0.125	0.140	3/16	1/4	5/16	3/8	1/2
2-32	0.0730	0.0730	0.0760	0.0760	0.0760	......	......	......	......	......
3-28	0.0860	0.0860	0.0860	0.0860	0.0890	0.0890	......	......	......	......
4-24	......	......	0.0980	0.0995	0.0995	0.0995	0.1015	......	......	......
5-20	......	......	0.1110	0.1110	0.1130	0.1130	0.1160	......	......	......
6-20	......	......	......	0.1200	0.1200	0.1200	0.1250	0.1250	......	......
8-18	......	......	......	0.1490	0.1490	0.1490	0.1520	0.1520	......	......
10-16	......	......	......	0.1660	0.1660	0.1660	0.1695	0.1719	0.1719	......
12-14	......	......	......	0.1910	0.1910	0.1910	0.1960	0.1960	0.1960	......
1/4-14	......	......	......	0.2210	0.2210	0.2210	0.2280	0.2280	0.2280	......
5/16-12	......	......	......	0.2810	0.2810	0.2810	0.2810	0.2900	0.2900	......
3/8-12	......	......	......	0.3438	0.3438	0.3438	0.3438	0.3438	0.3438	......

In Plastics								
	Phenol Formaldehyde				Cellulose Acetate, Cellulose Nitrate, Acrylic Resins, Styrene Resins			
	Hole Required	Drill Size No.	Depth of Penetration		Hole Required	Drill Size No.	Depth of Penetration	
Screw Size			Min.	Max.			Min.	Max.
2-32	0.0781	5/64	3/32	1/4	0.076	48	3/32	1/4
3-28	0.089	43	1/8	5/16	0.089	43	1/8	5/16
4-24	0.104	37	1/8	5/16	0.0995	39	1/8	5/16
5-20	0.116	32	3/16	3/8	0.113	33	3/16	3/8
6-20	0.125	1/8	3/16	3/8	0.120	31	3/16	3/8
8-18	0.147	26	1/4	1/2	0.144	27	1/4	1/2
10-16	0.1695	18	5/16	5/8	0.166	19	5/16	5/8
12-14	0.1935	10	3/8	5/8	0.189	12	3/8	5/8
1/4-14	0.228	1	3/8	3/4	0.221	2	3/8	3/4

NOTE: Because conditions may vary, it may be necessary to change the hole size to suit a particular application.

TD-12-46

Diameters of Wood Screws and Suggested Hole Sizes (Greenlee Co.)

The table of wood screw specifications simplifies the selection of the bit or drill size best suited to your requirements. The fractional equivalents and undersize and oversize decimals indicate how close a bit of given fractional size will bore to the actual screw dimension and whether the fit will be snug or loose. In selecting a tool size for the pilot hole (for threaded portion of screw), note that root diameters are average dimensions measured at the middle of the threaded portion. On some screws the root diameter tapers slightly from the end of the screw, increasing toward the head. It is usually good practice to bore the pilot hole the same size as the root diameter in hardwoods, such as oak, and about 15% smaller for softwoods, such as pine and Douglas fir. In some cases, allowances can be made to advantage for moisture content and other varying factors. This same rule can be used for shank holes. The ***shank diameters*** shown below are standard specifications subject to tolerances of $^{+.004}_{-.007}$. ***Maximum head diameters*** are also standard specifications which apply to flat and oval-head screws. Head sizes run from 5% to 10% smaller for round-head screws.

No. of Screw	Max. Head Dia.	Shank Diameter: Basic Dec. Size	Shank Diameter: Nearest Fractional Equivalent	Root Diameter: Average Dec. Size	Root Diameter: Nearest Fractional Equivalent	Threads per Inch	No. of Screw
0	.119	.060	1/16 Oversize .002	.040	3/64 Oversize .007	32	0
1	.146	.073	5/64 Oversize .005	.046	3/64 Basic Size	28	1
2	.172	.086	3/32 Oversize .007	.054	1/16 Oversize .008	26	2
3	.199	.099	7/64 Oversize .010	.065	1/16 Undersize .002	24	3
4	.225	.112	7/64 Undersize .003	.075	5/64 Oversize .003	22	4
5	.252	.125	1/8 Basic Size	.085	5/64 Undersize .007	20	5
6	.279	.138	9/64 Oversize .002	.094	3/32 Basic Size	18	6
7	.305	.151	5/32 Oversize .005	.102	7/64 Oversize .007	16	7
8	.332	.164	5/32 Undersize .007	.112	7/64 Undersize .003	15	8
9	.358	.177	11/64 Undersize .005	.122	1/8 Oversize .003	14	9
10	.385	.190	3/16 Undersize .002	.130	1/8 Undersize .005	13	10
11	.411	.203	13/64 Basic Size	.139	9/64 Oversize .001	12	11
12	.438	.216	7/32 Oversize .003	.148	9/64 Undersize .007	11	12
14	.491	.242	1/4 Oversize .008	.165	5/32 Undersize .009	10	14
16	.544	.268	17/64 Undersize .002	.184	3/16 Oversize .003	9	16
18	.597	.294	19/64 Oversize .003	.204	13/64 Undersize .001	8	18
20	.650	.320	5/16 Undersize .007	.223	7/32 Undersize .004	8	20
24	.756	.372	3/8 Oversize .003	.260	1/4 Undersize .010	7	24

TD-12-47

Dimensions of Square Bolts (USAS B18.2.1-1965)

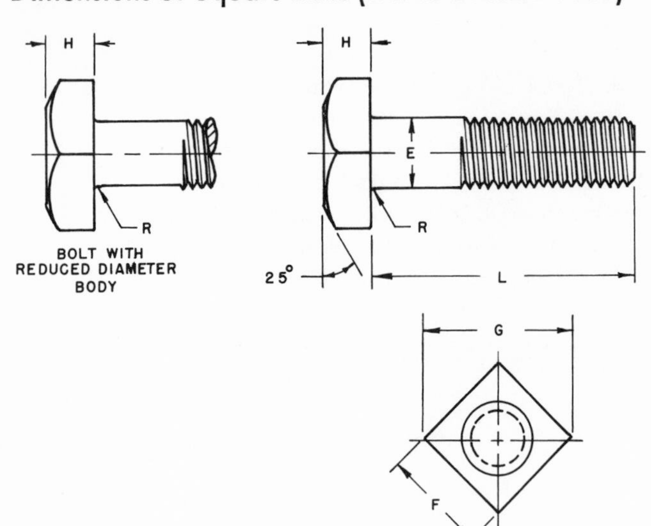

Nominal Size or Basic Product Dia.		Body Dia. E	Width Across Flats F	Width Across Corners G	Height H	Radius of Fillet R
		Max.	Basic	Max.	Basic	Max.
1/4	0.2500	0.260	3/8	0.530	11/64	0.031
5/16	0.3125	0.324	1/2	0.707	13/64	0.031
3/8	0.3750	0.388	9/16	0.795	1/4	0.031
7/16	0.4375	0.452	5/8	0.884	19/64	0.031
1/2	0.5000	0.515	3/4	1.061	21/64	0.031
5/8	0.6250	0.642	15/16	1.326	27/64	0.062
3/4	0.7500	0.768	1 1/8	1.591	1/2	0.062
7/8	0.8750	0.895	1 5/16	1.856	19/32	0.062
1	1.0000	1.022	1 1/2	2.121	21/32	0.093
1 1/8	1.1250	1.149	1 11/16	2.386	3/4	0.093
1 1/4	1.2500	1.277	1 7/8	2.652	27/32	0.093
1 3/8	1.3750	1.404	2 1/16	2.917	29/32	0.093
1 1/2	1.5000	1.531	2 1/4	3.182	1	0.093

TD-12-48

Dimensions of Hex Bolts (USAS B18.2.1-1965)

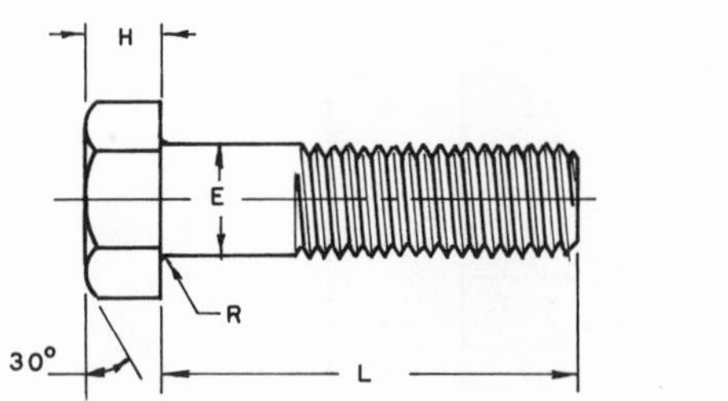

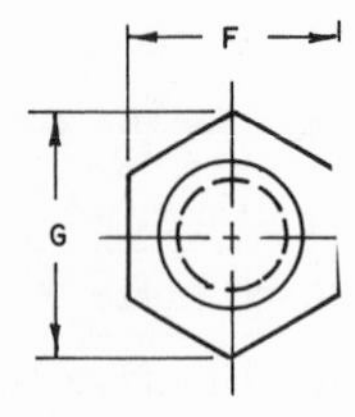

Nominal Size or Basic Product Dia.		Body Dia. E	Width Across Flats F	Width Across Corners G	Height H	Radius of Fillet R
		Max.	Basic	Max.	Basic	Max.
1/4	0.2500	0.260	7/16	0.505	11/64	0.031
5/16	0.3125	0.324	1/2	0.577	7/32	0.031
3/8	0.3750	0.388	9/16	0.650	1/4	0.031
7/16	0.4375	0.452	5/8	0.722	19/64	0.031
1/2	0.5000	0.515	3/4	0.866	11/32	0.031
5/8	0.6250	0.642	15/16	1.083	27/64	0.062
3/4	0.7500	0.768	1 1/8	1.299	1/2	0.062
7/8	0.8750	0.895	1 5/16	1.516	37/64	0.062
1	1.0000	1.022	1 1/2	1.732	43/64	0.093
1 1/8	1.1250	1.149	1 11/16	1.949	3/4	0.093
1 1/4	1.2500	1.277	1 7/8	2.165	27/32	0.093
1 3/8	1.3750	1.404	2 1/16	2.382	29/32	0.093
1 1/2	1.5000	1.531	2 1/4	2.598	1	0.093
1 3/4	1.7500	1.785	2 5/8	3.031	1 5/32	0.125
2	2.0000	2.039	3	3.464	1 11/32	0.125
2 1/4	2.2500	2.305	3 3/8	3.897	1 1/2	0.188
2 1/2	2.5000	2.559	3 3/4	4.330	1 21/32	0.188
2 3/4	2.7500	2.827	4 1/8	4.763	1 13/16	0.188
3	3.0000	3.081	4 1/2	5.196	2	0.188
3 1/4	3.2500	3.335	4 7/8	5.629	2 3/16	0.188
3 1/2	3.5000	3.589	5 1/4	6.062	2 5/16	0.188
3 3/4	3.7500	3.858	5 5/8	6.495	2 1/2	0.188
4	4.0000	4.111	6	6.928	2 11/16	0.188

TD-12-49

Dimensions of Heavy Hex Bolts (USAS B18.2.1-1965)

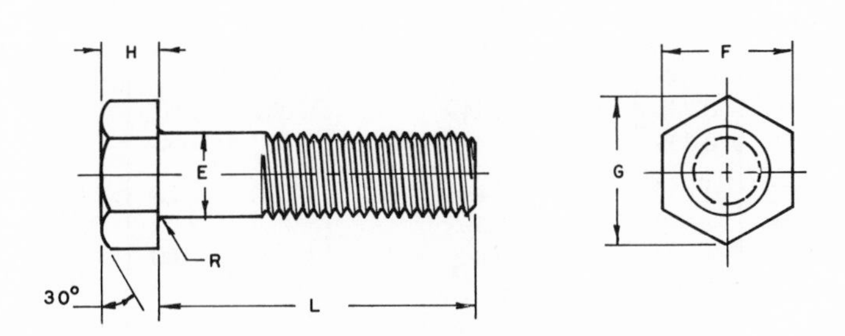

Nominal Size or Basic Product Dia.		Body Dia. E	Width Across Flats F	Width Across Corners G	Height H	Radius of Fillet R
		Max.	Basic	Max.	Basic	Max.
1/2	0.5000	0.515	7/8	1.010	11/32	0.031
5/8	0.6250	0.642	1 1/16	1.227	27/64	0.062
3/4	0.7500	0.768	1 1/4	1.443	1/2	0.062
7/8	0.8750	0.895	1 7/16	1.660	37/64	0.062
1	1.0000	1.022	1 5/8	1.876	43/64	0.093
1 1/8	1.1250	1.149	1 13/16	2.093	3/4	0.093
1 1/4	1.2500	1.277	2	2.309	27/32	0.093
1 3/8	1.3750	1.404	2 3/16	2.526	29/32	0.093
1 1/2	1.5000	1.531	2 3/8	2.742	1	0.093
1 3/4	1.7500	1.785	2 3/4	3.175	1 5/32	0.125
2	2.0000	2.039	3 1/8	3.608	1 11/32	0.125
2 1/4	2.2500	2.305	3 1/2	4.041	1 1/2	0.188
2 1/2	2.5000	2.559	3 7/8	4.474	1 21/32	0.188
2 3/4	2.7500	2.827	4 1/4	4.907	1 13/16	0.188
3	3.0000	3.081	4 5/8	5.340	2	0.188

TD-12-50

Dimensions of Hex Cap Screws (USAS B18.2.1-1965)

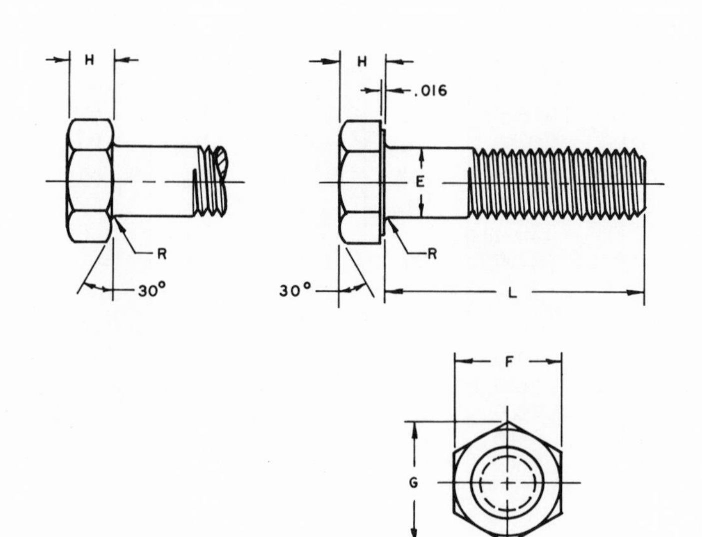

Nominal Size or Basic Product Dia.		Body Dia. E	Width Across Flats F	Width Across Corners G	Height H	Radius of Fillet R
		Max.	Basic	Max.	Basic	Max.
1/4	0.2500	0.2500	7/16	0.505	5/32	0.025
5/16	0.3125	0.3125	1/2	0.577	13/64	0.025
3/8	0.3750	0.3750	9/16	0.650	15/64	0.025
7/16	0.4375	0.4375	5/8	0.722	9/32	0.025
1/2	0.5000	0.5000	3/4	0.866	5/16	0.025
9/16	0.5625	0.5625	13/16	0.938	23/64	0.045
5/8	0.6250	0.6250	15/16	1.083	25/64	0.045
3/4	0.7500	0.7500	1 1/8	1.299	15/32	0.045
7/8	0.8750	0.8750	1 5/16	1.516	35/64	0.065
1	1.0000	1.0000	1 1/2	1.732	39/64	0.095
1 1/8	1.1250	1.1250	1 11/16	1.949	11/16	0.095
1 1/4	1.2500	1.2500	1 7/8	2.165	25/32	0.095
1 3/8	1.3750	1.3750	2 1/16	2.382	27/32	0.095
1 1/2	1.5000	1.5000	2 1/4	2.598	15/16	0.095
1 3/4	1.7500	1.7500	2 5/8	3.031	1 3/32	0.095
2	2.0000	2.0000	3	3.464	1 7/32	0.095
2 1/4	2.2500	2.2500	3 3/8	3.897	1 3/8	0.095
2 1/2	2.5000	2.5000	3 3/4	4.330	1 17/32	0.095
2 3/4	2.7500	2.7500	4 1/8	4.763	1 11/16	0.095
3	3.0000	3.0000	4 1/2	5.196	1 7/8	0.095

TD-12-51

Dimensions of Heavy Hex Structural Bolts (USAS B18.2.1-1965)

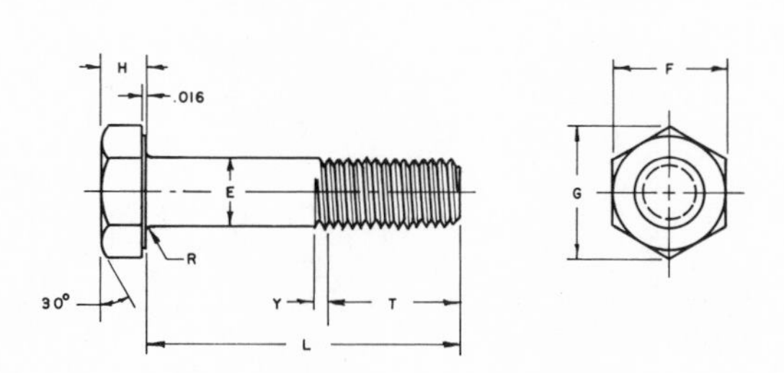

Nominal Size or Basic Product Dia.		Body Dia. E	Width Across Flats F	Width Across Corners G	Height H	Radius of Fillet R	Thread Length T	Vanish Thread Y
		Max.	Basic	Max.	Basic	Max.	Basic	Max.
1/2	0.5000	0.515	7/8	1.010	5/16	0.031	1.00	0.19
5/8	0.6250	0.642	1 1/16	1.227	25/64	0.062	1.25	0.22
3/4	0.7500	0.768	1 1/4	1.443	15/32	0.062	1.38	0.25
7/8	0.8750	0.895	1 7/16	1.660	35/64	0.062	1.50	0.28
1	1.0000	1.022	1 5/8	1.876	39/64	0.093	1.75	0.31
1 1/8	1.1250	1.149	1 13/16	2.093	11/16	0.093	2.00	0.34
1 1/4	1.2500	1.277	2	2.309	25/32	0.093	2.00	0.38
1 3/8	1.3750	1.404	2 3/16	2.526	27/32	0.093	2.25	0.44
1 1/2	1.5000	1.531	2 3/8	2.742	15/16	0.093	2.25	0.44

TD-12-52

Dimensions of Heavy Hex Screws (USAS B18.2.1-1965)

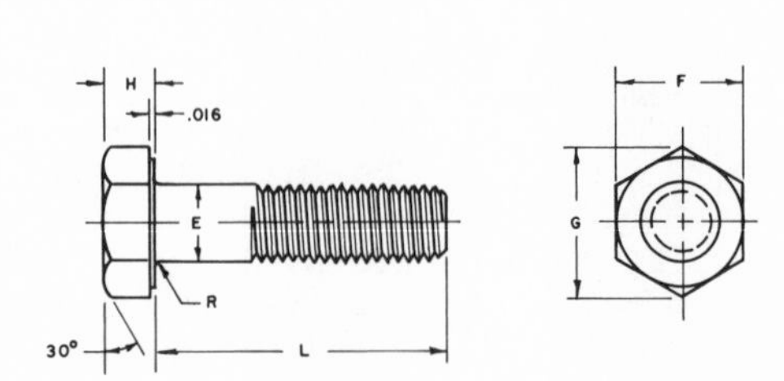

Nominal Size or Basic Product Dia.		Body Dia. E	Width Across Flats F	Width Across Corners G	Height H	Radius of Fillet R
		Max.	Basic	Max.	Basic	Max.
1/2	0.5000	0.5000	7/8	1.010	5/16	0.031
5/8	0.6250	0.6250	1 1/16	1.227	25/64	0.062
3/4	0.7500	0.7500	1 1/4	1.443	15/32	0.062
7/8	0.8750	0.8750	1 7/16	1.660	35/64	0.062
1	1.0000	1.0000	1 5/8	1.876	39/64	p.093
1 1/8	1.1250	1.1250	1 13/16	2.093	11/16	0.093
1 1/4	1.2500	1.2500	2	2.309	25/32	0.093
1 3/8	1.3750	1.3750	2 3/16	2.526	27/32	0.093
1 1/2	1.5000	1.5000	2 3/8	2.742	15/16	0.093
1 3/4	1.7500	1.7500	2 3/4	3.175	1 3/32	0.125
2	2.0000	2.0000	3 1/8	3.608	1 7/32	0.125
2 1/4	2.2500	2.2500	3 1/2	4.041	1 3/8	0.188
2 1/2	2.5000	2.5000	3 7/8	4.474	1 17/32	0.188
2 3/4	2.7500	2.7500	4 1/4	4.907	1 11/16	0.188
3	3.0000	3.0000	4 5/8	5.340	1 7/8	0.188

TD-12-53

Dimensions of Lag Screws (USAS B18.2.1-1965)

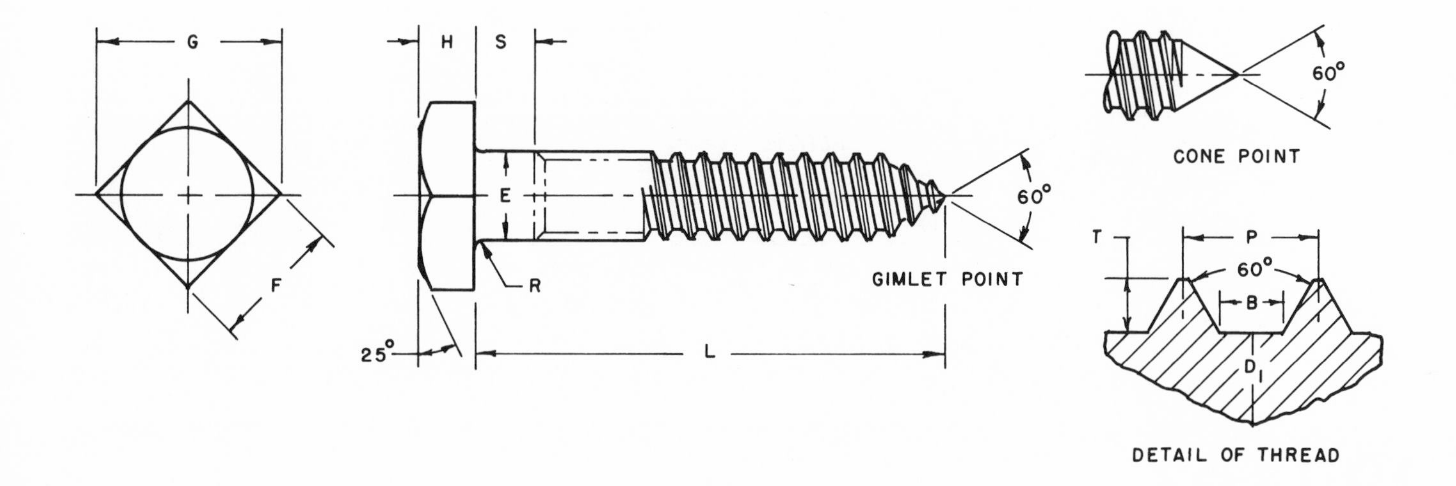

Nominal Size or Basic Product Dia.		Body or Shoulder Dia. E	Width Across Flats F	Width Across Corners G	Height H	Shoulder Length S	Radius of Fillet R	Threads per Inch	Thread Dimensions: Pitch	Flat at Root	Depth of Thread	Root Dia.
		Max.	Basic	Max.	Basic	Min.	Max.		P	B	T	D_1
No. 10	0.1900	0.199	9/32	0.398	1/8	0.094	0.031	11	0.091	0.039	0.035	0.120
1/4	0.2500	0.260	3/8	0.530	11/64	0.094	0.031	10	0.100	0.043	0.039	0.173
5/16	0.3125	0.324	1/2	0.707	13/64	0.125	0.031	9	0.111	0.048	0.043	0.227
3/8	0.3750	0.388	9/16	0.795	1/4	0.125	0.031	7	0.143	0.062	0.055	0.265
7/16	0.4375	0.452	5/8	0.884	19/64	0.156	0.031	7	0.143	0.062	0.055	0.328
1/2	0.5000	0.515	3/4	1.061	21/64	0.156	0.031	6	0.167	0.072	0.064	0.371
5/8	0.6250	0.642	15/16	1.326	27/64	0.312	0.062	5	0.200	0.086	0.077	0.471
3/4	0.7500	0.768	1 1/8	1.591	1/2	0.375	0.062	4 1/2	0.222	0.096	0.085	0.579
7/8	0.8750	0.895	1 5/16	1.856	19/32	0.375	0.062	4	0.250	0.108	0.096	0.683
1	1.0000	1.022	1 1/2	2.121	21/32	0.625	0.093	3 1/2	0.286	0.123	0.110	0.780
1 1/8	1.1250	1.149	1 11/16	2.386	3/4	0.625	0.093	3 1/4	0.308	0.133	0.119	0.887
1 1/4	1.2500	1.277	1 7/8	2.652	27/32	0.625	0.093	3 1/4	0.308	0.133	0.119	1.012

TD-12-54

Dimensions of Round Head Square-Neck Bolt (Carriage Bolt) (USAS B18.5-1952)

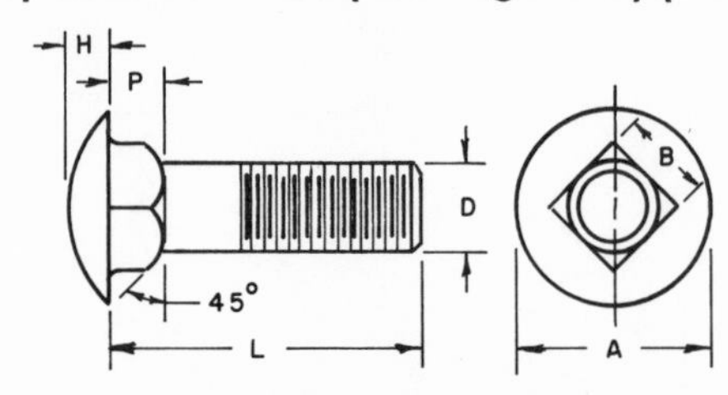

Size		Body Dia.	Diameter of Head A				Height of Head H			Depth of Square P		Width of Square B	
D	Tpi	Max.	Min.	Basic		Max.	Min.		Max.	Min.	Max.	Min.	Max.
No. 10	24	0.199	0.438	7/16	0.438	0.469	3/32	0.094	0.114	0.094	0.125	0.185	0.199
1/4	20	0.260	0.563	9/16	0.563	0.594	1/8	0.125	0.145	0.125	0.156	0.245	0.260
5/16	18	0.324	0.688	11/16	0.688	0.719	5/32	0.156	0.176	0.156	0.187	0.307	0.324
3/8	16	0.388	0.782	13/16	0.813	0.844	3/16	0.188	0.208	0.188	0.219	0.368	0.388
7/16	14	0.452	0.907	15/16	0.938	0.969	7/32	0.219	0.239	0.219	0.250	0.431	0.452
1/2	13	0.515	1.032	1 1/16	1.063	1.094	1/4	0.250	0.270	0.250	0.281	0.492	0.515
5/8	11	0.642	1.219	1 5/16	1.313	1.344	5/16	0.313	0.344	0.313	0.344	0.616	0.642
3/4	10	0.768	1.469	1 9/16	1.563	1.594	3/8	0.375	0.406	0.375	0.406	0.741	0.768
7/8	9	0.895	1.719	1 13/16	1.813	1.844	7/16	0.438	0.469	0.438	0.469	0.865	0.895
1	8	1.022	1.969	2 1/16	2.063	2.094	1/2	0.500	0.531	0.500	0.531	0.990	1.022

Dimensions of Round Head Short Square-Neck Bolt (USAS B18.5-1952)

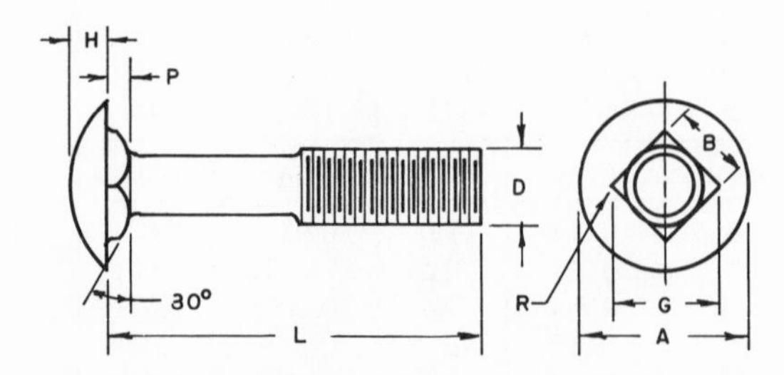

Size		Body Dia.	Dia. of Head A	Height of Head H	Depth of Square P	Width of Square B	Width Across Corners G	Radius Corners of Square R
D	Tpi	Max.	Min.	Min.	Min.	Min.	Max.	Max.
1/4	20	0.260	0.563	0.125	0.093	0.245	0.368	1/32
5/16	18	0.324	0.688	0.156	0.093	0.307	0.458	1/32
3/8	16	0.388	0.782	0.188	0.125	0.368	0.549	3/64
7/16	14	0.452	0.907	0.219	0.125	0.431	0.639	3/64
1/2	13	0.515	1.032	0.250	0.125	0.492	0.728	3/64
5/8	11	0.642	1.219	0.313	0.187	0.616	0.908	5/64
3/4	10	0.768	1.469	0.375	0.187	0.741	1.086	5/64

TD-12-56

Dimensions of Round Head Bolt (Button Head) (USAS B18.5-1952)

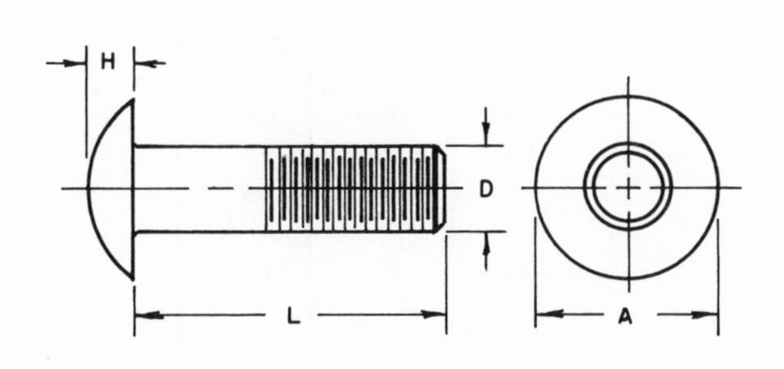

Size		Body Diameter	Diameter of Head A	Height of Head H
D	Tpi	Max.	Basic	Max.
No. 10	24	0.199	7/16	0.114
1/4	20	0.260	9/16	0.145
5/16	18	0.324	11/16	0.176
3/8	16	0.388	13/16	0.208
7/16	14	0.452	15/16	0.239
1/2	13	0.515	1 1/16	0.270
5/8	11	0.642	1 5/16	0.344
3/4	10	0.768	1 9/16	0.406
7/8	9	0.895	1 13/16	0.469
1	8	1.022	2 1/16	0.531

TD-12-57

Dimensions of Countersunk Bolt (USAS B18.5-1952)

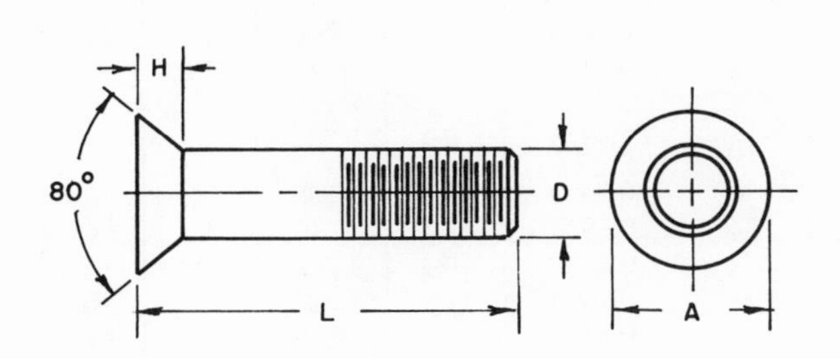

Size		Body Dia.	Dia. of Head A	Depth of Head	Width of Slot	Depth of Slot
D	Tpi	Max.	Max. Sharp	H	Max.	Max.
1/4	20	0.260	0.493	0.140	0.075	0.069
5/16	18	0.324	0.618	0.176	0.075	0.084
3/8	16	0.388	0.740	0.210	0.084	0.094
7/16	14	0.452	0.803	0.210	0.094	0.103
1/2	13	0.515	0.935	0.250	0.106	0.103
5/8	11	0.642	1.169	0.313	0.133	0.137
3/4	10	0.768	1.402	0.375	0.149	0.171
7/8	9	0.895	1.637	0.438	0.167	0.206
1	8	1.022	1.869	0.500	0.188	0.240
1 1/8	7	1.149	2.104	0.563	.....	.....
1 1/4	7	1.276	2.337	0.625	.....	.....
1 3/8	6	1.403	2.571	0.688	.....	.....
1 1/2	6	1.530	2.804	0.750	.....	.....

TD-12-58

Dimensions of Square Nuts (USAS B18.2.2-1965)

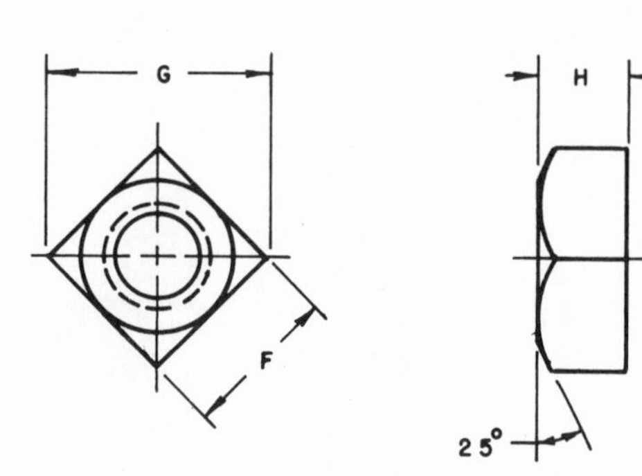

Nominal Size or Basic Major Dia. of Thread		Width Across Flats F	Width Across Corners G	Thickness H
		Basic	Max.	Basic
1/4	0.2500	7/16	0.619	7/32
5/16	0.3125	9/16	0.795	17/64
3/8	0.3750	5/8	0.884	21/64
7/16	0.4375	3/4	1.061	3/8
1/2	0.5000	13/16	1.149	7/16
5/8	0.6250	1	1.414	35/64
3/4	0.7500	1 1/8	1.591	21/32
7/8	0.8750	1 5/16	1.856	49/64
1	1.0000	1 1/2	2.121	7/8
1 1/8	1.1250	1 11/16	2.386	1
1 1/4	1.2500	1 7/8	2.652	1 3/32
1 3/8	1.3750	2 1/16	2.917	1 13/64
1 1/2	1.5000	2 1/4	3.182	1 5/16

TD-12-59

Dimensions of Hex Nuts and Hex Jam Nuts (USAS B18.2.2-1965)

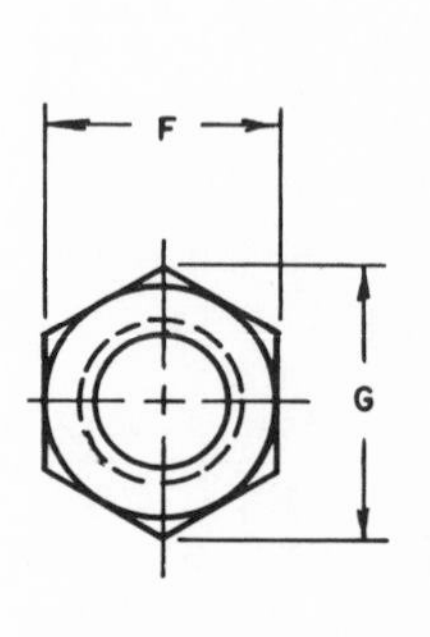

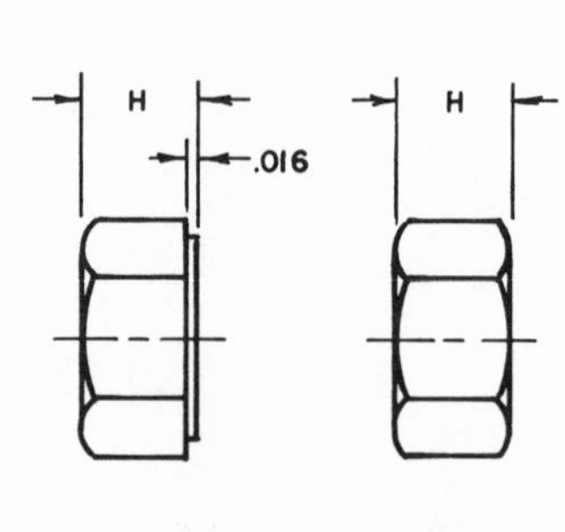

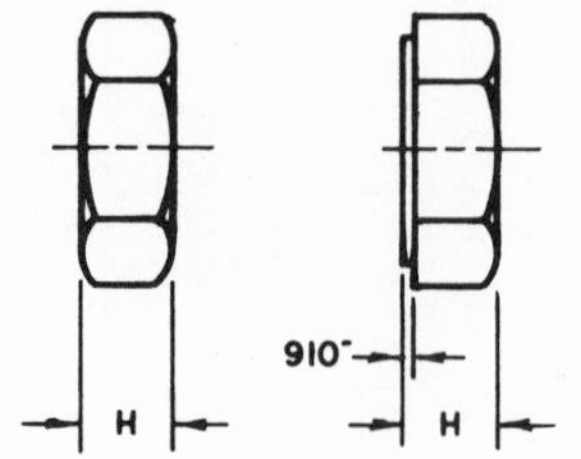

Nominal Size or Basic Major Dia. of Thread		Width Across Flats F	Width Across Corners G	Thick-ness Hex Nuts H	Thick-ness Hex Jam Nuts H
		Basic	Max.	Basic	Basic
1/4	0.2500	7/16	0.505	7/32	5/32
5/16	0.3125	1/2	0.577	17/64	3/16
3/8	0.3750	9/16	0.650	21/64	7/32
7/16	0.4375	11/16	0.794	3/8	1/4
1/2	0.5000	3/4	0.866	7/16	5/16
9/16	0.5625	7/8	1.010	31/64	5/16
5/8	0.6250	15/16	1.083	35/64	3/8
3/4	0.7500	1 1/8	1.299	41/64	27/64
7/8	0.8750	1 5/16	1.516	3/4	31/64
1	1.0000	1 1/2	1.732	55/64	35/64
1 1/8	1.1250	1 11/16	1.949	31/32	39/64
1 1/4	1.2500	1 7/8	2.165	1 1/16	23/32
1 3/8	1.3750	2 1/16	2.382	1 11/64	25/32
1 1/2	1.5000	2 1/4	2.598	1 9/32	27/32

TD-12-60

Dimensions of Hex Flat Nuts and Hex Flat Jam Nuts (USAS 18.2.2-1965)

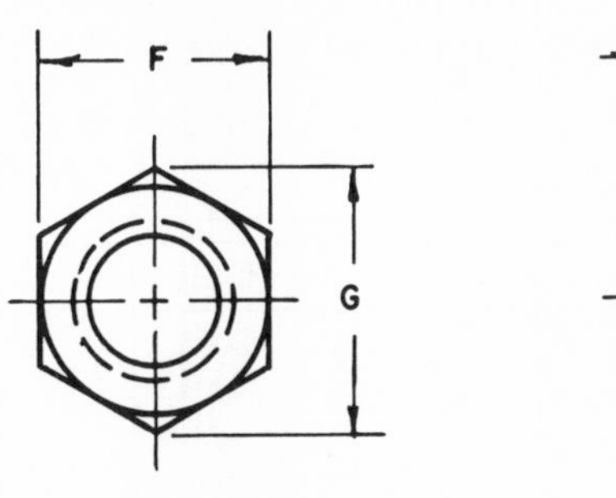

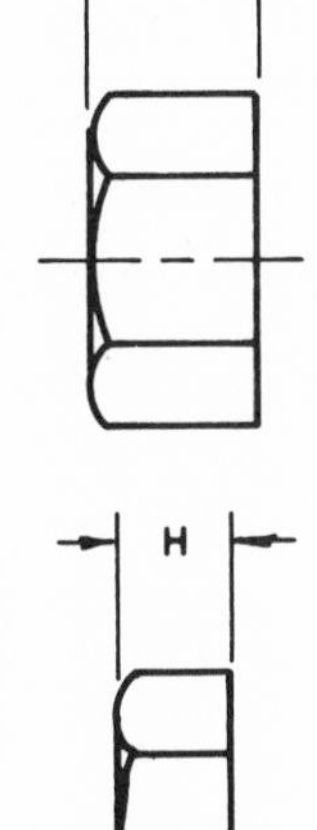

Nominal Size or Basic Major Dia. of Thread		Width Across Flats F	Width Across Corners G	Thickness Hex Flat Nuts H	Thickness Hex Flat Jam Nuts H
		Basic	Max.	Basic	Basic
1 1/8	1.1250	1 11/16	1.949	1	5/8
1 1/4	1.2500	1 7/8	2.165	1 3/32	3/4
1 3/8	1.3750	2 1/16	2.382	1 13/64	13/16
1 1/2	1.5000	2 1/4	2.598	1 5/16	7/8

TD-12-61

Dimensions of Square and Hexagon Machine Screw Nuts (USAS B18.6.3-1962)

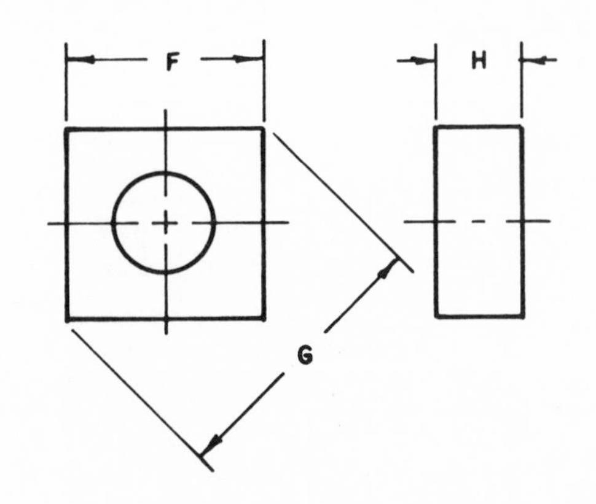

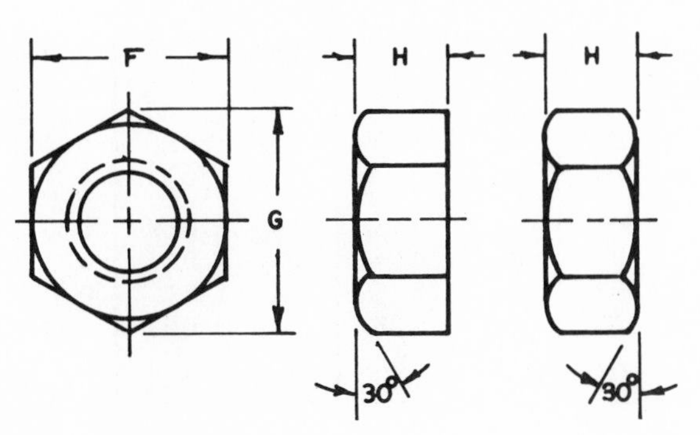

Nominal Size	Major Diameter of Thread	F Width Across Flats	G Width Across Corners Square	G Width Across Corners Hex.	H Thickness
	Basic	Basic	Max.	Max.	Nom.
0	0.0600	5/32	0.221	0.180	3/64
1	0.0730	5/32	0.221	0.180	3/64
2	0.0860	3/16	0.265	0.217	1/16
3	0.0990	3/16	0.265	0.217	1/16
4	0.1120	1/4	0.354	0.289	3/32
5	0.1250	5/16	0.442	0.361	7/64
6	0.1380	5/16	0.442	0.361	7/64
8	0.1640	11/32	0.486	0.397	1/8
10	0.1900	3/8	0.530	0.433	1/8
12	0.2160	7/16	0.619	0.505	5/32
1/4	0.2500	7/16	0.619	0.505	3/16
5/16	0.3125	9/16	0.795	0.650	7/32
3/8	0.3750	5/8	0.884	0.722	1/4

TD-12-62

Dimensions of Hex Castle Nuts (USAS B18.2.2-1965)

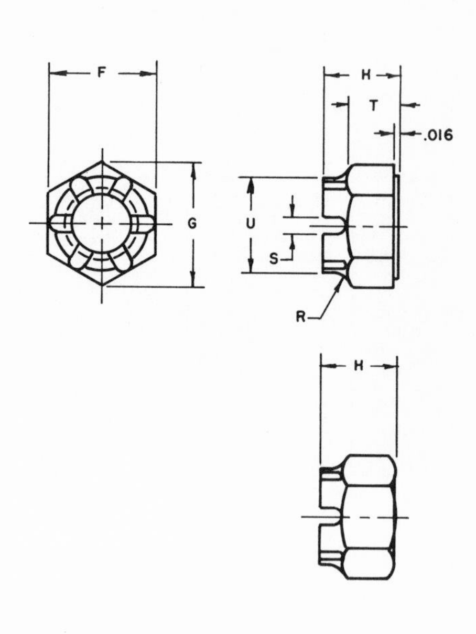

Nominal Size or Basic Major Dia. of Thread		Width Across Flats F	Width Across Corners G	Thickness H	Height of Flats	Unslotted Thickness T	Width of Slot S	Radius of Fillet R	Dia. of Cylindrical Part U
		Basic	Max.	Basic	Nom.	Max.	Max.	±.010	Min.
1/4	0.2500	7/16	0.505	9/32	3/16	0.20	0.10	0.094	0.371
5/16	0.3125	1/2	0.577	21/64	15/64	0.24	0.12	0.094	0.425
3/8	0.3750	9/16	0.650	13/32	9/32	0.29	0.15	0.094	0.478
7/16	0.4375	11/16	0.794	29/64	19/64	0.31	0.15	0.094	0.582
1/2	0.5000	3/4	0.866	9/16	13/32	0.42	0.18	0.125	0.637
9/16	0.5625	7/8	1.010	39/64	27/64	0.43	0.18	0.156	0.744
5/8	0.6250	15/16	1.083	23/32	1/2	0.51	0.24	0.156	0.797
3/4	0.7500	1 1/8	1.299	13/16	9/16	0.57	0.24	0.188	0.941
7/8	0.8750	1 5/16	1.516	29/32	21/32	0.67	0.24	0.188	1.097
1	1.0000	1 1/2	1.732	1	23/32	0.73	0.30	0.188	1.254
1 1/8	1.1250	1 11/16	1.949	1 5/32	13/16	0.83	0.33	0.250	1.411
1 1/4	1.2500	1 7/8	2.165	1 1/4	7/8	0.89	0.40	0.250	1.570
1 3/8	1.3750	2 1/16	2.382	1 3/8	1	1.02	0.40	0.250	1.726
1 1/2	1.5000	2 1/4	2.598	1 1/2	1 1/16	1.08	0.46	0.250	1.881

TD-12-63

Dimensions of Hex Slotted Nuts (USAS B18.2.2-1965)

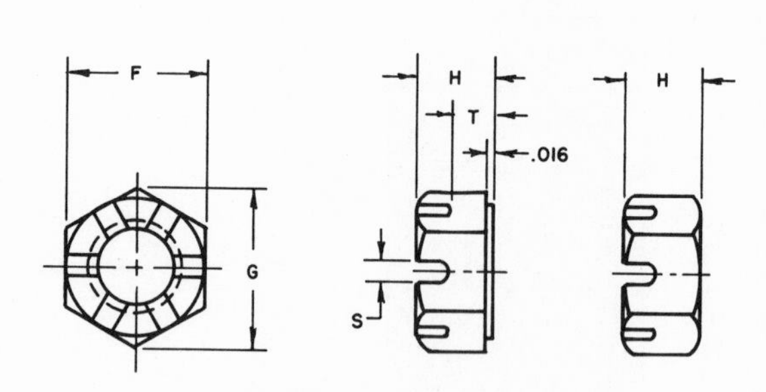

Nominal Size or Basic Major Dia. of Thread		Width Across Flats F	Width Across Corners G	Thickness H	Unslotted Thickness T	Width of Slot S
		Basic	Max.	Basic	Max.	Max.
1/4	0.2500	7/16	0.505	7/32	0.14	0.10
5/16	0.3125	1/2	0.577	17/64	0.18	0.12
3/8	0.3750	9/16	0.650	21/64	0.21	0.15
7/16	0.4375	11/16	0.794	3/8	0.23	0.15
1/2	0.5000	3/4	0.866	7/16	0.29	0.18
9/16	0.5625	7/8	1.010	31/64	0.31	0.18
5/8	0.6250	15/16	1.083	35/64	0.34	0.24
3/4	0.7500	1 1/8	1.299	41/64	0.40	0.24
7/8	0.8750	1 5/16	1.516	3/4	0.52	0.24
1	1.0000	1 1/2	1.732	55/64	0.59	0.30
1 1/8	1.1250	1 11/16	1.949	31/32	0.64	0.33
1 1/4	1.2500	1 7/8	2.165	1 1/16	0.70	0.40
1 3/8	1.3750	2 1/16	2.382	1 11/64	0.82	0.40
1 1/2	1.5000	2 1/4	2.598	1 9/32	0.86	0.46

TD-12-64

Dimensions of Preferred Sizes of Plain Washers, Type A (USAS B27.2-1965)

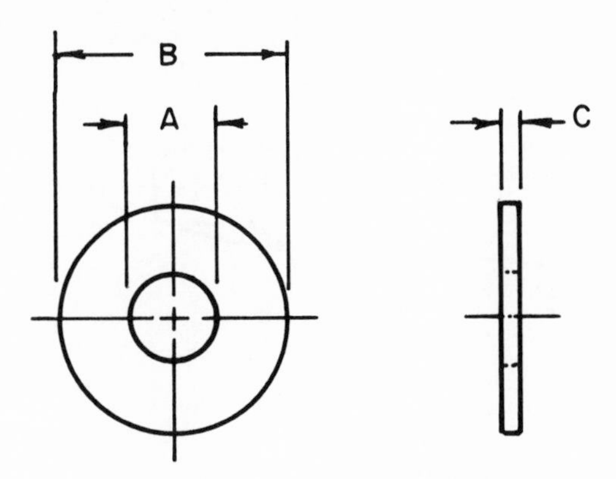

Nominal Washer Size**			Inside Dia. A Basic	Outside Dia. B Basic	Thickness C Basic
—	—		0.078	0.188	0.020
—	—		0.094	0.250	0.020
—	—		0.125	0.312	0.032
No. 6	0.138		0.156	0.375	0.049
No. 8	0.164		0.188	0.438	0.049
No. 10	0.190		0.219	0.500	0.049
3/16	0.188		0.250	0.562	0.049
No. 12	0.216		0.250	0.562	0.065
1/4	0.250	N	0.281	0.625	0.065
1/4	0.250	W	0.312	0.734*	0.065
5/16	0.312	N	0.344	0.688	0.065
5/16	0.312	W	0.375	0.875	0.083
3/8	0.375	N	0.406	0.812	0.065
3/8	0.375	W	0.438	1.000	0.083
7/16	0.438	N	0.469	0.922	0.065
7/16	0.438	W	0.500	1.250	0.083
1/2	0.500	N	0.531	1.062	0.095
1/2	0.500	W	0.562	1.375	0.109
9/16	0.562	N	0.594	1.156*	0.095
9/16	0.562	W	0.625	1.469*	0.109
5/8	0.625	N	0.656	1.312	0.095
5/8	0.625	W	0.688	1.750	0.134
3/4	0.750	N	0.812	1.469	0.134
3/4	0.750	W	0.812	2.000	0.148
7/8	0.875	N	0.938	1.750	0.134
7/8	0.875	W	0.938	2.250	0.165
1	1.000	N	1.062	2.000	0.134
1	1.000	W	1.062	2.500	0.165
1 1/8	1.125	N	1.250	2.250	0.134
1 1/8	1.125	W	1.250	2.750	0.165
1 1/4	1.250	N	1.375	2.500	0.165
1 1/4	1.250	W	1.375	3.000	0.165
1 3/8	1.375	N	1.500	2.750	0.165
1 3/8	1.375	W	1.500	3.250	0.180
1 1/2	1.500	N	1.625	3.000	0.165
1 1/2	1.500	W	1.625	3.500	0.180
1 5/8	1.625		1.750	3.750	0.180
1 3/4	1.750		1.875	4.000	0.180
1 7/8	1.875		2.000	4.250	0.180
2	2.000		2.125	4.500	0.180
2 1/4	2.250		2.375	4.750	0.220
2 1/2	2.500		2.625	5.000	0.238
2 3/4	2.750		2.875	5.250	0.259
3	3.000		3.125	5.500	0.284

*The 0.734 in., 1.156 in., and 1.469 in. outside diameters avoid washers which could be used in coin operated devices.

**Sizes are designated "Standard Plate" and "SAE." SAE size is designated "N" (narrow) and the Standard Plate "W" (wide).

TD-12-65

Dimensions of Regular Helical Spring Lock Washers (USAS B27.1-1965)

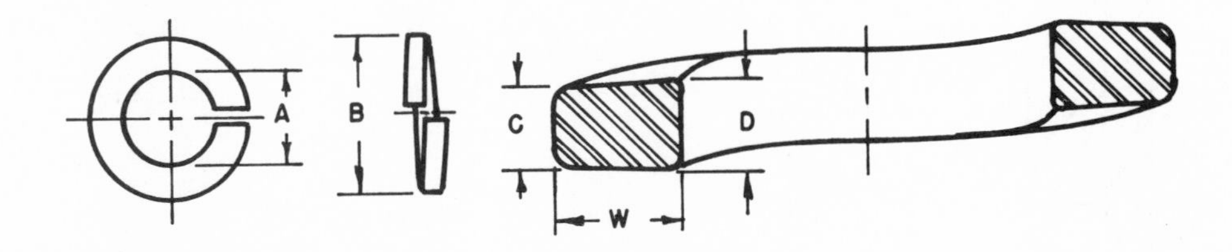

Nominal Washer Size		Inside Diameter A		Outside Diameter B	Washer Section Width W	Washer Section Thickness $\frac{D+C}{2}$
		Min.	Max.	Max.	Min.	Min.
No. 2	0.086	0.088	0.094	0.172	0.035	0.020
No. 3	0.099	0.101	0.107	0.195	0.040	0.025
No. 4	0.112	0.115	0.121	0.209	0.040	0.025
No. 5	0.125	0.128	0.134	0.236	0.047	0.031
No. 6	0.138	0.141	0.148	0.250	0.047	0.031
No. 8	0.164	0.168	0.175	0.293	0.055	0.040
No. 10	0.190	0.194	0.202	0.334	0.062	0.047
No. 12	0.216	0.221	0.229	0.377	0.070	0.056
1/4	0.250	0.255	0.263	0.489	0.109	0.062
5/16	0.312	0.318	0.328	0.586	0.125	0.078
3/8	0.375	0.382	0.393	0.683	0.141	0.094
7/16	0.438	0.446	0.459	0.779	0.156	0.109
1/2	0.500	0.509	0.523	0.873	0.171	0.125
9/16	0.562	0.572	0.587	0.971	0.188	0.141
5/8	0.625	0.636	0.653	1.079	0.203	0.156
11/16	0.688	0.700	0.718	1.176	0.219	0.172
3/4	0.750	0.763	0.783	1.271	0.234	0.188
13/16	0.812	0.826	0.847	1.367	0.250	0.203
7/8	0.875	0.890	0.912	1.464	0.266	0.219
15/16	0.938	0.954	0.978	1.560	0.281	0.234
1	1.000	1.017	1.042	1.661	0.297	0.250
1 1/16	1.062	1.080	1.107	1.756	0.312	0.266
1 1/8	1.125	1.144	1.172	1.853	0.328	0.281
1 3/16	1.188	1.208	1.237	1.950	0.344	0.297
1 1/4	1.250	1.271	1.302	2.045	0.359	0.312
1 5/16	1.312	1.334	1.366	2.141	0.375	0.328
1 3/8	1.375	1.398	1.432	2.239	0.391	0.344
1 7/16	1.438	1.462	1.497	2.334	0.406	0.359
1 1/2	1.500	1.525	1.561	2.430	0.422	0.375

TD-12-66

Dimensions of Extra Duty Helical Spring Lock Washers (USAS B27.1-1965)

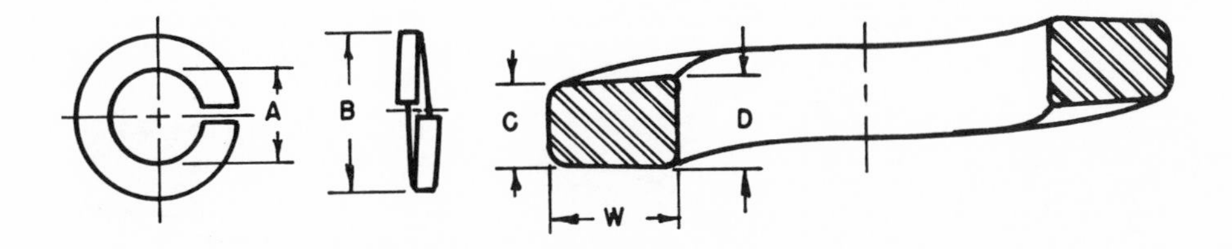

Nominal Washer Size		Inside Diameter A		Outside Diameter B	Washer Section: Width W	Washer Section: Thickness $\frac{D+C}{2}$
		Min.	Max.	Max.	Min.	Min.
No. 2	0.086	0.088	0.094	0.208	0.053	0.027
No. 3	0.099	0.101	0.107	0.239	0.062	0.034
No. 4	0.112	0.115	0.121	0.253	0.062	0.034
No. 5	0.125	0.128	0.134	0.300	0.079	0.045
No. 6	0.138	0.141	0.148	0.314	0.079	0.045
No. 8	0.164	0.168	0.175	0.375	0.096	0.057
No. 10	0.190	0.194	0.202	0.434	0.112	0.068
No. 12	0.216	0.221	0.229	0.497	0.130	0.080
1/4	0.250	0.255	0.263	0.535	0.132	0.084
5/16	0.312	0.318	0.328	0.622	0.143	0.108
3/8	0.375	0.382	0.393	0.741	0.170	0.123
7/16	0.438	0.446	0.459	0.839	0.186	0.143
1/2	0.500	0.509	0.523	0.939	0.204	0.162
9/16	0.562	0.572	0.587	1.041	0.223	0.182
5/8	0.625	0.636	0.653	1.157	0.242	0.202
11/16	0.688	0.700	0.718	1.258	0.260	0.221
3/4	0.750	0.763	0.783	1.361	0.279	0.241
13/16	0.812	0.826	0.847	1.463	0.298	0.261
7/8	0.875	0.890	0.912	1.576	0.322	0.285
15/16	0.938	0.954	0.978	1.688	0.345	0.308
1	1.000	1.017	1.042	1.799	0.366	0.330
1 1/16	1.062	1.080	1.107	1.910	0.389	0.352
1 1/8	1.125	1.144	1.172	2.019	0.411	0.375
1 3/16	1.188	1.208	1.237	2.124	0.431	0.396
1 1/4	1.250	1.271	1.302	2.231	0.452	0.417
1 5/16	1.312	1.334	1.366	2.335	0.472	0.438
1 3/8	1.375	1.398	1.432	2.439	0.491	0.458
1 7/16	1.438	1.462	1.497	2.540	0.509	0.478
1 1/2	1.500	1.525	1.561	2.638	0.526	0.496

TD-12-67

Dimensions of Hi-Collar Helical Spring Lock Washers (USAS B27.1-1965)

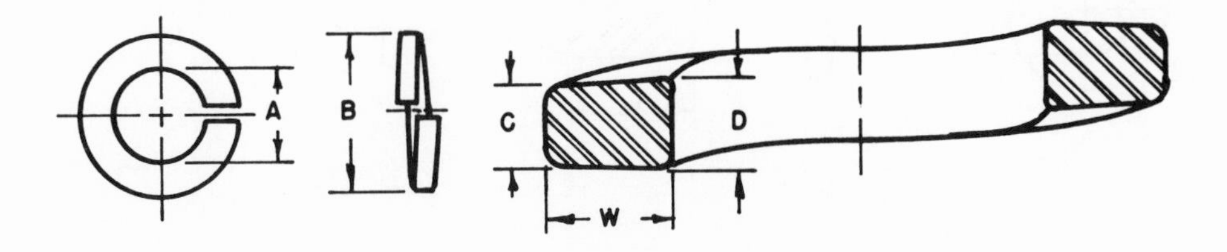

Nominal Washer Size		Inside Diameter A		Outside Diameter B	Washer Section Width W	Washer Section Thickness $\frac{D+C}{2}$
		Min.	Max.	Max.	Min.	Min.
No. 4	0.112	0.115	0.121	0.173	0.022	0.022
No. 5	0.125	0.128	0.134	0.202	0.030	0.030
No. 6	0.138	0.141	0.148	0.216	0.030	0.030
No. 8	0.164	0.168	0.175	0.267	0.042	0.047
No. 10	0.190	0.194	0.202	0.294	0.042	0.047
¼	0.250	0.255	0.263	0.365	0.047	0.078
5⁄16	0.312	0.318	0.328	0.460	0.062	0.093
⅜	0.375	0.382	0.393	0.553	0.076	0.125
7⁄16	0.438	0.446	0.459	0.647	0.090	0.140
½	0.500	0.509	0.523	0.737	0.103	0.172
⅝	0.625	0.636	0.653	0.923	0.125	0.203
¾	0.750	0.763	0.783	1.111	0.154	0.218
⅞	0.875	0.890	0.912	1.296	0.182	0.234
1	1.000	1.017	1.042	1.483	0.208	0.250
1⅛	1.125	1.144	1.172	1.669	0.236	0.313
1¼	1.250	1.271	1.302	1.799	0.236	0.313
1⅜	1.375	1.398	1.432	2.041	0.292	0.375
1½	1.500	1.525	1.561	2.170	0.292	0.375
1¾	1.750	1.775	1.811	2.602	0.383	0.469
2	2.000	2.025	2.061	2.852	0.383	0.469
2¼	2.250	2.275	2.311	3.352	0.508	0.508
2½	2.500	2.525	2.561	3.602	0.508	0.508
2¾	2.750	2.775	2.811	4.102	0.633	0.633
3	3.000	3.025	3.061	4.352	0.633	0.633

TD-12-68

Dimensions of Internal Tooth Lock Washers (USAS B27.1-1965)

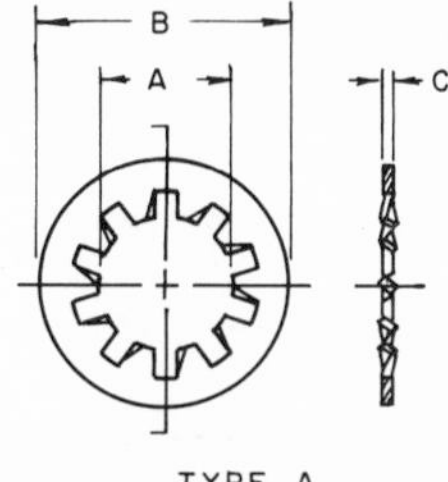

TYPE A

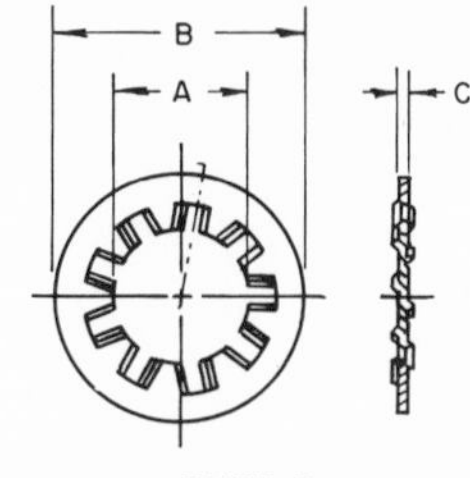

TYPE B

Nominal Washer Size		A Inside Diameter		B Outside Diameter		C Thickness	
		Min.	Max.	Max.	Min.	Max.	Min.
No. 2	0.086	0.089	0.095	0.200	0.175	0.105	0.010
No. 3	0.099	0.102	0.109	0.232	0.215	0.019	0.012
No. 4	0.112	0.115	0.123	0.270	0.245	0.019	0.015
No. 5	0.125	0.129	0.136	0.280	0.255	0.021	0.017
No. 6	0.138	0.141	0.150	0.295	0.275	0.021	0.017
No. 8	0.164	0.168	0.176	0.340	0.325	0.023	0.018
No. 10	0.190	0.195	0.204	0.381	0.365	0.025	0.020
No. 12	0.216	0.221	0.231	0.410	0.394	0.025	0.020
1/4	0.250	0.256	0.267	0.478	0.460	0.028	0.023
5/16	0.312	0.320	0.332	0.610	0.594	0.034	0.028
3/8	0.375	0.384	0.398	0.692	0.670	0.040	0.032
7/16	0.438	0.448	0.464	0.789	0.740	0.040	0.032
1/2	0.500	0.512	0.530	0.900	0.867	0.045	0.037
9/16	0.562	0.576	0.596	0.985	0.957	0.045	0.037
5/8	0.625	0.640	0.663	1.071	1.045	0.050	0.042
11/16	0.688	0.704	0.728	1.166	1.130	0.050	0.042
3/4	0.750	0.769	0.795	1.245	1.220	0.055	0.047
13/16	0.812	0.832	0.861	1.315	1.290	0.055	0.047
7/8	0.875	0.894	0.927	1.410	1.364	0.060	0.052
1	1.000	1.019	1.060	1.637	1.590	0.067	0.059
1 1/8	1.125	1.144	1.192	1.830	1.799	0.067	0.059
1 1/4	1.250	1.275	1.325	1.975	1.921	0.067	0.059

TECHNICAL DATA

Dimensions of Heavy Internal Tooth Lock Washers (USAS B27.1-1965)

1/4	0.250	0.256	0.267	0.536	0.500	0.045	0.035
5/16	0.312	0.320	0.332	0.607	0.590	0.050	0.040
3/8	0.375	0.384	0.398	0.748	0.700	0.050	0.042
7/16	0.438	0.448	0.464	0.858	0.800	0.067	0.050
1/2	0.500	0.512	0.530	0.924	0.880	0.067	0.055
9/16	0.562	0.576	0.596	1.034	0.990	0.067	0.055
5/8	0.625	0.640	0.663	1.135	1.100	0.067	0.059
3/4	0.750	0.768	0.795	1.265	1.240	0.084	0.070
7/8	0.875	0.894	0.927	1.447	1.400	0.084	0.075

TD-12-70

Dimensions of External Tooth Lock Washers (USAS B27.1-1965)

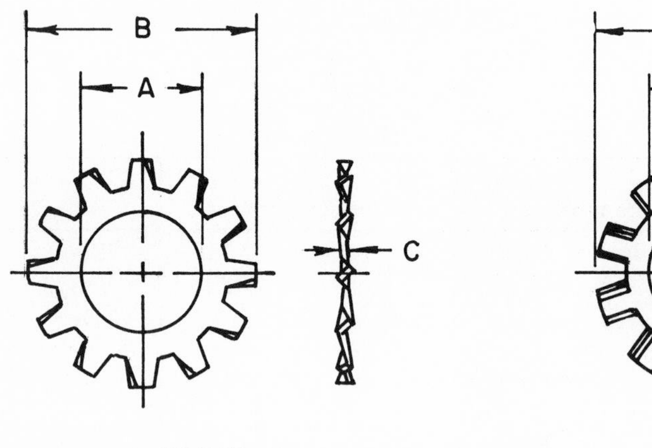

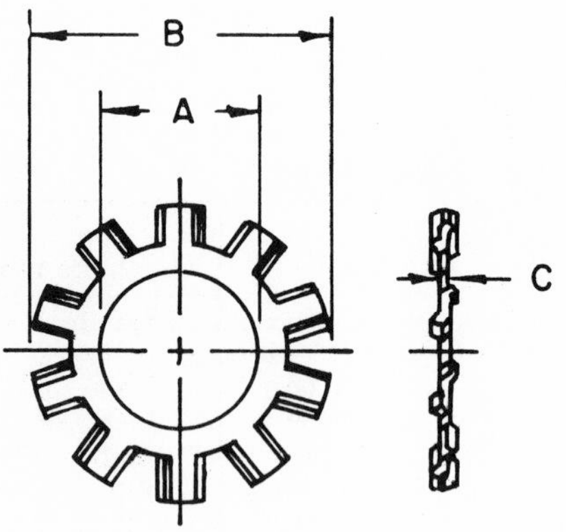

Nominal Washer Size		A Inside Diameter		B Outside Diameter		C Thickness	
		Min.	Max.	Max.	Min.	Max.	Min.
No. 4	0.112	0.115	0.123	0.260	0.245	0.019	0.105
No. 6	0.138	0.141	0.150	0.320	0.305	0.022	0.016
No. 8	0.164	0.168	0.176	0.381	0.365	0.023	0.018
No. 10	0.190	0.195	0.204	0.410	0.395	0.025	0.020
No. 12	0.216	0.221	0.231	0.475	0.460	0.028	0.023
1/4	0.250	0.256	0.267	0.510	0.494	0.028	0.023
5/16	0.312	0.320	0.332	0.610	0.588	0.034	0.028
3/8	0.375	0.384	0.398	0.694	0.670	0.040	0.032
7/16	0.438	0.448	0.464	0.760	0.740	0.040	0.032
1/2	0.500	0.513	0.530	0.900	0.880	0.045	0.037
9/16	0.562	0.576	0.596	0.985	0.960	0.045	0.037
5/8	0.625	0.641	0.663	1.070	1.045	0.050	0.042
11/16	0.688	0.704	0.728	1.155	1.130	0.050	0.042
3/4	0.750	0.768	0.795	1.260	1.220	0.055	0.047
13/16	0.812	0.833	0.861	1.315	1.290	0.055	0.047
7/8	0.875	0.897	0.927	1.410	1.380	0.060	0.052
1	1.000	1.025	1.060	1.620	1.590	0.067	0.059

TD-12-71

Dimensions of Square and Flat Keys (USAS)

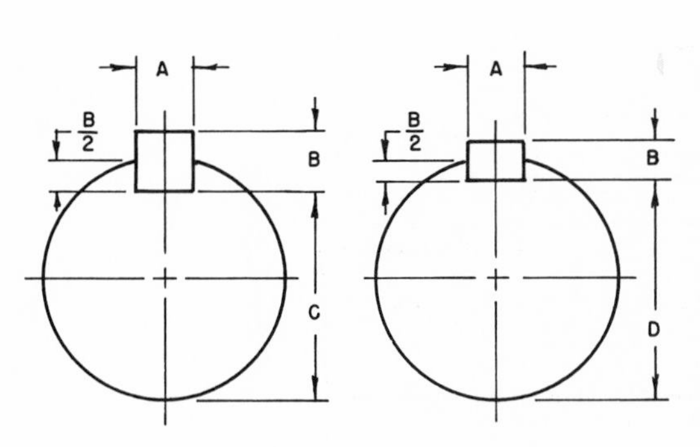

Shaft Diameter	Square key A x B	Flat key A x B	Bottom of keyseat to opposite side of shaft: Square key C	Bottom of keyseat to opposite side of shaft: Flat key D
1/2	1/8 x 1/8	1/8 x 3/32	0.430	0.445
9/16	1/8 x 1/8	1/8 x 3/32	0.493	0.509
5/8	3/16 x 3/16	3/16 x 1/8	0.517	0.548
11/16	3/16 x 3/16	3/16 x 1/8	0.581	0.612
3/4	3/16 x 3/16	3/16 x 1/8	0.644	0.676
13/16	3/16 x 3/16	3/16 x 1/8	0.708	0.739
7/8	3/16 x 3/16	3/16 x 1/8	0.771	0.802
15/16	1/4 x 1/4	1/4 x 3/16	0.796	0.827
1	1/4 x 1/4	1/4 x 3/16	0.859	0.890
1 1/16	1/4 x 1/4	1/4 x 3/16	0.923	0.954
1 1/8	1/4 x 1/4	1/4 x 3/16	0.986	1.017
1 3/16	1/4 x 1/4	1/4 x 3/16	1.049	1.081
1 1/4	1/4 x 1/4	1/4 x 3/16	1.112	1.144
1 5/16	5/16 x 5/16	5/16 x 1/4	1.137	1.169
1 3/8	5/16 x 5/16	5/16 x 1/4	1.201	1.232
1 7/16	3/8 x 3/8	3/8 x 1/4	1.225	1.288
1 1/2	3/8 x 3/8	3/8 x 1/4	1.289	1.351
1 9/16	3/8 x 3/8	3/8 x 1/4	1.352	1.415
1 5/8	3/8 x 3/8	3/8 x 1/4	1.416	1.478
1 11/16	3/8 x 3/8	3/8 x 1/4	1.479	1.542
1 3/4	3/8 x 3/8	3/8 x 1/4	1.542	1.605

TD-12-72

Dimensions of Woodruff Keys (USAS B-17 f-1930-R 1955)

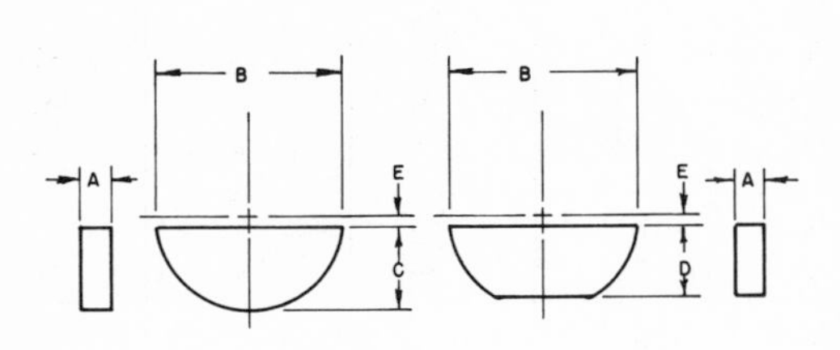

Key No.	Nominal key size A x B	Width of key A Max.	Dia. of key B Max.	Height of key C Max.	Height of key D Max.	Distance below center E
204	1/16 x 1/2	0.0635	0.500	0.203	0.194	3/64
304	3/32 x 1/2	.0948	0.500	.203	.194	3/64
305	3/32 x 5/8	.0948	0.625	.250	.240	1/16
404	1/8 x 1/2	.1260	0.500	.203	.194	3/64
405	1/8 x 5/8	.1260	0.625	.250	.204	1/16
406	1/8 x 3/4	.1260	0.750	.313	.303	1/16
505	5/32 x 5/8	.1573	0.625	.250	.240	1/16
506	5/32 x 3/4	.1573	0.750	.313	.303	1/16
507	5/32 x 7/8	.1573	0.875	.375	.365	1/16
606	3/16 x 3/4	.1885	0.750	.313	.303	1/16
607	3/16 x 7/8	.1885	0.875	.375	.365	1/16
608	3/16 x 1	.1885	1.000	.438	.428	1/16
609	3/16 x 1 1/8	.1885	1.125	.484	.475	5/64
807	1/4 x 7/8	.2510	0.875	.375	.365	1/16
808	1/4 x 1	.2510	1.000	.438	.428	1/16
809	1/4 x 1 1/8	.2510	1.125	.484	.475	5/64
810	1/4 x 1 1/4	.2510	1.250	.547	.537	5/64
811	1/4 x 1 3/8	.2510	1.375	.594	.584	3/32
812	1/4 x 1 1/2	.2510	1.500	.641	.631	7/64

TD-12-73

Dimensions of Pratt and Whitney Round-End Keys

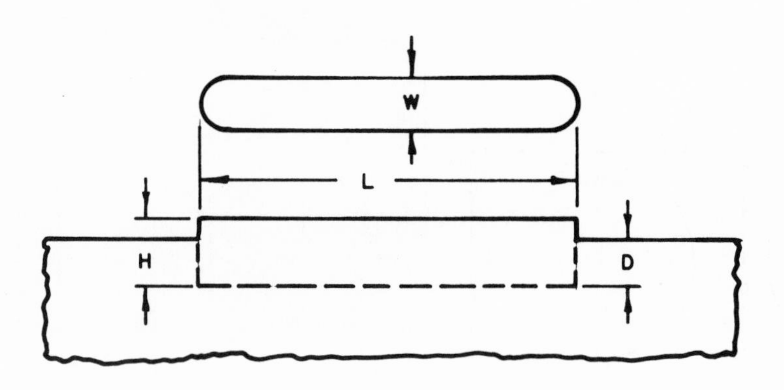

No. of key	L	W	H	D
1	1/2	1/16	3/32	1/16
2	1/2	3/32	9/64	3/32
3	1/2	1/8	3/16	1/8
4	5/8	3/32	9/64	3/32
5	5/8	1/8	3/16	1/8
6	5/8	5/32	15/64	5/32
7	3/4	1/8	3/16	1/8
8	3/4	5/32	15/64	5/32
9	3/4	3/16	9/32	3/16
10	7/8	5/32	15/64	5/32
11	7/8	3/16	9/32	3/16
12	7/8	7/32	21/64	7/32
A	7/8	1/4	3/8	1/4
13	1	3/16	9/32	3/16
14	1	7/32	21/64	7/32
15	1	1/4	3/8	1/4
B	1	5/16	15/32	5/16
16	1 1/8	3/16	9/32	3/16
17	1 1/8	7/32	21/64	7/32
18	1 1/8	1/4	3/8	1/4
C	1 1/8	5/16	15/32	5/16
19	1 1/4	3/16	9/32	3/16
20	1 1/4	7/32	21/64	7/32
21	1 1/4	1/4	3/8	1/4
D	1 1/4	5/16	15/32	5/16
E	1 1/4	3/8	9/16	3/8

No. of key	L	W	H	D
22	1 3/8	1/4	3/8	1/4
23	1 3/8	5/16	15/32	5/16
F	1 3/8	3/8	9/16	3/8
24	1 1/2	1/4	3/8	1/4
25	1 1/2	5/16	15/32	5/16
G	1 1/2	3/8	9/16	3/8
51	1 3/4	1/4	3/8	1/4
52	1 3/4	5/16	15/32	5/16
53	1 3/4	3/8	9/16	3/8
26	2	3/16	9/32	3/16
27	2	1/4	3/8	1/4
28	2	5/16	15/32	5/16
29	2	3/8	9/16	3/8
54	2 1/4	1/4	3/8	1/4
55	2 1/4	5/16	15/32	5/16
56	2 1/4	3/8	9/16	3/8
57	2 1/4	7/16	21/32	7/16
58	2 1/2	5/16	15/32	5/16
59	2 1/2	3/8	9/16	3/8
60	2 1/2	7/16	21/32	7/16
61	2 1/2	1/2	3/4	1/2
30	3	3/8	9/16	3/8
31	3	7/16	21/32	7/16
32	3	1/2	3/4	1/2
33	3	9/16	27/32	9/16
34	3	5/8	15/16	5/8

TD-12-74

Dimensions of Straight Pins (USAS B5.20-1947)

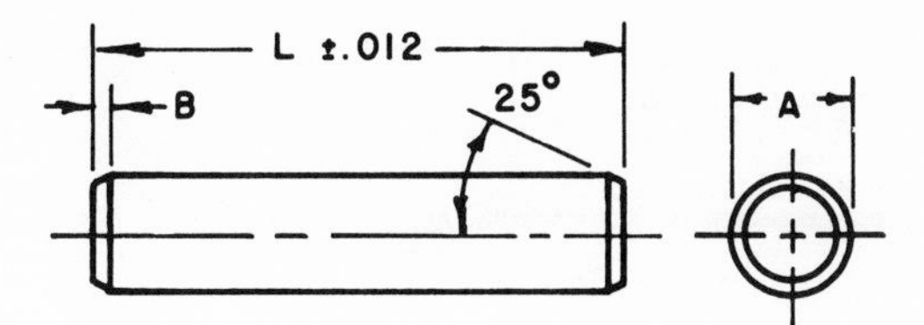

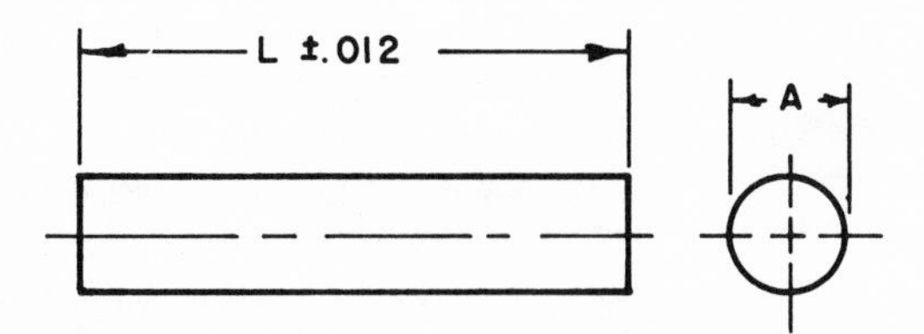

Nominal Diameter	Diameter A Max.	Diameter A Min.	Chamfer B
0.062	0.0625	0.0605	0.010
0.094	0.0937	0.0917	0.010
0.109	0.1094	0.1074	0.010
0.125	0.1250	0.1230	0.010
0.156	0.1562	0.1542	1/64
0.188	0.1875	0.1855	1/64
0.219	0.2187	0.2167	1/64
0.250	0.2500	0.2480	1/64
0.312	0.3125	0.3095	1/32
0.375	0.3750	0.3720	1/32
0.438	0.4375	0.4345	1/32
0.500	0.500	0.4970	1/32

TD-12-75

Dimensions of Cotter Pins (USAS-B5.20-1954)

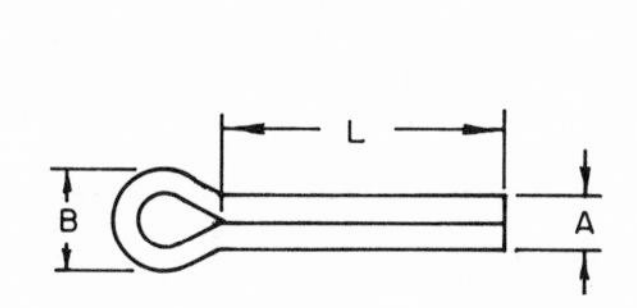

Diameter Nominal	Diameter A Max.	Outside Eye Dia. B Min.	Hole Sizes Recommended	Diameter Nominal	Diameter A Max.	Outside Eye Dia. B Min.	Hole Sizes Recommended
0.031	0.032	1/16	3/64	0.188	0.176	3/8	13/64
0.047	0.048	3/32	1/16	0.219	0.207	7/16	15/64
0.062	0.060	1/8	5/64	0.250	0.225	1/2	17/64
0.078	0.076	5/32	3/32	0.312	0.280	5/8	5/16
0.094	0.090	3/16	7/64	0.375	0.335	3/4	3/8
0.109	0.104	7/32	1/8	0.438	0.406	7/8	7/16
0.125	0.120	1/4	9/64	0.500	0.473	1	1/2
0.141	0.134	9/32	5/32	0.625	0.598	1 1/4	5/8
0.156	0.150	5/16	11/64	0.750	0.723	1 1/2	3/4

TD-12-76

Rivet Clinch Allowance (Chicago Rivet and Machine Co.)

Rivet Shank Diameter	.060″	.065″	.088″	.098″	1/8″	9/64″	5/32″	3/16″	7/32″	1/4″	5/16″
Clinch Allowance: Semi Tubular	.032″	.032″	.045″	.055″	.062″	.093″	.093″	.110″	.140″	.156″	.187″
Clinch Allowance: Split and Deep Hole			.062″	.078″	.093″	.125″	.125″	.156″	—	.187″	.187″
Diameter of Hole in Assembly	.067″	.070″	.093″	.104″	.128″	.152″	.165″	.196″	15/64″	.265″	21/64″
Drill Number	51	50	42	37	30	24	19	9	15/64″	17/64″	21/64″

TD-12-77

Common Nails, Box Nails

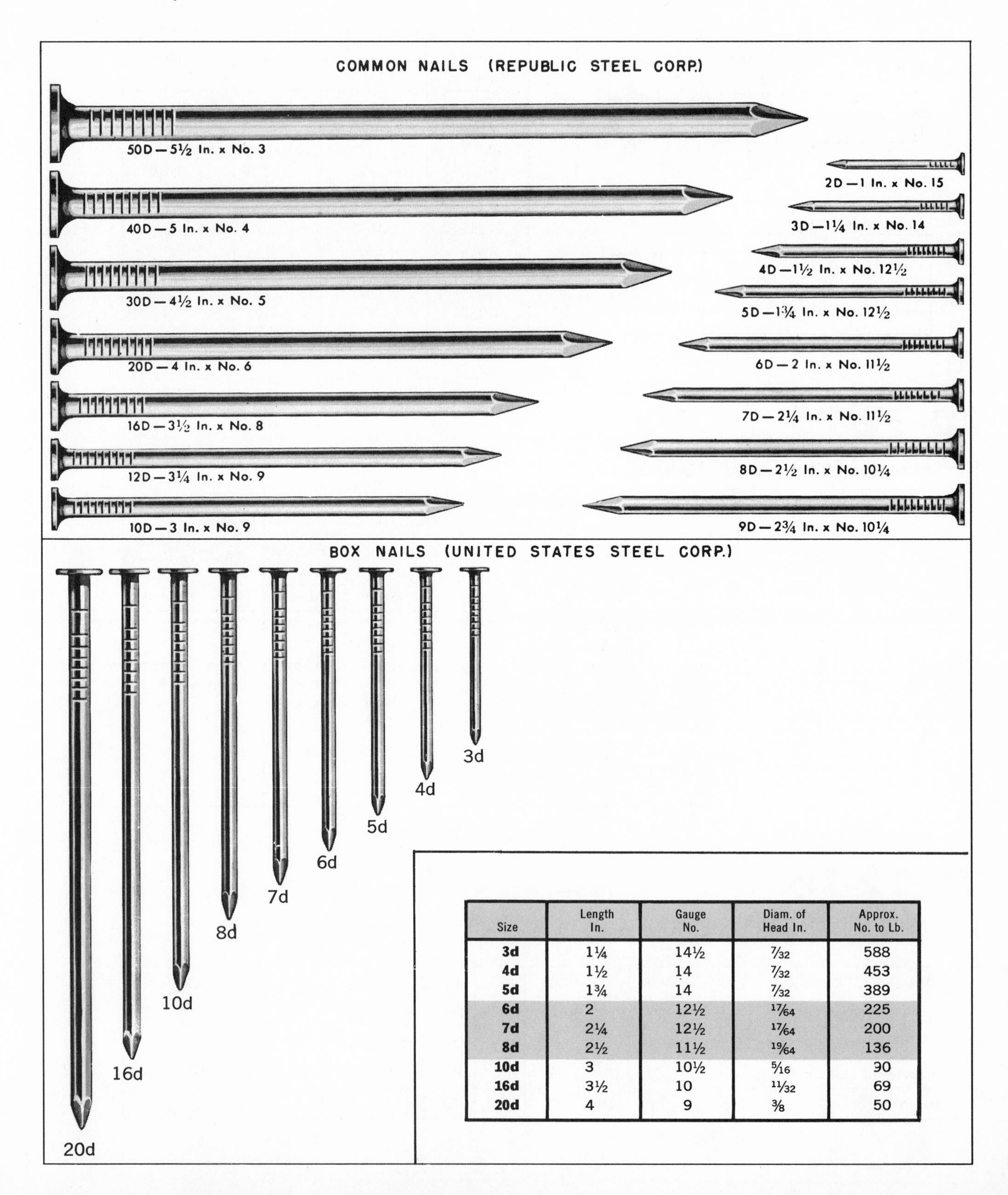

Size	Length In.	Gauge No.	Diam. of Head In.	Approx. No. to Lb.
3d	1¼	14½	7/32	588
4d	1½	14	7/32	453
5d	1¾	14	7/32	389
6d	2	12½	17/64	225
7d	2¼	12½	17/64	200
8d	2½	11½	19/64	136
10d	3	10½	5/16	90
16d	3½	10	11/32	69
20d	4	9	3/8	50

TD-12-78

Casing Nails, Finishing Nails, Tack Sizes, Countersunk Finishing Washers, Glaziers Points

CASING NAILS (UNITED STATES STEEL)

STANDARD SIZES

Size	Length In.	Gauge No.	Degree Countersunk	Diam. of Head Gauge No.	Approx. No. to Lb.
4d	1½	14	32	11	489
6d	2	12½	32	9½	244
8d	2½	11½	32	8½	147
10d	3	10½	32	7½	96
16d	3½	10	32	7	74

4d 6d 8d 10d 16d

FINISHING NAILS (UNITED STATES STEEL)

STANDARD SIZES

Size	Length In.	Gauge No.	Diam. of Head Gauge No.	Approx. No. to Lb.
3d	1¼	15½	12½	880
4d	1½	15	12	630
6d	2	13	10	288
8d	2½	12½	9½	196
10d	3	11½	8½	124

10d 8d 6d 4d 3d

TACK SIZES (ATLAS TACK CORP.)

1½	2	2½	3	4	6	8	10	12	14	16	18	20	22	24
7/32"	1/4"	5/16"	3/8"	7/16"	1/2"	9/16"	5/8"	11/16"	3/4"	13/16"	7/8"	15/16"	1"	1 1/8"

Ounce	**1½**	**2**	**2½**	**3**	**4**	**6**	**8**	**10**	**12**	**14**	**16**	**18**	**20**	**22**	**24**
Carpet	....	....	....	....	1600	1248	1104	880	....	....	....	....	....	....	....
Upholsterers	....	5600	4032	3000	2400	1760	1440	1200	1040	800	720	640	576	512	440
Trimmers	8000	6400	5600	4000	3008	2640	1792	1440	1200	1024	896	....	....	....	....
Bill Poster's	....	....	....	1264	960	608	544	496	....	....	....	....	....	....	....
Gimp	....	....	5000	3488	2992	2496	1840	1600	....	....	....	....	....	....	....

COUNTER SUNK FINISHING WASHERS (ATLAS TACK CORP.)

#6 15/32" diameter

#8 17/32" diameter

#10 19/32" diameter

#12 21/32" diameter

#14 23/32" diameter

#16 25/32" diameter

GLAZIERS POINTS (ATLAS TACK CORP.)

2½ oz.

#3 — 11/32"

#2 — 13/32"

#1 — 15/32"

#0 — 17/32"

TD-12-79

Double-Point Flat Wire Tacks, Fence Staples

DOUBLE POINT, FLAT WIRE TACKS (ATLAS TACK CORP.)

	#8	#9	#10	#11	#12	#14
Width Inside Crown	3/16"	7/32"	1/4"	9/32"	5/16"	5/16"
Length Inside Leg	13/32"	7/16"	15/32"	1/2"	5/8"	11/16"
Wire Gauge	16	16	16	15	15	14
Approx. Count Per Pound	1,250	1,150	1,050	770	670	490

FENCE STAPLES, 9 GAUGE (UNITED STATES STEEL CORP.)

1⅛" 1" ⅞"

Bright In.	Galvanized Wire In.	Approx. Count Per Lb.—Bright
⅞"	—	122
1"	1	106
1⅛"	1⅛	97
1¼"	1¼	87
1½"	1½	72
1¾"	—	61

Inside spread at shoulders is ¼ inch.
Length from underside of crown to tips of points.

TD-12-80

Flat Head Wire Nails, Wire Brads, Approximate Number of Wire Nails per Pound

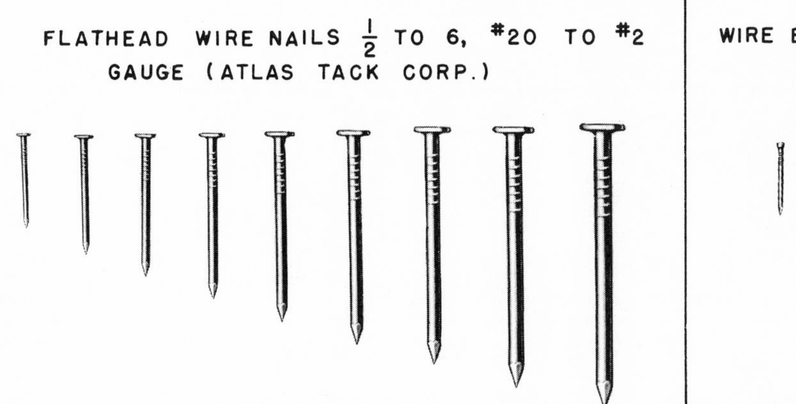

WIRE BRADS $\frac{3}{8}$ TO 4, #20 TO #5 GAUGE
(ATLAS TACK CORP.)

APPROXIMATE NUMBER OF WIRE NAILS PER POUND

Steel Wire Gauge	LENGTH																			
	3/16	1/4	3/8	1/2	5/8	3/4	7/8	1	1 1/8	1 1/4	1 1/2	1 3/4	2	2 1/4	2 1/2	2 3/4	3	3 1/2	4	4 1/2
2	.....	.....	....	....	....	....	....	60	54	48	41	35	31	28	25	23	21	18	16	14
3	.....	.....	....	....	....	....	....	67	60	55	47	41	36	32	29	27	25	21	18	16
4	.....	.....	....	....	....	....	....	81	74	66	55	48	41	37	34	31	29	25	22	20
5	.....	.....	....	....	....	....	....	90	81	74	61	52	45	41	38	35	32	28	24	22
6	.....	.....	....	213	174	149	128	113	101	91	76	65	58	52	47	43	39	34	29	26
7	.....	.....	....	250	205	174	148	132	120	110	92	78	70	61	55	53	51	40	35	31
8	.....	.....	....	272	238	198	174	153	139	126	106	93	82	74	66	61	56	48	42	38
9	.....	.....	....	348	286	238	213	185	170	152	128	112	99	87	79	71	67	58	50	45
10	.....	.....	....	469	373	320	277	242	216	196	165	142	124	111	100	91	84	71	62	55
11	.....	.....	....	510	417	366	323	285	254	233	200	171	149	136	122	111	103	87	77	69
12	.....	.....	....	740	603	511	442	405	351	327	268	229	204	182	161	149	137	118	103	95
13	.....	.....	1356	1017	802	688	590	508	458	412	348	297	260	232	209	190	175	153	138	123
14	.....	2293	1664	1290	1037	863	806	667	610	536	459	406	350	312	278	256	233	201	176	157
15	.....	2890	2213	1619	1316	1132	971	869	787	694	578	501	437	390	351	317	290	246	220	196
16	.....	3932	2720	2142	1708	1414	1229	1090	973	872	739	635	553	496	452	410	370	318	277	248
17	.....	5316	3890	2700	2306	1904	1581	1409	1253	1139	956	831	746	666	590	532	486	418	360	322
18	.....	7520	5072	3824	3130	2608	2248	1976	1760	1590	1338	1150	996	890	820	740	680	585	507	448
19	.....	9920	6860	5075	4132	3508	2816	2556	2284	2096	1772	1590	1390	1205	1060	970	895	800	....	....
20	18620	14050	9432	7164	5686	4795	4230	3596	3225	2893	2412	2070	1810	1620	1450	1315	1215	1035	....	....

These approximate numbers are an **Average** only,

TECHNICAL DATA

TD-12-81

Machine Screws — Tap Drill and Clearance Drill Sizes (South Chester Corp.)

Screw Size		Threads per Inch		Drill Sizes	
No.	O.D.	N.C.	N.F.	Tap	Clear
0	.060		80	3/64	#51
1	.073	64		#53	#47
1	.073		72	#53	#47
2	.086	56		#50	#42
2	.086		64	#50	#42
3	.099	48		#47	#37
3	.099		56	#46	#37
4	.112	40		#43	#31
4	.112		48	3/32	#31
5	.125	40		#38	#29
5	.125		44	#37	#29
6	.138	32		#36	#27
6	.138		40	#33	#27
8	.164	32		#29	#18
8	.164		36	#29	#18
10	.190	24		#26	#9
10	.190		32	#21	#9
12	.216	24		#16	#2
12	.216		28	#15	#2
Fractional Sizes Start Here					
1/4	.250	20		#7	17/64
1/4	.250		28	#3	17/64
5/16	.312	18		F	21/64
5/16	.312		24	I	21/64
3/8	.375	16		5/16	25/64
3/8	.375		24	Q	25/64
7/16	.437	14		U	29/64
7/16	.437		20	25/64	29/64
1/2	.500	13		27/64	33/64
1/2	.500		20	29/64	33/64
9/16	.562	12		31/64	37/64
9/16	.562		18	33/64	37/64
5/8	.625	11		17/32	41/64
5/8	.625		18	37/64	41/64
3/4	.750	10		21/32	49/64
3/4	.750		16	11/16	49/64
7/8	.875	9		49/64	57/64
7/8	.875		14	13/16	57/64
1	1.000	8		7/8	1 1/64
1	1.000		14	15/16	1 1/64

Tap Drill Sizes shown give approximately 75% depth of thread.

TD-12-82

Decimal Equivalents of Drill Sizes (South Chester Corp.)

Letter Sizes		Number Sizes			
Letter	Size in Inches	No.	Size in Inches	No.	Size in Inches
A	.234	1	.2280	41	.0960
B	.238	2	.2210	42	.0935
C	.242	3	.2130	43	.0890
D	.246	4	.2090	44	.0860
E	.250	5	.2055	45	.0820
F	.257	6	.2040	46	.0810
G	.261	7	.2010	47	.0785
H	.266	8	.1990	48	.0760
I	.272	9	.1960	49	.0730
J	.277	10	.1935	50	.0700
K	.281	11	.1910	51	.0670
L	.290	12	.1890	52	.0635
M	.295	13	.1850	53	.0595
N	.302	14	.1820	54	.0550
O	.316	15	.1800	55	.0520
P	.323	16	.1770	56	.0465
Q	.332	17	.1730	57	.0430
R	.339	18	.1695	58	.0420
S	.348	19	.1660	59	.0410
T	.358	20	.1610	60	.0400
U	.368	21	.1590	61	.0390
V	.377	22	.1570	62	.0380
W	.386	23	.1540	63	.0370
X	.397	24	.1520	64	.0360
Y	.404	25	.1495	65	.0350
Z	.413	26	.1470	66	.0330
		27	.1440	67	.0320
		28	.1405	68	.0310
		29	.1360	69	.0292
		30	.1285	70	.0280
		31	.1200	71	.0260
		32	.1160	72	.0250
		33	.1130	73	.0240
		34	.1110	74	.0225
		35	.1100	75	.0210
		36	.1065	76	.0200
		37	.1040	77	.0180
		38	.1015	78	.0160
		39	.0995	79	.0145
		40	.0980	80	.0135

TD-12-83

Standard Wire Gauges (South Chester Corp.)

This table shows the standard gauges and the names of major commodities for which each is used. To determine the gauge used for any commodity, notice the number in parenthesis opposite the commodity named and find the gauge column below bearing the same number in parenthesis.

Aluminum (2) except Tubing (1)
Bands (1)
Brass Tubing (3/8″ O.D. and larger) (1)
Brass Tubing (smaller than 3/8″ O.D.) (2)
Brass Sheets (2)
Brass Strips (2)
Brass Wire (2)
Copper Sheets (2)
Copper Wire (2)
Flat Wire (1)
Hoops (1)
Iron Wire (4)
Monel Metal Sheets (3)
Music Wire (5)
Nickel Sheets (3)
Nickel Silver Sheets (2)
Nickel Silver Wire (2)
Phosphor Bronze Strip (2)
Spring Steel (1)
Stainless Steel (3)
Steel Plates (6)
Steel Sheets (6)
Steel Tubing, seamless and welded (1)
Steel Wire (4) Exceptions:
  Music Wire (5)
  Armature Binding Wire (2)
  Flat Wire (1)
Strip Steel (1)

Ga. No.	(1) Birming-ham or Stubs	(2) American or Browne & Sharp	(3) U.S. Standard	(4) Washburn & Moen	(5) Music Wire (Std.)	(6) Mfgrs. Std. Ga. for Sheet Metal
1/0	.340	.3249	.3125	.3065	.009	
1	.300	.2893	.2812	.2830	.010	
2	.284	.2576	.2656	.2625	.011	
3	.259	.2294	.2500	.2437	.012	.2391
4	.238	.2043	.2343	.2253	.013	.2242
5	.220	.1819	.2187	.2070	.014	.2092
6	.203	.1620	.2031	.1920	.016	.1943
7	.180	.1443	.1875	.1770	.018	.1793
8	.165	.1285	.1718	.1620	.020	.1644
9	.148	.1144	.1562	.1483	.022	.1495
10	.134	.1019	.1406	.1350	.024	.1345
11	.120	.0907	.1250	.1205	.026	.1196
12	.109	.0808	.1093	.1055	.029	.1046
13	.095	.0719	.0937	.0915	.031	.0897
14	.083	.0640	.0781	.0800	.033	.0747
15	.072	.0570	.0703	.0720	.035	.0673
16	.065	.0508	.0625	.0625	.037	.0598
17	.058	.0452	.0562	.0540	.039	.0538
18	.049	.0403	.0500	.0475	.041	.0478
19	.042	.0359	.0437	.0410	.043	.0418
20	.035	.0319	.0375	.0348	.045	.0359
21	.032	.0284	.0343	.0317	.047	.0329
22	.028	.0253	.0312	.0286	.049	.0299
23	.025	.0225	.0281	.0258	.051	.0269
24	.022	.0201	.0250	.0230	.055	.0239
25	.020	.0179	.0218	.0204	.059	.0209
26	.018	.0159	.0187	.0181	.063	.0179
27	.016	.0142	.0171	.0173	.067	.0164
28	.014	.0126	.0156	.0162	.071	.0149
29	.013	.0112	.0140	.0150	.075	.0135
30	.012	.0100	.0125	.0140	.080	.0120
31	.010	.0089	.0109	.0132	.085	.0105
32	.009	.0079	.0101	.0128	.090	.0097
33	.008	.0071	.0093	.0118	.095	.0090
34	.007	.0063	.0085	.0104	.100	.0082
35	.005	.0056	.0078	.0095	.106	.0075
36	.004	.0050	.0070	.0090	.112	.0067
37		.0044	.0066	.0085	.118	.0064
38		.0039	.0062	.0080	.124	.0060

TECHNICAL DATA

selected references

This list is not intended to be exhaustive. It is intended to be recent (within the last ten years) and to provide information supplementary to that in this text. The numbers appearing in parentheses at the end of each entry refer to the chapters which should be of most value.

Art of Good Lettering, The. Detroit, Michigan: American Institute of Design and Drafting, 18465 James Couzens Highway. (Chapter 7).

Beitler, B. C., and E. L. J. Lockhart, *Design for You.* New York: John Wiley & Sons Inc., 1961 (Chapter 13).

Carlson, Richard F., *Metal Stamping Design.* Englewood Cliffs, New Jersey: Prentice-Hall, Inc., 1961. (Chapter 6).

Gibby, Joseph C., *Technical Illustration.* New York: McGraw-Hill Book Co., Inc., 1960. (Chapter 2).

Glenn, William H., and Donovan A. Johnson. *Adventures in Graphing.* St. Louis, Missouri: Webster Publishing Company, 1961. (Chapter 4).

Johnson, Donovan A., *Curves in Space.* St. Louis, Missouri: Webster Publishing Company, 1963. (Chapter 4).

Johnson, Donovan A., and William H. Glenn. *Topology: The Rubber-Sheet Geometry.* St. Louis, Missouri: Webster Publishing Company, 1961. (Chapters 4 and 8).

Laughner, Vallory H., and Donald W. Conover, *Handbook of Fastening and Joining Metal Parts.* New York: McGraw-Hill Book Co., Inc., 1954. (Chapter 12).

Nelson, Carl Erwin, *Microfilm Technology.* New York: McGraw-Hill Book Co., Inc., 1965. (Chapter 9).

Norton, M. Scott, *Geometric Constructions.* St. Louis, Missouri: Webster Publishing Company, 1963. (Chapter 4).

Panero, Julius, *Anatomy for Interior Designing.* New York: Library of Design. (Chapter 13).

Pare, Eugene, Lyman Francis, and Jack Kimbrell, *Introduction to Engineering Design*. New York: Holt, Rinehart, and Winston, 1963. (Chapter 13).

Skeist, Irving (Ed), *Handbook of Adhesives*. New York: Reinhold Publishing Company, 1962. (Chapter 12).

Thomas, T. A., *Technical Illustration*. New York: McGraw-Hill Book Co., Inc., 1960. (Chapter 2).

Van Doren, Harold L., *Industrial Design*. New York: McGraw-Hill Book Co., Inc., 1954. (Chapter 13).

Vezzani, A. A., *Reading and Detailing Assembly Drawings*. Detroit, Michigan: Dies Royalle Publishing Company, 1961. (Chapter 13).

Woodson, Wesley E., and Donald W. Conover, *Human Engineering Guide for Equipment Designers*. Berkeley, California: University of California Press, 1965. (Chapter 13).

selected films

The teacher will want to consult his audio-visual department for current catalogs and additional sources. This list is quite selective. Items are recommended by the author to supplement instruction in the chapters indicated in parentheses at the end of each entry.

According to Plan Black and White 9 min.
An introduction to drafting as a communication tool for industry. (Follow-up film strip available)
McGraw-Hill Book Co.
Text-Film Dept.
New York, N.Y. (Ch. 1)

Auxiliary Views: Double Auxiliaries Black and White 15 min.
Presents and illustrates double-auxiliary projection. (Follow-up film strip available)
McGraw-Hill Book Co.
Text-Film Dept.
New York, N.Y. (Ch. 10)

Auxiliary Views: Single Auxiliaries Black and White 20 min.
Presents and illustrates single-auxiliary projection. (Follow-up film strip available)
McGraw-Hill Book Co.
Text-Film Dept.
New York, N.Y. (Ch. 10)

Blueprint for Action Color 28 min.
The industry of reproducing drawings.
Modern Talking Picture Service
1212 Avenue of the Americas
New York, N.Y. 10036 (Ch. 1)

Creative Attitude Color 27 min.
Outlines effective ways to spark new ideas.
General Motors Corporation
Public Relations Staff, Film Library
General Motors Building
Detroit, Michigan 48202 (Ch. 13)

DAC-I (Design Augmented by Computers) Color 13 min.

An excellent visual presentation of use of a computer to aid in design.

General Motors Corporation
Public Relations Staff-Film Library
General Motors Building
Detroit, Michigan 48202 (Ch. 14)

Drawings and the Shop Black and White 15 min.

Relationships between the shop operations and their requirements on a drawing. (Follow-up film strip available)

McGraw-Hill Book Co.
Text-Film Dept.
New York, N.Y. (Ch. 6)

Forging in Closed Dies Color 28 min.

The story of modern drop forging equipment and methods.

Modern Talking Picture Service
1212 Ave. of the Americas
New York, N.Y. 10036 (Ch. 6)

Freehand Lettering and Figures Black and white film strip

Presents pointers on how to make freehand letters on drawings.

McGraw-Hill Book Co.
Text-Film Dept.
New York, N.Y. (Ch. 7)

Holding Power Color 23 min.

The story of production and use of industrial steel fasteners.

Modern Talking Picture Service
1212 Ave. of the Americas
New York, N.Y. 10036 (Ch. 12)

Orthographic Projection Black and white 20 min.

Principles of orthographic projection explained and illustrated. (Follow-up film strip available)

McGraw-Hill Book Co.
Text-Film Dept.
New York, N.Y. (Ch. 3)

Principal Dimensions, Reference Surfaces, and Tolerances Black and white 11 min.

Use and interpretation of reference surfaces and tolerances.

Visual Aids Service
University of Illinois
Division of University Extension
Champaign, Illinois (Ch. 11)

Scales: Flat and Triangular Black and white film strip

Explains the uses of common types of scales.

McGraw-Hill Book Co.
Text-Film Dept.
New York, N.Y. (Ch. 3)

Sections and Conventions Black and white 14 min.
How interior detail is exposed by a sectional view. (Follow-up film strip available)
McGraw-Hill Book Co.
Text-Film Dept.
New York, N.Y. (Ch. 5)

Seeing Color Color 18 min.
How the eye sees color and effects of lighting on color. Interchemical corporation)
Modern Talking Picture Service
1212 Avenue of the Americas
New York, N.Y. 10036 (Ch. 13)

Selections of Dimensions Black and White 20 min.
Principles of governing the selection of dimensions for drawings. (Follow-up film strip available)
McGraw-Hill Book Co.
Text-Film Dept.
New York, N.Y. (Ch. 8)

Up from Clay Color 26 min.
Car styling and design.
General Motors Corporation
Public Relations Staff, Film Library
General Motors Building
Detroit, Michigan 48202 (Ch. 13)

index